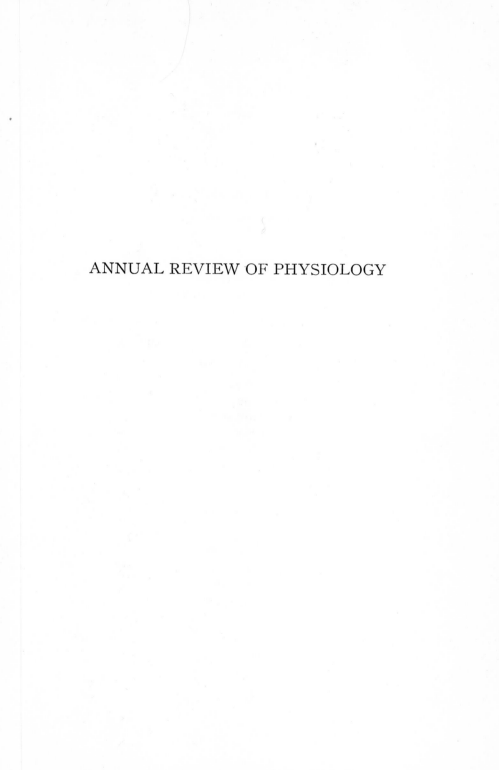

ANNUAL REVIEW OF PHYSIOLOGY

ANNUAL REVIEW OF PHYSIOLOGY

VICTOR E. HALL, *Editor*
University of California, Los Angeles

ARTHUR C. GIESE, *Associate Editor*
Stanford University

RALPH R. SONNENSCHEIN, *Associate Editor*
University of California, Los Angeles

VOLUME 32

1970
ANNUAL REVIEWS, INC.
4139 EL CAMINO WAY
PALO ALTO, CALIFORNIA, U.S.A.

ANNUAL REVIEW, INC.
PALO ALTO, CALIFORNIA, U.S.A.

© 1970 BY ANNUAL REVIEWS, INC.
ALL RIGHTS RESERVED

Standard Book Number 8243-0332-6
Library of Congress Catalog Card Number 39–15404

FOREIGN AGENCY
Maruzen Company, Limited
6 Tori-Nichome, Nihonbashi
Tokyo

PRINTED AND BOUND IN THE UNITED STATES OF AMERICA
BY GEORGE BANTA COMPANY, INC.

PREFACE

The thirty-second volume of the Annual Review of Physiology appears with its customary freight of the precious ore of physiology concentrated and refined in considerable degree. Those of us who are responsible for its editing feel that the quality of the chapters contributed to the Annual Review has been for the last several years distinctly superior to those of earlier years. It is now a rare chapter that deserves the criticism frequently made in the past that it is nothing more than a string of abstracts arranged under conventional headings. By far the lion's share of the credit for this advance belongs of course to the authors and reflects the ever-growing sophistication of our science and its devotees. The editors claim credit only for laying down in our invitation letter the type of review we would like to receive: an analysis of the literature of the specific field revealing the past year's advances, describing, evaluating, and placing in context the more significant contributions by a creative use of the author's own orientation and interests. Bibliographic completeness was to be foresworn, even at the cost of possible neglect of meritorious papers. And this, we are happy to say, is just what our authors are doing. It was a long and slow process but we have substantially reached a new high level of performance. What further changes the future may demand of us remains veiled.

Last year we saluted the greatly esteemed retiring Editor-in-Chief of the *Annual Reviews,* Dr. J. Murray Luck. This is the first volume to appear under the general supervision of his successor, Dr. Robert R. Schutz, whom we greet with happy expectation.

Like most volumes this suffered the loss of several chapters announced. The scheduled articles on cellular mechanisms of hormone action; kidney, water, and electrolytes; hearing; and activities of the CNS: motor have been deferred to Volume 33; the articles on control of cell behavior through cell contact and endocrine control of energy metabolism will not appear.

We also wish to express our sorrow at learning of the death of Dr. Robert K. S. Lim, the notable and beloved American physiologist. We are happy that he was able to complete the modest and informative chapter on Pain which appears in this volume.

And still once again warmest thanks and appreciation are due to the human dynamo which powers the Annual Review, our Assistant Editor Joann Huddleston, and to our printer Banta Press whose performance can best be appreciated by those who have worked with other presses.

V. E. H.
A. C. G.
R. R. S.

CONTENTS

A WORD ABOUT REPRINTS

The reader may be puzzled by the conspicuous number (1017 to 1036) aligned in the margin with the title of each review in this volume, it is a key for use in the ordering of reprints. These are priced uniformly at $0.95 each, postpaid. Payment must accompany the order if the purchase totals less than $10.00. All payments are to be made to Annual Reviews, Inc., in U.S. dollars. California orders are subject to 5 per cent sales tax. Delivery in the U.S.A. will require approximately 2 to 6 weeks.

Reprints, also at $0.95 each, are available from the *Annual Review of Biochemistry* and the *Annual Review of Psychology* (since 1961 in both cases) and from the *Annual Review of Microbiology* starting with Volume 22 (1968).

The sale of reprints of articles published in the *Reviews* was initiated with Volume 30 in the belief that reprints in individual copies, in sets covering stated topics, and in quantity for classroom use will have a special appeal to students and to teachers.

加藤元一先生之像

Genichi Kato

THE ROAD A SCIENTIST FOLLOWED 1037

Notes of Japanese Physiology as I myself experienced it

GEN-ICHI KATO

Department of Physiology, School of Medicine, Keio University
Tokyo, Japan

BY WAY OF PREFACE

There are many reminiscences in my long academic life of more than fifty years that was spent with the nerve. The most impressive and unforgettable are the presentation of the theory of decrementless conduction in nerve (1) and the success in isolating a single nerve fiber in conductible state (2). The descriptions will, therefore, be centered on these two.

When I first presented the decrementless theory in Japan in 1923, it was as though a stone was thrown into a pool. Ripples spread for over a decade broadly, so much so that pros and cons were hotly discussed even in popular magazines and daily news papers. In the end I had to go on a journey to Stockholm in 1926, to separate the sheep from the goats at the XII International Physiological Congress by giving open experiments in public.

The success in the isolation of a single nerve fiber in conductible state was the second event. It forced many textbooks to be rewritten, and encouraged me in 1932 to go as far as to Rome over the Indian Ocean and via Suez Canal to attend the XIV International Physiological Congress, and it motivated my invitation as the guest of honor to the XV International Physiological Congress at Leningrad and Moscow in 1935, to show the isolation experiment of a single nerve fiber in conductible state and to open to the public the experiments demonstrating the all-or-none law with the isolated single nerve fiber. Those are too impressive for me to forget even today after some forty years.

That which served to adorn the last chapter of my academic life, to add a few words, was the XXIII International Congress of Physiological Sciences which was held in Japan in 1965 under my presidency (3). I was and am more than glad to have had it since it was the first such event in Asia and it was what had long been dreamed to be realized.

THE THEORY OF DECREMENTLESS CONDUCTION AND ITS BEGINNING

In the early part of the 20th century Max Verworn and his school's theory of decremental conduction prevailed throughout the physiological

1

world (4): according to this theory, the nerve impulse which is conducted without decrement and follows the all-or-none law in the *normal* nerve would be so altered in the *narcotized* (abnormal) region that decrement would occur in both the impulse's intensity and velocity during conduction in disobedience to the all-or-none law. Of course, I was one of those adherents of this decrement theory at first. Be that as it may, Verworn and Keith Lucas (5), although both of 'decrement' school, had different opinion as to the *form* of decrement. At that time, nobody had any doubt regarding the existence of decrement, but I was curious to know which was right, Verworn or Lucas. The desire led a research associate of my Department (Dr. R. Maki) to make experiments to determine the right form of decrement by narcotizing different lengths of nerves, taking advantage of big Japanese toads. That was the introduction of my decrementless theory.

Dr. Maki showed me his experimental results, which, contrary to my expectation, showed that the length of the narcotized regions had nothing to do with the extinction time (the time necessary to suspend conduction in narcotized region), or in the longer narcotized region the extinction time approached or became the same as that in the short one, after the repetition of one experiment after another. That implies the nonexistence of decrement. With that result so unexpected before me, I reflected for a while as follows. It may be summarized in two points: (*a*) The decrement theory admits *qualitative* difference between normality and abnormality in the nerve. In other words, there is no decrement in intensity and velocity in its conduction under normal condition, but if once the nerve is put under abnormal (narcotized) condition, the nerve impulse turns to suffer decrement and does not follow the all-or-none law. Then where should the demarcation line be drawn between normality and abnormality? Where, then, is the borderline of qualitative change? Practically nerves are taken out of living bodies and preserved in Ringer solution before experimentation, sometimes several hours for next day's use. It is understandable that the nerve is normal when it stays in the living body, but it sounds quite unreasonable to regard it as normal until it is narcotized, and as abnormal from the moment it is narcotized. (*b*) Everybody knows and believes that there is no decrement in conduction in the normal nerve. But this (nondecremental conduction) is possible only in regions where there is locally a supply of new energy necessary for conduction. Then, the conduction with decrement under narcosis must be considered to be made with the initial energy only, without any supply of new energy being added during conduction (see p. 5 Fundamental difference of two theories). If so, it will imply that narcotics can transform the normal conduction principle wholly, once it is applied to the nerve. This is not a reasonable idea; narcotics applied cannot change the nature of conduction in principle, although the energy to be supplied locally during conduction may be reduced by narcosis. That is, there may take place *quantitative* change by narcosis, but never a qualitative change. Then, the size of nerve impulse may be reduced in the narcotized part of the nerve as compared with that in the normal nerve, but as in the normal nerve there will not be any decrement. This leads to a supposition that the extinction time is independent of the length of the narcotized part of the nerve.

When my speculation reached this far, my idea ran that the result Dr. Maki had obtained—the extinction time is not dependent on the length of the narcotized region—might be true. I almost cried to myself that it was a world-shaking affair. With the combined efforts of my whole laboratory, comparative experiments in respect of narcotized region of different lengths were repeated hundreds of times. The results led me to establish the decrementless theory at last with confirmed evidences derived from these experiments.

General outline of the decrementless theory.—To summarize the theory:

(*a*) The intensity of nerve impulse, even though reduced in the narcotized region, does not decrease gradually as it is conducted along the narcotized region. In other words, there is no decrement: the reduction is to be determined by the depth of narcosis (the grade of abnormality); the deeper the narcosis the greater the reduction. In this new theory, accordingly, the extinction time (the time necessary for suspension of conduction from outside electrode) is dependent on the depth of narcosis only, and not on the length of the narcotized region. In other words, extinction time is the same whether the narcotized region is longer or shorter.

(*b*) The conduction velocity is not subject to decrement during conduction, although it gets reduced in the narcotized region. The velocity remains even along the whole narcotized region, though it is smaller than that in the normal nerve. The reduction of velocity is determined by the depth of narcosis.

(*c*) The narcotized region also follows the all-or-none law. It is true that the size of nerve impulse elicitable by stimulus applied at the narcotized region is smaller than that at the non-narcotized normal region, but it is not dependent on the intensity of the stimulus applied, and is only dependent on the depth of narcosis. As narcosis proceeds the size of impulse becomes smaller, but the intensity of stimulus never affects the size of impulse produced. Here still the all-or-none law remains the iron law.

The experiments which formed the basis of the decrementless theory count several dozens, and they are fully described in the following two monographs:

(*a*) *The Theory of Decrementless Conduction* (1924), Nankodo, Tokyo, Japan.

(*b*) *The Further Studies on Decrementless Conduction* (1926), Nankodo, Tokyo, Japan.

Criticism of the experiments upon which the decrement theory is based. —Upon what foundation was based, then, the decrement theory (old conduction theory)? how did it get its justifiable acceptance? It was very unlikely, I reasoned, that the great authorities like Verworn, Lucas, and E. D. Adrian could easily commit any errors in their experiments. But to err is human.

Error lurks hidden in the most unlikely place. Professor A. Forbes of the Harvard University and his collaborators (6) read their paper on "conduction without decrement" and later described in printed essay that Kato and his school had not only advocated a decrementless theory, but also found the sources of the errors which had led to the inference of conduction with decrement: (*a*) an effect due to the diffusion of narcotics near the edge of the narcotizing chamber and (*b*) the spread of stimulating electric current. A few words have to be spent here as to these two items.

(*a*) Measurement of the time necessary to suspend conduction (extinction time) in different lengths of narcotized nerve was the first source of error. The experimental result that the extinction time was shorter in the longer narcotized region than that in the shorter one had supplied the basis for the old decrement theory. One of the most important sources of the error in this result lay in neglect to take into consideration the diffusion of narcotics near the edge of the narcotizing chamber (it must also be added here that the branching points[1] are specially sensitive to narcotics). When a narcotizing solution is put in a narcotizing chamber, the whole length of nerve within the chamber is, theoretically, to be evenly narcotized at the same depth, but practically not: narcosis is shallower near the edge of the narcotizing chamber (both near the upper and lower edge by about 3 mm). For this reason, when narcosis has proceeded to the depth necessary to suspend conduction in the longer narcotized region (longer than 6 mm), narcosis in the shorter region (shorter than 6 mm)[2] is still so shallow as to permit conduction. In other words, the depth of narcosis necessary to suspend conduction is sooner reached in the longer narcotized region than in the shorter one; that is, the former reaches the extinction time sooner than the latter. The reasoning may mislead one to the conception of decrement. This is due to the diffusion of narcotics near the edges of the narcotizing chamber, and not by any means is the result of decrement. Here Verworn took it as due to the existence of decrement in narcotized region. (Comparison must not be made between the narcotized nerves of longer than 6 mm and shorter than 6 mm in respect of extinction time.) In his famous experiments, Adrian compared 9.0 mm with 4.5 mm (5). This is one of the gravest errors the old theorists committed.

(*b*) Difference of effects between different strengths of stimuli was the second source of error. There is a stage of narcosis in which a weak electric stimulus applied within the narcotized region is not able to produce a

---

[1] The sciatic nerve of Japanese toad has four branches and these branching points are specially sensitive to narcotics. We have experimentally proved that this is due to the fact that these spots are liable to suffer some slightest damage unaware during the operation of taking the nerve out of the body. And the conduction suffers block at these spots, while the nonbranching part is still conducting. The longer the narcotized region, the more such spots may possibly be contained within it. This is another of the sources of error, which Professor Forbes has omitted to mention.

[2] We named 6 mm the "limit length".

contraction of muscle attached, whereas a stronger stimulus causes a contraction of the muscle. This experimental fact afforded a theoretical foundation for Verworn's theory that the narcotized region does not follow the all-or-none law. In fact, however, this is due to current spread, and is not to be taken as evidence of not following of the all-or-none law. It was because the strong electrical stimulus could spread to outside of the narcotizing chamber and stimulate the peripheral unnarcotized part of the nerve, and so the muscle contracted. And a weak electric stimulus cannot spread so far as outside the chamber, and so cannot cause any contraction of the muscle. This was where I took the greatest effort and pains in the research of decrementless theory. I, at last, was able to contrive a new invention to measure the distance of current spread. By means of the contrivance the point of nerve which is stimulated by the spreading current is clearly pointed out as being outside of the chamber when the stimulus is strong (so as to cause the muscle to contract). That the strong electrical stimulus can make the muscle contract comes from a different cause from the one which is presumed to be involved with the all-or-none law, but that experimental fact supplied Verworn with a supposition which made him declare that the narcotized region does not follow the all-or-none law. It was this spread of stimulating current that led him astray. To prove the above, you can see no muscle contraction when a mechanical stimulus (cut by a pair of scissors) is used instead of an electrical stimulus. This is because a mechanical stimulus does not run or spread like an electrical one. This was one of three experiments we have demonstrated at the XII International Physiological Congress at Stockholm (see p. 7 and 9, Cut-experiment).

Fundamental difference of two theories.—The decrement theory and the decrementless theory can be said to rest on fundamentally different theoretical standpoints. The former seems to hold that an impulse is conducted by its initial energy supplied *only* at its start which, being consumed as it propagates and having no supply of new energy during its conduction, gradually diminishes, in other words, suffers decrement (Verworn might not have gone so far), but the latter theory postulates that the impulse is conducted by means of new energy necessary for conduction produced *locally* as it is propagated, so it can be conducted in a decrementless manner (see Figure 2, p. 14). What is important here is that, while those supporting the decrement theory held that the nerve (a living tissue in general) would change its nature qualitatively when condition changed, we, in our decrementless theory, inferred that it would remain unchanged in its nature under changed conditions, and only be subject to quantitative change. Therefore, our way of thinking was fundamentally different from theirs, not being concerned merely with the phenomenal fact as to whether conduction is decremental or decrementless (nondecremental). In this sense the discussion on the right or wrong of our theory came to exert a great influence on the fundamental thought in the biological world.

Presentation of the decrementless theory.—It was at the II Japanese Physiological Congress in 1923 that the theory was first enunciated in our country. I was glad or even proud of it before the presentation. It was not only my first attendance at the meeting of Japanese physiologists since I came to Keio University, but I had secretly anticipated some praise which Professor Ishikawa, my honored teacher and scientist, would offer me, and which I did not even doubt. But unexpectedly, when I was about to step down with exultant air from the platform after reading my paper, he, turning crimson with rage, stood up and said to me to the effect that, "It's an act of arrogance to try criticism on Professor Verworn with such infantile research as yours. Do you believe such extensive research results as those by Professor Verworn and Dr. Lucas can be explained with such a trash idea as decrementless theory? Give me two hours and I'll smash the Keio theory to pieces! What do you say?" (7) A bolt from the blue! He was an earnest follower of those two scientists. He studied several years under Verworn. I was forced to a standstill, ghastly pale, at the corner of the platform without any words imaginable to answer his violent reproach. With downcast eyes I came back to my seat. Nothing had been more shocking in my life. I could not understand why Professor Ishikawa was that red with anger, because I had firmly believed he would praise me. I was foolish enough not to know how to measure other's corn by my own bushel. We, four members from my laboratory, came to a conclusion, after being smashed to pieces in such a way, that nothing would go well in Japan so far as our study on this line was concerned under such circumstances, however hard we might try. There, three years ahead, lay the 1926 XII International Physiological Congress at Stockholm. We were determined to join it and ask the world to inquire into the rights and wrongs of the matter by opening the experiments upon which our decrementless theory is based.

After that time, superhuman activities were started literally with the fury of a lion in attack in our laboratory. The whole laboratory were in general mobilization to devote ourselves to the completion of the decrementless theory. I was kept exceptionally busy. At that time all the lectures of physiology were in my charge; I had to prepare myself for them besides the research. There were some twenty members in my Department. I assigned each member his theme, and gave detailed instruction for the experiment each time, and late at night typed in English the results obtained. Of course I was exclusively confined to the laboratory. We worked double tides. It was in the midst of such dogged endeavour that the Great Earthquake (September 1, 1923) occurred which destroyed our string galvanometer which fell from the table. It also prevented us from getting the toads necessary for the experiments, though luckily the laboratory building escaped from the spreading fire. To continue the planned experiments, toads had to be caught by ourselves by going out into the suburban fields during daytime so that experiments had to be done at night. At last, overwork, physical and mental, sent me to the hospital where I had to make corrections in the English version of the book on my theory while in the hospital bed.

The monograph *The Theory of Decrementless Conduction* was thus completed in 1924, and copies were sent to universities and research institutes, European and American.

A little later in December 1924, Professor Forbes of Harvard (6) read his papers on "Conduction without Decrement", based on his cat's nerve experiment, at the American Physiological Congress at Washington. Then followed the publication of the paper of Koch (8), Köln University, confirming the finding of decrementless conduction. Studies on my decrementless theory made such headway abroad (its supporters looking askance at domestic unfavorable criticisms against it) that by the beginning of 1926 almost all the problems involved in it seemed to have been solved. Our painstaking efforts devoted to the problem were beyond description during that spell of time. Unyielding and unflinching will power and efforts were thus rewarded, and the following book, as well as the English version of the *Further Studies on Decrementless Conduction,* was completed in 1926; copies were sent abroad extensively.

The XII International Physiological Congress attended.—The year 1926 was our hoped-for year, when the XII International Physiological Congress was to be held at Stockholm. In spite of the high esteem in America and Europe of our achievements, we were still surrounded by foes in our own country. Decidedly and resolutely we were determined to attend the International Congress to ask for justice to be done to our decrementless theory by making a great drive to show the open demonstrations ourselves. The destination was Stockholm. The party included three members of my laboratory besides me. To point out the errors in the experiments on which the old theory was based and to endorse the correctness of our position, we were to perform the following three kinds of experiments at the congress with Japanese toads and the experimental equipment which had to be carried there with us all the way from Japan. The demonstrations were: (*a*) measurement of extinction time by narcotizing the longer and shorter regions of nerve (Dr. R. Maki), (*b*) the validity of all-or-none law in the narcotized region (Dr. R. Miyake), (*c*) cut-experiment (Dr. R. Uchimura, who was to show that the difference of effects caused by strong or weak electric stimuli is due to current spread and does not serve to support the negation of the all-or-none law). As the leader, I was in charge of leading the experiments, and making their explanation and answering to the questions of the spectators. There was another important task assigned to me. I had to deliver a lecture for an hour entitled, "The Decrementless Conduction Theory," and to participate in a panel discussion attached to it.

From early in the new year, our three members started, high-spiritedly, their assigned work to stand in the world arena for the first time. There was yet a long period of six months ahead before the experiments to be shown, but they wanted to see to it that there should not be anything left to be desired, because the performance was to be done before men of profound learning from all over the world.

The schedule was that we would leave Tokyo in May and arrive at Stockholm by the end of the month via Siberia; then there would be spare time of as long as two months, since the Congress was scheduled to be in August. July would be spent in preparing for the demonstration—that meant we would be allowed to enjoy a month's trips in June throughout Europe. What worried us most was how to carry big toads necessary for the experiments which were more than a hundred and a half in number. They would all die if sent in gunnysacks or something like that, though it would be the easiest way. And we knew that they would not eat anything but living (moving) food. That made it impossible for them to be packed in a freight car. The final idea on how to tackle this hardest thing was to make three refrigerator-like boxes with many shelves in them, and to put each of those toads on a shelf in line, taking care of them in our passenger car. That was the baggage most troublesome to handle. In addition, all the railroads and stations were occupied by laborers and farmers of the new Soviet Russia including Siberia since the successful revolution by Lenin, so that passing through that expanse of wasteland was not always safe. Therefore I asked the late Count Shimpei Goto for the insurance of a "Protection Certificate" from the Russian authority. This piece of paper was of great service to us.

It was May 31 when we reached Stockholm, going from Moscow through Leningrad into Finland and Helsinki. Two months were ahead of us before our demonstration was to be given; the Congress was scheduled to be held at the early part of August (3, 4, 5, and 6). A month was enough to prepare for the demonstration. Therefore, after having traveled in June through some European countries, we set to the preparation. Except two rooms with tables and some batteries provided us by the Karolinska Institute, whole sets of apparatus necessary for the demonstrations had already been carried in with us from Japan. Misfortunes visit us when most unawares; all the Japanese toads turned out to be dead. But substitutes appeared in the form of Dutch frogs, which we had already arranged to be available in such case during our trip through Europe. However, we had to keep it in mind that a couple of months since we left Tokyo had kept us from actual experimentation, with our skill in operation[3] lowered. Therefore, we had to brush up our ability for the preparation, or even to make it more efficient than before. One month, July, was spent mainly for this purpose.

The open experiment day came at last! My lecture on "Decrementless Theory" in the morning was successful as had been expected. The problem was left in the afternoon experiments. Before the demonstration I had given

---

[3] Special care and skill are needed in the operation of taking the nerve out of its body, in order to keep the branching points free from slightest damage. See footnote 2, p. 4.

instructions to three doctors who were in charge of the experiments that they should not answer any question, if asked. I would reply, because thinking in English or German on their parts would distract their attention from the experimentation, which was the most important thing. Meanwhile, scholars of every nationality were coming in twos and threes. When it seemed that all the guests were all on hand, I declared the opening of the demonstrations, with concise comments on the following three experiments. Firstly, measurement of the extinction time in the longer and shorter narcotized regions; in the old theory (decrement theory) its experimental and then theoretical basis was that the extinction time was shorter when the narcotized region was longer, wherein lay an error; that was to be caused by the existence of branches[4] and by the diffusion of the narcotics near the edge of the narcotizing chamber; with the caution to be shown presently and using the narcotized region longer than the limit length (6 mm), the extinction time should be just the same in the longer region as in the shorter one. Secondly, corroborative experiment in narcotized nerve which would show the validity of the all-or-none law; any impulse, either large or small, would be extinguished in the narcotized region at the same time. Thirdly, the last one, the cut-experiment in which the different effect of two electrical stimuli, strong and weak, applied within the narcotized part of the nerve would be proved to be due to the spread of the stimulating current, wheras Verworn erroneously interpreted this phenomenon to be due to not following the all-or-none law and made it as a basis for the decrement theory.

Now, the first experiment was started. Dr. Föhlich (Verworn's follower) was all attention to it with his eyes wide open. In the narcotizing chamber two pieces of sciatic nerves (3.0 cm and 1.5 cm long) were strung, taken out of right and left sides of one and the same frog from Holland. Extinction time was going to be measured in the presence of all the spectators. The results were: the conduction was suspended at 24 minutes and 16 seconds in the longer one, and in the shorter one 24 minutes and 15 seconds, the latter taking a bit shorter time by 1 second, but both times being almost or just the same. My announcement of these results was later said to have been too strained or rather sounded falsetto, with overjoy and overwhelming impression. I was not so much worrying about the second experiment because much less failure was likely to be involved in it. As expected, two impulses, large and small, disappeared at the same moment. Yet there was left the third one, the cut-experiment. There I had regained much calmness in my mind. Upon coming of extinction time in the narcotized region two electrical stimuli, strong and weak, were given at the narcotized region. The weak stimulus did not cause any muscular contraction while the strong one did; up to this point, things were as Verworn had insisted. Immediately after that, the narcotized region was to be cut at the spot where electrical stimuli had been given. It was to show that the strong electrical stimulus would cause a contraction of the muscle, but the cutting (mechanical stimu-

[4] See footnote 2, p. 4.

lation) would bring about no contraction. When Dr. Uchimura, just after applying the electrical stimulation, took a cutting pose, there came a voice from far behind of the room, "No muscle state can be seen from here!" Indeed, many of the observers wanted to witness whether the muscle would contract or not with their own eyes. It was Dr. Buytendijk, Professor of the University of Groningen, Holland, who offered to announce if the muscle moved or not, because he was nearest to the table. Dr. Uchimura took up scissors once again and brought them near the nerve to cut it. But his hand was trembling; that might cause some sort of straining on the nerve to make the muscle contract. I had no courage to see the cutting instant. Seconds fled. Suddenly sounded, "Keine Zuckung!! No twitch!!". It was Prof. Buytendijk's voice. And then followed another voice, "Revolution der Physiologie!", from whom I could not identify. Scholar after scholar they presented me with congratulations and handshakes. Professor Cremer, Berlin, and Professor Ascher, Bern University, patted me on the shoulder and said, "Demonstration experiments do not go so well as they have always been. But those today were an unusual success, excellent ones." Here in Japan where I was born, I had never been so sympathetically treated that those compassions nearly made tears well up in my eyes in spite of myself.

Newly discovered marvels by us seemed to run from scholar to scholar, from scholars to citizens all through the city where we were staying, because we found ourselves the objects of attention wherever we went from the next day on. Daily papers also reported our public demonstrations with capital headlines, saying a revolutionary new fact in the world of physiology happened. When we were leaving Stockholm where we spent forty-odd days, some unseen string was detaining us as does the familiar city where we were born and bred. Since our brilliant success in demonstrations on the decrementless theory at the XII International Physiological Congress as well as our announcement of the theory four years before in Japan, they began to take the theory into textbooks of physiology in various parts of the world. Besides them, it may be worthy of note that in the *Selected Readings in the History of Physiology* (1930), Dr. Fulton (9), Professor of the Yale University, counted the decrementless theory as one of 85 most outstanding achievements or discoveries in the physiological field during 2300 years since Aristotle up to then.

ISOLATION OF A SINGLE NERVE FIBER IN CONDUCTIBLE STATE

When the XIII International Physiological Congress was held at Harvard in 1929, I attended it with five members of my laboratory. On our way home from the Congress, the ship we were on was heading for Hawaii over the calm Pacific Ocean. Early fall was beautiful. Under the serene sky, I was looking up, lying in a cosy sofa, letting my eyes wander and entrusting my meditations to develop one after another. I was reflecting—that, up until 1929, we were discussing the characteristics of nerve fibers, on the basis of the experimental results which were obtained from bundles of nerve fibers (the sciatic nerve, for instance), but that this is not convincing, because the nerve impulse is conducted by individual nerve fibers each isolatedly, and that every fiber in the sciatic nerve is not necessarily of the same nature. And the senses of pain, warmth, cold, touch and so on, for example, are produced by afferent fibers of different kinds in the same nerve trunk. They may have different diameter, different conduction velocity and so on, my thinking ran. Then there arose many questions in my mind: (a) What role is being played by which fiber? (b) How can the essential nature of the nerve fiber be examined more closely and precisely? (c) How about the axon or the myelin sheath respectively? (d) What is the function of the nodes of Ranvier in the myelinated fiber? Thinking about these fundamental problems in nerve physiology, I came to the conclusion that the experiments done hitherto, using the nerve trunk in the form of a bundle of nerve fibers, would no longer be sufficient to solve these questions. Contrivance must be made so as to enable us to experiment directly with an isolated single nerve fiber in conductible state.

I landed in Yokohama with a final and fixed determination in my mind: that the isolation of a single nerve fiber in conductible (living) state shall be done by our hand.

Immediately upon getting back to my laboratory, I started the effort to isolate a single nerve fiber, with six assistants chosen from among my research associates. The trial continued every day from morning till midnight. But the truth defied our challenge. Our first trial was to isolate a single fiber under the microscope by means of a micromanipulator, but in vain. Painstaking efforts one after another ended in a complete failure. The whole year of 1929 was thus spent vainly without any effect. I once heard that Columbus was about to be thrown into the sea by his grumbling sailors, as they approached the American Continent. I should actually have been thrown out by my assistants if our effort had not been first rewarded in the early part of 1930. A single muscle fiber (not nerve fiber) was first isolated in living state and its contraction was actually seen under a microscope.

Compared with the muscle fiber, the nerve fiber is not only thinner but also more fragile. It was in summer of 1930 that a single nerve fiber was at last successfully isolated, under naked eyes, in conductible state. I can remember now, as if it were yesterday, my first impression upon seeing the first nerve fiber ever isolated in a conductible state in the world.

After that, for a couple of years, all the members of my laboratory, some twenty in numbers, were busily engaged on the single fiber problem, some working on its narcotization, the others on the node of Ranvier and so on.

Experimental results obtained from isolated single nerve fiber.—What new significant discovery was added to nerve physiology by the success in isolating a single nerve fiber in conductible state? From 1930 to 1932 all the members of our laboratory devoted themselves exclusively to experiments

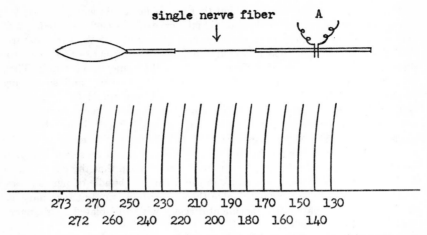

FIG. 1. All-or-none response of single-nerve-fiber-muscle preparation. Experimental result obtained at the XV International Physiological Congress. Numerals indicate coil distance in millimeters of the induction shock applied at electrode A.

using the single nerve fiber. What was accumulated as the results was collected and arranged in a new volume in 1934, entitled *Microphysiology of Nerve* in English (2), copies of which were sent over to various institutes in Europe and America.

Let me pick up some interesting items from it.

(*a*) The nerve[5] fiber follows the all-or-none law. On examination of action currents produced by various stimuli, strong and weak, applied to the isolated single nerve fiber, the action current turned out to be of the same intensity, regardless of the intensity of the applied stimuli.

(*b*) Two different kinds of motor fibers were found. They can be classified into the *quick* fibers (8.0 to 14.0 μ in diameter) and the *slow* fibers (4.0 to 8.0 μ in diameter). The former is an ordinary motor fiber, stimulation of which produces a muscle twitch or tetanus, while the latter is one which does not produce any visible contraction by a single stimulus, but by tetanic stimuli presents a slight wormlike visible muscle contraction only, the conduction velocity being half as much of the former [Tasaki (11)].

(*c*) When a muscle is connected to a galvanometer after isolating a single nerve fiber of the sciatic nerve supplying this muscle (keeping it in contact to the spinal cord *in situ*), the discharge of one and the single motor cell of the spinal cord can be examined. According to this, the frequency of discharge changes in accordance to the muscle force evolved, but the magnitude of individual nerve impulse remains constant regardless of the muscle force evolved.

(*d*) The existence of two different kinds of synapses (10) was demon-

---

[5] Muscle fiber too.

strated. When a certain point on the sole of the cat's paw is slightly stimulated with a pinpoint after a single nerve fiber (9 to 11 μ in diameter) has
been isolated from the nerve trunk of N. plantaris med, reaching the sole,
there appears a series of afferent impulses in this fiber which enters the spinal cord. Then this train of impulses causes simultaneously the contraction
of the toe-flexor and the inhibition of extensor muscle (M. soleus). To put
it in another way, the same impulse produces primarily an excitation on the
one hand and on the other an inhibition. This strongly suggests the existence of two different kinds of synapses.

(e) The inhibitory fibers to the heart were identified. Among fibers of
various diameters included in the vagus nerve, it is only those of about 6 μ
in diameter that serve to inhibit the heart (in the toad). This fact was not
found until single nerve fibers of the vagus nerve were isolated.

(f) The role of the Ranvier node was revealed. It had formerly been
believed that when a nerve was electrically stimulated, the excitation occurred at the cathode of the stimulating electrode. But it was found by single nerve fiber experiments that the excitation takes place only at Ranvier
nodes, regardless of the seat of the electrode.

(g) The role of the myelin sheath was studied. The myelin sheath is a
highly insulating substance and so electricity runs in and out of the fiber
only at the Ranvier node. When electric current flows outward at the node,
the node is so stimulated that an excitation occurs.

(h) The saltatory conduction (11) was demonstrated. Excitation is conducted saltatorily from R_1 to R_2 and from R_2 to R_3 (see Figure 2, p. 32), the
energy necessary for conduction being supplied locally at each Ranvier node
on its way. It results in an extreme difference of conduction velocity between
the myelinated fibers (which has Ranvier nodes) and the unmyelinated
fibers. In warm-blooded animals the velocity in the former is some 100 m
per second while in the latter as slow as 1 to 2 m.

(i) Ranvier nodes follow the all-or-none law. The action potential generated at the Ranvier node (electromotive force) keeps always constant, regardless of the intensity of the stimulus applied to it. It depends only on the
condition of the Ranvier node at the time.

(j) Narcotics affect the nerve fiber at the Ranvier node. If the narcotic
solution is above the critical concentration, the Ranvier node is immediately
so affected that no action current is generated at all, but if the concentration
is below the critical concentration, the excitability of the node is lowered in
accordance to the concentration used; in proportion to this lowered excitability, the size of action current is reduced. But the strength of stimulus
does not give any difference in the size of action current.

*Theory of decrementless conduction in the light of single nerve fiber
physiology (12).*—Isolated single nerve fiber in conductible state revealed to
us many new hitherto unknown facts as described in the above. In the light
of those new findings, it is of profound interest to look back upon the decre-

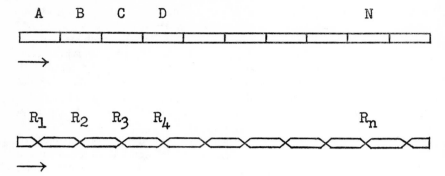

R: Ranvier node

FIG. 2. Diagram of nervous conduction—*above:* decrementless conduction; A, B, C, etc.: section of nerve imagined to be set in excitation at the same moment; *below:* single nerve fiber physiology.

mentless theory. The theory was formed before the success of the isolation of single nerve fiber: the former in 1923 and the latter in 1930. At the time when the decrementless theory was established, nobody in the world had ever dreamed of the possibility of isolating a single nerve fiber in conductible state, still less that of making experiments using it, and I myself was no exception. What gave me pleasure and even admiration was how well the various results obtained from experiments by the use of a single nerve fiber corresponded to and corroborated the assertions which had been made in the decrementless theory.

The essential theorization of the decrementless theory lies in the reasoning that the conduction in nerve is performed by the *local* supply of energy necessary for conduction during its propagation. To speak with the inserted diagram: the impulse is conducted along the nerve by the energy supplied at section A to the next section B, and by the energy supplied at B to section C, and thus it can propagate further on without any decrement. The theory further insists that there is only a quantitative difference, but no qualitative difference, between nerves normal and abnormal (narcotized). With the advancement of the research on single nerve fibers in a conductible state, the former expression which was quite abstract, such as the conduction from section A to B and from B to C by local supply of energy, came to be so scientifically concrete—the energy-supplying point was exactly located. This is, as is shown in the diagram, in nodes of Ranvier R_1, R_2, R_3 ——. In toad, for example, the internodal distance is about 2 mm, so that the impulse, by energy supplied at R_1, has only to reach to R_2, 2 mm ahead, and then by the energy supplied at R_2 it goes on to R_3, another node 2 mm farther, each traveling saltatorily. Even under narcotized (abnormal) circumstances, this mode of conduction would never change, and the size of impulse (which is expressed in terms of the intensity of action potential generated at the Ranvier node) would become small in quantity in proportion to its abnormality, but does not produce any change in quality: it still observes the all-or-none law, with no decrement in conduction.

Presentation of the success of isolating a single nerve fiber in conductible state.—The success of isolation of a single nerve fiber in conductible state was first made public in Japan in 1930. And next at the XIV International Physiological Congress held in Rome in 1932. There, the result was received with great surprise. After reading my paper, I was about to step down from the platform where the film of an isolated single nerve fiber was presented and the all-or-none law was proved with it, when, all of a sudden, Professor Louis Lapicque from France whose name is well-known by "chronaxie", came almost running up to me, from a back seat of the auditorium, and extended his hand, exclaiming before the audience,

"Congratulations! Congratulations!"

I grabbed his hand and shook it up and down a couple of times, being flushed with excitement. Upon getting back to our hotel, I learned that Professor Pavlov and many other professors stared in wonder at what we did. News came everywhere. That was perhaps the strong motivation for Professor Pavlov to invite me to the XV International Physiological Congress to witness our experiments.

In 1934 a monograph entitled *Microphysiology of Nerve* (2) was published.

Invitation to the XV International Physiological Congress.—The next Congress, the fifteenth, was scheduled to be held at Leningrad and Moscow, in 1935 under the presidency of Professor Pavlov. On a certain day in a certain month a letter came from Professor Pavlov himself. It said to the effect that, having heard our marvelous research in which single nerve fibers were isolated in conductible state, he heartily wished for us to come over there and actually let them observe the experiments at the XV International Congress, and felt it a privilege to invite me as Guest of Honor. Reading the letter, I recalled the long train journey of 1926 through Siberia. It was too much, I felt. I said to myself that I would not go. It was because our worries and difficulties ten years before were remembered when we had passed through Siberia to make our public experiments in the XII Congress at Stockholm to prove our decrementless theory with living toads brought all the way from Tokyo. After a few days a representative from the Soviet authorities visited me and assured me any service necessary for the journey and for the experiments in the Congress. The answer for it, however, was kept pending. In spite of earnest encouragement by the younger researchers in my laboratory, I was by no means inclined to go. When the representatives made second visit on me, my response was "I might if you so insist, but here is my proposal. We have to carry a lot of

Japanese toads in *hibernation* as subjects for our experimentation in Summer. Can you satisfy our necessity of supplying ice enough in amount to keep them in hibernation at every designated station along the Siberian Railroad?" Russian Minister of Railroad, Mr. Kaganovich, was willing to accept it, and that made me at last accept the invitation of CCCP. Members who accompanied me were six, including Dr. T. Tomita, present professor of physiology, Keio University, and Dr. I. Tasaki who is now active at NIH, USA. Unlike the previous trip through Siberia in 1926, this trip was the invited one, owing to the earnest request of CCCP. We could rely on them for everything—train, hotel, luggage and so on. There was no disagreeable check on our way to our belongings which were of course limitless. Besides, on arrival at Vladivostok, we were welcomed by Soviet representatives of the Far East and an English speaking interpreter was given us as our escort. A special freight car was attached to our train for the toads we carried. The dining car was decorated with two flags crossing, Japanese and Russian, and there was nothing more to want.

The success of our experiments, as had been expected, are detailed in my followers' notes, and it runs as follows:—Day of demonstrations was fixed as the 12th of August, and the experiments were scheduled to start at 3:00 p.m. Three rooms were allotted for us, from the institute belonging to Professor Bykof. We started to prepare for the demonstrations from the very day we arrived at Leningrad, the 1st of August. Visitor after visitor came to us to watch our demonstrations already during our preparation. That forced us to give a special exhibition for 200 Russian Physiologists on the 6th to avoid too much crowding on the scheduled day. On the very day, the 12th, it was so crowded with spectators that two members of the Professor Bykof's Institute were not enough for regulating them, and so two Japanese embassy officials from Moscow were added to help. The single nerve fiber preparations isolated on that day turned out as many as 33 pieces, and for the repeated experiments using those isolated fibers to prove the all-or-none law, Professor Kato himself served as explainer and interpreter. Stuffiness in the rooms because of crowded visitors raised the room temperature to 30° C from initial 23° C. The whole demonstrations were finished at half past 6:00 p.m. with a great success in rains of applause and admiration. The visitors numbered 600 and more, which was said to be a record-breaking number since the beginning of the International Physiological Congresses 46 years before.

In addition to the above cited synopsis of my followers' notes, there was contributed an outstanding article in *Pravda* by one of the most well-known female writers, Marietta Shaginyan of Russia, headed "Prof. Kato's Experiment" reporting details of our experiments. The article was so impressive and subtle like a woman writer, describing her observation in her own way which was far from such a matter as physiology. By her writing, our achievements bore more interest and significant meaning in a sense than by a specialist's report, and the contribution was translated into many foreign languages to be spread all over the world. Its Japanese translation was distributed by the Russo-Japanese Communication Press throughout this country.

TWENTY-THIRD INTERNATIONAL CONGRESS OF PHYSIOLOGICAL SCIENCE (3)

As we all know, this Congress which was formerly called "International Physiological Congress" is one of the oldest of its kind. Its origin dates as far back as 80 years ago. The first Congress was held at Basel in 1889.

From my early medical days, I have been highly interested in this congress and I have had opportunities to attend several of them. In those days traveling was highly time-consuming without air transportation. From Japan to Europe where most of the International Physiological Congress were held, one had to go through the Indian Ocean and the Suez Canal before reaching his destination, Marseilles. Therefore only a few scientists from this country were able to attend the Congresses.

I attended the 12th Congress in Stockholm, the 13th in Boston, the 14th in Rome, and the 15th in Leningrad and Moscow. What impressed me most was the friendly and peaceful atmosphere in which scientists of different countries of the world exchanged scientific data and opinions to promote their respective research programs. At each congress I attended, I could not help but smile to see how happy the delegates seemed, when they shook hands with their old friends they had not seen for three years, or made new acquaintances whose names were already familiar but only through scientific papers. Needless to say how moved I was, to feel the cordiality offered to the guests from abroad, by the ladies and other family members of the host countries. Since then, it has been my long lasting wish, that Japan could someday act as the host to the congress.

The first congress in Asia.—The XXIII International Congress of Physiological Sciences held in Tokyo, Japan, from 1 to 9 September 1965, as I recall, was the first congress ever held in Asia, and it was no doubt a long-lasting wish not only of me myself but also of all the Japanese scientists in the field to have the Congress here. I believe this wish had much to do with the success of the meeting—if it could ever be called a kind of success. Here, I should like to report how things were done and why they were done so, hoping that it will be of some help to the organizers of future congresses.

The Japanese Union of Physiological Sciences (JUPS), which was the host of the Congress, was organized and affiliated with the International Union of Physiological Sciences (IUPS) in 1950. In 1959, I invited IUPS, on behalf of the Japanese Union, to hold the XXIII Congress in Japan. Upon application, however, I learned that the American Physiological Society had also been very eager to have the Congress in Philadelphia in commemoration of the 300th anniversary of the founding of the University of Pennsylvania. The final decision was actually made at the Council Meeting held on 10 September 1962 in Leiden in favor of our Society, thanks to the concession offered by Professor Carl Schmidt of the American Physiological Society. I can never forget how much I was moved by his fairness, and at the same time I made up my mind then that I would try my best to make the XXIII Congress successful.

General arrangement.—In February 1963, two years and a half before the meeting, 37 Organizing Committee members were elected from the ten national societies affiliated to the JUPS, the Science Council of Japan, and a few governmental offices concerned. The ten societies of our Union are: the Physiological Society of Japan; the Japanese Pharmacological Society; the Japanese Biochemical Society; the Japanese Society of Hygiene; the Zoological Society of Japan; Japanese Society of Plant Physiologists; the Vitamin Society of Japan; the Japanese Endocrinological Society; the Agricultural Chemical Society of Japan; and the Japanese Physical Fitness Society. The membership to these societies at the time of the Congress, in the meanwhile, amounted to over 10,000.

To make our arrangements favorable and effective as well as to save time, a few subcommittees[6] were established in our Organizing Committee as follows:

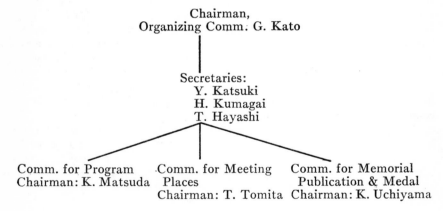

Chairman,
Organizing Comm. G. Kato

Secretaries:
Y. Katsuki
H. Kumagai
T. Hayashi

Comm. for Program   Comm. for Meeting   Comm. for Memorial
Chairman: K. Matsuda   Places   Publication & Medal
                   Chairman: T. Tomita   Chairman: K. Uchiyama

In the lobby of the main meeting place, the National Education Center, the following offices were prepared: registration office for active members; general information center; pigeonholes; registration and information office for ladies; bank; post office; Japan travel bureau; and service center for slide presentation.

This Congress consisted of 2864 members (not including 423 associate members) of which 1655 were from 45 different countries outside Japan and 1209 were from Japan. It was indeed a great pleasure that so many members from abroad could join us, in spite of the long distance to the far east and

---

[6] The Fund-raising Committee was separately established under the chairmanship of Professor G. Kato.

the expensive travel. We were truly happy to have such a large participation.

Scientific program.—The free communications submitted numbered 1238, of which 949 were from abroad and 289 domestic. The free communications were given mainly in the mornings all through the congress period, while the special (invited) lectures and symposia were scheduled for the afternoon sessions. There were twelve invited lectures and twelve symposia. After delivery, the lectures were open to discussions by the scientists of the highest level in their special field of work. For this purpose we invited some seventy world-famous leading scientists. These special lectures and symposia were of special interest especially to the young scientists and did not fail to encourage and inspire them.

Ladies' program.—As our country has its original culture much different from those of western countries, we had an advantage of making our Ladies' Program full of variety. All the activities were well attended, but among them the following programs were most popular; Japanese tea-ceremony party in a Japanese garden; show of Japanese flower arrangement and traditional handicrafts; visits to famous shrines and temples; a tea party with the attendance of Princess Takamatsu at her residence; and a "Kimono" show. The arrangements for all the programs for Ladies were made by the Ladies' Program Committee consisting of the wives of the Organizing Committee. They were housewives who were not used to this sort of work, and I supposed they might have numerous difficulties in organizing and operating the program. Therefore, at the Closing Session on the 9th of September, I was very happy to hear Mrs. Zotterman express, on behalf of all the visiting Ladies, her thanks to our Ladies' Program Committee for their services.

Visiting Japan.—We are proud of our customs, natural beauty, and historical sights. We sincerely hoped that our members' busy schedule allowed them to enjoy some of these treasures which Japan has to offer. For this purpose, we chose five courses for post-congress excursions (to Kyoto and Nara, both ancient capitals of Japan, for example) which I am sure, led them to many places of scenic beauty and of historical interest, well worthy of seeing.

Some closing words.—I do not think it necessary to emphasize here the important role which this Congress has played in the furthering of the physiological sciences, and besides, I believe that, through personal contacts of members and their accompanying associate members, this Congress has provided an excellent opportunity for making personal acquaintances and also for furthering international cooperation and mutual understanding among scientists from all over the world.

LITERATURE CITED

1. Kato, G. *The Theory of Decrementless Conduction,* Monograph, 1–166, (Nankodo, Tokyo, 1924)
   Kato, G. *The Further Studies on Decrementless Conduction,* Monograph, 1–163 (Nankodo, Tokyo, 1926)
2. Kato, G. *Microphysiology of Nerve,* Monograph, 1–138 (Maruzen, Tokyo, 1934) and its 2nd ed. (Nakayama Publ. Co., Tokyo, Japan)
3. Fenn, W. O. *History of the International Congress of Physiological Sciences 1889–1968,* Monograph, 59–68 (Sponsored by the IUPS and published by Am. Physiol. Soc., 1968)
4. Verworn, M. *Erregung and Lähmung,* 119–41 (Gustav Fischer, Jena, 1914)
5. Lucas, K. *The Conduction of the Nervous Impulse,* Monograph, 1–102 (Longmans, Green, London, 1917);
   Adrian, E. D. *J. Physiol.,* **14,** 389 (1912)

6. Forbes, A. and collaborators. *Am. J. Physiol.,* **72,** 177 (1925); **76,** 488–71 (1926)
7. Ishikawa, H. *The Studies in the Fundamental Phenomena of Life,* Monograph (1924);
   (Criticism of Ishikawa's opinion) Davis, H., *Physiol. Rev.,* **6,** 548–55, 577 (1926)
8. Koch, E. *Z. Biol.,* **87,** 249–57 (1928)
9. Fulton, J. *The Selected Readings in the History of Physiology,* Monograph, 225–28 (Thomas, Springfield, Ill., 1930)
10. Kato, G., Kaku, Z., Tasaki, I. *The Problems of Nervous Physiology and Behavior,* Monograph, 203–6 (Georgian branch Acad. Sci. USSR, 1936)
11. Tasaki, I. *Nervous Transmission,* (1962)
    Monograph, 1–106 (Thomas, Springfield, Ill., 1953)
12. Kato, G. *Arch. Intern. Pharmacol. Therap.,* **139,** No. 3–4, 540–46 (1962)

TRANSPORT ACROSS CELL MEMBRANES   1038

R. Whittam and K. P. Wheeler

Department of Physiology, University of Leicester, England

INTRODUCTION

We have been asked to write a critical article with references to only about a hundred key papers of the past eighteen to twenty-four months. There has been a great increase in publications on transport, even omitting work on microorganisms and intracellular organelles, such as mitochondria and vesicles, and inevitably we have had to make an arbitrary selection of approximately one paper out of every five we have read. Of course, much other good published work is not mentioned, but we hope that the bibliography will be an adequate guide to the literature. Further references can be found in several monographs (1, 2) and reviews (3–7) which have appeared since the last article in this series.

The most striking development is an emphasis on the study of the transport of one substance in relation to the transport of other substances or to another cellular activity. Thus, sugars and amino acids can influence the transport of each other, and the movements of both require Na. The well-established linkage between Na and K transport through the Na pump now seems to be matched by a similar relationship for movements in the opposite direction which are also mediated by the Na pump. The metabolism of cells is increasingly being shown to be governed by transport across cell membranes. Again, the potential difference (PD) across membranes and epithelia is related to ion movements brought about by the Na pump. Sodium seems to play a unique role which has led to the concept that the movement of other substances is related to the magnitude of the concentration difference of Na ions across a membrane or epithelium.

The feature of transport which has become best established and the most currently investigated is the nature of the ATPase reaction catalyzed by cell membranes. Perhaps the most obvious trend here is the interpretation of results in terms of conformational changes, or similar structural changes, of the ATPase molecule according to its ionic environments. The number of observations currently explained in this way is already large. It should be emphasized at the outset, however, that in spite of the large amount of chemical work, little study has been made to relate rates of ATPase activity with rates of transport. Moreover, it is becoming apparent that conclusions relating to the function of cells and organs cannot be uncritically drawn from work with preparations of membranes from fragmented cells. This ar-

21

ticle will deal with transport and secretion across epithelia, transport in single cells, the relationship between metabolism and transport, and finally the molecular mechanism of active transport insofar as ATPase activity and carriers are concerned.

TRANSPORT ACROSS EPITHELIA

Vasopressin.—The toad bladder has the same physiological function as the epithelium of distal portions of the renal tubule in the mammal in the reabsorption of electrolyte into the tissue fluids of the animal. NaCl is reabsorbed into the body fluids from the urine and this is accomplished by the active transport system in the cells of the bladder. The bladder is in the form of a single layer of specialized epithelial cells supported on connective tissue which contains bundles of smooth muscle and capillaries. Since the toad bladder responds to hormones in the same way as the kidneys, it has proved to be a useful model system for studying the action of neurohypophyseal hormones. The main problems recently investigated relate to the influence of vasopressin and aldosterone as regards both transport and intermediary metabolism.

In the first place, vasopressin causes an increase in the permeability of the bladder to water. The net transfer of water is proportional to the transepithelial osmotic gradient and is markedly raised by vasopressin (8). Water moves passively in accordance with the osmotic gradient, probably by flow through pores whose diameter is increased by vasopressin. The osmotic gradient is due largely to Na transport which is stimulated when vasopressin is added to the fluid bathing the serosal side of the isolated bladder. More Na is able to enter the cells with vasopressin whose action is to lower the permeability barrier to Na, and the increased Na transport follows from the raised intracellular Na. The increased O_2 consumption arises from the greater energy requirement for this transport and is not a direct effect of the hormone, unlike the case with aldosterone. Ouabain acts on the Na pump on the serosal side of the cell and thereby stops the transport, which suggests that Na is actively transported across the epithelium essentially by means of the Na pump in the serosal membrane. A similar action is found in frog skin.

One question recently investigated is whether cyclic 3',5'-AMP is necessary to elicit the action of vasopressin. Cuthbert & Painter (9) concluded from measuring the membrane potentials across the outer and inner facing membranes of frog skin that it was not necessary to involve cyclic AMP to explain the effects of vasopressin. Vasopressin increased the potential across the outer membrane and decreased the resistance, whereas cyclic AMP caused a biphasic change in potential and an increase in skin resistance. Civan & Frazier (10) showed a decreased dc resistance of toad bladder accompanying the action of vasopressin. Ninety-eight per cent of the change due to vasopressin occurred at the mucosal or apical membrane of the epithelial cell, although this membrane contributed only 54 per cent of the total transbladder resistance. By measuring the resistance under different conditions, further evidence was provided that vasopressin acts to increase the permeability of the mucosal membrane of the toad bladder so that Na enters the cells more readily.

Aldosterone.—Another major influence on Na transport in toad bladder is aldosterone, which also stimulates the transport of Na *in vivo* in the mammalian nephron. Its mechanism of action involves RNA-mediated protein synthesis in both systems [see Fanestil et al. in (5); (11)]. This hormone also differs from vasopressin in causing a direct stimulation of metabolism. The secretion of Na is increased only when pyruvate or other substances that yield pyruvate are available and there is an increased utilization of keto acids. The possibility that the activity of an enzyme involved in the tricarboxylic acid cycle may be increased in a way correlated with the enhanced Na transport has been tested. Measurements have been made of the activities of a number of relevant enzymes (12). Physiological concentrations of aldosterone caused an increased activity of several enzymes of the tricarboxylic acid cycle localized in mitochondria. Significantly, there was no change in the activities of enzymes involved in glycolysis. Consistent with the increase in enzyme activity due to aldosterone is the enhancement of CO_2 production from the 6 position of glucose. The effects of glucose on metabolism and Na transport were shown by Kirchberger et al. (13) to have the same time course of onset and the same dependence on the concentration of aldosterone. The enhanced Na transport and general increase in activity of a number of enzymes does not prove a causal relationship, but a positive correlation between the condensing enzyme and Na transport is likely. Thus the time courses of the effects with aldosterone are similar. The general increase of enzyme activity seems related to the increased energy requirement for Na transport.

These changes certainly are related to the physiological response to aldosterone. Further, agents such as puromycin and actinomycin which inhibit protein synthesis also prevent the increment in Na transport otherwise found with the hormone. A difficulty in drawing this conclusion is that deprivation of Na did not prevent the increase in enzymatic activity induced by aldosterone. This observation means that aldosterone induced a potential for Na transport even in the absence of Na. When Na was added after the exposure of the toad bladder to aldosterone in the absence of Na, there was an immediate increase in NaCl secretion. These results are consistent with a hormonal action effectively increasing the energy available to the Na pump. Most data with toad bladder can be summarized thus: 1. Na moves passively into the cell across the mucosal membrane and is later transported by the Na pump across the serosal membrane against a concentration and electrical potential difference; 2. vasopressin increases the permeability of the mucosal membrane whereas aldosterone increases the energy supply for the Na pump; and 3. both hormones raise transepithelial movement of NaCl and water.

One of the new diuretics in treatment of oedema and salt retention is amiloride which prevents Na transport in the distal part of the mammalian nephron. It also prevents Na transport across amphibian bladder and skin. Its action in these epithelia occurs when it is present on the apical side of the skin or bladder as if it prevents the ready entry of Na into the cells. Another possibility for its action is an effect on the transepithelial Na transport at the serosal side of the cell. Crabbé et al. (14) studied the action of amiloride with special reference to its effect on the response of toad skin to aldosterone. They found that amiloride did not affect the response of the skin to vasopressin or to aldosterone; but Bentley (15), in a detailed study of the action of amiloride on the toad bladder, found that amiloride counteracted the response of the bladder to vasopressin, cyclic AMP, and aldosterone. He further showed that it is a thousand times more active at the mucosal surface than at the serosal surface. The available evidence suggests that amiloride inhibited the action of the two hormones, both by restricting the entry of Na and by inhibiting the response to aldosterone. These findings with toad bladder are consistent with amiloride inhibiting Na transport in the mammalian kidney.

Another bladder which possesses the active mechanism for the reabsorption of NaCl is that of the freshwater turtle which differs from the amphibian bladder in having independent mechanisms for the transport of cations and anions. Solinger et al. (16) showed that ouabain causes a reversal of the sign of the PD across the bladder so that the serosal fluid becomes negative to the mucosal fluid. There was also a reversal of the direction of the short-circuit current across the epithelium, and the resistance of the bladder was doubled. The transport of anions was unaffected by ouabain whereas the transport of Na was inhibited, which suggests that the transfer of anions and cations occurs by independent mechanisms.

Renal tubules.—It is widely believed that reabsorption of Na in the renal tubule involves the breakdown of ATP when Na is transported from the lumen to the perilymph fluid by the action of the Na pump. It follows that when an increased load of NaCl is presented to the renal tubular epithelium an increased activity of the Na,K-activated ATPase would be expected. To test this possibility Katz & Epstein (17) examined the effect of large changes in the tubular reabsorptive load of Na on this ATPase activity in kidney homogenates. Glomerular filtration and tubular reabsorption were raised by uninephrectomy, and there was a parallel increase in ATPase activity in the contralateral kidney. There was no increase in the activity of several other enzymes such as glucose 6-phosphatase, succinic dehydrogenase, and glutaminase. A similar relationship was found when Na reabsorption was stimulated in two other ways—by feeding rats on a high-protein diet or after injection of methylprednisolone. These important experiments show that the renal ATPase can be increased in an adaptive way when the reabsorption of Na is chronically increased. Further work showed that the increase was due to the quantity of plasma membrane per cell rather than an increase in enzyme activity per unit of membrane (18). Another way of altering renal function is to bring about a decrease by adrenalectomy. This caused a fall of 35 to 40 per cent in ATPase activity concomitant with development of adrenal insufficiency (19). A high-Na diet counteracted the decrease in enzymatic activity. Increase in ATPase activity in response to changes in secretory activity necessitated by environmental changes has also been found in the gills of seawater eels (20) and in goldfish intestine (21).

Somewhat less direct evidence for a role of the Na pump in Na reabsorption comes from the measurements of PD across several segments of the nephron especially with regard to the effect of ouabain. There was no measurable PD across the proximal tubule of the isolated perfused nephron of the rabbit kidney; this indicates that active fluid absorption, which is secondary to NaCl transport, does not require or generate a PD (22). On the other hand, there was a PD in the collecting (distal) tubule which was abolished by ouabain. It fell from a mean control value of 23 mV (lumen negative) to zero in 10–35 min. The results suggest that the PD may be related to active Na transport. It is not possible to say whether the Na pump maintains the PD by virtue of the Na and K gradients set up by the Na pump or as a consequence of a separation of charge arising from an electrogenic Na pump.

Intestine

Discussion will be limited to the transfer of nonelectrolytes and amino acids across the intestine in which there have been recent advances; other aspects, including the transport of salts and water, have been fully reviewed recently (3, 6) and will not be considered here.

Nonelectrolytes.—Earlier work showed that glucose is actively absorbed better than most other sugars and that all the hydroxyl groups are involved in binding to the transport system during some part of the process. A convenient way of elucidating the involvement of hydroxyl groups in the C-1 and C-6 position is to use analogues of galactose. This sugar is not metabolized like glucose, yet is absorbed at about the same rate. The structural requirements for the active transport of hexoses across the intestine of the rat and hamster have thus been further clarified. Barnett et al. (23) extended earlier work and showed that the absorption of glucose involves hydrogen bonding at the C-6 position of the sugar. From analogues and structural isomers of glucose it was proposed that hydrogen bonding is also required in the C-1 position. A decrease in active transport occurs when replacements are made in positions 1, 2, 3, 4, and 6 of the sugar molecule, suggesting that contact at five points is necessary between the sugar and the membrane to bring about transport.

The involvement of the C-1 position is related to the discovery of Neale & Wiseman (24) and Caspary & Crane (25) that L-glucose is actively transported across the small intestine of the rat and hamster.

To demonstrate absorption of L-glucose, the animal must be in a semistarved or fully starved state. The movement of L-glucose against its concentration gradient fills the requirements of active transport: it needed oxygen, it was abolished by reducing the temperature to 27°C, and it was inhibited by phlorhizin and by D-glucose. As was previously shown for the transport of D-glucose, there was a requirement of Na ions at a concentration of 83 mM or greater (24). A possible interpretation of these findings is that L-glucose was converted to the D isomer, which was then absorbed, but this was shown not to be the case. It is now clear that the carrier mechanism for D-glucose probably transports L-glucose, thus the hypothesis that the transported hexoses must possess the D-pyranose structure is no longer tenable. These findings on intestinal absorption of glucose are similar to the results with rats and dogs in which it has been shown that D- and L-glucose share a common pathway in renal tubular absorption (26).

Another feature of absorption—of both sugars and amino acids—is inhibition by ouabain acting at the serosal side of the intestine owing to stoppage of the Na pump and dissipation of the Na concentration gradient between cells and extracellular fluid. Ouabain inhibits the transfer of amino acids at a lower concentration than is required to prevent absorption of sugars (27). This observation throws doubt on the existence of a common mechanism for the transport of sugars and amino acids (see later also). A possible explanation is that the influence of the Na concentration on the affinity of a carrier may be different for sugars and amino acids. These effects of ouabain seem to be related to the influence of amino acids and sugars on the transmural PD. Amino acids raise the PD, which suggests a correlation between transport and PD as was found with sugars. The Na pump is immediately stimulated by glucose or galactose and if amino acids act in the same way then the PD would seem to arise from separation of positive charges by the Na pump (electrogenic action) (6, 28). A further possibility is that Cl movements might contribute to the PD (29). A PD is produced only by those sugars that are actively transported, and it seems also with amino acids that it is those compounds which are transported by a special mechanism that generate an electrical potential. It is significant that the effects of amino acids and hexoses are additive as regards the PD, for this is in keeping with the view from other data that separate carriers are involved.

The absorption of disaccharides has been studied in amphibian small intestine by Parsons & Prichard (30). With maltose and trehalose, hydrolysis of the sugar occurred in the lumen, and the disaccharidases, maltase, and trehalase were found in the intestinal wall. Hydrolysis to the monosaccharide was closely related to the absorption mechanism. There was no evidence for lactase in any of the animals studied (*R. temporaria, R. pipiens,* and *B. vulgaris*). There is also a high concentration of trehalase in mammalian intestine and kidney. This finding, together with the fact that enzymes are present which catalyze the synthesis of trehalose from glucose, led Sacktor (31) to suggest that trehalase has a role in the absorption of glucose across the intestinal mucosa. His scheme involves the utilization of ATP in the transport of glucose and the formation of trehalose as an intermediate in the process. The evidence for the scheme lies in the localization of the enzymes which synthesize and hydrolyze trehalose.

Malathi & Crane (32) have criticized the scheme, however, on the grounds that phlorhizin or the absence of Na had no effect on the activity of trehalase, whereas these conditions prevent the transport of the product of hydrolysis (glucose). Another point is that trehalase and also lactase are located in a region of brush border external to the active transport process for sugars. Further rigorous tests on the location of these enzymes are required. Disaccharidases are undoubtedly important physiologically in the young animal, and most work has been concerned with lactase. In a study of maltase, Karrer & Parsons (33) followed the development of enzymic activity in the small intestine of embryos and chicks up to 6 weeks of age. There was an exponential increase *in ova* and constant levels were later achieved. These results point to the importance of the age of the animal in assessing the physiological significance of enzymic activities in relation to function.

Interaction between sugars and amino acids.—It is clear that transport of many sugars and amino acids in the intestine occurs by similar Na-activated processes which probably involve combination of substrate with specific membrane carriers. Moreover, reciprocal inhibitory effects among amino acids and sugars indicate that interactions between these two classes of compounds must take place somewhere in the transport process. However, controversy arises over the nature and level of this interaction and the site of interaction remains unresolved. Mention has been made of difficulties arising from the inhibition by ouabain and the PD generated by these substances so far as the notion of a common carrier is concerned. Further aspects of this problem are well presented in papers by Munck (34, 35) and Alvarado (36).

Munck has shown that galactose inhibits the transport of both valine and proline in everted sacs of rat small intestine, whereas glucose either has no effect (with small sacs) or actually stimulates (with large sacs). In addition, glucose completely abolishes the inhibitory effects of galactose. Munck suggests that glucose acts by providing an energy supplement which permits amino acid transport to continue in spite of the simultaneous expenditure of energy on sugar accumulation. Newey & Smyth (6) reached a similar conclusion in relation to the absorption of competing sugars. Large increments in net water flow from mucosal to serosal fluid accompany the increased amino acid fluxes in large sacs with glucose, and if this water movement is produced by different means, the amino acid flux is similarly stimulated. Glucose, therefore, acts by increasing the net transintestinal water flux and possibly by providing energy directly. As further evidence against interactions between sugars and amino acids at the carrier level, Munck (35) showed that the addition of high concentrations of sugars to the mucosal fluid does not increase the flux of previously equilibrated leucine back into this compartment. Again, high concentrations of amino acids do not affect the backflow of previously equilibrated galactose, whereas increased efflux of leucine is effected by addition of amino acids, and increased efflux of galactose by sugars. These results can only be explained by supposing that separate carriers mediate the transport of sugars and amino acids.

In contrast, Alvarado (36) has provided convincing evidence that sugars inhibit the flux of amino acids across the mucosal membrane of hamster small intestine by direct action at an external carrier site. The crucial observations were that galactose inhibits the initial rate of uptake of the nonmetabolizable amino acid, cycloleucine, into pieces of everted intestine *before* galactose has entered the tissue and whilst the cycloleucine is being transported down its own concentration gradient. These findings rule out the possibilities of stimulation from the inner side of the membrane and competition for a common energy source. Alvarado (36) suggested that these, and other, conflicting findings may be explained by species differences; but it seems that identical experiments with intestine from the different species should be performed before this explanation can be unreservedly accepted.

AMINO ACID TRANSPORT IN CELLS

Most current investigations of amino acid transport can be placed into one of two main groups dealing with: the classification of transport systems; interactions between cations and amino acids.

Classification of transport systems.—The two extreme classifications are that all amino acids enter a given cell via a single, common pathway, or that each amino acid moves through its own separate system. However, it seems unlikely that either of these extremes exists; instead all cells and tissues examined possess a limited number of distinct systems each of which serves for a number of amino acids, though usually with some overlap. Discrimination and classification of the several transport systems is achieved first by kinetic analysis of the interactions which occur among different amino acids during transport processes, and second by studying the effects of variation of other parameters, such as pH or ionic composition of the incubation medium. Christensen (37) has recently reviewed this topic and we confine ourselves to a few papers illustrating the current trends. One method which could help delineate the various transport systems more sharply is the production of an amino acid which is transported by only one pathway, in contrast to most natural amino acids which can be transported by more than one route. Knowledge of the structure and conformation of such a model substrate then provides useful information about the detailed structural requirements of the individual transport pathways. Christensen and his colleagues (38) have developed this approach in synthesizing a new amino acid by introducing an amino and a carboxyl group onto carbon 2 of the bicycloheptane ring of norcamphor. The two isomers obtained are transported by the system normally used in all cells and tissues tested for amino acids with nonpolar, branched side chains, such as valine and leucine.

Another trend is to consider movements of amino acids in both directions across the cell membrane, rather than to study uptake and accumulation by the cells. Thus Christensen & Handlogten (39) measured the efflux of several amino acids from the Ehrlich ascites tumour cell and reached the important conclusion that these amino acids escape from the cell via the same mediating routes used for their uptake. However, the apparent K_m values for efflux are in general much higher than those for influx, whereas the V_{max} values for the two directions are similar. A relatively small loss of neutral α-amino acids occurs also by a nonsaturable process, again corresponding to the findings for uptake.

Clayman, Belkhode & Scholefield (40, 41) have emphasized the importance of exchange diffusion of amino acids across cell membranes. From detailed studies with slices of mouse pancreas and both Novikoff and Ehrlich ascites tumour cells, they showed that exchange processes can lead to large increments in the flux of certain amino acids; that these are independent of the presence of cations and of whether the amino acid is intra- or extracellular; that they are characterized by a molar influx to efflux ratio which approaches 1:1, and that they have half-maximum values equal to the K_m values for transport. An amino acid on one side of a membrane can exchange with a different amino acid on the other side (heteroexchange), as well as with another molecule of the same compound (homoexchange), depending on the amino acids involved and the conditions. It seems reasonable to assume that homo- and heteroexchange are important *in vivo*. Many of these findings are not completely new, and extrapolation to other cells and tissues may not be warranted, but it does seem important to emphasize that all these complicating processes should be considered when amino acid transport is investigated.

Interactions between cations and amino acids.—Much work is devoted to finding out exactly how Na and K exert their effects on amino acid transport in various tissues, and how energy is obtained for the concentrative uptake of the amino acids. As with the interrelations between sugars and amino acids, no unique and common answer has emerged. The following examples illustrate the experimental approaches and results obtained with three widely different tissues. Thier (42) examined the two possibilities that Na activates amino acid uptake either by direct coupling at the carrier site, energy coming from the movement of the Na down its concentration gradient, or by an indirect mechanism which Na acts in a nonspecific role in the production of cellular energy for transport. He found that in isolated toad bladder the net uptake of amino acids occurs through the serosal surface of the epithelial cells, the mucosal surface being impermeable to amino acid movement in either direction. The uptake of γ-aminoisobutyric acid is Na dependent, ouabain sensitive, and unaffected by anaerobiosis. Replacement of serosal Na with choline, Mg, or K abolished the net uptake of the amino acid. The author suggests that the transport of amino acids and transepithelial Na movement are independent—but this conclusion requires qualification. Certainly, operation of the Na pump is necessary for amino acid uptake. The requirement for Na would seem to be for downhill Na movement across the serosal membrane, and clearly this can only occur so long as the Na pump maintains a low internal Na concentration so that Na can indeed move downhill inwards.

In a comprehensive series of experiments with mouse Ascites tumor cells, Eddy (43) has provided further evidence in support of the theory that glycine accumulation against its concentration gradient depends on the simultaneous spontaneous movements, down their respective concentration gradients, of Na and K. Cells were depleted of ATP and then incubated with various concentrations of external Na, K and glycine, measuring net movements of the ions and water, as well as of glycine. Cyanide was also added to stop mitochondrial ATP production. Variation of the cellular concentrations of Na and K was achieved during the preliminary treatment of the cells. Glycine accumulation (ΔGly) is accompanied by net increases of cellular Na (ΔNa) and water, together with a loss of K (ΔK). Mean values of ΔNa/ΔGly and ΔK/ΔGly are 0.9 and 0.6, respectively. In addition, the ratio of the concentrations of internal to external glycine attained is inversely proportional to the ratio of the Na concentrations, such that intracellular glycine exceeds the extracellular concentration only when the converse situation holds for Na. The exact quantitative relationship depends to a minor extent on the K concentration gradient. Contrary evidence comes from the work of Margolis & Lajtha (44), who have studied the concentrative uptake of several amino acids by mouse brain slices. Among other findings they showed that in the absence of external K the concentration of cellular Na is greater than extracellular Na before incubation, yet amino acid accumulation still occurs. Uptake also occurs during incubation in media containing low concentration of Na, when the intra- and extracellular Na concentrations are approximately equal. Since no consistent correlation is apparent between tissue levels of ATP and the extent of concentrative uptake of individual amino acids, these authors concluded that the energy source remains obscure and that although these processes depend on the extracellular concentrations of Na and K, the presence of a physiological Na gradient between tissue and medium is not necessary.

The mixture of common and contrasting observations in the work outlined above suggests either that marked differences exist among the various tissues examined or that some complicating factor has been overlooked. One possibility is a complication arising from exchange diffusion of the test amino acids with endogenous amino acids. Another is the production of ATP by glycolysis which is actually raised by cyanide. This point is relevant to Eddy's conclusion that whilst uptake by an exchange involving Na diffusion could not be excluded, the available evidence favors the idea of another source of energy. In view of the high glycolytic rate in tumour cells, ATP seems the likely source.

Lowenstein, Smith & Segal (45) have studied another interesting aspect of this topic by measuring the uptake of amino acids by slices of rat renal papilla under conditions of high external Na and sucrose concentrations (greater than 800 milliosmolal) and low oxygen tension, thus simulating the peculiar physiological environment of this part of the kidney. They found that the papilla can concentrate amino acids under these conditions, whereas active accumulation by the renal cortex is abolished or greatly reduced.

INTERDEPENDENCE BETWEEN ACTIVE TRANSPORT AND METABOLISM

Work has continued on the connection between metabolism and active transport. When transport has been measured in cells incubated under favorable and unfavorable metabolic conditions, the results continue to show that energy-giving reactions are needed for active transport. This view is only one side of the picture, and there has been more interest in the converse question as to the regulation of metabolism by the Na pump and the nature of the enzymic reactions at which control is exerted. Thus, lactate production in human red cells is the sole source of energy, and can be divided into two parts—one which is constant in magnitude and insensitive to operation of the Na pump, and another which is directly proportional to the rate of operation of the Na pump (46). This means that active transport is a pacemaker of metabolism. The magnitude of the transported-regulated component was from about 25 to 75 per cent of the constant component. This variable part of lactate production depends on external K being available for inward movement and internal Na for outward movement; it is regulated by the concentrations of these ions which determine the rate of operation of the pump. Ouabain inhibits the lactate production stimulated by external K and has no effect in the absence of K in the medium.

Since the Na pump converts ATP to ADP, the question arises as to the site at which ADP exerts its controlling influence over metabolism. Hoffman & Parker (47) showed that the Na pump regulates the metabolism of glucose to lactate in human red cells at the point of conversion of 1,3-diphosphoglycerate (1,3-DPG) and ADP to 3-phosphoglycerate and ATP through the action of phosphoglycerate kinase. The interaction between the sodium pump and this enzyme occurs in the cell membrane. This study further confirmed that the Na pump determined the rate of lactate production whether the metabolite was glucose or a purine nucleoside. Deoxynucleosides, like nucleosides, also produce lactate without the involvement of hexokinase and phosphofructokinase. Ouabain should therefore decrease lactate production from deoxynucleosides—a prediction verified by Wiley (48) who showed that inhibition of the Na pump decreases lactate production from deoxyadenosine and deoxyinosine.

The situation with respiring tissues is somewhat more complicated because of the complexity of the exergonic reactions. Nevertheless, the view that the Na pump regulates mitochondrial O_2 consumption through its production of ADP has been verified in Landon's (49) work. He examined the effect of isolated membrane fragments of kidney cortex on the respiration of kidney mitochondria *in vitro*. The membranes stimulated respiration in a manner indicating interaction between mitochondrial ATP production and ATPase activity of the Na pump. The control seems attributable to the generation of ADP and Landon found no evidence for a direct coupling between the electron transport pathway of mitochondria and the Na pump. On the other hand, involvement of a high-energy intermediate has been suggested at various times and recently claimed in the work of Klahr et al. (50) with turtle bladder and Levinson & Hempling (51) with tumor cells. Their view is that ATP generated from glycolysis is able to produce a high-energy intermediate of the electron transport system. This intermediate would then energize the Na pump in a way sensitive to ouabain.

These claims were based on work with cells possessing a special feature not found in either red cells or kidney cortex. This is a high Pasteur effect, and more study of metabolism as such is needed, especially of the factors regulating glycolysis. Thus, in Hempling's work, there is a difficulty of interpretation in terms of known metabolic pathways, in that the respiratory activity of ascites tumour cells was raised to the same level by adding either external K or DNP. The effect of external K was abolished by ouabain, as it is in other cells, yet adding DNP together with K did not raise O_2 consumption more than adding one alone, although the site of action of K is the external surface of the membrane whereas DNP acts on mitochondria. Is their similar effect on O_2 consumption fortuitous or does it imply a connection in relation to cell metabolism? This is the crucial question, and an unequivocal answer has not been found. Both the Na pump and oxidative phosphorylation may involve the turnover of a high-energy intermediate. One observation suggesting that active transport is energized by such an intermediate which may be common to both processes is that oligomycin prevents the response to external K, but not to DNP.

This finding is similar to that of Klahr et al., who found that DNP stimulated glycolysis in turtle bladder which they attribute to hydrolysis by DNP of the high-energy intermediate of the Na pump. The crux of their hypothesis is that energy is dissipated by this proposed action of DNP, but experimental evidence on this point is lacking. Their view differs from that of Hempling in not invoking a high-energy intermediate of oxidative phosphorylation; it is still ATP which is the source of energy from metabolism for the Na pump.

Considerable clarification of these views is given in the work of Gordon & de Hartog (52) who also worked with Ehrlich ascites tumour cells. Their important paper shows that K may cross the membrane in two ways. There is first transport through the normal Na pump, which elicits an increase in glycolysis that is almost completely abolished by ouabain. This observation is comparable to the situation in red blood cells. However, there is also a loss of intracellular K which can be initiated by adding valinomycin. This response was still found with ouabain when there was an increase in the rate of glycolysis some six to eight times over control values. The changes in K transport and glycolysis were attributed to an action of valinomycin on mitochondrial membranes as well as on the plasma membrane so that there was passive diffusion of K out of the cell. The results showed clearly that K transport regulates the rate of glycolysis in intact cells and point further to a possible role of mitochondrial ion transport in the maintenance of the ionic balance of the tumour cell. It is evident that enough different kinds of cell exist as regards the pattern of metabolism to test critically whether mitochrondria are directly involved in chemical reactions of the Na pump in the plasma membrane.

A clear demonstration of the influence of external cations on cellular respiration is shown in the work of Rang & Ritchie (53). They studied the effect of external K and other cations on the O_2 consumption of rabbit desheathed vagus nerves at rest and during activity. There was a resting O_2 consumption, and extra O_2 was consumed as a result of electrical stimulation. The extra O_2 consumption was virtually abolished by ouabain and was taken to reflect the pumping of ions to restore the ionic imbalance following electrical activity. This component of O_2 consumption was dependent on external K and, as would be expected, K could be replaced by other ions which simulate it in the activity of the Na pump. There is also an effect of K on the O_2 consumption of slices of brain cortex from rabbits (54). The tissue oxygen consumption is markedly raised in a high-K Ringer, and the response is abolished by ouabain, oligomycin, and deprivation of Na. It seems that the metabolic response of brain cortex slices, like that of peripheral nerve, depends on the operation of the Na pump.

PASSIVE PERMEABILITY TO IONS

A cell's ionic balance is determined by passive permeability as well as by active transport. Most interest is centred on the Na pump, but remember that its activity is regulated by the concentration of internal Na which, in turn, depends on the membrane permeability. To maintain a steady state with an unchanging level of internal Na it follows that if a cell membrane is leaky so that external Na readily enters the cell, then an active pump would need to work equally fast to make good the inward leakage. A similar point applies, *mutatis mutandis,* as regards K. There is a finite limit to the rate of function of the Na pump—at least in red cells—which means that there must be an upper limit to the passive permeability, for otherwise there would be an imbalance between entry and exit of Na and K. The question arises: is passive permeability kept at a low level in a way that depends on metabolism or is the low permeability an inherent property of the cell membrane influenced by such factors as fixed positive charges, lipid composition, and Ca? There is much evidence for the view [see Lepke & Passow in (7)] that large changes in the permeability of cations following variations in pH and ionic strength can be related to changes in the density of fixed positive charges of the membrane. At the same time, metabolic inhibitors such as iodoacetate, fluoride, and lead act synergistically with calcium to cause a selective increase in passive K movements. An observation still not fully explained is the enhancement of this permeability change with metabolites such as adenosine and other nucleosides. Whatever the mode of action of these compounds, the K loss undoubtedly depends on Ca because complexing agents prevent their effect.

Some preliminary work (55) on the increase in permeability to K due to metabolic inhibitors suggested that their effects arise from a failure of the Ca pump in the cell membrane which maintains a very low intracellular Ca concentration (56). Considerable advance in the mechanism of the control of passive permeability has recently come from the work of Gárdos (57) and Parker (58). Gárdos (57) found that bisulphite ions cause a hydrolysis of 2,3-DPG and also a loss of K which is found only when Ca is present in the Ringer solution. The main finding to explain is the selective increase in permeability to K and not to Na. This change has been described under a variety of conditions. The early work relates to the influence of metabolic inhibitors which act synergistically with Ca to increase the permeability of human red cell membranes to K. The recent work with bisulphite shows the same phenomenon, although there is a difficulty since Parker (58) produced an increase in permeability to both Na and K and did not need Ca, whereas Gárdos (57) found that Ca was necessary to elicit the permeability change just to K. There is also a difference of interpretation of the effects of bisulphite. Thus, Gárdos (57) suggests that the consequential change in permeability to K arises from interference with the metabolism of 2,3-DPG. Bisulphite inhibits the enzyme 2,3-DPG phosphatase and blocking of this enzyme in a way dependent on Ca ions is held to be responsible for the high rate of outflow of K. An alternative view (58) is that the effects of bisulphite are related more to the reducing potential of this anion than to its interference with the metabolism of 2,3-DPG. Support for this view is that the effects on cation permeability were independent of the level of 2,3-DPG and that oxidizing agents reversed the permeability changes caused by bisulphite. Whatever the correct explanation, the interesting discovery is that the permeability of red cells to Na and K can be reversibly influenced by changes in the state of oxidation as determined by oxidizing and reducing agents.

This whole question has become of great topical interest in view of two other findings on the control of cation permeability. The first finding is due to Sutherland, Rothstein & Weed (59) and Garrahan & Rega (60). They found that slowly penetrating organic mercurial compounds such as para-chloromercuribenzene sulphonate (PCMBS) interacted with the membranes of intact red cells so as to produce alterations in permeability to Na and K. Sulphydryl groups involved in the control of cation permeability comprise only between 4–18 per cent of those in the membrane, and seem to be located within the interior of the membrane and not readily accessible to either the intracellular or extracellular fluid. The permeability changes due to PCMBS are reversed by cysteine, thus providing a method for changing the cation concentration of cells.

The other (unrelated) way of influencing passive permeability is with cyclic antibiotics such as valinomycin, which selectively increases the permeability to K but not to Na (61). The permeability change in this case depends primarily on steric factors, particularly the relationship between the diameter of the ring and the effective diameter of the ion. Such antibiotics are potentially of great value in characterizing the kinds of molecules within the membrane which are involved in regulating cell permeability. An attractive hypothesis is that cyclic peptides with an hydrophobic outer shell and a hydrophilic inner region might be able to allow K ions, but not Na ions, to pass through the inner hydrophilic region. Work with these antibiotics opens up the possibility that the formation of such a structure in the red cell membrane might be the cause of the selective loss of K under the various conditions mentioned above. Passive permeability and the control of downhill ion movements is obviously not a static property of membranes but is a dynamic one, as is well known for the ionic fluxes responsible for nervous conduction.

WATER MOVEMENTS IN THE RED BLOOD CELL

Two outstanding problems concerning the permeability of red cells to water have been thoroughly investigated by Solomon and his associates. There is a discrepancy between the rate of swelling of the red cell under hypotonic conditions and its rate of shrinkage under hypertonic conditions with the same osmotic pressure difference. This led Rich et al. (62) to examine the effect of external osmolarity on net water movements. They measured the osmotic permeability coefficient, for both human and dog red cells, as a function of the osmolarity of the bathing medium and showed that the coefficient decreases as the external osmolarity is raised and vice versa. Moreover, the value of the coefficient is independent of the direction of water movement, of the solute used to provide the osmotic pressure gradient, and of pH in the range 6 to 8: it depends only on the final osmolarity of the medium. From these results, and the practically instantaneous responses to changes in external osmolarity, it seems likely that a thin layer at the outside of the cell membrane may control water movements.

Gary-Bobo & Solomon (63) have provided convicing experimental evidence to support a novel explanation for the apparent anomalous osmotic behavior of the human red cell. They found that calculations according to the van't Hoff equation give osmotic volumes for the human red cell considerably in excess of total cell water when the pH is below the isoelectric point of haemoglobin. The van't Hoff equation is, therefore, inapplicable for measurement of the solvent properties of the red cell; yet the previously suggested explanation, that part of the cell water is unable to participate in osmotic phenomena, was based on assumptions inherent in this equation. Hence this explanation must be considered untenable, a conclusion supported by *in vitro* measurements of osmotic and other properties of haemoglobin solutions, which failed to show any salt exclusion by the protein. Accordingly, a new hypothesis was developed, based solely on thermodynamic principles, which predicts that, at constant pH, the net charge on the haemoglobin molecule decreases with increasing concentration of haemoglobin. Such a change in charge of the macromolecule would result in the movement of counterions across the cell membrane and cause the apparent anomalous osmotic behavior. Experimental tests of this thesis provided quantitative agreement between the anion shift predicated by the equation and that observed in response to osmotic gradients. As the authors point out, this mechanism could provide an electrical transducer for osmotic signals, and its operation in other tissues could be of wide physiological importance.

ION MOVEMENTS, CHEMICAL REACTIONS, AND THE SODIUM PUMP

Ion movements and ATP.—As was suspected from earlier work with giant axons of the squid, a high ratio of ATP/ADP is required for optimum operation of the Na pump and it is unnecessary to have arginine phosphate (64). When the ratio is lowered, Na efflux becomes insensitive to external K. Brinley & Mullins (65) internally dialyzed giant axons and investigated the influence of eleven naturally occurring high-energy phosphate compounds of which only ATP fully supported the normal Na efflux. The efflux increased nonlinearly with increase of internal ATP and there was no evidence of saturation even when the ATP concentration was 10 mM. Deoxy-ATP supported 25 to 50 per cent of the Na efflux. Partial support of active K influx was also found when deoxy-ATP was present in human red cells, but again ATP was more effective (66). It has been possible to compare the energy expenditure for the Na pump in the isolated squid axon and the human erythrocyte; a minimum of 20 per cent of the total energy produced by each cell is used for Na extrusion. This work with nerve axons and red cells reinforces the view that ATP is a proximate energy source for the Na pump.

The dependence of the Na pump on ATP raises the question whether passive movements of Na and K might lead to synthesis of ATP by backwards running of the pump. Garrahan & Glynn (67) tested this possibility with ghosts of human red cells and found that radioactive orthophosphate (*P_i) was incorporated into ATP. Whatever the distribution of ions across the membrane and irrespective of the presence of ouabain, there was always a rather constant level of labelling of ATP. However, when ghosts rich in K and poor in Na were incubated in K-free Na Ringer, additional labelling was found which was inhibited by ouabain. Under these conditions there is a driving force for the entry of Na and exit of K. This extra labelling was also prevented if the external medium was isotonic KCl. It seems that a labelling of ATP occurs at about 2 per cent of the rate of ATP splitting, and that both reactions are mediated by the Na pump according to the direction of the Na and K movements. The chemical reaction is driven or depends upon the downhill ion movements when ATP is labelled just as much as the uphill (active) transport depends upon ATP splitting. In the latter case the chemical reaction does not occur unless the ions are transported, so for both downhill and uphill ion movements there is a coupling with the chemical reaction. Since a salient feature of the Na pump is the coupled movement of Na and K, the further question arises: does the ouabain-sensitive labelling of ATP require downhill movements of *both* Na and K?

Lant & Whittam (68) found that the ouabain-sensitive labelling of ATP did not occur when a migration of only Na or K was allowed to occur across the membrane; downhill movements of both ions were needed for the labelling. Furthermore, small amounts of external K which were sufficient to facilitate normal operation of the Na pump also prevented labelling. Although net synthesis of ATP has not been demonstrated because of the large amount of ATPase activity, it appears that there is a connection between downhill ion movements and ATP synthesis of the same kind as the connection between uphill ion movements and ATP splitting. Energy made available by the hydrolysis of ATP supports ion movements, and the opposite form of energy transformation further suggests that the incorporation of $*P_i$ into ATP can be driven by a coupled flow of Na and K down concentration gradients.

The ion movements which accompany the ouabain-sensitive labelling of ATP have been characterized. A component of unidirectional K efflux from cells is sensitive to ouabain, even when the Ringer solution is K free, so that it cannot be balanced by K entry. When external Na is not present because of its replacement with choline, this ouabain-sensitive component of K efflux was found [see Glynn & Lüthi in (7); (69)]. Two further tests have been made to explain the nature of the K efflux. First, there is the question of the accompanying ions. Unidirectional measurements of Na entry and exit were made to see whether there is an excess of entry over exit which is ouabain sensitive and the same magnitude as the K efflux. A complication in these measurements is that the bulk of the ouabain-sensitive Na fluxes represents exchange diffusion catalyzed by the Na pump (70–72). This exchange of internal for external Na occurs only in the absence of external K. Nevertheless, in addition to this exchange diffusion, there is a small excess of ouabain-sensitive Na entry over exit which matches the ouabain-sensitive K loss (73). These results with tracers show that small parts of the downhill movements of Na and K are inhibited by ouabain. These results were checked by measuring net movements of Na and K, and a small amount of K loss and Na gain was found to be inhibited by ouabain (69).

The general conclusion from these studies is that Na and K can move down concentration gradients (Na inwards and K outwards), across the membrane of the human red cell in a coupled manner, and in a way catalyzed by the Na pump and associated with the labelling of ATP with P_i. When allowance is made for the ATP splitting which occurs when ATP is being labelled, a comparison is possible of the number of ions moving down the concentration gradients in relation to the incorporation of 1 mole of $*P_i$ into ATP. The ratio is in the region of 2—a value close to the ratio for the active transport of Na and K relative to ATP splitting (74). An anal-

ogy to interpret the results is a fixed-gear bicycle in which the pedals rotate
in the same relationship to the wheels whether the bicycle is moving for-
wards on the level or uphill, or moving backwards downhill. The wheels
represent the Na and K movements and the crank the chemical reaction.

CHARACTERIZATION OF ION MOVEMENTS MEDIATED BY THE SODIUM PUMP

Ion movements across cell membranes can be conveniently divided into
those mediated by and those independent of the Na pump. The pump is inhibited by ouabain, and the paramount question is whether all of the unidirectional fluxes thus inhibited are those which lead to net movements or
whether they are of the kind called exchange diffusion. The characteristics
of ouabain-sensitive fluxes have recently been thoroughly studied. Besides
the well-known uptake of K and extrusion of Na, this work has shown that
the Na pump can catalyze other movements of both Na and K. Thus, two
other kinds of ion fluxes have been described which do not cause net movements and yet cannot be attributed to leakages of ions by diffusion.

Exchange diffusion of Na through the Na pump.—One kind of ion exchange is of internal Na for external Na. In human red cells (69–73), squid
giant axons (75), and frog muscle (76, 77) there is exchange diffusion of
Na which is ouabain sensitive, and this exchange is abolished when external
K is added. This process has been clarified in the work of Garrahan &
Glynn (70, 71, 78) and Baker et al. (75). The ouabain-sensitive Na exchange is progressively suppressed, synchronous with a progressive increase
in the exchange of internal Na for external K, as the external K concentration is raised from zero to 5 mM. The Na:K exchange represents active
transport, and it is significant that the concentration of external K required
for half-maximal activation is 1–2 mM for Na:K exchange and the same
value for abolition of Na:Na exchange (72). This observation adds weight
to the belief that the Na:Na exchange is brought about by a modified operation of the Na pump.

The involvement of the pump in the exchange diffusion process is further suggested by the requirement for ATP demonstrated with red cell
ghosts. The ghosts must contain concentrations of ATP, ADP, and P_i such
that the ratio of $[ATP]/[ADP] \cdot [P_i]$ is low (71). ATP is not measurably
hydrolyzed by the Na pump because there is no external K, but it may be
needed to convert the ATPase (see later) into the phosphorylated form,
which would seem to accelerate Na exchange. It follows that raising the internal concentration of P_i or decreasing that of ATP alike facilitate Na:Na
exchange, provided the external medium is free of K.

The same features of Na:Na exchange have been found in similar experiments with squid giant axons. When the Na efflux is measured from
axons immersed in K-free seawater, the ouabain-sensitive component is approximately the same magnitude as the ouabain-sensitive component of Na
influx. These axons were partially poisoned by 2,4-dinitrophenol and under
these conditions the membrane catalyzed a ouabain-sensitive exchange dif-

fusion of external and internal Na. In the squid axon, as in the human red blood cell, internal Na can be exchanged for external K or external Na according to whether the medium contains K or is without it. A further finding with squid axons relates to the specificity of the internal and external transport sites towards different alkali metals (75). The Na:Na exchange is specific for Na, for even external Li is unable to replace external Na, and Na:Li exchange is not found.

Exchange diffusion of K.—It is clear that the Na pump catalyzes Na:Na exchange in the absence of external K, and the question arises whether a comparable K:K movement can also be facilitated. Results suggesting that this is so have been described by Glynn & Lüthi (see 7) and Lant & Whittam (69). Potassium efflux must occur by carrier-mediated exchange if it is stimulated on increasing the external K concentration, and this has been found in red cells. The ouabain-sensitive K efflux was 25 per cent higher when the Ringer solution contained K than in K-free Ringer. This finding suggests that K efflux is linked to K influx and that this exchange occurs during normal operation of the Na pump.

Activation by external K.—The nature of the interaction between external K and external Na has been further clarified in work with human red cells and squid giant axons. Perhaps the most significant finding as regards mechanism is the influence of changes in the concentration of external K on ion movements. In nerve axons immersed in a solution containing 460 mM-Na, the ouabain-sensitive Na efflux increases along a sigmoid curve as the external K concentration is raised from 0–100 mM. There are signs of saturating at high K concentrations. Furthermore, the dependence of ouabain-sensitive K influx on external K concentration is similar to that for the ouabain-sensitive Na efflux.

Similar results were found in human red cells by Priestland & Whittam (79), and in these cells external Na competed with K with an inhibitor constant of about 5–10 mM Na. The results show that the K influx was markedly affected by the concentration of external Na. Competition with other ions has also been described (80), Na again being held to compete with external K whereas some other ions (e.g. tetraethylammonium) may act on some part of the transport system other than the K-sensitive site. All these results lead to the interpretation that external K stimulates Na efflux with a requirement for more than one K ion on the transport site facing the outside medium. This conclusion may have a connection with the stoichiometry of Na and K coupled movements in relation to ATP hydrolysis since approximately two K ions are transported inwards per molecule of ATP hydrolyzed (81). A sequential attachment of K ions seems likely, although the molecular nature of the reaction is quite unknown.

A sigmoid response has also been found in the hydrolysis of ATP with respect to activation by K using fragmented membranes, and it has been suggested that this connotes an allosteric mechanism. Such a mechanism is likely on general grounds inasmuch as the ATPase and Na pump are spatially asymmetrical since activation by internal Na depends on the presence of external K. Evidence for this kind of mechanism with intact cells is somewhat equivocal, however, since the sigmoid response is found only in the presence of external Na, whereas the Na pump in intact cells operates independently of external Na. The question arises: why is external Na needed to elicit the sigmoid response, if this response is indeed a feature of the Na pump, since it must be remembered that Na efflux and ATPase activity are stimulated by external K without being influenced by external Na and, in the absence of external Na, the response is that of a rectangular hyperbola? The sigmoid response found with intact cells therefore appears to arise largely from competition at external sites of the transport mechanism between Na and K (75, 79, 80).

Stimulation of Na efflux by external ions and insulin.—Further study has been made of the influence of the internal Na concentration on Na efflux from human red cells (82) and its dependence on external cations. The evidence fits with the view that Na efflux depends partly on the amount of Na in cells and partly on the counterion in the external medium which is transported inwards as Na is transported outwards. The influence of the external ion on the amount of Na efflux is K > Cs > Rb > Li when the internal Na concentration is greater than 30 meq/liter cells. With lower values the sequence of activating external ions is different. The effects of these ions on Na efflux resemble some of the effects obtained with artificial membranes such as those made of glass, and the type discussed by Diamond & Wright (83).

Na fluxes in rat diaphragm muscle have been shown to increase after treatment with insulin and the response is unaffected by deprivation of external glucose (84). Few effects of insulin on ion transport have previously been described and the effects may be summarized as an increase in K content and decrease in Na content, both changes being accompanied by an increase in the exchange of these ions. These effects are consistent with a stimulation of the Na pump by insulin which would produce an increase in membrane potential by electrogenic operation of the Na pump. The physiological role of insulin in regulation of the ionic balance of tissues remains to be elucidated.

Ion Movements Independent of the Sodium Pump

When the Na pump is inhibited, some of the unidirectional movements of Na and K occur by diffusion and these are thought of as leakages of ions determined solely by the driving force in the form of the concentration gradient (or, more correctly, the electrochemical potential gradient). Only a part of the ouabain-sensitive fluxes can be accounted for by diffusion. Thus, besides the exchanges of ions described above which depend on operation of the Na pump, a second kind of carrier-mediated transport of Na has been described when Na ions cross the membrane independent of the Na pump. Interest in this connection has been stimulated by the suggestion of Hoffman (85) that part of the ouabain-insensitive Na movements might occur because of a second Na pump.

Frog skeletal muscle.—There is good evidence with frog skeletal muscle (76, 77, 86) and human red cells (87) that the Na exchange persists in the presence of ouabain and is not a passive leak with the characteristics of a diffusion process but an exchange mediated by a carrier. Several lines of work lead to this conclusion. Keynes & Steinhardt (76) and Sjodin & Beaugé (77) found that in frog muscle the Na exchange was markedly influenced by the concentrations of external and internal Na. When external Na was replaced by Li, the ouabain-insensitive component of Na efflux was strikingly reduced, and this component was insensitive to external K. The inability to replace external Na with Li shows that the exchange system is specific for Na like the modified action of the Na pump which also catalyzes Na:Na exchange (76, 86). The salient difference between the ouabain-sensitive and ouabain-insensitive exchange diffusion of Na is that the former but not the latter is abolished by external K. Another point arises from the fact that Na efflux should depend on the concentration of internal Na as well as on external Na. Two lots of muscles were prepared containing either about 5 meq Na/kg or 15–30 meq/liter. A comparison was made of Na efflux from both lots of muscles in the presence and absence of ouabain. (The ouabain-sensitive component showed the features to be expected from previous work. However, although the ouabain-sensitive components of Na efflux and K influx were raised on increasing internal Na concentration, the important point has not yet been established whether the Na pump becomes saturated by elevated internal Na concentrations.) A component of Na efflux was ouabain insensitive. Thus, muscles poor in internal Na showed a fall in Na efflux when Na in the Ringer solution was replaced by Li, but the fall was greater with muscles rich in internal Na. The general conclusion is that replacement of external Na with Li decreases Na efflux caused by a ouabain-insensitive mechanism. There are notable differences between different cells in their responses to external Li, for example among squid axons, frog striated muscle, and human erythrocytes, although the three kinds of cells show the same features as regards the normal Na pump.

Red blood cells.—Similar findings were described in human red cells by Lubowitz & Whittam (87). Exchange diffusion implies that Na influx should depend on the concentration of internal Na, and they found that entry of Na in the presence of ouabain was stimulated by raising the level of internal Na; there was also an increase in Na efflux on raising external Na. Exchange diffusion of Na, therefore, occurs in the presence of ouabain. External K had no effect on the exchange. These results suggest that red cell membranes possess a carrier system which can catalyze Na:Na exchange in the presence of ouabain but which is not able to bring about net increase or decrease of Na. This kind of Na exchange is inhibited by ethacrynic acid. The part of Na efflux which depended on external Na was the same magnitude as the part which was inhibited by ethacrynic acid when the measurements were made in the presence of external Na. There are considerable difficulties in interpreting results with this compound inasmuch as it is a sulphydryl inhibitor which also decreases ATPase activity and the Na and K movements of the Na pump. The results are most simply explained in terms of exchange diffusion independent of the Na pump. Both with red cells and squid axons (65), there was no indication of a Na pump which was not coupled to the entry of external K (88).

In summary, Na and K movements consist of

1. exchange of internal Na for external K through the Na pump,
2. exchange diffusion of internal and external Na in a way inhibited by ouabain and external K,
3. exchange diffusion of internal and external K sensitive to ouabain,
4. exchange diffusion of internal and external Na insensitive to ouabain and to external K,
5. leakage of Na and K independent of a carrier system.

CALCIUM MOVEMENTS

The concentration of ionized Ca is extremely low in most living cells and Ca plays a part in several cellular functions. In muscle fibers it is one of the factors regulating activity of the contractile system, and there are marked changes in membrane permeability due to Ca. New mechanisms by which cells maintain a low internal Ca concentration have been discovered in recent work with red blood cells and giant axons of the squid.

Red blood cells.—The permeability of the human red cell membrane to Ca is very low and the ion penetrates the membrane only with great difficulty. It has been known for some time, however, that Ca enters the cells more readily when they are depleted of metabolites and it is under these conditions that intracellular Ca increases the membrane permeability generally. The question therefore arises whether an outwardly directed calcium pump exists to maintain the internal concentration at a lower value than the external.

Convincing evidence for a Ca pump in human red cells has been adduced by Schatzmann & Vincenzi (56). The efflux of Ca was measured with tracer in cells subjected to reversible haemolysis so that the membranes of the ghosts had become reconstituted to resemble those of the initial cells. The cell membranes possess a mechanism for the outward extrusion of Ca so that the internal free ionic Ca is maintained at a much lower level than the extracellular concentration. Calcium extrusion from ghosts was shown to depend on ATP which was hydrolyzed; without ATP there was no transport. During the initial phase of Ca transport about 0.8 mole Ca was extruded per mole P_i produced. The ATPase activity of the membrane was stimulated by internal and not by external Ca. The striking feature of the Ca pump is that it is independent of the Na pump, and the Ca-activated ATPase of the red cell membrane is insensitive to Na, K, ouabain, and oligomycin.

Squid nerve axons: Na efflux linked to Ca influx.—A new mechanism for Ca movements in axons of *Loligo forbesi* has been discovered by Hodgkin & Baker and their colleagues (89, 90) in a penetrating study of the complex relationship between the fluxes of Na and Ca. When external Na is replaced by Li, choline, or glucose there is an increase in Na efflux and in following up this early unexplained finding, further surprising effects were found. Na efflux is normally decreased markedly by ouabain but the increase on replacing external Na with Li was unaffected. However, this increment was abolished when Ca was left out of the artificial seawater bathing the axons. This key observation suggests that there is a component of Na efflux which is insensitive to ouabain and depends on external Ca (89). Calcium-dependent Na efflux is most evident in axons in Na-free medium, and as external Na is added it decreases to a small level. In other systems there is competition between Na and Ca and tests were made to see if this accounts for the different effects of external Ca. The entry of Ca was measured as well as Na efflux. It emerged that external Na caused a parallel decrease of both Ca influx and the Ca-dependent part of Na efflux. The somewhat complicated effects of external Na depended to some extent on the other solute used as replacement, but the results agree with a model in which there is competition between Na and Ca for a carrier molecule. Activation of Na efflux by external Ca fitted a Michaelis curve in accordance with equations derived for the model. Calcium influx was raised five- to fortyfold on decreasing external Na, and three- to tenfold on raising internal Na. The influence of internal Na on Ca entry has a bearing on the cardiotonic action of cardiac glycolysis, and Baker et al. (89) advance an interesting hypothesis, amenable to experimental test, for a link between the Na pump, Ca entry, and the contractile system in heart muscle.

The effects of external Ca were insensitive to ouabain and therefore independent of the operation of the Na pump. A precise coupling ratio was not determined because of variation in the values and because the fluxes could not be measured on the same axon. However, the indications are that some two to five Na ions move out as one Ca ion moves inwards and that the ions move in a linked way on a carrier molecule. The coupled movements are most marked when internal Na is high and external Na is low.

Squid nerve axons: Ca efflux coupled to Na influx.—Since a carrier system brings about a linked movement of Na out and Ca in, the question arises whether movements in the opposite direction might similarly be coupled. In the first situation with Na-free Ringer both ions are moving downhill, with their respective electrochemical potential gradients, whereas in the second case Ca would be moving uphill and Na downhill. Blaustein & Hodgkin (90) measured Ca efflux from squid axons and found that it was not affected by ouabain but was reduced on replacing external Na with Li, choline, or glucose, or by replacing external Ca with Mg. On the other hand, surprisingly, metabolic inhibition with cyanide caused an increase to 5–15 times the normal value. This observation means that a metabolic inhibitor promoted an uphill movement, and an explanation lies in the fact that cyanide causes an increase of some thirtyfold in the consideration of internal ionized Ca. After increase in Ca efflux due to cyanide, removal of external Na and Ca caused a fall of twentyfold in Ca efflux. The large efflux of Ca caused by cyanide is therefore mainly an exchange of internal Ca for external Na and Ca. The effects of deprivation of external Na and Ca are greater with poisoned than with unpoisoned axons because a greater amount of internal Ca is available for outward movement (90). The results, that both external Ca and Na promote Ca efflux, suggest an exchange diffusion of Ca for Ca and, in addition, a coupled movement of Na inwards and Ca outwards. Some of the energy for extruding Ca from squid axons therefore seems to come from the downhill movement of Na. This is a novel kind of linkage in that an uphill ion movement occurs without a direct dependence on ATP. Energy is, of course, used in maintaining the low internal Na concentration needed for there to be a driving force for Na to move inwards. Many far-reaching questions arise from this work. There might still be an ATP-dependent pump in nerve axons similar to that in red cells since some ATP would be available from glycolysis which is not inhibited by cyanide. Nevertheless, it is clear that a part of the normal Ca efflux is related to Na influx.

MEMBRANE ATPase ACTIVITY

In this section we shall use the term ATPase to describe only the adenosine triphosphatase activity which depends on the presence of Mg, Na, and K, and which is completely inhibited by ouabain, since this is the reaction associated with the transport of Na and K. Similarly, we shall limit the term phosphatase to mean only the Mg plus K-dependent phosphatase activity of the ATPase preparations.

Mechanism of the ATPase reaction.—Recent work on the detailed mechanism of the membrane ATPase reaction has consolidated earlier concepts and most of the findings concerning phosphorylated intermediates, the phosphatase activity of ATPase preparations, and the effects of cardioactive steroids and other reagents now present a fairly consistent picture. A few anomalies and discrepancies still exist, however, and these are noted below.

The simplest reaction sequence for the ATPase reaction that will account for all the reported experimental results is:

$$1. \quad \text{ATP} \quad + \quad E \underset{}{\overset{\text{Mg}^{++}, \text{Na}^+}{\rightleftharpoons}} E_1\text{-P} \quad + \quad \text{ADP}$$

$$2. \quad E_1\text{-P} \xrightarrow{\text{Mg}^{++}} E_2\text{-P}$$

$$3. \quad E_2\text{-P} \xrightarrow{\text{K}^+} E \quad + \quad P_i$$

In this scheme E_1–P and E_2–P represent two different forms of a phosphorylated enzyme intermediate. Most of the evidence supporting this sequence has been described previously and the publications discussed below either provide further support for or deal with more uncertain aspects of it.

Formation of an intermediate.—Evidence for the formation of a phosphorylated intermediate during the ATPase reaction was originally obtained only with a few extremely active ATPase preparations isolated from kidney, brain, and the electroplax of *Electrophorus electricus.* Several attempts to show ATPase-dependent phosphorylation in red blood cell membranes were unsuccessful and these failures were particularly disappointing in view of the immense volume of information about Na and K transport accumulated through studies of this tissue (46, 85, 88). There is now good evidence, however, for the formation of a phosphorylated intermediate in red blood cell membranes as well as in other tissues. The difficulty with red cell membranes apparently arises from the unusually high level of nonspecific phosphorylation that obscures the small amount associated with the ATPase reaction. By careful selection of the experimental conditions, both Blostein (91) and Bader et al. (92) overcame this problem and demonstrated the formation of intermediate with properties similar to those found in other tissues.

Bader and his colleagues, in addition, examined the relationship between enzymic activity and the phosphorylated intermediate of ATPases isolated from a total of six tissues and eleven species. They detected a phosphorylated intermediate in each preparation and also showed that the amount was related to the enzymic activity. The ratio of ATPase activity to the amount of intermediate fell within a twofold range, in spite of a 400-fold range in the specific activities of the ATPases. There was a comparable relation with phosphatase activity. Digestion of the phosphorylated enzymes with pepsin or pronase yielded identical ^{32}P-labelled peptides after electrophoretic separation; the available evidence therefore suggests that the mechanism of the membrane ATPase reaction is likely to be similar in most tissues and animal species.

Nucleotide specificity.—The question of nucleotide specificity of the membrane ATPase has been thoroughly examined by Schöner et al. (93), because of the contradictory results published during recent years. They found that ATP, ITP, and GTP are substrates for ATPases prepared from human red blood cells and from ox brain, the ratio of optimum reaction rates for the latter enzyme being ATP:ITP:GTP $= 27:2:1$. Similarly, when each of these nucleotides is labelled in the γ position with ^{32}P$_i$ there is incorporation of ^{32}P into the brain ATPase via a Na-dependent process; and subsequent addition of K leads to a rapid decrease in labelling. All three nucleotides appear to be hydrolyzed via the same acceptor group and the contradictory reports on nucleotide specificity in the literature might result from different sensitivities of the assay systems employed. In their latest paper dealing with the electroplax ATPase, Fahn, Koval & Albers (94) found a different effect with ITP. Phosphorylation does not occur if IT^{32}P is used in place of $AT^{32}P$, and this failure is unlikely to be explained in terms of the assay system. One possible explanation is that the electroplax ATPase is probably a purer form of the enzyme than most of those extracted from other tissues. These findings might be important in connection with work concerning the effects of nucleotides on inhibition by oligomycin and cardioactive steroids, and on phosphatase activity, because some of the arguments developed depend on the assumption that only ATP can phosphorylate the ATPase.

ATP-ADP exchange.—The first step in the reaction sequence can be regarded as an ADP-ATP exchange reaction requiring Mg and Na. This view has been questioned, however, because of the findings that in several ATPase preparations much of the exchange activity can be separated physically from the ATPase activity. This point has been examined in detail by Stahl (95) and Swanson (96), using brain preparations from rat and guinea pig respectively. Blostein (91) also examined this aspect of the red blood cell membrane ATPase. The results described by all three authors leave no doubt that a large proportion of Mg-dependent ADP-ATP exchange activity is not associated with the membrane ATPase activity. Nevertheless, the important point seems to be that the ATPase always exhibits some exchange activity which is stimulated by Na in the presence of low $(0.1–0.2\ \mathrm{m}M)$ but not high $(3\mathrm{m}M)$ Mg concentrations. This exchange reaction elicited by Na is stimulated by oligomycin, in contrast to the overall ATPase reaction and associated cation movements, which are inhibited by this antibiotic. The quantitative relationship between the exchange reaction and ATPase activity remains to be established. Although there is a note of caution in these reports, the general conclusion is that some of the Na-dependent exchange reaction is a component of the membrane ATPase system.

Reversal of reactions 2 and 3 in the above scheme is not found with fragmented membranes: no P_i–ATP exchange has been demonstrated. Yet with intact erythrocyte ghosts there is ouabain-sensitive labelling of ATP with $^{32}P_i$ (67, 68). If this does indeed represent a reversal of the Na pump and if the phosphorylated intermediates are an integral part of the ATPase reaction, then they must also participate in the reverse reactions which lead to incorporation of $^{32}P_i$ into ATP. In this case it follows that each step of the reaction sequence should be reversible.

Two forms of the intermediate.—Impressive support for the existence of the phosphorylated intermediate in two distinct forms comes from the work of Fahn et al. (94) and Post et al. (97). There is a requirement of a low Mg concentration for the ADP-ATP exchange reaction whereas phosphorylation occurs in the presence of a higher Mg concentration. Another indication of differences comes from treatment of the ATPase with *n*-ethylmaleimide (NEM) which abolishes the ATPase activity but enhances the exchange reaction. Moreover, the amount of the phosphorylated intermediate in the NEM-treated enzyme is not reduced in the presence of K, which suggests that treatment with NEM inhibits conversion of E_1–P to E_2–P. Oligomycin has an effect similar to that of treatment with NEM (94). Thus two forms of the phosphorylated enzyme should be distinguishable by their sensitivity to addition of ADP or of K. Addition of ADP should split only E_1–P, whereas addition of K should split only E_2–P.

These tests have been applied to native ATPase and to NEM-treated ATPase isolated from guinea pig kidney (97). The intermediate formed with the native enzyme is hydrolyzed by K but not by ADP, whereas that formed after NEM treatment responds to ADP but not K. The two phosphorylated forms of the enzyme yield the same peptic fragments after digestion and electrophoresis, which indicates that they are chemically very similar. Finally, a further series of experiments, which cannot be adequately described here, provided additional evidence for this sequence of phosphorylated intermediates in the native ATPase, untreated with NEM (97).

The action of ouabain has also been studied in more detail (97). Unfortunately the results must be interpreted with caution because a few apparently conflicting observations were made. There is fairly substantial evidence that ouabain interacts with the E_2–P form of the ATPase and not with the E_1–P form. Furthermore, treatment of the dephospho form of the ATPase with ouabain in the presence of Mg and at low ionic strength slowly makes it resistant to phosphorylation by $AT^{32}P$. Addition of P_i accelerates this inhibitory action. Also, $^{32}P_i$ by itself rapidly phosphorylates the ouabain-treated enzyme (97, 113, 120). Evidence that combination of ouabain with the enzyme after phosphorylation with $AT^{32}P$ yields the same product as phosphorylation by $^{32}P_i$ after treatment with ouabain was provided by electrophoretic comparison of the peptic fragments obtained by digestion of the enzyme after these reactions. On the basis of these findings it seems necessary to modify the reaction sequence as follows (97):

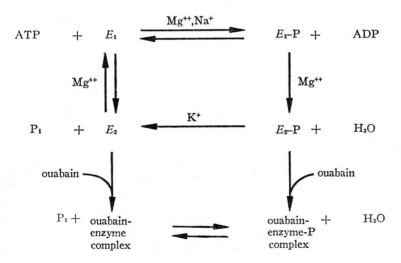

Chemical nature of the phosphorylated intermediate.—Several studies have already indicated that the phosphorylated intermediate described above is an acyl phosphate (E–CO–P$_i$). This conclusion is based on its sensitivity to alkaline hydrolysis and to hydrolysis by purified acyl phosphatase or by hydroxylamine:

$$E\text{–CO–P}_i + NH_2OH \rightarrow E\text{–CONHOH} + P_i$$

If the hydroxylamine-sensitive intermediate is linked to an amino acid residue of the enzyme which is not C-terminal, the most likely candidates for the acyl phosphate would seem to be L-glutamyl-γ-phosphate and L-aspartyl-β-phosphate. Kahlenberg et al. (98) have devised a method based on this view for the isolation and characterization of an acyl phosphate residue in phosphorylated ATPase prepared from pig brain. Their procedure was to digest phosphorylated and nonphosphorylated samples of the enzyme with pepsin and then form a radioactive hydroxamate derivative of the acyl phosphate intermediate by reacting the peptides produced with ^{3}H-labelled N-(*n*-propyl)hydroxylamine. A peptide fraction of each form of the ^{3}H-labelled enzyme was further degraded with pronase and the products were separated by chromatographic and electrophoretic techniques. Samples of both L-glutamyl-γ-N-(*n*-propyl) hydroxamate and L-aspartyl-β-N-(*n*-propyl) hydroxamate were synthesized and used as carriers and markers in the separation systems. ^{3}H-labelled residues from the enzyme migrated with authentic L-glutamyl-γ-N-(*n*-propyl) hydroxamate in a total of seven separation systems; no radioactive residues migrated with the authentic L-aspartyl-β-N-(*n*-propyl) hydroxamate in five of the seven systems. At the last stage of purification the amount of radioactivity from phosphorylated enzyme which migrated with the glutamyl derivative was 2.5 times that from the nonphosphorylated enzyme. From these, and other data, the phosphorylated intermediate in the ATPase appears to be L-glutamyl-γ-phosphate (P_i–CO–CH$_2$–CH$_2$–CH(NH$_2$)COOH).

One outstanding problem connected with the phosphorylated intermediate is the discrepancy between the effects of hydroxylamine on the intermediate and on the complete ATPase reaction. Although there is general agreement that hydroxylamine hydrolyzes the intermediate, some workers have failed to find a significant effect on the ATPase reaction itself. Chignell & Titus (99) have recently examined this problem, using both hydroxylamine and N-methylhydroxylamine with ox brain ATPase. They found that hydroxylamine contains traces of ammonia, which can substitute for K in the ATPase reaction, so that results obtained with this reagent are difficult to interpret. Fahn et al. (94) have also reported that hydroxylamine can act as a partial substitute for K with the electroplax ATPase. When N-methylhydroxylamine is used in place of hydroxylamine, it is difficult to differentiate between a mechanism involving an acyl phosphate which is inaccessible to the reagent from one in which the acyl phosphate is not an intermediate (99). In contrast, Fahn et al. (94), working with the electric organ ATPase, found that the dephosphorylating effect of hydroxylamine and its inhibitory effect on the ATPase reaction are in good agreement, with 30 per cent and 25 per cent changes respectively. These results add weight to the view that the intermediate is part of the overall ATPase reaction.

Relationship between ATPase and phosphatase activities.—This aspect of the subject continues to attract much attention and recent studies provide considerable insight into the ATPase reaction. Interest in the phosphatase activity stems from the demonstration that the ATPase reaction consists of two main steps: a Na-dependent phosphorylation of the enzyme followed by a K-dependent hydrolysis of the phosphorylated intermediate (see above). The latter step is similar in many respects to the phosphatase reaction catalyzed by the same enzyme preparations, so that it is possibly a different manifestation of the same process. On the other hand, doubt has been thrown on this interpretation by the finding that oligomycin partially inhibits the ATPase but not the phosphatase, and that the two reactions show different quantitative responses to various substrates and other inhibitors. Attempts to resolve these differences have been made in recent work in which the phosphatase reaction has been measured under conditions closely resembling those required for the ATPase reaction. Current opinion seems to be that the phosphatase activity is indeed another manifestation of the terminal step of the ATPase reaction.

To simulate the conditions used in the ATPase reaction, the effects of ATP and Na on the phosphatase activity of a variety of ATPase preparations have been extensively investigated. These studies have confirmed and extended earlier reports that either inhibition or stimulation can occur, depending on the exact conditions employed. Inhibition results when Na and ATP, separately or together, are present in the millimolar concentrations suitable for optimum ATPase activity (100). Na competes with K (101) and ATP inhibits competitively when either *p*-nitrophenylphosphate or acetylphosphate is the substrate (100), although the finding that other anions can also inhibit suggests that this effect might be nonspecific (102). Stimulation of the phosphatase is brought about by adding ATP at a concentration of about 0.1 mM, this effect either requiring or being enhanced by the presence of millimolar concentrations of Na (101–103). Other monovalent cations cannot substitute for Na (104) but ITP, CTP, or ADP can replace ATP (102, 103). This activation caused by Na plus ATP is prevented by the addition of oligomycin (102), hydroxylamine (101), or ethyleneglycoltetraacetic acid (105), the latter effect being overcome if sufficient Ca is also added. Besides activating the phosphatase, ATP and Na afford some protection against inactivation by heating (103), treatment with fluoride (103, 106), or treatment with diisopropyl fluorophosphate (100). In contrast, the presence of Mg is essential for each of these inactivating effects which are further enhanced by K. Another comparable action of ATP and Na is to increase the sensitivity of the phosphatase to ouabain (103, 105). It seems, therefore, that in the presence of ATP and Na the phosphatase activity of these preparations tends to resemble closely the ATPase activity.

Now the question arises: how does the presence of ATP and Na bring about these changes in behaviour of the phosphatase? The activation caused by the Na plus ATP is associated with a marked decrease in the K_m for K (101, 103) and with increases in both the K_m and V_{max} values for p-nitrophenylphosphate (101). The findings, taken together with those described above, lead to the view that Na plus ATP produces some conformational or other structural change in the enzyme. In view of the effect of hydroxylamine this change may be associated with the phosphorylation of the enzyme by ATP (101). This conclusion is supported by kinetic analysis of the inhibition of the ATPase reaction by oligomycin, which indicates that the enzyme acquires its affinity for oligomycin only after interaction with Na plus ATP (107). Previous work has established that the formation of the phosphorylated intermediate is insensitive to this inhibitor (see preceding section). On the other hand, phosphorylation may not be involved because the change in the behavior of the phosphatase can also be produced by Na plus ADP, ITP, or CTP as well as by ATP and several studies have indicated that these other nucleotides do not give a phosphorylated intermediate (102, 103) (see preceding section). A possibility is that the presence of the nucleotide together with Na causes the change by acting at a site different from that which binds ATP so that the phosphorylated intermediate is formed (102).

A further point of similarity between the ATPase and the phosphatase reactions is shown by the finding that Tl can replace K in both of them; and in each case the K_m for Tl is only one tenth of that for K (104, 108). Interestingly, in both rats and dogs a comparison of plasma disappearance of Tl and K, and of uptake of these ions by tissue, indicated that their movements *in vivo* are closely related (109).

STRUCTURAL ASPECTS OF THE ATPASE

Very little is known about the chemical composition and structure of the membrane ATPase, in spite of the many studies of it. The ATPase is referred to as an enzyme but this is not meant to imply a single chemical entity, such as just protein, since lipid is probably a component of the catalytic unit. Another point is whether the ATPase is really a combination of a phosphokinase and a phosphatase. Formation and hydrolysis of the phosphorylated intermediate of the reaction occurs by a combination of these two activities. It seems likely that the intermediate is a phosphorylated form of the enzyme itself, though it is relevant that phosphatase activity is exhibited without phosphokinase activity when p-nitrophenylphosphate or acetylphosphate is the substrate. Recent publications deal with the effects of both proteases and phospholipase on the ATPase activity and with the molecular weight of the enzyme.

Digestion with proteases.—Somogyi (110) showed that incubation of a rat brain ATPase with trypsin, chymotrypsin, or subtilisin A causes a progressive loss of the enzymic activity. Trypsin is much more potent than either chymotrypsin or subtilisin A, even though the latter two enzymes effect five or six times more proteolysis of the ATPase than does trypsin under the same conditions. These results suggest that trypsin, in contrast to chymotrypsin and subtilisin A, acts at the region of the active centre of the ATPase. Since trypsin splits peptide bonds involving the carboxylic groups of basic amino acids, it seems likely that either lysine or arginine is closely associated with the active centre. This inhibitory action of trypsin on the ATPase activity is partly counteracted by the presence of Na, K or Mg, separately or in combination, and the further addition of ATP modifies the protective effect of the cations. The action of Mg is abolished by ATP; the protection by K, in the presence of Mg, is lessened by ATP; but the protection by Na, in the presence of Mg, is not influenced by ATP. Somogyi interpreted these effects as manifestations of conformational changes in the ATPase molecule, such that the presence of ATP + Mg + Na stabilizes one form, whereas adding ATP + Mg + K stabilizes another. These are the combinations of ions which cause changes in the form of the phosphorylated intermediate. The configuration of the molecule would seem to depend on whether or not it is phosphorylated.

Function of phospholipids.—Suggestions that phospholipids play an important role in cation transport and ATPase activity are a constant feature of the literature, yet few facts appear to be established because of the many conflicting reports. This problem has been considered again by Emmelot & Bos (111) who have examined the effects of lipid extraction and phospholipase treatment on both the ATPase and the phosphatase activities of plasma membranes isolated from rat liver. Both enzyme activities are abolished by extracting membrane lipids with a mixture of petroleum ether and *n*-butanol, and both are partly inhibited after treatment with phospholipase C. Addition of either synthetic or crude animal lecithin does not restore the enzyme activities of the lipid-extracted membranes, though a slight reactivation of both activities is obtained with the phospholipase-treated samples. There is some doubt about the latter action, however, because of uncertainty about the effect of lecithin on the corresponding activities of the controls. Solubilization of the membranes with deoxycholate or saponin also results in complete loss of the ATPase activity, and this is not recovered after removal of the detergent by dialysis.

Interpretation of these findings is difficult because of the possibility of protein denaturation by the treatment with organic solvents and because of the presence of other biologically active substances in the phospholipase C preparation. General denaturation does not occur because similar solvent extraction does not affect the 5′-nucleotidase or the Mg-insensitive *p*-nitrophenylphosphatase activities of these membranes. Also, the inhibitions induced by phospholipase C are not caused by inhibitory substances which are bound by serum albumin. Additional evidence for the involvement of phospholipids in the ATPase reaction has been provided by earlier work, with some recent support (100), so that it may be tentatively concluded that the membrane ATPase and phosphatase activities depend on a lipid component of the preparation. As Emmelot & Bos (111) point out, however, there is no clear evidence that the associated phospholipid participates as a cofactor in the enzyme process. An alternative function for the lipid is structural in that it may keep the protein in the conformation required for enzymic activity.

Molecular weight.—The complex nature of the ATPase preparations implies that determination of the precise molecular weight of the functional enzyme in the usual sense might be impossible. Nevertheless, Mizuno et al. (112) have estimated the smallest particle size possessing ATPase activity, using an ATPase prepared from pig brain by differential centrifugation and treatment with both deoxycholate and sodium iodide. The enzyme was then disrupted into smaller particles by sonication. The final preparation was active, completely inhibited by ouabain, and remained in the supernatant fluid after centrifugation at 100,000 *g*. The preparation was subjected to gel filtration through a column of Sepharose 4B and part of the protein in it was retarded over a wide range. Fractions of retarded material were eluted and then rechromatographed through the same column. They were also retarded in the same way, showing that the heterogeneous peaks of the original chromatogram corresponded to particles of various sizes. Estimations were made with the use of centrifugation techniques of the partial specific volume and molecular weight of samples of eluted protein corresponding to the smallest particle size. A value of about 500,000 was obtained for the molecular weight.

INHIBITION OF CATION TRANSPORT PROCESSES BY CARDIOACTIVE GLYCOSIDES

The increasing number of publications on this topic owes much to the availability of isotopically labelled cardiac glycosides, which permit new experimental approaches, although several other methods of investigating the action of these inhibitors have also been devised. Albers et al. (113) have measured the rate of interaction of a number of cardioactive glycosides with an ATPase from *Electrophorus* electric organ by monitoring the reaction continuously with a pH-stat, while Baker & Manil (114) have measured the rate of action of ouabain on the efflux of Na from squid axons with a special apparatus for effecting rapid solution changes. The former group showed that the addition of cardioactive glycosides during the course of the ATPase reaction produces a time-dependent inhibition which is a function of the nature of the glycoside, its concentration, and the concentration of Na and K. Thus the rates of inhibition produced by equimolar concentrations of different glycosides, fall in the order: strophanthidin $>$ scillaren A $>$ digitoxin $>$ ouabain $>$ digoxin. The rate of inhibition increases with increasing concentration of glycoside but decreases if the K concentration is raised in the presence of very low concentrations of inhibitor. In contrast to these time-dependent effects, the addition of 1 mM Ca decreases the rate of reaction instantaneously relative to the time resolution of the method. In support of these findings we have observed, with a similar assay method and a kidney ATPase incubated with MgATP and Na, that the addition of K produces an immediate increase in the hydrolysis rate, whereas subsequent addition of ouabain causes a time-dependent inhibition (unpublished observations). Somewhat similar results have been reported by Baker & Manil (114) who showed that even in 1 mM ouabain (a concentration 10^4 greater than that required for 100 per cent inhibition of the Na pump in squid axons) the rate of inhibition of Na efflux from the axon is three or four times slower than that caused by removal of K from the bathing solution. They also found that replacement of the Na in the external solution by Li, K, choline, or dextrose affects the rate of action of ouabain. The rates in Na and Li media are similar and almost ten times faster than in choline or dextrose, while the rate in all-K medium is intermediate between these extremes.

Binding of glycosides.—More details concerning the rates of interaction of cardiac glycosides with membranes have been obtained by measuring the binding of tritiated ouabain or digoxin to intact and fragmented red blood cells (115, 116) and to a number of different ATPases (113, 117, 118). The common picture emerging from these studies is that in the presence of ATP, or other nucleoside di- or triphosphates, the addition of Mg and Na increases the rate of binding of these steroids, whereas K decreases it. Again, as found with the phosphorylated intermediate and with phosphatase activity, there are opposite effects with Na and K in the presence of Mg and ATP. A discrepancy arises with fragmented red blood cell membranes, Na apparently having no effect on ouabain binding (115) although Na is necessary for binding of digoxin (116). The addition of other cardioactive steroids decreases the amount of digoxin which is bound whereas inactive steroids have no effect (117); and the amount of ouabain bound parallels the inhibition of the ATPase activity (113). Schwartz et al. (118) found that the rate constant for digoxin binding to their ATPase is similar to that for ^{32}P incorporation from AT^{32}P, and further correlation is shown by estimates of the ratio of ouabain binding to Na-dependent phosphorylation in the range from 0.5 for the *Electrophorus* electric organ ATPase to 1.0 for a cat brain ATPase (113). However, these authors conclude that the lack of specificity of ATP in the binding reactions indicates that phosphorylation of the ATPase is not essential for binding (113, 115, 118). This view is supported by the fact that binding occurs in the presence of P_i without a nucleotide. On the other hand, the findings of Schöner et al. (93) raise certain difficulties (see section concerning the phosphorylated intermediate).

It is not clear whether the effects of the various ions described above are merely kinetic, modifying only the rates of interaction of the glycosides with the tissues, or whether they also limit the absolute amount of inhibitor bound. Some of the data presented by Albers et al. (113) suggest that both the rate and the absolute amount of ouabain binding are governed by the ionic environment, but it is difficult to distinguish between a very slow rate of inhibition and partial inhibition of the ATPase reaction.

Hoffman & Ingram (115) noted that ouabain binding to intact red blood cells continues after maximum inhibition of K influx has been attained, but by measuring the amount bound as soon as maximum inhibition was reached they were able to estimate the number of ouabain molecules bound per cell. Their figure of 250 molecules per red cell is surprisingly low and, if there is one binding site per pump, leads to the conclusion that about 100 ions are transported per site per second. Ellory & Keynes (116), working with fragmented human red cell membranes, also estimated that about 200 molecules of digoxin are bound per cell.

Nature of the binding and of the complexes formed.—Examination of the stabilities of the complexes formed between ouabain and the tissues has revealed an interesting difference between intact cells and an ATPase preparation, in that the binding of ouabain to intact cells might be influenced by cell metabolism. The complex formed between tritiated ouabain and the *Electrophorus* electric organ ATPase is extremely stable. Washing the enzyme with water or neutral buffer solution fails to remove the ouabain and no exchange of the bound radioactive steroid occurs with nonradioactive ouabain either in neutral Tris or in Tris plus Na, Mg, or ATP (113). The complex is dissociated, however, by exposure to acid, boiling, or extraction with methanol. In contrast to these observations, Mayhew & Levinson (119) have shown that the inhibition of cation transport and cell division induced by ouabain in Ehrlich ascites tumour cells is readily reversible, both processes being restored after washing the cells and incubating them in fresh medium.

These contradictory results are perhaps partially explained by the findings of Baker & Manil (114): prolonged washing of squid axons after brief exposure to ouabain fails to restore ouabain-sensitive Na efflux, although a large ouabain-sensitive Na efflux is obtained if the axon is first poisoned with cyanide before treatment with ouabain. (The ouabain and cyanide are removed by washing before Na efflux is measured.) In view of this effect of cyanide, it seems significant that Mayhew & Levinson (119) incubated their tumour cells anaerobically during exposure to ouabain and during the washing process, but aerobically for the subsequent determination of Na and K movements. Possibly poisoning with cyanide, or anoxia, allows membranes to react reversibly with ouabain, whereas the untreated membranes firmly bind the glycoside.

The nature of the bonds formed between the cardioactive glycosides and receptor molecules in tissues, and the changes involved which lead to inhibition of ATPase activity and cation transport, remain obscure. The general conclusion that conformational changes in the membrane ATPase must be involved is strongly supported by the work on the phosphorylated intermediate (97, 120). Albers et al. (113) suggest that the interaction of the cardioactive steroids with the ATPase may be lipophilic, because of the ready removal of bound ouabain by methanol extraction and because the rate of interaction of the glycosides is inversely related to the number of hydroxyl and sugar substituents. They also point out that the essentially irreversible nature of the binding of cardioactive glycosides invalidates the concept of K acting as a straightforward competitive inhibitor of the interaction.

ISOLATION AND IDENTIFICATION OF CARRIERS

Many models proposed for membrane transport processes assume that the first step is a specific binding of the transported substance ("substrate") to a receptor site of a hypothetical "carrier" molecule which is situated in the membrane. This binding reaction is followed by translocation of the substrate-carrier complex through the membrane and subsequent release of the substrate inside the cell. In the case of facilitated transport the movement is down a concentration gradient; in exchange diffusion there is a movement of equal magnitude in the opposite direction; and in active transport movement occurs against a concentration gradient. The only satisfactory way of testing these model schemes is the actual isolation and identification of carriers. Attempts have been made to this end and during the past few years considerable progress has been made. The rationale behind this approach, its applicability to a wide range of biological systems, the techniques, and most of the important results have been admirably summarized recently by Pardee (121). We shall describe only a few of the latest publications representative of current work.

Oxender and his colleagues (122, 123) have extended their work on a "leucine-binding protein" (LBP) isolated from *E. coli* K-12 cells by osmotic shock. There is a loss of leucine transport activity in these cells following osmotic shock concomitant with the appearance of the LBP in the shock fluid, and the protein has now been purified by chromatography and crystallization. The crystalline protein is homogeneous as judged by polyacrylamide electrophoresis, ultracentrifugation, and immunodiffusion. Its molecular weight has been estimated as 24,000 by ultracentrifugation, 36,000 by gel filtration, and 34,000 by amino acid analysis. It contains a low fraction of sulphur-containing amino acids. Binding of amino acids by LBP is highly specific for the L isomers of the branched-chain amino acids, such as leucine and valine, and the dissociation constants of the complexes are less than 1 μM. Changes in pH and ionic strength have little effect on the binding activity. The localization of LBP in the *E. coli* cell was examined by an immunocytochemical technique, using rabbit antibody against LBP, and it appears to be present only in the cell envelope and not in the cytoplasm (123). The concept of LBP being a carrier molecule is well supported by these results and by those showing first, that the kinetic constants for cellular transport of amino acids parallel the binding activity of the isolated protein, and second, that the synthesis of LBP and the transport of branched-chain amino acids are repressed in cells grown on leucine. To account for the maximal rate of transport observed with the intact cell, each cell must contain about 10^4 molecules of LBP, with a turnover number of about 200 per minute. Practically every aspect of the results of this work shows a remarkable similarity to that of Pardee's group on the sulphate-binding protein isolated from *Salmonella typhimurium* (121).

Anraku (124) also isolated LBP as well as a galactose-binding protein (GBP) from a mutant of *E coli* K-12 that lacks galactokinase. Again, this protein shows many similarities to LBP: its molecular weight is about 35,000 and it binds galactose and glucose with dissociation constants for the complexes of the order 1 μM. The complexes appear to consist of one molecule of sugar or amino acid combined with one molecule of protein. Anraku has also studied the process of restoration of active transport in the osmotically shocked cells (125). He showed that both LBP and GBP can interact with these cells, by a process showing saturation kinetics, and that this interaction increases the ability of the cells to transport leucine and galactose. However, to restore transport activity to nearly the original level, the addition of another nondialyzable substance found in the shock fluid is essential. This substance has no binding properties. Metabolic energy also appears to be necessary for restoration of cellular uptake of the amino acids and sugars.

Work with animal cells has not advanced to the level described above, but progress along similar lines is being made as the following example illustrates. Faust et al. (126) have shown that D-glucose is preferentially bound both by intact brush border membrane preparations from mucosa of hamster jejunum and by such preparations after they have been disrupted by treatment with Tris. Density gradient centrifugation of the latter preparation indicates that D-glucose is bound to a fraction containing the inner materials of the microvilli. Sugars which are actively transported competitively inhibit the binding of D-glucose, whereas those which are not actively transported, and all amino acids tested, have no effect on the binding. D-Glucosamine, which is not actively transported, inhibits both the active transport of D-glucose by everted sacs of jejunum and the preferential binding of D-glucose to the brush border preparation. Sulphydryl reagents and Ca and Li ions all inhibit the binding, whereas Mg stimulates it, and Na, K, and ammonium ions have no effect. These results clearly suggest that the preferential binding of D-glucose to the brush border is related to the initial step in the active transport of sugars by the small intestine.

A different approach to the problem of the identification of membrane carriers is illustrated by the experiments of LeFevre and his associates (127, 128). They are primarily concerned with the facilitated diffusion of monosaccharides through the red blood cell membrane and have examined various factors involved in the formation of complexes between membrane phospholipids and glucose. Their approach to the problem has been to induce the migration of glucose from water into chloroform by adding to the organic phase lipids which had been extracted from membranes. The addition of phospholipids extracted from human red blood cell membranes increases the apparent chloroform/water partition coefficient, but adding the neutral lipids does not. This induced migration of the sugar is not accompanied by comparable movement of water into the organic phase; and the extent of sugar solubilization is directly proportional to the concentration of phospholipid added, whereas the concurrent solubilization of water into the chloroform layer shows saturation kinetics. When the concentration of glucose in the aqueous phase is increased, keeping that of the phospholipid in the chloroform layer constant, the extent of glucose migration is again directly proportional to its concentration, with no sign of saturation.

These experiments were extended by the use of a three-phase system, $H_2O/CHCl_3/H_2O$, in which the effect on water-to-water transfer of glucose of adding erythrocyte membrane phospholipids to the chloroform layer was examined (128). The addition of the phospholipids accelerates the passage of glucose through the unstirred layer of chloroform, though the increase in flux is not correlated systematically with the induced migration described above. In the three-phase system the lecithin-rich fractions of the phospholipids are disproportionately effective in enhancing the glucose movement. Under steady-state conditions the sugar gradient in the chloroform layer is indetectably small, which indicates the interfaces as the sites of primary resistance to sugar movement. In somewhat similar work on the formation of complexes between amino acids and possible carrier molecules, Reiser & Christiansen (129) have recently reported that a lipid fraction extracted from intestinal mucosa will take up valine and glucose from aqueous solutions. The uptake was subject to inhibition by other amino acids and sugars, respectively, and there was no cross inhibition between the two classes of compound.

LITERATURE CITED

1. Stein, W. D. *The Movement of Molecules Across Cell Membranes* (Academic, New York, London, 369 pp., 1967)
2. Robertson, R. N. *Protons, Electrons, Phosphorylation and Active Transport* (Cambridge, 96 pp., 1968)
3. Whole issue on "Intestinal Absorption." *Brit. Med. Bull.*, **23**, No. 3 (1967)
4. Whole issue on "Structure and Function of Membranes." *Brit. Med. Bull.*, **24**, No. 2 (1968)
5. Järnefelt, J., Ed. *Regulatory Functions of Biological Membranes* (Elsevier, Amsterdam, 1968)
6. Newey, H., Smyth, D. H. The Digestive System. *The Biological Basis of Medicine* (Bittar, E. E., Ed., Academic, New York, 1969)
7. *J. Gen. Physiol.*, **51**, No. 5, Part 2, Suppl. Issue on *Cell Membrane Biophysics* (1968)
8. Leaf, A. *Am. J. Med.*, **42**, 745–56 (1967)
9. Cuthbert, A. W., Painter, E. *J. Physiol. (London)*, **199**, 593–612 (1968)
10. Civan, M. M., Frazier, H. S. *J. Gen. Physiol.*, **51**, 589–605 (1968)
11. Fimognari, Grace M., Fanestil, D. D., Edelman, I. S. *Am. J. Physiol.*, **213**, 954–62 (1967)
12. Kirsten, E., Kirsten, R., Leaf, A., Sharp, G. W. G. *Pflügers Arch.*, **300**, 213–25 (1968)
13. Kirchberger, M. A., Martin, D. G., Leaf, A., Sharp, G. W. G. *Biochim. Biophys. Acta*, **165**, 22–31 (1968)

14. Crabbé, J., Ehrlich, E. N. *Pflügers Arch.*, **304**, 284–96 (1968)
15. Bentley, P. J. *J. Physiol. (London)*, **195**, 317–30 (1968)
16. Solinger, R. E., Gonzalez, C. F., Shamoo, Y. E., Wyssbrod, H. R., Brodsky, W. A. *Am. J. Physiol.*, **215**, 249–61 (1968)
17. Katz, A. I., Epstein, F. H. *J. Clin. Invest.*, **46**, 1999–2011 (1967)
18. Manitius, A., Bensch, K., Epstein, F. H. *Biochim. Biophys. Acta*, **150**, 563–71 (1968)
19. Jørgensen, P. L. *Biochim. Biophys. Acta*, **151**, 212–24 (1968)
20. Kamiya, M., Utida, S. *Comp. Biochem. Physiol.*, **26**, 675–85 (1968)
21. Smith, M. W., Colombo, V. E., Munn, E. A. *Biochem. J.*, **107**, 691–98 (1968)
22. Burg. M. B., Isaacson, L., Grantham, J., Orloff, J., *Am. J. Physiol.*, **215**, 788–94 (1968)
23. Barnett, J. E. G., Jarvis, W. T. S., Munday, K. A. *Biochem. J.*, **109**, 61–67 (1968)
24. Neale, R. J., Wiseman, G. *J. Physiol. (London)*, **198**, 601–11 (1968)
25. Caspary, W. F., Crane, R. K. *Biochim. Biophys. Acta*, **163**, 395–400 (1968)
26. Huang, K. C., Woosley, R. L. *Am. J. Physiol.*, **214**, 342–47 (1968)
27. Newey, H., Sanford, P. A., Smyth, D. H. *J. Physiol. (London)*, **194**, 237–48 (1968)
28. Kohn, P. G., Smyth, D. H., Wright, E. M. *J. Physiol. (London)*, **196**, 723–46 (1968)
29. Taylor, A. E., Wright, E. M., Schultz, S. G., Curran, P. F. *Am. J. Physiol.*, **214**, 836–42 (1968)
30. Parsons, D. S., Prichard, J. S. *J. Physiol. (London)*, **199**, 137–50 (1968)
31. Sacktor, B. *Proc. Natl. Acad. Sci.*, **60**, 1007–14 (1968)
32. Malathi, P., Crane, R. K. *Biochim. Biophys. Acta*, **163**, 275–77 (1968)
33. Karrer, O., Parsons, D. S. *Life Sci.*, **7**, 85–89 (1968)
34. Munck, B. G. *Biochim. Biophys. Acta*, **150**, 82–91 (1968)
35. Munck, B. G. *Ibid.*, **156**, 192–94 (1968)
36. Alvarado, F. *Nature*, **219**, 276–77 (1968)
37. Christensen, H. N. *Advances in Enzymol.*, **32**, 1–20 (1969)
38. Christensen, H. N., Handlogten, M. E., Lam. I., Tager, H. S., Zand, R. *J. Biol. Chem.*, **244**, 1510–20 (1969)
39. Christensen, H. N., Handlogten, M. E. *J. Biol. Chem.*, **243**, 5428–38 (1968)
40. Clayman, S., Scholefield, P. G., *Biochim. Biophys. Acta*, **173**, 277–89 (1969)
41. Belkhode, M. L., Scholefield, P. G. *Biochim. Biophys. Acta*, **173**, 290–301 (1969)
42. Thier, S. O. *Biochim. Biophys. Acta*, **150**, 253–62 (1968)
43. Eddy, A. A. *Biochem. J.*, **108**, 195–206, 489–98 (1968)
44. Margolis, R. K., Lajtha, A. *Biochim. Biophys. Acta*, **163**, 374–85 (1968)
45. Lowenstein, L. M., Smith, I., Segal, S. *Biochim. Biophys. Acta*, **150**, 73–81 (1968)
46. Whittam, R. The Molecular Mechanism of Active Transport in *The Neurosciences*, 313–26 (Quarton, G. C., Melnechuk, T., Schmitt, F. O., Eds., Rockefeller Univ. Press, New York, 962 pp., 1967)
47. Hoffman, J. F., Parker, J. C. *J. Gen. Physiol.*, **50**, 893–916 (1967)
48. Wiley, J. S. *Biochim. Biophys. Acta*, **135**, 1071–74 (1967)
49. Landon, E. J. *Biochim. Biophys. Acta*, **143**, 518–21 (1967)
50. Klahr, S., Bourgoignie, J., Bricker, N. S. *Nature*, **218**, 769–70 (1968)
51. Levinson, C., Hempling, H. G. *Biochim. Biophys. Acta*, **135**, 306–18 (1967)
52. Gordon, E. E., de Hartog, M. *Biochim. Biophys. Acta*, **162**, 220–29 (1968)
53. Rang, H. P., Ritchie, J. M. *J. Physiol. (London)*, **196**, 163–81 (1968)
54. Ruščák, M., Whittam, R. *J. Physiol. (London)*, **190**, 595–610 (1967)
55. Whittam, R. *Nature*, **219**, 610 (1968)
56. Schatzmann, H. J., Vincenzi, F. F. *J. Physiol. (London)*, **201**, 369–95 (1969)
57. Gárdos, G. *Acta Biochim. Biophys. Acad. Sci. Hung.*, **1**, 139–48 (1966)
58. Parker, J. C. *J. Clin. Invest.*, **48**, 117–25 (1969)
59. Sutherland, R. M., Rothstein, A., Weed, R. I. *J. Cell. Physiol.*, **69**, 185–98 (1967)
60. Garrahan, P. J., Rega, A. F. *J. Physiol. (London)*, **193**, 459–66 (1967)
61. Tosteson, D. C., Cook, P., Andreoli,

T., Tieffenberg, M. *J. Gen. Physiol.*, **50**, 2513–25 (1967)
62. Rich, G. T., Sha'afi, R. I., Romualdez, A., Solomon, A. K. *Ibid.*, **52**, 941–54 (1968)
63. Gary-Bobo, C. M., Solomon, A. K. *J. Gen. Physiol.*, **52**, 825–53 (1968)
64. De Weer, P. *Nature*, **219**, 730–31 (1968)
65. Brinley, F. J., Jr., Mullins, L. J. *J. Gen. Physiol.*, **52**, 181–211 (1968)
66. Whittam, R., Wiley, J. S. *J. Physiol. (London)*, **191**, 633–52 (1967)
67. Garrahan, P. J., Glynn, I. M. *J. Physiol. (London)*, **192**, 237–56 (1967)
68. Lant, A. F., Whittam, R. *J. Physiol. (London)*, **199**, 457–84 (1968)
69. Lant, A. F., Whittam, R. *Ibid.*, **201**, 52–54P (1968)
70. Garrahan, P. J., Glynn, I. M. *J. Physiol. (London)*, **192**, 159–74 (1967)
71. Garrahan, P. J., Glynn, I. M. *Ibid.*, **192**, 189–216 (1967)
72. Levin, M. L., Rector, F. C., Jr., Seldin, D. W. *Am. J. Physiol.*, **214**, 1328–32 (1968)
73. Priestland, R. N., Whittam, R. *J. Physiol. (London).* **204**, 49–50P (1969)
74. Glynn, I. M., Lew, V. L. *J. Physiol. (London)*, **202**, 89–90P (1969)
75. Baker, P. F., Blaustein, M. P., Keynes, R. D., Manil, J., Shaw, T. I., Steinhardt, R. A. *J. Physiol. (London)*, **200**, 459–96 (1969)
76. Keynes, R. D., Steinhardt, R. A. *J. Physiol. (London)*, **198**, 581–99 (1968)
77. Sjodin, R. A., Beaugé, L. A. *J. Gen. Physiol.*, **52**, 389–407 (1968)
78. Garrahan, P. J., Glynn, I. M. *J. Physiol. (London)*, **192**, 175–88 (1967)
79. Priestland, R. N., Whittam, R. *Biochem. J.*, **109**, 369–74 (1968)
80. Sachs, J. R. *J. Clin. Invest.*, **46**, 1433–41 (1967)
81. Garrahan, P. J., Glynn, I. M. *J. Physiol. (London)*, **192**, 217–35 (1967)
82. Maizels, M. *J. Physiol. (London)*, **195**, 657–79 (1968)
83. Diamond, J., Wright, E. M. *Ann. Rev. Physiol.*, **31**, 581–646 (1969)
84. Creese, R. *J. Physiol. (London)*, **197**, 255–78 (1968)
85. Hoffman, J. F. *Am. J. Med.*, **41**, 666–80 (1966)
86. Beaugé, L. A., Sjodin, R. A. *J. Gen.*

Physiol., **52**, 408–23 (1968)
87. Lubowitz, H., Whittam, R. *J. Physiol. (London)*, **202**, 111–31 (1969)
88. Hoffman, J. F., Kregenow, F. M. *Ann. N.Y. Acad. Sci.*, **137**, 566–76 (1966)
89. Baker, P. F., Blaustein, M. P., Hodgkin, A. L., Steinhardt, R. A. *J. Physiol. (London)*, **200**, 431–58 (1969)
90. Blaustein, M. P., Hodgkin, A. L. *J. Physiol. (London)*, **200**, 497–527 (1969)
91. Blostein, R. *J. Biol. Chem.*, **243**, 1957–65 (1968)
92. Bader, H., Post, R. L., Bond, G. H. *Biochim. Biophys. Acta*, **150**, 41–46 (1968)
93. Schöner, W., Beusch, R., Kramer, R. *European J. Biochem.*, **7**, 102–10 (1968)
94. Fahn, S., Koval, G. J., Albers, R. W. *J. Biol. Chem.*, **243**, 1993–2002 (1968)
95. Stahl, W. L. *J. Neurochem.*, **15**, 499–509 and 511–18 (1968)
96. Swanson, P. D. *J. Neurochem.*, **15**, 1159–67 (1968)
97. Post, R. L., Kume, S., Sen, A. K., Tobin, T., Orcutt, B. (Presented at Symp. Membrane Proteins, New York Heart Assoc. and Heart Fund, Nov. 1968)
98. Kahlenberg, A., Galsworthy, P. R., Hokin, L. E. *Arch. Biochem. Biophys.*, **126**, 331–42 (1968)
99. Chignell, C. F., Titus, E. *Biochim. Biophys. Acta*, **159**, 345–51 (1968)
100. Formby, B., Clausen, J. *Z. Physiol. Chem.*, **349**, 909–19 (1968)
101. Rega, A. F., Garrahan, P. J., Pouchan, M. I. *Biochim. Biophys. Acta*, **150**, 742–44 (1968)
102. Askari, A., Koyal, D. *Biochem. Biophys. Res. Commun.*, **32**, 227–32 (1968)
103. Yoshida, H., Nagai, K., Ohashi, T., Nakagawa, Y. *Biochim. Biophys. Acta*, **171**, 178–85 (1969)
104. Britten, J. S., Blank, M. *Biochim. Biophys. Acta*, **159**, 160–66 (1968)
105. Pouchan, M. I., Garrahan, P. J., Rega, A. F. *Biochim. Biophys. Acta*, **173**, 151–54 (1969)
106. Yoshida, H., Nagai, K., Kamei, M., Nakagawa, Y. *Biochim. Biophys. Acta*, **150**, 162–64 (1968)
107. Inturrisi, C. E., Titus, E. *Mol. Pharmacol.*, **4**, 591–99 (1968)
108. Inturrisi, C. E. *Biochim. Biophys. Acta*, **173**, 567–69 (1969)

109. Gehring, P. J., Hammond, P. B. *J. Pharmacol. Exptl. Therap.*, **155**, 187–201 (1967)

110. Somogyi, J. *Biochim Biophys. Acta*, **151**, 421–28 (1968)

111. Emmelot, P., Bos, C. J. *Biochim. Biophys. Acta*, **150**, 341–53 (1968)

112. Mizuno, N., Nagano, K., Nakao, T., Tashima, Y., Fujita, M., Nakao, M. *Biochim. Biophys. Acta*, **168**, 311–20 (1968)

113. Albers, R. W., Koval, G. J., Siegel, J. *Mol. Pharmacol.*, **4**, 324–36 (1968)

114. Baker, P. F., Manil, J. *Biochim. Biophys. Acta*, **150**, 328–30 (1968)

115. Hoffman, J. F., Ingram, C. J. 420–24, *Proc. 1st Intern. Symp. Metabolism and Permeability of Erythrocytes and Thrombocytes* (G. Thieme, Stuttgart, 479 pp., 1969)

116. Ellory, J. C., Keynes, R. D. *Nature*, **221**, 776 (1969)

117. Matsui, H., Schwartz, A. *Biochim. Biophys. Acta*, **151**, 655–63 (1968)

118. Schwartz, A., Matsui, H., Laughter, A. H. *Science*, **159**, 323–25 (1968)

119. Mayhew, E., Levinson, C. *J. Cell. Physiol.*, **72**, 73–76 (1968)

120. Lindenmayer, G. E., Laughter, A. H., Schwartz, A. *Arch. Biochem. Biophys.*, **127**, 187–92 (1968)

121. Pardee, A. B. *Science*, **162**, 632–37 (1968)

122. Penrose, W. R., Nicholalds, G. E., Piperno, J. R., Oxender, D. L. *J. Biol. Chem.*, **243**, 5921–28 (1968)

123. Nakane, P. K., Nicholalds, G. E., Oxender, D. L. *Science*, **161**, 182–83 (1968)

124. Anraku, Y. *J. Biol. Chem.*, **243**, 3116–27 (1968)

125. Anraku, Y. *Ibid.*, **243**, 3128–35 (1968)

126. Faust, R. G., Leadbetter, M. G., Plenge, R. K., McCaslin, A. *J. Gen. Physiol.*, **52**, 482–94 (1968)

127. Yung, C. Y., Chaney, J. E., LeFevre, P. G. *Arch. Biochem. Biophys.*, **126**, 664–76 (1968)

128. LeFevre, P. G., Yung, C. Y., Chaney, J. E. *Ibid.* **126**, 677–91 (1968)

129. Reiser, S., Christiansen, P. A. *J. Lipid Res.*, **9**, 606–12 (1968)

ENDOCRINE REGULATION OF CALCIUM METABOLISM[1]

D. H. COPP

Department of Physiology, University of British Columbia
Vancouver, Canada

INTRODUCTION

The calcium concentration in the body fluids of a marine invertebrate such as the lobster is almost identical with that of the surrounding seawater. In contrast, marine vertebrates are able to maintain a calcium concentration which is considerably lower (1). The efficiency of calcium regulation increases with vertebrate evolution, and in man, the diurnal fluctuation in plasma calcium has been reported as ±3 per cent (2). In higher vertebrates, calcium regulation is facilitated by the action of two endocrine tissues which arise in the embryo from the branchial pouches. The oldest tissue phylogenetically is the ultimobranchial, which is found in sharks and fishes as well as land vertebrates. In lower vertebrates, it persists as a separate endocrine gland, but in most mammals it is imbedded in the thyroid as the parafollicular or "C" cells. These cells secrete the recently discovered hormone calcitonin (3), which apparently is involved in controlling hypercalcemia. The second endocrine tissue is the parathyroid which is absent from fishes, but is present in all air-breathing vertebrates. It secretes parathormone, which has an important function in combatting hypocalcemia.

The regulating action of these endocrine glands is based on a negative feedback control of parathormone and calcitonin secretion, and the action of

[1] *Nomenclature and units: parathormone* (abbreviation PTH) will be used to designate the parathyroid hormone; biological activity will be expressed in terms of U.S. Pharmacopoeia (USP) units. One milligram pure bovine parathormone is equivalent to 2500 USP units.

The original name *calcitonin* (abbreviation CT) will be used to designate the hypocalcemic hormone from ultimobranchial cells rather than the alternative term *thyrocalcitonin*. Calcitonin has been designated as the official name for the hormone by the World Health Organization. Biological activity is expressed in Medical Research Council (MRC) units based on Thyroid Calcitonin Research Standards A or B as provided by the Division of Biological Standards of the National Institute for Medical Research, Mill Hill, England. One milligram pure porcine hormone contains approximately 200 MRC units.

these hormones on gut, kidney, and skeleton. In mammals, the bone provides a vast reservoir of calcium (1 kg in an adult man) which plays a critical role in calcium homeostasis. Inorganic phosphate and magnesium ions also have an important effect on calcium metabolism. As shown in Figure 1, Sanderson, Marshall & Wilson (5) found that the rapid and precise restoration of the initial plasma calcium in young dogs following induced hypocalcemia and hypercalcemia was grossly impaired when the sources of parathormone and calcitonin were removed by thyroparathyroidectomy, indicating the importance of the endocrine controls in these animals.

During the 5-year period from July 1, 1964, which is covered in this review, there has been a tremendous upsurge of interest in the hormones involved in calcium regulation. The seeds were planted by such pioneers as Joseph Aub, Fuller Albright, Baird Hastings, and Franklin McLean, and nurtured by the Macy Conferences on Metabolic Interrelations and the Gordon Conferences on the Structure and Function of Bones and Teeth. The discovery in 1961 of a second calcium-regulating hormone, calcitonin (4), stimulated and broadened the field.

Most of the work on calcitonin has been carried out during the period covered by this review. There have also been four important international conferences dealing with this hormone—the 2nd Parathyroid Conference held in Noordwijk aan Zee, The Netherlands, August 25–29, 1964 (6); the Symposium on Thyrocalcitonin and the C Cells, held in London, July 17–20, 1967 (7); the 3rd Parathyroid Conference held at Mont Gabriel, Quebec, Canada, October 16–20, 1967 (8); and the 2nd Symposium on Calcitonin and the C Cells held in London, July 21–24, 1969 (9). Readers are referred to the published proceedings of these conferences (6–9) for more details of the exciting experimental work in this field. There have also been a number of excellent reviews on parathormone (10–12), calcitonin (13–16), and endocrine control of calcium homeostasis (17–20).

HISTORY

The importance of the parathyroid glands in calcium regulation has been recognized since the classical paper of MacCallum & Voegtlin published 60 years ago (21). The second calcium-regulating hormone, calcitonin, was discovered 9 years ago (4, 22) and most of the work in this field is confined to the past 5 years.

Parathyroid—parathormone.—The parathyroid glands were described and named by Sandström in 1880 (23) and their significance in calcium metabolism was demonstrated by MacCallum & Voegtlin in 1909 (21). The first biologically active extract was prepared by Collip in 1925 (24) and highly purified parathormone was isolated by Aurbach (25) and Rasmussen & Craig (26) in 1959. There is still some uncertainty as to its precise structure.

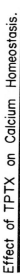
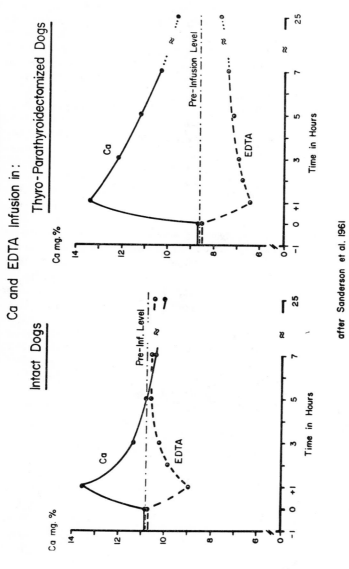

FIG. 1. Effect of thyroparathyroidectomy on precise control of plasma calcium. Recovery from hypercalcemia or hypocalcemia induced by a 1 hr infusion of calcium gluconate or EDTA. Curves for young dogs with intact glands are shown on the left, and for thyroparathyroidectomized dogs on the right. Replotted from the data of Sanderson et al. (5) with permission.

Ultimobranchial—calcitonin.—In 1961, Copp et al. (4, 22) observed that perfusion of the isolated thyroid-parathyroid gland complex in the dog with high-calcium blood caused a fall in plasma calcium which was much too rapid to be accounted for by suppression of parathormone production. The perfusates also lowered plasma calcium when injected into another dog. On the basis of these results, they postulated the existence of a second calcium-regulating hormone which they named *calcitonin* because it was apparently involved in regulating the level or "tone" of calcium in blood. These results were confirmed 2 years later by Kumar, Foster & MacIntyre (27). Originally attributed to the parathyroid, it soon became apparent that the hormone was derived from cells present in the mammalian thyroid. In 1963, Hirsch, Gauthier & Munson (28) reported that acid extracts of rat thyroid had a very potent hypocalcemic and hypophosphatemic effect when injected into young rats. They proposed the alternative name for the hormone, *thyrocalcitonin,* to indicate the gland of origin (28, 29). This discovery was of great importance, for it opened the way to chemical and physiological studies. The thyroid origin of the hormone in the mammal was soon confirmed in a number of laboratories (30–32).

It was later found, however, that calcitonin was not produced by the regular colloid-containing follicular cells of the thyroid, but was limited to the scattered (and often overlooked) parafollicular or "C" cells (33, 34) which Pearse & Carvalheira (35) proved to be of ultimobranchial origin. Inspired by these observations, Copp, Cockcroft & Kueh showed that in chickens (36) and dogfish sharks (37) the ultimobranchial glands contained high concentrations of calcitonin in contrast to the inactivity of thyroid extracts from these animals. This work was confirmed independently by Tauber (38) and successfully repeated by Moseley et al. (39). Calcitonin has now been extracted from the ultimobranchial glands of representative species of all classes of jawed vertebrates in which the gland is separate from thyroid (40), and in mammals has been demonstrated in the parathyroid and thymus as well as the thyroid (41). The discovery that the long-neglected ultimobranchial gland is the source of calcitonin has opened up new vistas in comparative endocrinology, and studies in lower vertebrates may prove of great value in understanding the fundamental mechanisms of action of the hormone in mammals.

Embryology and Morphology

As shown in Figure 2, both glands develop from a somewhat similar *Anlage* in the branchial pouches—the parathyroids from pouches 3 and 4, and the ultimobranchial from the terminal pouch. Since the gills have an important role in ion regulation in fishes, it may be significant that these glands, and the aortic and carotid bodies, develop from branchial tissue.

Ultimobranchial—The ultimobranchial was first described in 1886 (42) by van Bemmelen in elasmobranchs and named by him the suprapericardial

Derivatives of Branchial Pouches

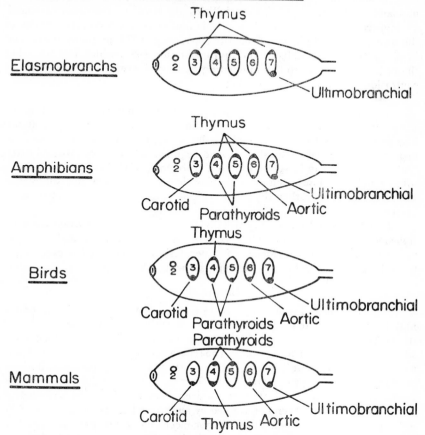

FIG. 2. Embryological development of glandular derivatives of the branchial pouches in various classes of vertebrates. Adapted from Fig. 11.26, p. 291 in: H. Smith, *Evolution of Chordate Structure,* Holt, Rinehart & Winston, New York, 1960.

body because of its location on the dorsal surface of the pericardium. The term *ultimobranchial* was introduced by Greil in 1905 (43), and seems more appropriate since the gland invariably develops from the last branchial pouch, and in higher vertebrates is usually located at some distance from the heart and in most mammals is imbedded in thyroid. Watzka (44) has given a very comprehensive review of the morphology of the ultimobranchial in all vertebrate classes in which it occurs and has noted that it is absent from cyclostomes. In elasmobranchs, the gland consists of well-defined follicles

(1, 45) and is found on the left side only. In bony fishes, the ultimobranchial is bilateral and consists of cords and sheets of polygonal cells. In amphibians, birds, and reptiles, both follicles and cords of cells may be found.

Hypercalcemia stimulates hyperplasia and increased secretory activity in
the ultimobranchial glands of teleosts (46), frogs (47), and birds (48), and
in the parafollicular cells of the thyroid of rats (49), which indicates that
the cells are sensitive to the stimulating effect of increased calcium ion concentration.

Parathyroids.—These glands appear first in amphibians at the time of
metamorphosis when they move from an aquatic to a terrestrial habitat.
The parathyroids are present in all air-breathing vertebrates. Their development may be related to the shift from a regimen low in phosphate and often
high in calcium (as in seawater) to a terrestrial life where the opposite is
often true (i.e., low calcium, high phosphate). Thus they are threatened
with hypocalcemia rather than hypercalcemia, as is the case for sea vertebrates.

The parathyroid glands are usually four in number, and are frequently
imbedded in the thyroid. They consist of cords of polygonal cells. In
tissue culture, there is evidence of hyperplasia and increased secretory activity by these cells when the medium is low in calcium (50, 51).

CHEMISTRY

Parathormone.—Twenty-four years elapsed between the isolation of the
first biologically potent extract from the parathyroids by Collip (24) and
the preparation of highly purified hormone (25, 26). The amino acid composition of bovine (52) and porcine (53) parathormone has now been determined and is shown in Table I. Both are straight-chain peptides with a molecular weight of approximately 9500. Sucrose density gradient studies with
human parathormone indicate that its size is similar (54). The structure of
bovine calcitonin has been determined by amino acid sequence analysis (52),
although there is still some uncertainty concerning certain regions. The biologically active portion of the molecule includes a sequence of 35 amino
acids, including the N terminus, and has full immunological activity.

Calcitonin.—In contrast to the above, progress in elucidating the chemistry of the calcitonins has been very rapid. Within 5 years after biologically
active extracts were prepared from rat (28) and hog (29) thyroid, pure porcine calcitonin was isolated, its structure was determined by amino acid sequence analysis (55–57), and the hormone was synthesized (58). The amino
acid composition of porcine and bovine calcitonin is shown in Table I where
it is compared with parathormone.

Porcine calcitonin contains 32 amino acid residues, with a 1–7 intrachain
disulfide bridge at the N terminus and prolinamide at the C terminus. It
thus has some similarity to arginine vasopressin and oxytocin, which also

TABLE I

AMINO ACID COMPOSITION OF BOVINE AND PORCINE PTH AND CT

Amino acid	Parathormone		Calcitonin	
	Bovine[a]	Porcine[b]	Bovine[c]	Porcine[d]
Alanine	6	7	1	1
Glycine	4	6	3	3
Leucine	7	10	3	3
Isoleucine	3	3	0	0
Serine	7	6	4	4
Threonine	0	2	2	2
Valine	8	7	1	1
Aspartic acid	10	8	4	4
Glutamic acid	12	11	1	1
Arginine	5	5	2	1
Lysine	9	9	0	1
Histidine	3	4	1	1
Tryptophane	1	1	1	1
Proline	3	3	2	2
Tyrosine	1	1	1	2
Phenylalanine	2	2	3	2
Cysteine	0	0	2	2
Methionine	2	1	1	1
	—	—	—	—
Total	83	86	32	32
Molecular weight	9476	9622	3585	3573

[a] Potts et al. (52).
[b] Littledike & Hawker (53).
[c] Potts, J. T. (Personal communication).
[d] Potts et al. (56).

have an intrachain disulfide ring at the N terminus and an amide at the C terminus. The entire molecule appears to be necessary for full biological activity, and such a simple step as deamidating the prolinamide at the C terminus results in loss of 97 per cent of the activity (59).

Human thyroid normally contains very small amounts (0.4 U/g) of calcitonin (60), but this was increased 100-fold in two cases of pseudohypoparathyroidism (61). The highest levels (143 U/g) were observed in medullary cell carcinoma of thyroid (62, 63) which is presumably a tumor of ultimobranchial cells. With such tumor tissue used as starting material, human calcitonin was isolated (64) and its structure determined (65). It occurs in a monomer (M) and dimer (D) form, the latter resulting from a disulfide cross linkage. The monomer has the same basic structure as the porcine hormone, but there are eighteen amino acid changes in the midpart of the molecule.

The third calcitonin to be characterized is that derived from salmon ultimobranchial glands. In the summer and fall of 1968, we collected over 200 pounds of septal tissue containing the ultimobranchials from approximately 500 tons of salmon. The glands were bulk-processed by Armour Pharmaceutical Company of Kankakee, Illinois, and final purification and amino acid analysis were carried out in our laboratory (66, 67). The structure was determined by Niall et al. (68), and the hormone was recently synthesized (69). The structure of human and salmon calcitonin is shown in Figure 3. It will be seen that the basic structure of all the calcitonins so far analyzed is very similar, although there are many amino acid changes in the middle of the molecule. The salmon hormone has only a single aromatic amino acid and contains more hydrophilic groups. This may explain why it was less retarded than porcine on a calibrated Sephadex G-50 column (70), which led to the erroneous conclusion that its molecular weight was higher.

With the standard assay procedure of Sturtridge & Kumar (71), salmon calcitonin had a biological potency of 5000 U/mg (67), compared to 200 U/mg for porcine calcitonin and 120 U/mg for human calcitonin. Salmon calcitonin is one of the most potent biological substances known. In the young rat, a dose of 0.25 ng (3.5 ng/kg) is sufficient to lower the plasma calcium 10 per cent; it requires 10,000 times as much of the parathormone peptide to produce a corresponding rise in plasma calcium.

In addition to its higher biological potency, salmon calcitonin also has a more prolonged action than that of porcine (72). Figure 4 shows the changes in plasma calcium following i.v. injection of hormone into young 2-kg rabbits. The response to 10 units (2 μg) of salmon calcitonin was much greater and more prolonged than the effect of 10 units (50 μg) of porcine hormone. This difference may be explained in part by the greater stability of the salmon hormone when incubated at 37°C in rabbit serum (72). Porcine calcitonin was completely inactivated in 1 hr; salmon calcitonin retained almost full activity for 4–6 hr. Similar differences were obtained with human serum. In one male subject with parathyroid carcinoma and hypercalcemia, the salmon peptide appeared to be at least 200 times as potent as porcine calcitonin (73). The higher potency and more prolonged action of salmon calcitonin would appear to offer real advantages in human therapy.

STANDARDS AND BIOASSAY

Parathormone.—Reliable standards and assay methods are essential for hormone purification and quantitative physiological studies. There is at present no international standard for parathormone and most investigators use the crude commercial extract prepared by the E. Lilly Co. of Indianapolis as a reference. The original dog assay of Collip & Clark (74) is still the basis of standardization of this preparation, as specified in the U.S. Pharmacopoeia. One USP unit is defined as 1 per cent of the amount of hormone or extract which will raise the serum calcium of normal mature male dogs by 1 mg per cent within 16–18 hr. More dependable assays are based on the hy-

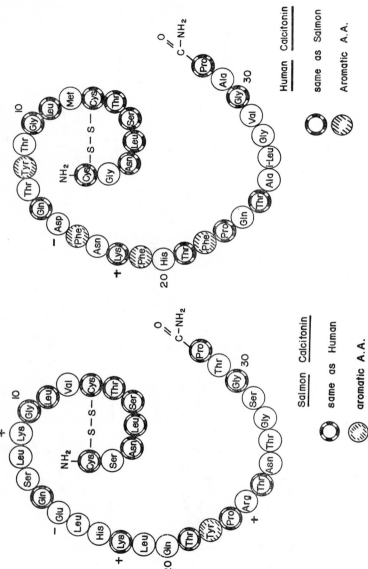

FIG. 3. Comparison of the structure of salmon (68) and human (65) calcitonin. Note that the salmon hormone has a net charge of +2 while the human hormone is essentially neutral.

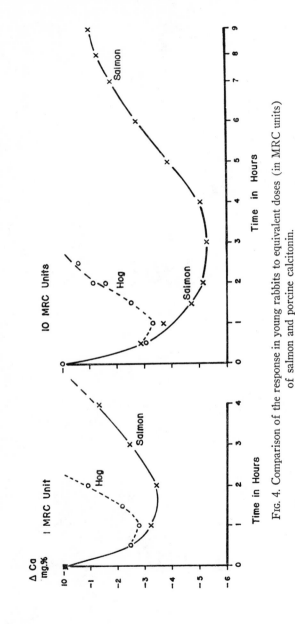

FIG. 4. Comparison of the response in young rabbits to equivalent doses (in MRC units) of salmon and porcine calcitonin.

percalcemic effect of the hormone in rats (75, 76) and mice (77), the phosphaturic effect in rats (78), and the release of calcium from 6-day-old mouse calvaria in tissue culture (79). The last two methods can detect very low levels of parathormone.

Calcitonin.—Shortly after the calcitonin field began to expand in 1964, the Division of Biological Standards of the National Institute for Medical Research, Mill Hill, London, provided investigators with a relatively crude standard of extract from porcine thyroid which was referred to as the Medical Research Council (MRC) Thyroid Calcitonin Research Standard A. 1 MRC unit was defined as 40 mg of this material and was equivalent to approximately 100 Hirsch units (29) and 1000 Hammersmith units (80). A second more purified preparation of porcine hormone (Research Standard B) is now available, and shortly there will also be standards for human calcitonin and possibly salmon hormone. The original bioassay methods (29, 80) were based on the fall in plasma calcium 50–60 min after administration of the hormone. A number of improvements in these methods have been proposed (71, 81). Copp & Kuczerpa have developed an assay based on the integrated hypocalcemic response as measured by the area between the plasma-calcium curve following i.v. injection of hormone into rats, and the control plasma-calcium level in rats injected with vehicle (82). This method is particularly age-sensitive, the response to a given dose being almost 20 times as great in 30-day-old rats as in mature 9-month-old animals. Phosphate is also a factor in assay. Simultaneous injection of phosphate increased the response to calcitonin (81), while sensitivity was greatly reduced in animals fed a low-phosphate diet (82).

IMMUNOASSAY

Parathormone.—Very sensitive methods of immunoassay have been developed based on complement fixation (83) or on competitive binding of radioiodine-labelled pure peptide (84–86). The radioimmunoassay of Berson et al. (84) measures bovine parathormone (PTH) in the range of 0.25–1 μg (0.6–2.5 mU) per ml, and also measures human PTH. The method has been used to study parathormone levels in the blood in human disease (85, 86) and is of great value in diagnosing hypo- and hyperparathyroidism. Antibodies to bovine PTH apparently react with rat PTH, for when injected into rats, they produce the same effect as parathyroidectomy (87).

Calcitonin.—In spite of its low molecular weight, calcitonin is weakly antigenic, and antibodies can be produced with the use of suitable adjuvants. Tashjian & Munson (88) reported that antibodies produced in rabbits against porcine calcitonin would neutralize the hypocalcemic effect of extracts of porcine and bovine thyroid, but would not affect the activity of extracts of rat and monkey thyroids. Three separate laboratories have developed sensitive radioimmunoassays for porcine calcitonin (89–91) capable of detecting as little as 0.02 ng (4 μU).

CONTROL OF SECRETION

Parathormone.—The gland-perfusion studies of Copp et al. (22) clearly showed that changes in the calcium concentration in the perfusing blood could alter the endogenous secretion of parathormone or calcitonin without mediation of the pituitary or the central nervous system. More quantitative studies have been carried out in cattle using radioimmunoassay to determine

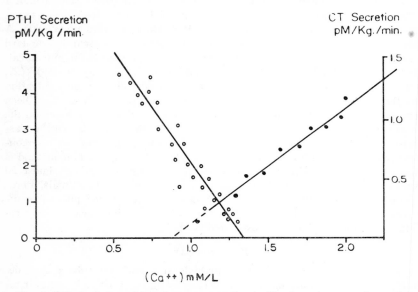

FIG. 5. Effect of the calcium ion concentration in blood on the rate of secretion of parathormone in the cow (92) and calcitonin in an adult sheep (98), measured in picomoles of hormone per kg per min.

the circulating blood level of the hormone (92). This increased in direct proportion to the fall in plasma calcium. However, if plasma calcium was kept constant, changes in phosphate did not affect parathormone levels (93). On the other hand, with constant calcium concentrations, lowering plasma magnesium stimulated secretion of PTH while high magnesium levels inhibited it (94). The half-life of injected parathormone is 20 min (95) and knowing this and the volume distribution of the hormone and the plasma concentration, one can estimate the secretion rate. In Figure 5, the rate of secretion of PTH in picomoles per kg per min is plotted against the ionic calcium concentration in millimoles per liter. The latter was calculated from the original data by A. Baird Hastings of the Scripps Institute, La

Jolla, California, using the McLean-Hastings nomogram (96). The relationship is linear and can be expressed by the equation:

$$d\mathrm{PTH}/dt = 7.36 - 5.45 \ (\mathrm{Ca^{++}}) \ \mathrm{picomoles/kg/min}$$

where $(\mathrm{Ca^{++}})$ represents the concentration of ionic calcium in plasma in millimoles per liter.

Calcitonin.—A similar direct proportional control of calcitonin secretion has been demonstrated by Care et al. (97, 98). A technique was developed for perfusing the thyroid gland of the pig or sheep with blood containing various concentrations of calcium. The venous effluent was collected and calcitonin (CT) was determined by bioassay (81). Their data has been recalculated as for PTH, and is plotted against ionic calcium in Figure 5. The relationship is linear and can be expressed by the equation:

$$d\mathrm{CT}/dt = 0.975 \ (\mathrm{Ca^{++}}) - 0.867$$

where $d\mathrm{CT}/dt$ is in picomoles/kg/min, and $(\mathrm{Ca^{++}})$ is the estimated calcium ion concentration in the perfusing blood. It will be noted that the two lines intersect at 1.18 mM $\mathrm{Ca^{++}}$/liter which is close to the normal plasma value. This provides a highly efficient negative-feedback control. There is substantial evidence that calcitonin is secreted at normal plasma levels in rats (99), rabbits (100), and man (101). Both cyclic AMP (102) and glucagon (103) stimulate release of calcitonin from pig thyroid, which suggests that adenyl cyclase may act as a facilitator or activator.

ACTION

Blood calcium and phosphate.—Administration of parathormone to dogs and humans causes a rise in plasma calcium and a fall in plasma phosphate which begins within 30–60 min and may persist for 12–24 hr. Injection of 0.2 mg pure bovine parathormone i.v. into young rats caused a prompt rise in plasma calcium which lasted for at least 30 hr (104). When actinomycin D was injected 2 hr before the PTH at a dose of 2 μg/g body weight, it had no effect on the initial rise in plasma calcium, but it completely suppressed the hypercalcemic effect after 6 hr. Actinomycin D has also been observed to inhibit the bone resorption induced by parathormone and vitamin A in bone organ cultures (105). The antibiotic is assumed to inhibit DNA synthesis, and thus protein synthesis. The initial response may be due to release of preformed enzymes, while the continued response apparently requires synthesis of new protein. An increased RNA synthesis by bone cells has been observed following administration of parathormone (106, 107).

Calcitonin normally lowers both plasma calcium and phosphate, but its effect is much more rapid than that of parathormone, and is not inhibited by actinomycin D (108). The hypocalcemic response is greatest in young actively growing mammals, and falls off rapidly with increasing age (82, 109, 110). It is correlated directly with growth rate (82) and presumably **bone** remodeling. However, ageing does not affect the rate of secretion of calcitonin (111). The hypocalcemic effect of calcitonin has been observed in parathyroidectomized, nephrectomized (29), and eviscerated (112) rats, so that it does not require the presence of these organs. There were also no significant changes in soft tissue Ca and P (113), so that it seemed logical to conclude that the target organ was bone.

Bone.—Parathormone stimulates, while calcitonin inhibits bone resorption in organ cultures of limb-bone rudiments from mouse embryos (114), rat embryos (115), and calvaria from newborn mice (116). Calcitonin also inhibits bone resorption induced in newborn mouse calvaria by toxic levels of vitamin A (117, 118). In this system, salmon calcitonin appeared to be 2500 times as effective as porcine hormone and had a more prolonged effect. In cultures of mouse calvaria (119), parathormone stimulated adenyl cyclase activity in the bone cells, thus increasing the intracellular formation of 3',5' cyclic adenosine monophosphate (cAMP). Calcitonin had no effect on the enzyme.

Wells & Lloyd (120) postulated that parathormone functions by activating adenyl cyclase to produce cAMP which, according to Vaes (121), acts as a secondary messenger to stimulate the synthesis and release of osteolytic lysosomal enzymes. It is significant that dibutyryl cyclic AMP, which can penetrate cells and mimics the action of cAMP, has a parathormone-like action in organ cultures of bone (122) and in parathyroidectomized rats (123). Cyclic AMP is hydrolyzed by cyclic nucleotide phosphodiesterase, an enzyme within the cell which is activated by imidazole. Since the latter has a hypocalcemic and hypophosphatemic effect when injected into rats, Wells & Lloyd suggested that calcitonin may exert its effect by also activating phosphodiesterase (120, 124). However, Chase et al. (119) observed no effect of parathormone or calcitonin on phosphodiesterase.

The effects of the hormones on bone *in vivo* parallel those observed in organ cultures. It has long been known that parathormone stimulates osteoclast activity and bone resorption with concomitant increase in urinary excretion of hydroxyproline (125). This is presumably derived from the collagen in resorbing bone. Administration of calcitonin reduces urinary excretion of hydroxyproline (126) which is taken as an index of bone breakdown. Calcitonin also inhibits the removal of bone salts (127) and hydroxyproline (128) from bone. The most striking experiments were those carried out by Foster et al. (129) in parathyroidectomized young rats (40–60 g). These were given four injections of calcitonin per day in a dose of 40 mU/rat/injection and killed after 4 weeks. Treated rats had a reduced osteoclast count and showed an increase in trabecular and cortical bone. Foster et al. (130) also studied the effect of calcitonin on the experimental osteoporosis produced in rats by administration of massive doses of vitamin A. Young rats were given 2500 I.U. vitamin A three times weekly for 4 weeks, by which time they were stunted and their bones osteoporotic. Daily administration of 400 mμ porcine calcitonin per rat completely prevented the stunting and osteoporosis produced by these toxic doses of the vitamin. The lowering of plasma calcium in the CT-treated animal was small (approximately 10 per cent according to a personal communication from G. V. Foster). For this reason, it seems unlikely that lowering of plasma calcium was a factor in the remarkable effect of the hormone in maintaining the animals in health in spite of the toxic doses of vitamin A which were administered. This suggests that calcitonin may have a more generalized effect on the cells of the body in addition to its specific effect on bone.

Milhaud et al. (131) studied the effect of calcitonin on calcium kinetics and found that treatment for 3 days lowered bone catabolism from 56.1 mg/day to .4 mg/day. There was also a reduction in bone anabolism (from 100 mg/day to 63 mg/day) which may have been due to the lowered plasma calcium.

In an isolated blood-perfused tibia, administration of parathormone caused a negative arteriovenous calcium difference (132), while calcitonin had the opposite effect (133). This confirms the fact that both hormones affect the net movement of calcium in and out of bone.

An inhibitory effect of calcitonin on bone atrophy was observed by Fujita et al. (134) but not by Ziegler & Delling (135). However, the latter claimed that administration of the hormone enhanced osteogenic activity. Delling et al. (136) also reported that calcitonin enhanced callus formation and osteogenesis in healing tibial fractures. In organ cultures of bone, Gaillard (114) observed that calcitonin caused an increase in osteoblast activity as well as suppression of osteolysis, and he concluded that the hormone caused a shift from bone destruction to bone formation. In addition, Wase et al. (137) reported an increase in positive calcium balance with an increased incorporation of radiocalcium into bone, suggesting that treatment with calcitonin enhanced bone formation.

In hereditary osteopetrosis ("thick bone disease") associated with the grey-lethal factor in mice, Walker (138) observed a great increase in parafollicular cells in the thyroid, and concluded that the bone abnormalities might be due to high calcitonin levels. Krook et al. (139) suggested the same explanation for the marked osteopetrosis in bulls fed a high-calcium diet, since this condition was associated with ultimobranchial tumors and C cell hyperplasia.

Gastrointestinal tract.—Parathyroidectomy depressed calcium absorption from the gut in the rat (140), while administration of parathyroid extract restored or even enhanced calcium absorption from intestinal loops *in vivo* (141, 142) or *in vitro* (143). Administration of effective hypocalcemic doses of pig and chicken calcitonin had no effect on absorption of calcium, magnesium, or phosphate from healed intestinal loops in dogs (144), but they did cause increased excretion of phosphate in the urine.

Kidney.—Increased urinary excretion of phosphate was one of the first effects observed following administration of parathyroid extract (24), and formed the basis of the original Albright hypothesis of action of the hormone. Parathormone also appears to enhance tubular reabsorption of calcium (145), and this may account in part for the hypercalcemia associated with hyperparathyroidism.

There is some controversy concerning the phosphaturic effect of calcitonin observed in the rat (146) and man (147), but not in dogs (148).

Cell membranes.—Borle (149) observed that purified parathormone would enhance uptake of calcium by monkey kidney cells by as much as 3–30 fold, with a significant effect observed by 1 hr, and a maximum effect at 6 hr. Associated with this was an increase in cellular calcium and calcium turnover. PTH also increased the calcium flux inward through isolated frog-skin (150). Rasmussen & Tenenhouse (151) have proposed that parathormone activates adenyl cyclase, and that the resulting increase in cAMP increases the permeability of the cell membrane to Ca^{++}. They feel that intracellular Ca^{++} has a very important role in regulating metabolic events within the cell, so that some cellular regulation of this ion is essential. According to Parkinson & Radde (152), calcitonin has the opposite effect on human red cells loaded with calcium and ^{47}Ca, increasing the calcium efflux by 40 per cent. This would suggest a basic function of PTH and CT in protecting the intracellular calcium from the effects of hypocalcemia and hypercalcemia respectively.

Miscellaneous.—Charbon (153) observed a rapid and selective vasodilator effect when essentially pure parathormone was injected into dogs. There was an increase in blood flow of up to 60 per cent in the celiac trunk and up to 40 per cent in the renal artery. A good correlation between the logarithm of the dose and the response was recorded.

Prolonged i.v. infusion of pure parathormone in young rats produced severe nephrocalcinosis; this effect was blocked by simultaneous administration of calcitonin (154). Calcitonin also blocked the skin calcification (calcergy) induced by an i.v. injection of lead acetate followed by subcutaneous injection of polymyxin (155).

COMPARATIVE ENDOCRINOLOGY

Parathormone.—Greep (156) has presented a comprehensive review of comparative aspects of parathyroid physiology up to the year 1962. There has been very little work since. Administration of bovine parathyroid extract to frogs produced hypercalcemia (157) and hypophosphatemia (158). When injected daily into the lizard *Dipsosaurus dorsalis* (159) the hormone extract caused hypercalcemia and increased urinary excretion of calcium and phosphate just as in the mammal. Avian parathyroid physiology has been reviewed recently by Urist (160). The parathyroids hypertrophy, as do the ultimobranchials, during the calcium stress of egg laying. Injection of bovine parathyroid extract produces hypercalcemia, just as it does in other vertebrates.

Calcitonin.—The recent discovery of the function of the ultimobranchial gland as the source of calcitonin in lower vertebrates has given a great impetus to comparative studies in this field. The work is largely confined to the past 2 years, and has been reviewed by Copp et al. (72). Chan (46) observed that the hypercalcemia following removal of the corpuscles of Stannius in the Asiatic eel was associated with hypertrophy of the ultimobranchial glands. Removal of the ultimobranchial glands in this species (one of the few fish in which such an operation is feasible) resulted in a significant rise in plasma calcium (46). Administration of porcine calcitonin caused a fall in plasma calcium in the European eel (161) and in the catfish *Ictalurus melas* (162) but not in *Fundulus heteroclitus* (163).

In the frog *Rana pipiens,* hypercalcemia caused reversible hypertrophy of the ultimobranchial glands (47), while removal of the glands caused a significant rise in plasma calcium (164). There was also progressive depletion of calcium carbonate from the paravertebral lime sacs which serve as a calcium storage organ in the frog. In bone, there was a decrease in osteoblasts and an increase in osteoclasts. Robertson (165) suggests that calcitonin may have an inhibitory effect on flux of calcium out of the lime sacs and may stimulate osteogenesis and inhibit bone resorption. Ultimobranchialectomy also increased urinary excretion of calcium; this was restored to normal by transplanting the glands back into the frog.

Injecting calcitonin into chickens had no hypocalcemic effect in normal birds (160) but did lower the plasma calcium in parathyroidectomized cockerels (166). When the plasma calcium was raised from 9.7 to 11.9 mg per cent in young turkeys by i.v. infusion of calcium, the plasma calcitonin rose 0.29 to 2.15 MRC units/liter (72). One hour after removal of the ultimobrachial glands, calcitonin could not be detected. Removal of the ultimobranchial glands also impaired the control of hypercalcemia induced by infusion of calcium (167) or parathyroid extract (168).

STUDIES IN MAN

The past 5 years have added little to our knowledge of parathyroid disease. Hyperparathyroidism is usually treated by surgical removal of the hyperfunctioning tumor or tissue, while hypoparathyroidism and the resulting hypocalcemia are normally controlled by high dietary intake of calcium and vitamin D.

However, in the calcitonin field, all clinical studies have been carried out during this period. Injection of calcitonin has very little effect on the plasma calcium of normal subjects (16, 73, 130, 169, 170), but this is not surprising in view of the slow rate of bone turnover. Significant lowering of plasma calcium was observed in patients with hypercalcemia due to osteolytic bone disease (16, 130) and in patients with Paget's disease with normal plasma calcium levels (171). In the latter, there was also relief of bone pain and a dramatic improvement in the patient's condition, so that it is now generally agreed that calcitonin is the treatment of choice in this condition. Some benefit has also been claimed in senile osteoporosis (172), although the evidence is not as clear-cut.

ROLE IN HOMEOSTASIS

The direct proportional control which the Ca^{++} concentration exerts on secretion of both hormones (see Figure 5) provides an elegant negative feedback control, and it is significant that the two regression lines intersect at the normal plasma calcium level. The significance of the parathyroids in calcium homeostasis has long been recognized, since removal of the glands in most cases causes a very significant decrease in the plasma calcium level. The role of calcitonin is more difficult to demonstrate since removal of the thyroid in mammals does not result in any significant elevation in plasma calcium. As a result, the importance of the hormone in homeostasis has been questioned by Bronner et al. (173). Removal of the ultimobranchial cells by thyroidectomy does impair control of hypercalcemia induced by injection of parathyroid extract in dogs (174) and rats (175) or by calcium infusion in rats (176). This was also the case when the ultimobranchials were removed during calcium infusion in young turkeys (167) or when parathyroid extract was injected into ultimobranchialectomized chickens (168). When hyperparathyroidism was produced in rats by intramuscular transplantation of 20–40 or 80 isologous parathyroid glands, the simultaneous transplantation of a similar number of isologous thyroid lobes prevented the hypercalcemia and greatly reduced the incidence of renal stones (177). One of the most significant series of experiments was carried out by Gray & Munson (178) in thyroidectomized rats with functioning parathyroid transplants. They found that even a modest dose of calcium administered by stomach tube, or a hastily consumed calcium-rich meal, would cause significant elevation in plasma calcium. This did not occur in sham-operated animals with intact thyroids. Thyroidectomized rats with parathyroid transplants were found to be more sensitive to the hypocalcemic effect of chicken and rat calcitonin (179). In nephrectomized rats, plasma calcium levels were significantly higher in animals with intact thyroids, and this was also true for the hypercalcemia induced by a high phosphate challenge (180). The explanation for these findings is still obscure.

SUMMARY

Precise homeostatic control of plasma calcium in the mammal is facilitated by negative-feedback controls involving two glands which arise from the epithelium of the branchial pouches. Parathormone from the parathyroid glands controls hypocalcemia, while calcitonin from ultimobranchial tissue controls hypercalcemia. Although calcitonin was discovered less than 10 years ago, more is now known about its chemistry, function, and role in other vertebrates than is the case for parathormone. In the mammal, the action of both hormones appears to be mediated primarily by their effects on bone. This may not be the case in lower vertebrates, and attention is now turning to the effects on calcium movement across cell membranes. Calcium homeostasis has become an exciting and challenging field for comparative endocrinologists, for those concerned with biological control systems, and for those confronted with the problems of the diseases involving calcium metabolism.

ACKNOWLEDGMENTS

The author would like to express his appreciation to Mrs. Valerie Walker and Mrs. Mary Forsyth for assistance with the manuscript, and to Mr. Kurt Henze for preparation of the illustrations. Experimental work from this laboratory reported in the review was supported by grants from the Medical Research Council and the British Columbia Medical Research Foundation.

LITERATURE CITED

1. Copp, D. H. The ultimobranchial glands and calcium regulation. In *Fish Physiology*, 2, 377–98 (Hoar, W. S., Randall, D. J., Eds., Academic, New York, 1969)
2. Carruthers, B. M., Copp, D. H., McIntosh, H. W. Diurnal variation in urinary excretion of calcium and phosphate and its relation to blood levels. *J. Lab. Clin. Med.*, 63, 959–68 (1964)
3. Copp, D. H. Hormonal control of hypercalcemia. Historic development of the calcitonin concept. *Am. J. Med.*, 23, 648–55 (1967)
4. Copp, D. H., Davidson, A. G. F., Cheney, B. A. Evidence for a new parathyroid hormone which lowers blood calcium. *Proc. Can. Fed. Biol. Soc.*, 4, 17 (1961)
5. Sanderson, P. H., Marshall, F., III, Wilson, R. E. Calcium and phosphorus homeostasis in the parathyroidectomized dog: evaluation by means of ethylenediaminetetraacetate and calcium tolerance tests. *J. Clin. Invest.*, 39, 662–70 (1960)
6. Gaillard, P. J., Talmage, R. V., Budy, A. M. *The Parathyroid Glands. Ultrastructure, Secretion and Function* (Univ. Chicago Press, Chicago, 353 pp., 1965)
7. Taylor, S. *Calcitonin. Proceedings of a Symposium on Thyrocalcitonin and the C Cells* (Heinemann Med. Books, London, 402 pp., 1968)
8. Talmage, R. V., Bélanger, L. F., Eds. *Parathyroid Hormone and Thyrocalcitonin (Calcitonin)* (Excerpta Med. Found., Amsterdam, 535 pp., 1968)
9. Taylor, S. *Calcitonin 1969. Proceedings of the Second International Symposium, London, 20–24 July, 1969* (Heinemann Med. Books, London, 1970) (In press)
10. Aurbach, G. D., Potts, J. T., Jr. Editorial. Parathyroid Hormone. *Am. J. Med.*, 42, 1–8 (1967)
11. Talmage, R. V. Aspects of parathyroid physiology in mammals. *Am. Zool.*, 7, 825–33 (1967)
12. Arnaud, C. D., Tenenhouse, A., Rasmussen, H. Parathyroid Hormone. *Ann. Rev. Physiol.*, 29, 349–72 (1967)
13. MacIntyre, I. Calcitonin: a general review. *Calcif. Tiss. Res.*, 1, 173–82 (1967)
14. Copp, D. H. Calcitonin. *Advan. Internal Med.*, 14, 55–82 (1968)
15. Munson, P. L., Hirsch, P. F., Brewer, H. B., Reisfeld, R. A., Cooper, C. W., Wästhed, A. B., Orimo, H., Potts, J. T., Jr. Thyrocalcitonin. *Recent Progr. Hormone Res.*, 24, 589–637 (1968)
16. Foster, G. V. Calcitonin. A review of experimental and clinical investigations. *Postgrad. Med. J.*, 44, 411–22 (1968)
17. Copp, D. H. Parathyroid hormone,

calcitonin and calcium homeostasis. In Ref. 7, 25–42

18. Copp, D. H. Endocrine control of calcium homeostasis. *J. Endocrinol.*, **43**, 137–61 (1969)

19. Copp, D. H. Calcitonin and Parathyroid Hormone. *Ann. Rev. Pharmacol.*, **9**, 327–44 (1969)

20. Copp, D. H. Parathormone, calcitonin and calcium homeostasis. In *Mineral Metabolism*, **III**, 453–513 (Comar, C. L., Bronner, F., Academic, New York, 1969)

21. MacCallum, W. G., Voegtlin, C. On the relation of tetany to the parathyroid glands and to calcium metabolism. *J. Exptl. Med.*, **11**, 118–51 (1909)

22. Copp, D. H., Cameron, E. C., Cheney, B. A., Davidson, A. G. F., Henze, K. G. Evidence for calcitonin—a new hormone from the parathyroid that lowers blood calcium. *Endocrinology*, **70**, 638–49 (1962)

23. Sandström, I. V. Glandulae parathyroideae. *Upsala Laekarefoer. Foerh.*, **15**, 441–71 (1880)

24. Collip, J. B. The extraction of a parathyroid hormone which will prevent or control parathyroid tetany and which regulates the level of blood calcium. *J. Biol. Chem.*, **63**, 395–438 (1925)

25. Aurbach, G. D. Isolation of parathyroid hormone after extraction with phenol. *J. Biol. Chem.*, **234**, 3179–81 (1959)

26. Rasmussen, H., Craig, L. C. Purification of parathyroid hormone by counter-current distribution. *J. Am. Chem. Soc.*, **81**, 5003 (1959)

27. Kumar, M. A., Foster, G. V., MacIntyre, I. Further evidence for calcitonin. A rapid-acting hormone which lowers plasma calcium. *Lancet*, **2**, 480–82 (1963)

28. Hirsch, P. F., Gauthier, G. F., Munson, P. L. Thyroid hypocalcemic principle and recurrent laryngeal nerve injury factors affecting the response to parathyroidectomy in rats. *Endocrinology*, **73**, 244–52 (1963)

29. Hirsch, P. F., Voelkel, E. F., Munson, P. L. Thyrocalcitonin: hypocalcemic hypophosphatemic principle of the thyroid gland. *Science*, **146**, 412–13 (1964)

30. Talmage, R. V., Neuenschwander, J., Kraintz, L. Evidence for the existence of thyrocalcitonin in the rat. *Endocrinology*, **76**, 103–7 (1965)

31. Foster, G. V., Baghdiantz, A., Kumar, M. A., Slack, E., Soliman, H. A., MacIntyre, I. Thyroid origin of calcitonin. *Nature*, **202**, 1303–5 (1964)

32. Care, A. D. Secretion of thyrocalcitonin. *Nature*, **205**, 1289–91 (1965)

33. Foster, G. V., MacIntyre, I., Pearse, A. G. E. Calcitonin production and the mitochondrion-rich cells of the dog thyroid. *Nature*, **203**, 1029–30 (1964)

34. Bussolati, G., Pearse, A. G. E. Immunofluorescent localization of calcitonin in the "C" cells of pig and dog thyroid. *J. Endocrinol.*, **37**, 205–9 (1967)

35. Pearse, A. G. E., Carvalheira, A. F. Cytochemical evidence for an ultimobranchial origin of rodent thyroid C cells. *Nature*, **214**, 929–30 (1967)

36. Copp, D. H., Cockcroft, D. W., Kueh, Y. Ultimobranchial origin of calcitonin. Hypocalcemic effect of extracts from chicken glands. *Can. J. Physiol. Pharmacol.*, **45**, 1095–99 (1967a)

37. Copp, D. H., Cockcroft, D. W., Kueh, Y. Calcitonin from ultimobranchial glands of dogfish and and chickens. *Science*, **158**, 924–25 (1967b)

38. Tauber, S. D. The ultimobranchial origin of thyrocalcitonin. *Proc. Natl. Acad. Sci.*, **58**, 1684–87 (1967)

39. Moseley, J. M., Matthews, E. W., Breed, R. H., Galante, L., Tse, A., MacIntyre, I. The ultimobranchial origin of calcitonin. *Lancet*, **1**, 108–10 (1968)

40. Copp, D. H., Parkes, C. O. Extraction of calcitonin from ultimobranchial tissue. In Ref. 8, 74–84

41. Galante, L., Gudmundsson, T. V., Matthews, E. W., Tse, A., Williams, E. D., Woodhouse, N. J. Y., MacIntyre, I. Thymic and parathyroid origin of calcitonin in man. *Lancet*, **11**, 537–38 (1968)

42. van Bemmelen, J. F. Über vermutliche rudimentäre Kiemenspalten bei Elasmobranchiern. *Mitt. Zool. Stat. Neapel*, **16**, 165 (1886)

43. Greil, A. Über die Anlage der Lungen sowie der ultimobranchialen (postbranchialen, suprapericardialen) Körper bei anuren Amphi-

bien. *Arb. Anat. Inst., Wiesbaden,* **29,** 447–503 (1905)

44. Watzka, M. Vergleichende Untersuchungen über den ultimobranchialen Körper. *Z. Mikroskop. Anat. Forsch.,* **34,** 485 (1933)

45. Camp, W. E. The development of the suprapericardial (postbranchial, ultimobranchial) body in *Squalus acanthias. J. Morphol.,* **28,** 369–415 (1917)

46. Chan, D. K. O. Endocrine regulation of calcium and inorganic phosphate in fresh-water adapted teleost fish, *Anguilla anguilla* and *A. Japonica. Proc. 3d Intern. Congr. Endocrinol., Mexico City, 1968* (Excerpta Med. Found.) (In press)

47. Robertson, D. R. The ultimobranchial body in *Rana pipiens.* IV. Hypercalcemia and glandular hypertrophy. *Z. Zellforsch. Mikroskop. Anat.,* **85,** 441–52 (1968a)

48. Chan, A. S., Cipera, J. D., Bélanger, L. F. The ultimobranchial gland of the chick and its response to a high calcium diet. *Rev. Can. Biol.,* **28,** 19–31 (1969)

49. Matsuzawa, T., Kurosumi, K. Morphological changes in the parafollicular cells of the rat thyroid glands after administration of calcium shown by electron microscopy. *Nature,* **213,** 927 (1967)

50. Raisz, L. G. Regulation by calcium of parathyroid growth and secretion *in vitro. Nature,* **197,** 1115–16 (1963)

51. Roth, S. I., Raisz, L. G. Effect of calcium concentration on the ultrastructure of rat parathyroid in organ culture. *Lab. Invest.,* **13,** 331–45 (1964)

52. Potts, J. T., Jr., Keutmann, H. T., Niall, H., Deftos, L., Brewer, H. B., Jr., Aurbach, G. D. Covalent structure of bovine parathyroid hormone in relation to biological and immunological activity. In Ref. 8, 44–53

53. Littledike, E. T., Hawker, C. D. Extraction, purification and partial characterization of porcine parathyroid hormone. *Endocrinology,* **81,**(2), 261–66 (1967)

54. O'Riordan, J. L. H., Condliffe, P. G., Potts, J. T., Jr., Aurbach, G. D. Density gradient centrifigation of human and bovine parathyroid hormone. *Endocrinology,* **81,** 585–90 (1967)

55. Bell, P. H., Barg, W. F., Jr., Colucci, D. F., Davies, M. V., Dziobkowski, C., Englert, M. E., Heyder, E., Paul, R., Snedeker, E. H. Purification and structure of porcine calcitonin-1. *J. Am. Chem. Soc.,* **90,** 2704–6 (1968)

56. Potts, J. T., Jr., Niall, H. D., Keutmann, H. T., Brewer, H. B., Jr., Deftos, L. J. The amino acid sequence of porcine thyrocalcitonin. *Proc. Natl. Acad. Sci.,* **59,** 1321 (1968)

57. Neher, R., Riniker, B., Zuber, H., Rittel, W., Kahnt, F. W. Thyrocalcitonin. II. Struktur von α-Thyrocalcitonin. *Helv. Chim. Acta,* **51,** 917–24 (1968)

58. Rittel, W., Brugger, M., Kamber, B., Riniker, B., Sieber, P. Thyrocalcitonin. III. Die synthese des α-Thyrocalcitonins. *Helv. Chim. Acta,* **51,** 924–28 (1968)

59. Sieber, P., Brugger, M., Kamber, B., Riniker, B., Rittel, W., Maier, R., Staehelin, M. Synthesis and biological activity of peptide sequences related to porcine α-thyrocalcitonin. In Ref. 9 (In press)

60. Aliopoulios, M. A., Voelkel, E. F., Munson, P. L. Assay of human thyroid glands for thyrocalcitonin activity. *J. Clin. Endocrin. Metab.,* **26,** 897–901 (1966)

61. Tashjian, A. H., Jr., Frantz, A. G., Lee, J. B. Pseudohypoparathyroidism: assays of parathyroid hormone and thyrocalcitonin. *Proc. Natl. Acad. Sci.,* **56,** 1138–42 (1966)

62. Tashjian, A. H., Jr., Melvin, K. E. W. Medullary carcinoma of the thyroid gland. Studies of thyrocalcitonin in plasma and tumor extracts. *New England J. Med.,* **279,** 279–83 (1968)

63. Cunliffe, W. J., Black, M. M., Hall, R., Johnston, I. D. A., Hudgson, P., Shuster, S., Gudmunsson, T. V., Joplin, G. F., Williams, E. D., Woodhouse, N. J. Y., Galante, L., MacIntyre, I. A calcitonin-secreting thyroid carcinoma. *Lancet,* **2,** 63–66 (1968)

64. Riniker, B., Neher, R., Maier, R., Kahnt, F. W., Byfield, P. G. H., Gudmundsson, T. V., Galante, L., MacIntyre, I. Menschliches Calcitonin. I. Isolierung und Charakterisierung. *Helv. Chim. Acta,* **51**(7), 1738–42 (1968)

65. Riniker, B., Neher, R., Rittel, W., Zuber, H. Menschliches Calcitonin. III. Struktur von Calcitonin M und D. *Helv. Chim. Acta,* **51,** 1900–5 (1968)

66. O'Dor, R. K., Parkes, C. O., Copp, D. H. The amino acid composition of salmon calcitonin. *Proc. Can. Fed. Biol. Soc.,* **12,** 13 (1969)

67. O'Dor, R. K., Parkes, C. O., Copp, D. H. Amino acid composition of salmon calcitonin. *Can. J. Biochem.,* **47,** 823–25 (1969)

68. Niall, H., Keutmann, H. T., Copp, D. H., Potts, J. T., Jr. Amino acid sequence of salmon ultimobranchial calcitonin. *Proc. Natl. Acad. Sci.,* **64,** 771–78 (1969)

69. Guttmann, v. St., Pless, J., Huguenin, R. L., Sandrin, E., Bossert, H., Zehner, K. Synthese von Salm-Calcitonin, eineme hochaktiven hypocalcämischen Hormon. *Helv. Chim. Acta,* **52,** 1789–95 (1969)

70. O'Dor, R. K., Parkes, C. O., Copp, D. H. Biological activities and molecular weights of ultimobranchial and thyroid calcitonins. *Comp. Biochem. Physiol.,* **29,** 295–300 (1969)

71. Sturtridge, W. C., Kumar, M. A. An improved bioassay for calcitonin. *J. Endocrinol.,* **42,** 501–3 (1968)

72. Copp, D. H., Brooks, C. E., Low, B. S., Newsome, F., O'Dor, R. K., Parkes, C. O., Walker, V., Watts, E. G. Calcitonin and ultimobranchial function in lower vertebrates. In Ref. 9 (In press)

73. Potts, J. T., Jr., Parsons, J. A., Neer, R. M., Krane, S. M., Deftos, L. J., Shields, C. L. Pharmacology of calcitonin: human and animal studies. In Ref. 9 (In press)

74. Collip, J. B., Clark, E. P. Further studies on the physiological action of a parathyroid hormone. *J. Biol. Chem.,* **64,** 485–507 (1925)

75. Munson, P. L. Biological assay of parathyroid hormone. In *The Parathyroids,* 94–113 (Greep, R. O., Talmage, R. V., Eds., Thomas, Springfield, Ill., 1961)

76. Causton, A., Chorlton, B., Rose, G. A., An improved assay for parathyroid hormone, observing the rise of serum calcium in thyroparathyroidectomized rats. *J. Endocrinol.,* **33,** 1–12 (1965)

77. Bethune, J. E., Inoue, H., Turpin, R. A. A bioassay for parathyroid

hormone in mice. *Endocrinology,* **81,** 67–70 (1967)

78. Treacher, R. J. Bioassay of parathyroid hormone in rats by determination of plasma calcium, urinary 32P excretion and serum alkaline phosphatase. *J. Endocrinol.,* **35,** 229–38 (1966)

79. Zanelli, J. M., Lea, D. J., Nisbet, J. A. A bioassay method *in vitro* for parathyroid hormone. *J. Endocrinol.,* **43,** 33–46 (1969)

80. Kumar, M. A., Slack, E., Edwards, A., Soliman, H. A., Baghdiantz, A., Foster, G. V., MacIntyre, I. A biological assay for calcitonin. *J. Endocrinol.,* **33,** 469–75 (1965)

81. Cooper, C. W., Hirsch, P. F., Toverud, S. U., Munson, P. L. An improved method for the biological assay of thyrocalcitonin. *Endocrinology,* **81,** 610–16 (1967)

82. Copp, D. H., Kuczerpa, A. V. A new bioassay for calcitonin and effect of age and dietary Ca and P on the response. In Ref. 7, 18–24

83. Tashjian, A. H., Jr., Levine, L., Munson, P. L. Immunoassay of parathyroid hormone by quantitative complement fixation. *Endocrinology,* **74,** 244–53 (1964)

84. Berson, S. A., Yalow, R. S., Aurbach, G. D., Potts, J. T., Jr. Immunoassay of bovine and human parathyroid hormone. *Proc. Natl. Acad. Sci.,* **49,** 613–17 (1963)

85. Berson, S. A., Yalow, R. S. Parathyroid hormone in plasma in adenomatous hyperparathyroidism, uremia, and bronchogenic carcinoma. *Science,* **154,** 907–9 (1966)

86. Riess, E., Canterbury, J. M. A radioimmunoassay for parathyroid hormone in man. *Proc. Soc. Exptl. Biol. Med.,* **128,** 501–4 (1968)

87. Kooh, S. W., Fraser, D. Experimental parathyroid hormone deficiency produced by injection of antibodies to bovine parathyroid hormone. *Can. J. Physiol. Pharmacol.,* **46,** 441–48 (1968)

88. Tashjian, A. H., Jr., Munson, P. L. Antibodies to porcine thyrocalcitonin: effects on the hypocalcemic activity of calf, rat, and monkey thyroid extracts. *Endocrinology,* **77,** 520–28 (1965)

89. Deftos, L. J., Lee, M. R., Potts, J. T., Jr. A radioimmunoassay for thyrocalcitonin. *Proc. Natl. Acad. Sci.,* **60,** 293–99 (1968)

90. Arnaud, C. D., Littledike, T., Tsao, H. S., Kaplan, E. L. Radioimmunoassay of calcitonin: a preliminary report. *Mayo Clin. Proc.*, **43**, 496–502 (1968)

91. Tashjian, A. H., Jr. Immunoassay of thyrocalcitonin. I. The method and its serological specificity. *Endocrinology*, **84**(1), 140–48 (1969)

92. Potts, J. T., Jr., Buckle, R. M., Sherwood, L. M., Ramberg, C. F., Jr., Mayer, G. P., Kronfeld, D. S., Deftos, L. J., Care, A. D., Aurbach, G. D. Control of secretion of parathyroid hormone. In Ref. 8, 407–16

93. Sherwood, L. M., Mayer, G. P., Ramberg, C. F., Jr., Kronfeld, D. S., Aurbach, G. D., Potts, J. T., Jr. Regulation of parathyroid hormone secretion: proportional control by calcium, lack of effect of phosphate. *Endocrinology*, **83**, 1043 (1968)

94. Buckle, R. M., Care, A. D., Cooper, C. W., Gitelman, H. J. The influence of plasma magnesium concentration on parathyroid hormone secretion. *J. Endocrinol.*, **42**, 529–34 (1968)

95. Melick, R. A., Aurbach, G. D., Potts, J. T., Jr. Distribution and half life of I¹³¹-labelled parathyroid hormone in the rat. *Endocrinology*, **77**, 198–202 (1965)

96. McLean, F. C., Hastings, A. B. Clinical estimation and significance of calcium-ion concentrations in the blood. *Am. J. Med. Sci.*, **189**, 601–13 (1935)

97. Care, A. D., Cooper, C. W., Duncan, T., Orimo, H. The direct measurement of thyrocalcitonin secretion rate *in vivo*. In Ref. 8, 417–27

98. Care, A. D., Cooper, C. W., Duncan, T., Orimo, H. A study of thyrocalcitonin secretion by direct measurement of *in vivo* secretion rates in pigs. *Endocrinology*, **83**, 161–69 (1968)

99. Klein, D. C., Talmage, R. V. Evidence for the secretion of thyrocalcitonin at normal and subnormal plasma calcium levels. *Endocrinology*, **82**, 132–36 (1968)

100. Lee, M. R., Deftos, L. J., Potts, J. T., Jr. Control of secretion of thyrocalcitonin in the rabbit as evaluated by radioimmunoassay. *Endocrinology*, **84**, 36–40 (1969)

101. Sturtridge, W. C., Kumar, M. A. Assay of Calcitonin in Human Plasma. *Lancet*, **1**, 725–26 (1968)

102. Care, A. D., Gitelman, H. J. Possible role of adenyl cyclase in thyrocalcitonin release in the pig. *J. Endocrinol.*, **41**, xxi (1968)

103. Care, A. D., Bates, R. F. L., Gitelman, H. J. The role of glucagon in the release of thyrocalcitonin. *J. Endocrinol.*, **43**, lv-lvi (1969)

104. Rasmussen, H., Arnaud, C., Hawker, C. Actinomycin D and the response to parathyroid hormone. *Science*, **144**, 1019–20 (1964)

105. Raisz, L. G. Inhibition by actinomycin D of bone resorption induced by parathyroid hormone or vitamin A. *Proc. Soc. Exptl. Biol. Med.*, **119**, 614–17 (1965)

106. Steinberg, J., Nichols, G., Jr. Stimulation of bone RNA synthesis by parathyroid hormone. In Ref. 8, 226–41

107. Park, H. Z., Talmage, R. V. Relation of endogenous parathyroid secretion to ³H-cytidine incorporation into bone cells. *Endocrinology*, **80**, 552–60 (1967)

108. Tashjian, A. H., Jr. Homeostasis of plasma calcium: effects of actinomycin D, parathyroidectomy and thyrocalcitonin. *Endocrinology*, **77**, 375–81 (1965)

109. Care, A. D., Duncan, T. Age as a factor in the response to thyrocalcitonin secretion. *J. Endocrinol.*, **37**, 107–8 (1967)

110. Milhaud, G., Perault-Staub, A. M., Moukhtar, M. S. Thyrocalcitonine: Effet de l'âge sur l'hypocalcémie et l'hypophosphatémie. *Compt. Rend. Acad. Sci.*, **264**, 110–13 (1967)

111. Duncan, T., Hinde, F., Phillippo, M. The lack of effect of age on thyrocalcitonin secretion. *J. Endocrinol.*, **40**, 9–10 (1968)

112. Aliopoulios, M. A., Munson, P. L. Thyrocalcitonin. *Surg. Forum*, **16**, 55–57 (1965)

113. Kenny, A. D., Heiskell, C. A. Effect of crude thyrocalcitonin on calcium and phosphorus metabolism in rats. *Proc. Soc. Exptl. Biol. Med.*, **120**, 269–71 (1965)

114. Gaillard, P. J. Bone culture studies with thyrocalcitonin. *Koninkl. Ned. Akad. Wettenschap.*, **70**, 309–20 (1967)

115. Raisz, L. G., Niemann, I. Early effects of parathyroid hormone and

thyrocalcitonin on bone in organ culture. *Nature,* **214,** 486–87 (1967)

116. Aliopoulios, M. A., Goldhaber, P., Munson, P. L. Thyrocalcitonin inhibition of bone resorption induced by parathyroid hormone in tissue culture. *Science,* **151,** 330–31 (1966)

117. Reynolds, J. J. Inhibition by calcitonin of bone resorption induced *in vitro* by vitamin A. *Proc. Roy. Soc. B,* **170,** 61–69 (1968)

118. Reynolds, J. J., Minkin, C. Bone studies *in vitro:* use of calcitonin as a specific inhibitor of bone resorption. In Ref. 9 (In press)

119. Chase, L. R., Fedak, S. A., Aurbach, G. D. Activation of skeletal adenyl cyclase by parathyroid hormone *in vitro. Endocrinology,* **84,** 761–68 (1969)

120. Wells, H., Lloyd, W. Possible involvement of cyclic AMP in the actions of thyrocalcitonin and parathyroid hormone. In Ref. 8, 332–33

121. Vaes, G. The role of lysosomes and of their enzymes in the development of bone resorption induced by parathyroid hormone. In Ref. 8, 318–28

122. Vaes, G. Parathryoid hormone-like action of N^6-2′-O-dibutyryladenosine-3′5′(cyclic)-monophosphate in tissue culture. *Nature,* **219,** 939–40 (1968)

123. Wells, H., Lloyd, W. Hypercalcemic and hypophosphatemic effects of dibutyryl cyclic AMP in rats after parathyroidectomy. *Endocrinology,* **84**(4), 861–67 (1969)

124. Wells, H., Lloyd, W. Hypocalcemic effect of imidazole in rats. *Endocrinology,* **83,** 521–29 (1968)

125. Bates, W. K., McGowen, J., Talmage, R. V. Influence of the parathyroids on hydroxyproline levels. *Endocrinology,* **71,** 189–95 (1962)

126. Martin, T. J., Robinson, C. J., MacIntyre, I. The mode of action of thyrocalcitonin. *Lancet,* **1,** 900–2 (1966)

127. Klein, D. C., Morii, H., Talmage, R. V. Effect of thyrocalcitonin, administered during peritoneal lavage, on removal of bone salts and their radioisotopes. *Proc. Soc. Exptl. Biol. Med.,* **124,** 627–33 (1967)

128. Klein, D. C., Talmage, R. V. Thyro-

calcitonin suppression of hydroxyproline release from bone. *Proc. Soc. Exptl. Biol. Med.,* **127** 95–99 (1968)

129. Foster, G. V., Doyle, F. H., Bordier, P., Matrajt, H. Effect of thyrocalcitonin on bone. *Lancet,* **2,** 1428–31 (1966a)

130. Foster, G. V., Clark, M., Doyle, F. H., Joplin, G. F., Singer, F. R., Fraser, T. R., MacIntyre, I. Clinical applications of calcitonin. In Ref. 8, 100–7

131. Milhaud, G., Moukhtar, M. S., Cherian, G., Perault-Staub, A. Effet l'administration de thyrocalcitonine sur les principaux paramétres du metabolisme du calcium du rat normal et du rat thyroparathyroidectomisé. *Compt. Rend.,* **262,** 511–14 (1966)

132. Parsons, J. A., Robinson, C. J. A rapid indirect hypercalcemic action of parathyroid demonstrated in isolated blood-perfused bone. In Ref. 8, 329–31

133. MacIntyre, I., Parsons, J. A., Robinson, C. J. The effect of thyrocalcitonin on the blood-bone calcium equilibrium in the perfused tibia of the cat. *J. Physiol.,* **191,** 393–405 (1967)

134. Fujita, T., Orimo, H., Ohata, M., Yoshikawa, M., Nakanishi, K., Misaka, E. Prevention of experimental bone atrophy by thyrocalcitonin. *Endocrinol. Japon.,* **15,** 8–12 (1968)

135. Ziegler, R., Delling, G. The effect of calcitonin on atrophy and new formation of bone. *Acta Endocrinol. Suppl. 138,* 183 (1969)

136. Delling, G., Schaefer, A., Ziegler, R. The effect of calcitonin on fracture healing and ectopic bone formation in the rat. In Ref. 9 (In press)

137. Wase, A. W., Peterson, A., Rickes, E., Solewski, J. Some effects of thyrocalcitonin on the calcium metabolism of the rat. *Endocrinology,* **79,** 687–91 (1966)

138. Walker, D. G. Elevated bone collagenolytic activity and hyperplasia of parafollicular light cells of the thyroid gland in parathormone-treated grey-lethal mice. *Z. Zellforsch.,* **72,** 100–24 (1966)

139. Krook, L., Lutwak, L., McEntee, K. Dietary calcium and ultimobranchial tumors and osteopetrosis in

the bull. *Am. J. Clin. Nutr.*, **22**, 115–18 (1969)

140. Shah, B. G., Draper, H. H. Depression of calcium absorption in parathyroidectomized rats. *Am. J. Physiol.*, **211**, 963–66 (1966)

141. Cramer, C. F. Participation of parathyroid glands in control of calcium absorption in dogs. *Endocrinology*, **72**, 192–96 (1963)

142. Care, A. D., Keynes, W. M. The role of parathyroid hormones in the absorption of calcium and magnesium from the small intestine. *Proc. Roy. Soc. Med.*, **57**, 867–68 (1964)

143. Lifshitz, F., Harrison, H. C., Harrison, H. E. Influence of parathyroid function upon the *in vitro* transport of calcium and phosphate by the rat intestine. *Endocrinology*, **84**, 912–17 (1969)

144. Cramer, C. F., Parkes, C. O., Copp, D. H. The effect of chicken and hog calcitonin on some parameters of Ca, P, and Mg metabolism in dogs. *Can. J. Physiol. Pharmacol.*, **47**, 181–84 (1969)

145. Peacock, M., Robertson, W. G., Nordin, B. E. C. Relation between serum and urinary calcium with particular reference to parathyroid activity. *Lancet*, **1**, 384–86 (1969)

146. Robinson, C. J., Martin, T. J., MacIntyre, I. Phosphaturic effect of thyrocalcitonin. *Lancet*, **2**, 83–84 **(1966)**

147. Haas, H. G. Phosphaturic effect of thyrocalcitonin. *Lancet*, **2**, 280 (1966)

148. Clark, J. D., Kenny, A. D. Hog thyrocalcitonin in the dog: urinary calcium phosphorus, magnesium and sodium responses. *Endocrinology*, **84**(5), 1199–1205 (1969)

149. Borle, A. B. Effects of purified parathyroid hormone on the calcium metabolism of monkey kidney cells. *Endocrinology*, **83**, 1316–22 (1968)

150. Watlington, C. O., Burke, P. K., Estep, H. L. Calcium flux in isolated frog skin; the effect of parathyroid substances. *Proc. Soc. Exptl. Biol. Med.*, **128**, 853–56 **(1968)**

151. Rasmussen, H., Tenenhouse, A. Cyclic adenosine monophosphate, Ca⁺⁺, and membranes. *Proc. Natl. Acad. Sci.*, **59**, 1364–70 (1969)

152. Parkinson, D. K., Radde, I. C. Calcitonin action on membrane ATPase—a hypothesis. In Ref. 9 (In press)

153. Charbon, G. A. A rapid and selective vasodilator effect of parathyroid hormone. *Europ. J. Pharmacol.*, **3**, 275–78 (1968)

154. Rasmussen, H., Tenenhouse, A. Thyrocalcitonin, osteoporosis and osteolysis. *Am. J. Med.*, **43**, 711–26 (1967)

155. Gabbiani, G., Tuchweber, B., Côté, G., Lefort, P. Action of thyroxine and calcitonin on experimental soft-tissue calcification. *Calcif. Tiss. Res.*, **2**(1), 30 (1968)

156. Greep, R. O. Parathyroid glands. In *Comp. Endocrinol.*, **1**, *Glandular Hormones*, 325–70 (1963)

157. Cortelyou, J. R. The effect of commercially prepared parathyroid extract on plasma and urine calcium levels in *Rana pipiens*. *Gen. Comp. Endocrinol.*, **9**, 234–40 (1967)

158. Cortelyou, J. R., Quipse, P. A., McWhinnie, D. J. Parathyroid extract effects on phosphorus metabolism in *Rana pipiens*. *Gen. Comp. Endocrinol.*, **9**, 76–92 (1967)

159. McWhinnie, D. J., Cortelyou, J. R. Influence of parathyroid extract on blood and urine mineral levels in Inquanid lizards. *Gen. Comp. Endocrinol.*, **11**, 78–87 (1968)

160. Urist, M. R. Avian parathyroid physiology: including a special comment on calcitonin. *Am. Zoologist*, **7**, 883–95 (1967)

161. Chan, D. K. O., Chester-Jones, I., Smith, R. N. The effect of mammalian calcitonin on the plasma levels of calcium and inorganic phosphate in the European eel (*Anguilla anguilla* L.). *Gen. Comp. Endocrinol.*, **11**, 243–45 (1968)

162. Louw, G. N., W. W., Kenny, A. D. Action of thyrocalcitonin in the teleost fish *Ictalurus melas*. *Nature*, **215**. 888–89 (1967)

163. Pang, P. K. T., Pickford, G. E. Failure of hog thyrocalcitonin to elicit hypocalcemia in the teleost fish, *Fundulus heteroclitus*. *Comp. Biochem. Physiol.*, **21**, 573–98 (1967)

164. Robertson, D. R. The ultimobranchial body of *Rana pipiens*. VIII. Effects of extirpation upon calcium distribution and bone cell types.

Gen. Comp. Endocrinol., **12**, 479–90 (1969)

165. Robertson, D. R. The ultimobranchial body in *Rana pipiens*. IX. Effects of extirpation and transplantation on urinary calcium excretion. *Endocrinology*, **84**, 1174–78 (1969)

166. Kraintz, L., Intscher, K. Effect of calcitonin on the domestic fowl. *Can. J. Physiol. Pharmacol.*, **47**, 313–15 (1969)

167. Walker, V. R., Low, B. S., Copp, D. H. Effect of ultimobranchialectomy during calcium infusion in young turkeys. *Proc. Can. Fed. Biol. Soc.*, **12**, 13 (1969)

168. Brown, D. M., Perey, D. Y. E., Dent, P. B., Good, R. A. Effect of chronic calcitonin deficiency on the skeleton of the chicken. *Proc. Soc. Exptl. Biol. Med.*, **130**, 1001–4 (1969)

169. Bell, N. H., Barrett, R. J., Patterson, R. Effects of porcine thyrocalcitonin on serum calcium, phosphorus and magnesium in the monkey and man. *Proc. Soc. Exptl. Biol. Med.*, **123**, 114–18 (1966)

170. Milhaud, G., Job, J. C. Thyrocalcitonin: effect on idiopathic hypercalcemia. *Science*, **154**, 794–96 (1966)

171. Bijvoet, O. L. M., van der Sluys Veer, J., Jansen, A. P. Effects of calcitonin on patients with Paget's disease. *Lancet*, **1**, 876–81 (1968)

172. Baud, C. A., Langer, B., Mach, R. S., Siebenthal, J., Tupling, M. R. Effects of prolonged thyrocalcitonin administration in human senile osteoporosis: a clinical histological and microcardiographical study. In Ref. 9 (In press)

173. Bronner, F., Sammon, P. J., Nichols, C., Stacey, R. E., Shah, B. G. Thyrocalcitonin and plasma calcium homeostasis in the rat. In Ref. 8, 353–69

174. Copp, D. H. Calcitonin—a new hormone from the parathyroid which lowers blood calcium. *Oral Surg.*, **16**, 872–77 (1963)

175. Hirsch, P. F., Munson, P. L. Importance of the thyroid glands in the prevention of hypercalcemia in rats. *Endocrinology*, **79**, 655–58 (1966)

176. Kumar, M. A., Sturtridge, W. C. Calcium homeostasis in chronic thyrocalcitonin deficiency. *Endocrinology*, **81**, 1297–1300 (1967)

177. Gittes, R. F., Radde, I. C. Experimental hyperparathyroidism from multiple isologous parathyroid transplants: homeostatic effect of simultaneous thyroid transplants. *Endocrinology*, **78**, 1015–22 (1966)

178. Gray, T. K., Munson, P. L. Thyrocalcitonin: Evidence for function in normal physiology. *Science* (In press)

179. Talmage, R. V., Kennedy, J. W. III. Influence of the thyroid on the response of rats to administered calcitonins. *Endocrinology*, **84**, 1026–31 (1969)

180. Talmage, R. V., Neuenschwander, J., Minkin, C. Influence of the thyroid on calcium and phosphate concentrations in extracellular fluid compartments. *Endocrinology*, **84**, 1016–25 (1969)

SKELETAL MUSCLE[1]   1040

ALEXANDER SANDOW

Division of Physiology, Institute for Muscle Disease, New York, N.Y.

This review deals with the research on skeletal muscle, predominantly of the vertebrate, published during the 2-year period ending early July 1969. Findings on other kinds of muscle or from earlier periods will be considered only when they bear on the problems of immediate concern. However, work on muscle has been so greatly expanded and diversified that no single brief review can possibly cover all kinds of muscle and skeletal muscle requires its own special review as do cardiac or smooth or insect muscle.

During the 2 years of interest the research on skeletal muscle alone has produced a tremendous outpouring of publications that reflects the fascination and excitement aroused by the problems and rich progress of current muscle research. This great productivity, however, can be embarrassing for it becomes almost impossible (even for a reviewer!) just to keep track of it all, let alone critically digest it. And this problem is qualitative as well as quantitative. For muscle is so varied structurally and functionally that the methods used in its study include almost every discipline used by biologists, biochemists, and biophysicists, and this demands that the student who wishes to critically comprehend the extremely variegated papers on muscle must have mastered an unusually wide range of subjects. Apart from the question whether anyone has such mastery, it seems to me that in a review such as this one the reader should be presented with what the editors of this journal request, a "synthetic overview of the principal trends and accomplishments" in the assigned subject. This is what I shall attempt to do, even though here and there I may have to limit my presentation to mere description and omit a more critical evaluation of some evidently outstanding papers.

Communication in general evidently goes on among myologists essentially as described in the last review of this series (1). As a New Yorker, I compliment the PHILADELPHIA MYO-BIO Group for their continuing devotion to dinners involving informal but critical discussion of muscle re-

[1] Abbreviations used: E-C coupling, excitation-contraction coupling; FRT, filament resting tension; LR, latency relaxation; PC, phosphorylcreatine; SR, sarcoplasmic reticulum; TS, transverse (tubular) system; STS, sarcotubular system (this being the combined SR + TS, or internal membrane system); SREC, short-range elastic component.

search. It is time a similar means was developed in New York to eat and discuss muscle. An interesting new feature concerned with improving communication is the call by Hoyle (2) for all interested to send both relevant electronmicrographs and reprints to build up his laboratory's library on comparative muscle physiology.

As is to be expected in so active a field as ours, reviews are plentiful. The Symposium on Muscle held in 1966 in Budapest has now been published (3), and for the most part it makes very interesting reading. The coverage was limited almost entirely to mechanisms of contraction, but the discussion, deliberately planned to be free, was remarkably spontaneous and wide-ranging, so that the published proceedings sparkle with much liveliness and valuable information. The comparative features of muscle, especially of the invertebrate, were covered in great detail by Hoyle (2). Two books essentially on skeletal muscle have appeared, one nicely brief and elementary (4) and the other, by Bendall (5), aptly entitled *Muscles, Molecules and Movement,* giving a quite detailed summary account, garnished here and there by the author's own provocative speculations, of the biochemistry and the protein chemistry of striated muscle in relation to all physiological features of the contraction-relaxation cycle. Bendall's book is highly recommended for the beginner who especially wishes an experimentally grounded introduction to the research on the molecular level that has provided so much of the foundation of our present knowledge of muscle activity. Essentially also a book is Mommaerts' comprehensive presentation of the historical, didactic, and current aspects of the energetics of muscle (5a).

The review by Ebashi & Endo (6) on the role of calcium in contraction is welcome as a fine, definitive account of information on this all-embracing feature of muscular activity. More specialized reviews of considerable interest have appeared: (a) X-ray diffraction studies of muscle by Hanson (7) who, though considering herself an "amateur who does not practice X-ray diffraction", has written a comprehensive and highly informative account of this subject that is easy to follow and extremely useful for all of us other X-ray amateurs; (b) various aspects of contractile proteins (8, 9); (c) membrane systems in special relation to excitation-contraction coupling (10); (d) mechanochemical transformation (11); (e) structure of both skeletal and cardiac sarcotubular systems given in an excellently condensed and clear form (12); (f) ion selective channels in relation to the action potential (13) which, though discussed directly for the nerve fiber, is usefully relevant to the muscle fiber; (g) pharmacological effects of ryanodine on muscle (14); (h) certain highly specialized pharmacological and biochemical features related to sympathomimetic amines (15) and to cyclic AMP (16); (i) two accounts of the "trophic" influences of nerve and muscle (17, 18). Special mention should be made of Caldwell's (19) detailed review of the movement and distribution of inorganic ions in both resting and excited muscle and nerve fibers, which includes critical consideration of the problems of active transport. Happily, this review treats muscle permeability so thoroughly that I need not consider that subject here. More particular consideration of the hydrogen ion is discussed in a review on intracellular pH (20).

Heart muscle has been very actively studied lately and this is reflected in detail in admirable reviews (21–24). The Somlyos (25) have given us an extremely comprehensive and detailed review of the structure, pathology, biochemistry, and biophysics of vascular smooth muscle; and this is only Part I of their work; Part II will deal with the responses of smooth muscle to particular chemical and physical agents. For contractile mechanisms of smooth muscle imaginatively considered in particular relation to sliding-filament mechanisms, read Ruegg's review (26), and for pharmacological aspects of excitation-contraction coupling, especially of smooth muscle (though with interesting material on slow and on dystrophic skeletal muscle), see the recent symposium (27).

The rich development of research on muscle is naturally having a considerable impact on studies of motility in general, which frequently in turn reflexly affect their parent field. This can be seen in various reviews, as well as symposia and their publications (8–11, 28–31).

Another most significant development, connected with the diseases of muscle, essentially stems from the two decades of farsighted policy of the Muscular Dystrophy Associations of America, Inc., to give generous support to basic research on muscle as an integral means coupled with clinical work and research to achieve its main goal to conquer muscular dystrophy. As one recent expression of this policy, the MDAA sponsored its fourth international conference, in 1966; this is now published as a highly informative, elegantly printed volume (32) which covers the basic and medical research aspects of dystrophy and related disorders. The muscle physiologist concentrating on fundamental mechanisms will find much of interest here, e.g. the nearly 100 pages of discussion on fiber types. The MDAA also sponsored a 2-day international conference on regeneration of muscle, held in New York, 28–29 March 1969, which it is hoped will be published, and which dealt with, among other subjects, the possible role of satellite cells (33) in general muscle economy and regeneration. Under stimulation from the MDAA, similar medically and basically oriented groups have been set up and are flourishing in Canada, England, Italy, Czechoslovakia, and Japan. The English "Research Committee of the Muscular Dystrophy Group" recently published the proceedings of its fourth (1968) symposium (34). And as these pages are being written, an International Congress on Muscle Diseases is being held in Milan (19–23 May 1969) sponsored by the "Unione Italiana Lotta Alla Distrofia Musculare". Finally, one should note the publication of a very detailed account of normal and diseased muscle structure as seen electronmicroscopically (35), and the book by Dubowitz (36) on the histochemistry of developing and diseased muscle.

MECHANICAL OUTPUT SYSTEMS

SLIDING-FILAMENT MECHANISMS

General behavior.—There is general agreement that changes in muscle length involve in each sarcomere a relative sliding of thin and thick filaments which maintain their length constant but vary in amount of interdigitation (e.g. 37). As previously reviewed (1), the amount of tension produced at plateau of isometric tetanus is, in general, a function of the amount and kind (whether single or double) of overlap, with cross-bridge involvement in accordance with the sliding-filament theory. But the situation is a bit clouded for isotonic contraction. Although there is evidence (38, 39) that considerable active sliding can occur and not essentially affect the isometric tension that should develop according to theory at the fully shortened length, an apparently serious challenge to the theory for active shortening has appeared in some work from Sjöstrand's laboratory (40, 41). In fact, such contradictory evidence was proposed earlier by Sjöstrand (42) where he claimed that during isotonic contractions of both electrically stimulated live muscles of the frog, or corresponding ATP activated glycerinated fibers, the increase of interdigitation was less than that expected from the amount of sarcomere shortening and that this discrepancy was related to the formation of "contraction bands" which appeared as an abnormal increase in density of filament material at the A-I junctions. It was claimed that these bands developed because of a change in the configuration of the thick and thin filaments which was different from that expected from only a simple increase in interdigitation.

Incidentally, "contraction bands"—as a term, and even as an observed entity in some respects like Sjöstrand's—are not new (43-44a). However, H. E. Huxley (45), noting that he and Hanson had discussed these bands as early as 1954 (46), not only offered a reasonable explanation for their occurrence but showed that shortening occurred generally without their appearance and that instead interdigitation increased in simple accordance with theory. It is therefore rather surprising to see now the new articles (40, 41) in which the "contraction bands" are studied in detail, but without benefit from, or even reference to, Huxley's analysis (45).

It seems to me that the new work does not add much to the original reports, except perhaps that "contraction bands" can be reversed (41). And while the claim may be true that "contraction band formation . . . is a feature which clearly distinguished fibers fixed during [isotonic] contraction . . ." (40), much evidence (37, 45) clearly shows that the reverse is not true: i.e., isotonic contraction does not always cause formation of "contraction bands", and that "these have no direct bearing on the basic process of contraction, but arise as an occasional and non-essential side effect, either of contraction or of preparation for electron microscopy" (45). Thus we can conclude that the essential interdigitational features of the original sliding-filament theory still hold good even for isotonic contraction.

Cross-bridge activity.—The results indicating that tension production in isometric contraction is basically associated with the presence of the cross bridges tell us no details as to how these structures perform their function; nor evidently are these results convincing enough to some workers to exclude other mechanisms for producing the basic interfilamentary motive force that do not depend on cross-bridge linkage to actin. However, some highly significant papers involving low-angle X-ray studies of frog skeletal muscle have appeared from the laboratories of H. E. Huxley (47–51) and of Elliott (52, 53) which certainly tell us much about some features of cross-bridge behavior during contraction and which strongly indicate that the bridges do produce the elementary force which underlies active tension production. Some results of a very extensive paper (48) have already been reviewed (1) on the basis of a preliminary report (47), so only certain additional features will be mentioned here. [For a very full account of this and related work, see Hanson's review (7).] There has been an impressive improvement in low-angle technique both in speed and in capacity to resolve as many as 20 or more meridional reflections within a maximum diffraction angle of about one degree. Both in rigor and in normal contraction, the meridional X-ray patterns indicate that for all practical purposes the thin and thick filaments do not change length; or rather this is true to within ± 0.2 per cent for the thin filament, but the thick filaments show an increase of about 1 per cent in their repeat unit. The cross bridges, however, without any significant change in axial spacing, seem to both rotate and extend radially in a plane perpendicular to the long axis of their thick-filament backbone. Furthermore, there is indication of much more disorder of the cross bridges during contraction than in rigor, this evidently corresponding to the reasonable view that the bridges are fluctuating cyclically in contraction but are locked in fixed position in rigor. Especially noteworthy is the result that the cross bridges show great asynchrony in their disordered behavior during normal contraction, for this seems to rule out the suggestions, as inferred from certain alleged mechanical features of contracting frog skeletal muscle, that cross bridges undergo synchronous cycles of activity (54) and that sarcomeres dither (55), the latter in any case being contradicted by other work on single fibers of frog muscle (56).

A most interesting feature of the X-ray work that demonstrates simply and directly the great power of the method for revealing practically the molecular properties of the contractile material within the living muscle is the change in the intensity ratio of the 10 and 11 equatorial reflections. I_{11}/I_{10} (49, 53). These reflections essentially represent the material of the myosin and the actin filaments, respectively, as organized in their hexagonal lattice, and the intensities of the reflections are proportional to the respective masses of substance at the lattice positions of the two kinds of filament. Although past findings were in disagreement (see 49 for review), the present results from the H. E. Huxley (49) and the Elliott (53) laboratories now agree that during contraction the value of I_{11}/I_{10} increases. One interpretation (53) of the increase is that contraction produces an increased order of the actin filaments in a limited part of overlap region, possibly the part including only the tapered ends of the myosin filaments. But, another view (49) is that the increased value of I_{11}/I_{10} is produced by a shift of substance from the thick to the thin filaments, as would occur if the activated heavy meromyosin side arms of the myosin swung from a postion close to their myosin backbone to a position of attachment on the actin filament and so formed the actual cross-bridge linkages by which the contractile force is supposed to be developed. A similar result has been obtained by a rather different type of study of X-ray intensity changes produced by contracting insect flight muscle (57).

Taken as a whole, these results, and many other finer details (48), powerfully support the view that the cross bridges mediate the active relative sliding of the filaments by linking to the actin filaments, and so generate the force of muscular contraction. Some conception of the extreme complexity of the cross-bridge activity during contraction can be seen in the work of Reedy (50, 51) which indicates that in insect muscle, at least, myosin has a left-handed, but actin a right-handed helical structure. This work also proves that in a state of rigor the cross bridges are so angled as to indicate that they have pushed rather than pulled the actin filaments toward the M-line center of the sarcomere. Whether this also occurs in vertebrate muscle is not known. One odd finding for the contracting sliding filaments is, as already mentioned, that although the actin filaments stay at constant length, the repeat unit of the myosin definitely increases by about 1 per cent. Actually an increase should be expected for both types of filament, for when they are developing force they are put under tension and should therefore both elongate. The failure of the actin filaments to do so may indicate that the aggregate of them in a sarcomere has a greater stiffness than that of all the associated myosin filaments (but see 48). At any rate, the constancy of thin-filament length invalidates the suggestion (58) that the series-elastic element, which is of course stretched during contraction, may be identified with the actin filaments.

Long-range interfilament forces.—Apart from the possibility that the actin and myosin filaments may interact by means of cross-bridge linkages, there must also be interactions based on relatively long-range electrical and van der Waals forces. The experimental basis for this view, which has been developed mainly in Elliott's laboratory (52, 53, 59–62), is that the constant volume relation (which holds for the filament lattice of sarcomeres varying in length from about 2.0 to 3.6 μ and which involves variation of the center-to-center separation of the actin and myosin filaments from about 250 to 187 Å in typical skeletal fibers) is not invariant, but depends strongly on the nature of the medium. Thus, Rome (61) shows in general, but more clearly for glycerinated fibers than for intact ones, that at a given sarcomere length the lateral lattice dimensions diminish and thus also does the lattice volume, the less the pH (9.0 to 4.0), the greater the ionic strength, and the higher the valence (1 or 2) of the predominant cation in the medium. Since the filament system is in stable equilibrium, these results indicate the presence of long-range repulsive electrical forces between the filaments, which are balanced by van der Waals attractive forces and are modified in general by hydration effects.

These results could be of prime importance in elucidating certain sliding-filament mechanisms such as may be operating in variously treated muscle fibers (63–65a) whose contractile output diminishes with increased internal ionic strength. It is curious, however, that a lattice behavior most like that of living muscle appears when the experimentally treated fibers are immersed in a glycerol medium of a very low ionic strength, $\mu = 0.015$ (61). For this value is probably only about one twentieth as great as the ionic strength of the living myoplasm (67).

Elliott and his co-workers (52, 53, and see also 66) make much of the problem of the filamentary gap, i.e., that the condition of constant lattice volume demands that the cross bridges be long enough to link myosin to actin filaments even in the shortened (e.g. 2.0 μ) sarcomere, where the distance between axial centers of the thick and thin filaments is about 250 Å, and where therefore the cross bridges would have to act over a distance some 60 Å greater than in the lengthened (e.g. 3.6 μ) sarcomere. Oddly, one might think that such a problem exists because in some diagrams of the sliding-filament structures (e.g. 48) the cross bridges are pictured as if they were short, straight, inextensive rods, unable even to bridge the gap between the pictured thick and thin filaments! But compare with this the diagram projecting the latest view (68).

Be that as it may, the activation of myosin-ATPase by actin evidently involves complexing of myosin and actin and this must depend on the heavy meromyosin of the cross bridges. Clearly this sort of reaction occurs in the living fiber (69–71), even in very short sarcomeres, and in such a way, furthermore, that the ATPase activity per cross bridge remains constant despite considerable changes in filamentary spacing. This complexing, moreover, must involve very tight binding since the dissociation constant is about 10^{-6} (72). And the possibility that such binding occurs in normally organized fibrils is strongly suggested by Bárány's (73, 74) work, based on the use of 1-fluoro-2,4-dinitrobenzene as a probe, which shows in various model and living muscle systems that the reactivity of myosin with the reagent is less in the contracted state than in the resting, thus indicating that myosin undergoes a conformational change during contraction which we may presume develops in reaction to the complexing of actin and myosin by means of cross-bridge linkages. Furthermore, the work of Pepe (75) indicates that the heavy meromyosin constituting the cross bridges has inherent properties and also variable ways of sticking out from the thick filaments which indicate that it could reach out for as much as 800 Å and so ensure that the cross bridges could contact the actin over any conceivable distance that would occur during physiological functioning of the sliding filaments.

Further details of the above and a constructively imaginative elaboration of them into a definite linkage theory of cross-bridge action will be found in the latest article by H. E. Huxley (68). Especially pertinent in this respect is the newest paper by Lowey and her collaborators (75a) which elaborates her recent work characterizing the physicochemical properties of the sub-fragments of the myosin molecule in relation to the general structure of the thick filament and especially in regard to the possible action of the cross bridges in contraction.

In view of all the evidence, I think we can safely conclude that the cross bridges produce the interfilamentary sliding force and that they do so by making contact with reactive sites on the actin filaments. Long-range forces, however, may nevertheless play an important secondary role of modulating the chemical reactions of the cross bridges with the actin and the mechanical consequences of these reactions.

Theoretical elaboration.—An interesting addition (76) to the A. F. Huxley (77) mathematical theory of cross-bridge action frees the theory from its original limitation to steady states of contraction, such as occurs in the force-velocity relation, and provides a basis for handling the kinetics of such processes as the twitch and the tetanus. This is achieved by introducing a time-dependent scheme for altering the value of Huxley's forward rate constant f by assuming that this depends not only on the position of a particular cross bridge relative to a neighboring reactive site on an actin filament, as originally assumed by Huxley, but also on the instantaneous amount of binding of activator Ca^{2+} and the subsequent removal of it from the myofibrils through reaccumulation by the SR. Also added to the theoretical model is a passive series elasticity with properties like that of the series-elastic component of muscle. With the original theory thus elaborated, quite realistic curves can then be predicted for the kinetics of force production in the twitch, the tetanus, the effects of quick releases and stretches, and, by another addition to the theory, the special behavior of insect fibrillar muscle.

The Huxley (77) theory has been subjected to another sort of treatment by T. L. Hill & White (78–81) who use the methods of equilibrium statistical thermodynamics. Although Hill (78) first attempted to treat the sliding-filament mechanism as if it exhibited a first-order phase transition, this had to be abandoned because certain features of the theory obviously contradicted some basic physiological features of the actual mechanism. In the later papers, detailed use is made of sophisticated stochastic methods of analysis based on random-walk processes as a means of learning about physicochemical systems at the level of first principles, and those who have the knowledge and the taste for such methods will find much to engage their attention. Evidently, one general conclusion deriving from this work is that the essentials of the Huxley theory do not run afoul of the basic principles of statistical thermodynamics. One rather odd feature of the Hill theory, however, is the prediction that the force developed per cross bridge is inversely proportional to the length of the bridge (80). This is contradictory to the fact that, at least over the range of frog fiber sarcomere lengths from 3.65 to 2.00 μ, which as mentioned above evidently involve variation in the interfilamentary gap and hence possibly of the length of the cross bridges from about 190 to 250 Å, there is no change in the force generated *per cross bridge.*

Although much of the foregoing indicates that the sliding-filament theory, even involving cross-bridge attachment, seems more solidly entrenched than ever, a completely different theory has appeared which would in effect commit the sliding-filament mechanism to limbo (82). The new theory places the basic origin of muscular force in an alleged tendency of the Z-bands to expand when activated, so that, since the constant volume condition is assumed to hold, the sarcomeres would tend to shorten and thus account for axial tension. This mechanism requires presence of a tensile boundary at the fiber surface, e.g. the sarcolemma, to serve as a "container" for constant volume maintenance but not to transmit active tension, this being accomplished by means of "the intermolecular forces of the sarcoplasmic fluid". As for the filaments, their function is turned inside-out, for they are supposed to contribute only to resting tension by cross-bridge action and then, by losing this in the activated fibril, slide passively and behave morphologically in conformance with observation. A complete discussion of all the serious weaknesses of this theory is too lengthy to be given here. But critically undermining it are the following: (*a*) Natori (83) preparations of myofibrils contract on appropriate activation when immersed in an aqueous medium (6, 83, 84) and therefore free of anything like a sarcolemma or even a boundary possessing surface tension; (*b*) it does not appear possible that the intermolecular forces of the aqueous interfilament solution of a Natori preparation could transmit a force in the sense of the theory when, as happens, the preparation contracts in an aqueous medium which is free to flow; and (*c*) contractions occur in preparations with damaged Z-disks (84a) or, even more important, in certain muscles, which though having some sort of sliding filaments, do not have Z-disks as assumed in the theory (26, 85, 86).

Miscellaneous structural details.—As an indication that contraction of muscle depends universally on an interaction between two types of filaments, it now appears that even in the previously doubtful case of vertebrate smooth muscle (87) thick, as well as thin, filaments are present in chicken gizzard and guinea pig taenia coli, and they are evidently composed of myosin (86–88). The existence of still a third type of (ultrathin, 25 Å) so-called T-filament in striated muscle as proposed by Hoyle (89, 90) was considered moot (1). And I think so, too, partly for reasons already given (1) but also because I do not think Hoyle has yet proved that certain passive elastic properties of fibers, which he believes can only be explained by his new filament, cannot be attributed to the sarcoplasmic reticulum, especially in those fibers having effectively continuous columns of sarcotubular membranes running the whole length of the fiber, as emphasized for other reasons elsewhere (90, 91). Perhaps the best position is that, according to Hoyle himself (2), "the reader should consider the evidence, judge for himself and await further developments." Some suggestive developments have occurred, in fact. A third type of filament has been reported to appear in myofibrillogenesis in larval newts, but these are not ultrathin and they seem not to transform into contractile elements (92). But most interesting, "thin whiskers" about 20 Å thick and 1000 Å long attached to "'arrowheads" have appeared in electronmicrographic studies of formation of actomyosin (93). These evidently consist of units of the light meromyosin moiety of myosin which have not been incorporated into a myosin thick filament. Now, Hoyle's T-filaments are structurally very similar to the "thin whiskers", and I therefore wonder whether they may be so actually, and have appeared in Hoyle's preparations as light meromyosin pieces sloughed off from thick filaments. Such an explanation of the filaments Hoyle reports would suggest they are only artifacts and would preclude the need for hypothesizing a new sliding-filament mechanism of contraction as proposed by Hoyle (90).

A new looping-filament configuration has been proposed for the structure of the Z-line in vertebrate muscle so now we have four models of Z to choose from (92, 94). However, the material of these lines has been selectively completely extracted from chick cardiac muscle by 1 M urea (95) and it is suggested that lipid-protein association occurs in the Z-line. Further indication that the Z-line contains tropomyosin is found in the disposition in certain cardiac muscles of material that is crystallographically like tropomyosin (96). However, α-actinin is also reported to be in the Z-band (97); and this is further strikingly indicated in that both M- and Z-lines can be removed from rabbit psoas fibers by a special procedure and that the Z-, but not the M-line can then be reconstituted, at least in part, by soaking the treated fibers in a medium containing α-actinin (97a). The M-line is itself evidently composed of a new protein (98). Furthermore, this line seems to have a very complicated structure involving short longitudinal M-filaments as well as the previously described transverse cross bridges (99). Structural details of the Z- and M-lines probably play a significant role in the sliding-filament mechanism by providing transverse anchorages for the filaments and thus keeping them in proper alignment.

Further interesting findings regarding sarcomeric organization deal with (a) oblique striations (85), (b) an indication that some tropomyosin may be located on the thick filaments (100), (c) some special findings in muscle prepared for electronmicroscopy without fixation (101), and (d) embryonic mechanisms producing myofibrils (102). A study of the general structure of tortoise skeletal muscle (103) reveals nothing electronmicroscopically visible in the filaments to account for the extreme slowness of mechanical response of these muscles. The structure of the sarcobubular system is also of no help in this regard: the fact that the T-tubules form a three-dimensional network which involves double sets of triads in each sarcomere should, if anything, increase the speed of response. The contradictory structural features highlight all the more the great importance of Bárány's finding (104) that the speed of mechanical action is determined basically by the rate of actomyosin-ATPase action. Finally, Goldspink (105) has demonstrated that the postnatal increase in length of the biceps brachii muscle of the mouse is only about 75 per cent accounted for by increase in number of sarcomeres, the remaining 25 per cent being due to increase in sarcomere length, which involves decrease in overlap but no change in length of the filaments. This finding is very interestingly discussed in relation to the variation in sarcomere length along the length of the fiber. Other papers from Goldspink's laboratory will be found of great interest concerning grosser features of muscle morphology and function as modified by genetic (106), developmental (107), hypertrophy-inducing (108), and dystrophic (109) factors.

MECHANICAL BEHAVIOR OF MUSCLES

Short-range elastic component.—D. K. Hill (110) has demonstrated most interestingly that the normal resting sartorius muscle of frog and toad has a special short-range elastic component (SREC), which is most clearly revealed at rest lengths where ordinary parallel elasticity is effectively absent. The SREC produces tension (elastic modulus, E_{SREC}, of about 1.5 kg/cm^2) as the muscle is being stretched at velocities of about 10–100 μ/sec; but when the stretch is as little as 50 μ (about 0.2 per cent muscle length), an "elastic limit" is reached and then as further stretch occurs the tension is maintained as a constant "frictional resistance". When the muscle is now allowed to return passively to its original length, these changes of the SREC reverse. The value of E_{SREC} is not changed by increase in the length of the muscle at which a stretch is impressed. It is, however, greatly increased in hypertonic media (up to 10 kg/cm^2 in $2 \times R$) and reduced in hypotonic media. And in hypertonic solutions (about 1.5–$2 \times R$) the value of E_{SREC} is rather independent of the velocity of the stretch for values from 0.1 to 100μ/sec, but it then very rapidly increases severalfold as the velocity increases to 40,000 μ/sec. Hill has also shown that mere increase in hypertonicity of the medium, e.g. to 2.5 times normal, causes the resting tension of the muscle to rise by about 0.1 P_0. Though not so called by Hill, this is evidently a contracture, as is definitely suggested by the increase in Ca flux induced by hypertonicity (111, 112). At any rate, Hill attributes this tension to the presence of a relatively small number of activated cross bridges in even the normal resting muscle, and thus calls such behavior "filamentary resting tension" (FRT). Moreover, he identifies this as the basis for the elastic behavior of the SREC, especially since the value of E_{SREC} increases in hypertonic media in parallel with the value of the FRT.

These findings and the many others Hill presents—including especially those on the latency relaxation, which I will mention later—undoubtedly reflect some very significant features of the muscle mechanical system. The reader must refer to the original article to obtain the full account of the results and to appreciate the full flavor of Hill's speculations on their possible significance. In outline, Hill proposes as a working hypothesis that the SREC is an elastic system that comes into evidence as a reaction of the cross bridges which are producing the FRT. Thus, the actively linked cross bridges causing the FRT are supposed to be bent and stretched as the muscle is stretched, and hence produce the short-range elastic effects of interest. At the "elastic limit" of the SREC it is supposed that the cross bridges "slip" at their actin contact points; and, as further strain is impressed on the filaments, ". . . the rate of slip, and the 'relaxation rate' increase rapidly and then, while the length change continues at the same velocity, the tension levels off to give a constant frictional resistance."

Some of Hill's results seriously question the validity of his hypothesis to explain the FRT and the SREC. Thus, the value of E_{SREC} remained remarkably constant (average deviation of ± 3 per cent) as the initial muscle length was increased so as to increase the sarcomere length from 2.0 to about 3.0 μ and thus reduce the filament overlap from approximately 1.6 to 0.6 μ. Hence, the value of E_{SREC} per unit of overlap was increased 2.7 times by lengthening the muscle. Hill also proves that a similar effect holds for the FRT. Taken at face value, these results make it difficult to believe that the SREC and FRT depend on action of the cross bridges. True, the filament spacing decreases under sarcomere stretch; but calculation based on the constant volume relation shows that at 3.0 μ the decrease would only be about 18 per cent of the spacing at 2.0 μ and it is hard to see how this could account for a 2.7 $\times$ increase in effectiveness of the overlap cross bridges in producing the observed effects on the SREC and the FRT. However, to further test the factor of filament spacing, Hill used a very clever procedure involving length and osmotic compensations to maintain lateral-filament spacing constant and found that E_{SREC} per unit of overlap was some 25 times greater at the short length than at the long, which is qualitatively opposite to the length effect just discussed and seems to contradict the theory of cross-bridge involvement even more than does the finding mentioned above. But Hill mentions other evidence of his experiments which suggest that this contradiction may be explained by the increase in "nonionic sarcoplasmic solutes" that is associated with the short fibers having the much larger E_{SREC}. While such an association does occur in the cited experiment, the proportion of nonelectrolytes in the fibers is small (67), and anyway the relevant increase in nonelectrolyte concentration could have been only about 2 times, so it is difficult to see how this would cause a 25 times increase in the specific value of SREC. Taking into consideration all the evidence, I think that it is not proved that the SREC involves the hypothesized dependence on the cross bridges.

Latency relaxation.—An additional most interesting feature of Hill's work (110) is the proposal that the latency relaxation (LR) originates as a transitory reduction of the FRT, i.e. as a reduction of tension of the SREC. Before discussing this we should note other attempts to explain the LR that have postulated a reduction in electrostatic repulsion between the filaments (48, 113), or some sort of change of the sarcotubular system, which might be osmotic (91), or an osmotic change in the myoplasm (1). These mechanisms might conceivably be consequences of the release of activator Ca²⁺ during E-C coupling. Such Ca²⁺ might, for example, increase the ionic strength of the medium between the filaments and thus reduce the electrostatic repulsive force between them, which would then become evident as a reduction in axial tension, i.e. the LR. Or such a reduction in tension could reflect changes in osmotic pressure in either the SR or the myoplasm or both, which could develop as the Ca is translocated from SR to myoplasm during E-C coupling. However, in considering the problem of the source of the LR in general, two features, as stressed elsewhere (91), should be kept in mind: (a) the kinetics of the LR in relation to the temporal ordering of the processes of E-C coupling; and (b) the possibility that the essentially continuous columns of the STS, in at least amphibian and mammalian skeletal muscle, comprise a mechanical element that could contribute to the passive axial tension of a muscle and, by changing elasticity or length, produce the LR.

Returning to Hill's work on the latency relaxation, it is interesting, first of all, that he has found and made much use of the finding that strongly hypertonic solutions, which greatly suppress positive tension output, produce little change in the magnitude of the LR but greatly slow up its course by a factor of about 10. Now, Hill's hypothesis that the LR represents reduction of the FRT is plausible, but it requires that some feature of activation (Ca²⁺?) arrive at the overlap region and break the FRT cross bridges just before the full activation of contraction of the sliding-filament mechanism. Thus the onset of the LR in a muscle such as the frog sartorius should be delayed in a stretched muscle (91), but it is slightly hastened. However, a more serious difficulty of the hypothesis is, as Hill pointed out, that, contrary to the general expectation that the depth of the LR should increase in parallel with increase in FRT, the LR remains of constant magnitude in hypertonic media which very greatly increase both FRT and E_{SREC}.

In conclusion, then, the above general discussion indicates that we do not yet know definitely what causes the latency relaxation. It is clear, however, that there are now at least three different possible mechanisms involving, respectively, interfilamentary electrostatic forces, breakage of cross bridges, and the osmotic action associated with the release of activator Ca²⁺ from the sarcoplasmic reticulum. It should be interesting to follow developments concerned with resolving this problem, and, furthermore, with utilizing the results to elucidate certain mechanisms of E-C coupling as it occurs in the intact, normally functioning muscle.

Active-state mechanisms.—Brady (21) in his admirable review of active state in cardiac muscle, which has much of value about the active state in skeletal muscle, quotes Hill (114) to the effect that quick stretch experiments to determine the "active state" have not always been done rigorously so that "in the end one begins to wonder whether the term has any exact meaning!" Despite this, recent studies (21) on the active state in heart muscle abound and there are a few interesting ones for skeletal muscle, as well, which I will discuss in the following but with concern for more varied active-state parameters than mere kinetics.

Active-state properties of the rat gastrocnemius muscle have been studied *in situ* (115), this condition being advantageous to assure continuous and adequate oxygenation of the muscle. But this procedure necessarily introduces certain disadvantages such as the high temperature of 37–38°, the unparallel geometry of the fibers, and the inability to provide massive stimulation for simultaneous activation of all longitudinal segments of the fibers. Nevertheless, the various results quite clearly confirm Hill's active-state concepts, in general, for this muscle, e.g. that there is a definite duration of an active-state plateau, even though this is only about 1.5 msec long. However, Desmedt & Hainaut (116; see also 117) have elegantly recorded contractions and associated action potentials of the human *in situ* adductor pollicis muscle subjected to indirect stimulation by double-shock stimuli of variable interval, and they show that with proper control for refractory period effects, the active state due to a single stimulation does not reach a plateau of maximal intensity. They have also studied the staircase behavior in the adductor pollicis muscle and find, incidentally, that preceding the usual positive effect an initial "negative" staircase appears [which, though generally neglected, has already been studied thoroughly by Colomo & Rocchi (118) in frog single muscle fiber preparations and has recently been described in heart muscle (119)]. But in the potentiated twitches of the positive staircase they find that both the time to peak and the half-relaxation time have decreased, rather than increased as found generally in chemically potentiated twitches (120). They thus conclude that this staircase twitch potentiation is not due to prolongation, but to intensification of the active state in respect especially to the capacity for shortening, rather than for tension output (but see 121). Furthermore, they attribute the increased shortening speed to an enhanced release of activator Ca^{2+}, in accordance with earlier work (e.g. 122), and the faster relaxation to an increase in the rate of uptake of this Ca^{2+} by the sarcoplasmic reticulum. Quite similar effects on the twitch have been observed during posttetanic potentiation of isolated rat extensor digitorum longus muscle at 35°C, although following very long tetani both the contraction and relaxation periods are prolonged (123). However, for these results, in general, an augmented release of Ca^{2+} is also inferred which would account for the increased contraction speed, but this release would be so augmented for the very long tetani as to prolong the active state and thus also prolong both the contraction and relaxation periods.

This work in general (see also 124) suggests that in mammalian muscle at high temperature, as found previously for isolated frog muscle at room temperature (125), the active state's shortening capacity does not achieve fullest maximal value in a normal twitch and that it can be intensified by various interventions, which suggests (125) that certain features of twitch potentiation may result from increasing the turnover rate of the cross bridges, thus increasing shortening speed, without necessarily altering the capacity of the bridges to produce force. But a further factor of interest may be an increase in number of fully activated myofibrils in each muscle fiber (123), a point to be developed later in relation to inward spread of activation. All the foregoing does not mean, however, that Hill's model of the active state is "not in fact adequately substantiated and can be abandoned", as stated by Desmedt & Hainaut in their article (116) as it originally appeared but rather, as stated in the reprints of this article, that "Hill's model, while valid in first approximation for frog muscle at 0°C, does not apply to mammalian muscle at body temperature." (Dr. Desmedt has informed me that this difference in the two versions of the general conclusion of his article developed because the article was printed before corrected proof had been received!)

Another rather different case in which force and velocity do not change together is found in the velocity transients produced by single-fiber preparations (126) when there is a sudden release from the fully active state, as measured by the isometric force P_0, to another state of maximal activity involving a smaller load under isotonic conditions. The velocity transients at around 3°C may last for 10 msec or more before the new steady-state velocity is attained, even though the force is essentially steady at its new value. These velocity transients are related to the motion of cyclic contraction mechanisms essentially as in the turnover of cross bridges in the A. F. Huxley (77) theory. This work indicates, in accordance with the A. F. Huxley model, that the iterative units of action of the cross bridges involve movements of the order of 100 Å, with corresponding weak force, rather than of only 5–10 Å with associated strong force.

Mention should be made of the report (54) of an entirely different sort of change in rate of contraction, a series of stepwise increases in rate of tension development at the start of the isometric twitch of skeletal muscle. Such changes have not been observed by others (115, 122) and, as discussed elsewhere (127), it is now clear that they were artifacts produced by inadequate stimulation of the muscle.

Mashima (128) has used the novel procedure of applying the isometric quick-release method for studying the kinetics of decay of the active state in partially and fully tetanized muscles rather than in mere twitch of a muscle, to determine the effect of the duration of the tetanus on the decay of activity. Unfortunately, no measurements were made of the tetanus relaxation latency, i.e., the duration of maintained tetanus plateau following the last shock, so the curves indicating decay of activity cannot be properly interpreted. However, the use of the quick-release method on tetanized muscle should have considerable interest in connection with study of relaxation to be discussed later.

Matsumoto (129–131) has mathematically analyzed certain basic experimentally measured mechanical proporties of frog sartorius muscle, and finds that the Hill force-velocity relation holds true with constant values of a/P_0 and b/l_0 at all lengths of a muscle less than l_0 (129), thus confirming older work (132). The series-elastic component (129) has the same properties for both isometric contractions, in which the strain due to shortening of the contractile component varies with time (e.g. during the tetanus contraction period), and isotonic contractions, in which the strain is constant with time for any one load. In particular, when the developed tension is P_0, the series elasticity has lengthened, and thus the contractile component has shortened by 5.3 per cent of l_0. Since the X-ray evidence indicates that the only lengthening in the sarcomere during contraction is the 1 per cent increase in length of the myosin filaments, this leaves about 4 per cent of l_0 to be attributed to other components of the series elasticity, e.g. tendon. I question some of Matsumoto's procedures, both experimental and theoretical, e.g. the failure to use massive stimulation and the assumption that rise of tension in tetanus is exponential. Incidently, these two inadequacies are connected, for the much better synchronization of contraction under massive stimulation would have produced experimental curves somewhat closer in shape to the assumed exponential one.

Bahler and co-workers (133–136) have analytically studied the dynamical behavior of a mammalian muscle, the rat gracilis anticus. Of particular interest is the essentially novel determination of the active-state dynamics of this muscle (134) under the assumption that "the contractile component is a force generator which is shunted by a velocity-sensitive internal load", and that part of the force internally generated is dissipated in the internal load in proportion to the velocity of shortening. The full development of this model gives the time variation of the active-state intensity—i.e., of the time-dependent force of the internal force generator. For the twitch of the studied muscle at about 17°C, the active-state kinetics is similar to Hill's classic curve (137) except that: (a) it reaches a maximal intensity of only $0.92\ P_0$, (b) there is no flat plateau at this maximum, and (c) the curve peaks rather late in the contraction period. The theory has some striking successes in that it predicts, in accordance with fact, that the active state is a function of muscle length, that tetanus and twitch differ in respect to the muscle length for generating maximal tension, and that, therefore, the twitch-to-tetanus ratio varies with muscle length.

Though the basic assumptions of the theory seem to hark back to the early thirties when muscle was thought to be a viscoelastic system, the details are worked out in a new and imaginative fashion. Nevertheless, and despite its successes, the theory seems weak—as the authors admit, though with reservations (134)—in that a shortening muscle should liberate heat in proportion to the energy dissipated in the internal load, and "unfortunately such a finding has not appeared in the literature." Furthermore, some interesting speculations (138) regarding operations of the cross bridges in connection with the force-velocity relation suggest an alternative to a dissipative internal load.

Taylor (139) has considered the problem of the active state theoretically in an entirely different manner. He starts with an outline scheme for E-C coupling (140) and then relates this mathematically to certain other processes of both E-C coupling and relaxation-factor activity so as to predict the kinetics of flux of activator Ca at the myofibrils. A basic assumption of the theory is that the intensity of the active state varies in proportion to the varying concentration of Ca-M, a complex between Ca and the contractile machinery. The theoretical system is quite realistic and thus very complex, and it has to be studied by means of an analog computer. The theory predicts curves of tension as a function of time and rate of change of tension that are in good agreement with experiment for normal, both types A and B potentiated, and summated twitches, and for simple and quick-release redeveloped tetani. In the twitch, the active-state kinetics is like that of Hill's pattern (137) but, somewhat as in Bahler's result (134), the maximal intensity of activity is only 88 per cent of P_0. I will consider Taylor's work again later in specific relation to certain aspects of the E-C coupling scheme (140) he uses in his theory.

It is interesting that both Taylor's (139) and Bahler's (134) theories predict that the intensity of the active state of the normal twitch does not peak at the potentially maximal value defined by P_0, the plateau tension of tetanus, for this is in agreement with the implications that Desmedt & Hainau (116) derive from their rather special experiments on *in situ* human muscle. Taylor's theory is of particular interest in this regard since he defines the active state as identical with a specific molecular entity, i.e. the complex Ca-M, and then calculates the kinetics of Ca-M from his theoretical system of chemical reactions underlying the contraction-relaxation cycle. In this scheme Ca-M fails to peak at tetanus value in a twitch, evidently because oncoming relaxation reactions are already removing Ca from the active complex very soon after stimulation. Julian (76), though also dealing with binding of Ca to the contractile machinery, considers that this is the essential basis of what he calls "activation" of contraction. He rather arbitrarily fixes the kinetics of the calcium binding to the myofibrils, introducing, among other features, the condition that even in a twitch "activation" attains its fullest possible value, and then shows that his theory leads to a distinction between "activation" and "active state." Thus, although there are currently different approaches to the analysis of activity, it is most interesting that they involve attempts to identify the active state with the properties of a complex of Ca and the contractile material. Evidence supporting this view will be presented later in discussion of the regulation of contractile activity.

Relaxation.—It is understandable that by far the bulk of the studies of muscle mechanics deals with contraction. But the recent upsurge of research on the relaxing factor (see later) presages increasing attention to the actual mechanics of relaxation and its relation to the relaxing factor. Recent studies of relaxation have been concerned essentially with decay of the active state (e.g. 128, 141) and have dealt more with kinetics than with mechanism. Relaxation mechanics appears generally in a relatively simple form in isometric tetanus relaxation (142). Specially interesting, the actual curves of decrease of tension during tetanus relaxations of frog sartorius muscles, though differing greatly in kinetics because of variation in temperature, chemical treatment, disease, etc., all follow essentially the same ("canonical") curve when normalized for tension in units of P_0, and for time in units of half-relaxation time, $t_{0.5}$. Equivalent normalization does not yield a "canonical" curve for isometric tetanus contraction, though such a result is claimed to hold for isotonic contractions (131). The canonical normalization of relaxation suggests that the different speeds of actual relaxations result from relatively simple variations in kinetics of a single reaction basically determining the process of relaxation. The nature of this reaction is suggested by an analysis (143) which indicates that Ca^{2+}, considered as an activator of contraction, disappears exponentially during relaxation. This suggests that the basic reaction may be an exponential accumulation of Ca^{2+} by the sarcoplasmic reticulum and that it is the time constant of this process that is changed by various muscle treatments so as to produce the observed variations in actual relaxation speed.

Relaxation is reportedly caused by an elongating force developed in an internal elasticity in the sarcomere (144). As previously mentioned, the myosin filaments are stretched by 1 per cent during contraction, and this might conform to an elasticity within the contracted sarcomere. But since the cross-bridge linkages between the filaments disappear during relaxation and the recoil of the system would involve shortening of the thick filaments, it is difficult to see how this would cause the sarcomere to lengthen.

ENERGETICS

Experimental.—Although at the time of the last review (1) activation heat and shortening heat both seemed to elude attachment to some definite chemical or physical source, the present situation indicates some improvement in this respect. The finding (145) that there is no ATP breakdown in a frog sartorius during relaxation from a brief tetanus, which contradicts earlier work by the Davies group (146), seems to allow enough breakdown of ATP during contraction to include an adequate chemical counterpart for heat liberated during activation. This has also been suggested and nicely discussed by Gibbs & Vaughan (147). The authors reject the views that activation heat results from release of activator Ca into the sarcoplasm or (at least entirely) from internal shortening and suggest that it arises in the sense that Hill (148) proposed originally in attempting to account for this heat. As for shortening heat, Chaplain (149), has introduced a quite new kind of approach by recording the heat output of glycerinated insect muscle performing isotonic shortening under the action of a nonhydrolyzable analog of ATP. Shortening heat appeared in such muscle, it was a linear function of the amount of shortening, and it obviously could not be attributed to energy released by hydrolysis of a substrate. Chaplain suggests that the heat was produced by a conformational change within the contractile protein. It may be asked whether this is the basis for the entropic source of shortening heat proposed by Davies (150).

It is pleasant to report some certainties regarding energetics. The *in vivo* enthalpy of PC breakdown in either twitches or tetani is -10.6 kcal/mole (with a standard error of $\pm$ 1.5) (151), or -11.0 ± 0.23, as determined later in the same laboratory by means of a new "integrating thermopile" (152). This value also represents indirectly, though with good assurance, the enthalpy of ATP hydrolysis *in vivo*. Woledge (138) has made a thorough study of tortoise skeletal muscle and has confirmed certain long-held predictions about its energetics that had been inferred from its great slowness relative to frog muscle's speed and its more concave force-velocity curve. Thus, as compared to the frog sartorius the tortoise rectus femoris muscle has: a smaller value of the shortening heat constant *a,* and this value *does not depend on the load* (153); a much smaller maintenance heat rate, which though still equal to the product $a\,b$ ($b = v_{max}a/P_0$), does not decrease during a long tetanus (154); and a greater efficiency in converting free energy into work. This study includes interesting speculations on the special energetics of the tortoise muscle in terms of the action of its cross bridges and in regard to evolutionary significance. The odd feature of skeletal muscle, the "Feng effect" or "stretch response", i.e., the increase in metabolism produced by stretch, has been studied myothermically (155) and found to increase with length in about the same way as does rest tension, to be increased by type A, but not type B potentiators (156) and, very strangely, by procaine also; and it is inferred to be mediated by a direct effect of stretch on the sarcolemma (i.e., including the excitable membrane) which is then relayed inward to affect the metabolism of the contractile system. A new myothermic method, "gradient-layer calorimetry", has been introduced (157–159) which is inherently slow, half-response time of about 1 min, and so is limited to measuring total heat output in a series of contractions. The results so far on both isometric (155, 156) and isotonic (157) contractions generally agree with older results. The authors present some exemplary discussion, however, stressing the difficulties in appraising myothermic data because they are so variable and so uncertain as to level of baseline.

According to Wilkie (152), "it remains a melancholy fact that we still do not know the efficiency [i.e., thermodynamic efficiency, A.S.] of the contractile process." Yet Davies and co-workers (160, 161) present extensive determinations of this property and find values which vary of course with shortening velocity, but which at a medium velocity can be up to 55 per cent for the overall energetics of a contraction-relaxation cycle. By taking into account the energy used to drive the relaxing factor's Ca pump, however, and thus determining the efficiency of the contractile process alone, values of the efficiency of 90 per cent and even higher have been calculated. These extremely high values may turn out to be completely delusive if as already mentioned (145) it is verified that no ATP hydrolysis occurs during relaxation.

Theoretical.—Caplan (162–164) has introduced an essentially new approach to the study of muscle energetics by applying the methods of irreversible thermodynamics. Space limitations prohibit even an introduction to Caplan's novel theoretical developments and to the criticisms they have provoked, so the reader should refer to the original articles for full details, or read Wilkie's report (165) for a general description and commentary. However, there is no doubt that the new theory as originally proposed achieved some important successes, such as the predictions of an essentially correct force-velocity curve, and of the relationship of the shape of this curve to the thermodynamic efficiency in agreement with experimental results (138). Wilkie & Woldege (166) claim, however, to have found some fatally incorrect predictions of the theory. But Caplan (164) criticizes and rejects their objections, at the expense of having to face the rejoinder of his critics (167) that his theory "has lost its seductive youthful simplicity and put on weight" and that "the new features that protect the theory from the chill winds of disproof do so only by preventing it from making any exact predictions whatever." The issue seems hardly settled, not merely because of Caplan's comment on this rejoinder (168) but especially because a most recent contribution (169) seems to have confirmed the essentials of the theory in regard to those features that had been subject to such seemingly devastating attacks (166).

Evidently, Caplan has started a very lively approach to problems of muscle energetics and we should all watch for further developments. For, as put by Wilkie (165), the new approach avoids the aridity of classical thermodynamics that derives from the restriction to states of equilibrium which cannot reveal specific mechanisms, and it emphasizes, instead, fluxes of energy. In muscle, this means that the new methods deal with coupling of release of chemical energy to the production of heat and mechanical work and may therefore suggest the means by which muscle converts chemical into mechanical energy.

REGULATORY SYSTEMS

Present knowledge tells us a most pleasing feature of muscles, the division of their main functions into those directly producing mechanical change and those regulating that change. Mechanical activity, as already discussed, is performed, in the first place, by the sliding filaments. But the regulatory activities, which now concern us, primarily involve the system of external and internal membranes, composed of plasma membrane, T-tubules, sarcoplasmic reticulum, triads, etc., whose general function is to control the availability of activator Ca, the free Ca^{2+} that activates the sliding filaments to contract. The regulatory functions divide rather neatly into excitation-contraction coupling which releases activator Ca^{2+}, and the Ca-pumping activity of the sarcoplasmic reticulum which removes this Ca^{2+} and so determines relaxation. Furthermore, it is striking that a key component in regulating the activating effect of Ca^{2+} is troponin, a built-in component of the sliding-filament machinery.

INTERNAL MEMBRANE SYSTEMS

General structure and function.—First, a matter of terminology. The internal membrane system is generally agreed to consist of two rather distinct basic parts, the sarcoplasmic reticulum (SR) and the transverse tubular system (TS), composed predominantly of longitudinal and transverse elements, respectively. The terminology generally used conforms to this distinction (1, 170) but on occasion (e.g. 12, 103) "sarcoplasmic reticulum" is used as inclusive of the T-tubules. I suggest adherence to the usage which distinguishes between sarcoplasmic reticulum and T-tubules. Furthermore, I shall use "sarcotubular system" (STS), in accordance with the practice of some authors, to name the entire internal membrane system.

A rigorously controlled study (170) based on the entrance of ferritin selectively into the T-tubes of muscle fibers shows that the STS is generally the same in frog and toad sartorius muscles and that, in particular, the TS is sharply localized to a longitudinal region only 0.2 μ wide at the level of the Z-line. This work also indicates that both surface area and volume of the T-system are about 30 per cent greater than previously determined (171). As already mentioned, skeletal muscle of the tortoise is like that of the frog in certain respects, but different in others (103), especially in the odd distribution of the T-tubules and their associated triads, thus pointing up the species variability in STS structures. Incidentally, I note also the sharp variations in such structures in cardiac muscle, not only between species (172–174) but also between different types of fibers within a given heart (175, 176).

Guinea pig muscle, studied partly by the relatively novel freeze-etch technique (177–179), has T-tubules which are continuous with the exterior of the fibers, either directly in cardiac fibers, or by way of subsarcolemmal caveolae in skeletal fibers. The findings about the caveolae are especially important in indicating that each T-tubule, though relatively simple as it envelopes a fibril, subdivides tortuously into as many as three or four caveollae just under the sarcolemma and then communicates by means of these to the exterior. The caveollae are interesting because their presence in other fibers may account for the difficulties experienced in detecting the mouth of the T-tubules at the plasma membrane, and they may add extra volume to that ordinarily determined by the T-tubules themselves. Further predominantly descriptive results of interest are concerned with developmental features of differentiation of the STS (180–184), with the curious penetration and anastomosing of SR extensions into the myofibril in an insect muscle (185), and with the astonishing case of a very fast crustacean fiber having three quarters of its space taken up by SR (186, 186a).

A functionally significant finding of greatest interest is that the T-system can be selectively disrupted by a special two-phased treatment of skeletal muscle involving first an exposure to a Ringer's solution made hypertonic by glycerol, and then a return to ordinary Ringer's (187–189). A thorough study of this effect (190) shows that up to 98 per cent of the T-tubules of a frog sartorius muscle are disrupted. These highly significant results will be discussed later in relation to the regulatory mechanisms performing electromechanical coupling.

Elements of the STS of both skeletal and cardiac muscle of different species vary sensitively, most obviously in volume, in response to changes in external ionic composition and osmotic pressure (191–194). The impressed alterations, though generally not easy to interpret, give valuable indications regarding the electrical and permeability properties of the elements of the STS. Birks & Davey (195) have made a quantitative study of one of these effects, the anomalous swelling of the SR in frog sartorius muscles immersed in hypertonic media, and their carefully controlled analysis shows that this anomalous behavior of the SR is just sufficient to account for previously discovered discrepancies in the osmotic behavior and ionic distribution in muscle fibers. Most strikingly, the authors conclude that the SR is effectively an extracellular compartment of the muscle, and this is to say, essentially, that the sucrose and the extra NaCl they used to make the external solution hypertonic had penetrated into the SR across the triadic junctional membranes. Perhaps certain special structural features of these junctions (196) have something to do with this.

Taken at face value, these results and their general conclusions seem definite and they have obvious and very important connotations, e.g., for problems of permeability of the various membranes of the STS and for mechanisms of E-C coupling, some of which Birks & Davey (195) discuss. These results also concern the site of action in the living fiber of a variety of substances, mainly certain lyotropic anions and divalent heavy metal ions, which potentiate contraction (156) and might produce this effect, in part, by interfering with the uptake of Ca by the SR (197, 198). However, several questions about this work need clarification, such as the selective effect of the external hypertonicity on the SR, since other workers (e.g. 192, 199, 200) have found swelling also of the transverse tubules, even when the external medium was isotonic but had half the NaCl replaced by an osmotically equivalent amount of sucrose (191). Then, the implication of this work that NaCl can pass into the SR seems to be contradicted by the finding that external Na could enter only the TS of frog fibers (201).

Chemical features: the relaxing factor.—The physiological role of Ca in all of its biophysical chemical detail is the prime feature of chemical interest in the regulation of muscular activity. Two excellent reviews (6, 202) provide an extensive introduction to this general topic. Our immediate concern, however, is only with the mechanism of accumulation of Ca by the SR, an essential reaction of the "relaxing factor" and especially the part played in this by ATP and by binding of Ca. We shall consider later the question of the release of this Ca in activating contraction. Both the mentioned reviews and especially Weber's detailed paper (203), although mainly oriented to the role of active transport and the associated ATPase activity in the Ca-pumping function of the SR, present indirect though strong arguments that a good part of the Ca accumulated in the SR in the presence of oxalate is bound and not free. But this inference is clouded by the quite unphysiological involvement of the oxalate. Carvalho (197, 198, 204, 205) has studied this problem in oxalate-free preparations in terms of the cation exchange properties of the extracted SR rather than of the active transport processes. He finds that rabbit SR has a total cation-binding capacity of 350 μeq/g protein for which normally Ca, Mg, K, and H ions compete. The binding is electrostatic and evidently involves especially imidazole from proteins and the phosphatidyl serine and lecithin in the membrane structure. In presence of ATP, however, the binding is remarkably altered so that Ca selectively becomes about 1000-fold more potent in competing against the other cations for the available binding sites. ATP may produce this alteration by causing a conformational change at the binding sites (198), and certain rather direct evidence seems to substantiate this view (206). Carvalho has yet to determine whether this action depends on hydrolysis of the ATP.

An important feature of Carvalho's work is his provocative discussion of current conceptions of accumulation of Ca by the SR. He questions the validity of the conclusion regarding the state of the accumulated Ca as inferred from the results obtained by means of oxalate; and he raises for consideration the possibility that ATP causes accumulation not by hydrolyzing, and thus energizing an active transport carrier, but by altering the binding sites of the SR in favor of uptake of Ca. Furthermore, he stresses the implication of his results that 80 per cent or more of the total Ca of the SR is electrostatically bound and thus cannot contribute to the activity of the ion in the vesicles. His work leaves uncertain the state of the remaining Ca, but if we assume that this is free and that the total concentration is 10-20 mM, then the intravesicular concentration of Ca^{2+} of living muscle might be about 1-2 mM and therefore close to that of the normal external medium. If we accept the conclusion (195) that the SR vesicles are effectively in direct contact with the external medium, then the intravesicular free Ca^{2+} would always tend to equilibrate with the external Ca^{2+} concentration, thus suggesting that any transported Ca would either be bound to the SR or diffuse to the external medium.

Weber & Herz (208), elaborating their earlier abstract, show that caffeine (1–10 mM) reduces the Ca-accumulating capacity of isolated SR from frog and rabbit skeletal muscle and also the rate of this uptake. The drug (8 mM), furthermore, releases enough free Ca^{2+} from SR, which has been thoroughly loaded with Ca, to account for the maximal contracture produced by caffeine in intact frog muscle. Weber (209) suggests that the drug uncouples ATPase activity of the SR from the inward transport of Ca and thus both reduces the uptake and increases the release of Ca. Noteworthily, caffeine has no effect at all on the Ca which is electrostatically bound either passively (ATP absent) or actively (ATP present) (198, 205), but it acts on the Ca which is taken up in excess of the electrostatically bound moiety, and this finding is confirmed in terms of internal evidence of the results of Weber & Herz (208). Thus the Ca fully loading the SR divides into two parts: the electrostatically bound portion, about 80 per cent or more of the maximum amount (205), which is unaffected by caffeine, and a more labile portion that accumulates in the SR presumably only after all the binding sites have been filled up. The labile portion may be in free solution within the vesicle, and, as previously indicated, possibly in equilibrium with the Ca^{2+} of the external medium.

The various aforementioned findings, in conjunction with others regarding the exchangeability of Ca of the SR (198), support the inferences, previously drawn from studies of Ca flux in living muscles (210, 211), that the ability of caffeine and of quinine to release Ca from the SR can account for the contracture and twitch potentiation these alkaloids produce in living muscle. Also of interest in this general context are the results (197, 198) concerned with other effects on the SR of drugs and of anionic and divalent cationic twitch potentiators of muscle. Quinine, though acting somewhat like caffeine on live muscle, causes a general release of Ca^{2+} from SR: it affects not only the labile, but also the electrostatically bound portion of Ca. Such a difference may be of help in determining the molecular mechanisms by which the SR releases activator Ca^{2+} in the myofibrillar space. In this particular context, and also because of more general pharmacological interest, I should cite certain additional studies of the control of Ca accumulation and release by the SR of either cardiac or skeletal muscle (212–24).

Still further results generally indicating topochemical aspects of SR are the following. With an electronmicroscopic method using thorium dioxide as stain, calcium-binding sites have been located in the SR but not in the TS of fish branchial muscle (225). Tetanus toxin, insofar as it binds to skeletal muscle, has been found localized in T-tubules and in terminal sacs of the SR, and may thus exert some of its toxic effects by affecting the regulatory functions of these structures (226). Three studies (227–229) very significantly show that the membrane of the sarcotubular vesicles is asymmetrical, the outside surface (the surface directed toward the myofibrillar space) being studded at intervals of about 100 Å with little knoblike elements about 20–40 Å in diameter. Various tests suggest that these structures may be involved in transport of Ca across the membrane and that therefore, as already suggested (6), it is this surface facing the myofibrils that is important for calcium transport into the SR vesicles. As for enzymes, in addition to those previously mentioned (1), there are new reports that the TTS contains adenylcyclase (230)—although this is not involved in the action of caffeine on SR (109), acetylcholinesterase in T-tubules of rat extraocular muscle fibers (231), and Mg-activated ATPase which is either only in the terminal sacs (mouse skeletal muscle) (232, 233) or possibly in both the terminal sac and the more central (H-zone) region of the SR (234).

CALCIUM AND REGULATION OF THE CONTRACTION-RELAXATION CYCLE

The troponin-tropomyosin complex.—It is now clear that this protein complex plays a critical role in relaying the regulatory role of Ca to the contractile filaments. This subject has been so thoroughly and excellently reviewed by Ebashi & Endo (6) (in whose laboratory most of the pertinent work has been done) that I need hardly discuss it here. In summary, the Ebashi group has shown that the troponin-tropomyosin complex is bound uniformly along the whole length of the actin filaments and so the thin filaments in reality are composed not merely of actin, but of an association of actin, troponin, and tropomyosin. At rest, this tripartite complex prevents interaction of the actin and myosin filaments, i.e. prevents cross-bridge formation, and relaxation is maintained. In the presence of sufficient free Ca^{2+}, troponin, acting specifically as the Ca-receptive protein of the whole complex, binds the Ca and by some reaction necessarily involving tropomyosin as a sort of intermediary lifts the inhibition and thus permits the contractile actomyosin complex to develop. Hence, what we call "Ca-activation" of contraction does not involve formation of a contractile Ca-actomyosin complex, but rather the Ca acts "as a releasing factor of an existing repression" of contraction (235). This occurs only in the presence of the troponin-tropomyosin complex, the "sensitizer" normally inducing formation of actomyosin. Evidently, then, Ca is not directly involved in the essential cross-bridge action causing contraction, as Davies (236) assumed in his theory of contraction. Further details about the troponin-tropomyosin complex and its function will be found in (237–39); especially significant is that the action of troponin in binding of exchangeable Ca is quite specific in comparison with binding by tropomyosin, actin, myosin, or thick filaments, and is more than adequate for the binding of Ca to myofibrils needed to account for the full activation of contraction (235, 240).

In view of the foregoing, it is evident that restoration of the relaxed state of the myofibrils requires that Ca must be removed from the troponin-tropomyosin to permit repression of contraction. But, to quote Weber (241): "The regulation of actomyosin contraction by Ca is a process of considerable complexity." Specifically, this is indicated by her results which extend our knowledge of the participation of Mg and intact ATP in the mechanism of relaxation by showing that MgATP is necessary for relaxation, even when effectively no activator Ca at all remains on the contractile protein, so that the role of the Mg is not merely to displace Ca. Thus relaxation requires not only that the SR remove activator Ca from the sliding filaments, but also that special relaxing actions occur in the myofibrils themselves, which involve, at the least, MgATP as well as troponin and tropomyosin.

Activation by Ca.—In a careful study of glycerinated crab fibers, which among other factors involved control of the role of diffusion of Ca^{2+} through the sarcomere both lengthwise and crosswise, Gillis (242) has demonstrated that no matter how much the sarcomere is stretched and regardless of where the activator is applied, the Ca^{2+} must diffuse to the cross bridges, i.e. to the overlap region of the A-band, to produce contraction. An interesting implication of Gillis's work is that mere binding of Ca^{2+} to the troponin on the thin filaments does not in itself involve any effects on the contractility of the sliding filaments: e.g. there is no variation in sensitivity of the Ca activation finally developed, in relation to the point of Ca binding along the length of the thin filament. Work from Podolsky's laboratory (243) on the Natori (83) stripped-fiber preparation shows that, on activation by applied Ca^{2+}, slow fibers shorten much more slowly than fast ones, which indicates that the low speed of the slow fiber is inherent in the contractile mechanism. This difference in speed may depend on a parallel difference in rate of ATPase activity of the respective actomyosins of the two types of muscle (104). An intriguing feature of the above results (243) is that a Ca-activated contraction spreads much further in the slow than in the fast fibers, this difference evidently being the physiological consequence of the relative paucity of SR in slow fibers. In another paper from this laboratory (244), force production has been objectively recorded from frog fast muscle fibers after application of different buffered concentrations of Ca^{2+} to a stripped region, and it is shown that the outputs of force at threshold, 50 per cent, and maximal values occur for pCa's of 7.5, 6.8, and 6.0, respectively, thereby forming a typical S-shaped curve in rather close agreement with results for "contractile activity" (syneresis and ATPase activity) in myofibril preparations (245). The force vs. pCa relation has also been determined (246) for glycerinated fibers of a wide variety of muscles, with results in general like those just described. But, in correlated studies, ATP breakdown always showed a threshold at a greater pCa value, as was also found in relating APTase activity to syneresis of myofibrils (245).

Ca transients.—This term (247) nicely designates the quick pulse of rise and fall of free Ca^{2+} concentration that occurs within a muscle fiber when it is activated to contract. Such transients have been almost directly detected in toad sartorii by use of murexide, whose absorption spectrum changes on combination with Ca (248), and in barnacle single fibers by means of aequorin, which luminesces on combination with Ca (247, 249). These results dramatically confirm with almost perfect certainty what had been suggested by a wealth of indirect evidence (6, 156, 202): (*a*) that the free Ca^{2+} in resting muscle is extremely low and so relaxation is maintained; (*b*) that, on depolarization of the membrane, there is a sudden release into the sarcoplasm of a relatively large amount of free Ca^{2+} which serves to activate contraction; and (c) that this free Ca^{2+} then relatively slowly disappears as the response runs its course and the relaxed state returns. There are still formidable problems in elucidating the exact relation of the Ca transient to the course of the tension output in a contraction. These problems arise in part because of the inherent properties of the Ca indicator systems. But the kinetics of the aequorin system has been carefully studied (249a) and it seems that, if the muscle responses are sufficiently slow, slower than in vertebrate muscle, then the Ca-induced aequorin luminescence should give a reasonably true record of the variation of the free Ca^{2+} concentration during a response. I will discuss later other features of these problems concerned with the relations of the Ca transients to changes in membrane potential and, as partly discussed earlier with respect to the active state, to dependence of activation of the myofibrils on their bound Ca, rather on the free Ca^{2+} in the sarcoplasm.

Ca fluxes in relation to Ca activation.—Disturbances in distribution of Ca within muscle fibers can be inferred from studies of changes in flux of Ca, generally as ^{45}Ca, between muscles and their external media. An extended study of this sort (250) has determined the movements of Ca between blood plasma and various muscles within the rat of either sex and at different stages of growth, under conditions of both rest and activity. Bianchi (251) has demonstrated that lidocaine, though not increasing the ^{45}Ca flux of the frog sartorius, causes contracture by itself, and, in a special sense, potentiates caffeine contracture, these results being in strong contrast to the quite opposite effects of other local anesthetics, such as procaine and tetracaine. Furthermore, lidocaine does not potentiate caffeine contracture in the absence of Ca or in a depolarized muscle, and these effects, especially, are taken to signify that the various actions of this drug are attributable to a direct action on the T-tubules which causes a release of "trigger" Ca which then is supposed in turn to cause a release of activator Ca^{2+} from the SR. Such studies at least indicate that Ca fluxes in whole muscle can be rather complex and that Ca functions in a number of ways which are located at different parts of the STS. Both influx and efflux of ^{45}Ca increase in rat skeletal muscle after denervation and this is especially marked on treatment of such muscles with caffeine (210). The latter effect apparently explains the susceptibility to caffeine contracture which develops in these muscles after denervation, and it therefore suggests that the capacity of the SR to release Ca at least under the action of caffeine is regulated by some neurotrophic influence, and that such an influence may be of general importance in determining the function of the STS.

ELECTROMECHANICAL COUPLING

Normally, the response of a muscle fiber starts with an electrical change, a depolarization of the plasma membrane, which is somehow relayed inward so as to effect coupling with and activation of the mechanical system. Some of us (156) have been using the term excitation-contraction (E-C) coupling synonymously with electromechanical coupling, but this practice is rather lax because there are important cases of electromechanical coupling in which excitation and its special electrical sign, the action potential, are absent, as in naturally functioning amphibian slow muscles or experimentally voltage-clamped fibers. In terms of the general features of the various processes, this laxity is perhaps permissible, but differences appear which are very significant, as will be seen in the following, and so we should use our terms precisely, especially reserving "E-C coupling" for cases of electromechanical coupling involving the action potential.

General mechanisms.—In this section our main interest is in studies giving no direct evidence of details of inward spread but concerned generally with correlating initial and final events of electromechanical coupling and thus attempting to develop inferences about coupling mechanisms. Gainer (252), using the K-contracture technique, finds that in very small bundles of lobster skeletal muscle fibers the characteristic sigmoid relation between tension and depolarization is essentially the same (with the mechanical threshold at about -60 mV and saturation attained near to -20 mV) in the absence or in the presence of external Cl^-, and this suggests, contrary to a proposed hypothesis (253), that influx of Cl^- is not involved in electromechanical coupling in these fibers. A similar result indicating lack of dependence on a Cl^- current has been reported also for crayfish fibers (254, 255). In the presence of the normal external Ca^{2+}, 24 mM, activation of the lobster muscles by 100 mM K^+ to produce a maximal contracture causes a 15 min influx of 3.6 mmoles Ca/kg muscle, or 0.24 mmoles/kg/min (252). The Ca influx during the first minute alone is enough to fully activate the myofibrils (see later), and it therefore raises the question whether activator Ca^{2+} to produce contracture in this crustacean muscle is obtained at all from internal stores. Taylor et al. (127) have compared the effects of a variety of substances that either raise or lower the mechanical threshold of K contractures with their effects on the isometric twitch. They conclude that although it is not possible in their work to specify definite values of the mechanical threshold associated with the E-C coupling in the twitches of their muscles, such thresholds do operate in association with the depolarizing effects of the action potential, and, qualitatively, the lower the threshold, the speedier the onset of tension in the twitch and the greater the peak tension output.

New approaches to the problems of electromechanical coupling involve, in general, for the electrical part, voltage clamping of the membrane for controllable time intervals and measurement of associated membrane currents. These studies confirm, refine, and importantly extend the conclusions drawn from earlier studies based, e.g., on the studies of K contractures, as indicated in the following. (*a*) There are definite membrane voltages for mechanical threshold and mechanical saturation (253, 254, 256–262), though, very significantly, these are not fixed at "critical" values, but are generally more positive (internal potential indication), i.e., require greater depolarization, the shorter the duration of the depolarization (e.g. 253, 256, 257, 259, 261, 262). (b) The mechanical threshold is lowered by caffeine (260) and lyotropic anions (263) and raised by extra Ca (264). (c) The degree of mechanical activation is generally proportional to the duration of the depolarization (140, 265, 266). (d) Following a relatively long depolarization, it takes time for the coupling system to be "reprimed", or lose its "refractoriness" (267) (though this "refractoriness" should not operate at all when the depolarization is very brief, as for the action potential). (e) There are certain apparent relations between a given depolarization and the development of the active state of the contractile system (257, 259, 265).

Especially interesting are the quite novel results obtained by these new methods, such as the dependence of mechanical threshold and saturation potentials on the duration of the depolarization. Furthermore, various workers have demonstrated that electromechanical coupling seems to be independent of both Na activation (though see later) and delayed rectification (260, 262–264). Another very important finding is that mechanical activation does not increase in proportion to membrane current (254, 257, 260) and this is apparently contrary to the "channeled-current" hypothesis for E-C coupling (253). But the dependence of the degree of electromechanical coupling on a strength-duration relation for the voltage change at the membrane suggests that a certain amount of charge must be displaced in the coupling structures for a given mechanical activation to occur. And our use of ordinary membrane currents in electromechanical coupling may be misleading since the currents flowing only in the T-tubules may be of critical significance, and these are not known.

The work from the Hodgkin laboratory (262) includes many additional interesting features that I must forego discussing, except to mention the hypothesis to explain the strength-duration curve of the mechanical threshold. This relates changes in membrane potential to both the rate of release of an activator (Ca^{2+}?) from an unspecified store and the rate of return of the activator to this store, and it is assumed that increase in concentration of the activator at the myofibrils to some critical level causes a threshold mechanical response. Thus, a relation is derived which predicts the membrane potential that is just necessary to cause threshold activation in a given time. But no attempt is made to analyze this overall correlation between membrane potential and mechanical response into possible component electromechanical coupling mechanisms of, e.g., the T-tubules or the SR. It is interesting, however, that the equation for the strength-duration relation predicts a reasonable fit if only the release of the activator is voltage dependent, the uptake being regarded as constant. This would seem to be the formal equivalent of having the SR release Ca^{2+} in response to a depolarization, but reaccumulate it by a relatively voltage-independent process—as seems to be true according to considerable evidence discussed elsewhere in this review and in an earlier one (156).

T-tubule participation.—I have previously mentioned that T-tubules in frog fibers can be selectively disrupted by a special treatment (187–190). The treated fibers do not respond mechanically to electrical stimulation, but they do produce action potentials and K depolarizations (188, 190, 268, 269) and they seem to have quite normal contractile systems since they respond fairly normally in caffeine contractures (187, 188). Hence, their inability to respond mechanically to electrical stimulation proves quite directly, as had already been supposed (for review: 6, 156), that the T-tubules are required in electromechanical coupling to convey an inwardly moving electrical signal which causes the SR to release activator Ca^{2+}. Such dependence on T-tubules does not seem to hold for frog slow muscle (270), which suggests that such fibers may be able to respond mechanically by uptake of Ca directly across their plasma membrane, and thus indicates again the likeness of frog slow muscle to heart muscle (see 156).

Although it is claimed that caffeine contractures occur normally after disruption of T-tubules, an extended study (271) shows that the ordinary caffeine contracture tension output is statistically only about 60 per cent of that of normal muscles. Yet contractures of normal strength are obtained when frog muscles, which had been equilibrated at room temperature to a subcontracture dose of caffeine, are suddenly exposed to very low temperature (272). Also the very interesting sarcomeric oscillations set up in frog fast fibers by subcontracture doses of caffeine (273) are almost completely prevented by previous disruption of the T-tubules, which suggests that some part of the tubules may be involved in releasing the Ca^{2+} that presumably activates the oscillations.

The fibers with disrupted T-tubules have yielded some electrophysiological results of the greatest interest (269, 274, 275), indicating: (*a*) that the T-tubules provide a great part of the capacitance of the normal fiber, as already indicated by other means (e.g. 276); (*b*) that about two thirds of K conductance of the entire fiber (per cm^2 of fiber surface) occurs across the T-tubule membrane, with the remainder across the surface membrane; (*c*) that perhaps only the surface membrane shows anomalous rectification; (*d*) that the Cl conductance is effectively zero through the T-tubule; (*e*) that the T-tubule seems to be the source of both the early and late afterpotentials following the spike, of the creep in potential which develops on passing hyperpolarizing currents into fibers, and of the relative slowness in repolarizing a muscle on removal of excess external K^+ (277), all of these effects evidently being consequences of the high K conductance of the T-tubules. Disruption of the T-tubules, however, has no effect on Ca efflux of resting fibers, which suggests that such outward movement of Ca occurs solely across the surface membrane (278). It would be of great interest, however, to determine whether the T-tubules play any role in the transport of Ca released from the SR by activity set up by some form of electromechanical coupling or by some chemical agent such as caffeine or quinine.

Transverse spread of activation: the mechanism of T-tubule action.—In view of the foregoing we can conclude that, in the normal fiber, the various signs of electrically evoked transverse spread of activation of contraction reflect inward movement of some sort of signal, most likely electrical, along the T-tubules. That the STS is electrically active during electromechanical coupling is indicated by experiments on skinned fibers whose myofibrils were activated by direct application of electric currents or chemicals acting presumably by reducing the potential difference across the STS membranes (279). These experiments, however, are unclear as to whether the SR or the T-tubules became depolarized to activate contraction. Generally, the mechanical activation was graded and so production of a minimal effect obeyed a strength-duration relation for applied electric pulses, this behavior evidently being the equivalent of the previously mentioned cases of strength-duration relationship in electromechanical coupling. But, oddly, all-or-none responses occasionally appeared, as if the STS were capable of producing a propagated response, as also indicated by certain results of Natori (280). Furthermore, the responses in general were considerably distributed within a skinned fiber not only radially but, especially, also longitudinally over a number of successive sarcomeres. The longitudinal spread suggested that "the triadic junction in the skinned fiber offers a low resistance to the passage of inorganic ions, so that the entire internal membrane system is connected by the relatively low resistance of the luminal fluid." Obviously, this is consistent with the indications (195) that despite the triadic junctions the SR is effectively in direct communication with the extracellular medium.

By means of a very ingenious method Gonzalez-Serratos (281) has determined that the velocity of the T-tubule signal is 3, 6, and 8 cm/sec at 5, 12, and 19.5°C. Thus at room temperature the velocity would be so great that in an average frog skeletal muscle fiber, activation of the innermost fibrils would be delayed by only about 0.5 msec after activation had occurred at the surface. Adrian et al. (282), using quite sophisticated voltage-clamp techniques, determined that the space constant for the T-tubules depends on the radius, and is about 60 μ for a 50 μ fiber. Falk (283) has studied theoretically the inward spread of an electrotonic signal in a simple linear model of a T-tubule by assuming certain equivalent circuit models and component values for frog muscle fibers determined in earlier work (276). She determines the time course of the depolarization across the T-tubule capacitance —this assumed to be the essential electrical change causing activation— when a given depolarization occurs across the plasma membrane. For the case of an action potential at the surface, her model 3, which is reasonably realistic, predicts that the depolarization of the T-tubule membranes at the axis of the fiber will develop with a delay of 0.25 msec relative to the timing of the action potential and also show an attenuation to only about 0.5 of the original surface depolarization. These values are consistent with the just cited findings on measured speed of inward activation and with latent period

timing, and with mechanical threshold features assumed to occur in a typical twitch at room temperature. These results are especially noteworthy for
they are based on an assumed passive, electrotonic spread of the inward-
moving signal of electromechanical coupling, and thus suggest that development of the fully intense active state of the twitch need not involve a regenerative process in the T-tubules. Adrian et al. (262) have extended Falk's
treatment by theoretically analyzing the cable properties of variously struc-
tured networks of tubules, and they find that a voltage step at the surface of
an 80 μ fiber would reach half its final value at the axis in about 0.5 msec,
again indicating that electrotonic spread in the TS could be sufficiently rapid
to be consistent with the brevity of the latent period in the twitch of a fast
muscle. [For other possible factors determining the duration of the latent
period, see (156).]

Particularly interesting is the question whether the electrical effects of
an action potential could be conveyed by the T-tubules with not only sufficient rapidity but also ample strength to fully activate the whole of a fiber.
Falk's theoretical analysis (283) of an electrotonic mechanism suggests that
this could occur, and the combined experimental and theoretical analyses of
Adrian et al. (262), also oriented to an electrotonic propagation, come to
essentially the same conclusion. Further work (282) indicates, however,
that a passive, electrotonic mechanism would just allow a normal action potential, at room temperature, to activate the most central fibrils of a muscle
fiber, and that an active potential change in the T-tubules must occur if E-C
coupling is to have an adequate safety factor. This raises a question as to
the validity of Taylor's reliance, in his theory of the active state (139), on
certain values of the membrane potential obtained from K contractures
(140) to determine the effectiveness of a given action potential in E-C
coupling. He points out, however, that according to his analysis the significant
events determining the kinetics of the active state are not so dependent on
the assumed mechanically significant profile of the action potential. Much
more important are the features of the released calcium, such as its total
amount and the kinetics of its binding to the contractile filaments and pumping back into the SR, which occur during the relatively long period of
mechanical activity following the action potential. Furthermore, as for the
action potential itself, account should be taken of the possibility that the propagation of its effects into the interior of the fiber is not limited to a mere
electronic process, as indicated in the following.

Now, in all of the aforementioned experimental work with voltage
clamps, Na activation of the fibers was suppressed by tetrodotoxin, evidently
to expedite the experimental procedure, and also presumably to limit the
system to passive, electrotonic behavior and so test the possibility (284) that
inward spread might not involve active processes. But, results of my own
laboratory show that reduction of the action potential spike in normal fibers
by as much as 30–35 mV by means of Na deficiency (70 per cent, with
sucrose replacement) has no effect on the peak twitch tension in either frog

single fast fibers (285) or whole sartorii (286), which indicates that the full, normal action potential does function with an E-C coupling safety factor. [Other results from my laboratory regarding effects of Na depletion to the contrary (287) are to be disregarded because the effects were not properly controlled for osmotic changes.] It is also very interesting that Costantin (288) finds in frog twitch fibers that with tetrodotoxin omitted and only partial suppression of Na activation by appropriate choline substitution, a given clamped voltage produces changes which penetrate into the fiber more effectively than when Na activation is completely inhibited. These results suggest that "inward spread of a surface action potential normally occurs, not by passive electrotonus, but by propagation of an action potential along the T-system" (288). Could there not be another possibility, an abortive response in the T-tubule, which would be active, though limited, in respect to Na activation and propagate with a decrement, as may actually be the case (284)? We are obviously faced with a most provocative problem regarding the function of the T-tubules and it will be fascinating to see the future developments.

Ca and the mechanical threshold.—Note that much of the work on mechanisms of T-tubule function discussed in the foregoing is based on experimentally obtained correlations between surface depolarizations and mechanical activity, e.g. on the mechanical threshold. Hence, the associated theoretical developments, limited as they are to T-tubule processes, take no account of the events of electromechanical coupling that must involve the triadic junction, the SR vesicles, the diffusion of the released Ca^{2+} to the sliding filaments, etc. The theoretical findings must therefore be interpreted as indicating proposed mechanisms that are at most consistent with the facts of electromechanical coupling as a whole. Obviously, more information about the various links of electromechanical coupling may help us in appraising more definitely the significance of the T-tubular processes in relation to the overall function of electromechanical coupling.

As a first approach to this consider that the electromechanical coupling events determining the mechanical threshold may be divided into two linked components, which I will call electro-Ca coupling and Ca-mechanical coupling (cf. 23). The reasons for assigning a pivotal role to Ca in this subdivision are evident as follows. The Ca transients (248, 249) clearly show that the first observationally defined major step in electromechanical coupling is electro-Ca coupling—the coupling of an electrical membrane change to the release of free Ca^{2+} in the myoplasm. Then, all the work discussed here and elsewhere (e.g. 6, 156, 245) about Ca^{2+} as activator of contraction concerns Ca-mechanical coupling, the second major component of electromechanical coupling. The question that now arises is, what part does each of these linked processes play in determining the mechanical threshold?

Certain evidence suggests that electro-Ca coupling does not involve a threshold. Thus, some results on Ca transients (249) suggest that a small enough depolarization releases a measurable amount of Ca^{2+} but does not cause any contraction. And a similar inference follows from the results that both quinine and caffeine in low enough doses increase the flux of internal Ca without causing contracture (211) and that considerable increases in metabolism of frog muscle, which evidently depend on release of free Ca^{2+}, occur when the muscles are depolarized by subcontracture concentrations of K^+ (289, 290). Thus, there may not be a threshold for electro-Ca coupling, or, if there is one, the depolarization to attain this is less than that of the mechanical threshold. These considerations obviously tell us nothing directly about how the T-tubules, the triadic (or dyadic) junctions, and the terminal sacs of the SR are each involved in turn in electro-Ca coupling. But the possibilities that passive electrotonic conduction may occur in the T-tubules (either by itself or as a forerunner of production of active processes), or that graded "channeled current" conduction occurs in T-tubules (253), suggest that T-tubule activity does not involve a threshold and that therefore a threshold for electro-Ca coupling, if it exists at all, is a functional feature of the junctions or the terminal sacs.

Calcium-mechanical coupling does clearly entail a threshold. This is frequently represented in terms of the concentration of free Ca^{2+} in the medium of a contractile system—generally about 10^{-7} M—which is just sufficient to cause minimal contractile activity (244, 245). It is delusive, however, to consider the Ca-mechanical threshold simply in this way, because it is not the free Ca^{2+}, but the bound Ca on the myofibrils, that activates contraction, and the bound Ca is in very much greater amount than the free. Thus, from Weber's results (245) it can be shown that the extra Ca that must be bound on the myofibrils of intact muscle for a threshold effect is about 120×10^{-6} moles/kg wet muscle, which is some $1200 \times$ greater than that of the corresponding free Ca^{2+}. And, incidentally, for saturation of contraction, the free Ca^{2+} would be about $10^{-6} M$, but the bound about $200 \times$ greater. These differences in free and bound Ca are not always taken into account: in some recent attempts (253, 291) to determine the amount of electric charge that must be displaced and the corresponding current that must flow in electromechanical coupling, only the free Ca^{2+} was considered. Thus, the calculated amounts of charge or current were too small by a factor of about 1200 regarding threshold effects and by about 200 for saturation.

However, my main point is that Ca-mechanical coupling operates with a definite threshold, and, in view of the possibility that electro-Ca coupling is free of a threshold, what we call the mechanical threshold may really represent an almost direct relationship between a certain depolarized level of membrane potential (which must be further removed from the resting potential, the briefer the depolarization) and the release of enough Ca to bind to the myofibrils to initiate a minimal response. Probably the same sort of relationship holds for activation beyond the mechanical threshold. If so, the theories about operation of the T-tubules may give the essential basis for determining the quantitative effectiveness of a given change in membrane potential, as for example the action potential, in setting up the active state of contraction. In respect to kinetics, however, such analyses would still deal only with the action potential and its effects down the T-tubules. There would then remain the need to determine the overall kinetics of E-C coupling by taking into account the events not merely of the T-tubules but of all the elements, such as diffusion (156) and binding (139) of Ca^{2+} to the reactive sites of myofibrils, involved in finally coupling membrane depolarization to activation of the contractile system.

In concluding this entire section on regulatory systems, it is clear that the STS is involved in both activation and relaxation of contraction. In E-C coupling, the action potential switches on activation by causing the SR to release Ca^{2+}. But what turns off the release of the Ca^{2+}, and then switches on the function of the SR as relaxing factor is not known, although this may develop by simple cessation of the action potential (or rather the spike of the action potential), which terminates the release of activator Ca^{2+} and thus establishes the conditions for the SR to reaccumulate the Ca^{2+} and permit relaxation. A system of this sort is used in Taylor's theory (139). In any case, special studies of relaxation, such as those previously discussed (128, 141–143), should help in clarifying not only relaxation mechanisms themselves but also the integration of these with E-C coupling processes to give a general account of the regulation of the complete contraction-relaxation cycle.

TYPES OF SKELETAL MUSCLE

General structure and function.—New evidence continues to appear that skeletal muscles, regardless of species source, contain fibers which tend to show differences of the slow versus the fast type. But these differences are such that, in general, there is a whole spectrum of muscle types whose classification on the basis of one criterion, e.g. speed of contraction, does not necessarily mesh with that involving some other property, such as structure, color, or histochemistry. As Hess (292) puts it: "A muscle is a muscle is a muscle." Examples of these differences are found in (293-306a). A comparative study of rat fast and slow muscle (307) in relation to the frog sartorius helps to clarify the problem (307a) of the relative sensitivity to caffeine of mammalian and amphibian muscle.

Excitability.—Pilar (308), continuing the controversy with Bach-y-Rita discussed in detail previously (1), now seems to have clearly shown electrophysiologically that the slow fibers of the cat superior oblique extraocular muscle are true tonic fibers as in frog slow muscle. Other indications of such slow fibers in extraocular muscles of the human (309) and the cat (310), and in back muscles of the chicken (311), have been demonstrated by the response of the muscles to acetylcholine or cholinomimetic drugs. An excellent study (312) of the electrical and mechanical properties of red and white fish muscle fibers reports the remarkable result that contracture could not be produced in the typical, twitch, white fibers by even 40 times the normal concentration of K, which caused more than 50 mV depolarization.

Histochemistry.—Histochemical (and biochemical) differences among the various types of muscle fibers are being studied in great detail, but space limitations are so stringent that I can only touch on a few significant developments. Introductions to this field are provided by the reviews of Padykula & Gauthier (313) and Dubowitz (36) and by the detailed studies by Romanul, Engel, and others (314–317). In general, in mammals and amphibia there are at least two histochemically fairly distinct fiber types. "Type I" is rich in myoglobin and in enzymes of lipid and mitochondrial oxidative metabolism, but low in both phosphorylase and myofibrillar ATPase; and it is the preponderant kind of fiber in red, slow muscles. "Types II" ("glycolytic") has opposite characteristics: it is poor in myoglobin and in lipid and mitochondrial enzymes, but rich in both phosphorylase and myofibrillar ATPase, and it is preponderant in white, fast muscles. But exceptions to these concordances do occur (317a). The distinction regarding the ATPase, however, accords with the biochemical and physiological findings (104, 243). In newborn guinea pigs, rats, and cats, the soleus, a typical slow muscle, contains a mixture of about equal numbers of Types I and II fibers (316). But with maturation, this muscle becomes wholly Type I in the guinea pig and practically so in the rat and cat, this being attributed to a developmental transformation of Type II into Type I fibers. This change can be prevented by neonatal sciatic denervation but not by tenotomy, which indicates that the histochemical organization of the tested muscles is neuronally regulated. To a certain degree these histochemical differences parallel the changing mechanical ones that appear in the maturing soleus, which becomes fully slow only after maturation of the animal (318). Interesting variations in the differentiation of the two major types of fiber appear in the development of slow and fast muscles of the dystrophic chicken (319). Noteworthily, the Ca-binding activity of SR from slow muscles of the rabbit is much less than that from fast muscles, which suggests that this difference may be involved in determining the relatively long twitch time of slow muscles (320, 321).

Neuronal regulation.—That the mechanical behavior of mammalian muscle depends on its innervation is demonstrated again in the findings (*a*) that posttetanic potentiation of the isometric twitch, normally present in the extensor digitorum longus (fast) muscle of the rat but absent (or rather replaced by posttetanic depression) in the soleus (slow), shows reversed localization after these two muscles are cross innervated (322); and (*b*) that in kittens cross innervation of slow and fast muscles transforms the effect of lowered temperature on the twitch of these muscles in accordance with the new innervation (323). In the toad, however, Close & Hoh (324) show that the typical mechanical responses of twitch fibers ('which make up the whole of the sartorius) and slow-graded fibers (which make up part of the posterior semitendinosus) are not changed at all by cross innervation lasting up to 200 days. Since these experiments were done on fairly mature animals, one wonders whether the results would be different if very much younger animals were used.

The histochemical and the biochemical composition of muscle fibers is also dependent on innervation, at least in mammals, as shown by previously mentioned results (316), and by the finding that after cross innervation, the properties of the myosin-ATPase and lactic dehydrogenase of originally fast muscle change completely to properties characteristic of these enzymes in the normally slow muscle, and that the reverse change also occurs but only partially (325). Similar effects of cross innervation occur for myoglobin (326) and for certain oxidative and glycolytic enzymes (327). The speeding up of the cross-innervated soleus muscle of the guinea pig and the accompanying, appropriate change in histochemical pattern (appearance of Type II fibers) studied by Robbins et al. (328) is especially interesting because it indicates that all the fibers of the cross-innervated soleus were partially speeded-up and not that some fibers were completely speeded-up to the kinetic level of true fast fibers.

By far the most important problem in this field is to elucidate the mechanism by which motor nerve fibers determine the metabolic and mechanical properties of the muscle fibers they innervate. This has been very thoroughly discussed and reviewed in previously mentioned publications (17, 18). It is very interesting that the specialists in this field, who used to speak rather forthrightly about the possibility that the key process of interest was a neurotrophic influence—implying thereby that the nerve fiber delivered to the muscle fiber a substance (or substances), or at least some influence apart from the traffic of nerve impulses, that regulated the general state of the muscle fiber—now are more chary. They prefer to designate the key influence as "trophic" (i.e., in quotation marks), and define "trophic" effects as "interactions between nerves and other cells which initiate or control molecular modifications in the other cell" (18). Furthermore, there is a general feeling that the pattern of nerve impulses activating a muscle fiber may, after all, have something to do in the "interactions" making up the "trophic" influence.

The importance of the nerve impulse pattern has been stressed especially by Vrbová (329), and in her latest publication (330) she demonstrates that the speeding up of the isometric twitch kinetics of the rabbit soleus muscle that develops following decreased activity due to tenotomy and spinal section can be reversed by long-term *in situ* electrical stimulation of the muscle at frequencies of about 10/sec, but not 20 or 40/sec. Thus she concludes "that the almost continuous low frequency discharge of motoneurones innervating postural muscles plays an important part in establishing and maintaining the slow time course of contractions of these muscles." General support for this view is found in work in which changes in mechanical speed were induced by changes in activity of the muscle produced by tenotomy (331), immobilization (332), contralateral deafferentation (333), and compensatory hypertrophy (334, 335). But the situation is far from settled, for Gutmann and his associates have shown (335, 336) that while an increase in tonic activity causes a muscle to become slower, and develop consistent enzymatic changes, e.g. decrease in myofibrillar ATPase, an increase in phasic activity has opposite effects both mechanically and metabolically. Thus it is now clear that the issue is at least actively joined as to whether nerve impulses, and their effects in patterning the activity of muscle, comprise a factor of the "trophic" influence. However, it would be well in attempting to appraise this factor and to approach a general solution of the problem to recall that there is evidence (e.g. 337) of a traffic of chemical substance down a motor nerve and then into muscle cells, which may be taken as a model of the delivery of neurotrophic material. Furthermore, Drachman (338, 339) reports striking denervation-like effects caused by substances, such as botulinum toxin, that interfere with the function of acetylcholine at neuromuscular junctions; and he hypothesizes that acetylcholine, as normally released spontaneously in production of miniature endplate potentials, may serve to transmit the trophic influence from motor nerves to muscles. These various findings were critically discussed at the conference on "trophic" action (18), and there seemed to be general agreement that acetylcholine, whether released spontaneously or by nerve impulses, may act neurotrophically by producing certain permeability changes that would facilitate passage of "trophic" material from nerve into muscle fibers.

ACKNOWLEDGMENTS

This review was written under the support of a grant from the Muscular Dystrophy Associations of America and during the tenure of grant NB-04262-07 from the United States Public Health Service. I take pleasure in thanking my associates Drs. Michael Barany, Arselio P. Carvalho, and Louis A. Mulieri and Mr. Edwin S. Geffner for many stimulating discussions that greatly aided me in clarifying my thinking on the varied problems I have discussed. I am grateful to various persons for permitting me to discuss their unpublished observations or their papers in press. And, finally, I thank Miss Cathleen Francis and Miss Gladys Roberts for secretarial assistance, and Mrs. Latissia Sanchez for much help in keeping the bibliography in order.

LITERATURE CITED

1. Peachey, L. D. Muscle. *Ann. Rev. Physiol.*, **30**, 201–440 (1968)
2. Hoyle, G. Comparative aspects of muscle. *Ann. Rev. Physiol.*, **31**, 43–84 (1969)
3. Ernst, E., Straub, F. B., Eds. *Symposium on Muscle. Symp. Biol. Hungarica,* 8 (Akad. Kiado, Budapest, 259 pp., 1968)
4. Wilkie, D. R. *Muscle* (St. Martin's Press, New York, 63 pp., 1968)
5. Bendall, J. R. *Muscles, Molecules, and Movement* (Heinemann Educational Books, London, 219 pp., 1969)
5a. Mommaerts, W. F. H. M. Energetics of muscular contraction. *Physiol. Rev.,* **49**, 427–508 (1969)
6. Ebashi, S., Endo, M. Calcium ion and muscle contraction. *Progr. Biophys. Mol. Biol.,* **18**, 123–83 (1968)
7. Hanson, J. Recent X-ray diffraction studies of muscle. *Quart. Rev. Biophys.,* **1**, 177–216 (1968)
8. Perry, S. V. The role of myosin in muscular contraction. In *Aspects of Cell Motility,* 1–16 (See Ref. 29)
9. Szent-Gyorgyi, A. G. The role of actin-myosin interaction in contraction. In *Aspects of Cell Motility,* 17–42 (See Ref. 29)
10. Podolsky, R. J. Membrane systems in muscle cells. In *Aspects of Cell Motility,* 87–100 (See Ref. 29)
11. Pringle, J. W. S. Mechano-chemical transformation in striated muscle. In *Aspects of Cell Motility,* 67–86 (See Ref. 29)
12. Page, S. Structure of the sarcoplasmic reticulum in vertebrate muscle. *Brit. Med. Bull.,* **24**, 170–73 (1968)
13. Baker, P. F. Nervous conduction: some properties of the ion-selective channels which appear during the action potential. *Brit. Med. Bull.,* **24**, 179–82 (1968)
14. Jenden, D. J., Fairhurst, A. S. The pharmacology of ryanodine. *Pharmacol. Rev.,* **21**, 1–25 (1969)
15. Bowman, W. C., Nott, M. W. Actions of sympathomimetic amines and their antagonists on skeletal muscle. *Pharmacol. Rev.,* **21**, 27–72 (1969)
16. Robinson, G. A., Butcher, R. W., Sutherland, E. W. Cyclic AMP.

Ann. Rev. Biochem., **37**, 149–74 (1968)
17. Guth, L. "Trophic" influences of nerve on muscle. *Physiol. Rev.,* **48**, 645–87 (1969)
18. "Trophic" effects of vertebrate neurons. In *Neurosci. Res. Progr. Bull.,* **7**, No. 1 (Guth, L., Chairman, NRP Work Session June 23–25, 1968, 73 pp., 1968)
19. Caldwell, P. C. Factors governing movement and distribution of inorganic ions in nerve and muscle. *Physiol. Rev.,* **48**, 1–64 (1968)
20. Waddell, W. J., Bates, R. G. Intracellular pH. *Physiol. Rev.,* **49**, 285–329 (1969)
21. Brady, A. J. Active state in cardiac muscle. *Physiol. Rev.,* **48**, 570–600 (1968)
22. Langer, G. A. Ion fluxes in cardiac excitation and contraction and their relation to myocardial contractility. *Physiol. Rev.,* **48**, 708–57 (1968)
23. Sonnenblick, E. H., Stam, A. C., Jr. Cardiac muscle: activation and contraction. *Ann. Rev. Physiol.,* **31**, 647–74 (1969)
24. Braunwald, E., Ross, Jr., J., Sonnenblick, E. H. *Mechanisms of Contraction of the Normal and Failing Heart* (Little, Brown, Boston, 205 pp., 1967)
25. Somlyo, A. P., Somlyo, A. V. Vascular smooth muscle. I. Normal structure, pathology, biochemistry and biophysics. *Pharmacol. Rev.,* **20**, 197–272 (1968)
26. Ruegg, J. C. Contractile mechanisms of smooth muscle. In *Aspects of Cell Motility,* 45–66 (See Ref. 29)
27. Bianchi, C. P., Ed. Pharmacology of Excitation-Contraction Coupling. *Fed. Proc.,* **28**, 1624–69 (1969)
28. Stracher, A., Ed. Proceedings of a Symposium on the Contractile Process, *J. Gen. Physiol.,* **50**, No. 6, Pt. 2 (Rockefeller Univ. Press, New York, 292 pp., 1967)
29. *Aspects of Cell Motility. Symposia of the Society for Experimental Biology,* No. XXII (Academic Press, New York, 370 pp., 1968)
30. Kinosita, H., Murakami, A. Control of ciliary motion. *Physiol. Rev.,* **47**, 53–82 (1967)
31. Gibbons, I. R. The biochemistry of

motility. *Ann. Rev. Biochem.,* **37,** 521–46 (1968)

32. Milhorat, A. T., Ed. *Exploratory Concepts in Muscular Dystrophy and Related Disorders* (Excerpta Med. Found., Amsterdam, 420 pp., 1967)

33. Mauro, A. Satellite cell of skeletal muscle fibers. *J. Biophys. Biochem. Cytol.,* **9,** 493–95 (1961)

34. Research in Muscular Dystrophy. *Proc. 4th Symp. Muscular Dystrophy* (Edited by Res. Comm. Muscular Dystrophy Group, Pitman Med. Publ. Co., London, 472 pp., 1968)

35. Pellegrino, C., Franzini-Armstrong, C. Recent contributions of electron microscopy to the study of normal and pathological muscle. *Intern. Rev. Exptl. Pathol.,* **7,** 139–226 (1969)

36. Dubowitz, V. *Developing and Diseased Muscle. A Histochemical Study* (SIMP Res. Monograph, Spastics Intern. Med. Publ. in association with Wm. Heineman Med. Books, New York, 106 pp., 1968)

37. Huxley, A. F. Muscle. *Ann. Rev. Physiol.,* **26,** 131–52 (1964)

38. Edman, K. A. P. The relation between sarcomere length and active tension in isolated semitendinosus fibres of the frog. *J. Physiol.,* **183,** 407–17 (1966)

39. Gordon, A. M., Huxley, A. F., Julian, F. J. The variation in isometric tension with sarcomere length in vertebrate muscle fibres. *J. Physiol.,* **184,** 170–92 (1966)

40. Sjöstrand, F. S., Jagendorf-Elfvin, M. Ultrastructure studies of the contraction-relaxation cycle of glycerinated rabbit psoas muscle. I. The ultrastructure of glycerinated fibers contracted by treatment wih ATP. *J. Ultrastruct. Res.,* **17,** 348–78 (1967)

41. Jagendorf-Elfvin, M. Ultrastructure of the contraction-relaxation cycle of glycerinated rabbit psoas muscle. II. The ultrastructure of glycerinated fibers relaxed in EDTA and ATP-induced contraction. *J. Ultrastruct. Res.,* **17,** 379–400 (1967)

42. Sjöstrand, F. S. Ultrastructural changes in skeletal muscle myofibrils in connexion with contraction. *Nature,* **201,** 45–47 (1964)

43. Jordan, H. E. The structural changes in striped muscle during contraction. *Physiol. Rev.,* **13,** 301–24 (1933)

44. Sandow, A. Diffraction patterns of the frog sartorius and sarcomere behavior during contraction. *J. Cell. Comp. Physiol.,* **9,** 55–75 (1936)

44a. Huxley, A. F., Neidergerke, R. Measurement of the striations of isolated muscle fibres with the interference microscope. *J. Physiol.,* **144,** 403–25 (1958)

45. Huxley, H. E. Structural evidence concerning the mechanism of contraction in striated muscle. In *Muscle. Proc. Symp. Fac. Med., Univ. Alberta,* 3–28 (Pergamon, London, 584 pp., 1965)

46. Huxley, H., Hanson, J. Changes in the cross-striations of muscle during contraction and stretch and their structural interpretation. *Nature,* **173,** 978–87 (1954)

47. Huxley, H. E. Recent X-ray diffraction and electron microscope studies of striated muscle. *J. Gen. Physiol.,* **50,** 71–83 (1967)

48. Huxley, H. E., Brown, W. The low-angle X-ray diagram of vertebrate striated muscle and its behavior during contraction and rigor. *J. Mol. Biol.,* **30,** 383–434 (1967)

49. Huxley, H. E. Structural difference between resting and rigor muscle; evidence from intensity changes in the low-angle equatorial X-ray diagram. *J. Mol. Biol.,* **37,** 507–20 (1968)

50. Reedy, M. K. Cross-bridges and periods in insect flight muscle. *Am. Zool.,* **7,** 465–81 (1967)

51. Reedy, M. K. Ultrastructure of insect flight muscle. *J. Mol. Biol.,* **31,** 155–76 (1968)

52. Elliott, G. F. Variations of the contractile apparatus in smooth and striated muscles. *J. Gen. Physiol.,* **50,** 171–84 (1967)

53. Elliott, G. F., Lowy, J., Millman, B. M. Low-angle X-ray diffraction studied of living striated muscle during contraction. *J. Mol. Biol.,* **25,** 31–45 (1967)

54. Foulks, J. G., Perry, F. A. The time course of early changes in the rate of tension development in electrically stimulated frog toe muscle: effects of muscle length,

temperature and twitch potentiators. *J. Physiol.*, **185**, 355–81 (1966)

55. Larson, R. E., Kushmerick, M. J., Haynes, D. H., Davies, R. E. Internal work during maintained tension of isometric tetanus. *Biophys. J.*, **8**, A-8 (1968)

56. Clewerth, D., Edman, K. A. P. Laser diffraction studies on single skeletal muscle fibers. *Science*, **163**, 296–98 (1967)

57. Tregear, R. T., Miller, A. Evidence of crossbridge movement during contraction of insect flight muscle. *Nature*, **222**, 1184–85 (1969)

58. Galey, F. R. Elastic properties of fixed and fresh muscle. *J. Ultrastruct. Res.*, **26**, 424–41 (1969)

59. Elliott, G. F. Force-balances and stability in hexagonally packed polyelectrolyte systems. *J. Theoret. Biol.*, **21**, 71–87 (1968)

60. Rome, E. Light and X-ray diffraction studies of the filament lattice of glycerol-extracted rabbit psoas muscle. *J. Mol. Biol.*, **27**, 591–602 (1967)

61. Rome, E. X-ray diffraction studies of the filament lattice of striated muscle in various bathing media. *J. Mol. Biol.*, **37**, 331–44 (1968)

62. Shear, D. B. The electrical double layer, long range forces, and muscle contraction. *Biophys. J.*, **9**, A184 (1969)

63. Edman, K. A. P., Andersson, K.-E. The variation in active tension with sarcomere length in vertebrate skeletal muscle and its relation to fibre width. *Experientia*, **24**, 134–36 (1968)

64. April, E., Brandt, P. W., Reuben, J. P., Grundfest, H. Muscle contraction: the effect of ionic strength. *Nature*, **220**, 182–84 (1968)

65. Podolsky, R. J., Sugi, H. The influence of external hypertonic solutions on the contractile mechanism of skeletal muscle fibers. *J. Gen. Physiol.*, **50**, 2496–97 (1967)

65a. Caputo, C. Volume and twitch tension changes in single muscle fibers in hypertonic solutions. *J. Gen. Physiol.*, **52**, 793–809 (1968)

66. Brandt, P. W., Lopez, E., Reuben, J. P., Grundfest, H. The relationship between myofilament packing density and sarcomere length in frog striated muscle. *J. Cell Biol.*, **33**, 255–63 (1967)

67. Dubuisson, M. *Muscular Contraction* (Thomas, Springfield, Ill., 243 pp., 1954)

68. Huxley, H. E. The mechanism of muscular contraction. *Science*, **164**, 1356–65 (1969)

69. Sandberg, J. A., Carlson, F. D. The length dependence of phosphorylcreatine hydrolysis during an isometric tetanus. *Biochem Z.*, **345**, 212–31 (1966)

70. Chaplain, R. A. Changes of ademosine triphosphatase activity and tension with fibre elongation in glycerinated insect fibrillar flight muscle. *Pflügers Arch.*, **307**, 120–26 (1969)

71. Hayashi, Y., Tonomura, Y. Dependence of activity of myofibrillar ATPase on sarcomere length and calcium ion concentration. *J. Biochem. (Tokyo)*, **63**, 101–18 (1968)

72. Young, M. Studies on the structural basis of the interaction of myosin and actin. *Proc. Natl. Acad. Sci.*, **58**, 2393–2400 (1967)

73. Bárány, M., Bailin, G., Bárány, K. Reaction of myosin with 1-fluoro-2,4-dinitrobenzene at low ionic strength. *J. Biol. Chem.*, **244**, 648–57 (1969)

74. Bárány, M., Bárány, K. Change in reactivity of myosin during muscular contraction (Personal communication)

75. Pepe, F. A. The myosin filament. II. Interaction between myosin and actin filaments observed using antibody staining in fluorescent and electron microscopy. *J. Mol. Biol.*, **27**, 227–36 (1967)

75a. Lowey, S., Slayter, H. S., Weeds, A. G., Baker, H. Substructure of the myosin molecule. I. Subfragments of myosin by enzyme degradation. *J. Mol. Biol.*, **42**, 1–29 (1969)

76. Julian, F. J. Activation in a skeletal muscle contraction model with a modification for insect fibrillar muscle. *Biophys. J.*, **9**, 547–70 (1969)

77. Huxley, A. F. Muscle structure and theories of contraction. *Progr. Biophys.*, **7**, 255–318 (1957)

78. Hill, T. L. Phase transition in the sliding-filament model of muscular contraction. *Proc. Natl. Acad. Sci.*,

54, 1194–1200 (1968)

79. Hill, T. L. On the sliding-filament model of muscular contraction. II. *Proc. Natl. Acad. Sci.,* **61,** 98–105 (1968)

80. Hill, T. L., White, G. M. On the sliding-filament model of muscular contraction. III. Kinetics of cross-bridge fluctuations in configuration. *Proc. Natl. Acad. Sci.,* **61,** 514–21 (1968)

81. Hill, T. L., White, G. M. On the sliding-filament model of muscular contraction. IV. Calculation of force-velocity curves. *Proc. Natl. Acad. Sci.,* **61,** 889–96 (1968)

82. Ullrick, W. C. A theory of contraction for striated muscle. *J. Theoret. Biol.,* **15,** 53–69 (1967)

83. Natori, R. The property and contraction process of isolated myofibrils. *Jikeikai Med. J.,* **1,** 119–26 (1954)

84. Hellam, D. C., Podolsky, R. J. Force measurements in skinned muscle fibres. *J. Physiol.,* **200,** 807–19 (1969)

84a. Stephens, R. E. Analysis of muscle contraction by ultraviolet microbeam disruption of sarcomere structure. *J. Cell Biol.,* **25,** 129–39 (1965)

85. Rosenbluth, J. Obliquely striated muscle. IV. Sarcoplasmic reticulum, contractile apparatus, and endomysium of the body muscle of a Polychaete, Glycera, in relation to its speed. *J. Cell Biol.,* **36,** 245–59 (1968)

86. Nonomura, Y. Myofilaments in smooth muscle of guinea pig's taenia coli, *J. Cell Biol.,* **39,** 741–63 (1968)

87. Kelly, R. E., Rice, R. V. Localization of myosin filaments in smooth muscle. *J. Cell Biol.,* **37,** 105–16 (1968)

88. Kaminer, B. Synthetic myosin filaments from vertebrate smooth muscle. *J. Mol. Biol.,* **39,** 257–64 (1969)

89. McNeill, P. A., Hoyle, G. Evidence for superthin filaments. *Am. Zool.,* **7,** 483–98 (1967)

90. Hoyle, G. Discussion on ultrastructure of muscle fibrils. In *Symposium on Muscle, Symp. Biol. Hung.,* 34–55 (See Ref. 3)

91. Sandow, A. Latency relaxation: a brief analytical review. *Med. Coll. Virginia Quart.,* **2,** 82–89 (1966)

92. Kelly, D. E. Myofibrillogenesis and Z-band differentiation. *Anat. Rec.,* **163,** 403–26 (1969)

93. Ikemoto, N., Kitagawa, S., Nakamura, A., Gergely, J. Electron microscopic investigations of actomyosin as a function of ionic strength. *J. Cell Biol.,* **39,** 620–29 (1968)

94. Kelly, D. E. Models of muscle Z-band structure based on a looping filament configuration. *J. Cell Biol.,* **34,** 827–39 (1967)

95. Rash, J. E., Shay, J. W., Biesele, J. J. Urea extraction of Z-bands, intercalated disks, and desmosomes. *J. Ultrastruct. Res.,* **24,** 181–89 (1968)

96. Fawcett, D. W. The sporadic occurrence in cardiac muscle of anomalous Z-bands exhibiting a periodic structure suggestive of tropomyosin. *J. Cell Biol.,* **36,** 266–70 (1968)

97. Masaki, T., Endo, M., Ebashi, S. Localization of 6 S component of α-actinin at Z-band. *J. Biochem.,* **62,** 630–32 (1967)

97a. Stromer, M. H., Hartshorne, D. J., Mueller, H., Rice, R. V. The effect of various protein fractions on Z- and M-line reconstitution. *J. Cell Biol.,* **40,** 167–78 (1969)

98. Masaki, T., Takaiti, O., Ebashi, S. "M-substance", a new protein constituting the M-line of myofibrils. *J. Biochem. (Tokyo),* **64,** 909–10 (1968)

99. Knappeis, G. G., Carlsen, F. The ultrastructure of the M line in skeletal muscle. *J. Cell Biol.,* **38,** 202–11 (1968)

100. Corsi, A., Muscatello, U., Ronchetti, I. Electron miscroscope observations of the location of actin and tropomyosin in the rabbit myofibril. *J. Ultrastruct. Res.,* **19,** 260–72 (1967)

101. Pease, D. C. Structural features of unfixed mammalian smooth and striated muscle prepared by glycol dehyration. *J. Ultrastuct. Res.,* **23,** 380–403 (1968)

102. Fischman, D. A. An electron microscope study of myofibril formation in embryonic chick skeletal muscle. *J. Cell Biol.,* **32,** 557–75 (1967)

103. Page, S. G. Fine structure of tortoise skeletal muscle. *J. Physiol.,* **197,** 709–15 (1968)

104. Bárány, M. ATPase activity of myosin correlated with speed of muscle shortening. *J. Gen. Physiol.*, **50**, 197–218 (1967)

105. Goldspink, G. Sarcomere length during post-natal growth of mammalian muscle fibres. *J. Cell Sci.*, **3**, 539–48 (1968)

106. Luff, A. R., Goldspink, G. Large and small muscles. *Life Sci.*, **6**, 1821–26 (1967)

107. Goldspink, G., Rowe, R. W. D. Studies on postembryonic growth and development of skeletal muscle. II: Some physiological and structural changes that are associated with the growth and development of skeletal muscle fibres. *Proc. Roy. Irish Acad.*, **66**, 85–99 (1968)

108. Rowe, R. W. D., Goldspink, G. Surgically induced hypertrophy in skeletal muscles of the laboratory mouse. *Anat. Rec.*, **161**, 69–76 (1968)

109. Goldspink, G., Rowe, R. W. D. The growth and development of muscle fibres in normal and dystrophic mice. In *Proc. 4th Symp. in Muscular Dystrophy* (See Ref. 34)

110. Hill, D. K. Tension due to interaction between the sliding filaments in resting striated muscle: The effect of stimulation. *J. Physiol.*, **199**, 637–84 (1968)

111. Homsher, E., Briggs, F. N. Effects of hypertonicity on calcium fluxes in frog sartorius muscles. *Fed. Proc.*, **27**, 375 (1968)

112. Isaacson, A. Caffeine-induced contractures and related calcium movements of muscle in hypertonic media. *Experientia* (In press)

113. Huxley, H. E. Muscle cells. In *The Cell*, **4**, 365–481 (Brachet, J., Mirsky, A. E., Eds., Academic, New York, 511 pp., 1960)

114. Hill, A. V. *Trails and Trials in Physiology* (Williams & Wilkins, Baltimore, 374 pp., 1965)

115. Wilander, B. Active state duration of rat gastrocnemius muscle. *Acta Physiol. Scand.*, **68**, 1–17 (1966)

116. Desmedt, J. E., Hainaut, K. Kinetics of myofilament activation in potentiated contraction: staircase phenomenon in human skeletal muscle. *Nature*, **217**, 529–32 (1968)

117. Desmedt, J. E., Emeryk, B., Renoirte, P., Hainaut, K. Disorder of muscle contraction processes in sex-linked (Duchenne) muscular dystrophy with correlative electromygraphic study of myopathic involvement in small hand muscles. *Am. J. Med.*, **45**, 853–72 (1968)

118. Colomo, F., Rocchi, P. Staircase effect and post-tetanic potentiation in frog nerve-single muscle fibre preparations. *Arch. Fisiol.*, **64**, 189–266 (1965)

119. Brown, A. M., Orkand, R. K. A down then up staircase in frog ventricle due to altered excitation-contraction coupling. *J. Physiol.*, **197**, 295–304 (1968)

120. Sandow, A. Potentiation of muscular contraction. *Arch. Phys. Med. Rehabil.*, **45**, 62–81 (1964)

121. Rosenfalck, P. Staircase phenomenon of human muscle: relation to the active state. *Nature*, **218**, 958–59 (1968)

122. Sandow, A., Preiser, H. Muscular contraction as regulated by the action potential. *Science*, **146**, 1470–72 (1964)

123. Close, R., Hoh, J. F. Y. Post-tetanic potentiation of twitch contractions of cross-innervated rat fast and slow muscles. *Nature*, **221**, 179–81 (1969)

124. Buller, A. J., Lewis, D. M. The rate of tension development in isometric tetanic contractions of mammalian fast and slow skeletal muscle. *J. Physiol.*, **176**, 337–54 (1965)

125. Sandow, A., Seaman, T. Muscle shortening velocity in normal and potentiated contractions. *Life Sci.*, **3**, 91–96 (1964)

126. Civan, M. M., Podolsky, R. J. Contraction kinetics of striated muscle fibres following quick changes in load. *J. Physiol.*, **184**, 511–34 (1966)

127. Taylor, S. R., Preiser, H., Sandow, A. Mechanical threshold as a factor in excitation-contraction coupling. *J. Gen. Physiol.*, **54**, 352–68 (1969)

128. Mashima, H. On the active state developed by repetitive stimuli in the frog skeletal muscle. *J. Physiol. Soc. Japan*, **29**, 708–9 (1968)

129. Matsumoto, Y. Validity of the force-velocity relation for muscle contraction in the length region. *J. Gen. Physiol.*, **50**, 1125–37 (1967)

130. Matsumoto, Y. Theoretical series elastic element length in *Rana*

pipiens sartorius muscles. *J. Gen. Physiol.*, **50**, 1139–56 (1967)

131. Matsumoto, Y. Normalization of shortening of *Rana pipiens* sartorius muscle. *J. Theoret. Biol.*, **18**, 387–95 (1968)

132. Abbott, B. C., Wilkie, D. R. The relation between velocity of shortening and the tension-length curve of skeletal muscle. *J. Physiol.*, **120**, 214–23 (1953)

133. Bahler, A. S. Series elastic component of mammalian skeletal muscle. *Am. J. Physiol.*, **213**, 1560–64 (1967)

134. Bahler, A. S., Fales, J. T., Zierler, K. L. The active state of mammalian skeletal muscle. *J. Gen. Physiol.*, **50**, 2167–76 (1967)

135. Bahler, A. S. Modeling of mammalian skeletal muscle. *Bio-Med. Eng.*, **15**, 249–57 (1968)

136. Bahler, A. S., Fales, J. T., Zierler, K. L. The dynamic properties of mammalian skeletal muscle. *J. Gen. Physiol.*, **51**, 369–84 (1968)

137. Hill, A. V. The abrupt transition from rest to activity in muscle. *Proc. Roy. Soc. B,* **136**, 399–420 (1949)

138. Woledge, R. C. The energetics of tortoise muscle. *J. Physiol.*, **197**, 685–707 (1968)

139. Taylor, C. P. S. Isometric muscle contraction and and the active state, an analong computer study. *J. Biophys.*, **9**, 759–80 (1969)

140. Sandow, A., Taylor, S. R., Preiser, H. Role of the action potential in excitation-contraction coupling. *Fed. Proc.*, **24**, 1116–23 (1965)

141. Parmley, W. W., Sonnenblick, E. H. Relation between mechanics of contraction and relaxation in mammalian cardiac muscle. *Am. J. Physiol.*, **216**, 1084–91 (1969)

142. Sandow, A., Preiser, H. Tetanus and active state indications in normal and caffeinized muscle. *Biophys. J.*, **8**, A-12 (1968)

143. Sandow, A., Preiser, H., Geffner, E. S. Tetanus relaxation: generalized mechanics and a Ca-mechanism theory. *Abstr. 3rd Intern. Biophys. Congr., Intern. Union Pure Appl. Biophys.*, 273 (1969)

144. Parsons, C., Porter, K. R. Muscle relaxation: Evidence for an intra-fibrillar restoring force in vertebrate striated muscle. *Science,* **153**, 426–27 (1966)

145. Mommaerts, W. F. H. M., Wallner, A. The break-down of adenosine triphosphate in the contraction cycle of the frog sartorius muscle. *J. Physiol.*, **193**, 343–57 (1967)

146. Davies, R. E., Kushmerick, M. J., Larson, R. E. Lack of ATP splitting equivalent to activation and shortening heat. *Fed. Proc.*, **26**, 553 (1967)

147. Gibbs, C. L., Vaughan, P. The effect of calcium depletion upon the tension-independent component of cardiac heat production. *J. Gen. Physiol.*, **52**, 532–49 (1968)

148. Hill, A. V. The onset of contraction. *Proc. Roy. Soc. B,* **136**, 242–54 (1949)

149. Chaplain, R. A. Molecular nature of the heat of shortening of muscle. *Nature,* **223**, 63–64 (1969)

150. Davies, R. E. ATP, activation, and the heat of shortening of muscle. *Nature,* **214**, 148–51 (1967)

151. Carlson, F. D., Hardy, D., Wilkie, D. R. The relation between heat produced and phosphorylcreatine split during isometric contraction of frog's muscle. *J. Physiol.*, **186**, 209–35 (1967)

152. Wilkie, D. R. Heat work and phosphorylcreatine break-down. *J. Physiol.*, **195**, 157–83 (1968)

153. Hill, A. V. The effect of load on the heat of shortening of muscle. *Proc. Roy. Soc. B,* **159**, 297–318 (1964)

154. Aubert, X. *Le Couplage Énergétique de la Contraction Musculaire* (Éditions Arscia, Brussels, 313 pp., 1956)

155. Clinch, N. F. On the increase in rate of heat production caused by stretch in frog's skeletal muscle. *J. Physiol.*, **196**, 397–414 (1968)

156. Sandow, A. Excitation-contraction coupling in skeletal muscle. *Pharmacol. Rev.*, **17**, 265–320 (1965)

157. Fales, J. T., Crawford, W. J., Zierler, K. L. Gradient-layer calorimetry of muscle: relation between length, twitch tension, and heat. *Am. J. Physiol.*, **213**, 1427–32 (1967)

158. Fales, J. T., Zierler, K. L. Relation between length, tension, and heat: frog sartorius muscle, brief tetani. *Am. J. Physiol.*, **216**, 70–75 (1969)

159. Fales, J. T. Muscle heat production and work: effect of varying iso-

tonic load. *Am. J. Physiol.*, **216**, 1184–87 (1969)

160. Davies, R. E., Kushmerick, M. J. The thermodynamic efficiency of muscle contraction. *Abstr. Intern. Congr. Biochem., 7th, Tokyo, 1967*, Symp. VI-3.5

161. Kushmerick, M. J., Davies, R. E. Energetics and efficiency of maximally working frog sartorius muscles at 0°C. *Fed. Proc.*, **26**, 727 (1967)

162. Caplan, S. R. A characteristic of self-regulated linear energy converters—the Hill force-velocity relation for muscle. *J. Theoret. Biol.*, **11**, 63–86 (1966)

163. Caplan, S. R. Autonomic energy conversion. I. The input relation: Phenomenological and mechanical 1146–66 (1968)

164. Caplan, S. R. Autonomic energy conversion. II. An approach to the energetics muscular contraction. *Biophys. J.*, **8**, 1167–94 (1968) considerations. *Biophys. J.*, **8**,

165. Wilkie, D. Energetic aspects of muscular contraction. In *Symposium on Muscle, Symp. Biol. Hung.*, **8**, 207–23 (See Ref. 3)

166. Wilkie, D. R., Woledge, R. C. The application of irreversible thermodynamics to muscular contraction. Comments on a recent theory by S. R. Caplan. *Proc. Roy. Soc. B*, **169**, 17–29 (1967)

167. Wilkie, D. R., Woledge, R. C. Autonomic energy conversion. *Biophys. J.*, **8**, 1195–96 (1968)

168. Caplan, S. R. Comments from S. R. Caplan. *Biophys. J.*, **8**, 1197 (1968)

169. Bornhorst, W. J., Minardi, J. E. Comparison of Caplan's irreversible thermodynamic theory of muscle contraction with chemical data. *Biophys. J.*, **9**, 654–65 (1969)

170. Peachey, L. D., Schild, R. E. The distribution of the T-system along the sarcomeres of frog and toad sartorius muscles. *J. Physiol.*, **194**, 249–58 (1968)

171. Peachey, L. D. The sarcoplasmic reticulum and transverse tubules of the frog's sartorius. *J. Cell Biol.*, **25**, 209–31 (1965)

172. Staley, N. A., Benson, E. S. The ultrastructure of frog ventricular cardiac muscle and it's relationship to mechanism of excitation-contraction coupling. *J. Cell Biol.*, **38**, 99–114 (1968)

173. Sommer, J. R. Chicken cardiac muscle: A transitional stage between amphibian and mammalian cardiac muscle. *J. Cell Biol.*, **39**, 127a (1968)

174. Sommer, J. R., Steere, R. L. Apropos transverse tubules in chicken cardiac muscle. *Fed. Proc.*, **28**, 328 (1969)

175. Sommer, J. R., Johnson, E. A. A comparative study of purkinje fibers and ventricular fibers. *J. Cell Biol.*, **36**, 297–526 (1968)

176. Forssmann, W. G., Matter, A., Daldrup, J., Girardier, L. A study of the T system in the heart muscle by means of horseradish peroxidase tracing. *J. Cell Biol.*, **39**, 45a (1968)

177. Rayns, D. G., Simpson, F. O. Transverse tubule apertures in mammalian myocardial cells: surface array. *Science*, **156**, 656–57 (1967)

178. Rayns, D. G., Simpson, F. O., Bertaud, W. S. Surface features of striated muscle. I. Guinea-pig cardiac muscle. *J. Cell Sci.*, **3**, 267–474 (1968)

179. Rayns, D. G., Simpson, F. O., Bertaud, W. S. Surface features of striated muscle. II. Guinea-pig skeletal muscle. *J. Cell Sci.*, **3**, 475–82 (1968)

180. Walker, S. M., Schrodt, G. R. Triads in foetal skeletal muscle. *Nature*, **216**, 985–88 (1967)

181. Walker, S. M., Schrodt, G. R., Bingham, M. Electron microscope study of the sarcoplasmic reticulum at the Z-line level in skeletal muscle fibers of fetal and newborn rats. *J. Cell Biol.*, **39**, 469–75 (1969)

182. Walker, S. M., Schrodt, G. R., Bingham, M. Evidence for connections of the sarcoplasmic reticulum with the sarcolemma and with the Z line in skeletal muscle fibers of fetal and newborn rats. *Am. J. Phys. Med.*, **48**, 63–77 (1969)

183. Ishikawa, H. Formation of elaborate networks of T-system tubules in cultured skeletal muscle with special reference to the T-system formation. *J. Cell Biol.*, **38**, 51–67 (1968)

184. Schiaffino, S., Margreth, A. Coordinated development of the sarcoplasmic reticulum and T system

during postnatal differentiation of rat skeletal muscle. *J. Cell Biol.,* **41,** 855–75 (1969)

185. Reger, J. F. The organization of sarcoplasmic reticulum in direct flight muscle of the dipidopteran Achalarus lyciades. *J. Ultrastruct. Res.,* **18,** 595–99 (1967)

186. Rosenbluth, J. Sarcoplasmic reticulum of an unusually fast-acting crustacean muscle. *J. Cell Biol.,* **42,** 534–47 (1969)

186a. Mendelson, M., Van der Kloot, W. G. Electrical and mechanical characteristics of a very fast lobster muscle. *J. Cell Biol.,* **42,** 548–64 (1969)

187. Howell, J. N., Jenden, D. J. T-tubules of skeletal muscle: morphological alterations which interrupt excitation-contraction coupling. *Fed. Proc.,* **26,** 553 (1967)

188. Howell, J. N. A lesion of the transverse tubules of skeletal muscle. *J. Physiol.,* **201,** 515–33 (1969)

189. Krolenko, S. A. Changes in the T-system of muscle fibres under the influence of influx and efflux of glycerol. *Nature,* **221,** 966–68 (1969)

190. Eisenberg, B., Eisenberg, R. S. Selective disruption of the sarcotubular system in frog sartorius muscle. A quantitative study with exogenous peroxidase as a marker. *J. Cell Biol.,* **39,** 451–67 (1968)

191. Rapoport, S. I., Freygang, W. H., Jr., Peachey, L. D. Swelling of transverse tubular system of frog sartorius. *Biophys. J.,* **8,** A-116 (1968)

192. Freygang, Jr., W. H., Rapoport, S. I., Peachey, L. D. Some relations between changes in the linear electrical properties of striated muscle fibers and changes in ultrastructure. *J. Gen. Physiol.,* **50,** 2437–58 (1967)

193. Brandt, P. W., Reuben, J. P., Grundfest, H. Physiological studies on isolated single muscle fibers. II. The properties of the cray fish transverse tubular system: localization of the sites of reversible swelling. *J. Cell Biol.,* **38,** 115–29 (1968)

194. Legato, M. J., Spiro, D., Langer, G. A. Ultrastructural alterations produced in mammalian myocardium by variations in perfusate

ionic composition. *J. Cell Biol.,* **37,** 1–12 (1968)

195. Birks, R. I., Davey, D. R. Osmotic responses demonstrating the extracellular character of the sarcoplasmic reticulum. *J. Physiol.,* **202,** 171–88 (1969)

196. Armstrong, C. F. The triadic junction in frog muscle fibers. *J. Cell Biol.,* **39,** 6a (1968)

197. Carvalho, A. P. Effects of potentiators of muscular contraction on binding of cations by sarcoplasmic reticulum. *J. Gen. Physiol.,* **51,** 427–42 (1968)

198. Carvalho, A. P. Calcium-binding properties of sarcoplasmic reticulum as influenced by ATP, caffeine, quinine, and local anesthetics. *J. Gen. Physiol.,* **52,** 622–42 (1968)

199. Huxley, H. E., Page, S., Wilkie, D. R. An electron microscopic study of muscle in hypertonic solutions. *J. Physiol.,* **169,** 325–29 (1963)

200. Freygang, W. H., Jr., Goldstein, D. A., Hellam, D. C., Peachey, L. D. The relation between the late after-potential and the size of the transverse tubular system of frog muscle. *J. Gen. Physiol.,* **48,** 235–63 (1964)

201. Zadunaisky, J. A. The location of sodium in the transverse tubules of skeletal muscle. *J. Cell Biol.,* **31,** C11–C16 (1966)

202. Weber, A. Energized calcium transport and relaxing factors. *Curr. Top. Bioenerg.,* **1,** 203–54 (1966)

203. Weber, A., Herz, R., Reiss, I. Study of the kinetics of calcium transport by isolated fragmented sarcoplasmic reticulum. *Biochem. Z.,* **345,** 329–69 (1966)

204. Carvalho, A. P. Binding of cations by microsomes from rabbit skeletal muscle. *J. Cell. Physiol.,* **67,** 73–84 (1966)

205. Carvalho, A. P., Leo, B. Effects of ATP on the interaction of Ca^{++}, Mg^{++}, and K^+ with fragmented sarcoplasmic reticulum isolated from rabbit skeletal muscle. *J. Gen. Physiol.,* **50,** 1327–52 (1967)

206. Landgraf, W. C., Inesi, G. ATP dependent conformational change in "spin labelled" sarcoplasmic reticulum. *Arch. Biochem. Biophys.,* **130,** 111–18 (1969)

207. Hasselbach, W. Relaxing factor and

the relaxation of muscle. *Progr. Biophys.*, **14**, 167–22 (1964)

208. Weber, A., Herz, R. The relationship between caffeine contracture of intact muscle and the effect of caffeine on reticulum. *J. Gen. Physiol.*, **52**, 750–59 (1968)

209. Weber, A. The mechanism of the action of caffeine on sarcoplasmic reticulum. *J. Gen. Physiol.*, **52**, 760–72 (1968)

210. Isaacson, A., Sandow, A. Caffeine effects on radiocalcium movement in normal and denervated rat muscle. *J. Pharmacol. Exptl. Therap.*, **155**, 378–88 (1967)

211. Isaacson, A., Sandow, A. Quinine and caffeine effects on ^{45}Ca movements in frog sartorius muscle. *J. Gen. Physiol.*, **50**, 2109–28 (1967)

212. Inesi, G., Watanabe, S. Temperature dependence of ATP hydrolysis and calcium uptake by fragmented sarcoplasmic membranes. *Arch. Biochem. Biophys.*, **121**, 665–71 (1967)

213. Fuchs, F. Inhibition of sarcotubular calcium transport by caffeine: species and temperature dependence. *Biochim. Biophys. Acta,* **172**, 566–70 (1969)

214. Fuchs, F., Gertz, E. W., Briggs, F. N. The effect of quinidine on calcium accumulation by isolated sarcoplasmic reticulum of skeletal and cardiac muscle. *J. Gen. Physiol.*, **52**, 955–68 (1968)

215. Lain, R. F., Hess, M. L., Gertz, E. W., Briggs, F. N. Calcium uptake activity of canine myocardial sarcoplasmic reticulum in the presence of anesthetic agents. *Circ. Res.*, **23**, 597–604 (1968)

216. Van der Kloot, W. G. Inhibitors of active Ca^{2+} uptake by fragments of the sarcoplasmic reticulum of lobster muscle. *Comp. Biochem. Physiol.*, **17**, 75–86 (1966)

217. Van der Kloot, W. Calcium uptake by isolated sarcoplasmic reticulum treated with dithiothreitol. *Science,* **164**, 1294 (1969)

218. Klaus, W., Lee, K. S. Influence of cardiac glycosides on calcium binding in muscle subcellular components. *J. Pharmacol. Exptl. Therap.*, **166**, 68–76 (1969)

219. Chimoskey, J. E., Gergely, J. Effect of norepinephrine, ouabain, and pH on cardiac sarcoplasmic reticulum. *Arch. Intern. Pharmacodyn.*, **176**, 289–97 (1968)

220. Hess, M. L., Briggs, F. N., Shinebourne, E., Hamer, J. Effect of adrenergic blocking agents on the calcium pump of the fragmented cardiac sarcoplasmic reticulum. *Nature*, **220**, 79–80 (1968)

221. Yu, B. P., Masoro, E. J., DeMartinis, F. D. Imidazole and sequestration of calcium ions by sarcoplasmic reticulum. *Nature*, **216**, 822–24 (1967)

222. Chimoskey, J. E., Gergely, J. Effect of ions on sarcoplasmic reticulum fragments. *Arch. Biochem. Biophys.*, **128**, 601–5 (1968)

223. Balzer, H., Makinose, M., Hasselbach, W. The inhibition of the sarcoplasmic calcium pump by prenylamine, reserpine, chlorpromazine and imipramine. *Arch. Exptl. Pathol. Pharmakol.*, **260**, 444–55 (1968)

224. Balzer, H., Makinose, M., Fiehn, W., Hasselbach, W. The bindings of the calcium transport inhibitors reserpine, chlorpromazine, and prenylamine to the lipids of the membranes of the sarcoplasmic reticulum. *Arch. Exptl. Pathol. Pharmakol.*, **260**, 456–73 (1968)

225. Philpott, C. W., Goldstein, M. A. Sarcoplasmic reticulum of striated muscle: localization of potential calcium binding sites. *Science,* **155**, 1019–20 (1967)

226. Zacks, S. I., Sheff, M. F. Tetanus toxin; fine structure localization of binding sites in striated muscle. *Science,* **159**, 643–44 (1968)

227. Hasselbach, W., Elfvin, L. G. Structural and chemical asymmetry of the calcium-transporting membranes of the sarcotubular system as revealed by electron microscopy. *J. Uultrastruct. Res.*, **17**, 598–622 (1967)

228. Ikemoto, N., Sreter, F. A., Nakamura, A., Gergely, J. Tryptic digestion and localization of calcium uptake and ATPase activity in fragments of sarcoplasmic reticulum. *J. Ultrastruct. Res.*, **23**, 216–32 (1968)

229. Martonosi, A. Sarcoplasmic reticulum. V. The structure of sarcoplasmic reticulum membranes. *Biochim. Biophys. Acta.*, **150**, 694–704 (1968)

230. Entman, M. L., Levey, G. S., Epstein, S. E. Demonstration of adenyl cyclase activity in canine cardiac sarcoplasmic reticulum. *Biochem. Biophys. Res. Commun.*, **35**, 728–33 (1969)

231. Teravainen, H. Distribution of acetylcholinesterase in extraocular muscle fibres of the rat. *Histochemie*, **18**, 174–76 (1969)

232. Lane, B. P. Localization of products of ATP hydrolysis in mammalian smooth muscle cells. *J. Cell Biol.*, **34**, 713–20 (1967)

233. Schulze, W., Wollenberger, A. Zytochemische Lokalisation und Charakterisierung von phosphatabspaltenden Fermenten im sarkotubularen System quergestreifter Muskeln. *Histochemie*, **10**, 140–53 (1967)

234. Gauthier, G. F. On the localization of sarcotubular ATPase activity in mammalian skeletal muscle. *Histochemie*, **11**, 97–111 (1967)

235. Ebashi, S., Kodama, A., Ebashi, F. Troponin. I. Preparation and physiological function. *J. Biochem.*, **64**, 465–77 (1968)

236. Davies, R. E. A molecular theory of muscle contraction: calcium-dependent contractions with hydrogen bond formation plus ATP-dependent extensions of part of the myosin-actin bridges. *Nature*, **199**, 1068–74 (1963)

237. Nonomura, Y., Drabikowski, W., Ebashi, S. The localization of troponin in tropomyosin paracrystals. *J. Biochem.*, **64**, 419–22 (1968)

238. Wakabayashi, T., Ebashi, S. Reversible change in physical state of troponin induced by calcium ion. *J. Biochem.*, **64**, 731–32 (1968)

239. Yasui, B., Fuchs, F., Briggs, F. N. The role of the sulfhydryl groups of tropomyosin and troponin in the calcium control of actomyosin contractility. *J. Biol. Chem.*, **243**, 735–42 (1968)

240. Fuchs, F., Briggs, F. N. The site of calcium binding in relation to the activation of myofibrillar contraction. *J. Gen. Physiol.*, **51**, 655–76 (1968)

241. Weber, A., Herz, R., Reiss, I. The role of magnesium in the relaxation of myofibrils. *Biochemistry*, **8**, 2266–70 (1969)

242. Gillis, J. M. The site of action of calcium in producing contraction in striated muscle. *J. Physiol.*, **200**, 849–64 (1969)

243. Costantin, L. L., Podolsky, R. J., Tice, L. W. Calcium activation of frog slow muscle fibres. *J. Physiol.*, **188**, 261–71 (1967)

244. Hellam, D. C., Podolsky, R. J. Force measurements in skinned muscle fibres. *J. Physiol.*, **209**, 807–19 (1969)

245. Weber, A., Herz, R., Reiss, I. The regulation of myofibriller activity by calcium. *Proc. Roy. Soc. B*, **160**, 489–501 (1964)

246. Schädler, M. Proportionale Aktivierung von ATPase-Aktivität und Kontraktionsspannung durch Calciumionen in isolierten contractilen Strukturen verschiedener Muskelärten. *Pflügers Arch.*, **296**, 70–90 (1967)

247. Ridgway, E. B., Ashley, C. C. Calcium transients in single muscle fibers. *Biochem. Biophys. Res. Commun.*, **29**, 229–34 (1967)

248. Jöbis, F. F., O'Connor, M. J. Calcium release and reabsorption in the sartorius muscle of the toad. *Biochem. Biophys. Res. Commun.*, **25**, 246–52 (1966)

249. Ashley, C. C., Ridgway, E. B. Simultaneous recording of membrane potential, calcium transient and tension in single muscle fibres. *Nature*, **219**, 1168–69 (1968)

249a. Hastings, J. W., Mitchell, G., Mattingly, P. H., Blinks, J. R., Van Leeuwen, M. Response of aequorin bioluminescence to rapid changes in calcium concentration. *Nature*, **222**, 1047–50 (1969)

250. Stoclet, J.-C. Mouvements du calcium dans le muscle au repos et en activité chez le rat in vivo. *J. Physiol.*, **58**, Suppl. 4, 1–131 (1966)

251. Bianchi, C. P., Bolton, T. C. Action of local anesthetics on coupling systems in muscle. *J. Pharmacol. Exptl. Therap.*, **157**, 388–405 (1967)

252. Gainer, H. The role of calcium in excitation contraction coupling of lobster muscle. *J. Gen. Physiol.*, **52**, 88–110 (1968)

253. Reuben, J. P., Brandt, P. W., Garcia, H., Grundfest, H. Excitation-contraction coupling in crayfish. *Am. Zool.*, **7**, 623–45 (1967)

254. Dudel, J. Rüdel, R. Voltage controlled contractions and current voltage relations of crayfish muscle fibers in chloride-free solutions. *Pflügers Arch.*, **308**, 291–314 (1969)

255. Zachar, J., Zacharová, D. Potassium contractures in single muscle fibres of the crayfish. *J. Physiol.*, **186**, 596–618 (1966)

256. Hagiwara, S., Takahashi, K., Junge, D. Excitation-contraction coupling in a barnacle muscle fiber as examined with voltage clamp technique. *J. Gen. Physiol.*, **51**, 157–75 (1968)

257. Dudel, J., Morad, M., Rüdel, R. Contractions of single crayfish muscle fibers induced by controlled changes of membrane potential. *Pflügers Arch.*, **299**, 38–51 (1968)

258. Morad, M., Trautwein, W. The effect of the duration of the action potential on contraction in the membrand heart muscle. *Pflügers Arch.*, **299**, 66–82 (1968)

259. Dudel, J., Rüdel, R. Temperature dependence of electro-mechanical coupling in crayfish muscle fibers. *Pflügers Arch.*, **301**, 16–30 (1968)

260. Heistracher, P., Hunt, C. C. The relation of membrane changes to contraction in twitch muscle fibres. *J. Physiol.*, **201**, 589–611 (1969)

261. Sugi, H. Local activation of frog fibres with linearly rising currents. *J. Physiol.*, **199**, 549–67 (1968)

262. Adrian, R. H., Chandler, W. K., Hodgkin, A. L. The kinetics of mechanical activation in frog muscle. *J. Physiol.*, **204**, 207–30 (1969)

263. Kao, C. Y., Stanfield, P. R. Actions of some anions on electrical properties and mechanical threshold of frog twitch muscle. *J. Physiol.*, **198**, 291–309 (1968)

264. Costantin, L. L. The effect of calcium on contraction and conductance threshold in frog skeletal muscle. *J. Physiol.*, **195**, 119–32 (1968)

265. Edman, K. A. P., Grieve, D. W., Nilsson, E. Studies of the excitation-contraction mechanism in skeletal muscle and the myocardium. *Pflügers Arch.*, **290**, 320–34 (1966)

266. Fozzard, H. A., Hellam, D. C. Relationship between membrane voltage and tension in voltage-clamped cardiac purkinje fibres. *Nature*, **218**, 588–89 (1968)

267. Heistracher, P., Hunt, C. C. Contractile repriming in snake twitch muscle fibres. *J. Physiol.*, **201**, 613–26 (1969)

268. Gage, P. W., Eisenberg, R. S. Action potentials without contraction in frog skeletal muscle fibers with disrupted transverse tubules. *Science*, **158**, 1702–3 (1967)

269. Gage, P. W., Eisenberg, R. S. Action potentials, afterpotentials, and excitation-contraction coupling in frog sartorius fibers without transverse tubules. *J. Gen. Physiol.*, **53**, 298–310 (1969)

270. Stefani, E., Steinbach, A. Persistence of excitation contraction coupling in "slow" muscle fibres after a treatment that destroys transverse tubules in "twitch" fibres. *Nature*, **218**, 681–82 (1968)

271. Geffner, E. S., Sandow, A. (Unpublished results)

272. Sakai, T., Sandow, A. (Unpublished results)

273. Marco, L. A., Nastuk, W. L. Sarcomeric oscillations in frog skeletal muscle fibers. *Science*, **161**, 1357–58 (1968)

274. Gage, P. W., Eisenberg, R. S. Capacitance of the surface and transverse tubular membrane and frog sartorius muscle fibers. *J. Gen. Physiol.*, **53**, 265–78 (1969)

275. Eisenberg, R. S., Gage, P. W. Ionic conductances of the surface and transverse tubular membranes of frog sartorius fibers. *J. Gen. Physiol.*, **53**, 279–97 (1969)

276. Falk, G., Fatt, P. Linear electrical properties of striated muscle fibres observed with intracellular electrodes. *Proc. Roy. Soc. B*, **160**, 69–123 (1964)

277. Nakajima, S., Nakajima, Y., Peachey, L. D. Speed of repolarization and morphology of glycerol-treated muscle fibres. *J. Physiol.*, **200**, 115–116P (1969)

278. Van der Kloot, W. G. The effect of disruption on the T-tubules on calcium efflux from frog skeletal muscle. *Comp. Biochem. Physiol.*, **26**, 377–79 (1968)

279. Costantin, L. L., Podolsky, R. J. Depolarization of the internal membrane system in the activation of frog skeletal muscle. *J. Gen. Physiol.*, **50**, 1101–24 (1967)

280. Natori, R. Propagated contractions in isolated sarcolemma-free bundle

of myofibrils. *Jikeikai Med. J.*, **12**, 214–21 (1965)

281. Gonzalez-Serratos, H. Inward spread of contraction during a twitch. *J. Physiol.*, **185**, 20P–21P (1966)

282. Adrian, R. H., Costantin, L. L., Peachey, L. D. Radial spread of contraction in frog muscle fibres. *J. Physiol.*, **204**, 231–57 (1969)

283. Falk, G. Predicted delays in the activation of the contractile system. *Biophys. J.*, **8**, 608–25 (1968)

284. Huxley, A. F. Local activation in muscle. *Ann. N.Y. Acad. Sci.*, **81**, 446–52 (1969)

285. Mulieri, L. P. (Unpublished results)

286. Geffner, E. S., Sandow, A. (Unpublished results)

287. Sandow, A., Preiser, H., Taylor, S. R. Excitation-contraction coupling in skeletal muscle under variations in external Na and Ca. *Abstr. 24th Intern. Congr. Physiol. Sci.* (In press)

288. Costantin, L. L. (Unpublished results)

289. Novotny, I., Vyskocil, F. Possible role of Ca ions in the resting metabolism of frog sartorius muscle during potassium depolarization. *J. Cell Physiol.*, **67**, 159–68 (1966)

290. Van der Kloot, W. G. Potassium-stimulated respiration and intracellular calcium release in frog skeletal muscle. *J. Physiol.*, **191**, 141–65 (1965)

291. Ashley, C. C. The role of cell calcium in the contraction of single cannulated muscle fibers. *Am. Zool.*, **7**, 647–59 (1967)

292. Hess, A. The structure of vertebrate slow and twitch muscle fibers. *Invest. Ophthalmol.*, **6**, 217–28 (1968)

293. Fernand, V. S. V., Hess, A. The occurrence, structure and innervation of slow and twitch muscle fibres in the tensor tympani and stapedius of the cat. *J. Physiol.*, **200**, 547–54 (1969)

294. Forssmann, W. G., Matter, A. Ultrastruktureller Nachweis von zwei Myofibrillentypen in den Muskelfasern des Rattenzwerchfells. *Experientia*, **22**, 816–20 (1966)

295. Close, R. Properties of motor units in fast and slow skeletal muscles of the rat. *J. Physiol.*, **193**, 45–55 (1967)

296. Shafiq, S. A., Gorycki, M. A., Milhorat, A. T. An electron microscope study of fibre types in normal and dystrophic muscles of the mouse. *J. Anat.*, **104**, 281–93 (1969)

297. Shafiq, S. A., Gorycki, M., Goldstone, L., Milhorat, A. T. Fine structure of fiber types in normal human muscle. *Anat. Rec.*, **156**, 283–302 (1966)

298. Brust, M., Cosla, H. W. Contractility of isolated human skeletal muscle. *Arch. Phys. Med. Rehabil.*, **48**, 543–55 (1967)

299. Eberstein, A., Goodgold, J. Slow and fast twitch fibers in human skeletal muscle. *Am. J. Physiol.*, **215**, 535–41 (1968)

300. McComas, A. J., Thomas, H. C. Fast and slow twitch muscles in man. *J. Neurol. Sci.*, **7**, 301–7 (1968)

301. Buchtal, F., Schmalbruch, H. Spectrum of contraction times of different fibre bundles in the brachial biceps and triceps muscles of man. *Nature*, **222**, 89 (1969)

302. Nishihara, H. Studies on the fine structure of red and white fin muscles of the fish *(Carassius auratus)*. *Arch. Histol. (Okayama)*, **28**, 425–47 (1967)

303. Kilarski, W. The fine structure of striated muscles in teleosts, *Z. Zellforsch., Mikroskop. Anat.*, **79**, 562–80 (1967)

304. Rayner, M. D., Keenan, M. J. Role of red and white muscles in the swimming of the skipjack tuna., *Nature*, **214**, 392–93 (1967)

305. Smith, R. S., Lannergren, J. Types of motor units in the skeletal muscle of *Xenopus laevis*. *Nature*, **217**, 281–83 (1968)

306. Jahromi, S. S., Atwood, H. L. Ultrastructural features of crayfish phasic and tonic muscle fibers. *Can. J. Zool.*, **45**, 601–6 (1967)

306a. Cochrane, D. G., Elder, J. Y., Usherwood, P. N. R. Electrical, mechanical and ultrastructural properties of tonic and phasic muscle fibers in the locust *(Schistocerca gregaria)*. *J. Physiol.*, **200**, 68P–69P (1969)

307. Isaacson, A., Hinkes, M., Taylor, S. R. Contracture and twitch potentiation of fast and slow muscles of the rat at 20 and 37 C. *Am. J. Physiol.* (In press)

307a. Frank, G. B., Buss, W. C. Caffeine-induced contractures in mammalian skeletal muscle. *Arch. Intern. Pharmacodyn.*, **170**, 343–49 (1967)

308. Pilar, G. Further study of the electrical and mechanical responses of slow fibers in cat extraocular muscles. *J. Gen. Physiol.*, **50**, 2289–300 (1967)

309. Kaufman, L. General anaesthesia in ophthalmology. *Proc. Roy. Soc. Med.*, **60**, 1275–80 (1967)

310. Sanghvi, I. S., Smith, C. M. Characterization of stimulation of mammalian extraocular muscles by cholinomimetics. *J. Pharmacol. Exptl. Therap.*, **167**, 351–64 (1969)

311. Fedde, M. R. Electrical properties and acetylcholine sensitivity of singly and multiply innervated avian muscle fibers. *J. Gen. Physiol.*, **53**, 624–37 (1969)

312. Hidaka, T., Toida, N. Biophysical and mechanical properties of red and white muscle fibres in fish. *J. Physiol.*, **201**, 49–59 (1969)

313. Padykula, H. A., Gauthier, G. F. Morphological and cytochemical characteristics of fiber types in normal mammalian muscle. In *Exploratory Concepts in Muscular Dystrophy and Related Disorders*, 117–28 (Excerpta Med. Found., Amsterdam, 420 pp., 1967)

314. Romanul, F. C. A., Van der Meulen, J. P. Slow and fast muscles after cross innervation. *Arch. Neurol.*, **17**, 387–402 (1967)

315. Engel, W. K., Irwin, R. L. A histochemical-physiological correlation of frog skeletal muscle fibers. *Am. J. Physiol.*, **213**, 511–18 (1967)

316. Karpati, G., Engel, W. K. Neuronal trophic function. A new aspect demonstrated histochemically in developing soleus muscle. *Arch. Neurol.*, **17**, 542–45 (1967)

317. Beatty, C. H., Basinger, G. M., Bocek, R. M. Differentiation of red and white fibers in muscle from fetal, neonatal and infant Rhesus monkeys. *J. Histochem. Cytochem.*, **15**, 93–103 (1967)

317a. Hall-Braggs, E. C. B. The contraction times and enzyme activity of two rabbit laryngeal muscles. *J. Anat. (London)*, **102**, 241–55 (1968)

318. Buller, A. J., Eccles, J. C., Eccles, R. M. Differentiation of fast and slow muscles in the cat hind limb. *J. Physiol.*, **150**, 399–416 (1960)

319. Cosmos, E., Butler, J. Differentiation of fiber types in muscle of normal and dystrophic chickens. A quantitative and histochemical study of the ontogeny of muscle enzymes. In *Exploratory Concepts in Muscular Dystrophy and Related Disorders*, 197–206 (See Ref. 313)

320. Yamamoto, T. The relaxing factor system in rabbit red muscle. *Sapporo Med. J.*, **31**, 210–18 (1967)

321. Harigaya, S., Ogawa, Y., Sugita, H. Calcium binding activity of microsomal fraction of rabbit red muscle. *J. Biochem.*, **63**, 324–31 (1968)

322. Close, R., Hoh, J. F. Y. Post-tetanic potentiation of twitch contractions of cross-innervated rat fast and slow muscles. *Nature*, **221**, 179–81 (1969)

323. Buller, A. J., Ranatunga, K. W., Smith, J. Influence of temperature on the isometric myograms of cross innervated mammalian fast twitch and slow twitch skeletal muscles. *Nature*, **218**, 877–78 (1968)

324. Close, R., Hoh, J. F. Y. Effects of nerve cross-union on fast-twitch and slow-graded muscle fibres in the toad. *J. Physiol.*, **198**, 103–25 (1968)

325. Mommaerts, W. F. H. M. Muscle energetics: biochemical differences between muscles as determined by the innervation. *Proc. 24th Intern. Congr. Physiol. Sci.*, **6**, 116 (1969)

326. McPherson, A., Tokunaga, J. The effects of cross-innervation on the myoglobin concentration of tonic and phasic muscles. *J. Physiol.*, **188**, 121–29 (1967)

327. Prewitt, M. A., Salafsky, B. Effect of cross innervation on biochemical characteristics of skeletal muscles. *Am. J. Physiol.*, **213**, 295–300 (1967)

328. Robbins, N., Karpati, G., Engel, W. K. Histochemical and contractile properties of the cross-innervated guinea pig soleus muscle. *Arch. Neurol.*, **20**, 318–29 (1969)

329. Vrbová, G. The effect of motoneurone activity on the speed of contraction of striated muscle. *J. Physiol.*, **169**, 513–26 (1963)

330. Salmons, S., Vrbová, G. The in-

fluence of activity on some contractile characteristics of mammalian fast and slow muscles. *J. Physiol.*, **201**, 535–49 (1969)

331. Nelson, P. G. Functional consequences of tenotomy in hind limb muscles of the cat. *J. Physiol.*, **201**, 321–33 (1969)

332. Fischbach, G. D., Robbins, N. Changes in contractile properties of disused soleus muscles. *J. Physiol.*, **201**, 305–20 (1969)

333. Olson, C. B., Swett, C. P., Jr. Speed of contraction of skeletal muscle. *Arch. Neurol.*, **20**, 263–70 (1969)

334. Lesch, M., Parmley, W. W., Hamosh, M., Kaufman, S., Sonnenblick, E. H. Effects of acute hypertrophy on the contractile properties of skeletal muscle. *Am. J. Physiol.*, **214**, 685–90 (1968)

335. Gutmann, E., Hájek, I., Horský, P. Effect of excessive use on contraction and metabolic properties of cross-striated muscle. *J. Physiol.*, **203**, 46–47P (1969)

336. Gutmann, E., Hájek, I., Horský, P., Syrový, I., Rohlíček, V., Stepita-Klauco, M. Effect of repeated long lasting direct muscle stimulation on contraction and enzyme properties of muscles in organ cultures. *Physiol. Bohemoslov.*, **17**, 461 (1968)

337. Korr, I. M., Wilkinson, P. N., Chornock, F. W. Axonal delivery of neuroplasmic components to muscle cells. *Science*, **155**, 342–45 (1967)

338. Drachman, D. B. Is acetylcholine the trophic neuromuscular transmitter? *Arch. Neurol.*, **17**, 206–18 (1967)

339. Drachman, D. B., Houk, J. Effect of botulinum toxin on speed of skeletal muscle contraction. *Am. J. Physiol.*, **216**, 1453–55 (1969)

DIGESTION: INTESTINAL SECRETION[1]

THOMAS R. HENDRIX AND THEODORE M. BAYLESS

Division of Gastroenterology, Department of Medicine, Johns Hopkins University School of Medicine and Johns Hopkins Hospital

INTRODUCTION

Absorption, the primary function of the alimentary tract, involves two processes: secretion of digestive enzymes and diluting fluid; and absorption of the digested food materials and reabsorption of the diluting fluid. In recent years the second process, absorption, has been examined by a variety of ingenious *in vitro* (1–3) and *in vivo* (4, 5) techniques. Intestinal secretion, on the other hand, has been almost totally neglected by physiologists of the present generation. Even the *Handbook of Physiology* which contains one complete volume on secretion and another on absorption has not so much as a section on intestinal secretion. Although the intestine has a large mass of simple tubular glands, the crypts of Lieberkühn, to which physiologists and anatomists of an earlier day ascribed a secretory function, a perusal of today's literature leaves the reader with the impression that the major function of the crypts of Lieberkühn is to serve as the nursery for developing absorptive columnar cells destined for function on the villi.

The first problem encountered in a discussion of secretion is a satisfactory definition of the term. In 1924, Vincent (6) observed that "the term secretion is not used in a very definite or restricted sense, but has been applied and still is applied to several different processes." The situation is much the same today. "Transfer uphill, that is against a gradient, is termed active transport or secretion", is the definition of secretion found in a recent text (7). Although this may be correct, it is difficult to know exactly how to apply such a criterion to the discharge of mucus from a goblet cell or zymogen granules from a pancreatic acinar cell. Another author (8) writes "The basic concept of secretion, in most general terms, implies a chemical transformation." While work of some form is required for secretion and this work ultimately rests on chemical transformation, such definitions are difficult to apply to many types of observations. According to general usage and in the broadest sense "secretion" is the process by which material is separated, elaborated, and discharged by cells, especially by the epithelial cells of glands. As noted above, such a process implies the expenditure of energy but does not specify the source or mediation of this energy. We will use the

[1] Supported in part by USPHS NIH Graduate Training Grant AM09095, and Research Grants AM10581 and A108187.

term secretion in this general context; when a specific mechanism is implied or to be discussed it will be indicated.

If the secretory structure under study has a major duct, such as the parotid gland or the pancreas, the definition of its secretory product is simple, although the mechanism of elaboration may be complex and difficult to define. Characterization of the secretion of the intestinal glands in terms of volume and composition is difficult because it is discharged onto an actively absorbing surface. As Babkin (9) noted ". . . in none of the other digestive organs are both the process of secretion and that of absorption carried on simultaneously to such an extent." Most studies of intestinal secretion have employed intestinal fistulas and have equated the intestinal juice recovered with intestinal secretion. It is readily apparent that secretions will be recovered from an intestinal fistula only when the rate of secretion into the loop exceeds its absorptive capacity. If absorptive functions are intact, net fluid movement will always underestimate secretion.

The traditional view that intestinal secretion constitutes an important digestive juice responsible for the final intraluminal step before absorption has been discredited although it continues to appear in some textbooks. In 1940, Wright et al. (10) concluded that only enterokinase, an enzyme that converts trypsinogen to trypsin, and amylase were secreted into the lumen by the intestine. This work and that of Linderstrøm-Lang (11) indicated that most of the enzymatic activity attributed to the succus entericus was derived from enzymes released by desquamated intestinal cells and that these enzymes were normally active as "endocellular-enzymes". This view has been elegantly confirmed by Miller & Crane (12, 13) and Gray & Ingelfinger (14) who showed the dissacharidases to be located in and functionally active at the brush border of the columnar cells of the intestinal villi. Interest in intestinal secretion faded with acceptance of the view that the succus entericus had no important digestive function. On the other hand, scant attention has been given the suggestion advanced by Wright et al. (10) and repeated by Florey et al. (15) in their review of the secretions of the intestine. ". . . it may be assumed that during digestion a fluid is secreted which has other functions beside that of contributing enzymes. It is well recognized that water and salt solutions are rapidly taken up from the small intestine, and we have shown in this paper that duodenal secretion itself can be absorbed from the jejunum. It may be necessary for a constant secretion of fluid to take place from the crypts of Lieberkühn to keep the food particles in suspension while they are attacked by the pancreatic enzymes, and as the products of digestion are absorbed water and salts go with them. One may envisage a circulation of fluid during active digestion, the secretion passing out from the crypts of Lieberkühn into the lumen and back into the villi."

Recent interest in the pathogenesis of cholera and other diarrheal illnesses has necessitated a reexamination of our concepts of fluid transfer across the intestinal mucosa. To provide a basis for this reexamination the following will be reviewed: composition of intestinal secretion, control of intestinal secretion, morphologic evidence of intestinal secretion, origin of intestinal fluid, and examples of intestinal secretory states. The review will be limited to a consideration of jejunal and ileal function.

COMPOSITION OF INTESTINAL SECRETIONS

The succus entericus or fasting intestinal fluid is often considered to be intestinal secretion but is, in reality, the resultant of fluxes out of and into the intestine and only part of the latter can be considered to be truly secretion. Subsequent observations on the ionic composition of fasting intestinal contents agree with those reported by de Beer et al. (16); the concentrations of sodium, potassium, calcium, and total anions were relatively constant in jejunal and ileal loops and differed little from serum. On the other hand, the concentrations of chloride and bicarbonate showed a reciprocal relation. In jejunal juice the bicarbonate concentration was low and in the ileum it was high. (See Table I.) Similar concentrations in man were found by Phillips & Summerskill (17) by perfusing segments of jejunum and ileum with solutions of varying ionic compositions to determine the concentration of electrolytes that would not be altered by passage through the segment. Postprandial intestinal contents show the same stability of composition (18). Similar values have been obtained in the dog (19) by using the equilibration method of Swallow & Code (20).

The explanation of the differing anion concentrations in the upper and lower small intestine continues to be a subject for debate. In a study of acid-base balance of jejunal secretions in man, McGee & Hastings (21) found that the bicarbonate concentration was about one-half that of plasma while the CO_2 tension was twice that of venous blood. They suggested that

TABLE I

CONCENTRATION OF ELECTROLYTES IN SMALL INTESTINE (meq/liter)

Ref.	Na	K	Cl	HCO$_3$
Jejunum				
16	143	7	148	22
19	137	9.7	131	10.6
17	140	6	138	6
18	140	10	100	30[a]
Ileum				
16	151	4.7	78	84
19	137	9.2	83	69
17	138	6	104	40
18	140	6	60	60[a]

[a] Bicarbonate not measured directly, but calculated by $Na^+ + K^+ - Cl^-$, bile salts.

this was the consequence of the mixing of two hypothetical jejunal secretions, one acid and the other alkaline. Fordtran & Ingelfinger (22) have calculated that the addition of 15 mM of HCl per liter to an ultrafiltrate of plasma would produce the acid-base values observed by McGee & Hastings.

Using the equilibration concentration technique, Swallow & Code (20) found total CO_2 to be 5 meq/liter in the jejunum and 71 meq/liter in the ileum. They favored the suggestion of Parsons (23) and McGee & Hastings (21) that secretion of hydrogen ion into the jejunum is the cause of the low bicarbonate and high CO_2 tension. It was suggested that the difference between jejunum and ileum was due to a facility to secrete hydrogen ion which diminishes aborally along the small intestine. Bidirectional fluxes indicated that the rate at which CO_2 left the intestine was directly related to the luminal concentration whereas movement into the loop was not.

Recently Turnberg et al. (24) proposed a double-exchange model (sodium for hydrogen and chloride for bicarbonate) for ion movement across the ileal epithelium based on *in vivo* observations in man. Central to their argument is that ion transport in the ileum is nonelectrogenic. The validity of this model depends upon the sensitivity of their technique to recognize small changes in transmucosal potential difference which must be excluded to prove that a transport system is truly nonelectrogenic. Data from *in vitro* studies, on the other hand, can be explained by passive diffusion uncomplicated by exchange diffusion (25, 26). More studies will be required to resolve this difference which may be due to differences in behavior of intestinal mucosa *in vivo* and *in vitro* or may be more a matter of experimental design.

In addition to water and electrolytes in intestinal fluid, mucin is added by goblet cells (see morphology section). Desquamating cells add their enzymes to the intestinal fluid but there is no evidence that these enzymes have any function except when they are *in situ* in the mucosa.

All serum proteins enter the intestinal lumen in small amounts. On the other hand, considerable interest has centered around a special secretory mechanism for γ A-immunoglobulins in the intestine (27). Their role in defense against pathogenic bacteria and maintaining equilibrium between the host and the organisms residing in his gut is speculative.

CONTROL OF INTESTINAL SECRETION

Factors influencing or controlling intestinal secretion have been completely reviewed in the past (9, 15, 28). Most studies of neural and humoral effects on intestinal secretion have been performed on isolated loops (Thiry or Thiry-Vella fistulas) in dogs. Fluid accumulation in the loop was taken as evidence of secretion. These studies were conducted before nonabsorbable reference markers and unidirectional flux studies were employed. In addition, the choice of the dog for these studies was unfortunate since absorption from canine loops is avid and a considerable secretory response must be elicited before net secretion is evident. This point is clearly illustrated by a recent study comparing the effect of cholera toxin on rabbit and canine jejunal loops (29). In the rabbit, which has little or no net fluid absorption from the jejunum, the secretory response to cholera toxin was evident within 15 min. In the dog net secretion was not obvious until 2–3 hr after toxin exposure. On the other hand, when net fluid movement was monitored by a nonabsorbable reference material in control and toxin-treated animals, alteration in net fluid movement in the cholera dogs was significant within 30 min. What seemed to be a striking species difference to a secretory stimulus (cholera exotoxin) was, in fact, a difference in normal balance between absorption and secretion. Interestingly in this connection, in some species there normally is net secretion of fluid into the lumen of the small intestine (30, 31).

ROLE OF LOCAL STIMULATION

There is little or no fasting secretion in isolated canine intestinal loops, nor does fluid accumulate in these loops in response to feeding. It is not clear whether the transections of the intramural neural plexuses necessary for construction of the loops play any role in the unresponsiveness of the preparation. It is generally agreed that mechanical stimulation of the mucosa with a catheter or bolus leads to the production of a variable, but usually small, amount of intestinal fluid. Chemical stimulants such as mustard oil, 0.5 per cent HCl, soap, peptone, and sugar solutions increase the volume of fluid in the loop (9, 28). Although the suggestion has been made that these responses are mediated through changes in motor activity or blood flow of the stimulated loop, data are not available to judge whether absorption of digestion products can stimulate intestinal secretion. Substituted phenols, 2,4-dinitrophenol (DNP) and 2,4,5-trichlorophenol (TCP), when placed in canine jejunal loops at a concentration of 0.01 M/liter, cause secretion of fluid into the loop. Calculations of chloride movement were interpreted as demonstrating active transport into the lumen. Although DNP and TCP are known for their ability to uncouple oxidative phosphorylation, how this may lead to active chloride secretion is not clear (32). Secretion into the intestine increases above a mechanical obstruction but only after absorption decreases (33).

ROLE OF NEURAL STIMULATION

Wright et al. (10) were unable to confirm earlier reports that direct stimulation of the vagus produced intestinal secretion. Babkin (9) was inclined to believe that the failure to observe a vagal effect was due to epinephrine release and vasoconstriction which accompanied decerebration, the procedure used by Wright et al. to prepare their animals for study. Gregory (34) observed in conscious dogs that apomorphine caused a small but definite secretory response from Thiry-Vella loops which was blocked by thoracic vagotomy, and suggested that the secretion was due to central vagal excitation associated with apomorphine-induced nausea.

Parasympathomimetic drugs such as pilocarpine and physostigmine produce copious intestinal secretion which is blocked by atropine (10, 15). Tidball (35) has shown that the normal absorption of water and chloride from canine jejunal loops is reversed by bethanechol, a stable choline derivative. Furthermore, the chloride secretion induced by this cholinergic drug fulfilled criteria for active transport since this ion: 1. moved from a lower to higher chemical activity; 2. moved against an adverse electrical potential difference; and 3. moved in a way that could not be attributed to solvent drag because apparent chloride concentration in the transported fluid was higher than in the extracellular fluid from which it originated.

Section of all nerves to an intestinal loop is followed by a copious outpouring of fluid, "paralytic secretion", which returns to normal during the following 4–7 days (34). The same effect is produced by sectioning the preganglionic sympathetic nerves. This "paralytic secretion" is inhibited by stimulation of the distal ends of the cut nerves as well as by atropine (10); it is believed to be the result of unopposed acetylcholine stimulation of the intestinal glands. The relevance of these observations to normal function is not clear because no secretion by intestinal loops in response to a meal has been seen that could be interpreted as inhibition of "sympathetic tone" (10).

ROLE OF HUMORAL STIMULATION

Canine intestinal loops produce no net secretion in response to feeding, hence there has been little reason to look for a humoral mechanism for stimulation of intestinal secretion. Nevertheless, in a series of papers Nasset and co-workers (35–38) have described an acid-ethanol extract of dog and hog intestinal mucosa free of secretin activity (enterocrinin) which increased secretion from innervated as well as denervated loops of intestine. Babkin (9) appeared to have accepted the evidence presented by Nasset and co-workers, whereas Florey et al. (15) and Gregory (35) were skeptical. They were reluctant to accept the notion of enterocrinin because of two concerns: the fluid collected was the result of mechanical stimulation by a catheter or by negative pressure applied to a loop held open by a helical spring; the concentration of enzyme activity shown due to desquamated cells increased in the "enterocrinin stimulated fluid".

Our understanding of the control of intestinal secretion has advanced little since 1941, when Florey et al. (15) wrote the following in their review of secretions of the intestine: "Clearly knowledge must progress further before a definite view can be expressed as to which are the important factors in the control of intestinal secretion in the intact animal. It is still more difficult to estimate how all the factors involved are integrated and the cloud which covers this aspect of intestinal physiology is perhaps the cause of the fog surrounding many aspects of the pathology of the intestine."

MORPHOLOGIC EVIDENCE OF INTESTINAL SECRETION

Most physiologic studies of transport across the intestinal epithelium treat this tissue as though it is a homogeneous membrane or parallel array of membranes. Some justification for this view is provided by the demonstration that the majority of the cells of the intestinal epithelium arise by mitosis in the crypts of Lieberkühn and migrate up the villi where they accomplish their absorptive function and are shed from the villus tips (39–42). On the other hand, the intestinal epithelium is composed of a variety of differentiated cell types characterized by complex morphologic specialization. These features recently have been reviewed and beautifully illustrated by Trier (43).

The tips or crests of the villi are the prime site of absorption for substances with specific transport mechanisms (44). The membrane of the microvilli (brush border) of the columnar cells of the villus crests contains both digestive enzymes, e.g. disaccharidases, and transport sites, probably with an intimate relation between the digestive site and absorptive locus for a specific substrate (45). Materials that are believed to move by diffusion and solvent drag, e.g. urea, also probably leave the lumen in greatest quantity in the villus crest area in conjunction with the movement of actively transported solutes that generate osmotic and electrochemical gradients.

The crypts of Lieberkühn surround the bases of the villi and are the site of cell division, cell differentiation, and active protein synthesis (46, 47). A major secretory role for the crypts has been inferred on the basis of the structure of the undifferentiated crypt cells but without evidence from any physiologic studies (48). The rich vascular network around the crypts also is compatible with this notion (49). Other potential secretory cells in the intestinal epithelium include goblet cells, Paneth cells, and argentaffin cells. The net secretory capacity of the latter, however, appears to be small.

UNDIFFERENTIATED CRYPT CELLS

The undifferentiated cells are the most abundant cell type in the crypts. As demonstrated by Trier (50) their characteristics can be readily delineated by electronmicroscopy or by light-microscopic study. A distinct change in histochemical characteristics between crypt cells which lack alkaline phosphatase and villus cells which have abundant phosphatase has been demonstrated (47). In addition, the undifferentiated crypt cell differs from its progeny, the villous columnar absorptive cell, as follows: 1. greater affinity for basophilic dyes because of an abundance of ribosomes with a high content of ribonucleic acid, 2. frequent mitotic figures, 3. less well-developed microvilli and absent terminal web, and 4. secretory granules in the apical third of the cells. With transition into "adult" columnar cells at the junction of crypt and villus, the microvilli become tall and regular and develop enzymes characteristic of "adult" cells, e.g. leucine amino peptidase, adenosine triphosphatase, dissacharidases, and alkaline phosphatase as they advance toward the villus crest. In addition, in the villus all morphologic evidence of secretory activity abruptly disappears as well as mitotic activity (48).

The secretory granules, enclosed in a membrane, stain with periodic acid Schiff stain but not with Alcian blue, which suggests that they are composed, in part at least, of a neutral polysaccharide protein complex. These granules displace the microvilli as they are transferred to the crypt lumen by merocrine secretion. In addition, striking apocrine secretion with large pseudopods of cytoplasm pinching off into the lumen are seen from the undifferentiated crypt cells of man and to a lesser extent in the crypts of rodents. The latter form of secretion was described over 60 years ago but the probably more important merocrine secretion has only recently been described (50). Although the physiologic significance of these two types of secretion is not known, both are seen in biopsies from fasting man but are more prominent after stimulation by pilocarpine.

The physiologic factors that control the release of the secretory granules from the undifferentiated crypt cells have not been delineated. Although striking morphologic evidence of secretion by these cells is seen after pilocarpine administration, it is not known to what extent this contributes to the fluid recovered from an intestinal fistula after pilocarpine stimulation.

The anatomists' view (48) that ". . . the principal cells of the crypts are mainly secretory" finds support in these observations. In addition, the lumens of the crypts are dilated after pilocarpine stimulation and similar crypt dilatation is seen as well in experimental cholera, another "active" secretory state (50, 51). Further indirect evidence in support of the crypt as a source of secreted fluid is provided by the observation that cycloheximide administration, which damages the crypts before the villus crests, prevents the secretory response to cholera exotoxin (52).

GOBLET CELLS

Goblet cells are found both in the crypts and along the villi of the small intestine and become progressively more numerous from the midjejunum to terminal ileum. Their origin has been debated but since they appear to divide it is not necessary to postulate that they arise from undifferentiated crypt cells or villus absorptive cells. Labeled sulfur is incorporated in mucus granules in the supranuclear portion within 1 hr of administration and these labeled granules migrate to the apical surface and, by 12 hr, are secreted into the gut lumen (53). Recent evidence suggests that goblet cells discharge their mucus by a merocrine secretion rather than by an apocrine process (54).

The physiologic factors which control the release of mucus, as well as the volume and function of this secretion, are uncertain. As in other organs, mucus is generally considered a protective and lubricating material.

PANETH CELLS

Paneth cells are a stable cell population which lie at the base of the crypts of Lieberkühn throughout the length of the small intestine of many species, including man, monkey, ruminants, and rodent. These cells are rare or absent in other species such as pig, cat, dog, and raccoon. Morphologically there is little or no proliferation of Paneth cells. These cells are highly differentiated and have an elaborate well-organized rough endoplasmic reticulum which suggests great secretory potential. The granules in the apical cytoplasm can frequently be observed to be discharging into the crypt lumen even in the fasting state (55). Using tritrated leucine microautoradiography in fasting mice, Trier et al. (56) have recently shown that granules are synthesized and subsequently secreted in 5 to 12 hr.

Paneth cell granules are secreted also after feeding and after pilocarpine stimulation but their function is not known. The granules of man and rat have the histochemical staining characteristics of neutral polysaccharide-protein complexes. In mice there is also an acid mucopolysaccharide outer halo (57).

ARGENTAFFIN CELLS

Argentaffin or enterochromaffin cells are distributed throughout the mucosa of the gastrointestinal tract. In the small intestine they are most abundant in the crypts. The granules contain large quantities of serotonin and decrease as serotonin is released by reserpine (58). Because the apical portions of the argentaffin cells in the small intestine usually do not reach the intestinal lumen, these cells are thought to have an endocrine, rather than an exocrine, function.

A functional role for the argentaffin cells has not been determined, although they have been postulated to function in the regulation of gastrointestinal motility through the release of serotinin (59). Patients with disseminated argentaffin cell neoplasms (carcinoid tumors) have diarrhea in association with excessive blood levels of serotonin and bradykinin (60). The diarrhea is attributed to alterations in intestinal motor function. Whether any alteration of intestinal fluid transfer occurs independently of the motility alteration has not been determined, however.

VILLUS ABSORPTIVE CELLS

The absorptive cells of the villi have a striated luminal border composed of microvilli. The trilaminar membrane of the microvillus is wider than the plasma membrane at the lateral and basal surfaces of the cell.

Pores or fenestrations in the microvillus membrane have not been demonstrated by currently available techniques. A fine filamentous coat or "fuzz" which seems to arise from the outer portion of the microvillous membrane has recently been postulated to serve as a binding area for materials prior to digestion and absorption (61).

The extreme apical portions of the lateral cell membranes of adjacent villus cells are fused for a length of 0.1–0.2 μ to form a "tight junction" which completely encircles the cells and acts as a barrier between the gut lumen and the intercellular spaces. Peroxidase, an electron-dense material, when given intravenously enters the lateral intercellular spaces but does not cross the tight junction (62). It is believed that absorbed materials enter the interdigitated and expansile lateral intercellular spaces by first entering the cell through the apical microvillus membrane, passing through the cytoplasm and finally the lateral cell membrane. This intercellular space is a prominent feature of Curran's three-compartment model to be mentioned later.

ORIGIN OF INTESTINAL FLUID

It is generally agreed that water movement is passive (63–66), its direction and magnitude being determined in the final analysis by osmotic and hydrostatic pressure gradients. These gradients in turn are the result of the permeability characteristics of the intestinal membranes, active transport of solutes, and tissue pressure due to the effect of active transport and vascular and lymphatic pressure. Three mechanisms, not mutually exclusive, have been proposed to explain fluid and electrolyte movement into the intestinal lumen: 1. transfer by filtration generated by increased tissue pressure; 2. transfer generated by electrical and chemical gradients across a semipermeable membrane composed of the intestinal mucosa; and 3. transfer by active secretion by the crypts of Lieberkühn.

FILTRATION

"It is probable that secretion, as well as absorption, of fluid is a physical process, and transfer of fluid through the gut wall is regulated primarily by vascular reactions, both local and general" (67). This view, developed by Wells in a series of articles, was based on observations in ingenious but rather unphysiologic *in vivo* experiments in which hydrostatic pressure gradients were established across the mucosa by exposing it to subatmospheric pressure (68–70). These data were compatible with the conclusion that secretion or absorption was determined by the algebraic sum of hydrostatic and osmotic pressure gradients across the mucosa. Direct observation of the mucosa led the authors to state that "Secretion of fluid occurs only when hyperemia (active or passive or more often both) is present, the villi are tensely swollen and the mucosa is thickened and water logged. Capillary and tissue fluid pressures appear to be high" (67). The design of these experiments, of course, precluded any other association. It is clear, however, that hyperemia is not a necessary accompaniment of intestinal secretion. In recent morphologic studies of the pathogenesis of intestinal fluid production, the secreting intestinal mucosa in experimental cholera reveals no evidence that hyperemia and engorgement of the villi are necessary prerequisites for intestinal secretion (51).

The hypothesis presented by Wells was an oversimplification which effectively ignored several observations, e.g. 1. that when osmotic pressure gradients are reduced to zero by placing serum in the intestine, fluid is still absorbed, and 2. that the jejunal and ileal fluid have different ionic compositions. The design and interpretation of most recent experiments indicate that isotonic water movement is the consequence of active solute transport (71). On the other hand, it is not unreasonable to suppose that transport rates may be modified by changes in hydrostatic pressure gradients across the mucosa.

The relation between hydrostatic pressure and transmucosal fluid movement was recently reexamined in an *in vitro* preparation in which sheets of intestinal mucosa were tied over the end of a glass cylinder (72–74). The results were felt to be relevant to *in vivo* intestinal function because water transport from isotonic Krebs-bicarbonate Ringer solution depended on the presence of glucose in the mucosal solution, water was absorbed against an activity gradient, and uphill glucose movement and chloride impoverishment from the mucosal fluid were observed. Increasing pressure on the mucosal surface to as high as 22 cm H_2O did not alter the rate of fluid movement. On the other hand, fluid absorption was reduced to zero when "serosal" pressure was increased by 2–6 cm H_2O. Greater elevation of "serosal" pressure led to a reversal of net fluid movement and when "serosal" pressure was elevated to 20 cm H_2O the secretory rate was ten times the maximal absorptive rate. It was also reported that glucose was transported from serosal to mucosal fluid in direct proportion to the induced net fluid movement. It is unfortunate that careful histologic studies of the membranes were not included because the reported uphill transport of glucose as well as inulin from serosa to mucosa strongly suggests physical damage to the epithelium. *In vivo* there is no movement of glucose from blood to lumen when the direction of net water movement is changed from absorption to secretion by a hypertonic, nonabsorbable solute. Glucose appears in the luminal fluid only with solute concentrations that produce epithelial damage (75, 76). It was concluded "that the changes from net absorption to net secretion, whenever found in closed intestinal loops (as in the case of raised portal vein pressure, intestinal obstruction, and cholera), would in themselves be very suggestive evidence for increased secretory convective flow, possibly filtration" (74).

However, filtration seems an unlikely explanation for the secretory state of cholera because purging in cholera patients continues in spite of severe hypotension and hypovolemia (19). In animal studies in which the mesenteric artery pressure and flow could be manipulated, the rate of intestinal fluid production in response to exposure to cholera exotoxin was not decreased by a reduction of mesenteric artery pressure to less than 30 per cent of control values (77). In man portal venous and, as a consequence, intestinal capillary pressures have been recorded as high as 450 cm H_2O, yet a net fluid secretory state is not produced even though small increases in fecal protein loss may be encountered (78). Although the design and interpretation of most recent experiments lead to the conclusion that fluid movement is the consequence of active solute transport and in spite of the objections presented above, it is not unlikely that net fluid and electrolyte transport rates may be modified by changes in hydrostatic pressure gradients across the mucosa.

ACTIVITY GRADIENTS ACROSS A SEMIPERMEABLE MEMBRANE

Current concepts of intestinal absorption and its reverse, intestinal "secretion", draw heavily on the theories of transport across cell membranes developed in systems using single cells and simple epithelial surfaces such as frog skin or toad bladder. For a review of these concepts the reader is referred to Stein's monograph (79) and reviews by Curran & Schultz (80), Schultz & Curran (71), Fordtran & Ingelfinger (22), and Fordtran & Dietschy (81). In general terms the intestinal epithelium is treated as a lipoidal membrane perforated by water-filled pores, the rate and direction of water and electrolyte movement being determined by the porosity of the membrane and active transport systems within the membrane. Since the intestine is the primary organ of absorption, most studies have been designed to increase understanding of the factors involved in transferring fluid, electrolytes, and nutrients from the lumen. To account for this polarity of function, models consisting of a series of membranes have been proposed. The three-compartment model of Curran (82) seems to best fit the available data on sodium transport and volume flow. It is based on the belief that sodium is actively transported across the intestinal mucosa. Water movement is coupled to the sodium transport because sodium is concentrated in the intercellular space by active transport sites believed to be located in the membrane of lateral and basal aspects of the columnar cells. An osmotic gradient is established because the space is sealed off from the lumen by the tight junction (see above) and diffusion of sodium away from the immediate vicinity of the cell is impeded by the lamina propria. Water follows the activity gradient established and isotonic volume flow is the consequence.

Permeability characteristics of the intestine.—The jejunum and ileum have different absorptive characteristics. Since porosity of the intestinal membrane is one factor determining the transport characteristics of the intestine, its measurement should increase our understanding of functional differences along the intestine. Fordtran et al. (83) measured the apparent permeability of the small intestine of man by determining the reflection coefficients (ratio of observed to theoretic osmotic pressure) for nonlipid solutes of varying molecular size (urea, erythritol, and mannitol). The water movement into the intestinal lumen in response to perfusion with equimolar hypertonic solutions of the solutes was measured. Mannitol, which is not absorbed appreciably, exerted its full theoretic osmotic pressure. The smaller molecules, being able to leave the lumen, exerted less than their full theoretic osmotic effect. From such data it is possible to calculate a theoretic diameter for the "aqueous pores" in the membrane. Such calculations assume that the intestinal membrane is a homogenous structure with uniform perforations or pores, an assumption which may not be exact. Nevertheless, such treatment of the data permits quantification of some of the differences between upper and lower intestine. The filtration coefficient (the flow of water induced by an osmotic gradient) was nine times greater in the proximal jejunum than in the terminal ileum, which suggests that the "pores" in the jejunum were larger or more numerous. When the reflection coefficients of smaller molecules were compared according to the formulations of Renkin (84) and Solomon (85), the apparent effective pore radius was twice as large in the jejunum as in the ileum. Although not specifically stated, this formulation implies that the size of the pores determines the character of the fluid absorbed, the direction being determined by the orientation of the driving force.

Using this technique, Love (86) calculated that in experimental cholera the filtration coefficient was five times normal and the apparent pore radius was twice normal, and inferred from these results that intestinal permeability is increased in cholera. On the other hand, the data might alternatively indicate that the intestine's responsiveness to an osmotic gradient is increased in cholera.

Fordtran et al. (87), utilizing the simultaneous diffusion ratios of tritiated water and urea, calculated that pore size in patients with celiac disease (sprue) was markedly decreased from normal. This clearly indicates that the absorptive defect in this disease which involves water, electrolytes, and nonelectrolytes is based on more complex alteration than mere decreased surface area of the mucosa. In addition, the jejunum was found to be in a net secretory state with water, sodium, and potassium being added to the intestinal fluid. This observation could not be explained by concentration or osmotic gradients, for none were found and the calculated decreased pore size would have served to restrict fluid and electrolyte movement in both directions. There seem to be two possible explanations: 1. There is truly hypersecretion by the mucosa. Since the lesion of celiac disease is more accurately described as crypt hyperplasia than villous atrophy, hypersection may be merely a consequence of an increased mass of secretory cells (undifferentiated crypt cells). 2. Intestinal secretion is normal but a net secretory state is observed because of severe limitation of absorption.

Active transport of solutes across the epithelium.—It is beyond the scope of this review to discuss observations on solute transport and conclusions drawn from them relevant to fluid movement across the intestinal mucosa. The interpretation of much of these data is difficult because of the great variety of techniques, e.g. *in vivo, in vitro,* net flux, unidirectional flux, transmucosal potential differences, short-circuit current. Nevertheless, a few generalizations may help in the discussion of intestinal secretion. Most studies of intestinal transport have been conducted under circumstances in which the intestine was in a net absorptive state. Similar studies conducted when net fluid and electrolyte movement was into the lumen should give a more complete view of how the intestine accomplishes its functions.

Sodium: It is generally agreed that sodium is actively transported, i.e. moved against an electrochemical gradient, from the lumen of the intestine (82). This active transfer of sodium is increased by actively transported nonelectrolytes such as glucose and alanine (88, 89). This monosaccharide and amino acid effect of augmenting sodium transport has been shown to be additive, which suggests that different pathways are involved. On the other hand, the presence of an active sodium transport system does not necessarily indicate its physiologic importance *in vivo*. From studies in man, Fordtran et al. (90) have concluded that only a small fraction of total sodium absorption in the jejunum is mediated by active transport and the majority is by bulk flow along osmotic pressure gradients.

The transmucosal potential difference of 4–8 mV, serosa positive to mucosa, has been attributed to active sodium transport, because the short-circuit current (an externally applied current which reduces the transmucosal potential difference to zero) can be accounted for by sodium transport *in vitro* where it can be accurately measured (71). Barry et al. (91) took issue with this concept since net sodium flux and short-circuit current agreed in the rat jejunum only when glucose was in the fluid but not when it contained galactose or methylglucoside. Recently Taylor et al. (92) have shown that the discrepancy observed in the presence of a poorly metabolized sugar was due to an active secretion of chloride in jejunum as well as in ileum. These observations led them to suggest a neutral NaCl secretory mechanism related to the metabolic state of the tissue in which chloride is actively transported from the serosa to mucosa. In addition, recent evidence from *in vivo* experiments suggests that simple active sodium transport is not the whole story but rather sodium absorption is coupled with bicarbonate absorption. This is effected by a sodium-hydrogen exchange and the liberated CO_2 rapidly diffuses out of the intestine (24, 93). The authors state ". . . that jejunal Na absorption from HCO_3 solutions is entirely passive and that all apparently active Na absorption is, in fact, linked to HCO_3 transport" (93). Much work will be required to resolve the many discrepancies, for it is not clear how many are due to differences in *in vivo* and *in vitro* techniques, differences between jejunum and ileum, differences in species, or differences in the absorptive-secretory state of the preparation.

Chloride: The movement of chloride has been attributed to active chloride absorption (63, 94), active chloride secretion (32, 35, 92), passive diffusion (25, 26) and anion exchange (23, 24, 30, 93, 95). The differing conclusions are attributable in part, if not entirely, to differences in experimental design. *In vitro* studies of rabbit ileum have shown active chloride secretion in response to adenosine-3', 5' cyclic monophosphate, theophylline, a phosphodiesterase inhibitor, two prostagladins (PGA and PGE), and cholera exotoxin (96, 97).

Regardless of mechanisms involved, the intestinal mucosa can develop large chloride concentration gradients between lumen and plasma. Ingraham & Visscher (98) found that the canine ileum could reduce the chloride concentration of the luminal contents to 0.4 m*M,* a plasma-to-lumen chloride concentration ratio of approximately 250:1.

Bicarbonate: The concentration of bicarbonate is lower than plasma in jejunal contents and higher in ileal contents. This does not necessarily indicate, however, that bicarbonate is actively absorbed in the jejunum and secreted in the ileum. As noted in the discussion of the composition of intestinal secretion, apparent bicarbonate absorption can be the consequence of hydrogen ion secretion which results in the formation of water and CO_2; the latter readily diffuses out of the lumen without the mediation of any absorptive transport mechanism. Fordtran and co-workers (24) have recently postulated a double-exchange model in which sodium is exchanged for hydrogen and chloride for bicarbonate. When both cycles are balanced it functions as a neutral NaCl pump: NaCl is absorbed or secreted without generating an electrical potential difference across the mucosa. This formulation is compatible with the observation of Parsons that in the rat *in vivo* there is an inverse relation between net chloride and net bicarbonate flux (23).

Potassium: The movement of potassium seems to be adequately explained by passive movement in response to electrochemical gradients (81).

Nonelectrolyte solutes: Active transport of sugars and amino acids depends upon the presence of sodium in the luminal fluid. Conversely absorption of these nonelectrolyte solutes increases the rate of sodium absorption (71).

Recently Taylor et al. (92) have shown sodium movement from serosa to mucosa is more than doubled when glucose is added to the mucosal solution in *in vitro* preparations of rat jejunum. No such increase in serosa to mucosa flux was observed in ileal preparations. Fordtran et al. (90) found *in vivo* that glucose and bicarbonate enhanced the rate of sodium absorption even when net water movement was reduced to zero by adding a nonabsorbable solute, mannitol, to the luminal fluid. This effect, however, was not specific for sodium, since urea also was absorbed in the absence of net water flow and a concentration gradient. These findings led them to postulate a fluid circuit model for jejunal transport. To separate the bulk flow stream carrying sodium and urea out of the lumen from the opposite and equal fluid stream flowing into the lumen in response to mannitol, they suggested that bulk flow occurs through the tight junctions between cells into the intercellular space while flow in the opposite direction is across the luminal cell membrane. This is an ingenious model but its anatomic validity will be difficult to test. A simpler and more easily tested model to accomplish anatomic separation of the fluid streams moving in opposite directions is discussed in the next section.

SECRETION BY THE CRYPTS OF LIEBERKÜHN

Anatomists, physiologists, and experimental pathologists of an earlier generation had no hesitancy in ascribing a secretory function to the crypts of Lieberkühn. In 1881, from observations of choleraic stools, autopsy findings, and intestinal secretion stimulated by pilocarpine, Cohnheim (99) concluded that "the process of cholera may be interpreted by supposing that first, under the influence of the virus, which has probably entered the intestine from without, there takes place *an extra-ordinary* profuse secretion from the glands of the small intestine." Interest in the pathogenesis of intestinal fluid production induced by infection with *Vibrio cholerae* and in intestinal secretion in general has been revitalized in recent years. This interest has been facilitated by the recent development of reliable experimental models of the disease (100, 101). It has been reaffirmed that the massive outpouring of fluid from the intestine characteristic of cholera occurs without morphologic alteration of the intestinal epithelium as judged by light and electronmicroscopy (51). In addition, the response of the intestine, in fact the entire clinical picture of cholera, is attributable to local action of cholera exotoxin on the intestinal mucosa. It was originally suggested that the massive intestinal fluid and electrolyte losses in cholera were due to failure of intestinal absorption caused by inhibition of the sodium pump (102). This was effectively discredited when it was shown that sodium as well as glucose absorption was normal in cholera (103–105). In addition, in cholera glucose absorption was associated with the expected increase in sodium absorption (19).

The observation that glucose absorption and unidirectional sodium flux out of the lumen was normal in the presence or absence of glucose in spite of reversal of net fluid movement from "absorption" to "secretion" suggests that there might be, at least in part, an anatomic separation of absorption from secretion. Since a simple change in porosity of the intestinal membrane cannot explain these observations, Serebro et al. (106) were led to look for support for Cohnheim's hypothesis. If cholera toxin stimulated secretion by the crypts of Lieberkühn without altering the absorptive function of the villi, agents which damage the crypts preferentially would be expected to modify the secretory response to cholera toxin. This notion was substantiated by studies of the effect of cycloheximide, an antibiotic inhibitor of protein synthesis. On exposure to cycloheximide the epithelial cells of the crypts of Lieberkühn, having a higher protein synthetic rate, are affected earlier and by a smaller dose than the absorptive columnar cells of the villi. The earliest morphologic evidence of the reversible inhibition of protein synthesis is disappearance of mitotic figures from the crypts of Lieberkühn. This reversible inhibition of maturation has been shown to be caused by inhibition of protein synthesis necessary for cells to proceed from prophase to metaphase (107). With increasing levels of cycloheximide the crypt epithelium shows irreversible damage and finally the epithelium of the villi shows morphologic and functional derangement.

At a level causing only disappearance of mitotic figures from the crypts, cycloheximide inhibits the secretion of fluid that normally follows exposure of the intestinal mucosa to cholera toxin. This inhibition of cholera toxin-induced secretion occurs without depression of glucose absorption, a function of the villus crests. Calculations of bidirectional sodium fluxes indicate that the cycloheximide effect is due entirely to inhibition of the exotoxin-induced increase in blood to lumen flux (108). The available data may indicate that cholera exotoxin, while not influencing the absorptive function of the columnar cells of the villi, does cause the epithelial cells of the crypts to increase the rate of secretion of their normal product. Such a formulation explains the observation of intact absorption in the face of augmented movement of fluid of normal ionic composition into the intestinal lumen.

It is logical to ask whether the mechanism of fluid production in cholera is unique or whether it is involved in other situations characterized by net secretory states of the intestine. With this in mind, Halsted et al. (109) studied the intestinal fluid production induced by an intraluminal hypertonic solution. Cycloheximide at a concentration which prevented secretory response to cholera exotoxin limited fluid movement into the lumen induced by a hypertonic solution by 50 per cent. They suggested that the fluid secretion in response to hypertonic solutions is, in part, the result of osmotic forces acting to move water into the lumen and in part a secretory response of the crypts.

It would be worthwhile to determine if other net secretory states, such as those associated with cholinergic stimulation (35), metabolic inhibitors (32), and intestinal obstruction and distention (33, 110) and normally seen in the Herbivora (30), are caused by increased secretory activity of the crypts. With cholinergic stimulation, at least, there is physiologic evidence of active chloride secretion with net fluid secretion (35) and morphologic evidence of a secretory response in the crypts (49).

Is secretion only a response to abnormal stimuli such as cholera toxin and cholinergic drugs or is it, as Wright et al. (10) suggested, an integral component of the normal intestinal absorptive process? In a recent article describing effect of sugars on ion fluxes in the intestine it was noted that sodium flux into the jejunum during glucose absorption was more than twice that observed when there was no sugar in the intestinal lumen (92). Applying newer techniques and concepts of membrane transport it may be worthwhile to reexamine the fluid circuit hypothesis advanced by Ingraham, Peters & Visscher (111). Having observed that "Sodium chloride removal may proceed until the concentration ratio for chloride between blood and intestinal fluid may be 200 to 1," they suggested: "The type of uni-univalent salt impoverishment which is observed in the small intestine can be accounted for by assuming that there is a flow of water into the blood carrying out the univalent salt at a concentration at which it exists in the gut, and a simultaneous flow of water free from that salt into the intestine at another point. It is necessary to postulate a membrane which is in essence a mosaic, one portion of which is strictly semipermeable and through which water enters the gut, and another portion of which is permeable to uni-univalent salts through which the solution of such salts passes into the blood." If this is to be acceptable in the light of present concepts of intestinal function, several qualifications become necessary. First, the implication that water movement is primary is not compatible with the well-established membrane theory. Second, the postulated mosaic required to explain the fluid circuit may exist if crypts do, indeed, secrete as an integral part of intestinal absorption. Third, it is reasonable that if the crypts are the site for secreting excess hydrogen ions and the absorptive cells of the villi are the location of bicarbonate for chloride exchange, free water to aid in the dilution of hypertonic luminal contents would be generated.

In conclusion, more space has been devoted to the suggestion that the crypts of Lieberkühn are truly secretory glands and play an important role in normal absorption, as well as in the increased production of intestinal fluid in diarrheal states, than has been devoted to the other two mechanisms. From observations cited in this review, it seems probable that all three mechanisms, filtration, active transport and membrane permeability, and crypt secretion, contribute to the formation of intestinal fluid (the succus entericus). It remains, however, to determine the relative importance of each in various situations of net absorption or net secretion.

Finally any formulation of intestinal transport mechanisms that treats the intestinal segment under study as a homogeneous semipermeable membrane will be in error inasmuch as the secretory and absorptive functions of crypt and villus cells differ. The characteristic differences in jejunal and ileal transport never would have been identified if the small intestine had been studied only as a single unit.

SECRETORY STATES

In the intact man or animal, net intestinal secretion is not obvious until the amount discharged by the small intestine exceeds the capacity of the colon to absorb the fluid. Similarly, increased secretory activity in the small intestine is not apparent unless the volume of fluid moving into the lumen exceeds the normal absorptive capacity or the absorptive capacity is diminished. Application to secretory states of concepts and techniques that have been so important in advancing our understanding of absorption should be equally productive in defining intestinal secretion and its relation to absorption.

Powell et al. (30), studying net water and electrolyte movement in the jejunum, ileum, cecum, and colon of the guinea pig, found net lumen-to-blood transport (absorption) of water and electrolytes in the cecum and colon. On the other hand, despite glucose and chloride absorption in the jejunum and ileum, there was net blood-to-lumen movement (secretion) of water, sodium, potassium, and bicarbonate. The bicarbonate transport was against an electrochemical gradient. It has been reported that herbivorous animals have a larger percentage of their total body water within the lumen of the gut: 20 per cent in the guinea pig as compared to 6 per cent in the rat (112). A comparison of water and electrolyte fluxes at various levels of the gut in these animals should broaden our understanding of the relation of absorption to secretion.

A variety of humoral agents have been observed to produce intestinal secretion. Soergel et al. (113) demonstrated that antidiuretic hormone (vasopressin 1U/hr i.v.) decreased the rate of net movement of water and sodium out of the jejunum and ileum of man and in some instances produced net secretion into the lumen. Similar results were obtained by increased endogenous antidiuretic hormone induced by dehydration. The alteration in net water and sodium movement did not change the rate of glucose or xylose absorption, however. The observed effects were the result of increased secretion into the lumen or decreased sodium absorption. The normal sugar absorption makes increased secretion the more attractive suggestion.

Adrenalectomy has been reported to decrease net NaCl and water absorption in the rat (114) and the dog (115). It is not suggested, however, that the small intestine plays any essential role in regulation of total body sodium and plasma volume.

Several types of tumors have been reported to be associated with diarrhea. In many of these instances it is not clear whether the humoral agents thought to be responsible act primarily by altering fluid movement across the gut, by altering motility, or both. Some nongastrin-secreting adenomas of the pancreas are associated with such copious diarrhea that the term "pancreatic cholera" is sometimes applied to the syndrome. Since the diarrhea may be relieved by resection of the tumor, mediation by a humoral agent has been postulated but not proven (116). Recently secretin has been suggested as the active agent but secretin alone does not cause diarrhea in conscious dogs (117). Sympathetic nervous system tumors including ganglioneuromas, neuroblastomas, and ganglioneuroblastomas have been associated with diarrhea which was controlled by removal or destruction of the tumor. The catecholamines secreted do not seem to explain the altered intestinal function (118, 119). Medullary carcinomas of the thyroid with metastases are commonly accompanied by watery diarrhea. These tumors are associated with increased production of prostaglandins, a group of hydroxy fatty acids with pronounced and varied biologic activity (120). In this connection, the recent observation that prostaglandins cause net secretion in canine intestinal loops is of interest (96). It was suggested that cyclic AMP causes active chloride secretion (97) and that the prostaglandin effect was produced by inhibition of adenylcyclase with resultant increased tissue levels of cyclic AMP.

Hyperosmotic solutions such as encountered in the postgastrectomy dumping syndrome and with nonabsorbable solutes such as result from lactase deficiency lead to a net secretory state in the intestine (121). The net secretion has been assumed to be merely a manifestation of fluid movement across the intestinal epithelium in response to osmotic gradients. The observation that the response is limited by an agent that damages the crypts of Lieberkühn suggests a more complex explanation (109).

The characteristics and mechanism of the hypersecretion of cholera are discussed above in the section on secretion by the crypts of Lieberkühn. Two different, but not necessarily contradictory suggestions on the mediation of the effect of cholera toxin have been advanced recently: increased synthesis of proteins necessary for the secretory process (106); and increased tissue levels of cyclic AMP (97). There is evidence that the other organisms such as *E. coli* (122) and staphylococci (123) cause net secretion by the gut. It is not known if they share the same pathway involved in cholera fluid production. On the other hand, the bacterial flora may play an essential role in maintaining the integrity of the water-solute transport system in the intestinal epithelium (124).

Net secretory states have been described in disorders associated with damage and morphologic alteration of the mucosa. In the past attention has been directed toward the limited absorptive capacity in these disorders. Two recent studies indicate that in celiac disease (nontropical sprue) increased secretion plays a role in the overall abnormality (87, 125). Secretion not due to exudation has been described in experimental salmonella enterocolitis (126).

Finally net secretion may be the result of an absence of a specific transfer mechanism which has been proposed as an explanation for congenital chloridorrhea. This condition, in which large amounts of chloride are lost in the stool, may be due to a lack of a mechanism for the exchange of chloride for bicarbonate (127).

CONCLUSION

A review of intestinal secretion leads to the view that absorption and secretion are parts of the same process, the transfer of fluid and nutrients from the gut lumen into the organism, which is the prime function of the alimentary tract. Some of the differing conclusions about intestinal transport may be due, at least in part, to a failure to include a consideration of this interrelation into the analysis of the data. If the crypts have, as has been suggested, a prominent role in secretion, some apparent discrepancies may be related to differing crypt function. This may be especially relevant to differences between *in vitro* and *in vivo* observations.

LITERATURE CITED

1. Wilson, T. H., Wiseman, G. The use of sacs of inverted small intestine for the study of the transference of substances from the mucosal to the serosal surface. *J. Physiol.*, **123**, 116–25 (1954)
2. Ussing, H. H., Zerahn, K. Active transport of sodium as the source of electric current in the short circuited isolated frog skin. *Acta Physiol. Scand.*, **23**, 110–27 (1951)
3. Parsons, D. S. Methods for investigation of intestinal absorption. *Handbook of Physiology.* Sect. 6, *Alimentary Canal.* **III.** *Intestinal Absorption*, 1177–1216 (Code, C. F., Ed., Am. Physiol. Soc., Washington, D.C., 1570 pp., 1968)
4. Borgström, B., Dahlquist, A., Lundh, G., Sjövall, J. Studies of intestinal digestion and absorption in the human. *J. Clin. Invest.*, **36**, 1521–36 (1957)
5. Fordtran, J. S., Levitan, R., Bikerman, V., Barrows, B. A., Ingelfinger, F. J. The kinetics of water absorption in the human intestine. *Trans. Assoc. Am. Physicians*, **74**, 195–205 (1961)
6. Vincent, S. *An Introduction to the Study of Secretion*, 26 (Edward Arnold, London, 168 pp., 1924)
7. Langley, L. L. *Cell Function* (Reinhold, 2nd ed., 364 pp., New York, 1968)
8. DeRobertis, E. D. P., Morvinski, W. W., Saez, F. A. *Cell Biology*, 427 (Saunders, Philadelphia, 4th ed. of *General Cytology*, 446 pp., 1965)
9. Babkin, B. P. *Secretory Mechanism of the Digestive Glands*, 614–27 (Hoeber, New York, 2nd ed., 1027 pp., 1950)
10. Wright, R. D., Jennings, M. A., Florey, H. W., Lium, R. The influence of nerves and drugs on secretion by the small intestine and an investigation of the enzymes in intestinal juice. *Quart. J. Exptl. Physiol.*, **30**, 73–120 (1940)
11. Linderstrøm-Lang, K. Proteolytic enzymes. *Ann. Rev. Biochem.*, **8**, 37–58 (1939)
12. Miller, D., Crane, R. K. The digestive function of the epithelium of the small intestine. I. An intra-cellular locus of disaccharide and sugar phosphate ester hydrolysis. *Biochem. Biophys. Acta*, **52**, 281 (1961)
13. Miller, D., Crane, R. K. The digestive function of the epithelium of the small intestine. II. Localization of disaccharide hydrolysis in the isolated brush border portion of intestinal epithelial cells. *Biochim. Biophys. Acta*, **52**, 293–98 (1961)
14. Gray, G. M., Ingelfinger, F. J. Intestinal absorption of sucrose in man: the site of hydrolysis and absorption. *J. Clin. Invest.*, **44**, 390 (1965)
15. Florey, H. W., Wright, R. D., Jennings, M. A. The secretions of the intestine. *Physiol. Rev.*, **21**, 36–69 (1941)
16. de Beer, E. J., Johnston, C. G., Wilson, D. W. The composition of intestinal secretions. *J. Biol. Chem.*, **108**, 113–20 (1935)
17. Phillips, S. F., Summerskill, W. H. J. Water and electrolyte transport during maintenance of isotonicity in human jejunum and ileum. *J. Lab. Clin. Med.*, **70**, 686–98 (1967)
18. Fordtran, J. S., Locklear, T. W. Ionic constituents of gastric and small intestinal fluids after eating. *Am. J. Digest. Diseases*, **11**, 503–21 (1966)
19. Hendrix, T. R., Banwell, J. G. Pathogenesis of cholera. *Gastroenterology* (In press, 1969)
20. Swallow, J. H., Code, C. F. Intestinal transmucosal flux of bicarbonate. *Am. J. Physiol.*, **212**, 717–23 (1967)
21. McGee, L. C., Hastings, A. B. The carbon-dioxide tension and acid-base balance of jejunal secretions in man. *J. Biol. Chem.*, **142**, 893–904 (1942)
22. Fordtran, J. S., Ingelfinger, F. J. Absorption of water, electrolytes, and sugars from the human gut. *Handbook of Physiology.* Sect. 6, *Alimentary Canal.* **III.** *Intestinal Absorption*, 1457–90 (See Ref. 3)
23. Parsons, D. S. The absorption of bicarbonate-saline solutions by the small intestine and colon of the white rat. *Quart. J. Exptl. Physiol.*, **41**, 410–20 (1956)

24. Turnberg, L. A., Bieberdorf, F. A.,
    Fordtran, J. S. Ileal electrolyte
    transport in normal man. *J. Clin.
    Invest.*, **48**, 85a (1969)
25. Clarkson, T. W., Toole, S. R. Mea-
    surement of short-circuit current
    and ion transport across the ileum.
    Am. J. Physiol., **206**, 658–68
    (1964)
26. Schultz, S. G., Zalusky, R., Gass,
    A. E., Jr. Ion transport in isolated
    rabbit ileum. III. Chloride fluxes.
    J. Gen. Physiol., **48**, 275–378
    (1964)
27. Tomasi, T. B., Jr. On the mecha-
    nisms of transport and biological
    significance of antibodies in exter-
    nal secretions. *Arthritis Rheum.*,
    12, 45–50 (1969)
28. Gregory, R. A. *Secretory Mechanisms
    of the Gastro-intestinal Tract.
    Jejunal Glands*, 213–29 (Edward
    Arnold, London, 248 pp., 1962)
29. McGonagle, T. J., Serebro, H. A.,
    Iber, F. L., Bayless, T. M., Hen-
    drix, T. R. Time of onset of action
    of cholera toxin in the dog and
    rabbit. *Gastroenterology* (In press,
    1969)
30. Powell, D. W., Malawer, S. J.,
    Plotkin, G. R. Secretion of elec-
    trolytes and water by the guinea
    pig small intestine in vivo. *Am. J.
    Physiol.*, **215**, 1226–33 (1968)
31. Kokas, E., Phillips, J. L., Jr., Brunso,
    W. D., Jr. The secretory activity
    of the duodenum in chickens.
    Comp. Biochem. Physiol., **22**, 81–
    90 (1966)
32. Tidball, C. S. Effect of substituted
    phenols on movement of water
    and protein across the intestine.
    Am. J. Physiol., **200**, 305–8 (1961)
33. Shield, R. The absorption and secre-
    tion of fluid and electrolytes by
    the obstructed bowel. *Brit. J. Surg.*,
    52, 774–79 (1965)
34. Gregory, R. A. The nervous path-
    ways of intestinal reflexes asso-
    ciated with nausea and vomiting.
    J. Physiol., **106**, 95–103 (1947)
35. Tidball, C. S. Active chloride trans-
    port during intestinal secretion.
    Am. J. Physiol., **200**, 309–12
    (1961)
36. Nasset, E. S., Pierce, H. B., Murlin,
    J. R. Proof of a humoral control
    of intestinal secretion. *Am. J.
    Physiol.*, **111**, 145–58 (1935)
37. Fink, R. M., Nasset, E. S. The
    physiological response to entero-
    crinin considered quantitatively.

Am. J. Physiol., **139**, 626–32
(1942)
38. Heggeness, F. W., Nasset, E. S.
    Purification of enterocrinin. *Am.
    J. Physiol.*, **167**, 159–65 (1951)
39. Leblond, C. P., Messier, P. Renewal
    of chief cells and goblet cells in
    the small intestine as shown by
    radio-autography after injection
    of thymidine-H³ into mice. *Anat.
    Record*, **132**, 247–60 (1958)
40. Quastler, H., Sherman, F. G. Cell
    population kinetics in the intestinal
    epithelium of the mouse. *Exptl.
    Cell Res.*, **17**, 420–38 (1958)
41. Lipkin, M., Sherlock, P., Bell, B.
    Cell proliferation kinetics in the
    gastrointestinal tract of man. II.
    Cell renewal in stomach, ileum,
    colon and rectum. *Gastroenterol-
    ogy*, **45**, 721–29 (1963)
42. Shorter, R. G., Moertel, C. G., Titus,
    J. L., Reitemeier, R. J. Cell
    kinetics in jejunum and rectum of
    man. *Am. J. Digest. Diseases*, **9**,
    760–63 (1964)
43. Trier, J. S. Morphology of the epithe-
    lium of the small intestine. *Hand-
    book of Physiology. Sect. 6, Ali-
    mentary Canal.* **III.** *Intestinal
    Absorption*, 1125–75 (See Ref. 3)
44. Kinter, W. B., Wilson, T. H. Auto-
    radiographic study of sugar and
    amino acid absorption by everted
    sacs of hamster intestine. *J. Cell
    Biol.*, **25**, 19–39 (1965)
45. Crane, R. K. A perspective of
    digestive-absorptive function. *Am.
    J. Clin. Nutr.*, **22**, 242–49 (1969)
46. Cocco, A. E., Dohrmann, M. J., Hen-
    drix, T. R. Reconstruction of
    normal jejunal biopsy: Three-
    dimensional histology. *Gastroenter-
    ology*, **51**, 24–31 (1966)
47. Padykula, H. A., Strauss, E. W.,
    Ladman, A. J., Gardner, F. H.
    A morphologic and histochemical
    analysis of the human jejunal
    epithelium in non-tropical sprue.
    Gastroenterology, **40**, 735–65
    (1961)
48. Macklin, C. C., Macklin, M. T.
    Special Cytology, 252 (Cowdry,
    E. V., Ed., Hoeber, New York,
    552 pp., 1932)
49. Reynolds, R. D., Brim, J., Sheehey,
    T. W. The vascular archetecture
    of the small intestinal mucosa of
    the monkey (Mucaca mulatta).
    Anat. Record, **159**, 211–15 (1967)
50. Trier, J. S. Studies on small intesti-
    nal crypt epithelium. I. Evidence

for and mechanisms of secretory activity by undifferentiated cells of the human small intestine. *Gastroenterology*, **47**, 480–95 (1964)

51. Elliott, H. L., Carpenter, C. C. J., Sack, R. B. Yardley, J. H. Small bowel morphology in experimental canine cholera. *Am. J. Pathol.*, **52**, 15a (1968)

52. Serebro, H. A., Iber, F. L., Yardley, J. H., Hendrix, T. R. Inhibition of cholera toxin action in the rabbit by cycloheximide. *Gastroenterology*, **56**, 506–11 (1969)

53. Belanger, L. F. Autoradiographic visualization of S^{35} incorporation and turnover by the mucus glands of the gastrointestinal tract and other soft tissues of rat and hamster. *Anat. Record*, **118**, 755–72 (1954)

54. Trier, J. S. Studies on small intestinal epithelium. I. The fine structure of the crypt epithelium of the proximal intestine of fasting humans. *J. Cell Biol.*, **18**, 599–620 (1963)

55. Trier, J. S. The paneth cells: an enigma. *Gastroenterology*, **51**, 560–62 (1966)

56. Trier, J. S., Lorenzsonn, V., Groehler, K. Pattern of secretion of paneth cells of the small intestine of mice. *Gastroenterology*, **53**, 240–49 (1967)

57. Staley, M. W., Trier, J. S. Morphologic heterogeneity of mouse paneth cell granules before and after secretory stimulation. *Am. J. Anat.*, **117**, 365–83 (1965)

58. Benditt, E. P., Wong, R. L. On the concentration of 5-hydroxytryptamine in mammalian enterochromaffin cells and its release by reserpine. *J. Exptl. Med.*, **105**, 509–20 (1957)

59. Page, I. H. Serotonin (5-hydroxytryptamine). *Physiol. Rev.*, **39**, 563–88 (1954)

60. Oates, J. A., Melmon, K., Sjoerdsma, A., Gillespie, L., Mason, D. Release of kinin peptide in the carcinoid syndrome. *Lancet*, **1**, 514–17 (1964)

61. Fawcett, D. W. Surface specialization of absorbing cells. *J. Histochem. Cytochem.*, **13**, 75–91 (1965)

62. Hugon, J. S., Borgers, M. Absorption of horseradish peroxidase by the mucosal cells of the duodenum of mouse. I. The fasting animal. *J. Histochem. Cytochem.*, **16**, 229–36 (1968)

63. Curran, P. F., Solomon, A. K. Ion and water fluxes in the ileum of rats. *J. Gen. Physiol.*, **41**, 143–68 (1957)

64. Curran, P. F. Na, Cl, and water transport by rat ileum *in vitro*. *J. Gen. Physiol.*, **43**, 1137–48 (1960)

65. Clarkson, T. W., Toole, S. R. Measurement of short-circuit current and ion transport across the ileum. *Am. J. Physiol.*, **206**, 658–68 (1964)

66. Curran, P. F. Coupling between transport processes in intestine. *Physiologist*, **11**, 3–23 (1968)

67. Wells, H. S., Johnson, R. G. The intestinal villi and their circulation in relation to absorption and secretion of fluid. *Am. J. Physiol.*, **109**, 387–402 (1934)

68. Wells, H. S. The passage of materials through the intestinal wall. I. The relation between intraintestinal pressure and rate of absorption of water. *Am. J. Physiol.*, **99**, 209–20 (1931)

69. Wells, H. S. The passage of materials through the intestinal wall. II. The osmotic pressure of colloids of lymph from the lacteals as a measure of the absorbing force of the intestine. *Am. J. Physiol.*, **101**, 421–45 (1932)

70. Wells, H. S. The balance of physical forces which determine the rate and direction of flow of fluid through the intestinal mucosa. *Am. J. Physiol.*, **130**, 410–19 (1940)

71. Schultz, S. G., Curran, P. F. Intestinal absorption of sodium chloride and water. *Handbook of Physiology*. Sect. 6, *Alimentary Canal*. III. *Intestinal Absorption*, 1245–75 (See Ref. 3)

72. Hakim, A., Lester, R. G., Lifson, N. Absorption by an *in vitro* preparation of dog intestinal mucosa. *J. Appl. Physiol.*, **18**, 409–13 (1963)

73. Hakim, A. A., Lifson, N. Urea transport across dog intestinal mucosa *in vitro*. *Am. J. Physiol.*, **206**, 1315–20 (1964)

74. Hakim, A. A., Lifson, N. Effects of pressure on water and solute transport by dog intestinal mucosa *in vitro*. *Am. J. Physiol.*, **216**, 276–84 (1969)

75. Cocco, A. E., Salem, A. A., Hendrix, T. R. Demonstrations of a selective barrier affecting movement of

sugars from blood to intestinal lumen. *Bull. Johns Hopkins Hosp.*, **117**, 1–7 (1965)

76. Cocco, A. E., Hendrix, T. R. The effect produced by phlorizin and hypertonic saline on sugar movement from blood to intestinal lumen. *Bull. Johns Hopkins Hosp.*, **117**, 296–305 (1965)

77. Carpenter, C. C. J., Greenough, W. B. III, Sack, R. B. The relationship of superior mesenteric blood flow to gut electrolyte loss in experimental cholera. *J. Infect. Diseases*, **119**, 182–93 (1969)

78. Iber, F. L. Protein loss into the gastrointestinal tract in cirrhosis of the liver. *Am. J. Clin. Nutr.*, **19**, 219–22 (1966)

79. Stein, W. D. *The Movements of Molecules Across Cell Membranes* (Academic, New York, 369 pp., 1967)

80. Curran, P. F., Schultz, S. G. Transport across membranes: general principles. *Handbook of Physiology*. Sect. 6, *Alimentary Canal*. **III.** *Intestinal Absorption*, 1217–43 (See Ref. 3)

81. Fordtran, J. S., Dietschy, J. M. Water and electrolyte movement in the intestine. *Gastroenterology*, **50**, 263–85 (1966)

82. Curran, P. F. Ion transport in intestine and its coupling to other transport processes. *Fed. Proc.*, **24**, 993–99 (1965)

83. Fordtran, J. S., Rector, F. C., Jr., Ewton, M. F., Soter, N., Kinney, J. Permeability characteristics of the human small intestine. *J. Clin. Invest.*, **44**, 1935–44 (1965)

84. Renkin, E. M. Filtration, diffusion, and molecular sieving through porous cellulose membranes. *J. Gen. Physiol.*, **38**, 225–43 (1954)

85. Solomon, A. K. Measurement of the equivalent pore radius in cell membranes. *Membrane Transport and Metabolism*, 94–99 (Kleinzeller, A., Kotyk, A., Eds., Czech. Acad. Sci., Prague, 1961)

86. Love, A. H. G. Permeability characteristics of the cholera-infected small intestine. *Gut*, **10**, 105–7 (1969)

87. Fordtran, J. S., Rector, F. C., Locklear, T. W., Ewton, M. F. Water and solute movement in the small intestine of patients with sprue. *J. Clin. Invest.*, **46**, 287–98 (1967)

88. Schultz, S. G., Zalusky, R. Ion transport in isolated rabbit ileum. II. The interaction between active sodium and active sugar transport. *J. Gen. Physiol.*, **47**, 1043–59 (1964)

89. Schultz, S. G., Curran, P. F., Chez, R. A., Fuisz, R. E. Alanine and sodium fluxes across the mucosal border of rabbit ileum. *J. Gen. Physiol.*, **50**, 1241–60 (1967)

90. Fordtran, J. S., Rector, F. C., Jr., Carter, N. W. The mechanism of sodium absorption in the human small intestine. *J. Clin. Invest.*, **47**, 884–900 (1968)

91. Barry, R. J. C., Smyth, D. H., Wright, E. M. Short-circuit current and solute transfer by rat jejunum. *J. Physiol.*, **181**, 410–31 (1965)

92. Taylor, A. E., Wright, E. M., Schultz, S. G., Curran, P. F. Effect of sugars on ion fluxes in intestine. *Am. J. Physiol.*, **214**, 836–42 (1968)

93. Turnberg, L. A., Rector, F. C., Fordtran, J. S. Jejunal bicarbonate and sodium transport in normal man. *Clin. Res.*, **17**, 313 (1969)

94. Kinney, V. R., Code, C. F. Canine ileal chloride absorption: Effect of carbonic anhydrase inhibitor on transport. *Am. J. Physiol.*, **207**, 998–1004 (1964)

95. Hubel, K. A. Bicarbonate secretion and its dependence on intraluminal chloride. *Am. J. Physiol.*, **213**, 1409–13 (1967)

96. Greenough, W. B. III, Pierce, N. F., Al Awqati, Q., Carpenter, C. C. J. Stimulation of gut electrolyte secretion by prostoglandins, theophylline and cholera exotoxin. *J. Clin. Invest.*, **48**, 32a (1969)

97. Field, M., From, D., Wallace, C. K., Greenough, W. B. III. Stimulation of active chloride secretion in small intestine by cholera exotoxin. *J. Clin. Invest.*, **48**, 24a (1969)

98. Ingraham, R. C., Visscher, M. B. The production of chloride-free solutions by the action of the intestinal epithelium. *Am. J. Physiol.*, **114**, 676–80 (1936)

99. Cohnheim, J. F. *Lectures on General Pathology, A Handbook for Practioners and Students*. Sect. III, *The pathology of digestion*, 113,

949–60 (Transl. from 2nd German ed. by McKee, A. B., New Sydenham Soc., London, 1890)

100. Sack, R. B., Carpenter, C. C. J., Steenburg, R. W., Pierce, N. F. Experimental cholera, a canine model. *Lancet*, **1**, 206–7 (1966)

101. Sack, R. B., Carpenter, C. C. J. Experimental canine cholera. I. Development of the model. *J. Infect. Diseases*, **119**, 138–49 (1969)

102. Fuhrman, G. J., Fuhrman, F. A. Inhibition of active sodium transport by cholera toxin. *Nature*, **188**, 71–72 (1960)

103. Serebun, H. A., Bayless, T. M., Hendrix, T. R., Iber, F. L., McGonagle, T. Absorption of *d*-glucose by the rabbit jejunum during cholera toxin-induced diarrhoea. *Nature*, **217**, 1272–73 (1968)

104. Iber, F. L., McGonagle, T., Serebro, H. A., Leubbers, E. H., Bayless, T. M., Hendrix, T. R. The mechanism of fluid production in experimental cholera toxin-induced diarrhea. *J. Clin. Invest.*, **47**, 50a (1968)

105. Love, A. H. G. Permeability characteristics of the cholera-infected small intestine. *Gut*, **10**, 105–7 (1969)

106. Serebro, H. A., Iber, F. L., Yardley, J. H., Hendrix, T. R. Inhibition of cholera toxin action in the rabbit by cycloheximide. *Gastroenterology*, **56**, 506–11 (1969)

107. Verbin, R. S., Farber, E. Effect of cycloheximide on the cell cycle of the crypts of the small intestine of the rat. *J. Cell Biol.*, **35**, 649–58 (1967)

108. Grayer, D. I., Serebro, H. A., Hendrix, T. R. Effect of cycloheximide on Na+ fluxes in experimental cholera. *Fed. Proc.*, **28**, 718 (1969)

109. Halsted, C. H., Grayer, D. I., Luebbers, E. H., Yardley, J. H., Hendrix, T. R. Effect of cycloheximide on intestinal secretion induced by hypertonic glucose. *Gastroenterology*, **56**, 1252 (1969)

110. Herrin, R. C., Meek, W. J. Distension as a factor in intestinal obstruction. *Arch. Internal Med.*, **51**, 152–68 (1933)

111. Ingraham, R. C., Peters, R. C., Visscher, M. B. On the movement of materials across living membranes against concentration gradients. *J. Phys. Chem.*, **42**, 141–50 (1938)

112. Cizek, L. J. Total water content of laboratory animals with special reference to volume within the lumen of the gastrointestinal tract. *Am. J. Physiol.*, **179**, 104–10 (1954)

113. Soergel, K. H., Whalen, G. E., Harris, J. A., Green, J. E. Effect of antidiuretic hormone on human small intestinal water and solute transport. *J. Clin. Invest.*, **47**, 1071–82 (1968)

114. Stein, I., Wertheimer, E. Effect of adrenalectomy on intestinal absorption involving osmotic work in rats. *Proc. Soc. Exptl. Biol. Med.*, **46**, 172–74 (1941)

115. Dennis, C., Wood, E. H. Intestinal absorption in the adrenalectomized dog. *Am. J. Physiol.*, **129**, 182–90 (1940)

116. Espinor, E. A., Beaven, D. W. Nonspecific islet cell tumor of the pancreas with diarrhea. *Quart. J. Med.*, **31**, 447–71 (1962)

117. Zollinger, R. M., Tompkins, R. K., Amerson, J. R., Endahl, G. L., Kraft, A. R., Moone, F. T. Identification of the diarrheogenic hormone associated with non-beta islet cell tumors of the pancreas. *Ann. Surg.*, **168**, 502–21 (1968)

118. Stickler, G. B., Hallenbeck, G. A., Flock, E. V., Rosevear, J. W. Catecholamines and diarrhea in ganglioneuroblastoma. *J. Diseases Children*, **104**, 598–604 (1962)

119. Cameron, D. G., Warner, H. A., Szabo, A. J. Chronic diarrhea in an adult with hypokalemic nephropathy and osteomalacia due to a functioning ganglioneuroblastoma. *Trans. Am. Clin. Climat. Assoc.*, **78**, 205–17 (1966)

120. Sandler, M., Karim, S. M. M., Williams, E. D. Prostaglandins in aminepeptide-secreting tumours. *Lancet*, **2**, 1053–55 (1968)

121. Christopher, N. L., Bayless, T. M. Role of small bowel and colon in lactose induced diarrhea. *Gastroenterology*, **56**, 1250 (1969)

122. Taylor, J., Maltby, M. P., Payne, J. M. Factors influencing the response of ligated rabbit gut segments to injected *Escherichia coli*. *J. Pathol. Bacteriol.*, **76**, 491–99 (1958)

164   HENDRIX & BAYLESS

123. Lin, T. M., Nosh, J. F., Ensminger, P. W., Benslay, D. N. Mechanism study of the action of malethamen in stapholococcus enterotoxin-induced diarrhea in monkeys. *Arch. Intern. Pharmacodyn.*, **169**, 162–76 (1967)
124. Savage, D. C., Dubos, R. Alterations in the mouse cecum and its flora produced by antibacterial drugs. *J. Exptl. Med.*, **128**, 97–110 (1968)
125. Schmid, W. C., Phillips, S. F., Summerskill, W. H. J. Jejunal secretion of electrolytes and water in nontropical sprue. *J. Lab. Clin. Med.*, **73**, 772–83 (1969)
126. Powell, D. W., Plotkin, G. R., Maenza, R. M., Formal, S. B. Experimental diarrhea: intestinal electrolyte water transport in rat salmonella entercolitis. *Clin. Res.*, **16**, 290 (1968)
127. Evanson, J. M., Stanbury, S. W. Congenital chloridorrhoea or so-called congenital alkalosis with diarrhoea. *Gut*, **6**, 29–38 (1965)

CNS AT THE CELLULAR LEVEL: IDENTITY OF TRANSMITTER AGENTS

Catherine Hebb

Department of Physiology, A.R.C. Institute of Animal Physiology Babraham, Cambridge, England

Introduction

The subject of this review is the identity of transmitter agents in the central nervous system (CNS) of mammals. Its purpose is to discuss recent evidence relating to the identification of certain substances as central neurotransmitters and to consider some of the pathways in which they may function. The substances to be discussed are: acetylcholine (ACh); monoamines such as norepinephrine (noradrenaline), dopamine, and 5-hydroxytryptamine (5-HT); neutral amino acids, as inhibitory transmitters; and acidic amino acids, as excitatory transmitters. Possibly the most important advances in the field which have occurred in the period under review (1966–69) have come about as the result of investigations into the potential transmitter role of certain of the neutral amino acids. Because of the considerable theoretical importance of this work it is the topic which will be discussed at greatest length.

In scanning the literature on central transmitter agents one cannot fail to be impressed by the great caution with which most authors approach the subject. Almost all stress the complexity of the CNS, the difficulty, if not impossibility, of examining single neurons or homogeneous groups of neurons in isolation from one another, and the many diverse problems arising from this. For this reason great stress has been laid on the various criteria which have been found acceptable in the identification of neurotransmitters in the autonomic and peripheral nervous systems. But not all of them may be applicable to central pathways, some could be irrelevant and insistence on them may well hinder rather than promote the understanding of central transmission processes.

Nevertheless, some standard of proof is necessary and a recent article by Werman (1) provides a useful guide in considering which of the generally accepted criteria can best be applied to the study of central synapses. Of eight criteria which he discusses, the one on which he lays the greatest emphasis is the 'criterion of identical actions' while the next in importance is the 'criterion of pharmacological identity'.

165

Both criteria can be met in experiments in which the responses of single neurons are studied by the technique of microiontophoresis (2, 3) which makes it possible to apply various agents to the surface of the neuron while recording changes in its excitability, either by extra- or by intracellularly placed microelectrodes. Excitatory substances increase the rate of firing; inhibitory substances reduce either the spontaneous rate of firing, or the rate of firing induced in a cell by previous application of an excitatory agent. This information can be obtained by extracellular recording. As frequently urged by Curtis and his associates (3–5), and many others, critical evidence for 'identity of action' of the supposed transmitter depends upon intracellular recording. This provides the means of judging what the molecular mechanism responsible for the change in excitability is. In the case of an inhibitory agent it is particularly important to show whether its effect is accompanied by hyperpolarization as in the case of the natural transmitter. Further confirmatory tests utilizing the same technical approach are discussed by Werman in detail.

If the action of the natural transmitter is blocked or modified in any way by pharmacological agents the action of the substance suspected to be the transmitter should be modified in the same way. In this way evidence of pharmacological identity can be established. An example of this which will be discussed later is the effect of strychinine in blocking the action of the inhibitory transmitter on spinal neurons (3–5). But other examples, such as the blocking of ACh by atropine, will readily spring to mind.

When the identity of the transmitter is provisionally known, or approximated, important confirmatory criteria are: evidence that the enzyme for its synthesis is present in some part of the neuron which releases it; and, in certain circumstances, the 'collectability of the transmitter' during stimulation. An example is the collection of ACh from the cortex in response to various stimuli. However, this may not always be achieved because it is conceivable that the transmitter may be inactivated before it can be collected.

The presence of the transmitter is thought to be a criterion of less certain value, particularly the belief that a transmitter is necessarily stored at higher concentrations in the nerve terminals. Werman's arguments here are somewhat less convincing, perhaps, since they appear to overlook the probability that the release of transmitter from different types of nerves has many features in common which make it likely that within certain limits it is governed by the same general rules and release from a preformed store seems to be one of these. It may therefore be a criterion of considerable value if a suspected transmitter substance can be shown to be concentrated in the nerve endings or, even better, can be shown to be concentrated in vesicles at the endings, either by histochemistry (see below) or by the techniques of subcellular fractionation.

The criterion of the presence of an inactivating enzyme at, or near, the site of release of the transmitter, although generally accepted, is the one for which there is the least theoretical justification. The model here is the hydrolysis of ACh by cholinesterase but other methods of getting rid of the transmitter are possible. One is that it may be removed by diffusion and destruction at a distance, say in the blood. Alternatively, it might be absorbed into the cell on which it acts. A further possibility not mentioned by Werman is reuptake by the endings from which it was originally released, a process which seems to be important in the case of noradrenergic nerves (6).

In considering these criteria a distinction must necessarily be made between substances which are already established as transmitters, in the peripheral and autonomic nervous systems, and those for which such precedents do not exist. It may be right, in the case of acetylcholine, for example, to insist that central cholinergic neurons must conform in all respects to peripheral cholinergic neurons. Thus they may be expected to contain throughout their length the transmitter, the synthesizing enzyme, choline acetyltransferase (ChAc), and the hydrolyzing enzyme, acetylcholinesterase (AChE); and to synapse with membranes on which more AChE is located. In recent years, because of an adequate histochemical method, considerable reliance has been placed on the presence of AChE alone for the demonstration of central cholinergic neurons but since the function of the presynaptic AChE is not known and there are parts of the CNS where the distribution of ACh does not parallel that of AChE, this criterion could be misleading. Nevertheless, it is a valuable adjunct to other criteria and useful for preliminary exploration and mapping of putative cholinergic pathways.

Another special case is provided by norepinephrine, dopamine, and 5-HT because they are instances in which the presence of the transmitter can be demonstrated by fluorescence histochemistry, although it remains a difficulty that norepinephrine and dopamine can only be distinguished from each other by indirect pharmacological tests (7) or by supplementary biochemical analyses. For these three substances, then, the presence of the transmitter has been established and this provides the departure point for investigation of the other criteria.

A further speculative possibility is that the ultrastructure of each synapse may eventually provide information about the identity of the substance responsible for the transmission of impulses across it. For example, the presence of dense core, or granular, vesicles at its endings is generally recognized as evidence that a peripheral neuron is adrenergic and clearly distinguishes it from cholinergic neurons in which the agranular synaptic vesicles are the predominant population. From this the possibility naturally arises that central adrenergic nerve terminals can be similarly identified and investigations to this end have been carried out (8–10). Evidence recently discussed by Bloom (8) shows that the concentration of dense core vesicles in the brain can be correlated with the regional distribution of norepinephrine and other biogenic amines. Similarly, Wood (9, 10) finds that organelles containing the three brain amines, nonepinephrine, dopamine, and 5-HT, are identifiable as dense core vesicles by electronmicroscopy; and while in one paper (9) he reported that the method of staining did not distinguish between the three amines, he has subsequently (10) found a means of differentiating 5-HT from the catecholamines.

Of relevant interest is the use of electronmicroscope autoradiography for the identification of catecholamine storage sites. The application of the method to peripheral nerves has been carefully studied by Salpeter et al. (11). It may be of less use in mapping central synapses, however, since there is evidence that vesicles in noradrenergic nerve endings can take up 5-HT as well as norepinephrine (12).

It has been proposed by Bodian (13) that two morphologically distinct types of agranular vesicles found in synaptic bulbs on the surface of spinal motoneurons, in monkeys, may signify differences in the function, whether excitatory or inhibitory, of the endings in which they are found.

The possibility that a method for the identification of cholinergic endings had been found was indicated in experiments by Akert & Sandri (14). They obtained evidence to suggest that a mixture of osmium tetroxide and zinc iodide selectively stains synaptic vesicles characteristic of cholinergic nerve terminals; and it seemed possible that this would provide a specific staining method for this kind of ending. However, a similar positive reaction for nerves supplying the pineal gland (15) seems to show that the reaction is not specific for cholinergic nerve terminals.

ACETYLCHOLINE AS A CENTRAL TRANSMITTER

A question of current interest is the part played by cholinergic neurons in the ascending reticular system. Although it is not a new idea that ACh-releasing neurons form an important component of the cortical arousal system (16), the extent of their involvement is still a subject for investigation. That ACh is a transmitter in this system seems to be generally accepted; and it is possible too that within it cholinergic neurons may relay with one another and that successive neurons in the multisynaptic system are both cholinergic and cholinoceptive (17, 18). A question about which there is some disagreement is whether, apart from the motor cranial outflow, cholinergic neurons of the brain are only found in the reticular system. An alternative view is that they form one or more of the relaying neurons in the direct or 'specific' sensory pathways (19, 20) or are neurons specifically associated with these pathways.

The evidence for believing that cholinergic neurons are a component of the cortical arousal system has been summarized by Krnjević (21). About 16 to 25 per cent of the neurons examined in the cat cortex, by the technique of microiontophoresis, most of them concentrated in layer V, are excited by ACh. The excitation is typically slow in onset and prolonged, possibly an appropriate kind of action for the transmitter of the diffuse reticular system. ACh and the enzymes for its production and its hydrolysis are all present in the cortex but most of the neurons containing these substances are subcortical in origin. The observations that many cholinoceptive cortical cells cannot be excited by thalamic stimulation; that the effects of certain drugs on the release of ACh from cortical endings do not correspond with their effects on cortical activity produced by sensory stimulation; and that ACh-sensitive cells can be excited by stimulation of the midbrain reticular formation, which also increases the release of ACh from the cortex, all suggest that the cholinergic nerve fibres of the cortex originate in the reticular system and are unlikely to be part of the direct thalamocortical pathways. Krnjević suggests, however, that some specific thalamic nuclei may be linked selectively to certain ascending cholinergic fibres; in this way the same ascending system could be activated to produce general arousal as well as localized responses in the cortex.

In general agreement with this is the work of Lewis & Shute (17, 18) on the histochemical distribution of AChE in the brain which they have recently summarized in two extensive publications. One deals with what they call the cholinergic limbic system which consists of two groups of neurons: (a) afferent to the hippocampus; and (b) projecting from the hippocampal system to the medial cortex, to nuclei of the ascending reticular system, and to some nonneural tissue. The other paper deals with the ascending reticular system. In their opinion the AChE-containing pathways of the forebrain form the anatomical basis of this system. It consists of two pathways: (a) from the nucleus cuneiformis projecting to tectum, metathalamus, and thalamus; and (b) from the ventral tegmental area and the substantia nigra to subthalamus, hypothalamus, basal ganglia, and cortex. Under all these headings individual pathways are described in detail. In most cases their polarity was determined by making chronic lesions which caused AChE to accumulate on the perikaryal side of severed axons and to decrease on the other side.

The distribution described by Lewis & Shute fits with the expected distribution of neurons belonging to the ascending reticular arousal system; but does it exclude the possibility that cholinergic neurons exist elsewhere in other systems of the CNS?

Evidence from experiments on the cortical release of ACh by Mitchell and his colleagues (19, 22–24) and by Szerb (20) seems to show that cholinergic neurons must form part of other specific pathways to the cortex. In a study of the visual system of the rabbit, Collier & Mitchell (22) showed that unilateral stimulation of the lateral geniculate body produces a large increase in release of ACh from the corresponding primary visual area of cortex and a widespread but smaller increase from other areas including the contralateral visual area. From this and other evidence they concluded that two ascending cholinergic systems might exist: (a) the ascending reticular formation which is responsible for the general increase in ACh release which they had observed; and (b) a pathway specifically associated with the visual system, its activation being responsible for localized release of ACh from the stimulated cortex. The possibility that the specific cholinergic neurons were the primary thalamocortical afferents was dismissed for the same reasons that Krnjević (21) has given. Instead the authors suggested that the fibres responsible are those involved in augmenting and repetitive responses which are known to originate from the thalamus. In further experiments on anaesthetized rabbits (23) it was shown that a vertical lesion which separated the lateral geniculate from midline structures did not alter cortical release of ACh, in response to lateral geniculate stimulation, in any way; on the other hand, after the nucleus was separated from lower brain centres by a horizontal section the release of ACh from the contralateral visual area was no longer increased by stimulation of the lateral geniculate. This operation did not affect the spontaneous release of ACh which therefore could not have been due to activity in the ascending reticular system. The additional release of ACh which occurred in conscious rabbits, however, was attributed to the influence of the reticular system.

In contrast to these results, experiments done by Phillis (25) tend to show that the effect of sensory stimuli in increasing ACh release is mediated purely by the ascending reticular system. He found that stimulation of any of the appropriate modalities produced roughly the same increase in the release of ACh from the sensorimotor, parietal, auditory, and visual cortex. Direct cortical stimulation as well as stimulation of the reticular system also increased the release to a comparable extent in the various cortical areas. He argued therefore that the system of cholinergic neurons involved was probably the cortical arousal system. He also suggested that the part of Collier & Mitchell's findings which was not explained by the stimulation of the ascending reticular system could be explained by the activity of the intracortical cholinergic neurons described by Krnjević & Silver (26).

The general thesis that release of ACh from different areas of sensory cortex can be equally increased regardless of the sensory modality stimulated is not borne out by the work of Hemsworth & Mitchell (27). They have shown that on stimulation of the medial geniculate body the output of ACh from the auditory cortex is increased much more than the output from the visual cortex. They consider that Phillis failed to find a selective increase of ACh release in response to sensory stimulation, because of the short duration of the stimulus he applied. Although it would be adequate for direct thalamic stimulation, 15 min would produce in the case of a peripherally applied stimulus a relatively small response; hence it might be difficult to demonstrate the separate effect of the specific pathways.

The evidence on balance, therefore, favours the existence of a specific cholinergic pathway between the thalamus and cortex. But some uncertainty remains because of the failure so far to identify the neurons concerned. One possibility which in my opinion has not been altogether excluded is that the primary afferent fibres to the cortex of the auditory and visual systems, as fourth-order neurons, may themselves be cholinergic as originally postulated by Feldberg & Vogt (28). Recent experiments by Miller et al. (29) could be interpreted in favour of this concept. They showed on rabbits that removal of the striate cortex caused, with the ensuing retrograde degeneration and loss of cells, a 28 per cent fall in the ACh content of the lateral geniculate body;

enucleation of the contralateral eye reduced both the concentration in the geniculate by 23 per cent, and its content by 27 per cent. Together the two operations reduced the concentration by 35 per cent and the content by 56 per cent. The authors considered that sufficient time—30 days—had been allowed for retrograde degeneration to be complete and thought that the balance of ACh remaining in the tissue was probably due to contamination with other tissue. Possibly terminals of the cholinergic fibres said by Shute & Lewis (18) to supply the lateral geniculate body are the source of the residual ACh.

Whatever the explanation, the experiments seem to provide clear evidence that the cells destroyed by retrograde degeneration contain ACh; if so, they are probably cholinergic. An argument equally in favour of this conclusion is the effect of enucleation. Since the trunk of the optic nerve does not contain ACh (30) the fall in its concentration in the lateral geniculate following enucleation is not likely to be due to losses from the optic nerve terminals; the only other likely explanation is that it is an early effect of transsynaptic degeneration which is only certainly known to occur in the lateral geniculate body.

Although most authors have emphasized the excitatory actions of ACh on cerebral cortical cells (21, 31), Phillis & York (32, 33) have recently found that when Dial compound, alone or with diethyl ether, was used as anaesthetic, a large proportion of neurons in the cortex of the cat were depressed by ACh. Further analysis of the response indicated that some of these cells were innervated by ascending fibres of the reticular system; others were thought to be innervated by cholinergic inhibitory interneurons lying wholly within the cortex.

The interneurons postulated by Phillis & York may belong to the group of intracortical cells originally described by Krnjević & Silver (26). These probably give rise to the U-fibres that lie at the bottom of sulci between the grey and white matter; and according to Krnjević (21) they also may give rise to ascending collaterals which end as parallel fibres lying in the most superficial layer of the cortex.

It is of course not certain that the only function of ACh is that of neurotransmitter and its presence in neural tissue could have some other meaning. One indication in this direction is the evidence recently reported by Marchisio & Consolo (34) from which it seems that ACh plays some part in neurohistogenesis in the developing chick embryo. To account for their observations they suggest that ACh may control a metabolic pathway involved in the maturation process of the cell; and that this may be related to its well-known effect on phospholipid metabolism which was discovered by L. and M. Hokin and recently reviewed by them (35, 36). However, this metabolic effect of ACh on phospholipids need not be separate from its action as a transmitter. It could be a part of its total effect on the synaptic membrane (for discussion see 35). This seems more likely since atropine blocks its metabolic as well as its neuropharmacological actions.

It may be relevant here that Krnjević & Schwartz (37) found from intracellular recordings that ACh had a similar depolarizing action on responsive neurons and on unresponsive cells thought to be neuroglia. Depolarization was unaccompanied by any detectable change in membrane resistance in either type of cell. Krnjević & Schwartz suggest that in both cases ACh may be activating an electrogenic chloride pump and that in this respect the cortical cells could be compared to salivary gland cells in their response to ACh.

Whatever the explanation of its depolarizing action is, the finding that ACh depolarizes glial cells as well as neurons injects an element of doubt into the case for it being a neurotransmitter in the cortex. Moreover, the fact that it causes no change in membrane resistance when it depolarizes cortical cells is not in accordance with what is known of synaptic transmission nor with the actions of ACh at the neuromuscular junction and sympathetic ganglion. However, the possible similarity of its effects on cortical and salivary gland cells suggests another hypothesis, that these effects are typical of its action in excitatory muscarinic transmissions. Thus, it is possible that it is a transmitter in the cortex as at the neuromuscular junction but, because of a difference in the receptors on which it acts, the mechanism by which depolarization occurs differs in the two cases.

In spite of the doubts that have been raised, the evidence as a whole is impressively in favour of ACh being a transmitter of the CNS. There is evidence of: (a) the collectability of the transmitter; (b) the presence of the transmitter; (c) the presence of the synthesizing enzyme; (d) the presence of the inactivating enzyme; and (e) for some systems, pharmacological identity of actions of the transmitter and ACh. Its most important function is evidently as the transmitter of the cortical arousal system, although an inhibitory function now seems probable (32, 33); and there are indications that it is the transmitter in some neurons belonging to the specific afferent pathways as well. Evidence that some ascending and descending fibres of the spinal cord are cholinergic has also been found (38) but their function remains to be investigated.

MONOAMINES AS CENTRAL TRANSMITTERS

The distribution in the CNS of nerve fibres, and their cells of origin, which contain norepinephrine, dopamine, or 5-hydroxytryptamine (5-HT), has recently been reviewed by Fuxe, Hökfelt & Ungerstedt (39). A significant feature of the observed distribution is that with the exception of some catecholamine-containing cell groups in the hypothalamus all the cells of origin for these amines are located in the tegmentum of the midbrain, the pons and medulla oblongata. From these, fibres containing norepinephrine or 5-HT descend to innervate the grey matter of the spinal cord and ascend to innervate structures in the diencephalon and telencephalon, while others supply various nuclei of the lower brainstem. Relatively few 5-HT-containing fibres reach the cerebral cortex but a diffuse network of norepinephrine-containing fibres is found throughout its layers with the highest density in the cingular region.

Dopamine fibres and terminals are mostly ascending and innervate subcortical structures. Among these the nigrostriatal dopamine fibres are the best documented. Short dopamine neurons are also found to lie wholly within the retina. In most cases the origin of the terminals found in different parts of the brain cannot be directly traced by existing methods and have to be inferred from indirect, but convincing evidence, such as the histochemical changes which occur in anterograde and retrograde degeneration of the suspected pathways. The same group of workers (40) have also obtained evidence to show that norepinephrine terminals can be depleted of their amine by stimulation if resynthesis is prevented. This test might be regarded as a substitute for the criterion of collectability of the transmitter.

There has long been evidence to suggest that the reticular activating system involves adrenergic as well as cholinergic neurons (16) but tests of the actions of norepinephrine and dopamine on cortical cells of the cat showed that like 5-HT they had in general a depressant action (21). This together with other earlier evidence reviewed in two recent papers (18, 41) has suggested to some the possibility that monoaminergic fibres supplying the cortex are inhibitory and opposite in action to its cholinergic supply. However, it now appears from experiments done by Roberts & Straughan and their associates (42, 43) on *encéphale isolé* preparations that the predominant effect of norepinephrine is to excite cortical cells; about twice as many, 35 per cent of all tested, were excited as depressed. When N_2O-halothane was the anaesthetic 61 per cent of cells tested were excited, 14 per cent were depressed, and the rest responded with a mixed effect (7 per cent) or did not respond at all (18 per cent). With barbiturate anaesthesia, which is the anaesthesia commonly used for experiments of this kind, only 8 per cent of neurons were excited by norepinephrine while 62 per cent were depressed. From this it would appear that excitation is the more normal action of norepinephrine on most cerebral cortical cells; and this conclusion is strengthened by the additional evidence (43, 44) showing that, in 75 per cent of cases, excitation by norepinephrine could be blocked reversibly by α- and β-blockers; only 10 per cent of depressant responses could be similarly blocked.

These results do not imply that the normal response of central neurons is always excitatory. Apart from the evidence that some cortical cells continue to respond with an inhibitory change, Tebēcis (45) has found that norepinephrine has a predominantly inhibitory action on the medial geniculate nucleus of cats. N_2O-halothane was the anaesthetic used in these experiments. Brainstem stimulation and 5-HT had similar effects. Of considerable interest is the observation that in many cases the depressant actions of brainstem stimulation, of norepinephrine, and of 5-HT were greatly reduced by iontophoretic application of strychnine. This would suggest that both norepinephrine and 5-HT are inhibitory transmitters to the medial geniculate and the histochemical evidence quoted by the author supports this interpretation. Both inhibitory and excitatory responses to electrophoretically applied norepinephrine have been observed by Boakes et al. (46) in tests of brainstem neurons of the decerebrate cat. In some cases dopamine had the opposite effect on cells which were either excited or depressed by norepinephrine.

York (47) finds that dopamine itself is inhibitory on cells of the cat caudate nucleus; this inhibition was blocked by phenoxybenzamine. Other work from the same laboratory had shown that stimulation of the centromedian nucleus of the thalamus causes an increased output of dopamine from the caudate nucleus, and caudate cells which are inhibited by stimulation of the same thalamic nucleus are inhibited by dopamine. It was further shown that the inhibition in both cases can be blocked by phenoxybenzamine. Together with histochemical evidence showing the presence of the transmitter, these results go a long way towards proving the presence of inhibitory dopaminergic neurons reaching the caudate nucleus via the thalamus. The author also suggests from other evidence that the nigrostriatal pathway is an excitatory dopaminergic pathway.

The third amine, 5-HT, like norepinephrine has also been shown by Roberts & Straughan (48) to have both excitatory and depressant actions on cortical cells. Again the excitatory actions were revealed by the use of the *encéphale isolé* preparation (cat). In this preparation, 30 per cent of neurons tested, in the postsigmoid and suprasylvian gyri, were excited by 5-HT. The effect was seen as an increase in the rate of firing of spontaneously active cells or of cells minimally stimulated by glutamic acid. About the same proportion of cells (33 per cent) were depressed by 5-HT. As in the case of norepinephrine, excitation by 5-HT was blocked by antagonists which specifically block its action in the periphery; the depressant action, on all save two cells, was not blocked by these agents.

From this brief account it appears then that ascending monoaminergic pathways could play an important part in the cortical arousal system. In subcortical structures they may also have a significant activating rôle although in some regions both excitatory and inhibitory actions have been found (46, 49), and in the caudate nucleus it appears that the inhibitory input of dopaminergic neurons is of considerable importance.

The descending monoaminergic neurons might be expected to be inhibitory too since norepinephrine administered electrophoretically in the vicinity of either Renshaw cells or spinal interneurons in unanaesthetized cats depresses the synaptic responses of the interneurons and the sensitivity of both groups of cell to excitant amino acids (50, 51). However, its inhibitory action on these cells was not blocked by strychnine while strychnine readily blocked the inhibition induced either by pinching the ipsilateral hindpaw or by stimulating the contralateral medullary reticular formation (51).

The fact that both α- and β-blocking agents can suppress the responses of cortical neurons to norepinephrine led Johnson et al. (43) to suggest that the excitation by norepinephrine involves a mixed population of α- and β-receptors or a different type of receptor on cortical cells. Similarly, from their studies on brainstem neurons, Boakes et al. (46) concluded that norepinephrine-responsive receptors in these cells do not behave like peripheral adrenoreceptors.

NEUTRAL AMINO ACIDS AS INHIBITORY TRANSMITTER AGENTS

For some time it has been accepted that the inhibitory postsynaptic potential (IPSP) is produced by the release of a specific inhibitory substance from inhibitory presynaptic terminals; and that, in conditions regulating storage and release of the transmitter, inhibitory synapses are probably similar in all important respects to the excitatory ones (2). However, although many candidates have been proposed as inhibitory transmitters, Factor I, γ-aminobutyric acid (GABA), and some of the catecholamines among others, the evidence has in most cases been equivocal or insufficient (2, 3). GABA, one of a group of neutral amino acids, including taurine, α- and β-alanine, and glycine among others, which have a depressant action on all types of spinal neurons and on cortical neurons as well, has been one of the most promising transmitter suspects but for some time two pieces of evidence, which have been strongly emphasized by Curtis & Watkins (3), seemed to preclude its identification as an inhibitory transmitter.

If it were the transmitter its depressant effect should derive from the same conductance change in the subsynaptic membrane as that brought about by the physiologically released transmitter, and in the case of the spinal neurons at least its action should be antagonized by strychnine. However, when tested on single cells by microiontophoresis it produced depression of firing of motoneurons (3, 52) or of cortical cells (53) without producing the hyperpolarization expected if the conductance change were the same as that produced by the transmitter. Secondly, its depressant action, either on cortical or spinal cells, was not blocked by strychnine (3, 52, 54). The other depressant amino acids tested similarly failed these tests. The results suggested therefore that they and GABA both acted nonspecifically, not only on the receptor sites of the natural transmitter but on other parts of the neuronal membrane as well.

Put in another way, these substances failed the criteria of the 'identity of action' and of 'pharmacological identity'. Yet there were many converging lines of evidence implicating GABA as an inhibitory transmitter; and cumulatively, Curtis & Watkins's (3) own researches indicated that the biologically active amino acids (excitant and depressant) were interacting with receptor sites specific for the amino acid molecule. Consequently, they did not altogether exclude the possibility that GABA, and perhaps some other depressant amino acids, were inhibitory transmitter agents; and they suggested that some other explanation might account for the failure of experimentally applied GABA to reproduce all of the effects of the natural transmitter.

The developments with which the present review is concerned fully justify this caution since it is now clear that the effects of iontophoretically applied GABA are fully compatible with it being the transmitter in some parts of the CNS. These developments, which began with some preliminary observations in 1965 (55) and are still continuing, must be thought to have considerable importance since not only have they provided new information about the possible rôle of GABA in the vertebrate nervous system, they have also yielded evidence about other amino acids which may also be involved in neurotransmission, notably in the spinal cord. Much of this work has centred around the question of glycine as a possible transmitter of the inhibitory spinal interneurons. Although the research work on the two amino acids has been interconnected it will be convenient to consider them separately here.

Gamma-aminobutyric acid.—A preliminary report by Obata (55) disclosed that cells of Deiters nucleus are hyperpolarized by microiontophoretic application of GABA; this was subsequently amplified (56) in a detailed study of the pharmacology of postsynaptic inhibition of Deiters neurons induced by stimulation of Purkinje cell axons and by GABA. The chief finding, which favours the identity of actions of GABA and the inhibitory transmitter, was that microiontophoretic application of GABA caused hyperpolarization of the cells together with a large increase in membrane conductance; but it was also shown that the depression of Deiters neurons produced either by the natural inhibitory transmitter or by GABA was not blocked by strychnine or by tetanus toxin, both of which block or prevent inhibition of spinal motoneurons (57). Although the absence of a blocking effect does not contribute any positive evidence in favor of the identity of the transmitter it is important in showing a further similarity in the properties of GABA and the inhibitory transmitter belonging to the Purkinje cells. It also demonstrates clearly that the inhibitory process can differ in important respects, such as in its susceptibility to strychnine, in different parts of the CNS.

Cerebral cortical inhibition in cats is also resistant to strychnine (54, 58) and to tetanus toxin (54). This was shown by Krnjević and his colleagues who also showed that the depressant action of GABA on the cortex is not blocked by either substance, nor by a large number of other compounds, including picrotoxin; and these were also ineffective in blocking the cortical inhibitory transmitter. This strengthened earlier evidence from the same group implicating GABA as the inhibitory transmitter of the cerebral cortex. Subsequently, Krnjević & Schwartz (59–61) were able to demonstrate hyperpolarization of single neurons of the pericruciate cortex of cats in response to microiontophoretic application of GABA. Their evidence of the similarity between GABA and the transmitter was more complete than that of Obata et al. (56) since they were able to show that both the inhibitory transmitter and GABA were reversed by injecting chloride into the cell from the recording electrode. On the basis of these observations and that the reversal potentials for both physiological and GABA-induced inhibition were approximately similar, they concluded that GABA could be the main cortical inhibitory transmitter.

Krnjević & Schwartz (61) accounted for previous failures to demonstrate a hyperpolarizing action of GABA on cortical cells as due to the use of concentric or coaxial electrodes giving rise to artifacts which mask small changes in membrane potential. In their subsequent more successful experiments they used instead 'twin' micropipettes, an arrangment in which two micropipettes, one for recording from the interior of the cell and the other for ejecting GABA on to the exterior surface, are held parallel to one another. The arrangement of these seems to be similar in principle to the 'parallel' micropipettes described by Curtis (62) for intracellular recording from spinal motoneurons.

Considered as a whole the evidence which now favours GABA as an inhibitory transmitter of the mammalian brain is impressive. In the brain its highest concentration (ca. 10 μmoles/g tissue) is about 30 times higher than its lowest concentration (63) and there are even greater disparities between the brain and spinal roots. Although not compelling evidence in itself this kind of distribution is consistent with a transmitter function for GABA. Similarly, the evidence that both GABA (52, 64) and the enzyme which synthesizes it, L-glutamic acid decarboxylase (64), are both more concentrated in or near the Purkinje cells than in other parts of the cerebellum supports the conclusion that it is the inhibitory transmitter which these cells release. Kuriyama et al. (65) have also reported a distribution of GABA in the retina which suggests that it is concentrated in the amacrine or other intraretinal cells and so could be an inhibitory transmitter in this part of the nervous system as well.

There is also some evidence of stereospecificity of cortical receptors for GABA. Other amino acids with fewer groups between the amino and acidic groups are definitely less potent in blocking cortical neuron activity than GABA itself and other amino acids of similar chain length (66). In contrast, although GABA was at one time listed as being a more potent depressant of spinal neurons than β-alanine and glycine in that order (3) it now appears that, of the three, it is the least potent on spinal motoneurons (4, 67–69) and interneurons (5, 67–69) although the differences in the second case may be slight (67).

On cortical neurons GABA is estimated to have the same order of activity as the excitant L-glutamate, of which an amount as little as 10^{-14} moles causes excitation (66). This means that cortical cells are about as sensitive to GABA as the Mauthner neuron of the goldfish (70) and the neuromuscular junction of the crayfish (71).

Recent experiments of Kuriyama et al. (72) also support the idea that GABA is a synaptic transmitter. These experiments showed that a synaptic vesicle fraction isolated by differential centrifugation and hyposmotic shock from mouse brain retained relatively more of GABA (2.4 times), of glutamic decarboxylase (2.6 times), and of glutamic acid (1.7 times) than of lactic dehydrogenase which is generally regarded as a soluble cytoplasmic enzyme. Because of its diffusibility this degree of retention of GABA by the vesicles is probably significant. It is of interest that since GABA-transaminase was virtually absent from the vesicles, it would appear that the only glutamic acid present must be derived from some extravesicular source, whereas the GABA present is likely to have been formed from the glutamic acid also in the vesicles although some may be taken up from the surrounding cytoplasm. The isolated vesicle fraction was able to accumulate both GABA and glutamic acid, in the presence of sodium, at O° C. Evidence that GABA is concentrated in the nerve endings is also provided by some preliminary experiments of Iversen & Neal (73).

The indication that the transmitter and its synthesizing enzyme are present together in the synaptic vesicles is in apparent contrast with acetylcholine. It too is found in the vesicle fraction but the choline acetyltransferase of the nerve endings appears to be sited elsewhere (74). It is also of interest that glutamic acid is in the same fraction as GABA and presumably in the same vesicles since it provides the substrate for the synthesis of GABA. Kuriyama et al. (72) suggest that if the two amino acids are both present in the same vesicle both would be expected to be liberated simultaneously; and further, that whether the postsynaptic effect was excitatory or inhibitory would depend on their ratio in the vesicles at the time. That a switchover from GABA to glutamic acid release would occur seems unlikely, however, in view of the stability of the cortical inhibitory response and its resistance to fatigue (75, 76). On the other hand the close spatial association with the transmitter of glutamic acid, and of the enzyme which converts it to GABA, could be an important factor in preventing fatigue of the neurons.

The suggestion that a neuron might liberate either GABA or glutamic acid depending on its metabolic state finds an echo in the idea that the state of activity of the brain as a whole is in some way related to the relative levels of the two amino acids (64, 77–80).

Wiechert & Herbst (77) report that intracisternal injections of glutamic acid or of pyridoxal 5-phosphate (a coenzyme for both GABA-transaminase and glutamic acid decarboxylase but possibly with a preferential affinity for the first and hence stimulating the production of glutamic acid) cause epileptiform seizures which can be interrupted or prevented by intracisternal injections of GABA, or more obscurely, by pretreatment with methyl-α-ethylsuccinimide. Similarly, Essig (78) has found that treatment with amino-oxyacetic acid (an inhibitor of GABA-transaminase) reduces or prevents sodium barbital withdrawal convulsions. According to Roberts & Kuriyama (64) treatment of mice with amino-oxyacetic acid makes them less susceptible to convulsions in response to electric shock but only for a time: in their experiments, for 1.5 hr after treatment, a decrease in seizure incidence was correlated with the rise in the brain level of GABA but after that, although the level continued to rise, susceptibility to seizures increased.

More direct evidence of a possibly specific relation between GABA levels and excitability of the brain has been obtained by DeFeudis & Elliott (79). In confirmation of earlier work, they found that in rats which suffered convulsions following exposure to high oxygen pressures, the brain levels of GABA fell significantly below the levels in controls. It was further shown that both the convulsions and the fall in GABA were prevented by intraperitoneal injections of hyperosmotic solutions; and that the fall in GABA did not occur when the convulsions were produced by picrotoxin or by pentylenetetrazol.

Wood (80) has recently proposed that the accumulation of GABA which occurs during hypoxia, by causing a depression of neuronal activity, operates as a homeostatic device to conserve energy at a time when oxygen and metabolites are in short supply.

Is this scheme consistent with the rôle of GABA as transmitter? GABA-transaminase, the enzyme responsible for the metabolic removal of GABA, and for its entrance into the oxidative metabolic pathways of brain, seems to be located in the mitochondria (81). Its inactivity, therefore, will lead to overproduction of GABA in and near the mitochondria, probably in all parts of the neuron; and since treatment with amino-oxyacetic acid is effective, for a short time, in preventing or reducing seizures and electro-convulsions, the accumulated GABA must somehow escape from the cell to produce inhibition of other neurons. It is less clear that it does so solely in response to conducted nerve impulses. It appears more likely, since treatment with amino-oxyacetic acid can prevent the onset of convulsions (64), that when the level of GABA rises in the tissue it is released in part independently of inhibitory neuronal activity as an overflow. Raising the extracellular level in this case would be comparable in its effect to administration of GABA intracisternally.

In contrast, the occurrence of seizures in response to high oxygen pressure might well be due to a failure in the transmission process arising from the depletion of vesicular stores of GABA. L-Glutamic decarboxylase is significantly inhibited by high oxygen pressure (82) and this could account for a reduction of GABA both in the vesicles and elsewhere in the neuron.

It seems necessary then—at least to the present reviewer—to distinguish between GABA as a transmitter which is released from the nerve endings, probably from synaptic vesicles, only in response to a conducted nerve impulse, and metabolic GABA which is released into the extracellular space as the result of its accumulation within the cell. The synaptic release of GABA would not normally be subject to metabolic controls except in a permissive sense and it is difficult to see how it could fit in with Wood's suggested scheme; in contrast, release by overflow would be wholly dominated by metabolic events and it may well be that this does have a homeostatic function.

An earlier report by Jasper, Khan & Elliott (83) relating GABA release from the surface of the cortex to the state of activity of the brain does not seem to have been followed up. Recently, however, Mitchell & Srinivasan (84) have published a brief report of experiments in which they have studied the release of labelled GABA, with which the cortex had been allowed to equilibrate, in response to electrical stimulation of the cortex itself and the ipsilateral lateral geniculate body. The parameters of stimulation were chosen to produce inhibitory responses but it remains for further investigation to show that the observed release was in fact due to the activity of inhibitory neurons.

Of the original reasons for thinking that GABA is probably not a spinal inhibitory transmitter, the most important was that GABA could not be shown to hyperpolarize the motoneurons; another was that strychnine, which blocks the action of the natural inhibitor, did not reduce or prevent the inhibitory effect of GABA on any spinal neurons. The action of GABA is also not blocked by tetanus toxin although this blocks spinal inhibition; but whereas strychnine evidently acts postsynaptically (2, 3), tetanus toxin is thought to act presynaptically (2, 85) and would not therefore be expected to block effects of an agent which simulates the action of the natural inhibitor.

From more recent investigations with improved equipment [parallel as distinct from coaxial micropipettes (62)], it is now clear that GABA, in common with several other of the depressant amino acids, when applied by microiontophoresis, does cause hyperpolarization of the spinal motoneurons (4, 67). And on a number of quite rigorous tests its action on these cells appears to be identical with that of the transmitter (4). As we shall see later there is evidence that the transmitter of the inhibitory interneurons is glycine but this would not necessarily exclude GABA from having a similar function in the cord. More than one type of inhibitory interneuron may exist and descending neurons of upper or supraspinal origin offer other possible pathways in which it could be the transmitter.

One reason for thinking that GABA might be a spinal transmitter is its uneven distribution in the spinal cord. According to Graham et al. (86) its concentration in the dorsal grey matter of the lumbosacral region of the cat's cord is about five times higher than in the spinal roots. Other evidence, however, is against GABA being a spinal transmitter.

In the first place it appears to be distinctly less potent than glycine in its action on motoneurons (4) and spinal interneurons although it may be about equally effective with glycine as a depressant of Renshaw cells (5).

Secondly, the inhibitory action of GABA on the spinal motoneurons, as well as on the interneurons and Renshaw cells, is not blocked by strychnine (4, 5), except in concentrations which are higher than are required to block the natural inhibition (87). This argument may now be thought to have greater force than it did earlier from the fact that strychnine readily blocks the action of the α- and β-depressant amino acids, including glycine, on all three populations of cells (4, 5, 87).

A third argument against GABA is the failure to reduce its concentration significantly in any area of the cat's lumbar spinal cord in response to degenerative procedures. Asphyxial destruction of interneurons in the lumbar cord with the loss of inhibition and of polysynaptic reflexes produced only slight or inconsistent changes in the level of GABA; Davidoff et al. (88, 89) therefore suggested that it is not a major agent of segmental spinal inhibition. Nor, apparently, is it the transmitter of descending inhibitory pathways coming from the brain and upper spinal cord. Rizzoli (90) has found that no significant loss of GABA occurs in the lumbar region of the spinal cord up to 21 days after it has been transected in the thoracic region.

Considering all the evidence, therefore, it seems that the uneven distribution of GABA in the spinal cord must have some other significance or that it functions in some more obscure spinal inhibitory pathway. Rizzoli (90) suggests that it may originate in cells of the upper dorsal horn, possibly in the substantia gelatinosa. It is possible also that not all supraspinal pathways would have degenerated in the 21 days he allowed in his experiments since degeneration rates in the CNS may vary markedly with fibre sizes (91). It should also be considered whether the disappearance of GABA in a degenerating nerve will necessarily follow the same time course as that demonstrated for other transmitters such as ACh and norepinephrine. But perhaps a more important consideration is that the amount of GABA functioning as transmitter is likely to be only a small fraction of the whole—the concentrations of GABA in the spinal cord expressed on a molar basis are of the order of 100 times larger than concentrations of ACh found in the nervous system—and if only the transmitter fraction is initially reduced by transection this evidence of degeneration might not be detected. The same considerations might be thought to apply to the experiments of Davidoff et al. (88, 89) on the asphyxial destruction of the spinal interneurons but in that case the neuron as a whole was damaged directly and more general effects on the metabolism of the cell might be expected.

Glycine.—Of the recent developments in the search for neurotransmitters the most interesting is the evidence implicating glycine as the hypothetical inhibitory transmitter of the spinal interneurons (4, 5, 67–69, 86, 88, 89, 92, 93). Although its depressant properties had already been described, glycine had not been specially remarked except as one of the class of depressant amino acids whose properties were first fully investigated by Curtis & Watkins (94, 3) in a study of the structural relations between amino acids such as glutamate and aspartate, which excite, and those such as GABA and β-alanine, which depress spinal neurons when applied to them by the technique of microiontophoresis. In comparison with GABA, β-alanine, and taurine, glycine appeared to be a less powerful inhibitor, although it was rated more powerful than α-alanine and some other neutral amino acids found in nervous tissue (3).

The evidence which first drew attention to glycine as a likely transmitter suspect of the spinal cord was first published in full by Graham, Shank, Werman & Aprison (86). Their results showed that, among five amino acids found in the cat spinal cord, the level of glycine (7.1 μmoles/g) was the highest; that it was most concentrated in the ventral grey matter where the endings of spinal interneurons should be congregated; and that there was a tenfold difference between its concentration in this region and its concentration in the spinal roots where its level was lowest. This unevenness of distribution which is also exhibited by GABA, and by cystathionine (95), although these are present in lower concentrations, is consistent with, and to that extent evidence for, glycine being a transmitter. In the case of glycine the evidence was rather stronger than for the other two substances since not only was it present in a higher concentration but it appeared to be associated with the interneurons. The same group of workers therefore investigated the possible role of glycine further. Their attack, based on the theoretical treatment by Werman (1), was aimed at testing two criteria by which the transmitter status of glycine might be judged. One was the 'criterion of the presence of the transmitter' or was glycine concentrated in the spinal interneurons? The other was the 'criterion of identical actions' or could glycine be shown by intracellular recording to produce the same conductance change in the motoneurons as that produced by the inhibitory transmitter released from spinal interneurons?

To find out whether glycine is concentrated in the interneurons they measured the levels of glycine, GABA, glutamate, aspartate, and glutamine in the spinal cord under normal conditions and after asphyxial destruction of large numbers of interneurons (88, 89). As already mentioned the changes produced in GABA were slight and inconsistent; nor was glutamine affected; but there was a significant loss of each of the other three amino acids. Glycine was reduced in the white matter of the ventral and dorsal cord, and in the dorsal horn; but the largest reduction was in the ventral grey matter; moreover, a significant correlation was found between the concentration of glycine and the numbers of small neurons surviving the treatment, in different samples. Glutamate also showed a general reduction but the biggest change was in the dorsal grey matter and there was no correlation between the neuron count and its concentration. Aspartate was reduced in ventral and dorsal grey matter but not elsewhere and a correlation was found between its concentration and the numbers of small neurons remaining.

In interpreting these results Davidoff et al. (89) concluded that glycine is associated with the interneurons and is probably the transmitter of the inhibitory interneurons. They also suggested that aspartate is the transmitter of the excitatory interneurons and that glutamate may be the transmitter of the dorsal root afferents (see later discussion). However, the important result of these experiments is that they go a long way to establish the first criterion mentioned above, the presence of glycine in the inhibitory interneurons of the spinal cord. To test whether there was identity of action of glycine and the inhibitory transmitter of the interneurons, Werman et al. (67) adopted the method of the Canberra workers (3, 94) of applying substances to single cells by microiontophoresis whilst recording the response of the cell either through extra- or intracellularly placed electrodes. In the first case they recorded through the central barrel of a five-barrel micropipette, from whose outer four barrels the test compounds were ejected as required; in the second case they used twin or parallel micropipettes fixed side by side, one the recording electrode which penetrated the cell and the other the pipette from which glycine was ejected onto the outside of the cell. The glycine pipette could also be used as a recording electrode. In addition, the intracellular micropipette was sometimes double-barrelled.

By these means they were able to show, in agreement with earlier work of Curtis and his associates (3, 94), that the application of glycine decreases or abolishes the firing of about 90 per cent of all spinal neurons. On spinal interneurons glycine was slightly more effective in reducing their firing rate. With intracellular recording they made a rigorous comparison between this inhibitory action of glycine on the motoneurons and the action of the inhibitory transmitter and found a remarkable similarity between the two. Glycine blocked spike invasion into the soma, caused membrane hyperpolarization, and reduced the size of the excitatory postsynaptic potential, all effects which appeared to be closely related to the conductance change it produced. The inhibitory postsynaptic potential was also sensitive to glycine and there was evidence of competition between it and the transmitter. The hyperpolarization produced by glycine and that produced by the transmitter were both converted into depolarization when halides were injected into the cell (see also 2). The authors were also able to show that none of these effects could have been due to glycine acting presynaptically. The possibility, however, of some presynaptic effects by glycine is apparently not altogether excluded (96).

These results were subsequently confirmed by Curtis et al. (4, 5, 68, 69) who also showed that the hyperpolarizing action of glycine, like that of the inhibitory transmitter, is blocked by strychnine. Thus glycine, in its hyperpolarizing action on the motoneurons and its susceptibility to the blocking action of strychnine, satisfies both of the criteria for the inhibitory transmitter originally emphasized by Curtis & Watkins (3) as well as Werman's (1) other criterion of the presence of the transmitter. But some differences and doubts remain.

One difference is that according to Curtis et al. (5) glycine depresses the firing of a high proportion of Renshaw cells (their figures: 169 out of 170) while Werman et al. found no evidence for such an effect. On the other hand, both groups are agreed that the firing of most spinal interneurons, other than the Renshaw cells, can be depressed by glycine. The explanation of the difference might conceivably lie in the conditions of anaesthesia. The animals experimented on by Curtis et al. were fully anaesthetized with sodium pentobarbital; those used by Werman et al. were more lightly anaesthetized and kept immobile with d-tubocurarine. Although d-tubocurarine does not normally pass the blood-brain barrier, the possibility should not be overlooked that a slow leakage into spinal tissue may occur in an experiment in which initially some damage may have been done to the barrier in that region; if so it might interfere with the normal responses of the Renshaw

cells. This explanation may well not be the true one but where such competent investigators are concerned, results so different must be related to
differences in experimental conditions.

Another less serious difference concerns the action of strychnine. In
their recent papers Curtis and his associates (4, 5) have strongly emphasized their evidence that sensitivity to strychnine distinguishes the depressant actions both of the natural transmitter and of glycine from the depressant action of GABA which is not affected by strychnine. Further, the depressant actions of other α- and β-amino acids on spinal motoneurons, on
interneurons, on Renshaw cells, and in some cases on cortical cells are all
like that of glycine, opposed by strychnine while the depressant action of
GABA and of other ω-amino acids is not. This provides the basis for the
classification of the depressant amino acids into 'glycine-like' and 'GABA-
like'. Under the first heading, α-alanine, glycine, serine, and taurine were
found by Johnston (97) to be present in the spinal cord. Cystathionine is also
present in the cord but although its depressant action (95) was confirmed
(5) its sensitivity to strychnine was not tested.

The distinction between the strychnine-sensitive and strychnine-insensi-
tive amino acids found by Curtis's group has not been found to be so
clear-cut by Davidoff, Aprison & Werman (87). According to them the
difference is quantitative and not qualitative; in their hands strychnine can
reduce the inhibitory action of GABA on the spinal interneurons although
the reduction is less than the corresponding effect on glycine inhibition.
However, the concentration of strychnine solution used by Davidoff et al.
was ten times higher than the concentration used by Curtis et al. (4, 5).
Thus the quantitative difference is large enough to substantiate rather than
contradict the conclusions reached by Curtis et al.

Another, more recent difference in the findings of the two research
groups concerns the action of picrotoxin on spinal inhibition. According to
Eccles (2) picrotoxin blocks presynaptic inhibition and would not therefore
be expected to affect glycine inhibition if glycine is indeed the inhibitory
transmitter; but from evidence quoted by Curtis (52) and by Davidoff &
Aprison (96) it is possible that it can act postsynaptically. In commenting
on this evidence, Curtis (52) has argued that it is susceptible to other explanations and, in agreement with this view, he and his co-workers have found
no evidence that it can block the inhibitory action of glycine or the other
depressant amino acids on the spinal interneurons (5). In their tests picrotoxin was administered electrophoretically either as an anion at pH 11–12 or
as a cation at pH 2.5–3. On the other hand Davidoff & Aprison (96), in a
preliminary report, have described experiments in which picrotoxin, ejected
at pH 6.2 or 8, antagonized the action of glycine on almost all the spinal
interneurons studied. Since they found picrotoxin to be inactive at pH 2.5
and 11, they consider that the discrepancy between their results and those of
Curtis et al. can be explained on this basis. These results have so far only
been published in a preliminary form; and until further evidence is available

it is not certain how they will affect our present understanding of picrotoxin action, and the status of glycine as an inhibitory transmitter. It is evident that a rigorous reexamination of the evidence that the inhibition produced by glycine is due solely to a direct postsynaptic action will be necessary.

Glycine might also be the transmitter in inhibitory pathways of supraspinal origin, such as the descending fibres which inhibit the firing of Renshaw cells, since their inhibitory action can be reversibly reduced by strychnine (51). Since it has also been shown by the same group that glycine inhibits the Renshaw cells (see above) and that this inhibition is blocked by strychnine there is a *prima facie* case for identifying glycine or some closely related substance as the transmitter. Further, Rizzoli (90) has found that transection of the upper spinal cord produces a general reduction of glycine in the lumbar cord 21 days later; although the change was only large enough to be significant in the dorsolateral funiculus, the result suggests that glycine is associated with descending spinal axons.

Glycine may also be an inhibitory transmitter in neurons supplying the cuneate nucleus (98).

While GABA is a more potent depressant of cortical cells than glycine the reverse is true for spinal neurons. Curtis et al. (4, 5) found that when they attempted to depress homocysteic acid-induced firing of cortical cells glycine was such a weak depressant that it was often difficult to demonstrate an effect; they were able to show, however, that even this weak action was reversed by strychnine. Kelly & Krnjević (99) have also reported that glycine has a weaker action than GABA in blocking glutamate-induced firing of neurons in the cat's cortex. They also find that the membrane conductance, which is increased by GABA, is not increased by glycine as part of its depressant action.

To sum up, it seems reasonable to conclude at this time that glycine is an inhibitory transmitter of the spinal cord. Although the results of Curtis and his associates do not agree in all details with those from Aprison's group, each has produced positive evidence implicating glycine as the spinal transmitter and neither has obtained results incompatible with this interpretation. As with GABA, little or no evidence is available about how it is released and confirmation of its transmitter status will probably have to await evidence on this question.

ACIDIC AMINO ACIDS AS EXCITATORY TRANSMITTER AGENTS

It has long been clear that cholinergic and monoaminergic neurons could at best only represent a small proportion of the total numbers of central excitatory neurons; and that there must be many others which release other transmitter agents. Both glutamate and aspartate have been suggested as candidates for this rôle (66, 89, 100).

So far as glutamate is concerned this is not a new suggestion. It has been known for some time as a powerful excitant of neurons in both the brain (66) and the spinal cord (3, 94); and its presence in relatively large amounts in central nervous tissue, and its rapid, and rapidly reversible, action on various central neurons, have been cited as evidence that it is a neurotransmitter (66). But the view that its action in increasing the firing rate of neurons is unspecific seems to be more generally accepted (101). It is perhaps the fact that, like a number of other acidic amino acids, glutamate has been found to excite practically all central neurons on which it has been tested, that has lent greatest weight to this view. Recent evidence, however, shows that it may be more selective in its action than was previously thought. Steiner & Meyer (102) report that iontophoretic application of L-glutamate activated only about 50 per cent of the cells of the cuneate and gracilis nuclei. Moreover, Krnjević & Schwartz (37) found that unlike ACh, glutamate did not depolarize the unresponsive, probably neuroglial, cells of the cat's pericruciate cortex. In this one respect glutamate can be regarded as being more selective in its action than ACh.

Krnjević & Schwartz were also able to show by means of intracellular recording that the depolarizing action of glutamate on cortical nerve cells was accompanied by a fall in membrane resistance; the mechanism of its depolarizing action is therefore more in accordance with the expected behaviour of an excitatory transmitter than is the case for ACh.

In other papers from the same laboratory (98, 103) it has been suggested that glutamate is the transmitter released by first-order afferents to the cuneate nucleus. The cuneate neurons are very sensitive to glutamate and its application to them produces in many cases the same pattern of firing as the natural transmitter. This suggestion is supported by the work of Graham et al. (86) showing that dorsal roots contain 50 per cent more glutamic acid than ventral roots; and that within the cord its concentration is highest in the dorsal grey matter. Its concentration is also higher in the dorsal columns than in the ventral columns of white matter.

This distribution of glutamic acid in the spinal cord, according to Graham et al. (86) and Rizzoli (90), is in agreement with the suggestion that it is more concentrated in first-order somatic afferent neurons than in other neurons.

A significant loss of glutamate occurred in the dorsolateral funiculus in Rizzoli's (90) experiments 3 weeks after transection of the cord at a higher level, and in both the ventral and dorsal grey matter in experiments by Davidoff et al. (89) in which loss of interneurons was produced by asphyxia of the spinal cord. Neither of these experiments should have caused degenerative damage to the spinal afferents; and the loss of glutamic acid cannot therefore be explained as the result of such damage. It seems then that the operations had a more general damaging effect than the authors thought likely or there are other pathways in which glutamate is concentrated and therefore possibly a transmitter.

Graham et al. (86) also measured the distribution of aspartic acid in the cat's spinal cord. From the evidence that it is most concentrated in the dorsal grey matter (2.05 μmoles/g) and elsewhere considerably lower (1–1.3

μmoles/g) they concluded that it could be the transmitter of the excitatory interneurons of the spinal cord.

The subsequent paper from the same laboratory by Davidoff et al. (89) appeared to confirm this identification when it was shown that asphyxial damage of the cord caused a reduction of aspartate in the grey matter which could be correlated with the loss of spinal interneurons. But the authors concluded that physiological studies would be necessary to clarify this possibility. These remain to be done.

The known characteristics of the excitatory action of glutamate, and of aspartate although it has been less studied, make it probable that they have a direct postsynaptic action. This does not necessarily exclude a presynaptic action as well and it may be relevant that on some invertebrate preparations glutamate increases the quantal release of transmitter (104–106). For example, Florey & Woodcock (106) have reported evidence that glutamate enhances the spontaneous quantal release of transmitter from crab motor nerve terminals and that this action adds significantly to the direct effect of glutamate on the muscle fibres. Possibly glutamate can have analogous presynaptic effects in the mammalian CNS although this seems less probable in view of the temporal precision with which the firing of glutamate-sensitive cells can be controlled by its iontophoretic application.

CONCLUSION

Two kinds of transmitter agents have been discussed in this review. One group, ACh, norepinephrine, dopamine, and 5-HT, are synthetic products of the cells in which they are found, and are limited to the neurons that have specialized equipment for this production; while, too, they may have a part in controlling metabolism they are not metabolites in any ordinary sense of the word. But the second group, the amino acids, appear to have both a metabolic and a transmitter function and are apparently constituents of most central neurons. Because of this metabolic function it is difficult in some cases to apply the tests of presence of the transmitter and of its related enzymes as evidence for the transmitter function of such substances; and even their release in response to stimulation is open to more than one interpretation. Where the evidence is much stronger is in the analysis of their postsynaptic actions and comparison of these with the postsynaptic actions of the true transmitter. Evidence of this kind gives the most impressive support for GABA and glycine as inhibitory transmitters. It is somewhat less impressive in the case of the monoamines and ACh. But for them evidence of their presence in certain neurons, the related distribution of the enzymes which synthesize or inactivate them, their release in response to stimulation of the neural paths in which they are found, and evidence of pharmacological identity of action together form a case which makes it virtually certain that they are central transmitters.

It is frequently suggested that one or other of the substances considered here may not be true transmitters but 'regulators' or 'modulators' of neuronal activity. In making distinctions of this kind the critical question is how the substance is released. If it is released as the terminal effect of a conducted nerve impulse and as a result produces a change in the excitability of another neuron then it must be regarded as a transmitter. On the other hand, if a substance such as GABA is released from a resting nerve cell as a result of the metabolic state of the cell, and the effect of such overflow is to reduce the excitability of neighbouring cells, this process could hardly be described as neurotransmission. A substance released in this way might well have a generalized action and could then be fittingly described as a 'regulator'. If Wood's (80) ideas are right it may be that overflow, of this kind, of GABA and of glutamic acid does occur as the result of metabolic events; and whether or not they are also transmitters in the sense defined above, they could be regulators of neural activity.

Of any of the substances discussed here, it is not possible to say that the evidence in favour of their transmitter rôle is conclusive beyond all possible shadow of doubt! But the progress made in their study during the past three years has been considerable and has brought a better understanding of how transmitter agents work and so may open the way to the kind of experiments by which certainty may be achieved in one direction or the other.

ACKNOWLEDGEMENTS

I would like to thank Miss Catherine Page for her considerable help in preparing this manuscript, Mrs. Dorothy George for help in preparing the references, Miss Wendy Reynolds and Mr. Butcher for assistance in collecting the journals and books to which reference has been made, and Dr. Michael Smith for reading and criticizing an earlier version of the manuscript.

LITERATURE CITED

1. Werman, R. Criteria for identification of a central nervous system transmitter. *Comp. Biochem. Physiol.*, **18**, 745–66 (1966)
2. Eccles, J. C. *The Physiology of Synapses* (Springer, Berlin, 316 pp., 1964)
3. Curtis, D. R., Watkins, J. C. The pharmacology of amino acids related to gamma-aminobutyric acid. *Pharmacol. Rev.*, **17**, 347–91 (1965)
4. Curtis, D. R., Hösli, L., Johnston, G. A. R., Johnston, I. H. The hyperpolarization of spinal motoneurones by glycine and related amino acids. *Exptl. Brain Res.*, **5**, 235–58 (1968)
5. Curtis, D. R., Hösli, L., Johnston, G. A. R. A pharmacological study of the depression of spinal neurones by glycine and related amino acids. *Exptl. Brain Res.*, **6**, 1–18 (1968)
6. Gillespie, J. S. Adrenergic mechanisms. *Proc. Intern. Union Physiol. Sci., 24th, Washington, 1968*, **6**, 107–8
7. Fuxe, K. Localization and mapping of amine-containing neurons by fluorescent techniques. *Neurosci. Res. Progr. Bull.*, **5**, 18–21 (1967)
8. Bloom, F. E. Localization of norepinephrine in dense-core vesciles. *Neurosci. Res. Progr. Bull.*, **5**, 11–17 (1967)
9. Wood, J. G. Electron microscopic localization of amines in central nervous tissue. *Nature*, **209**, 1131–33 (1966)
10. Wood, J. G. Cytochemical localization of 5-hydroxytryptamine (5-HT) in the central nervous system (CNS). *Anat. Record*, **157**, 343–44 (1967)
11. Salpeter, M. M., Budd, C. The distribution of exogenous ^{3}H-norepinephrine within sympathetic

nerve. *J. Anat.*, **104**, 580 (1969)

12. Snipes, R. L., Thoenen, H., Tranzer, J. P. Fine structural localization of exogenous 5-HT in vesicles of adrenergic nerve terminals. *Experientia*, **24**, 1026–27 (1968)

13. Bodian, D. Electron microscopy: two major synaptic types on spinal motoneurons. *Science,* **151**, 1093–94 (1966)

14. Akert, K., Sandri, C. An electron-microscopic study of zinc iodide-osmium impregnation of neurons. I. Staining of synaptic vesicles at cholinergic junctions. *Brain Res.,* **7**, 286–95 (1968)

15. Pellegrino de Iraldi, A., Gueudet, R. Action of reserpine on the osmium tetroxide zinc iodide reactive site of synaptic vesicles in the pineal nerves of the rat. *Z. Zellforsch.,* **91**, 178–85 (1968)

16. Magoun, H. W. *The Waking Brain* (Thomas, Springfield, 135 pp., 1958)

17. Lewis, P. R., Shute, C. C. D. The cholinergic limbic system: projections to hippocampal formation, medial cortex, nuclei of the ascending cholinergic reticular system, and the subfornical organ and supra-optic crest. *Brain,* **90**, 521–40 (1967)

18. Shute, C. C. D., Lewis, P. R. The ascending cholinergic reticular system: neocortical, olfactory and subcortical projections. *Brain,* **90**, 497–520 (1967)

19. Mitchell, J. F. Acetylcholine release from the brain. In *Mechanisms of Release of Biogenic Amines Proc. Wenner-Gren Symp., 1965, Stockholm,* 425–37 (Pergamon, Oxford, 1966)

20. Szerb, J. C. Cortical acetylcholine release and electroencephalographic arousal. *J. Physiol. (London),* **192**, 329–43 (1967)

21. Krnjević, K. Chemical transmission and cortical arousal. *Anesthesiology,* **28**, 100–5 (1967)

22. Collier, B., Mitchell, J. F. The central release of acetylcholine during stimulation of the visual pathway. *J. Physiol. (London),* **184**, 239–54 (1966)

23. Collier, B., Mitchell, J. F. The central release of acetylcholine during consciousness and after brain lesions. *J. Physiol. (London),* **188**, 83–98 (1967)

24. Neal, M. J., Hemsworth, B. A., Mitchell, J. F. The excitation of central cholinergic mechanisms by stimulation of the auditory pathway. *Life Sci.,* **7**, 757–63 (1968)

25. Phillis, J. W. Acetylcholine release from the cerebral cortex: its role in cortical arousal. *Brain Res.,* **7**, 378–89 (1968)

26. Krnjević, K., Silver, A. A histochemical study of cholinergic fibres in the cerebral cortex. *J. Anat.,* **99**, 711–59 (1965)

27. Hemsworth, B. A., Mitchell, J. F. The characteristics of acetylcholine release mechanisms in the auditory cortex. *Brit. J. Pharmacol.,* **36**, 161–70 (1969)

28. Feldberg, W., Vogt, M. Acetylcholine synthesis in different regions of the central nervous system. *J. Physiol. (London),* **107**, 372–81 (1948)

29. Miller, E., Heller, A., Moore, R. Y. Acetylcholine in rabbit visual system nuclei after enucleation and visual cortex ablation. *J. Pharmacol. Exptl. Therap.,* **165**, 117–25 (1969)

30. Feldberg, W. Present views on the mode of action of acetylcholine in the central nervous system. *Physiol. Rev.,* **25**, 596–642 (1945)

31. Steiner, F. A. Influence of micro-electrophoretically applied acetylcholine on the responsiveness of hippocampal and lateral geniculate neurones. *Pflügers Arch.,* **303**, 173–80 (1968)

32. Phillis, J. W., York, D. H. Cholinergic inhibition in the cerebral cortex. *Brain Res.,* **5**, 517–20 (1967)

33. Phillis, J. W., York, D. H. Pharmacological studies on a cholinergic inhibition in the cerebral cortex. *Brain Res.,* **10**, 297–306 (1968)

34. Marchisio, P. C., Consolo, S. Developmental changes of choline acetyltransferase (ChAc) activity in chick embryo spinal and sympathetic ganglia. *J. Neurochem.,* **15**, 759–64 (1968)

35. Hokin, L. Response of phosphatidic acid and phosphatidyl inositol turnover to acetylcholine. *Neurosci. Res. Progr. Bull.,* **5**, 26–31 (1967)

36. Hokin, M. Molecular control of acetylcholine-responsive sodium pumps. *Neurosci. Res. Progr. Bull.,* **5**, 32–36 (1967)

37. Krnjević, K., Schwartz, S. Some

properties of unresponsive cells in the cerebral cortex. *Exptl. Brain Res.*, **3**, 306–19 (1967)

38. Gwyn, D. G., Silver, A., Wolstencroft, J. H. Evidence for ascending and descending cholinergic fibres in cat spinal cord. *J. Physiol. (London)*, **201**, 23–24P (1968)

39. Fuxe, K., Hökfelt, T., Ungerstedt, U. Distribution of monoamines in the mammalian central nervous system by histochemical studies. In *Metabolism of Amines in the Brain. Proc. Symp. Brit. Scand. Pharmacol. Soc., Edinburgh, 1968*, 10–22 (Hooper, G., Ed., Macmillan, London, 74 pp., 1969)

40. Reis, D. J., Fuxe, K. Depletion of noradrenaline in brainstem neurons during sham rage behaviour produced by acute brainstem transection in cat. *Brain Res.*, **7**, 448–51 (1968)

41. Malcolm, J. L., Saraiva, P., Spear, P. J. Cholinergic and adrenergic inhibition in the rat cerebral cortex. *Intern. J. Neuropharmacol.*, **6**, 509–27 (1967)

42. Roberts, M. H. T., Straughan, D. W. Actions of noradrenaline and mescaline on cortical neurones. *Arch. Exptl. Pathol. Pharmakol.*, **259**, 191 (1968)

43. Johnson, E. S., Roberts, M. H. T., Sobieszek, A., Straughan, D. W. Excitation of cortical neurones by noradrenaline. *Brit. J. Pharmacol.*, **34**, 221–22p (1968)

44. Johnson, E. S., Roberts, M. H. T., Straughan, D. W. Adrenergic responses in the cerebral cortex. *J. Physiol. (London)*, **201**, 21–22P (1969)

45. Tebēcis, A. K. Are 5-hydroxytryptamine and noradrenaline inhibitory transmitters in the medial geniculate nucleus? *Brain Res.*, **6**, 780–82 (1967)

46. Boakes, R. J., Bradley, P. B., Brookes, N., Candy, J. M., Wolstencroft, J. H. Effects of noradrenaline and its analogues on brain stem neurones. *J. Physiol. (London)*, **201**, 20–21P (1969)

47. York, D. H. The inhibitory action of dopamine on neurones of the caudate nucleus. *Brain Res.*, **5**, 263–66 (1967)

48. Roberts, M. H. T., Straughan, D. W. Excitation and depression of cortical neurones by 5-hydroxytrypta-

mine. *J. Physiol. (London)*, **193**, 269–94 (1967)

49. Weight, F. F., Salmoiraghi, G. C. Responses of spinal cord interneurons to acetylcholine, norepinephrine and serotonin administered by microelectrophoresis. *J. Pharmacol. Exptl. Therap.*, **153**, 420–27 (1966)

50. Engberg, I., Ryall, R. W. The action of mono-amines upon [cat] spinal neurones. *Life Sci.*, **4**, 2223–27 (1965)

51. Biscoe, T. J., Curtis, D. R. Noradrenaline and inhibition of Renshaw cells. *Science,* **151**, 1230–31 (1966)

52. Curtis, D. R. Pharmacology and neurochemistry of mammalian central inhibitory processes. In *Structure and Functions of Inhibitory Neuronal Mechanisms Proc. 4th Intern. Mtg. Neurobiologists, 1966, Stockholm*, 429–56 (Euler, U. S. v., Ed., Pergamon, 1968)

53. Krnjević, K. Microelectrophoretic studies with micropipettes. In *Neuropsychopharmacology*, **3**, 260–64 (Bradley, P. G., Flügal, F., Hock, P., Eds., Elsevier, Amsterdam, 1963)

54. Krnjević, K., Randić, M., Straughan, D. W. Pharmacology of cortical inhibition. *J. Physiol. (London)*, **184**, 78–105 (1966)

55. Obata, K. Pharmacological study on postsynaptic inhibition of Deiters' neurones. *Proc. Intern. Union Physiol. Sci., 23rd, Tokyo, 1965*, **5**, 406

56. Obata, K., Ito, M., Ochi, R., Sato, N. Pharmacological properties of the postsynaptic inhibition by Purkinje cell axons and the action of γ-amino-butyric acid on Deiters neurones. *Exptl. Brain Res.*, **4**, 43–57 (1967)

57. Curtis, D. R. The pharmacology of central and peripheral inhibition, *Pharmacol. Rev.*, **15**, 333–63 (1963)

58. Biscoe, T. J., Curtis, D. R. Strychnine and cortical inhibition. *Nature,* **214**, 914–15 (1967)

59. Krnjević, K., Schwartz, S. Cortical inhibition and GABA. *Fed. Proc.*, **25**, 627 (1966)

60. Krnjević, K., Schwartz, S. Is γ-aminobutyric acid an inhibitory transmitter? *Nature,* **211**, 1372–74 (1966)

61. Krnjević, K., Schwartz, S. The action

of γ-aminobutyric acid on cortical neurones. *Exptl. Brain Res., 3,* 320–36 (1967)

62. Curtis, D. R. A method for assembly of "parallel" micro-pipettes. *Electroenceph. Clin. Neurophysiol., 24,* 587–89 (1968)

63. Fahn, S., Côté, L. J. Regional distribution of γ-aminobutyric acid (GABA) in brain of the rhesus monkey. *J. Neurochem., 15,* 209–13 (1968)

64. Roberts, E., Kuriyama, K. Biochemical-physiological correlations in studies of the γ-aminobutyric acid system. *Brain Res., 8,* 1–35 (1968)

65. Kuriyama, K., Sisken, B., Haber, B., Roberts, E. The γ-aminobutyric acid system in rabbit retina. *Brain Res., 9,* 165–68 (1968)

66. Krnjević, K. Micro-iontophoretic studies on cortical neurons. *Intern. Rev. Neurobiol., 7,* 41–98 (1964)

67. Werman, R., Davidoff, R. A., Aprison, M. H. Inhibitory action of glycine on spinal neurons in the cat. *J. Neurophysiol., 31,* 81–95 (1968)

68. Curtis, D. R., Hösli, L., Johnston, G. A. R., Johnston, I. H. Glycine and spinal inhibition. *Brain Res., 5,* 112–14 (1967)

69. Curtis, D. R., Hösli, L., Johnston, G. A. R. Inhibition of spinal neurones by glycine. *Nature, 215,* 1502–3 (1967)

70. Diamond, J. The activation and distribution of GABA and L-glutamate receptors on goldfish Mauthner neurones: an analysis of dendritic remote inhibition. *J. Physiol. (London), 194,* 669–723 (1968)

71. Takeuchi, A., Takeuchi, N. Localized action of gamma-aminobutyric acid on the crayfish muscle. *J. Physiol. (London), 177,* 225–38 (1965)

72. Kuriyama, K., Roberts, E., Kakefuda, T. Association of the γ-aminobutyric acid system with a synaptic vesicle fraction from mouse brain. *Brain Res., 8,* 135–52 (1968)

73. Iversen, L. L., Neal, M. J. Subcellular distribution of endogenous and [³H]-GABA in rat cerebral cortex. *Brit. J. Pharmacol., 36,* 206–8P (1969)

74. Hebb, C. O. Synthesis and storage of acetylcholine (ACh) considered as a special example of a synaptic transmitter. *Proc. Intern. Union*

Physiol. Sci., 24th, Washington, 1968, 6, 277–78

75. Krnjević, K., Randić, M., Straughan, D. W. An inhibitory process in the cerebral cortex. *J. Physiol. (London), 184,* 16–48 (1966)

76. Krnjević, K., Randić, M., Straughan, D. W. Nature of a cortical inhibitory process. *J. Physiol. (London), 184,* 49–77 (1966)

77. Weichert, P., Herbst, A. Provocation of cerebral seizures by derangement of the natural balance between glutamic acid and γ-aminobutyric acid. *J. Neurochem., 13,* 59–64 (1966)

78. Essig, C. F. Possible relation of brain gamma-aminobutyric acid (GABA) to barbiturate abstinence convulsions. *Arch. Intern. Pharmacodyn., 176,* 97–103 (1968)

79. DeFeudis, F. V., Elliott, K. A. C. Convulsions and γ-aminobutyric acid content of rat brain. *Can. J. Physiol. Pharmacol., 46,* 803–4 (1968)

80. Wood, J. D. A possible role for gamma-aminobutyric acid in the homeostatic control of brain metabolism under conditions of hypoxia. *Exptl. Brain Res., 4,* 81–84 (1967)

81. Waksman, A., Rubinstein, M. K., Kuriyama, K., Roberts, E. Localization of γ-aminobutyric-α-oxoglutaric acid transaminase in mouse brain. *J. Neurochem., 15,* 351–57 (1968)

82. Wood, J. D., Watson, W. J., Ducker, A. J. Oxygen poisoning in various mammalian species and the possible role of gamma-aminobutyric acid metabolism. *J. Neurochem., 14,* 1067–74 (1967)

83. Jasper, H. H., Khan, R. T., Elliott, K. A. C. Amino acid released from the cerebral cortex in relation to its state of activation. *Science, 147,* 1448–49 (1965)

84. Mitchell, J. F., Srinivasan, V. The release of [³H]γ-aminobutyric acid from the surface of the brain by electrical stimuli which produce synaptic inhibition. *J. Physiol. (London)* (In press, 1969)

85. Curtis, D. R., de Groat, W. C. Tetanus toxin and spinal inhibition. *Brain Res., 10,* 208–12 (1968)

86. Graham, L. T., Shank, R. P., Werman, R., Aprison, M. H. Distribution of some synaptic transmitter

suspects in cat spinal cord: glutamic acid, aspartic acid, γ-aminobutyric acid, glycine, and glutamine. *J. Neurochem.*, **14**, 465–72 (1967)

87. Davidoff, R. A., Aprison, M. H., Werman, R. The effects of strychnine on the inhibition of interneurons by glycine and γ-aminobutyric acid. *Intern. J. Neuropharamcol.*, **8**, 191–94 (1969)

88. Davidoff, R. A., Shank, R. P., Graham, L. T., Aprison, M. H., Werman, R. Is glycine a neurotransmitter? *Nature*, **214**, 680–81 (1967)

89. Davidoff, R. A., Graham, L. T., Shank, R. P., Werman, R., Aprison, M. H. Changes in amino acid concentrations associated with loss of spinal interneurons. *J. Neurochem.*, **14**, 1025–31 (1967)

90. Rizzoli, A. A. Distribution of glutamic acid, aspartic acid, γ-aminobutyric acid and glycine in six areas of cat spinal cord before and after transection. *Brain Res.*, **11**, 11–18 (1968)

91. van Crevel, H. *The Rate of Secondary Degeneration in the Central Nervous System. An Experimental Study in the Pyramid and Optic Nerve of the Cat* (Doctoral thesis, Univ. Leiden, Ijdo, Leiden, 93 pp., 1958)

92. Aprison, M. H., Werman, R. The distribution of glycine in cat spinal cord and roots. *Life Sci.*, **4**, 2075–83 (1965)

93. Werman, R., Davidoff, R. A., Aprison, M. H. Inhibition of motoneurones by iontophoresis of glycine. *Nature*, **214**, 681–83 (1967)

94. Curtis, D. R., Watkins, J. C. The excitation and depression of spinal neurones by structurally related amino acids. *J. Neurochem.*, **6**, 117–41 (1960)

95. Werman, R., Davidoff, R. A., Aprison, M. H. The inhibitory action of cystathionine. *Life Sci.*, **5**, 1431–40 (1966)

96. Davidoff, R. A., Aprison, M. H. Picrotoxin antagonism of the inhibition of interneurons by glycine. *Life Sci.*, **8**, 107–12 (1969)

97. Johnston, G. A. R. The intraspinal distribution of some depressant amino acids. *J. Neurochem.*, **15**, 1013–17 (1968)

98. Galindo, A., Krnjević, K., Schwartz, S. Micro-iontophoretic studies on neurones in the cuneate nucleus. *J. Physiol. (London)*, **192**, 359–77 (1967)

99. Kelly, J. S., Krnjević, K. Effects of γ-aminobuytric acid and glycine on cortical neurones. *Nature*, **219**, 1380–81 (1968)

100. Johnston, G. A. R., de Groat, W. C., Curtis, D. R. Tetanus toxin and amino acid levels in cat spinal cord. *J. Neurochem.*, **16**, 797–800 (1969)

101. Salmoiraghi, G. C., Stefanis, C. N. A critique of iontophoretic studies of central nervous system neurons. *Intern. Rev. Neurobiol.*, **10**, 1–30 (1967)

102. Steiner, F. A., Meyer, M. Actions of L-glutamate, acetylcholine and dopamine on single neurones in the nuclei cuneatus and gracilis of the cat. *Experientia*, **22**, 58–59 (1966)

103. Galindo, A., Krnjević, K., Schwartz, S. Patterns of firing in cuneate neurones and some effects of Flaxedil. *Exptl. Brain Res.*, **5**, 87–101 (1968)

104. Kerkut, G. A., Walker, R. J. The effect of L-glutamate, acetylcholine and gamma-aminobutyric acid on the miniature end-plate potentials and contractures of the coxal muscles of the cockroach, *Periplaneta americana. Comp. Biochem. Physiol.*, **17**, 435–54 (1966)

105. Usherwood, P. N. R., Machili, P. Chemical transmission at the insect excitatory neuromuscular synapse. *Nature*, **210**, 634–36 (1966)

106. Florey, E., Woodcock, B. Presynaptic excitatory action of glutamate applied to crab nerve-muscle preparations. *Comp. Biochem. Physiol.*, **26**, 661–51 (1968)

THE FUNCTIONAL ORGANIZATION OF INVERTEBRATE GANGLIA

Eric R. Kandel and Irving Kupfermann

Departments of Physiology and Psychiatry, New York University Medical School
The Public Health Research Institute of the City of New York

INTRODUCTION

Invertebrate preparations have had a prominent role in the growth of cellular neurophysiology. The giant axons of squid and cuttlefish, introduced into neurophysiology by J. Z. Young (335, 336), were useful in developing and testing the ionic hypothesis of the resting and action potentials (103, 104, 105); studies on the giant synapse of the squid and the neuromuscular junction of the crab helped lay the foundation for modern ideas of synaptic excitation and inhibition (25, 26, 76, 94, 141); and the crayfish stretch receptor (163) and the eye of *Limulus* (98) provided excellent material for studying sensory processing. These and the parallel studies on the vertebrate neuromuscular junction and central and sensory neurons provided the interdigitating details of the relatively complete picture of the biophysical functioning of nerve cells that we now have. (For reviews see 64, 140.)

These comparative studies of nerve cells indicate that all neurons are qualitatively rather similar in their electrophysiological properties. Nevertheless, different nervous systems have greatly differing capacities for generating behavior. One nervous system therefore apparently differs from another not in the types of basic neurons used but rather in the number of neurons, in the way neurons are interconnected, and in the precise function of the interconnections. Because of the complex interconnections of their individual cells, even simple nervous systems show certain surprising or "emergent" properties which cannot be predicted from the properties of the individual neurons. Neural scientists are therefore beginning to tackle the more complex problem of the organization and function of interconnected systems of neurons. Descriptions on this level are an essential prerequisite for understanding behavior. Such analyses are also relevant to genetic studies of the nervous system. By specifying the precision involved in the interconnections among neurons and the rules determining their functional expression, these studies provide a blueprint of what genetic and developmental processes must accomplish.

As neural scientists begin to address themselves to the organization of

193

neuronal systems it seems necessary to ask: Will invertebrate preparations prove useful here? The solutions given by the studies of the squid giant axon and of invertebrate synapses are interesting because they are general and provide many of the principles for understanding cellular functioning in all nervous systems. Are the rules which govern the organization of invertebrate ganglia also likely to prove general and will they apply to the organization of other neuronal systems?

One could argue that the rules of neural organization will differ in vertebrates and invertebrates and that here a comparative and reductionist approach will fail. For example, man has behavioral capacities such as abstract thinking and language, which are not found among invertebrates and which clearly require unique types of neuronal organization. Although true, we think this is not the issue at hand. The question is not whether some behaviors and their neuronal organization are peculiar to the mammalian brain, but whether any behaviors are so general as to suggest common patterns of neuronal organization. Here the answer is clear: simple behavioral patterns such as elementary perception, motor coordination, and learning are found in higher invertebrates as well as vertebrates. It must be admitted that the existence of common behavioral capabilities in man and higher invertebrates does not *necessarily* mean that common neuronal mechanisms are involved; it does however suggest that the mechanisms may be general and should be explored fully in whatever preparation they can be studied in most effectively. For example, a complete and rigorous analysis of a simple learning task in any animal, no matter how humble, is likely to prove more instructive than incomplete or less direct studies of learning in complex forms. Even if the neural mechanisms are not identical, established differences between invertebrate and vertebrate mechanisms are nonetheless likely to yield important insights which will enrich our understanding of learning in all animals.

In this review we will consider several trends emerging from studies which have used invertebrate ganglia to analyze the organization and function of neuronal systems. We will limit this review to certain higher invertebrates: annelids, gastropod molluscs, and arthropods, where the most detailed cellular studies of functional organization are available. We will begin with some anatomical and developmental considerations which are relevant to the physiological analysis of invertebrate ganglia and which also illustrate the advantages offered by these preparations for the solution of certain physiological and genetic problems. We will then discuss afferent aggregates and central sensory systems, and motor aggregates and the control of movement. Finally we will consider some aspects of behavioral modifications in invertebrates, in particular, reflex habituation.

With the exception of some sections in Horridge's 1963 review (111), the functional organization of invertebrate ganglia has not been previously considered in the *Annual Reviews*. We will therefore consider some important earlier studies as well as recent papers. We make no attempt at a complete coverage of this vast field. We have been highly selective and have been primarily guided by our biases. Specifically we have tried to focus on problems of functional organization common to the invertebrate and vertebrate CNS. The interested reader should also consult Bullock & Horridge's important treatise on the invertebrate nervous system (27), as well as other more specialized reviews and symposia (32, 70, 111, 113, 277, 286, 306).

ANATOMICAL ORGANIZATION OF INVERTEBRATE GANGLIA

The central neurons of higher invertebrates are characteristically clustered together in ganglia which connect to symmetrical ganglia by means of commissures, to other ganglia by means of connectives, and to the periphery by means of mixed (afferent and efferent) nerves. Often the two symmetrical ganglia fuse, forming a single unit, and in addition, several of the head ganglia usually fuse to form the brain. For a general discussion of the ultrastructure of an invertebrate ganglion, Smith & Treherne's review should be consulted (260).

The typical invertebrate ganglion has three subdivisions: a surrounding sheath, a region of cell bodies, and a region of neuropile.

THE SHEATH

The sheath, or neural lamella, is a fibrous capsule containing collagen fibers, fibroblasts, and, in some cases muscle cells, all set in a finely granular matrix. The sheath encloses the CNS, including the ganglia, the connectives, the commissures, and the proximal parts of the peripheral nerves. Although often thickened around ganglia, the sheath seems to offer no particular barrier to the diffusion of small molecules (164, 260, 313, 314), and is primarily protective, providing structural support for the neural architecture. The capsule often penetrates into central ganglia, subdividing them into different regions (e.g. 42). In some species in which the nervous system is avascular the sheath is highly vascularized and contains within it numerous fine processes of the neurosecretory cells of the ganglion. In these cases the sheath seems also to serve as a neurohemal organ for storing and releasing the neurosecretory products (see e.g. 41, 80, 246, 259).

THE CELL BODY REGION

General.—As in all nervous systems, the substance of the invertebrate ganglion is divided into two zones: cellular and fibrous. This primary differentiation, however, occurs in very different ways in the invertebrate and the vertebrate CNS (27). In vertebrates the two zones are intermingled and axons enter into the cellular zone. In invertebrates the zones are separated. In the invertebrate ganglion the cell bodies of its neurons, almost all of which are monopolar, are gathered in a rind around the outside of the ganglion. This cellular region is devoid of axons and synapses. Each neuron sends its axon into a central region, the neuropile, which consists of the synaptic field made up of the connections between processes of neurons lying within the ganglion and the connections between neurons in this ganglion and axons from other ganglia or from the periphery. The central region also contains fibers of passage that run through without making synaptic connections.

This characteristic segregation in higher invertebrate ganglia into a peripheral cell body region and a central neuropile is of great experimental advantage. For example, the location of the cell bodies on the outer surface often makes it possible to see individual cells in the intact ganglion under the dissecting microscope. As a result, cells may be identified repeatedly from preparation to preparation by a number of purely visual criteria such as position, size, and pigmentation. In the past few years maps of cells so identified have been obtained in annelids, crustaceans, insects, and gastropod molluscs (45, 49, 62, 80, 199, 207, 237, 315). In these invertebrates there has been a remarkable constancy of prominently recognizable cells which applies not only to cell size, relative position, and morphological, electrophysiological, and biochemical properties but also to the central interconnections between cells in the few cases examined (12, 14, 133, 232). Some large cells must also be constant in the vertebrate CNS as is evident from such identifiable cells as the Mauthner and Mueller neurons (81, 248).

The identifiable invertebrate neurons are often large. For example some identified cell bodies in leech ganglia reach 100 μ in diameter, some in the lobster reach 200 μ, and occasional cells in marine gastropods (*Aplysia* and *Tritonia*) can reach 1000 μ. These large cells can be readily impaled with microelectrodes and it is usually not difficult to record from several cells simultaneously and to study their interactions. Because of their size, individual cells can also be dissected out by hand, and since the cell bodies are free of synapses, they provide relatively pure material for biochemical studies (88, 89, 207, 250). Finally, in annelids and molluscs, and perhaps in other invertebrates, the cell bodies contain chemosensitive receptors which appear to be similar to those found in the neuropile. Thus the cell body, although free of synapses, provides an experimental synaptic membrane for detailed studies of junctional properties (11, 49, 79, 153, 274). As a result of these several advantages the transmitter biochemistry and pharmacology of certain invertebrate preparations, such as the lobster and *Aplysia,* are quite advanced (for reviews see 87, 132, 151, 160, 272).

Functional and biochemical architecture of the cell body region.—The cell body of an invertebrate neuron is relatively free and dangles at the end of an axon held fixed by its connections in the neuropile. As a result of mechanical forces, a given cell body in a certain ganglion might be pushed into different positions in different individuals while still keeping a constant set of synaptic connections. In fact, slight variations in the position of identified cells are often found (80, 207). It might therefore seem that there should be no necessary correlation between the function of a cell and the topographical position of its cell body within the cortical surface of the ganglion. In the past 5 years, however, several maps of identified cells have been obtained which show correlations between topographical groupings in the cell body region and cellular function (45, 80, 200, 207).

A prototype of this class of study is that by Otsuka, Kravitz & Potter (207) on the abdominal ganglion of the lobster. Twenty-one pairs of neurons going to muscle were examined according to four criteria: position of the cell in the ganglion; which muscle the cell innervated; whether the innervation was inhibitory or excitatory; and whether the cell contained high concentration of either γ-aminobutyric acid (GABA), the inhibitory transmitter in this ganglion, or glutamate, the putative excitatory transmitter. Otsuka et al. (207) found that the cell bodies occurred in groupings which were relatively constant in location and composition and in which the constituent cells showed one or more common features. The most important characteristic of a grouping appeared to be the type of transmitter synthesized by the cells. For example, three cells which contained high concentrations of GABA were grouped together even though the cells mediated inhibition to three unrelated muscles. Two other high GABA-containing cells of unknown function were also located near this cluster. Given common transmitter synthesis, cells were next grouped according to reflex function. Fourteen cells were found to be excitatory motoneurons to muscle. These cells all contained high concentration of glutamate (and low GABA), and adjacent cells innervated the same or synergistic muscles. Finally, since these ganglia are symmetrical, each cell also had a functional partner of the same size and position on the opposite side of the ganglion.

Grouping of cells according to common transmitter has been examined in other ganglia and for two other transmitters, acetylcholine and 5-hydroxytryptamine (serotonin). Giller & Schwartz (88, 89) have provided a biochemical map of the abdominal ganglion of *Aplysia* of cells high in acetylcholine, based upon the demonstration of the synthesizing enzyme, choline transacetylase, in identified cell bodies. Only three of thirty identified cells examined contained choline transacetylase. Two of these cells are grouped together; the third cell (R2) is homologous with a cell in the left pleural ganglion which also contained the transferase. A fluorescence histochemical map for cells containing serotonin has now been obtained in the leech (74, 152, 250). In the most complete study, three pairs of symmetrical cells and one additional cell were found to be high in serotonin (250). These cells were not grouped together, however; each of the cells on one side was in a different packet.

The causal factors determining the grouping of cell bodies are unknown but Otsuka et al. (207) have now advanced a number of reasonable suggestions. They have suggested that in the lobster the cluster of inhibitory neurons containing GABA derive from a common embryological origin and that the grouping of cells according to motor function makes it easier to form common connections needed for common reflex functions (118). That grouping according to common transmitter takes precedence over grouping according to common reflex connections suggests that differentiation of transmitter biosynthesis occurs before the development of appropriate connections.

To summarize, certain biochemical and functional properties of neurons correlate well with the topographical location of their somata in the cell body region of the ganglion. This finding is encouraging, and suggests that there may also be at least a rough correlation between the position of a cell in relation to its neighbors in the cell body layer and the position of its axon in relation to that of its neighbor in the neuropile. If this relationship proved general it could provide useful clues for understanding the organization of the neuropile.

THE NEUROPILE REGION

In contrast to rapidly increasing understanding of the organization of the cell body layer, analysis of the neuropile of invertebrate ganglia proceeds slowly. In part this reflects the paucity of histological studies of invertebrate ganglia. Largely, however, the explanation involves the hopelessly complicated appearance of even the simplest neuropile, with the result that the neuropile of invertebrates seemed to offer no particular advantage to morphologists. However, several recent techniques based on using identifiable cells as reference points may bring important advances in understanding the neuropile region.

The analysis of the neuropile consists of two parts: morphological and functional. We will consider these below.

Morphological analysis of the neuropile.—The purpose of a morphological analysis of the neuropile is to understand the structural basis of organized neural action by describing the three-dimensional architecture of the neuropile—the course taken by the interconnecting fibers and their various subgroupings as well as the fine structure of the synaptic contacts.

Neuropile architecture is complex but seems to be organized into patterns which recur not only within the same CNS but in the CNS of differing organisms (185). For example, there is considerable similarity in the structure of the neuropile in the retinas of arthropods, cephalopod molluscs, and vertebrates, and in the olfactory systems of arthropods and vertebrates (188). Unknown are the patterns of functional interconnections resulting from different patterns of neuropile organization and how functional and neuropile patterns relate to behavior. To answer these questions several behavioral systems will have to be analyzed in morphological and physiological detail.

Histological analysis of the invertebrate neuropile using conventional silver-staining techniques has often not worked as well in the invertebrate CNS as in higher forms; however, recently Rowell (249) has developed a successful technique for silver staining which has now been applied to several invertebrate ganglia (73, 142, 237). Kendig (142) has used this method to analyze neuropile structure of the third abdominal ganglion of the crayfish. She found that the fibers entering the ganglion via the ventral nerve cord and the peripheral nerves formed distinctive bundles with characteristic paths and destinations. Of the other traditional histological stains, methylene blue is perhaps the most consistently useful for impregnating neurons and tracing their processes (e.g. 200, 234, 327).

Three promising new techniques have recently been used in invertebrates. A technique for identifying the course of the efferent axons of ganglion cells based on retrograde chromatolysis has been introduced by Cohen & Jacklet (45) using pyronine malachite green to stain for RNA. Cells whose axons were cut 2 weeks prior to fixation showed a characteristic perinuclear RNA ring. With this technique Cohen & Jacklet specified the peripheral distribution of the axons of sixty cells on one side of the metathoracic ganglion of the cockroach and found the corresponding symmetrical mates on the other side.

Osmium-fixed serial sections stained with heavy metals have been used by Coggeshall (41) to trace the major process of several large identified neurons in *Aplysia*. Osmium fixation has several advantages (312). Unlike methylene blue or Golgi it does not stain some cells to the exclusion of others. As a result it provides the best way to obtain a picture of every cell, intact and in place, and in appropriate proximity to its neighbors (312). It is also possible to combine light-microscopic scanning with electronmicroscopic examination of appropriate serial sections. With this technique Coggeshall was able to describe the types of synaptic boutons which end on the axons of the large identified cells in the abdominal ganglion.

A very promising new approach to the morphological study of the neuropile is that of intracellular injection of a fluorescent dye recently introduced by Stretton & Kravitz (267). They examined a large number of fluorescent procion dyes which bind covalently to macromolecules within the cell, to determine which diffused most satisfactorily to the fine neuronal terminal processes in the neuropile. Procion yellow M4RS was particularly useful because it was the most fluorescent. The advantage of this technique is that one or more cells can be selectively injected with dye and their processes traced without the confusion normally introduced by conventional stains which are taken up arbitrarily by many cells. The dye can be injected iontophoretically and appears to be nontoxic. Stretton & Kravitz have used the distribution of the dye to study the geometry of certain identified cells in lobster ganglia, by reconstructing a cell's shape through serial sections. By injecting a given cell in different ganglia they found that, despite some microheterogeneity in their finer branches, the general pattern of branching of the individual cells studied was quite characteristic. Moreover, by studying different cells and tracing their process they were able to begin an analysis of the organization of the neuropile.

The technique of Stretton & Kravitz can also be used to identify the location of the cell body of an identified axonal process. Remler, Selverston

& Kennedy (232) injected procion yellow by pressure into the lateral giant
fiber of the crayfish abdominal cord and identified its cell body in the contralateral ganglion. A similar technique was first used by Staub (264) who
injected trypan blue or trypan red intracellularly into the giant motor fibers
of the squid and located their cell bodies in the stellate ganglion. Remler et
al. (232) have now also used this method to analyze the connections made
between the medial and lateral giant fibers and seven flexor motoneurons in
the third abdominal ganglion. They found that some motoneurons receive
connections from all four giant fibers whereas others connect only with the
homolateral pair (148, 232, 255).

   Functional analysis of the neuropile.—The purpose of this analysis is to
describe the function of the anatomical interconnections between cells in a
ganglion. This analysis is facilitated in certain invertebrate ganglia because
the synaptic connections between an interneuron and a follower cell are detectable electrophysiologically by stimulating the interneuron with an intracellular electrode and by recording the elementary postsynaptic potential it
produces in the follower cell with another intracellular electrode. This technique is essentially an extension of the electroanatomical mapping used successfully in the vertebrate nervous system for examining connections between populations of neurons (64, 66, 135). With this technique a number
of direct connections of several identified interneurons and their follower
cells have been mapped in *Aplysia* (84, 133, 283); the interconnections between sensory neurons have been mapped in the leech ganglion (14); and
the intra- and interganglionic connections between the Retzius cells have
been specified (69, 93). Aso specified have been the interconnections between receptor cells in the eye of the nudibranch *Hermissenda* (59) and the
horseshoe crab *Limulus* (98); the connections of the giant cell in the gas-
troesophageal ganglia of the nudibranch *Anisodoris* (90); and the interconnections of cells in the crustacean cardiac ganglion (92).

   These studies can suggest what factors determine the functional expression of interconnections between cells in a neuronal population. For example, in *Aplysia* the connections of an identified interneuron (L10) have been
traced to fourteen identified follower cells in three different regions of the
abdominal ganglion and to an unspecified number of cells (probably 20–30)
in three identified cell groups in these regions (19, 133, 215, 282). The connections between the interneuron and its follower cells were examined both
electrophysiologically and pharmacologically to determine the following
four questions: must a neuron be specialized for inhibition or excitation or
can it be multivalent? does the neuron conform to Dale's principle (50) and
release the same transmitter from all of its terminals? is the sign of the synaptic action determined by the chemical structure of the transmitter substance released by the presynaptic neuron, or by the nature of the receptor
located on the postsynaptic cell? and must the postsynaptic cell have only
one receptor to the same chemical transmitter substance, or can it have
more than one receptor?

Examination of the various synaptic actions produced by the different branches of the interneuron showed it to be multiactioned and to mediate inhibition to the follower cells in one region, excitation to cells of another region, and conjoint excitation-inhibition to a cell in a third region. All of these synaptic actions could be accounted for by a single transmitter substance, acetylcholine, which was released by the different branches of the interneuron interacting with different receptors. The different receptors to acetylcholine determined the sign of the synaptic action by controlling different ionic conductance mechanisms: Na^+ for excitation, Cl^- for inhibition, and Na^+ and Cl^- for conjoint excitation-inhibition. In addition to activating different conductance mechanisms the transmitter may also activate an electrogenic Na^+ pump in the membrane to produce synaptic inhibition. Some postsynaptic cells had two receptors to the same transmitter. The functional expression of cholinergic transmission in this neural population is therefore determined by the postsynaptic element and depends on the type of receptor and the number and combination of receptors which the cell has. In turn, the number and even the permissible combination of receptors seem to be correlated with the region in the cell body layer of the ganglion in which the soma of the follower cell is located.

Some other interneurons in *Aplysia* are also multiaction (84, 133), but the extent to which such neurons are found in other invertebrate ganglia is unknown. There is now evidence that each eccentric cell of *Limulus* mediates conjoint excitation and inhibition to its neighboring cells (224, 225, 226), as do the receptor cells in the eye of *Hermissenda* (59). Also, the inhibitory cells to muscle in crustacea are double action (207). In all three cases however, the excitatory actions appear to be mediated by electrical means.

THE CONNECTIVES, COMMISSURES, AND PERIPHERAL NERVES

A typical invertebrate ganglion is connected to its symmetrical mate by a fiber tract called a commissure, to other ganglia by connectives, and to the periphery by peripheral nerves. One experimental advantage of the arthropod nervous system is that the connective tissue surrounding these various axon tracts is fairly loose, and as a result it is possible to divide the tract into small fiber bundles so as to progressively isolate individual units for study. This technique was first applied to primary motor and sensory fibers in peripheral nerves (97, 296, 297) but has now been extended to recording from, or stimulating, afferent and command interneurons whose axons run in the connectives. As with the cell body layer and the neuropile, the fiber tracts appear to be topographically organized and a given fiber can be repeatedly identified in the same general area in a cross-sectional diagram of the tract (301).

THE NEUROGLIAL CELLS

Despite the increasing amount of information becoming available about neuroglial cells, their role in the organization of the invertebrate ganglion is still not clear. For an excellent review of the current status of neuroglial cells, see Kuffler & Nicholls (164).

In most invertebrate ganglia there appear to be different types of glial cells in the different regions of the ganglion: the connectives, the cell body layer, and the neuropile (40–42, 311, 314).

The glial cells of the connective.—These cells seem primarily supportive; they contain many tonofilaments and appear to be relatively inactive metabolically. The relationship of the glial cells to axons of the connective sometimes varies according to the size of the axons (8, 41, 42). Small axons are frequently bundled together and enveloped by a single glial process. Medium-size axons are wrapped in bundles of two or three, whereas very large axons are individually wrapped often in the layers of processes from many glial cells (41). It would be interesting to know whether these glial wrappings serve to segregate functional neuronal groupings, as Palay (209) suggested for vertebrates. Invertebrate axons may on occasion be myelinated and one instance of saltatory conduction has been encountered (174).

The glial cells of the ganglion cell body layer.—These cells can serve to define different cell masses. This is particularly evident in the insect (311) and in the leech (42) where a single giant packet glial cell surrounds a large cluster of ganglion cell bodies. In addition, in ganglia which are avascular—such as those of the annelid worms, the insects, and the gastropod molluscs—the glial cells of the cell body region may have an additional nutritive function. In these ganglia, the glial cells appear to be metabolically active, containing few tonofilaments but an abundant Golgi apparatus, ribosomes, and mitochondria. These glial cells resemble cells with high rates of active transport, such as renal tubular or avian salt gland cells. This has led Wigglesworth (313), Coggeshall & Fawcett (42), and Coggeshall (40) to suggest that the glia of the cell body layer may facilitate the transfer of nutrients from the blood to the neurons in avascular nervous systems.

The possibility that glia may have nutritive functions in avascular nervous systems is supported by the finding that in these nervous systems the glia in the cell body layer contain large quantities of glycogen and some lipid (246, 247, 313). Moreover, the glial elements often invaginate neurons to form a "trophospongium" (106) in which a large surface area of neuron and glial cells are brought in close apposition. In the insect, neuronal glycogen is most concentrated in the region of the axon hillock where the glial invaginations are most extensive. In the cockroach, Wigglesworth (313) found that after being depleted by starvation, glycogen was restored rapidly at the axon hillock following feeding. This suggests that the extensive glial invaginations at this site may facilitate the transfer of glycogen from glia to neurons, but direct transfer of substrates from neurons to glia has yet to be demonstrated. In the leech, Wolfe & Nicholls (330) have found by autoradiography that neuronal cell bodies deprived of their glia could take up labeled glucose and convert it to glycogen. Moreover, under normal circumstances glucose can diffuse to the neurons from the bathing fluid via the intercellular spaces. Wolfe & Nicholls conclude that if transfer of glycogen from glia to neurons occurs, it probably does so as a long-term reservoir used only when the demands of the neuron cannot be met by the more direct supply route of the intercellular space.

The glial cells of the neuropile.—These cells resemble the glia of the connectives and the peripheral nerves, and appear not to be metabolically active. It is intriguing that the neuropile, where so much metabolic activity occurs, lacks a blood supply even in a vascular nervous system like that of the earthworm (40).

An important advance in the functional study of glia has recently been made by Kuffler, Nicholls, and their colleagues who have recorded intracellularly in glial cells in invertebrate ganglia (leech) as well as in the vertebrate CNS. A major new finding which bears on the organization of neuronal systems is that impulse activity in neurons produces a depolarization of the surrounding glial cells because of K^+ accumulation (13, 206). As a result the glial cells can sense the overall activity of neighboring neurons. This K^+-mediated depolarization may be important in triggering a trophic response in the glial cells (164). A similar depolarization of presumed glial cells has recently been demonstrated in the mammalian brain (36, 139).

SPECIFICITY OF NEURONS AND THEIR INTERCONNECTIONS IN THE ADULT GANGLION

On the basis of his studies of development and regeneration in lower vertebrates, Sperry (262, 263) has suggested that individual neurons and their connections are specific and normally invariable. From the studies so far available in vertebrates it is, however, difficult to determine the precise resolution of this specificity. How invariant is the number of neurons in a particular region of the brain and how precise are their interconnections? Is there a unique specificity, based on cell-to-cell matching of individual biochemical characteristics, so that each outgrowing axon can only connect with a unique postsynaptic cell? Or can the instruction for the presynaptic neuron be slightly more general so that it leads the outgrowing fiber to a specific site but does not specify with which of several cells the fiber can synapse? These questions attempt to separate inherent factors from environmental ones in order to specify what is invariant and what is left to local environmental factors, to learning, or even to chance.

The answers to these questions may be approached in the invertebrate nervous system where individual cells can be repeatedly identified and where it may be possible to investigate the genetic mechanisms which determine this specificity. We will first consider to what degree the number of neurons in a particular ganglion is specified (neuronal specificity) and then to what degree the connections of each neuron are specified (connection specificity).

Neuronal specificity.—The best case for invariance of number and uniqueness of neurons can be made for certain primary sensory and primary motor systems which contain a small population of neurons. Here recognition of distinct individuals is enhanced and it is possible to show, in all animals of a species, the consistent occurrence of some neuronal elements with constant properties and connections. For example, the abdominal stretch receptors of the crayfish are completely and rigidly predetermined in number, functional properties, and anatomical relations. Invariably in each abdominal segment there are two pairs of receptors, one slowly and the other rapidly adapting (307). Similarly the motor outflow to the crayfish abdominal muscles is mediated by a small and constant number of distinctive fibers (three to six depending on the muscle). Of these, one is an inhibitor, and the others are excitors. The motor fibers can be further distinguished from each other by their effects on muscle (4, 301, 302).

The central ganglia of lobster, crayfish, leech, cockroach, and gastropod molluscs all contain large cells which are highly distinctive in appearance and functional properties and which can be repeatedly identified. For example, among the neurons in the abdominal ganglion of *Aplysia* there are thirty identifiable cells, including several motoneurons, an interneuron, and a cluster of neurosecretory cells. Each of these cells has a characteristic position, size, appearance, firing pattern, afferent input, efferent axon pathway, and pharmacological response to acetylcholine (80). Similarly, in the leech Nicholls & Baylor (200) have described fourteen identified sensory neurons (six cells responding to touch, four to pressure, and four to noxious stimuli) each of which had its cell body in the central ganglion. Each cell of a group had a characteristic constellation of functional properties. A similar specificity has now also been noted by Ann Stewart (266) for seventeen pairs of motoneurons in the leech.

Whereas these findings show that some neurons are invariant, it would be incorrect to conclude that all neurons are invariant and that the number of neurons in the nervous system is fully specified. To the contrary, some cell types are clearly not invariant. For example, the hair receptors of the abdominal cerci of the house cricket increase in number from 50 to 750 as the animal goes through successive molts (70). These cells differentiate from ectodermal cells of the epidermis and send their axons into the CNS where they become functionally incorporated into the already established nervous system (314). Similarly, there is an increase with age in the size and the number of ommatidia in the eye of insects and of arachnids and a concomitant increase in the number of fibers they send to the CNS (21, 27, 285, 314). In addition to these sensory neurons, some central neurons are added to the nervous system of many and perhaps all invertebrates throughout postembryonic life (see section on Development of Invertebrate Ganglia). Moreover, as in mammals, the number of neurons may decrease progressively throughout later adult life in some invertebrates (e.g. 240).

The question of neuronal specificity therefore reduces itself to which cell types are invariant in number, which are not, and why. We will consider some data relevant to these questions below.

Connection specificity.—Evidence for connection specificity comes from two types of studies: those concerned with the normal interconnections of neurons and those concerned with regenerating connections.

In the few examples where connections between identified cells have been examined in detail they have been found invariant. For example, the interconnections of the fourteen identified sensory neurons in each segmental ganglion of the leech are constant (14), as are the connections to fourteen identified cells which have been demonstrated for an identified interneuron in *Aplysia* (133). Similarly, giant interneurons concerned with escape responses in insects, worms, and molluscs are also fixed in number, position, and physiological properties and presumably make invariant connections (27, 202).

Further evidence for connection specificity comes from studies of natural and experimental regeneration. For example in crustacea, regeneration can occur following natural injury such as the voluntary amputation of a limb (autotomy) or the removal of an eyestalk. When the leg of a crustacean is strongly stimulated the animal can reflexly cast it off (20, 331). When the castoff leg regenerates, normal reflex function is restored, which suggests that each regenerating sensory receptor, with its cell body in the periphery, must have regenerated from new cells and these sensory neurons may have then made the same central connections as the neurons of the amputated limb. Indeed the four main types of proprioceptors found in the normal leg are present in the regenerated limb (304).

Removal of the eyestalk in decapod crustacea by either natural or experimental trauma is also followed by regeneration, not of the eyestalk, but of another (heteromorphic) appendage which usually resembles a portion of the outer flagellum of an antennule (189). Behavioral responses in the heteromorph antennule are often similar to those in the original antennule, which suggests that at least some of the regenerating afferent fibers make specific central connections with neurons normally involved with antennular reflexes (186, 189). Some lobsters responded with strong reflex responses within a few days after the first appearance of the heteromorph and once evident, the response remained unchanged thereafter throughout months of observations. These data have led Maynard (186) to suggest that the reflex connections may develop in all-or-none manner. Central connections made by the regenerates have not been studied in detail and most of the inferences were based on behavioral analyses. These analyses, although suggestive, cannot resolve cell-to-cell connectivity patterns. To accomplish this resolution, more detailed electrophysiological experiments are necessary.

A step in this dirction has been taken by Edwards & Sahota (73) in studies in the cricket on the regeneration of transplanted abdominal (anal) cerci, sensory structures which contain hairs responsive to displacement by air movement. The afferent fibers from the normal cerci pass to the terminal ganglion where they apparently synapse with giant fibers that pass anteriorly. Cerci transplanted to the stump of a mesothoracic leg also formed synapses with giant fibers, but physiological data indicated that the synapses were located in the thoracic ganglion rather than the terminal ganglion. Edwards & Sahota suggest that the regenerating cercal fibers can recognize and synapse with the giant fibers on which they normally terminate, even at some distance from their normal site of synaptic contact. The fibers may be able to recognize the cell as a whole rather than some specific synaptic area.

Detailed studies of cellular regeneration are now being carried out in leech ganglia by Baylor & Nicholls (12). Each of 21 ganglia in the leech contains six particular cells, probably primary sensory neurons, which are sensitive to touch of the skin. Each of these touch cells when electrically stimulated produces three effects on the other five touch cells in the same ganglion and on ipsilateral touch cells in neighboring ganglia: an electrically mediated excitatory synaptic potential, a chemically mediated excitatory synaptic potential of longer latency, and a chemically mediated inhibitory synaptic potential of variable latency. The axons mediate these effects to neighboring ganglia, via the connectives. After being cut, the axons regenerate in 5 weeks and connections between the touch cells of neighboring ganglia are reestablished. The touch cells do not appear to make incorrect connections with other cells but the newly formed connections between touch cells are *not* identical with the original connections between touch cells. One of the two EPSPs originally present does not always reappear (12, 201).

These studies make it clear that certain synaptic connections can be highly specific. Whether all connections are this specific is not clear. For example, some systems appear to be randomly interconnected or seem as if they would not require much specificity. The motor innervation of the superficial abdominal flexor muscles in the crayfish consists of six fibers (five excitors and one inhibitor). Kennedy & Takeda (150) found that whereas there are regional differences in the distribution of the six axons, the distribution of axons within a region, as well as the combinations of different axons innervating the same muscle within that region, is approximately that to be anticipated on the basis of a random distribution. Thus Kennedy & Takeda suggest that "precise developmental mechanisms are not required to achieve a specific pattern of connections; the observed pattern could be brought about by a group of axons that grow into the muscle (for a distance determined in part by their diameter), and branch repeatedly to innervate muscle fibers with variable density". This suggestion was strengthened by the finding that a particular axon may innervate one muscle fiber and skip one or two before innervating another. Skipped innervation is also seen in the connections between eccentric cells in the lateral eye of *Limulus*

(*229*). The functional interconnections between eccentric cells seems to be organized primarily along a spatial gradient, a principle of organization which does not seem to require much specificity. Also, certain groups of cells like the 400 neuroendocrine cells of the bag cell cluster in *Aplysia* are very tightly interconnected, probably by means of electrical synapses (80, 169, 170), an arrangement which again seems not to require much specificity. Although skipped innervation and simple spatial gradient of connections suggest that these connections could develop randomly, the randomness could also be genetically specified and connections which appear to be nonspecific could nonetheless be specifically determined.

A possible example of nonspecific regeneration has now also been reported by Horridge (114) who found a persistence of normal behavioral responses in the locust following 180° rotation of the eye and subsequent regeneration of its connections with the optic lobe. The anatomical examination of the reconnections indicated that the outgrowing fibers connected to the cells immediately behind them, rather than to the cells to which they were originally connected.

To summarize, there is good evidence for the invariance of some neurons and for the specificity of their interconnections. These cells appear to be unique individuals which can make connections only with other unique individuals. However, at least some neurons may not be invariant and at least some of these cells may not be unique. Also, some patterns of interconnection may not be completely specific. The arguments for nonuniqueness are as follows: (*a*) Some cells continue to divide into adult life in the CNS of several invertebrates. (*b*) There are some types of interconnections as in the eye of *Limulus* and the neuromuscular innervation of crayfish which do not seem to require a great deal of specificity. (*c*) Nonspecific connections have been encountered following regeneration of the eye of the locust.

Although neither of these arguments is by itself very convincing, they raise the possibility that neurons may fall into two categories: large cells which are invariant and cannot divide; smaller cells which can divide. Consistent with this suggestion is Coggeshall's (41) finding that in the abdominal ganglion of *Aplysia* the density of DNA, as examined with a Feulgin stain, was the same in large cells with large nuclei (up to 500 μ) as it was in smaller cells with small nuclei. It appears that all the nuclei of all nerve cells in this ganglion are capable of repeated chromosomal replication, but that only in certain types of cells is chromosomal replication associated with cell division.

It is premature to draw conclusions from these limited data, but with the techniques and test systems now available, direct experiments can be done which could distinguish between genetic, environmental, and random factors in development. Specifically it would be important to know more about the increase in neuronal number during postembryonic life. How general is this process? What cell types tend to increase and what cell types remain constant? Do nondividing cells form more specific connections than do dividing cells? Is cell division which occurs late in development inherent or is it in response to a change in environmental or functional demand? A particularly useful approach to these problems is provided by analyses of the development of invertebrate ganglia.

DEVELOPMENT OF INVERTEBRATE GANGLIA

A review of the complex literature on invertebrate neurogenesis and postembryonic development is beyond our scope and we will limit ourselves to a few relevant issues. Interested readers should consult the valuable recent reviews by Edwards (70–72).

The distinctive feature of the development of higher invertebrates is that they do not proceed directly from embryo to adult. Instead, invertebrate postembryonic development involves one or more larval stages which may be accompanied by structural rearrangements in the CNS.

EMBRYONIC DEVELOPMENT

The most detailed information on the embryonic development of the invertebrate CNS comes from studies of insects (6, 182, 294), but similar developmental processes have been described for annelid worms (253) and for crustaceans (157). The behavior of the insect neuroblast was clearly described by Wheeler in 1904 and subsequent studies (6, 9, 211) have not basically altered his findings. Even before Wheeler, August Weisman had appreciated the nature of metamorphosis and described the reserve (imaginal) cells that give rise to the adult brain (292).

The first traces of the CNS in the insect become evident before the blastopore is closed (294). The ectoderm consists of two kinds of elements, one of which (the dermatoblasts) gives rise to the other (the neuroblasts). The neuroblasts in turn give rise to the neural elements of the nerve cord.

The neural structures develop in an anteroposterior direction beginning with the brain. The neuroblasts, which first differentiate as isolated cells or as small clusters, arise segmentally in each lateral half. As they increase in number they fill their segment and give rise to two long rows of cells that run the length of each half of the body from mouth to anus. Several changes occurring simultaneously produce further development of the nerve cord. These include: the proliferation of the neuroblasts, the formation of the connectives and commissures, and the development of the neurolemma. Each neuroblast divides asymmetrically, yielding a daughter neuroblast and a small preganglion cell, the ganglion mother cell (254). The ganglion mother cell then divides symmetrically into daughter cells that differentiate into neurons. Since the neuroblast remains in an outer or peripheral position, each gives rise to a column of daughter cells below it. With continued proliferation of daughter cells the columnar arrangement becomes distorted. The daughter cells send out axonal processes which soon ramify, giving rise to the neuropile of the ganglion. After the two ganglionic neuropiles in each segment are established, the connectives develop and join the isolated ganglionic masses in the two longitudinal rows; later the commissures become evident, joining the two ganglionic neuropiles of each segment. An outer and inner neurolemma are formed from epithelial walls freed up from the integument.

Before formation of connectives and commissures the ganglia occupy the whole of their respective segments and are only separated from one another by the intersegmental constrictions. After the formation of the connectives and commissures the ganglia separate further. As the embryo grows, the length of the individual segments is greatly increased and the nerve cord, which is attached both in the infraesophageal region and in the last abdominal segments, is forced to lengthen. The lengthening has little effect on the ganglia but the connectives are drawn out into thin threads denuded of ganglionic cells and covered only by the neurolemma. In the locust, the subesophageal ganglia remain close to each other and fuse as do the last abdominal ganglia. Later other ganglia may also fuse, further reducing the original number of ganglia. The degree of segmental fusion varies and further fusion often occurs during the pupal phase (39). For a discussion of the mechanism of connective shortening and its role in ganglionic fusion the papers by Pipa & Woolever (217–219) should be consulted.

There are several important similarities between neurogenesis in the insect CNS and that in vertebrates (258, 294). In each case the neuroblasts divide and give rise to daughter cells which ultimately differentiate into ganglion cells that send out axonal processes. In each case the neuroblasts retain their peripheral position in the CNS, close to the central canal in vertebrates or on the surface of the nerve cord in invertebrates. However there is at least one major difference. In vertebrates the ganglion cells migrate in relation to each other, whereas in the insects and probably in other invertebrates they are passively displaced inward by the newly proliferating sister cells.

To study this special feature of invertebrate neurogenesis, the passive displacement of the daughter cells along vertical columns, Carlson (33) has developed a hanging-drop method of tissue culture for the grasshopper nerve cord in which each neuroblast is identifiable.

POSTEMBRYONIC DEVELOPMENT

Postembryonic development varies greatly and may proceed either gradually without dramatic changes in body form (anamorphic development), or abruptly, with great physical transformations (metamorphic development). Among invertebrates metamorphic development is seen most clearly in insects where a further distinction is made as to whether the insect is holo- or hemimetabolous (181, 314).

Holometabolous insects undergo a complete metamorphosis and a pupal stage is interposed between the larva and the adult. In these insects the adult (imaginal) organs develop independently of the larval organs. In parts of the body where the most extreme metamorphosis occurs, the cellular precursors of the adult organs are already present at early embryonic stages in the form of clusters of undifferentiated embryonic cells, the imaginal disks. The imaginal disks grow at time of metamorphosis and replace almost all of the larval organs which break down completely (e.g. 181, 314).

Radical restructuring also occurs in the CNS during metamorphosis. Many neurons are replaced in all parts of the CNS but because the new axons tend to grow along the paths of older ones the pattern of peripheral innervation is sometimes not radically changed (27, 295). The adult nervous system is formed from neuroblasts which persist throughout the CNS during the postembryonic period either as groups of cells or as scattered individuals. These cells appear to have no nervous functions in the larva until metamorphosis when they differentiate into the neurons of the adult brain (181).

The postembryonic development of hemimetabolous insects is less radical and is more characteristic of other invertebrates. Hemimetabolous insects undergo an incomplete metamorphosis and the active immature larva is transformed directly into an adult. In these insects there is usually no segregation of adult and larval cells. Larval cells retain the capacity to develop adult characters throughout the larval period and for the most part the larval tissue is taken over directly by the adult and appropriately modified at the time of the last molt. This direct transformation of larval cells into adult also characterizes the postembryonic development of the CNS. Neuroblasts in the segmental ganglia degenerate before hatching and, to a large degree, the number of neurons and perhaps even the cellular architecture of the segmental ganglia of hemimetabolous insects appear to be specified during the embryonic phase and to remain relatively constant throughout development (72). However, the brain of these insects, particularly the corpora pedunculata and the optic lobe, retains some neuroblasts. These neuroblasts continue to divide throughout postembryonic life (72, 210), and increases of up to twentyfold have been described in the number of globuli cells of the corpora pedunculata (72).

Postembryonic changes in the structure of the nervous system are not limited to insects but also occur, at least to some degree, in certain annelid worms and gastropod molluscs (41, 205). These changes generally take the form of adding new neurons to an earlier CNS structure, and therefore resemble the development of the hemimetabolous insects.

In the earthworm, the number of neurons in most parts of the brain increases during postembryonic growth, but the percentage increase varies greatly (350–5000 per cent), depending upon the region and cell type (205). A particularly prominent increase in cell number occurs in ganglia which control the reproductive apparatus. A similar differential increase in neuronal number occurs in the abdominal ganglion of *Aplysia* (41, 80). The large identified cells in this ganglion appear to be invariant and can be recognized in young as well as old animals, but some small cells show significant increases (100 to 400 per cent) in number with age. The increase is not limited to one phase of maturation but continues throughout adult life (41) and, as in the earthworm, one cell group showing a prominent increase is concerned with reproduction (166).

In insects, newly added central neurons derive from primitive neuroblasts (see for example 204) but in molluscs they may actually derive from division of fully differentiated ganglion cells (41). The origin of these neurons might be found by autoradiography techniques for labeling mitotic activity (204, 258). The additional problem of what function the late arrivers have can also be examined. For example, in the abdominal ganglion of *Aplysia* the greatest increase in cell number (400 per cent) occurs in a group of neuroendocrine cells (the bag cells) which produce a substance that stimulates egg laying in mature animals (166). These neuronal additions may provide adequate hormone levels for the animal's reproductive phase. Perhaps the completion of other cell groups is similarly timed to serve needs that arise late in development or to keep pace with the gradually increasing demands of a growing organism. This is also suggested by the finding that there is an increase in the number of cells in the optic lobes of hemimetabolous insects correlated with an increase in afferent fibers reaching the optic lobe from the growing compound eye (72, 210).

Throughout development the proliferation of neurons is almost invariably accompanied by death of cells. Why some of the preganglion cells survive while others die is unknown. Edwards (72) has suggested that there is an overproduction of preganglion cells and a subsequent selection of cells destined to become functioning neurons based on their ability to establish appropriate connections. Proliferation may be designed to exceed requirements significantly and once these have been met, the excess cells, which have failed to make appropriate connections, are eliminated (72, 204).

These observations on proliferation and cell death in insects provide an interesting parallel to vertebrate neurogenesis where increases in peripheral load lead to neuronal proliferation and decreases in load lead to neuronal degeneration (96, 120). Studies of developmental eye mutants, to be reviewed below, further support the notion that in the insect visual system, a change in cell number may result from a change in peripheral load.

DEVELOPMENTAL MUTANTS

Genetic studies are facilitated in some invertebrates because the generation time is short (e.g. 12 days in *Drosophila*). Mutants have so far been primarily used to analyze morphogenetic interrelationships. For example, eye mutants of *Drosophila* have been used to analyze the relationship between the eye and the optic lobe and between the optic and antennular lobes [see in particular Bodenstein's review (21)]. Richards & Furron (235) and Power (220, 221) used a series of mutants with progressively smaller number of ommatidia, ranging from a full eye (780 facets) to total absence of ommatidia. The volume of each optic glomerulus varied linearly with numbers of ommatidia. In eyeless mutants there was complete hypoplasia of the external glomerulus which only receives incoming optic fibers. Other parts of the glomerulus which receive fibers from neural structures other than eye were less affected. Eyeless mutants also showed hypoplasia of their antennular sensory area (221) and, to a lesser degree, in the corpora pedunculata (102). Power concludes that the hypoplasia of the glomeruli is a secondary result of the ingrowth of fewer afferent fibers from the mutant eye disks. This effect on the glomeruli in turn affects other regions of the brain which are interconnected with it.

Recently Benzer (16) reasoned that since changes in the genes controlling the development and functioning of specific neural circuits will affect behavior, it might be possible to unravel the neural circuitry underlying certain behaviors by analyzing specific behavioral mutants. This approach could delineate what features of connectivity are coded for by single genes. Using this approach Hotta & Benzer (116) and Pak, Grossfield & White (208) described phototactic mutants of *Drosophila* with retinographic abnormalities, in which the eye pigments were normal. These observations suggested the existence of genetic blocks at sites beyond normal primary photoreceptors either in the retinular cells or in the first optic ganglion (116).

To summarize, increase in cell number may occur to some degree in the postembryonic growth of all invertebrates. It appears to involve only certain cell types and certain regions of the brain. Other cell types remain fixed in number throughout postembryonic life. The stimulus for cell division and the factors which permit the division of some cells but not others are unknown, but there is a correlation between increases of cell number and increased functional demands. Some cell types (see section on Postembryonic Development), often consisting of large cells, may be invariant because they never experience an increase in fuctional demand or, if they do, they do not respond to it by replicating. Other cell types, often consisting of smaller cells, may not be invariant but they can respond to an increased functional demand by replicating. An example of this correlation is provided in the abdominal ganglion of *Aplysia* where the two groups of neurosecretory cells, the white cells and the bag cells, respond differently to an apparently increased functional demand provided by the growth of the animal. Both white and bag cells increase the processes they send into the connective tissue sheath. In the white cells, a group of thirteen large identified cells, there is an increase in the number or processes that each cell sends into the sheath but no change in cell number. In the bag cells, a cluster of small cells, there is an increase in the number of cells as well as an increase in the number of processes per cell (41, 80).

THE FUNCTIONAL SYSTEMS WITHIN INVERTEBRATE GANGLIA
AFFERENT SYSTEMS

The usefulness of highly specialized invertebrate preparations is seen clearly in the study of sensory systems. There are literally millions of invertebrate species to choose from, and for a given neurophysiological problem it has often proved possible to select one or two invertebrate preparations that possess optimal features. As a result it has been possible to obtain a good idea of how receptor aggregates function and how the CNS processes sensory information.

Receptor aggregates.—An early notion of sensory systems conceived of a receptor as an independent entity which served to transmit to the CNS a relatively undistorted representation of the physical energy impinging on it. Higher stages of the nervous system would then transform this sensory information to forms that were maximally useful to the organism. Research on invertebrates has modified this view, and it is now widely accepted that in many instances first-order receptor neurons do not act as isolated units. Instead they can influence one another directly and can be affected by activity from the CNS. Thus, sensory information is transformed and modified at the earliest stage of neural processing. Receptor aggregates in invertebrates have proven useful not only for the analysis of sensory systems but also for studying the principles governing the interaction of mutually interconnected neurons.

A fruitful preparation for studying receptor aggregates has been the lateral eye of the horseshoe crab, *Limulus*. The lateral eye of adult *Limulus* is composed of about 1000 ommatidia, each consisting of about a dozen sensory cells (retinular cells) in close physical and electrical contact with a single neural element, the eccentric cell. Each eccentric cell sends one process to the brain via the optic nerve, and in addition gives off processes that synapse with other eccentric cells within a plexus immediately behind the ommatidia. Illumination of an ommatidium elicits all-or-none spikes that are propagated down the optic nerve. The main principle in the organization of the eye of *Limulus* is lateral inhibition: nerve impulses in one eccentric cell are inhibited by nerve impulses in adjacent eccentric cells. Selective stimulation of adjacent cells can be produced either by illumination of adjacent ommatidia (99) or by direct (electrical) antidromic stimulation of the isolated axons of adjacent eccentric cells (276). Thus, each eccentric cell makes inhibitory synaptic connections with adjacent eccentric cells. As far as can be determined, each eccentric cell produces the same type of action as any other but the strength of the inhibitory coupling decreases with distance between the cells (100).

Despite the fact that the lateral eye of *Limulus* is composed of hundreds of interacting units, many aspects of the *steady-state* functional activity of this eye have been described by relatively simple mathematical formulations (98, 228). This is possible because all elements can be treated as equivalent except for a gradient of the strength of synaptic interaction. The analysis of the *transient* responses of the eye of *Limulus* is much more complicated than that of the steady state, but even here mathematical and computer models have been developed (176, 229). The type of neural organization seen in the eye of *Limulus* occurs elsewhere in both vertebrates and invertebrates [e.g. in the lateral interaction among motor neurons in the spinal cord (65, 91, 233) and among fly motor neurons (197)], and the analysis that is possible here may prove to have wide application. In addition, this analysis may be useful for working out more complex systems which are organized as repeating units.

Despite its simple neural organization, the lateral eye of *Limulus* has many interesting functional properties. For example, by studying the output of the eccentric cells as a function of different patterns of light and dark projected on the eye, Hartline et al. (99) showed that lateral inhibition enhances border contrast between light and dark areas. Kirschfeld & Reichardt (155) have shown that contrast enhancement can rectify image distortion produced by the optical properties of the eye. Recently Ratliff et al. (230) have demonstrated that the eye of *Limulus* can function as a bandpass frequency filter, producing maximal output at a given input frequency. Thus lateral inhibition can function to produce sharpening in the time dimension as well as in the spatial dimension. Perhaps the most remarkable feature of lateral inhibition is that it can be used to model a number of visual perceptual phenomena seen in humans, including "Mach bands", backward masking, and figural aftereffects (83, 228, 293). For a more detailed account of the functioning of this system see (175, 228, 229, 329).

The receptor units that make up the eye of the nudibranch *Hermissenda* also show lateral inhibitory interactions (7, 59). Since this eye consists of only five receptor cells, all of which can be impaled with recording microelectrodes, certain features of lateral inhibition may be studied in more detail than in the eye of *Limulus*.

A receptor aggregate with a different type of lateral inhibition was discovered by Eckert (67, 68) in the stretch receptor system of the abdomen of decapod crustaceans. The stretch receptor organs are arranged in a linear array along the rostral-caudal axis of the abdomen. Activation of the receptor in one segment decreases the output of receptors in adjacent segments; however, the inhibition is not mediated by direct collateral connections as in the eye of *Limulus,* but is mediated instead by a reflex loop consisting of one or more interneurons. As in the eye of *Limulus* (224, 226, 265), activation of a given receptor not only inhibits adjacent receptors but also produces powerful self-inhibition. Fields (77) has suggested that lateral inhibition in the stretch receptor system increases the flexibility of the tail. He showed that contraction of the extensor muscles of one given segment stimulates the stretch receptor organs in adjacent segments as well as in the reference segment. A reflex elicited by the activity of the adjacent receptor organs tends to cause contraction of the extensor muscles adjacent to the reference segment. Thus, powerful inhibition of the response of adjacent muscle receptor organs may function to increase the independence of movement of a given abdominal segment. In this system, lateral inhibition does not sharpen sensory input as in the *Limulus* eye, but rather sharpens the motor output to a given segment. Fields, Evoy & Kennedy (78) suggest that lateral inhibition in the stretch receptor organs may also contribute to the proper phasing of tail movement, since the inhibition is not symmetrical, being greater in the rostral direction than in the caudal direction.

Although the predominant interaction between primary receptor neurons appears to be inhibitory, recent studies suggest that there may also be excitatory interactions between primary sensory neurons. For example in the leech, touch receptor neurons show mutual excitatory interactions mediated by electrical synapses made in the CNS (12, 14). In addition to these short-latency excitatory connections, the touch neurons produce mutual longer-latency inhibitory synaptic potentials, as well as another excitatory synatpic potential. These long-latency PSPs are probably not monosynaptic.

Another example of excitatory interactions between sensory neurons has been recently described in the lateral eye of *Limulus*. The long-duration IPSP produced by the action of one eccentric cell on another is preceded by a brief EPSP (225). Although the EPSP is small, it could have important functional consequences since it would significantly delay the inhibitory action of the IPSP. Since the connections between receptor neurons in the eye of *Hermissenda* and *Limulus* are apparently monosynaptic, the biphasic excitatory-inhibitory PSPs represent examples of conjoint synapses in primary sensory neurons. Such conjoint synaptic actions as well as multisynaptic excitatory and inhibitory actions (see above) considerably increase the integrative capacities of receptor aggregates.

Afferent interneurons.—Sensory information coming either from independent receptors or from receptor aggregates undergoes a series of transformations within the CNS. The nature of the resultant higher-order representation of sensory inflow has been studied in several invertebrate preparations. Wiersma and his colleagues have made an extensive analysis of sensory interneurons in the crayfish and their findings are probably representative of most arthropods (115, 121, 269). By dissecting out fine filaments from the connectives which contain the axons of primary and higher-order sensory fibers it was possible to make extracellular recordings from single units. Similar analyses have now been carried out both in the somatosensory and visual systems, thereby permitting comparisons with each other as well as with analogous data from the parallel mammalian systems.

(*a*) Somatosensory system: On the basis of their approximate position in the connective and of their characteristic firing pattern and receptive field, Wiersma has categorized more than 100 distinct sensory interneurons: the main finding is that afferent interneurons respond to a large variety of spatial combinations of sensory input. For example, some interneurons respond to tactile stimulation of a single abdominal segment; others respond to stimulation of a segment and one or more adjacent segments; still others may respond to tactile stimulation of any segment of the entire abdomen (308). Thus, the tactile receptive surface is represented by a series of unique, individual elements, some with very localized receptive fields and

others with broad and overlapping receptive fields. A given stimulus therefore activates a large number of parallel units (301, 302, 305, 308).

(b) Visual system: Spatial representation in the crayfish visual system
is similar to that found in the somatosensory system (305, 310). The optic
nerve contains a number of interneurons, each of which appears to be a
unique identifiable individual. For example, one class of fibers consists of
exactly fourteen units. These units, called "sustaining fibers", respond to
steady illumination. Each unit has its own specifiable receptive field. As in
the somesthetic system, some units have a moderately restricted field, such
as a small segment of a retinal quadrant, while other units have a broad and
overlapping field and respond to stimulation over a hemiretina or even over
a whole retina. In addition to the sustaining fibers, Wiersma and his colleagues have described a number of interneurons in the crayfish visual system which are unusual because of the complex stimuli necessary to affect
their firing. For example, one type of fiber responds only to moving stimuli.
When the animal moves its eye, these fibers are inhibited, and do not fire,
although there is movement of the visual field across the eye (310, see also
109). These units thus discriminate between real movement in the visual
world and apparent movement resulting from motion of the eye. Another
class of visual fibers in the crayfish (310) alters their receptive fields as a
function of the position of the animal in space (space-constant fibers). Thus
with the animal in an upright position, one particular unit will respond only
to visual stimulation of the dorsal part of the eye; but when the animal is
placed on its back, the unit responds only to stimulation of the ventral part
of the eye. The space-constant fiber thereby responds to stimuli in relation
to real space, independent of the locus of stimulation on the eye. This is apparently accomplished by means of proprioceptive input that inhibits the
output of the appropriate portion of the potential receptive field. When the
statocysts were removed these units could respond to stimuli anywhere in
the receptive field regardless of the position of the animal. Similar units
have now been described in the vertebrate CNS (108).

Abstracting ability of sensory units.—An important generalization about
the function of sensory systems which emerges from the studies of Wiersma
and others is that sensory interneurons operate so as to abstract certain features of the sensory input. The abstracting ability of some interneurons may
be related to their particular geometry. For example, in the crayfish there is
an interneuron that responds to any tactile stimulus applied to the left side
of the body, independent of the particular position (308). This unit does not
respond to stimulation from any place else on the body, and consequently it
is abstracting the quality of "leftness". Interestingly, this type of interneuron consists of a single long process that can receive synaptic input in each
segmental ganglion through which it runs. It can initiate spikes at any one
of multiple trigger zones (122, 146, 147). This type of arrangement permits
the interneuron to receive input from any combination of areas of the body

surface. An additional consequence of this structural organization of crayfish interneurons is that activation of an interneuron elicits impulses that both ascend and descend the fiber. Furthermore, impulses initiated from different segments can collide and cancel one another. A given stimulus can therefore produce a complex pattern of spikes. The possible functional significance of these complex spike patterns has not been determined.

A common way by which the nervous system determines the abstracting property of sensory neurons is by means of inhibitory gating. A neuron responds to some stimulus, but is inhibited from responding by some other event. Thus the sensory response to a particular stimulus becomes contingent upon the absence of some event. In the previously discussed crayfish movement fibers and space-constant fibers, the response of the unit to a visual stimulus was contingent upon the absence of eye movement or certain proprioceptive input. Another example of inhibitory gating is seen in the two L-fibers in the auditory system of an insect (269). The L-fiber responds to sound stimulation of the ipsilateral tympanic organ. However, the contralateral tympanic organ exerts a powerful inhibitory effect. This system accentuates slight differences in the degree of stimulation between the left and right tympanic organs, and consequently is ideally suited to signal directional information about the sound source. We have cited a number of examples in invertebrate sensory systems where individual neurons respond to certain abstract qualities of the sensory world, much as they do in the vertebrate CNS (108, 118, 179). We should emphasize, however, that each cell is only part of a more complicated sensory process and that to fully understand the function of a sensory neuron it is necessary to understand its relation to other neurons, and its relation to a final behavioral output (115, 118). This type of analysis may be possible in invertebrates because of the relatively few units composing their nervous system.

THE MOTOR SYSTEM

The control of movement in higher invertebrates has been most extensively investigated in arthropods largely because of their particularly favorable peripheral apparatus. Because of their exoskeleton, one can fix leads on the body surface and implant electrodes in muscle or around peripheral nerves without significantly interfering with the movement of the animal. The motoneurons are located within central ganglia and there is no peripheral nerve net to complicate the analysis as it sometimes does in molluscs and annelids. The motor system consists of relatively few units. For example, in the crayfish the motor supply to a single muscle typically consists of one inhibitor and one to five excitors each with a different distribution and action. The motor axons are usually quite large (up to 70 μ diam) and easy to dissect [see Bush (31) for review]. The extracellularly recorded action potential of each of the motor fibers to a given muscle is often distinctive, and it can be distinguished from its neighboring axons so that in some experimental conditions the whole population can be studied simultaneously

(149, 150). Atwood (4) and Usherwood (279) should be consulted for reviews of the recent literature on neuromuscular transmission in crustaceans and insects respectively.

Reflex control of movement.—

(a) Reflex reciprocity in proprioceptive reflexes: Two types of proprioceptive reflexes have been studied in the crayfish: one involves claw opening, the other the control of abdominal position. Each illustrates a different principle for achieving reflex reciprocity in the action of antagonistic muscles.

The opener muscle of the dactyl of the crayfish claw receives innervation from only two motoneurons, one excitator and one inhibitor (29, 280). The two motoneurons, although acting antagonistically, are not reciprocally related. Excitation of one does not lead to inhibition of the other. On the contrary, reflex activity often increases the firing rate of both motoneurons as if they formed part of a common motoneuron pool (325). Despite a lack of central reciprocal interactions, good separation of antagonistic functions is achieved peripherally by differential reflex actions on the two cells. Proprioceptive stimulation of the claw (passive flexion) produces reflex relaxation of the opener muscle. This occurs *without* central suppression of excitatory outflow, because the reflex increase in the activity of the inhibitor exceeds and overcomes the activity of the excitor. Tactile stimulation of the body surface produces reflex contraction of the opener muscle despite activity in the inhibitor, because of preferential increases in the activity of the excitor (29–31, 325). The lack of a central inhibitory mechanism for specifying the reciprocal actions of these two motoneurons may be attributed to several interrelated factors: 1. The peripheral postsynaptic inhibitory action on muscle is highly effective and can overcome a weak excitatory action if activated strongly. 2. The inhibitor supplies only the opener muscle but the excitor supplies the opener muscle as well as another muscle (the stretcher of the propodite). Central inhibition of the excitor, were it to exist, would therefore be nonspecific because it would affect both motor actions equally. 3. The inhibitor axon also produces a very powerful presynaptic inhibitory action (63) which is exclusively limited to the excitatory branch going to the opener. Kennedy et al. (144) suggest that presynaptic inhibition may therefore provide an alternative to central inhibition in cases such as this where the latter is impractical.

The muscles of the crayfish abdomen are segmented and bilaterally symmetrical, consisting of two groups: the fast extensors and flexors which are relatively massive and deep muscles that produce the tail flip escape response; and the slow extensors and flexors which are thin and superficial muscles that control abdominal posture. The more massive deep muscles respond with a powerful fast twitch to single impulses in their motor nerves (1, 149), whereas the thin superficial muscles respond with a slow contraction to repetitive stimulation of the motor nerves. The thin superficial slow extensors and flexors of each midabdominal segment are each innervated by five excitors and one inhibitor.

In contrast to the claw opener muscle, reciprocal innervation of flexors and extensors in the slow abdominal musculature is accomplished centrally (78, 144). With some exceptions, excitation of the excitatory axons is associated with inhibition of the inhibitor to the same muscle, and with activation of the inhibitor and central inhibition of all the excitator axons to the antagonistic muscle. In the abdominal musculature, central inhibition exists and peripheral inhibition seems to have a minor role, perhaps primarily designed to achieve repolarization and terminate the contraction of preceding excitatory action. Moreover, presynaptic inhibition is entirely lacking in this system (144).

(b) Postural adjustment through proprioceptive reflexes: Fields *(77)* studied the proprioceptive control of abdominal posture in crayfish by examining the reflex control of the superficial extensor muscles of the abdomen. In each half-segment there is a slowly adapting muscle receptor organ embedded in a specialized muscle strand which lies in parallel with the adjacent functional slow extensor muscles. The specialized muscle of the receptor organ is supplied by a branch from one, sometimes two or three, of the five motoneurons supplying the slow extensors. The receptor cell also receives an inhibitory axon of unknown behavioral function. In addition, the extensor muscles have rapidly adapting stretch receptors of unknown function.

Fields found that stretching the slowly adapting receptor produced reflex activation of the ipsilateral slow extensor muscles and had no effect on the twitch extensor muscles. The discharge of the slowly adapting receptor primarily activates one of the five motoneurons innervating the tonic extensor muscles. This motoneuron has a very wide distribution, innervating over 90 per cent of the tonic extensor muscles, but it is not a motoneuron that innervates the receptor muscle. There is therefore no positive feedback in the reflex loop. Activity of the slowly adapting receptor in one segment has a slight effect on the slow extensor motoneurons in adjacent segments but no significant effects on the contralateral segment.

The slowly adapting receptor responded to stretch of the extensor muscles so that passive flexion increased the receptor discharge and excited the major motoneuron to the extensors; this resulted in a compensatory extensor force. The receptor did not seem to be measuring length, however, but rather deviation of the abdomen from some set position. Recording of the stretch receptor discharge in intact moving animals showed that receptor activity did not correlate closely with the degree of flexion of the tail. Greatest discharge followed externally imposed flexion or active extension against a load. In voluntary extension the slow receptor discharged rapidly at the beginning of the movement and declined in frequency as the motion continued. This finding suggested to Fields *(77)* that the receptor served as an error detector in a length-servo system *(190)*, sensing the difference be-

tween the existing segment length and the new segment length demanded by
the discharge rate of the motoneurons innervating the receptor muscle as
well as extensor muscles. Thereby a fixed output to the receptor muscle
might result in a given degree of extension independent of variable external
load.

Evoy & Kennedy (75) subsequently studied the central control of these
postural reflexes by examining the effects of stimulating the axons of individual (command) interneurons acting on extensor and muscle receptor motoneurons. Two major types of effects were found: 1. Some interneurons selectively excite the motoneuron which sends branches both to the receptor
muscle and to some functional extensor muscles. Activity of these interneurons produces contraction of the receptor muscle, followed by discharge of
the muscle receptor and contraction of the functional extensors due to reflex
activation of the major (unshared) motoneuron. These interneurons therefore control receptor sensitivity and their activity alters the set point of the
length-servo system and influences to a considerable degree the position and
shape of the abdomen. 2. Some interneurons act only on the main extensor
muscles and not on the receptor muscle. These interneurons produce tension
increases without changing the peripheral reference signal maintained by
efferent control of the receptor. Unlike the first types, these interneurons do
not produce a specified amplitude of movement; the degree of movement
will vary depending upon the external load on the tail.

As a result of these two types of central controls, Fields et al. (78) proposed that Merton's suggestion (190) for control of movements in vertebrates might also be applicable to the crayfish (see also 44). Movement
might be initiated in two different ways: by interneurons acting on motoneurons which innervate the receptor muscle (along with a few extensors)
to produce a postural adjustment; and by interneurons acting on motoneurons which act only on the extensor muscles (and not on the receptor muscle) to produce an increase in tension. This system therefore contains certain functional parallels to vertebrate proprioceptive reflexes. The crayfish
motoneurons that innervate the receptors are analogous to mammalian
gamma motoneurons, whereas the crayfish motoneurons that exclusively innervate the extensor muscles are analogous to the mammalian alpha motoneurons.

Because each neuron in the system can be specified individually, the
crayfish provides an opportunity for exploring a number of general features
common to proprioceptive reflex organization in vertebrates as well as invertebrates. There are however a number of differences between the mammalian and crustacean systems. For example, the motoneuron innervating
the receptor muscle also acts on some functional extensor muscles (whose
contraction actually serves to unload the receptor), whereas the gamma motoneurons do not innervate extrafusal muscles. Another difference is the
presence of inhibitory neurons which act either on the receptor or on the

functional extensors and which are in turn selectively affected by the CNS.

Proprioceptive reflexes have also been studied in insects where different reflexes have been found to operate with widely differing speeds. As early as 1940, Pringle (222) described proprioceptive reflexes in the cockroach leg. Recently Wilson (319) showed that the timing of these reflexes is precisely controlled by their input even during most rapid leg movements. By contrast the proprioceptive reflex which controls wing beat frequency in the locust [(326), see also following section] operates with a time constant so slow that it exerts no phasic cycle-by-cycle influence. The proprioceptive reflexes of caterpillars are of intermediate speed (288); the proprioceptors provide phasic information but do not rigidly determine the locomotory sequence. Proprioceptive inputs can therefore be tonic as well as phasic. Tonic proprioceptive input does not provide timing information for the motor sequence but provides a general excitatory state which modulates a central time device (see following section).

Further evidence for a dual function of proprioceptive systems has been provided by Cohen (44) who showed that the crab has two classes of proprioceptors in its walking legs, the myochordotonal organ and the proximal organ. Both provide similar information about rate and direction of movement and about joint position and both initiate typical stretch reflexes. The myochordotonal organ differs from the proximal organ in being under efferent control; input from the myochordotonal organ feeds back on to the motoneuron innervating its own receptor muscles. Ablation of the proximal organ produced changes in joint position localized to the operated leg. Removal of myochordotonal organs, however, produces a generalized loss of muscle tone in unoperated as well as operated legs, so that movements although still coordinated are slowed down and the postural base of the animal is reduced. Thus whereas the proximal organ supplies the CNS with specific sensory information about joint movement, the myochordotonal organ seems to be involved in setting the general excitability level of motoneurons.

Central control of motor sequences.—Whereas there is general agreement that postural adjustments involve proprioceptive reflexes, a major question in the study of motor systems is to what degree motor sequences are reflexly controlled. Does cyclical locomotor behavior require proprioceptive feedback from peripheral structures for its maintenance and timing or can the CNS produce these patterns without information from the periphery? The work of Mott & Sherrington (196; see also 178, 257, 278) has suggested that locomotion results from information conveyed centrally from the periphery by the immediately preceding sensory input. Each phase of movement was thought to be triggered by a particular pattern of input from peripheral receptors. Locomotion might be initiated by input from exteroceptors, or even centrally, but once it is initiated, a cyclical proprioceptive reflex process would be required for its timing and maintenance. This view has now been shown to be incorrect for several locomotor patterns in invertebrates. The most detailed of these studies has been that of Donald Wilson on the flight of locusts.

Locusts beat their two pairs of wings at the same frequency (e.g. 17 beats/sec) in an approximately sinusoidal fashion. Each pair of wings beats synchronously, the hindwings leading the forewings by about 30° throughout the period (289, 291). The muscles that provide the wingstroke power are of the fast type and each wingstroke is triggered by a brief burst of impulses of the motoneurons located in the insect's thoracic ganglia. Each wing is controlled by 20 motoneurons so that 80 motoneurons drive the whole flight system (for review see 291, 318). By means of an aerodynamic apparatus originally described by Weis-Fogh (289), Wilson & Weis-Fogh (327) were able to study flight while the locust, fixed in space, was suspended in the wind stream of an open-jet wind tunnel. Wilson & Weis-Fogh implanted several intramuscular electrodes to monitor the activity of individual fibers in different muscle groups during flight. They specified when each motor unit was activated under various sets of aerodynamic conditions and described the activity of the population of motoneurons generating insect flight. The output pattern consisted of an orderly temporal sequence of firing of four groups of motoneurons that respectively control the hindwing elevators, forewing elevators, hindwing depressors, and forewing depressors. Each muscle unit receives either 0, 1, 2, or occasionally more impulses per wingbeat. This variation serves to control flight power and direction.

The flight control system was found to be located in the three thoracic ganglia and to be independent of the patterned activity coming to it from either the abdominal nervous system below or the supraesophageal ganglia above (290, 317). When these ganglia were isolated, flight continued unaffected. Wilson (317) also recorded from sensory nerves in the restrained flying animal. Two types of sensory input of the thoracic ganglia are relevant to flight: wind acting on wind-sensitive hairs on the head can initiate and maintain flight; and wind forces and wing movements acting on receptors located near the wings can maintain flight and control wingbeat frequency and other parameters controlling flight power. Flight probably begins with a jump which produces an air stream over the head hairs, exciting the flight system. Once established, movement of the animal through the air maintains flight as a result of the wind blowing on the head hairs and the movement of the wings affecting wing sense organs. Several receptors are located in the wing area. Proprioceptive hairs located on the tegulae at the base of the forewing discharge during the last half of the downstroke. The campaniform sensilla, about twenty mechanoreceptors located in the wing veins, probably measure lift forces during the downstroke. Finally, there is one stretch receptor in each hinge which discharges one or more impulses toward the end of the upstroke and signals wing position frequency, velocity, and amplitude. The flight-maintaining stimulus of wind on the head hair is steady and not phased with wing movement and could therefore not provide the reflex signals for the wingbeat cycle. However, the wings contain a variety of mechanoreceptors whose output is phased with wing position or movement. These receptors could in principle provide sufficient information for a purely reflex integration of the flight pattern.

To examine the role of this sensory feedback in maintaining rhythmic flight, Wilson (317) and Wilson & Gettrup (326) opened the sensory loop by systematically destroying the sense organs or the sensory nerves that provide the feedback. As long as wind continued to stimulate the head hairs, both the proprioceptive hairs and the campaniform sensilla could be removed without preventing flight. The main sequencing of the motoneuron pattern remained and its overall frequency was the same (317). Destroying all four stretch receptors resulted in a decrease in the wingbeat frequency to about one half of its normal value. Destroying only two or three stretch receptors had intermediate effects. Thus the elimination of all phasic sensory feedback from the wings did not disrupt the normal phase pattern of flight; it only produced a decrease in wingbeat frequency. Similarly, with the wing receptors intact, the head hair receptors could be removed and normal flight was still retained. In the absence of both wing receptors and head hair receptors, normal flight was not maintained but a normal wing phase pattern could be restored, at reduced wingbeat frequency, by electrically stimulating the CNS. The stimuli could be applied anywhere in the CNS from brain to abdominal cord. To be successful for maintaining flight the central stimulation did not have to be patterned in any way.

Thus, random stimuli containing no information for the timing of units worked perfectly well. Of further interest was the finding that many facilitating stimuli were needed to initiate the first response and that following the last stimulus there was a cyclical afterdischarge which sometimes lasted hundreds of cycles (317, 328). Direct stimulation of sensory nerves (326, 328) similarly indicated that phasing of the input was not necessary for a phased motor output.

Wilson (317, 321, 323) points out that these data indicate that the hypothesis of peripheral control and patterned feedback cannot explain wing movements in the locust. Instead, the patterned action of locust wing movements is produced by a pattern generator located in the CNS.

From these studies there emerges the following picture of the interaction of sensory information and central motor patterning device. The CNS receives two types of signals from the periphery, one steady (from head hairs) and the other phasic (from wing receptors). However, the timing information even from the phasic receptors is apparently little used. There is thus a disassociation between the motor output and the sensory input pattern. Whereas the output frequency determines the input frequency (because the motor output always bears a specific relationship to wing movements and the movements control the timing of the stretch receptors), the input pattern does not influence the output pattern.

Wilson (318, 323) suggests that the ganglion averages the input from the four stretch receptors and from its other flight receptors over a long time interval compared with the wingbeat period, and this average level of excitation determines the wingbeat frequency. Most of the detailed information about wing position, frequency, and amplitude is lost or discarded. The average level of excitatory input merely acts to turn on a central pattern generator but does not determine the main features of the pattern. The features are apparently inherent in the connections of the central network.

Given an inherent central program for locust flight, why does the animal need stretch reflexes at all? What is the function of reflex activity in insect flight? This problem has recently been approached in a highly imaginative study by Wilson (324). Wilson asked two questions: how perfect is the motor pattern (motor score) which is built into the thoracic ganglia? and how is the motor pattern modified by the removal of wings, thereby making the inherent score inappropriate? For this purpose Wilson studied animals in free flight or suspended as previously but with a new provision that permitted the animal to roll freely. Animals in free flight were observed with or without reduced sensory input produced by reducing visual input and by covering the wind-sensitive head hairs. Rolling behavior was studied with both normal and reduced visual input in animals mounted in front of a wind tunnel fitted with a movable simulated horizon. In addition, in some animals, flight muscles or single wings were removed.

In the absence of visual feedback, many suspended intact animals rolled consistently in one direction and there was asymmetry in the discharge pattern of the motoneurons. This centrally inherent asymmetry was corrected by unknown feedback in free flight or by the visual feedback provided by illuminating the simulated horizon. Similarly, removal of a wing produced changes in rolling torque in the absence of exteroceptive feedback which could also be corrected in free flight or in tethered flight with an illuminated horizon.

Wilson (324) suggests that in the locust flight system proprioceptive reflexes and exteroceptive sensory information supplement the preprogramed information built into the CNS so that the motor output can be modified. The need for modification may range from a fundamental mistake in the central program, such as provided by an inherent asymmetry in the output pattern, to a more transient change in the environmental condition for flight, such as might be produced by an alteration in wind direction. Thus the CNS has programed into it nearly everything that can be anticipated prior to actual flight. The sensory inputs supplement and complement this built-in information about the body and the environment that either cannot be anticipated genetically or is needed to compensate for minor genetic or developmental errors.

As a result of the interaction of genetic and sensory mechanisms, the insect flight control system is quite stable and overcompensated. No single motor or sensory structure is uniquely necessary for stable flight. Only as more and more of the whole flight system is damaged is flying ability progressively reduced.

Wilson's data and conclusions provide an elegant way of reviewing the interrelationship of environmental stimuli to genetically determined central patterns of connectivity and of function. Moreover, they illustrate a possible solution to the paradox posed by Lashley (177) who argued against the localization of function within specifically interconnected neurons because large brain lesion failed to eliminate certain behaviors. What emerges from Wilson's studies of insect flight is that highly specific patterns of afferent interconnections are distributed in space so that elimination of one reduces only a part of the safety margin without disrupting behavioral function. The apparent redundancy within the nervous system therefore can provide a double function: it provides a means whereby information processes in parallel can supplement and complement each other; and it provides a compensation against damage to the other parallel channels.

Evidence of central control of motor sequence is also available in other invertebrate systems. Hughes & Wiersma (123) and Ikeda & Wiersma (126) have shown that the typical metachronal rhythm of the thoracic and abdominal appendages in the crayfish is under central control. These appendages, called swimmerets, are used for swimming and feeding in some crustacea but the function of the five paired swimmerets in crayfish is not known. When the abdomen of the crayfish is removed from the rest of the body the swimmerets often start to beat in well-coordinated rhythmical movements which are essentially the same as those which occur in the intact animal; this may be due to a release of inhibition from higher centers (123). The discharge of the motoneuron to the swimmerets is signaled by a burst of impulses which can be recorded in the first root of any of the first five abdominal ganglia. The burst of motoneuron impulses is synchronous with the movement of the swimmerets which it innervates. The burst is composed of several units of which those associated with retraction and protraction of the swimmerets can be readily distinguished. The swimmerets on the two sides normally move together and the discharges recorded from the first two roots of any single abdominal ganglion show this synchrony. The cyclical bursts persist unaltered when the root is cut and the swimmeret removed. Moreover, the rhythmic coordinated motor discharge can persist following complete deafferentiation of the first five abdominal ganglia and their isolation from the rest of the CNS (126). The pattern is therefore centrally determined and no input is required to insure that the motor units normally involved in the rhythmic beat of the swimmerets discharge in their normal sequence.

Ikeda & Wiersma (126) analyzed several features of this motor sequence by examining the burst activity in several ganglia simultaneously. The central rhythm does not appear synchronously in all five ganglia; the rhythm originates in the most posterior (5th) ganglion and spreads to the more anterior ones. If the fifth ganglion is removed, the fourth replaces it as the pacemaker and occasionally even the third can replace the fourth following its removal. Only the second and first ganglia have no pacemaker capabilities. All potential pacemakers have comparable preferred frequencies of about 1.5 bursts per sec. The more posterior the ganglion the longer the discharge. This discharge is characteristic for each ganglion and is independent of whether the ganglion is the pacemaker or a follower.

To account for the sequencing of this rhythm Wiersma & Ikeda (309) suggested the following model. Each hemiganglion contains a single pacemaker neuron which connects with its partner on the other side as well as with the ipsilateral pacemaker cell in the next anterior ganglion. The pacemaker cells in the different ganglia vary in excitability. Those in the posterior are most exitable whereas those in the two anterior ganglia fire only when triggered by a posterior pacemaker cell. Discharge of pacemaker cells in any hemiganglion is rapidly followed by discharge of its partners in the other hemiganglion and, after some latency, by the discharge of the pacemaker cells in the next anterior ganglion. The pacemaker cells could be the motoneurons themselves or, alternatively, they could be independent cells which control motoneuron activity. Davis (54–58) has explored the effect on swimmeret beating of sensory input from the statocysts and from swimmeret muscle proprioceptors. As with insect flight, proprioceptive information supplements the centrally determined motor sequence. Decreasing the proprioceptive input from a given swimmeret decreases the strength of movement of the adjacent swimmerets on the same side.

Other instances in which evidence for a central control of motor sequence has been presented are the cicada song (95), the cricket song (119), the control of heartbeat in crustacea (92, 183, 184), the copulatory movements in the praying mantis (245), the respiration of insects (192–194), and the eye movement in crabs (28, 112). Deafferentation experiments now also indicate that proprioceptive feedback may not be essential for certain types of voluntary movements in lower vertebrates (332) as well as in primates (156, 270, 271).

Perhaps all motor sequences in invertebrates may prove to be centrally controlled. Until recently, insect walking appeared to be reflexively controlled because proprioceptive input plays a large role in the walking of certain insects and provides a partial explanation for the altered walking pattern assumed after leg amputation (see 320, 322). However, new experiments suggest that insect walking is also due to an inherent central rhythmicity (117, 212).

To summarize, postural adjustments appear to be highly reflexive and dependent upon proprioceptive input, but many types of cyclical motor behavior such as insect flight seem to be centrally determined and the basic pattern and phase are relatively independent of proprioceptive input. In cyclical motor sequences proprioceptive input serves primarily as supplementary information for the genetically determined central program.

Although we have a fairly good intuitive understanding of how reflexive mechanisms might work, little is known about the wiring diagram and cellular properties of the elements involved in generating a central program. Many of the models proposed for these central pattern generators postulate systems that have endogenous activity (see 321). But with the exception of the cardiac ganglion it has not been possible to record intracellularly in cell bodies of identified moto- and interneurons to demonstrate autochronous activity in systems controlling motor sequences. Indeed, three general questions can be asked. Can endogenous activity be rigorously demonstrated in any invertebrate neuron or network of neurons? How general a mechanism is endogenous activity? What types of mechanisms might be involved in the generation of complex patterns such as those which underlie motor sequences?

Endogenous rhythms and the generation of central patterns of neuronal activity.—In a number of invertebrate ganglia it has now been possible to demonstrate rigorously that single cells can manifest spontaneous activity in the complete absence of neural stimulation. A detailed study is that by Barbara Alving (3) in which she tied a ligature around the synapse-free cell body of several identified cells in *Aplysia* to isolate electrically the soma from the synapses in the neuropile. In the complete absence of neural input, the isolated cell body retained its characteristic firing pattern. The mechanism for this endogenous activity appears to reside in an intrinsically unstable membrane potential, a mechanism similar to that underlying the spontaneously active cells in the pacemaker regions of the vertebrate heart. (For discussions see 80, 268.) The frequency of occurrence of endogenously active cells has been examined in two neural populations. In the crustacean cardiac ganglion all nine cells are endogenously active (92, 183, 184, 187). In the abdominal ganglion of *Aplysia* 24 of 30 of the large and prominent (identified) cells were spontaneously active and in most cells the endogenous nature of this activity could be demonstrated (80).

The existence of autoactive neurons is of particular behavioral importance. Specifically such cells could explain the persistence of rhythmic coordinated swimmeret movements in the crayfish following isolation from the remainder of the nervous system. More generally, the presence of autoactive cells which sustain a level of ongoing activity in the CNS may provide a neural analog of the psychological concept of an internal drive state (243). And, as Strumwasser (268) has emphasized, endogenously active cells can maintain the neurally controlled circadian rhythms of bodily functions.

The best studied example of the generation of a complex spontaneous central pattern by interconnected endogenously active cells is provided by the cardiac ganglion found on the inner surface of the heart of higher crustacea [see reviews by Maynard (187) and Hagiwara (92)]. Typically this ganglion is made up of nine neurons whose rhythmic output drives the heart. All of these cells are capable of endogenous activity in the absence of sensory input; also they all interact with each other to initiate at regular intervals a burst of impulses which causes a brief tetanic contraction of the heart. The ganglion can be divided into two subpopulations of cells: a posterior group of four small cells which appear to be the pacemakers; and an anterior group of five large follower cells which are motoneurons to the heart. The four posterior cells fire first and provide the initial impulse of each burst. The posterior cells synapse on the anterior cells and produce EPSPs which cause them to discharge. Moreover, the follower cells are electrically coupled to each other and to the pacemakers, and their resultant positive feedback probably aids in the development of the avalanching burst of 20–100 spikes produced by the follower cells.

The pattern of impulses produced by the cardiac ganglion is truly endogenous, for it persists even when the ganglion is completely isolated from all sensory input (183). However, the pattern of activity in the ganglion can be modulated in three major ways: by direct inhibitor and accelerator fibers coming from the CNS; by indirect neural action acting on the valves of the heart to change the rate of filling which influences the stretching of the heart; and by hormonal influence via the neuroendocrine product released by the pericardial organ (47, 48, 92).

A system such as the cardiac ganglion has the properties necessary for generating the types of central rhythms which seem to account for the control of rhythmic movement in arthropods. In each case input is unnecessary for the basic rhythm but can provide an important modulation of the fundamental rhythm of the pacemaker cluster. Characteristically, several influences can interact with the endogenous rhythm.

What is still difficult to explain is how a central pattern is generated that requires external triggering, and persists for only seconds or minutes after the stimulus (126, 318, 326, 328). Perhaps here we have a transition case of cells with only limited potentialities for endogenous activity which cannot maintain this activity in the absence of an occasional neural input (see e.g. 167, 170).

Motor command elements.—Release of a central preprogramed motor sequence requires elements within the CNS capable of triggering behavioral sequences. Perhaps the most dramatic finding to emerge from recent studies of the invertebrate motor system is the discovery that single "command elements" can trigger complete preprogramed motor sequences. Although command elements were first described by Wiersma 30 years ago in the crayfish, the detailed study of such neurons in arthropods has begun only recently.[1]

The discovery of command elements began with the analysis of the giant fiber system in the crayfish. The crayfish nervous system contains a giant fiber system consisting of two pairs of longitudinal giant axons, the medial giants and the lateral giants, and many pairs of peripherally directed giant

---

[1] In 1938, Wiersma described fibers which produce blocks of behavior (296), but he first called them "command fibers" in 1964 (309).

motoneurons (129, 130). The medial giant neurons have their cell bodies in the brain, where they presumably receive a variety of sensory input (107, 298). Their axons run the length of the nerve cord from the brain to the last abdominal ganglion. The lateral giant neurons also run the length of the nerve cord but these giant fibers are segmented, being composed of units which are tightly coupled by electrical junctions. Each axon segment has its own large cell body contralateral to the axon (232). The lateral giants are therefore actually fused neurons, but the tightness of their electrical coupling makes them behave functionally as one unit (138, 284). The lateral giant fibers can be excited by stimulation of body segments posterior to the fourth thoracic. As early as 1924, Johnson (129) had shown that the four giant fibers serve to flip the crayfish tail but not until 1938 did Wiersma show that a single electrical stimulus applied to any one of the four giant fibers could produce a complete escape response consisting of turning in of the eyestalks, forward movement of the antennae and legs, pulling upward of the swimmerets, and a strong tail flip (296, 299). In addition, leg movement is inhibited (236). Each of the four giant fibers apparently synapses in every ganglion of the nerve cord and brings a similar although not identical peripheral output into play. The four giant fibers do however differ in the types of natural stimuli necessary to discharge them. The medial fibers respond to stimulation of the head region (pinching the flagella of the antenna and visual stimuli) whereas the lateral fibers respond to noxious stimuli in the tail region. In this sense the crayfish giant fiber system may be similar to an analogous giant fiber system in the earthworm (24).

Following the discovery of the command neurons for the escape response, Wiersma (299) discovered a single fiber in the circumoesophageal commissure which on repetitive stimulation triggered the defensive reflex. This reflex consists of the animal becoming opisthotonic and raising its claws and head while supporting its body on its tail and fourth and fifth thoracic legs.

A decade later Wiersma returned to studying command fibers and in collaboration with Hughes (123) and later with Ikeda (309) he described five command elements which upon repetitive stimulation (about 30/sec) caused rhythmic beating of the swimmerets. More recently Atwood & Wiersma (5) have described eight additional command elements in the circumoesophageal commissures controlling a variety of peripheral claw, leg, and abdominal movements, and Kennedy, Evoy, Dane & Hanawalt (75, 143, 145) have provided detailed evidence that single fibers command abdominal postural adjustments.

From analyses of a number of command fibers in crayfish several generalizations have emerged (5, 75, 144, 309).

(a) Command fibers generally exert a widespread effect controlling a total block or sequence of behavior. As a result they frequently have complex and differential effects upon different motor pathways, exciting some and inhibiting others. For example a command fiber controlling abdominal flexion will affect a number of segments, producing in each segment excitation of five flexor motoneurons, inhibition of the flexor inhibition, excitation of the extensor inhibitor, and inhibition of the five extensor motoneurons. This command element therefore affects the activity of at least 120 motoneurons (144). Some command fibers which control abdominal flexion also affect the caudal appendages or the swimmerets and may therefore influence as many as 300 motoneurons (145).

(b) More than one fiber can initiate a particular behavioral sequence and there is often overlap in the effector actions mediated by a number of different command fibers. For example any one of the four giant fibers can trigger the escape response (296, 299) and any one of five fibers can elicit beating of the swimmerets (309).

(c) Despite the overlap in effector actions among several command elements it is often possible to distinguish important differences in their detailed field of action, which suggests that the movement produced by each element may be unique. The actions of some command fibers are limited to a single motor system, whereas the action of others may include a second system. For example, some fibers controlling abdominal position activate only the abdominal musculature, whereas others also produce movement of the swimmerets or of the caudal appendages (75). In addition, almost all of the command fibers controlling abdominal posture differ from each other in the number of abdominal segments which they supply and in their relative efficacy in common segments. As a result, some produce strong discharge in caudal segments and weak discharges in rostral ones while others have the opposite effect. These findings have led Kennedy et al. (145) to suggest that despite the extensive overlap, each command fiber in a particular category may code for a unique body position or geometry.

(d) The quantitative relationship between behavioral output and frequency of firing of a command element is often complex. In some cases different firing frequencies of a simple command element may produce different types of behavior (5).

(e) Command fibers tend to have a very high threshold to sensory activation, and simultaneous stimulation of several different sensory inputs may be required to make them respond (5, 148).

(f) Certain interneurons in the CNS ("suppression" elements) inhibit the actions of command elements (75, 309).

Although most of the studies on command elements have been carried out on crayfish, similar elements have now been also encountered in annelid worms (24) and marine molluscs (168, 213, 316). It seems likely that they occur in all higher invertebrates as well as in some vertebrates (334).

As Atwood & Wiersma (5) point out, the term "command fiber" indicates only that its activity calls into play a readily recognizable behavioral act. The term is descriptively convenient but tells us nothing about the mechanisms by which these fibers engage their respective motoneurons. Atwood & Wiersma write: "These mechanisms may range in complexity from the direct coupling involved in the giant-fibre synapses to systems in which complex neural pacemaker and timing circuits are interposed between the command fibre and the motor axons." Clearly the major task in this area is to delineate the complete connectivity pattern formed by the command elements and the neuronal populations which they innervate. What are the principles of interconnections involved here? How do these cells mediate their reciprocal interactions? Do individual command elements mediate opposite synaptic actions directly to their different follower cells (133) or do they require interneurons?

A beginning toward an analysis of the connectivity pattern subserving the actions of a command element has been made by Roberts (236, 237), who studied the pattern of muscular and nervous activity resulting from a single impulse in the giant fiber system in the crayfish in the absence of peripheral reflexes. An impulse in one of these fibers produces the full escape response. The first response to an action potential in a central giant is an action potential in the motor giant which is electrically coupled to it (82) and which innervates the majority of the fast flexor muscles. The muscles are excited synchronously; and the characteristic pattern of the tail flip flexion movement results from the inherent arrangement and properties of the muscles themselves (231), not from any special pattern of impulses in the circuit of the escape response. The remaining excitor motoneurons, whose field of innervation is more restricted, fire shortly after the giant motoneuron. There appears to be a specific advantage to this double innervation. Whereas the muscle endplate potentials (EJPs) produced by the motor giants decline rapidly with repeated stimulation, the EJPs produced by the late-arriving activity of the other motoneurons facilitate. The activity in the nongiant motoneurons can therefore produce the flexion response even in the absence of a response to an impulse in the motor giant (149), and as a result the crayfish continues to be capable of repeated tail flips necessary for backward swimming.

Late in the cycle the motoneurons to the slow abdominal flexors are activated; their function may be to stabilize the tail, preparatory for another tail flip or for the reestablishment of postural tone. Neither fast nor slow extensors were activated by giant fiber activity.

In addition to these actions on motoneurons, Roberts (236) found that activity in any central giant fiber leads to central inhibition of the lateral giant fibers. The inhibition lasts 80 msec, the time the crayfish needs to complete one tail flip movement. Roberts suggests that the inhibition is mediated by an interneuron which receives recurrent collaterals from all of the giant axons. Central inhibition of the giant fiber system may limit the number of impulses produced in them by a single afferent volley and lead to coordination of successive escape responses.

OVERVIEW OF THE ORGANIZATION OF AFFERENT AND MOTOR SYSTEMS

Perhaps the area of greatest ignorance in the organization of the invertebrate nervous system is the functional interconnections between the afferent and motor systems. There are, however, two features common to the organization of both afferent and motor systems which may provide clues to their interconnectivity. 1. In both systems neurons code for position. In the motor system they code for position of movement and in the sensory system they code for the position of the sensory input on the body surface. 2. In both systems many units abstract only certain critical aspects of the stimulus.

The coding for position is best illustrated by considering studies of the crayfish abdomen. The afferent interneurons that collect input from the abdominal tactile receptors can be grouped into *segmental interneurons* which react only to stimulation of one segment and *multisegmental* interneurons which respond to stimulation of any one of several segments. A single sensory stimulus applied to the fourth abdominal segment activates about a dozen interneurons: one segmental interneuron which serves segment 4 alone, a multisegmental interneuron which serves segment 4 in combination with 5, a third which collects input from 3, 4, and 5, and so forth. Although each sensory area activates a number of interneurons, each interneuron appears to code for a unique spatial representation in the sensory field (122, 300). Similarly command fibers controlling abdominal position may act on only one segment, on two segments, on all segments, or on all segments as well as on the swimmerets or caudal appendages (143). Each command fiber therefore may act in a spatially unique way, coding for a unique motor representation of body geometry.

The abstracting capabilities of afferent interneurons have been considered in detail in an earlier section. Possible parallel abstracting capability of command elements is suggested by the findings that they may only respond to fairly complex stimuli. Although there are some notable exceptions (60, 266), the vast majority of afferent neurons and interneurons do not produce motor movement when they become active individually. This finding suggests that the afferent input to command elements may be complex, requiring a number of differing afferent interneurons activated by a specific and complex natural stimulus or combinations of stimuli. In a sense this is what we might expect. It now appears from studies of the sensory systems of mammals that the higher the order of a neuron in a sensory system the more complex its appropriate stimulus tends to be (118). Command elements are higher-order neurons to the highest-order afferent cells, and their appropriate stimulus should be more complex still.

Neurosecretory Systems

Neurosecretion is ubiquitous in invertebrates and the ratio of neurosecretory cells to ordinary neurons in many invertebrate ganglia appears to be greater than in the vertebrate brain. For example, in the abdominal ganglion of mature specimens of the mollusk *Aplysia,* one group of neurosecretory cells (the bag cells) accounts for almost half of the total number of neurons

(41). Experiments on invertebrates, particularly insects, have played a central role in establishing the hormonal function of neurosecretory cells, and there is an extensive literature on the endocrinological aspects of invertebrate neurosecretory cells (18, 252) [see (281) for distinction between neurosecretory and neuroendocrine cells]. On the other hand, there is scanty evidence on the neural functioning of neurosecretory cells even though in some invertebrates these cells are quite large and are easy to impale with microelectrodes.

We might ask whether neurosecretory cells have the basic properties of conventional neurons: are they electrically excitable, and do they generate action potentials? By extracellular (281, 333) and more recently by intracellular recordings (43, 49, 169, 170), neurosecretory cells in invertebrates have been found to resemble those of vertebrates (15, 131, 195) in behaving like conventional nerve cells. As in studies of vertebrate neurosecretory cells, a somewhat prolonged action potential has been described.

In addition to generating propagated action potentials, neurosecretory cells are also involved in integrative reflex activity in ways analogous to the activity of nonneurosecretory neurons. For example several studies in invertebrates have now demonstrated neuroendocrine reflexes in which neurosecretory cells function analogously to motoneurons as the final motor pathway affecting either muscle cells or glands. Wigglesworth (314) found that in the insect *Rhodnius* a blood meal elicited moulting by causing swelling of the abdomen and initiating a neurosecretory reflex involving the medial group of neurosecretory cells in the brain. The brain hormone released from the medial neurosecretory cells in turn stimulates the prothoracic gland to release the growth hormone, ecdysone. Subsequently Van der Kloot (281) reported that as predicted, stretching of the abdomen elicited impulses in the nervus cardiacum which contains the axons of the medial neurosecretory cells. Davey [52] reported that heart rate increases reflexly in cockroaches fed a meal of glucose. The receptors for this reflex are localized in one particular region of the labrum (a mouth part) and the reflex is abolished by sectioning the labrum nerve. The corpus cardiacum contains a cardioacceleratory substance, and destroying this organ abolished the reflex. Furthermore, injection of trypan blue, which blocks the cardioacceleratory effects of extracts from the corpus cardiacum, also blocks the cardioacceleratory feeding reflex. Davey therefore concluded that the acceleration of the heart resulted from the release of a neurosecretory product of the corpus cardiocum. Other neuroendocrine reflexes in insects involve oogenesis, water balance, and tanning (for a recent review see 227).

A possible mechanism for insuring the release of sufficient amounts of hormone by a neuroendocrine reflex has been studied in the bag cells, a group of neurosecretory cells located in the abdominal ganglion of the marine mollusk *Aplysia* (170). Anatomical studies by Coggeshall (80) have shown that the bag cells are filled with elementary "neurosecretory" granules and send processes into the sheath, which can function as a neurohemal organ. In the unstimulated isolated ganglion, intracellular recording showed that the bag cells are completely inactive. Brief electrical stimulation (sometimes a single shock) of the left or right pleurovisceral connective elicits bag cell spike activity, usually lasting 5–10 min, but occasionally persisting for up to 50 min. Functional studies on the bag cells indicate that they may be involved in an endocrinological reflex that results in the release of eggs (166). *In vitro* studies showed that brief electrical stimulation of a connective led to the release into the perfusate of a substance which released egg laying when injected into intact animals (169). The system appears designed to release a measured amount of a particular hormone, independent of the exact parameters of the triggering stimulus. This centrally controlled response of the bag cells is somewhat analogous to that of the control of flight in the locust, in which afferent input serves merely to trigger a preprogramed central response.

A significant feature in the functional activity of the bag cells is that they are all mutually excitatory, and as a result all 400 bag cells on one side of the ganglion fire in exact synchrony. The left and right groups of bag cells are also mutually excitatory, but the coupling is not as strong as between the cells on a given side. For that reason, as the frequency of firing decreases, the left and right groups of bag cells become desynchronized. These results indicate that a cluster of neurosecretory cells can show an elementary form of integrative activity as well as a purely secretory motor function. In this respect they are analogous to nonneurosecretory motor cells that also can have certain central integrative synaptic functions besides their direct motor functions. For example, spinal motoneurons synaptically innervate interneurons as well as muscle.

Although, on the whole, neurosecretory cells in invertebrates function analogously to nonneurosecretory *motor* cells, they can also function as *interneurons* or even as *sensory cells*. For example, Cooke [47) has shown that electrical stimulation of the pericardial organ causes the release of a cardioacceleratory substance presumably secreted by neurosecretory processes associated with the pericardial organ. The substance released from the pericardial organ does not act directly on the heart, but instead affects nerve cells in the cardiac ganglion which drives the heart (48). Therefore these neurosecretory cells function analogously to nonneurosecretory interneurons. A somewhat more complicated example in which nerve cells may mediate the effects of a neurohormone is indicated in a study by Davey (52). He suggested that a hormone in the corpora cardica of cockroaches stimulates the hindgut by causing the release of an indolalkylamine which then acts on the peripheral nerve net associated with the gut.

A number of studies have indicated a possible sensory function for neurosecretory cells in invertebrates. Waterman & Enami (287) have proposed that the structure of the lateral rudimentary eye of the horseshoe crab indicates it is a neurosecretory organ. There was no evidence that the secretory substance moves down the axons of the neurosensory cells, but instead it appeared that the cells secrete their product directly from the cell bodies into the surrounding connective tissue which is heavily vascularized. Another possible example of neurosecretion intimately associated with a sensory system is seen in the secondary visual units of the rudimentary eye of *Aplysia*. A possible neurosecretory function for these cells has been suggested by Jacklet (127) on the basis of the presence of elementary neurosecretory granules. Interestingly, these cells appear to discharge synchronously, like the bag cells of the abdominal ganglion of *Aplysia*. Similarly another cluster of neurosecretory cells in the abdominal ganglion of *Aplysia* (the white cells) may have a sensory function. In the isolated ganglion the white cells are tonically active, showing regular spike activity that is independent in each cell. Stimulation of peripheral nerves has a weak inhibitory influence (43, 80). Stimulation of the branchial nerve produces antidromic spikes, showing that the white cells send a long process into the branchial nerve. Chemical stimulation of the osphradium also results in antidromic spikes in the white cells (128). Since the white cells send extensive processes into the sheath, their long processes in the branchial nerve may not serve primarily as a source of release of the secretory product, but may function as a dendrite, activated either directly by chemical stimuli or synaptically by a primary sensory cell. Other possible examples of neurosecretory function of sensory organs have been discussed by Bern (17) and Davey (53).

FUNCTIONAL MODIFIABILITY OF INVERTEBRATE GANGLIA

The nervous systems of invertebrates have been used to study the mechanisms of a variety of behaviors (cf. 27, 60, 243). Learning and other behavioral modifications have been of particular interest. A reason for this interest is that neuronal plasticity is commonly encountered during the cellular studies now possible in invertebrates. Also, in contrast to certain instinctive behaviors that are species-specific, the mechanisms of behavioral modification promise to have wide generality across species, including man.

Rather than review all of the literature relevant to mechanisms of invertebrate learning, we will concentrate on habituation—the waning of a response that is repeatedly evoked. Habituation is remarkably general and parametrically similar forms of this response decrement occur in all higher metazoa. Moreover a number of different responses show habituation.[2]

[2] In invertebrates it is also possible to produce response decrement without utilizing repeated stimulation, and such behavior may be related to habituation. For example, the complex feeding response in the mollusk *Aplysia* which habituates when repeatedly evoked by a nonfood object (180) can also be inhibited without repeated stimulation if the animal is given a single strong electric shock (171). Response alternation is another example of a response decrement occurring outside of the usual habituation paradigm. This refers to the observation that in a number of invertebrates, when an animal makes either a left or right turn, there is a sharply decreased probability that the animal will subsequently make the same turn (61, 165).

Habituation has at least two of the features characteristic of the most advanced forms of learning (191) ; it can be relatively enduring, lasting days and even weeks (161, 162, 180) ; and it can be rapidly produced (101, 214, 216). Habituation may also be related to learning in two other ways : it involves the repeated presentation of an unreinforced stimulus and is operationally equivalent to the extinction procedure utilized in classical and operant conditioning; and a habituated response can be increased in magnitude by presenting a second stimulus (dishabituation). Operationally, dishabituation is similar to sensitization or pseudoconditioning, processes that have been considered to be a part of true classical conditioning. In addition, sensitization and pseudoconditioning (nonassociative forms of response increments) are likely to be precursors to true associative conditioning. Because of these features some workers feel that habituation is an example of simple learning (e.g. 275), but others do not consider it to be true learning (e.g. 191). Since the definition of learning is somewhat arbitrary it seems best to avoid semantic controversy by considering habituation as simply a "behavioral modification".

To understand the detailed neural mechanisms of a particular behavioral modification it is necessary to know in detail the wiring diagram of the behavior being modified. However, even in the relatively simple nervous systems of invertebrates, it is difficult to work out the circuit of any given behavior. For this reason, defensive escape and withdrawal responses which characteristically habituate provide a unique opportunity for studying the mechanisms of habituation. Most defensive reflexes are mediated by simple neuronal circuits involving only a few synaptic relays. This simplicity probably results from the requirement that defensive reflexes must be rapid to be effective. Another fortunate consequence of the necessity for speed and rapid coordination of the defensive reflexes is that they almost always involve giant nerve cells, which facilitate long-term intracellular recording of synaptic potentials. It is also easy to recognize and record the discharge of these giant fibers by means of extracellular recording.

In the remaining discussion we will only consider habituation of defensive responses in mollusks, annelids, and arthropods. We will first discuss behavioral studies and then studies of the neural mechanisms.

BEHAVIORAL STUDIES

Behavioral experiments are useful for determining whether habituation results from sensory adaptation or motor fatigue, rather than from a functional change in the CNS. Although physiological inferences from behavioral experiments are usually open to alternative explanations, several types of behavioral experiments support the notion that peripheral sensory or motor effects do not play a predominant role in habituation.

From the known rates of sensory adaptation and muscle fatigue one would predict that if habituation were due to these peripheral effects, its time course of recovery would be relatively short. The available data indicate that habituation usually lasts many minutes and even hours and days.

For example, habituation of the withdrawal response in polychaete worms does not fully recover in 3 to 17 hr following 20 to 55 trials separated by 1–3 min (38). Recovery from habituation can sometimes be further prolonged when the response is repeatedly habituated on a daily basis. Kuenzer (162) reported that the withdrawal response in earthworms did not fully recover after 10 days of rest following daily habituation for 10 days. In a more recent and better controlled experiment, Gardner (85) found that the habituated withdrawal response in the earthworm did not fully recover within 96 hr following an average of 24 habituating trials totaling only 6 sec of stimulation over a period of 7 min. Whereas these examples involve repeated stimulation, it is possible to obtain habituation of reasonably long duration following only a single stimulus. For example the defensive gill withdrawal response in *Aplysia* does not fully recover for 20 min following a single tactile stimulus (214, 216).

Dishabituation also argues against peripheral sensory or motor effects. In one of the earliest systematic accounts of habituation in invertebrates, Humphrey (124) found that a habituated withdrawal response in snails could transiently recover following the application of a strong stimulus. Dishabituation following a strong stimulus has also been reported for defensive withdrawal responses in worms (38, 85) and in *Aplysia* (e.g. 214, 216).

Another observation that argues against sensory accommodation or muscle fatigue is that strong stimuli produce slower habituation than weak stimuli. This has been described for withdrawal responses in polychaete and oligochaete worms (38, 162) and in *Aplysia* (214, 216). Moreover, habituation is often stimulus-specific. Animals fully habituated to one type of stimulus will often show responses when tested with a different type. This suggests that neither neuromuscular accommodation nor muscular fatigue can account for habituation, since defensive withdrawal responses are usually mediated by one set of final motor outputs. Stimulus-specific habituation of defensive reflexes has been described in both oligochaete (162) and polychaete worms (38, 251). Another observation that denies a crucial role for muscular fatigue comes from an interesting experiment by Clark (38) on nereid worms. Clark found that a series of very weak stimuli that elicited no responses nevertheless increased the rate of habituation produced when a stronger stimulus was subsequently used.

Two observations on the habituation of defensive reflexes relate specifically to the question of sensory accommodation. It has been reported in the habituation of withdrawal responses of worms (85, 110) that while one type of response may completely disappear during habituation, other types may still be present. Thus at least some elements of the sensory system must still be functioning, although one type of response no longer occurs. In addition, generalization of habituation argues against a crucial role for sensory accommodation. When a response is habituated by repeated tactile stimulation at one point, reflexes elicited by stimuli presented at nearby points are also depressed.

NEUROPHYSIOLOGICAL STUDIES

Horridge (110) investigated the locus of the critical neural changes involved in habituation of the polychaete worms *Nereis* and *Harmothoe*. The escape response in these worms involves several giant fibers that run the length of the animal. These fibers are excited by afferent input and, in turn, they excite motor cells that innervate the body musculature. The role of failure at the afferent-to-giant fibers pathway was tested by recording giant fiber responses extracellularly while directly stimulating sensory fibers by strong electric shocks applied to an anal cercus. At a stimulus rate of 4–20/sec the first and second stimulus usually elicited giant fiber responses. Subsequent stimuli were ineffective. Thus transmission at the sensory-to-giant synapse was extremely labile. Directly stimulating giant fibers and recording muscle action potentials led to a similar conclusion concerning the giant-to-motor synapse. Following repetitive stimulation at 5–12/sec, localized muscle action potentials failed in an all-or-none fashion. By directly stimulating motor fibers and recording muscle action potentials it was possible to show that the motoneuron-to-muscle junction does not readily fail, although the muscle action potentials decrease in size at stimulus frequencies above 1/sec.

By means of experiments similar to those of Horridge on polychaete worms, Roberts (239) concluded that the decline of the escape reflex in the earthworm is also due to failure at both the sensory-to-giant and giant-to-motor cell junctions. Roberts (238) has also studied the properties of the withdrawal response of *Myxicola*, a polychaete worm in which the giant fibers do not synapse with motoneurons, but instead directly innervate the body musculature (203). Therefore, contractions produced by direct stimulation of the giant fiber do not readily fatigue, as they do in the earthworm and ragworm. Since the withdrawal response in *Myxicola* rapidly habituates (238), Roberts assumed that this results from accommodation at sensory-to-giant synapses, although this point has not been directly investigated.

In neither of the experiments on worms was it possible to distinguish decreased effectiveness of excitatory synaptic action from increased inhibitory activity as a mechanism of reflex failure. Although the experiments with worms do not provide decisive information about the mechanism of habituation, they are in agreement with behavioral inferences that indicate that habituation is not a result of peripheral factors. The experiments primarily indicate the loci at which modifications in central synaptic transmission are occurring. It is interesting that in cases where two central synapses mediate the withdrawal response, both synapses show modification with repetitive stimulation. This does not necessarily mean that both synapses are importantly involved in reflex habituation. In a series-connected neural reflex circuit, failure at any one point will cause reflex failure. Therefore in worms, even though both synapses may rapidly fatigue, behavioral habituation may be largely or entirely due to failure at the junction that is most readily fatigued. To clarify this point it is necessary to show at least rough quantitative fits between the physiological and behavioral data. Unfortunately, the stimulus parameters used in the physiological experiments on worms have been quite different from those used in the behavioral studies on habituation.

Several workers using extracellular recording and stimulation techniques have also studied the possible loci of the neuronal changes that may underlie habituation of the defensive escape response in roaches. Pumphrey & Rawdon-Smith (223) found that with repetitive stimulation of an afferent nerve (cercal) in the roach, the giant fiber response failed, although the afferent volley remained unchanged. Failure occurred however only with relatively high-frequency stimulation (around 25/sec). Roeder, Kennedy & Samson (244) similarly found that failure at the sensory-to-giant junction required relatively high-frequency stimulation. However, stimulation of the giant fiber led to very rapid failure of the motor output (241-243), which led Roeder to suggest that habituation of the escape response in roaches is due to rapid adaptation of the giant-to-motoneuron synapse. A report by Baxter (10) supports this conclusion. He used natural stimuli (puffs of air) and recorded motor responses while simultaneously recording extracellularly from the giant fibers. Upon repetitive stimulation, the escape response decreased in intensity and finally disappeared, but the electrical activity of the giant fibers remained unchanged.

The conclusion that habituation of the escape response in roaches is entirely due to changes at the giant-to-motor synapse has been questioned by Hughes (121). In a quantitative study of the number of giant fiber spikes evoked by repetitive stimulation of the anal cerci, he found a decrease in spikes even with stimuli separated by 1 min intervals. As previously discussed for the worm, since the escape response in the roach is mediated by a series-connected neuronal system, the contribution, if any, of changes at any given point in the circuit can only be definitely established by quantitative comparisons of the changes at various points in the circuit, preferably using natural stimuli and behaviorally functioning preparations.

Although extracellular recording techniques are useful for recording the locus of the changes underlying habituation, more detailed elucidation of cellular mechanisms requires intracellular techniques. Krasne & Roberts (158, 159) have studied habituation of the crayfish escape response. They stimulated the giant fiber directly at the same rate used in behavioral experiments, and showed that reflex habituation was not mediated by changes at the giant-to-motor synapses. Intracellular recording from a lateral giant fiber showed that repetitive afferent stimulation led to a decrease of the excitatory synaptic potential in the giant fiber, with eventual failure of the giant fiber spike. To test whether this depression may have been due to an augmentation of inhibitory processes, the authors tested whether the repetitively evoked EPSP decreased in the presence of picrotoxin, which blocks many inhibitory synapses in the crayfish nervous system. Since picrotoxin did not lead to a decrease in the rate at which the repetitively evoked EPSP decreased, the authors concluded that inhibition probably does not play a role in habituation of the escape reflex in crayfish. They recognize, however, that this conclusion is based upon the unproven assumption that picrotoxin blocks all inhibitory synapses. Moreover since the afferent pathway to the lateral giant is not well specified it was not possible to specify the exact locus or mechanisms of the neuronal modification.

In an analysis of habituation and dishabituation of the defensive withdrawal of the gill in *Aplysia,* it has been possible to specify both the locus and the mechanism of the response decrement. When the mantle shelf of *Aplysia* is stimulated, the siphon, the mantle shelf, and the gill contract and withdraw into the mantle cavity. This reflex is completely controlled by the abdominal ganglion and its neural circuit has been largely specified (168). Tactile receptors in the mantle activate sensory fibers that make monosynaptic as well as polysynaptic excitatory connections with four motoneurons that innervate the gill.

Behavioral aspects of habituation of the gill reflex were studied in the intact *Aplysia* restrained in a small aquarium (214, 216). Repeated stimulation of the mantle produces habituation of the withdrawal response and presentation of a different tactile stimulus produces dishabituation. Habituation of the gill was shown to have features characteristic of habituation found in mammals (261). Moreover the time course of habituation could be relatively long. With repeated stimulation at 1–3 min intervals, the gill response habituated to roughly 30 per cent of control, and full recovery sometimes required more than an hour. In a semi-intact preparation intracellular recordings were made from identified gill motoneurons while gill contractions were recorded simultaneously. The animal was prepared in the same way as the intact preparation except that a small hole was made just anterior to the mantle region, and the abdominal ganglion with its connectives and peripheral nerves attached was lifted out and pinned to an illuminated stage. In this preparation motor responsiveness could be shown not to change significantly during habituation. In addition, the possibility that habituation resulted from changes in sensory input was excluded by showing that controlled electrical stimulation of a peripheral nerve also produced habituation. Instead, decreased gill contractions were associated with a decreased spike discharge of gill motoneurons, as a result of a decrease in the amplitude of the complex excitatory synaptic potential evoked by the repeated tactile stimulation (173). Dishabituation was associated with an increase in the size of the EPSP seen in the gill motoneurons. By means of a simplified preparation consisting of an isolated ganglion with only a piece of skin and nerve attached, it was possible to show that slow repetitive stimulation (once every 1 to 5 min) of a small area of skin led to a large decrease of the EPSP recorded from identified gill motoneurons (37). Since there was no change in the input resistance during habituation, this decrease could be attributed to a change in the synaptic drive impinging on the motoneurons. Moreover, it was possible to show decrement in a unitary monosynaptic

EPSP which was repeatedly evoked by stimulating a primary afferent fiber that synapsed on the motoneuron. The time course of decrement and recovery of the EPSP was comparable to the habituation of the gill demonstrated in behavioral experiments. These results show that at least part of the behavioral habituation is due to low-frequency depression of the monosynaptic EPSP produced by the afferent fibers on the motoneurons.

A similar analysis was undertaken for dishabituation. Facilitation of a decremented monosynaptic EPSP could be produced by stimulation of another nerve. This heterosynaptic facilitation occurred in the absence of a change in the passive properties of the motoneuron membrane, which indicates that the facilitation was a presynaptic facilitation of the decremented EPSP.

These studies indicate that plastic changes in excitatory synpatic transmission contribute significantly to, and perhaps could fully account for habituation and dishabituation in *Aplysia*.

The mechanisms for the plastic changes underlying habituation and dishabituation in *Aplysia* might have been expected from previous work. Response decrement of EPSPs due to homosynaptic depression (23, 136, 137), and heterosynaptic facilitation due to a presynaptic mechanism (137, 273) had been described in different cells in the abdominal ganglion. However, several studies have shown alternative mechanisms that could have equally accounted for these behavioral modifications. For example, habituation could have been caused by increased inhibitory drive on the motoneuron, presynaptic inhibition of the afferent fibers, or a decrease in the resistance of the motoneuron. Similarly, dishabituation could have been due to a number of known mechanisms (for reviews see refs. 22, 134, 172). In all of these earlier studies, however, the behavioral role played by the cells showing the plastic changes was not known; hence the behavioral significance, if any, of the observed modification could not be determined. It is apparent then that the key to analyzing behavioral modification is essentially electroanatomical. Once the neural circuit of the behavior is specified, the analysis of the locus and mechanism of behavioral modification is greatly simplified.

The studies in *Aplysia* indicate that habituation involves a change in the functional effectiveness of previously existing excitatory connections. Thus at least in this simple case it seems unnecessary to invoke electrical fields or growth of new connections in explaining a behavioral modification. These studies also shed light on the relationship of dishabituation to habituation. The data indicate that, as suggested by Humphrey (125), Sharpless & Jasper (256), and Spencer, Thompson & Neilson (261), dishabitation is not simply a removal of the habituatory process. Rather, dishabituation represents an independent process superimposed on habituation. Seen in this perspective, dishabituation is merely a special case of sensitization (quasiconditioning), the process whereby a strong stimulus enhances other responses. Humphrey (125) had suggested such a relationship between dishabituation and sensitization, on the basis of behavioral experiments. Thus, neurophysiological studies of behavioral modification not only can provide insight into neural mechanisms but also can supplement behavioral experiments in clarifying the relationship between various behavioral processes.

CONCLUSIONS

As recently as a decade ago, most knowledge about the functional organization of nervous systems was derived from studies of the vertebrate CNS. With rare exceptions (e.g. 2, 222) invertebrate nervous systems were primarily used for studying the biophysical mechanisms of cellular functioning. This situation began to change as the work of Wiersma and of Hartline & Ratliff yielded insights into the organization of invertebrate sensory and motor systems. Moreover it soon became evident that these insights were of general importance. The abstracting capabilities of units in the crayfish visual system found by Wiersma (305) were similar to those described by Lettvin et al. (179) in the frog and by Hubel & Wiesel (118) in the cat and the monkey. Similarly, the lateral inhibition found by Hartline & Ratliff (98) in the eye of *Limulus* has now been repeatedly encountered in vertebrate sensory and motor systems.

As neurophysiologists became aware of the possibility of using invertebrate ganglia for studying the integrative actions of neuronal systems, the number of functional studies of invertebrates increased and a greater variety of preparations began to be used. Whereas the older functional studies were largely carried out on crustaceans and on *Limulus,* recent studies have also examined the neural organization of annelid worms, gastropod molluscs, and insects. As a result of the increase in the number and types of preparations studied, the generality of certain earlier findings has been considerably extended. For example, the existence of uniquely identifiable neurons first described by Wiersma in the connectives and peripheral nerves of crayfish has been confirmed in studies of the central ganglia of all higher invertebrates examined including cockroach (45), crayfish (232, 237), leech (200), lobster (207), *Aplysia* (80), and *Tritonia* (62, 315).

In addition to new preparations, a number of new experimental approaches to studying the functional organization of invertebrates have been developed. Whereas earlier workers relied on descriptive information based on extracellular recordings from single units in fiber tracts, recent workers have also utilized intracellular recordings designed to specify neuronal mechanisms. In addition, microchemical analysis and intracellular dye injections have proven useful for the functional analysis of invertebrate ganglia. Microchemical techniques for studying transmitter substances in individual, identifiable neurons have made it possible to establish maps of cells containing known transmitters in several preparations (88, 89, 207, 250). Moreover, because of the large size of invertebrate neurons, the regulation of macromolecular synthesis can now be studied in individual cells using both radioautographic and biochemical methods. The intracellular injection of fluorescent dyes into neurons has greatly facilitated the tracing of anatomical connections made by identified cells (148, 232, 267).

As a result of these several advances, invertebrate neurophysiologists have made significant strides toward working out the central task facing neural science: the description of the neuronal circuits mediating different behaviors in terms of the physiological and biochemical properties of its individual elements. Although in no case has the wiring diagram for a complete behavior been worked out in detail, several functional wiring diagrams have been partially specified and these may contribute toward general solutions to several problems. These problems include: (a) the factors which determine the functional expression of interconnections between cells (132, 133); (b) the relationship between different connectivity patterns to different behaviors (12, 13, 148, 167, 168, 170, 207, 266); and (c) the functional changes underlying behavioral modifications (37, 158, 159, 173, 214, 216).

In some cases, as in the analysis of lateral inhibition, studies of invertebrates have provided new insights into neuronal organization; in other instances studies of invertebrates have helped to clarify well-established ideas. For example the finding of redundancy in neural organization has been repeatedly emphasized in experiment neurology. However, studies of invertebrate ganglia may permit a detailed analysis of the cellular mechanisms involved.

Redundancy is a prominent feature of invertebrate motor systems and a given motor sequence can often be controlled by several similar command elements (5). Although each element produces a slightly different effect, the differences between the elements of a set of command neurons are generally much smaller than are their similarities. A comparable redundancy in invertebrate sensory systems was found by Wilson (323) in his study of the proprioceptive control of insect flight. In the healthy intact organism, the subtle differences between otherwise similar elements may provide for precise and subtle sensory and motor function. However, in the case of injury to neuronal elements, this type of redundancy may provide the mechanism for the remarkable residual functioning after trauma that is characteristic of the CNS.

It is interesting that multiple determinancy is also being increasingly encountered even in elementary cellular processes. For example, in many invertebrate neurons the resting potential is in part maintained by two processes: a K^+ conductance and an electrogenic Na^+ pump (34, 154). In several examples, the action potential can also be generated by one of two processes: an increased conductance to Na^+ or to Ca^+ (35, 86). In addition, two types of hyperpolarizing afterpotentials (46, 198, 199) can coexist in the same neuron by utilizing parallel conductance and active transport mechanisms.

It is therefore evident that invertebrate neurophysiology can address itself in a relevant manner to some of the general problems of integrative organization of neural systems which previously could only be tackled in the vertebrate brain. Moreover invertebrates offer experimental advantages for the analysis of neural organization much as they did for earlier studies of cellular function. As the data from invertebrate axons and synapses complemented mammalian cellular neurophysiology, so can functional studies of invertebrate ganglia complement studies of the integrative action of the mammalian brain. The complementary nature of vertebrate and invertebrate research in the nervous system applies not only to studies of neural integration and learning but equally to studies of embryonic and postembryonic development. In these areas cellular biochemical, morphological, and genetic approaches are required adjuncts to neurophysiological ones, and invertebrate ganglia offer unique opportunities for combined neurobiological studies.

ACKNOWLEDGMENTS

Supported by Career Scientist Award No. KO 5-MH 18558-02 to E.R.K., and Research Scientist Development Award No. 1 KO1 MH 12240 to I.K. The original work cited in this review was supported by grants NB-07621-03 and NB-05980-05. We have benefited greatly from discussions with a number of colleagues and are particularly grateful for the detailed comments of Drs. J. S. Edwards, D. Kennedy, and D. Wilson on an earlier draft of this review.

LITERATURE CITED

1. Abbott, B. C., Parnas, L. Electrical and mechanical responses in deep abdominal extensor muscles of crayfish and lobster. *J. Gen. Physiol.*, **48**, 919–31 (1965)

2. Adrian, E. D. Synchronized reactions in the optic ganglion of *Dysticus*. *J. Physiol. (London)*, **91**, 66–89 (1937)

3. Alving, B. O. Spontaneous activity in isolated somata of *Aplysia* pacemaker neurons. *J. Gen. Physiol.*, **51**, 29–45 (1968)

4. Atwood, H. L. Crustacean neuromuscular transmission. *Am. Zool.*, **7**, 527–52 (1967)

5. Atwood, H. L., Wiersma, C. A. G. Command interneurons in the crayfish central nervous system. *J. Exptl. Biol.*, **46**, 249–61 (1967)

6. Baden, V. Embryology of the nervous system of the grasshopper, *Melanoplus differentialis (Acrididae; Orthoptera)*. *J. Morphol.*, **60**, 159–90 (1936)

7. Barth, J. Intracellular recording from photoreceptor neurons in the eyes of a nudibranch mollusc (*Hermissenda crassicornis*). *Comp. Biochem. Physiol.*, **11**, 311–15 (1964)

8. Batham, E. J. Infoldings of nerve fiber membranes in the opisthobranch mollusc *Aplysia californica*. *J. Biophys. Biochem. Cytol.*, **9**, 490–92 (1961)

9. Bauer, V. Zur Inneren Metamorphose des Zentralnervensystems der Insekten. *Zool. Jahrb. Abt. Anat.*, **20**, 123–52 (1904)

10. Baxter, C. Habituation of the roach to puffs of air. *Anat. Record*, **128**, 521 (Abstr.) (1957)

11. Baylor, D. A., Gerschenfeld, H. M., Nicholls, J. G. (Unpublished observations)

12. Baylor, D. A., Nicholls, J. G. Receptive fields, synaptic connections and regeneration patterns of sensory neurons in the central nervous system of the leech. In *Physiological and Biochemical Aspects of Neural Integration*, 3–16 (Carlson, F. D., Ed., Prentice-Hall, Englewood Cliffs, N.J., 391 pp., 1968)

13. Baylor, D. A., Nicholls, J. G. Potassium accumulation. *J. Physiol. (London)* (In press, 1969)

14. Baylor, D. A., Nicholls, J. G. Chemical and electrical synaptic connexions between cutaneous mechanoreceptor neurons in the central nervous system of the leech. *J. Physiol. (London)* (In press, 1969)

15. Bennett, M. V. L., Fox, S. Electrophysiology of caudal neurosecretory cells in the skate and fluke. *Gen. Comp. Endocrinol.*, **2**, 77–95 (1962)

16. Benzer, S. Behavioral mutants of *Drosophila* isolated by countercurrent distribution. *Proc. Natl. Acad. Sci. U.S.*, **58**, 1112–19 (1967)

17. Bern, H. A. On eyes that may not see and glands that may not secrete. *Am. Zool.*, **7**, 815–21 (1967)

18. Bern, H. A., Hagadorn, I. R. Neurosecretion. In *Structure and Function in the Nervous System of Invertebrates*, **1**, 356–429 (Bullock, T. H., Horridge, G. A., Eds., Freeman, San Francisco, 798 pp., 1965)

19. Blankenship, J., Wachtel, H., Kandel, E. R. Ionic mechanism of cholinergic excitatory inhibitory and dual responses produced by an identified interneuron (In preparation)

20. Bliss, D. E. Autotomy and regeneration. In *The Physiology of Crustacea*, **1**, 501–89 (Waterman, T. H., Ed., Academic, New York, 670 pp., 1960)

21. Bodenstein, D. Regeneration. In *Insect Physiology*, 866–67 (Roeder, K. D., Ed., Wiley, New York, 1953)

22. Bruner, J., Tauc, L. Long-lasting phenomena in the molluscan nervous system. *Symp. Soc. Exptl. Biol.*, **20**, 457–75 (1966)

23. Bruner, J., Tauc, L. Habituation at the synaptic level in *Aplysia*. *Nature*, **210**, 37–39 (1966)

24. Bullock, T. H. Functional organization of the giant fiber system of *Lumbricus*. *J. Neurophysiol.*, **8**, 55–71 (1945)

25. Bullock, T. H. Properties of a single synapse in the stellate ganglion of squid. *J. Neurophysiol.*, **11**, 343–64 (1948)

26. Bullock, T. H., Hagiwara, S. Intracellular recording from the giant

synapse of the squid. *J. Gen. Physiol.*, **40**, 565–77 (1957)

27. Bullock, T. H., Horridge, G. A., Eds. *Structure and Function in the Nervous System of Invertebrates* (Freeman, San Francisco, 2 vols., 2517 pp., 1965)

28. Burrows, M., Horridge, G. A. The actions of the eyecup muscles of the crab, *Carcinus,* during optokinetic movements. *J. Exptl. Biol.,* **49**, 223–50 (1968)

29. Bush, B. M. H. Peripheral reflex inhibition in the claw of the crab *Carcinus maenas* (L.). *J. Exptl. Biol.,* **39**, 71–88 (1962)

30. Bush, B. M. H. Proprioceptive reflexes in the legs of *Carcinus maenas. J. Exptl. Biol.,* **39**, 89–105 (1962)

31. Bush, B. M. H. A comparative study of certain limb reflexes in decapod crustaceans. *Comp. Biochem. Physiol.,* **10**, 273–90 (1963)

32. Carlson, F. D., Ed. *Physiological and Biochemical Aspects of Nervous Integration* (Prentice-Hall, Englewood Cliffs, N.J., 391 pp., 1968)

33. Carlson, J. G., Gaulden, M. E. Grasshopper neuroblast techniques. *Methods Cell Physiol.,* **1**, 229–76 (1964)

34. Carpenter, D. O., Alving, B. O. A contribution of an electrogenic Na⁺ pump to membrane potential in *Aplysia* neurons. *J. Gen. Physiol.,* **52**, 1–21 (1968)

35. Carpenter, D., Gunn, R. The dependence of pacemaker discharges on Na⁺ and Ca⁺⁺ in *Aplysia* neurons. *Fed. Proc.,* **28**, 425 (1969)

36. Castellucci, V., Goldring, S. Contribution to steady potential shifts of slow depolarization in cells presumed to be glial. *Electroencephal. Clin. Neurophysiol.* (In press, 1969)

37. Castellucci, V., Kupfermann, I., Pinsker, H., Kandel, E. R. Analysis of habituation and dishabituation in Aplysia. III. Cellular mechanisms in the isolated ganglion (In preparation)

38. Clark, R. B. Habituation of the polychaete Nereis to sudden stimuli. I. General properties of the habituation process. *Animal Behav.,* **8**, 83–92 (1960)

39. Cody, F. P., Gray, I. E. The changes in the central nervous system

during the life history of the beetle *Passalus cornutus* Fabricius. *J. Morphol.,* **62**, 503–17 (1938)

40. Coggeshall, R. E. A fine structure analysis of the ventral nerve cord and associated sheath of *Lumbricus terrestris* L. *J. Comp. Neurol.,* **125**, 393–438 (1965)

41. Coggeshall, R. E. A light and electronmicroscope study of the abdominal ganglion of *Aplysia californica. J. Neurophysiol.,* **30**, 1263–87 (1967)

42. Coggeshall, R. E., Fawcett, D. W. The fine structure of the central nervous system of the leech, *Hirudo medicinalis. J. Neurophysiol.,* **27**, 229–89 (1964)

43. Coggeshall, R. E., Kandel, E. R., Kupfermann, I., Waziri, R. A morphological and functional study on a cluster of identifiable neurosecretory cells in the abdominal ganglion of *Aplysia californica. J. Cell Biol.,* **31**, 363–68 (1966)

44. Cohen, M. J. The dual role of sensory systems: detection and setting of central excitability. *Cold Spring Harbor Symp. Quant. Biol.,* **30**, 587–99 (1965)

45. Cohen, M. J., Jacklet, J. W. The functional organization of motor neurons in an insect ganglion. *Phil. Trans. Roy. Soc. (London), B,* **252**, 501–27 (1967)

46. Connelly, C. M. Recovery process and metabolism in nerve. *Rev. Mod. Phys.,* **31**, 475 (1959)

47. Cooke, I. M. Electrical activity and release of neurosecretory material in crab pericardial organs. *Comp. Biochem. Physiol.,* **13**, 353–66 (1964)

48. Cooke, I. M. The sites of action of pericardial organ extract and 5-hydroxytryptamine in the decapod crustacean heart. *Am. Zool.,* **6**, 107–21 (1966)

49. Cooke, I. M. Potentials recorded intracellularly from neurosecretory terminals. *Am. Zool.,* **7**, 732–33 (1967)

50. Dale, H. Pharmacology and nerve-endings. *Proc. Roy. Soc. Med.,* **28**, 319–32 (1935)

51. Davey, K. G. The mode of action of the corpus cardiacum on the hind gut in *Periplaneta americana. J. Exptl. Biol.,* **39**, 319–24 (1962)

52. Davey, K. G. The release by feeding of a pharmacologically active fac-

tor from the corpus cardiacum of *Periplaneta americana. J. Insect Physiol.*, **8**, 205–8 (1962)

53. Davey, K. G. Neurosecretion and molting in some parasitic nematodes. *Am. Zool.*, **6**, 243–49 (1966)

54. Davis, W. J. The neuromuscular basis of lobster swimmeret beating. *J. Exptl. Zool.*, **3**, 363–78 (1968)

55. Davis, W. J. Lobster righting responses and their neural control. *Proc. Roy. Soc. (London), B*, **70**, 435–50 (1968)

56. Davis, W. J. Quantitative analysis of swimmeret beating in the lobster. *J. Exptl. Biol.*, **48**, 643–62 (1968)

57. Davis, W. J. The neural control of swimmeret beating in the lobster. *J. Exptl. Biol.*, **50**, 99–117 (1969)

58. Davis, W. J., Murphey, R. K. Discharge patterns of swimmeret motoneurones in the lobster, stimulated with a digital computer. *J. Exptl. Biol.*, **50**, 119–28 (1969)

59. Dennis, M. J. Interactions between receptor cells of a simple eye. In *Invertebrate Nervous Systems*, 259–62 (Wiersma, C. A. G., Ed., Univ. Chicago Press, 370 pp., 1967)

60. Dethier, V. G. Microscopic brains. *Science*, **143**, 1138–45 (1964)

61. Dingle, H. The occurrence of correcting behavior in various insects. *Ecology*, **43**, 727–28 (1962)

62. Dorsett, D. A. Giant neurons and axon pathways in the brain of *Tritonia. J. Exptl. Biol.*, **46**, 137–51 (1967)

63. Dudel, J., Kuffler, S. W. Presynaptic inhibition at the crayfish neuromuscular junction. *J. Physiol. (London)*, **155**, 543–62 (1961)

64. Eccles, J. C. *The Physiology of Nerve Cells* (Springer-Verlag, New York, 316 pp., 1964)

65. Eccles, J. C., Fatt, P., Koketsu, K. Cholinergic and inhibitory synapses in a pathway from motor axon collaterals to motoneurones. *J. Physiol. (London)*, **126**, 524–62 (1954)

66. Eccles, J. C., Ito, M., Szentagothai, J. *The Cerebellum as a Neuronal Machine* (Springer-Verlag, New York, 335 pp., 1967)

67. Eckert, R. O. Reflex relationships of the abdominal stretch receptors of the crayfish. I. Feedback inhibition of the receptors. *J. Cell. Comp. Physiol.*, **57**, 149–62 (1961)

68. Eckert, R. O. Reflex relationships of the abdominal stretch receptors of the crayfish. II. Stretch receptor involvement during the swimming reflex. *J. Cell. Comp. Physiol.*, **57**, 163–74 (1961)

69. Eckert, R. O. Electrical interaction of paired ganglion cells in the leech. *J. Gen. Physiol.*, **46**, 573–87 (1963)

70. Edwards, J. S. Some questions for the insect nervous system. In *Insects and Physiology*, 163–73 (Beament, J. W. L., Treherne, J. E., Eds., Oliver & Boyd, Edinburgh, 378 pp., 1967)

71. Edwards, J. S. Neural control of development in arthropods. In *Invertebrate Nervous Systems*, 95–110 (See Ref. 59)

72. Edwards, J. S. Postembryonic development and regeneration of the insect nervous system. *Advan. Insect Physiol.*, **6**, 97–137 (1969)

73. Edwards, J. S., Sahota, T. S. Regeneration of a sensory system: the formation of central connections by normal and transplanted cerci of the house cricket *Acheta domesticus. J. Exptl. Zool.*, **166**, 387–95 (1968)

74. Ehinger, B., Falck, B., Myhrberg, H. E. Biogenic amines in *Hirudo medicinalis. Histochemie*, **15**, 140–49 (1968)

75. Evoy, W. H., Kennedy, D. The central nervous organization underlying control of antagonistic muscles in the crayfish. I. Types of command fibers. *J. Exptl. Zool.*, **165**, 223–38 (1967)

76. Fatt, P., Katz, B. The effect of inhibitory nerve impulses on a crustacean muscle fiber. *J. Physiol. (London)*, **121**, 374–89 (1953)

77. Fields, H. L. The proprioceptive control of posture in the crayfish abdomen. *J. Exptl. Biol.*, **44**, 455–68 (1966)

78. Fields, H. L., Evoy, W. H., Kennedy, D. Reflex role played by efferent control of an invertebrate stretch receptor. *J. Neurophysiol.*, **30**, 859–74 (1967)

79. Frank, K., Tauc, L. Voltage clamp studies of molluscan neuron membrane properties. In *Symp. Cellular Functions of Membrane Transport, Woods Hole, Mass., 1963,*

113–35 (Hoffman, J. H., Ed., Prentice-Hall, Englewood Cliffs, N.J., 291 pp., 1964)

80. Frazier, W. T., Kandel, E. R., Kupfermann, I., Waziri, R., Coggeshall, R. E. Morphological and functional properties of identified cells in the abdominal ganglion of *Aplysia californica*. *J. Neurophysiol.*, **30**, 1288–351 (1967)

81. Furshpan, E. J., Furukawa, T. Intracellular and extracellular responses of the several regions of the Mauthner cell of the goldfish. *J. Neurophysiol.*, **25**, 732–71 (1962)

82. Furshpan, E. J., Potter, D. D. Transmission at the giant motor synapses of the crayfish. *J. Physiol. (London)*, **145**, 289–325 (1959)

83. Ganz, L., Mechanism of the figural after effects. *Physiol. Rev.*, **73**, 128–50 (1966)

84. Gardner, D. Symmetry and redundancy of interneuronal connections in the buccal ganglion of *Aplysia*. *Physiologist*, **12**(3), 232 (1969)

85. Gardner, L. E. Retention and overhabituation of a dual-component response in *Lumbricus terrestris*. *J. Comp. Physiol. Psychol.*, **66**, 315–18 (1968)

86. Geduldig, D., Junge, D. Sodium and calcium components of action potentials in *Aplysia* giant neurone. *J. Physiol.*, **199**, 347–65 (1968)

87. Gerschenfeld, H. M. Chemical transmitters in invertebrate nervous systems. *Symp. Soc. Exptl. Biol.*, **20**, 299–323 (1966)

88. Giller, E., Schwartz, J. H. Choline acetyltransferase: regional distribution in the abdominal ganglion of *Aplysia*. *Science*, **161**, 908–11 (1968)

89. Giller, E., Schwartz, J. H. Distribution of choline acetyltransferase in single neurons of the abdominal ganglion of *Aplysia*. *Fed. Proc.*, **28**, 2659 (1969)

90. Gorman, A. L. F., Mirolli, M. The input-output organization of a pair of giant neurones in the mollusc *Anisodoris nobilis*. *J. Physiol. (London)* (In press, 1969)

91. Granit, R., Renkin, B. Net depolarization and discharge rate of motoneurones, as measured by recurrent inhibition. *J. Physiol. (London)*, **158**, 461–75 (1961)

92. Hagiwara, S. Nervous activities of the heart in Crustacea. *Ergeb. Biol.*, **24**, 287–311 (1961)

93. Hagiwara, S., Morita, H. Electrotonic transmission of spikes between two neurons in a leech. *Fed. Proc.*, **21**, 361 (1962)

94. Hagiwara, S., Tasaki, I. A study of the mechanism of impulse transmission across the giant synapse of the squid. *J. Physiol. (London)*, **143**, 114–37 (1958)

95. Hagiwara, S., Watanabe, A. Discharges in motoneurones of cicada. *J. Cell. Comp. Physiol.*, **47**, 415–28 (1956)

96. Hamburger, V., Levi-Montalcini, R. Proliferation, differentiation and degeneration in the spinal ganglia of the chick embryo under normal and experimental conditions. *J. Exptl. Zool.*, **111**, 457–501 (1949)

97. Hartline, H. K., Graham, C. H. Nerve impulses from single receptors in the eye. *J. Cell. Comp. Physiol.*, **1**, 277–95 (1932)

98. Hartline, H. K., Ratliff, F. Inhibitory interaction of receptor units in the eye of Limulus. *J. Gen. Physiol.*, **40**, 357–76 (1957)

99. Hartline, H. K., Ratliff, F., Miller, W. H. Inhibitory interaction in the retina and its significance in vision. In *Intern. Symp. Nervous Inhibition, Friday Harbor, Washington, 1960*, 241–84 (Florey, E., Ed., Pergamon, New York, 475 pp., 1961)

100. Hartline, H. K., Wagner, H. G., Ratliff, F. Inhibition in the eye of Limulus. *J. Gen. Physiol.*, **39**, 651–73 (1956)

101. Hinde, R. A. Factors governing the changes in strength of a partially inborn response, as shown by the mobbing behaviour of the chaffinch (*Fringilla coelebs*). II. The waning of the response. *Proc. Roy. Soc. (London), B*, **142**, 331–58 (1954)

102. Hinke, W. Das relative postembryonale Wachstum der Hirnteile von *Culex pipiens, Drosophila melanogaster und Drosophila mutanten*. *Z. Morphol. Oekol. Tiere*, **50**, 81–118 (1961)

103. Hodgkin, A. L. *The Conduction of the Nervous Impulse* (Liverpool Univ. Press, 108 pp., 1964)

104. Hodgkin, A. L., Huxley, A. F., Katz, B. Ionic currents underlying activity in the giant axon of the

squid. *Arch. Sci. Physiol.* **3,** 129–50 (1949)

105. Hodgkin, A. L., Katz, B. The effect of sodium ions on the electrical activity of the giant axon of the squid. *J. Physiol. (London),* **108,** 37–77 (1949)

106. Holmgren, E. Beitrage zur Morphologie der Zelle. I. Nervenzellen. *Anat. Hefte,* **18,** 269–325 (1901)

107. Horiuch, E., Hayashi, H., Takahashi, I. Median giant fiber system in the crayfish cephalic ganglion. *Nature,* **212,** 831–32 (1966)

108. Horn, G., Hill, R. M. Modifications of receptive fields of cells in the visual cortex occurring spontaneously and associated with bodily tilt. *Nature,* **221,** 186–88 (1969)

109. Horn, G., Rowell, C. H. F. Medium and long-term changes in the behaviour of visual neurones in the tritocerebrum of locusts. *J. Exptl. Biol.,* **49,** 143–69 (1968)

110. Horridge, G. A. Analysis of the rapid responses of *Nereis* and *Harmothoë* (Annelida). *Proc. Roy. Soc. (London),* B, **150,** 245–62 (1959)

111. Horridge, G. A. Comparative physiology: Integrative action of the nervous system. *Ann. Rev. Physiol.,* **25,** 523–44 (1963)

112. Horridge, G. A. Optokinetic memory in the crab, *Carcinus. J. Exptl. Biol.,* **44,** 233–45 (1966)

113. Horridge, G. A. *Interneurons. Their Origin, Action, Specificity, Growth and Plasticity* (Freeman, San Francisco, 436 pp., 1968)

114. Horridge, G. A. Affinity of neurones in regeneration. *Nature,* **219,** 737–40 (1968)

115. Horridge, G. A., Scholes, J. H., Shaw, S., Tunstall, J. Extracellular recordings from single neurones in the optic lobe and brain of the locust. In *The Physiology of the Insect Central Nervous System,* 165–202 (Treherne, J. E., Beament, J. W. C., Eds., Academic, New York, 277 pp., 1965)

116. Hotta, Y., Benzer, S. Abnormal electroretinograms in visual mutants of Drosophila. *Nature,* **222,** 354–56 (1969)

117. Hoy, R. R., Wilson, D. M. Rhythmic motor output in the leg motor neurons of the milkweed bug *Oncopeltus. Fed. Proc.,* **28,** 1837 (1969)

118. Hubel, D. H., Wiesel, T. N. Receptive fields, binocular interaction and functional architecture in the cat's visual cortex. *J. Physiol. (London),* **160,** 106–54 (1962)

119. Huber, F. Central nervous control of sound production in crickets and some speculations on its evolution. *Evolution,* **16,** 429–42 (1962)

120. Hughes, A. F. W. *Aspects of Neural Ontogeny* (Logos, London, 249 pp., 1968)

121. Hughes, G. M. Neuronal pathways in the insect central nervous system. In *The Physiology of the Insect Central Nervous System,* 79–117 (See Ref. 115)

122. Hughes, G. M., Wiersma, C. A. G. Neuronal pathways and synaptic connexions in the abdominal cord of the crayfish. *J. Exptl. Biol.,* **37,** 291–307 (1960)

123. Hughes, G. M., Wiersma, C. A. G. The coordination of swimmeret movements in the crayfish, *Procambarus clarkii* (Girard). *J. Exptl. Biol.,* **37,** 657–70 (1960)

124. Humphrey, G. Le Chatellier's rule and the problem of habituation and dehabituation in *Helix albolabris. Psychol. Forsch.,* **13,** 113–27 (1930)

125. Humphrey, G. *The Nature of Learning in its Relation to the Living System* (Harcourt-Brace, New York, 1933)

126. Ikeda, K., Wiersma, C. A. G. Autogenic rhythmicity in the abdominal ganglia of the crayfish: The control of swimmeret movement. *Comp. Biochem. Physiol.,* **12,** 107–15 (1964)

127. Jacklet, J. W. Electrophysiological organization of the eye of *Aplysia. J. Gen. Physiol.,* **53,** 21–42 (1969)

128. Jahan-Parwar, B., Smith, M., Von Baumgarten, R. Activation of neurosecretory cells in *Aplysia* by osphradial stimulation. *Am. J. Physiol.,* **216,** 1246–57 (1969)

129. Johnson, G. E. Giant nerve fibers in crustaceans with special reference to *Cambarus* and *Palaemonetes. J. Comp. Neurol.,* **36,** 323–73 (1924)

130. Johnson, G. E. Studies on the functions of the giant nerve fibers of crustaceans with special reference to *Cambarus* and *Palaemonetes. J. Comp. Neurol.,* **42,** 19–33 (1926)

131. Kandel, E. R. Electrical properties of hypothalamic neuroendocrine

cells. *J. Gen. Physiol.*, **47**, 691–717 (1964)

132. Kandel, E. R. Dale's principle and the functional specificity of neurons. In *Psychopharmacology: A Review of Progress, 1957–67*, (Ifron, D. H., Ed., Public Health Serv. Publ. No. 1836, 1342 pp., 1968)

133. Kandel, E. R., Frazier, W. T., Waziri, R., Coggeshall, R. E. Direct and common connections among identified neurons in *Aplysia*. *J. Neurophysiol.*, **30**, 1352–76 (1967)

134. Kandel, E. R., Spencer, W. A. Cellular neurophysiological approaches in the study of learning. *Physiol. Rev.*, **48**, 65–134 (1968)

135. Kandel, E. R., Spencer, W. A., Brinley, F. J., Jr. Electrophysiology of hippocampal neurons. I. Sequential invasion and synaptic organization. *J. Neurophysiol.*, **24**, 225–42 (1961)

136. Kandel, E. R., Tauc, L. Heterosynaptic facilitation in neurones of the abdominal ganglion of *Aplysia depilans*. *J. Physiol. (London)*, **181**, 1–27 (1965)

137. Kandel, E. R., Tauc, L. Mechanism of heterosynaptic facilitation in the giant cell of the abdominal ganglion of *Aplysia depilans*. *J. Physiol. (London)*, **181**, 28–47 (1965)

138. Kao, C. Y. Post synaptic electrogenesis in septate giant axons. II. Comparisons of medial and lateral giant axons of crayfish. *J. Neurophysiol.*, **23**, 618–35 (1960)

139. Karahashi, Y., Goldring, S. Intracellular potential from "idle" cells in cerebral cortex of cat. *Electroenceph. Clin. Neurophysiol.*, **20**, 600–7 (1966)

140. Katz, B. *Nerve, Muscle and Synapse* (McGraw-Hill, New York, 193 pp., 1966)

141. Katz, B., Miledi, R. A study of synaptic transmission in the absence of nerve impulses. *J. Physiol. (London)*, **192**, 407–36 (1967)

142. Kendig, J. J. Structure and function in the third abdominal ganglion of the crayfish *Procambarus clarkii* (Girard). *J. Exptl. Zool.*, **164**, 1–20 (1967)

143. Kennedy, D., Evoy, W. H., Dane, B., Hanawalt, J. T. The central nervous organization underlying control of antagonistic muscles in the crayfish. *J. Exptl. Zool.*, **165**, 239–48 (1967)

144. Kennedy, D., Evoy, W. H., Fields, H. L. The unit basis of some crustacean reflexes. *Symp. Soc. Exptl. Biol.*, **20**, 75–109 (1965)

145. Kennedy, D., Evoy, W. H., Hanawalt, J. T. Release of coordinated behavior in crayfish by single central neurons. *Science*, **154**, 917–19 (1966)

146. Kennedy, D., Mellon, D., Jr. Synaptic activation and receptive fields in crayfish interneurons. *Comp. Biochem. Physiol.*, **13**, 275–300 (1964)

147. Kennedy, D., Mellon, D., Jr. Receptive-field organization and response patterns in neurons with spatially distributed input. In *Neural Theory and Modeling (Symposium, Ojai, California, 1962)* (Reiss, F., Ed., Stanford Univ. Press, Stanford, Calif., 427 pp., 1964)

148. Kennedy, D., Selverston, A. I., Remler, M. P. Analysis of restricted neuronal networks. *Science*, **164**, 1488–96 (1969)

149. Kennedy, D., Takeda, K. Reflex control of abdominal flexor muscles in the crayfish. I. The twitch system. *J. Exptl. Biol.*, **43**, 211–27 (1965)

150. Kennedy, D., Takeda, K. Reflex control of the abdominal flexor muscles in the crayfish. II. The tonic system. *J. Exptl. Biol.*, **43**, 229–46 (1965)

151. Kerkut, G. A. Biochemical aspects of invertebrate nerve cells. In *Invertebrate Nervous Systems*, 5–37 (See Ref. 59)

152. Kerkut, G. A., Sedden, C. B., Walker, R. J. Cellular localization of monoamines by fluorescence microscopy in *Hirudo medicinales* and *Lumbricus terrestris*. *Comp. Biochem. Physiol.*, **21**, 687–90 (1967)

153. Kerkut, G. A., Thomas, R. C. The effect of anion injection and changes in the external potassium and chloride concentrations on the reversal potentials of the IPSP and acetylcholine. *Comp. Biochem. Physiol.*, **11**, 199–213 (1964)

154. Kerkut, G. A., Thomas, R. C. An electrogenic sodium pump in small nerve cells. *Comp. Biochem. Physiol.*, **14**, 167–83 (1965)

155. Kirschfeld, K., Reichardt, W. Die Verarbeitung stationärer optischer Nachrichten in Komplexauge von *Limulus. Kybernetik,* **2,** 43–61 (1964)

156. Knapp, H. D., Taub, E., Berman, A. J. Effects of deafferentation on a conditioned avoidance response. *Science,* **128,** 842–43 (1958)

157. Korschelt, E. Ontogonie der Decapoden. *Bronn's Klassen,* **5,** 1, 7, 671–861 (1944)

158. Krasne, F. B. Excitation and habituation of the crayfish escape reflex: The depolarizing response in lateral giant fibers of the isolated abdomen. *J. Exptl. Biol.,* **50,** 29–46 (1969)

159. Krasne, F. B., Roberts, A. Habituation of crayfish escape response during release from inhibition induced by picrotoxin. *Nature,* **215,** 769–70 (1967)

160. Kravitz, E. A., Iversen, L. L., Otsuka, M., Hall, Z. W. Gamma-aminobutyric acid in the lobster nervous system; release from inhibitory nerves and uptake into nerve muscle preparations. In *Structure and Function of Inhibitory Neuronal Mechanisms,* Proc. 4th Intern. Mtg. Neurobiologists, Stockholm, 1966, 371–76 (Von Euler, C., Ed., Pergamon, Oxford, 563 pp., 1968)

161. Kuczka, H. Verhalten physiologische Untersuchungen über die Wischhandlung der intakten Erdkröte. *Z. Tierpsychol.,* **13,** 185–207 (1956)

162. Kuenzer, P. Verhalten physiologische Untersuchungen über das Zucken des Regenwurms. *Z. Tierpsychol.,* **15,** 31–49 (1958)

163. Kuffler, S. W., Eyzaguirre, C. Synaptic inhibition in an isolated nerve cell. *J. Gen. Physiol.,* **39,** 155–84 (1955)

164. Kuffler, S. W., Nicholls, J. G. The physiology of neuroglial cells. *Ergeb. Physiol.,* **57,** 1–90 (1966)

165. Kupfermann, I. Turn alternation in the pill bug (*Armadillidium vulgare*). *Animal Behav.,* **14,** 68–72 (1966)

166. Kupfermann, I. Stimulation of egg laying: possible neuroendocrine function of bag cells of abdominal ganglion of *Aplysia californica. Nature,* **216,** 814–15 (1967)

167. Kupfermann, I. Studies of a neurosecretory cluster in the abdominal ganglion of *Aplysia.* II. Neuroendocrine function (In preparation)

168. Kupfermann, I., Kandel, E. R. Neuronal controls of a behavioral response mediated by the abdominal ganglion of *Aplysia. Science,* **164,** 847–50 (1969)

169. Kupfermann, I., Kandel, E. R. Studies of a neurosecretory cluster in the abdominal ganglion of *Aplysia.* I. Electrophysiological properties (In preparation)

170. Kupfermann, I., Kandel, E. R., Coggeshall, R. Synchronized activity in a neurosecretory cluster in *Aplysia. Physiologist,* **9,** 223 (Abstr.) (1966)

171. Kupfermann, I., Pinsker, H. A behavioral modification of the feeding reflex in *Aplysia californica. Commun. Behav. Biol.,* **2,** 13–17 (1968)

172. Kupfermann, I., Pinsker, H. Plasticity in *Aplysia* neurons and some simple neuronal models of learning. In *Reinforcement,* 356–86 (Tapp, J., Ed., Academic, New York, 1969)

173. Kupfermann, I., Pinsker, H., Castellucci, V., Kandel, E. R. Analysis of habituation and dishabituation in *Aplysia.* II. Cellular concomitants in a semi-intact preparation (In preparation)

174. Kusano, K., La Vail, M. M. Functionally excitable area of a shrimp medullated giant fiber. *Biol. Bull.,* **135,** 427 (Abstr.) (1968)

175. Lange, D., Hartline, H. K., Ratliff, F. Inhibitory interaction in the retina: Techniques of experimental and theoretical analysis. *Ann. N.Y. Acad. Sci.,* **128,** 955–71 (1966)

176. Lange, D., Hartline, H. K., Ratliff, F. The dynamics of lateral inhibition of *Limulus.* In *Proc. Intern. Symp. Functional Organization Compound Eye,* 425–49 (Bernhard, C. G., Ed., Pergamon, Oxford, 591 pp., 1966)

177. Lashley, K. S. *Brain Mechanisms and Intelligence: A Quantitative Study of Injuries to the Brain* (Univ. Chicago Press, 186 pp., 1929)

178. Lessek, A. M. Inactivation of voluntary motor function following

rhizotomy. *J. Neuropathol. Exptl. Neurol.,* **12,** 83–87 (1953)

179. Lettvin, J. Y., Maturana, H. R., McCullough, W. S., Pitts, W. H. What the frog's eye tells the frog's brain. *Proc. IRE,* **47,** 1940–51 (1959)

180. Lickey, M. E. Learned behavior in *Aplysia vaccaria. J. Comp. Physiol. Psychol.,* **66,** 712–18 (1968)

181. Luscher, M. Insects as a medium for the study of differentiation. In *Insects and Physiology,* 39–51 Beament, J. W. L., Treherne, J. E., Eds., Oliver & Boyd, Edinburgh, 378 pp., 1967)

182. Malzacher, P. Die Embryogenese des Gehirns paurometaboler Insekten Untersuchungen an *Carausius morosus* und *Periplaneta americana. Z. Morphol. Oekol Tiere,* **62,** 103–61 (1968)

183. Maynard, D. M. Activity in a crustacean ganglion. II. Pattern and interaction in burst formation. *Biol. Bull.,* **109,** 420–36 (1955)

184. Maynard, D. M. Cardiac inhibition in decapod crustacea. In *Intern. Symp. Nervous Inhibition, Friday Harbor, Washington, 1966,* 144–78 (See Ref. 99)

185. Maynard, D. M. Organization of neuropil. *Am. Zool.,* **2,** 79–96 (1962)

186. Maynard, D. M. The occurrence and functional characteristics of heteromorph antennules in an experimental population of spiny lobsters, *Panilirus argus. J. Exptl. Biol.,* **43,** 79–106 (1965)

187. Maynard, D. M. Integration in crustacean ganglia. *Symp. Soc. Exptl. Biol.,* **20,** 111–49 (1966)

188. Maynard, D. M. Organization of central ganglion. In *Invertebrate Nervous Systems,* 231–55 (See Ref. 59)

189. Maynard, D. M., Cohen, M. J. The function of a heteromorph antennule in a spiny lobster, *Paniluris argus. J. Exptl. Biol.,* **43,** 55–78 (1965)

190. Merton, P. A. Speculations on the servo control of movement. In *The Spinal Cord,* 247–55 (Wolstenholme, G. E. W., Freeman, J. S., Eds., Churchill, London, 300 pp., 1953)

191. Miller, N. Certain facts of learning relevant to the search for its

physical basis. In *The Neurosciences,* 643–52 (Quarton, G. C., Melnechuck, T., Schmitt, F. O., Eds., Rockefeller Univ. Press, New York, 962 pp., 1967)

192. Miller, P. L. Respiration in the desert locust. I. The control of ventilation. *J. Exptl. Biol.,* **37,** 224–36 (1960)

193. Miller, P. L. Respiration in the desert locust. II. The control of spiracles. *J. Exptl. Biol.,* **37,** 237–63 (1960)

194. Miller, P. L. The central control of respiratory movements. In *The Physiology of the Insect Central Nervous System,* 141–55 (See Ref. 277)

195. Morita, H., Ishibashi, T., Yamashita, S. Synaptic transmission in neurosecretory cells. *Nature,* **191,** 183 (1961)

196. Mott, F. W., Sherrington, C. S. Experiments upon the influences of sensory nerves upon movement and nutrition of the limbs. Preliminary communication. *Proc. Roy. Soc. (London), B,* **57,** 481–88 (1895)

197. Mulloney, B. Organization of the flight motor neurons of *Diptera* (In preparation)

198. Nakajima, S., Takahashi, K. Posttetanic hyperpolarization and electrogenic Na pump in stretch receptor neurone of crayfish. *J. Physiol. (London),* **187,** 105–27 (1966)

199. Nicholls, J. G., Baylor, D. A. Longlasting hyperpolarization after activity of neurons in leech central nervous system. *Science,* **162,** 279–81 (1968)

200. Nicholls, J. G., Baylor, D. A. Specific modalities and receptive fields of sensory neurons in the central nervous system of the leech. *J. Neurophysiol.,* **31,** 740–56 (1968)

201. Nicholls, J. G., Baylor, D. A. (Personal communication)

202. Nicol, J. A. C. The giant axons of annelids. *Quart. Rev. Biol.,* **23,** 291–323 (1948)

203. Nicol, J. A. C. The giant nerve fibers in the central nervous system of *Myxicola (Polychaeta, Sabellidae). Quart. J. Microscop. Sci.,* **89,** 1–45 (1948)

204. Nordlander, R. H., Edwards, J. S. Morphological cell death in the postembryonic development of the

insect optic lobes. *Nature*, **218**, 780–81 (1968)

205. Ogawa, F. The nervous system of earthworm (*Pheretima communissima*) in different ages. *Sci. Rept. Res. Inst. Tohoku Univ.*, (4) **13**, 395–488 (1939)

206. Orkand, R. K., Nicholls, J. G., Kuffler, S. W. Effect of nerve impulses on the membrane potential of glial cells in the central nervous system of amphibia. *J. Neurophysiol.*, **29**, 788–806 (1966)

207. Otsuka, M., Kravitz, E. A., Potter, D. D. Physiological and chemical architecture of a lobster ganglion with particular reference to gamma-aminobutyrate and glutamate. *J. Neurophysiol.*, **30**, 725–52 (1967)

208. Pak, W. L., Grossfield, J., White, N. V. Nonphototactic mutants in a study of vision of *Drosophila*. *Nature*, **222**, 351–54 (1969)

209. Palay, S. The role of neuroglia in the organization of the central nervous system. In *Nerve as a Tissue* (Rodahl, K., Issekutz, Eds., Harper & Row, New York, 1966)

210. Panov, A. A. The origin and fate of neuroblasts, neurones, and neuroglial cells in the central nervous system of the Chinese silkmoth *Antheraca pernyi guer* (*Lepidoptera, Attacidae*). *Entomol. Obozrenie*, **42**, 337–50 (1963)

211. Paulson, D. F. Histogenesis, organogenesis and differentiation in the embryo of *Drosophila melanogaster* Meigen. In *Biology of Drosophila Melanogaster*, 168–74 (Demerec, M., Ed., Hafner, New York, 632 pp., 1965)

212. Pearson, K. (Personal communication)

213. Peretz, B., Strumwasser, F. Patterned gill movements elicited by nerves and single neurons in *Aplysia. Fed. Proc.*, **28**, 426 (1969)

214. Pinsker, H., Castellucci, V., Kupfermann, I., Kandel, E. R. Analysis of habituation and dishabituation in *Aplysia*. I. Behavioral studies in an intact preparation (In preparation)

215. Pinsker, H., Kandel, E. R. Synaptic activation of an electrogenic sodium pump. *Science*, **163**, 931–35 (1969)

216. Pinsker, H., Kupfermann, I., Castellucci, V., Kandel, E. R. Cellular analysis of behavioral reflex habituation in *Aplysia. Fed. Proc.*, **28**, 1836 (1969)

217. Pipa, R. L. Insect metamorphosis. III. Nerve cord shortening in a moth, *Galleria mellonella* (L.), may be accomplished by humoral potentiation of neuroglial motility. *J. Exptl. Zool.*, **164**, 47–60 (1967)

218. Pipa, R. L., Woolever, P. S. Insect neurometamorphosis. I. Histological changes during ventral nerve cord shortening in *Galleria mellonella* (L.) (Lepidoptera). *Z. Zellforsch.*, **63**, 405–17 (1964)

219. Pipa, R. L., Woolever, P. S. Insect neurometamorphosis. II. The fine structure of perineurial connective tissue, adipohemocytes, and the shortening ventral nerve cord of a moth, *Galleria mellonella* (L.). *Z. Zellforsch.*, **68**, 80–101 (1965)

220. Power, M. E. The effect of reduction in numbers of ommatidia upon the brain of *Drosophila melanogaster*. *J. Exptl. Zool.*, **94**, 33–71 (1943)

221. Power, M. E. An experimental study of the neurogenetic relationship between optic and antennal sensory areas in the brain of *Drosophila melanogaster*. *J. Exptl. Zool.*, **103**, 429–91 (1946)

222. Pringle, J. W. S. The reflex mechanism of the insect leg. *J. Exptl. Biol.*, **17**, 8–17 (1940)

223. Pumphrey, R. J., Rawdon-Smith, A. F. Synaptic transmission of nervous impulses through the last abdominal ganglion of the cockroach. *Proc. Roy. Soc. (London)*, B, **122**, 106–18 (1937)

224. Purple, R. L. *The integration of excitatory and inhibitory influences in the eccentric cell in the eye of Limulus* (Thesis, Rockefeller Inst., New York, 1964)

225. Purple, R. L. Effects of ion substitution and altered calcium-magnesium ratios on lateral inhibition in *Limulus. Fed. Proc.*, **28**, 104 (1969)

226. Purple, R. L., Dodge, F. A. Interaction of excitation and inhibition in the eccentric cell in the eye of *Limulus. Cold Spring Harbor Symp. Quant. Biol.*, **30**, 529–37 (1965)

254   KANDEL & KUPFERMANN

227. Ralph, C. L. Recent developments in invertebrate endocrinology. *Am. Zool.*, **7**, 145–60 (1967)
228. Ratliff, F. *Mach bands: Quantitative Studies on Neural Networks in the Retina* (Holden Day, San Francisco, 365 pp., 1965)
229. Ratliff, F., Hartline, H. K., Lange, D. The dynamics of lateral inhibition in the compound eye of *Limulus*. In *Proc. Intern. Symp. Functional Organization of the Compound Eye*, 399–424 (Bernhard, C. G., Ed., Pergamon, Oxford, 591 pp., 1966)
230. Ratliff, F., Knight, B. W., Toyoda, J., Hartline, H. K. Enhancement of flicker by lateral inhibition. *Science*, **158**, 392–93 (1967)
231. Rayner, M. D., Wiersma, C. A. G. Mechanisms of the crayfish tail flick. *Nature*, **213**, 1231–33 (1967)
232. Remler, M., Selverston, A., Kennedy, D. Lateral giant fibers of crayfish: location of somata of dye injection. *Science*, **162**, 281–83 (1968)
233. Renshaw, B. Central effects of centripetal impulses in axons of spinal ventral roots. *J. Neurophysiol.*, **9**, 191–204 (1946)
234. Retzius, G. *Biologische Untersuchungen*. Neue Folge II (Sampson Wallin, Stockholm, 1891)
235. Richards, M. H., Furron, E. Y. The eye and optic tract in normal and "eyeless" *Drosophila*. *Biol. Bull.*, **48**, 243–58 (1925)
236. Roberts, A. Recurrent inhibition in the giant-fibre system of the crayfish and its effect on the excitability of the escape response. *J. Exptl. Biol.*, **48**, 545–67 (1968)
237. Roberts, A. Some features of the central coordination of a fast movement in the crayfish. *J. Exptl. Biol.*, **49**, 645–56 (1969)
238. Roberts, M. B. V. The rapid response of *Myxicola infundibulum* (Grübe). *J. Marine Biol. Assoc. U.K.*, **42**, 527–39 (1962)
239. Roberts, M. B. V. The giant fibre reflex of the earthworm, *Lumbricus terrestris* L. II. Fatigue. *J. Exptl. Biol.*, **39**, 229–37 (1962)
240. Rockstein, M. The relation of cholinesterase activity to change in cell number with age in the brain of the adult worker honey bee. *J. Cell. Comp. Physiol.*, **35**, 11–23 (1950)
241. Roeder, K. D. Organization of the ascending giant fiber system in cockroach *Periplaneta americana*. *J. Exptl. Zool.*, **108**, 243–61 (1948)
242. Roeder, K. D. A physiological approach to the relation between prey and predator. In *Studies in Invertebrate Morphology*, 287–306 (Smithsonian Misc. Collections, **137**, Smithsonian Inst., Washington, D.C., 1959)
243. Roeder, K. D. *Nerve Cells and Insect Behavior* (Harvard Univ. Press, Cambridge, 188 pp., 1963)
244. Roeder, K. D., Kennedy, N. K., Samson, E. A. Synaptic conduction to giant fibers of the cockroach and the action of anticholinesterases. *J. Neurophysiol.*, **10**, 1–10 (1947)
245. Roeder, K. D., Tozian, L., Weiaut, E. A. Endogenous nerve activity and behavior in the mantis and cockroach. *J. Insect Physiol.*, **4**, 45–62 (1960)
246. Rosenbluth, J. The visceral ganglion of *Aplysia californica*. *Z. Zellforsch,.* **60**, 213–36 (1963)
247. Rosenbluth, J. Functions of glial cells. In *The Central Nervous System*, Intern. Acad. Pathol. *Monogr. 9*, 21–41 (Bailey, O. T., Smith, D. E., Eds., Williams & Wilkins, Baltimore, 364 pp., 1968)
248. Rovainen, C. M. Physiological and anatomical studies on large neurons of central nervous system of the sea lamprey (*Petramyzon marinus*). I. Müller and Mauthner cells. *J. Neurophysiol.*, **30**, 1000–23 (1967)
249. Rowell, C. H. F. A general method for silvering invertebrate central nervous systems. *Quart. J. Microscop. Sci.*, **104**, 81–87 (1963)
250. Rude, S., Coggeshall, R. E., Van Orden, L. S. Chemical and ultrastructural identification of 5-hydroxytryptamine in an identified neuron. *J. Cell Biol.*, **41**, 832–54 (1969)
251. Rullier, F. La vision et l'habitude chez *Mercierella enigmatica* Fauvel. *Bull. Lab. Maritime Dinard*, **30**, 21–27 (1948)
252. Scharrer, E., Scharrer, B. Hormones produced by neurosecretory cells. *Recent Progr. Hormone Res.*, **20**, 183–240 (1964)
253. Schmidt, G. A. Untersuchungen über

die Embryologie die Anneliden. I. Embryonalentwicklung von *Piscicola geometra. Blainu. Zool. Jahrb. (Anat.)*, **47**, 319–428 (1926)

254. Schrader, K. Untersuchungen über die Normalentwicklung des Gehirns und Gehirntransplantionen bei der Mehlmotte *Ephestia kuhniella* Zeller. *Biol. Zentr.*, **58**, 52–90 (1938)

255. Selverston, A. I., Remler, M. P., Kennedy, D. Crayfish motoneurons: intraganglionic architecture and activation by giant fibers. *Fed. Proc.*, **28**, 431 (1969)

256. Sharpless, S., Jasper, H. Habituation of the arousal reaction. *Brain, 79*, 655–80 (1956)

257. Sherrington, C. S. Quantitative management of contraction in lowest level coordination. *Brain*, **54**, 1–28 (1931)

258. Sidman, R. L., Miale, I. L., Feder, N. Cell proliferation and migration in the primitive ependymal zone: an autoradiographic study of biogenesis in the nervous system. *Exptl. Neurol.*, **1**, 322–33 (1959)

259. Simpson, L., Bern, H. A., Nishioka, R. S. Survey of evidence for neurosection in gastropod molluscs. *Am. Zool.*, **6**, 123–38 (1966)

260. Smith, D. S., Treherene, J. E. Functional aspects of the organization of the insect nervous system. *Advan. Insect Physiol.*, **1**, 401–84 (1967)

261. Spencer, W. A., Thompson, R. F., Neilson, D. R., Jr. Response decrement of the flexion reflex in the acute spinal cat and transient restoration by strong stimuli. *J. Neurophysiol.*, **29**, 221–39 (1966)

262. Sperry, R. W. Mechanisms of neuronal maturation. In *Handbook of Experimental Psychology*, 247–52 (Stevens, S. S., Ed., Wiley, New York, 1436 pp., 1951)

263. Sperry, R. W. Selective communications in nerve nets: Impulse specificity versus connection specificity. *Neurosci. Res. Bull.*, **3**(5), 37–43 (1965)

264. Staub, N. C. Demonstration of anatomy of the giant fiber system of the squid by microinjection. *Proc. Soc. Exptl. Biol. Med.*, **86**, 854–55 (1954)

265. Stevens, C. F. *A quantitative theory of neural interactions: theoretical and experimental investigations*

266. Stewart, A. *Excitatory and inhibitory motoneurons in the central nervous system of the leech* (Ph.D. dissertation, Yale Univ., New Haven, 1969)

267. Stretton, A. O. W., Kravitz, E. A. Neuronal geometry: determination with a technique of intracellular dye injection. *Science*, **162**, 132–34 (1968)

268. Strumwasser, F. Types of information stored in single neurons. In *Invertebrate Nervous Systems*, 291–319 (See Ref. 306)

269. Suga, N., Katsuki, Y. Central mechanism of hearing in insects. *J. Exptl. Biol.*, **38**, 545–58 (1961)

270. Taub, E., Berman, A. J. Avoidance conditioning in the absence of relevant proprioceptive and exteroceptive feedback. *J. Comp. Physiol. Psychol.*, **56**, 1012–16 (1963)

271. Taub, E., Berman, A. J. Movement and learning in the absence of sensory feedback. In *The Neuropsychology of Spatially Oriented Behavior* (Freedman, S. J., Ed., Dorsey Press, Homewood, Ill., 290 pp., 1968)

272. Tauc, L. Transmission in invertebrate and vertebrate ganglia. *Physiol. Rev.*, **47**, 521–93 (1967)

273. Tauc, L., Epstein, R. Heterosynaptic facilitation as a distinct mechanism in *Aplysia. Nature*, **214**, 724–25 (1957)

274. Tauc, L., Gerschenfeld, H. M. A cholinergic mechanism of inhibitory synaptic transmission in a molluscan nervous system. *J. Neurophysiol.*, **25**, 236–62 (1962)

275. Thorpe, W. H. *Learning and Instinct in Animals* (Harvard Univ. Press, Cambridge, 493 pp., 1958)

276. Tomita, T. Mechanism of lateral inhibition in eye of *Limulus. J. Neurophysiol.*, **21**, 419–29 (1958)

277. Treherne, J. E., Beament, J. W. L. *The Physiology of the Insect Central Nervous System* (Academic, New York, 277 pp., 1965)

278. Twitchell, T. E. Sensory factors in purposive movement. *J. Neurophysiol.*, **17**, 239–52 (1954)

279. Usherwood, P. N. Insect neuromuscular mechanisms. *Am. Zool.*, **7**, 553–82 (1967)

280. Van Harreveld, A., Wiersma, C. A. G.

The triple innervation of crayfish muscle and its function in contraction and inhibition. *J. Exptl. Biol.,* **14,** 448–61 (1937)

281. Van der Kloot, W. G. Neurosecretion in insects. *Ann. Rev. Entomol.,* **5,** 35–52 (1960)

282. Wachtel, H., Kandel, E. R. A direct synaptic connection mediating both excitation and inhibition. *Science,* **158,** 1206–8 (1967)

283. Wachtel, H., Waziri, R., Kandel, E. R. Interneurons (In preparation)

284. Watanabe, A., Grundfest, H. Impulse propagation at the septal and commissural junctions of crayfish lateral giant axons. *J. Gen. Physiol.,* **45,** 267–308 (1961)

285. Waterman, T. H. Relative growth and the compound eye in Xiphosura. *J. Morphol.,* **95,** 125–58 (1954)

286. Waterman, T. H., Ed. *The Physiology of Crustacea* (Academic, New York, 2 vols., 1351 pp., 1961)

287. Waterman, T. H., Enami, M. Neurosecretion in the lateral rudimentary eye of *Tachypleus,* a Xiphosuran. *Pubbl. Staz. Zool. Napoli,* **24** (Suppl.), 81–82 (1954)

288. Weavers, G. R. Proprioceptive reflexes and the coordination of locomotion in the caterpillar *Antheraea pernyi* (Lepidoptera). In *The Physiology of the Insect Central Nervous System,* 113–24 (See Ref. 277)

289. Weis-Fogh, T. Biology and physics of locust flight. II. Flight performance of the desert locust (*Schistocerca gregaria*). *Phil. Trans. Roy. Soc. (London), B,* **239,** 459–510 (1956)

290. Weis-Fogh, T. Biology and physics of locust flight. IV. Notes on sensory mechanisms in locust flight. *Phil. Trans. Roy Soc. (London), B,* **239,** 553–84 (1956)

291. Weis-Fogh, T. Control of basic movements in flying insects. *Symp. Soc. Exptl. Biol.,* **18,** 343–61 (1964)

292. Weisman, A. Die nachembryonale Entwicklung der Musciden nach Beobachtung an *Musca vomitoria* und *Sarcophaga carnaria. Z. Wiss. Zool.,* **14,** 187–336 (1864)

293. Weisstein, N. A Rashevsky-Landahl neural net: Simulation of meta-

contrast. *Psychol. Rev.,* **75,** 494–521 (1968)

294. Wheeler, W. M. A contribution to insect embryology. *J. Morphol.,* **8,** 1–160 (1893)

295. Whiteen, J. *Metamorphic Changes in Insects in Metamorphosis,* 43–105 (Etkin, W., Gilbert, L. I., Eds., Appleton-Century-Crofts, New York, 1968)

296. Wiersma, C. A. G. Function of the giant fibers of the central nervous system of the crayfish. *Proc. Soc. Exptl. Biol. Med.,* **38,** 661–62 (1938)

297. Wiersma, C. A. G. The efferent innervation of muscle. *Biol. Symp.,* **3,** 259–89 (1941)

298. Wiersma, C. A. G. Giant nerve fiber system of the crayfish. A contribution to comparative physiology of synapse. *J. Neurophysiol.,* **10,** 23–38 (1947)

299. Wiersma, C. A. G. The neuron soma. Neurons of arthropods. *Cold Spring Harbor Symp. Quant. Biol.,* **17,** 155–63 (1952)

300. Wiersma, C. A. G. On the functional connections of single units in the central nervous system of the crayfish, *Procambarus clarkii* (Girard). *J. Comp. Neurol.,* **110,** 421–71 (1958)

301. Wiersma, C. A. G. Reflexes and the central nervous system. In *The Physiology of Crustacea,* **2,** 241–79 (Waterman, T. H., Ed., Academic, New York, 681 pp., 1961)

302. Wiersma, C. A. G. The organization of the arthropod central nervous system. *Am. Zool.,* **2,** 67–78 (1962)

303. Wiersma, C. A. G. Unit properties as factors in transform functions. *Proc. Intern. Union Physiol. Sci., 20th Intern. Congr.,* **3,** 137–40 (1962)

304. Wiersma, C. A. G. Crayfish neurospecificity. *Neurosoc. Res. Progr. Bull.,* **3,** 45–53 (1965)

305. Wiersma, C. A. G. Integration in the visual pathway of crustacea. *Symp. Soc. Exptl. Biol.,* **20,** 151–77 (1966)

306. Wiersma, C. A. G., Ed. *Invertebrate Nervous Systems, Their Significance for Mammalian Neurophysiology,* Conf. Invertebrate Nervous Systems, Calif. Inst. Technol.,

1966 (Univ. Chicago Press, 370 pp., 1967)

307. Wiersma, C. A. G., Furshpan, E., Florey, E. Physiological and pharmacological observations on muscle receptor organs of the crayfish *Cambarus clarkii* (Girard). *J. Exptl. Biol.*, **30**, 136–50 (1953)

308. Wiersma, C. A. G., Hughes, G. M. On the functional anatomy of neuronal units in the abdominal cord of the crayfish, *Procambarus clarkii* (Girard). *J. Comp. Neurol.*, **116**, 209–28 (1961)

309. Wiersma, C. A. G., Ikeda, K. Interneurons commanding swimmeret movements in the crayfish *Procambarus clarkii* (Girard). *Comp. Biochem. Physiol.*, **12**, 509–25 (1964)

310. Wiersma, C. A. G., Yamaguchi, T. Integration of visual stimuli by the crayfish nervous system. *J. Exptl. Biol.*, **47**, 409–31 (1967)

311. Wigglesworth, V. B. The histology of the nervous system of an insect, *Rhodnius prolixus* (Hemiptera). II. The central ganglion. *Quart. J. Microscop. Sci.*, **100**, 299–313 (1954)

312. Wigglesworth, V. B. The use of osmium in the fixation and staining of tissues. *Proc. Roy. Soc. (London), B*, **147**, 185–99 (1957)

313. Wigglesworth, V. B. The nutrition of the central nervous system in the cockroach *Periplaneta americana* L. The role of perineurium and glial cells in the mobilization of reserves. *J. Exptl. Biol.*, **37**, 500–12 (1960)

314. Wigglesworth, V. B. *The Principles of Insect Physiology* (Methuen, London, 6th ed., 1965)

315. Willows, A. O. D. Behavioral acts elicited by stimulation of single identifiable brain cells. *Science*, **157**, 570–74 (1967)

316. Willows, A. O. D. Behavioral acts elicited by stimulation of single identifiable nerve cells. In *Physiological and Biochemical Aspects of Nervous Integration*, 217–43 (See Ref. 32)

317. Wilson, D. M. The central nervous control of flight in a locust. *J. Exptl. Biol.*, **38**, 471–90 (1961)

318. Wilson, D. M. The origin of the flight-motor command in grasshoppers. In *Neural Theory and Modeling*, 331–45 (Reiss, R. F., Ed., Stanford Univ. Press, 427 pp., 1964)

319. Wilson, D. M. The nervous coordination of insect locomotion. In *The Physiology of the Insect Central Nervous System*, 125–40 (See Ref. 277)

320. Wilson, D. M. Insect walking. *Ann. Rev. Entomol.*, **13**, 103–22 (1966)

321. Wilson, D. M. Central nervous mechanisms for the generation of rhythmic behavior in arthropods. *Symp. Soc. Exptl. Biol.*, **20**, 199–228 (1966)

322. Wilson, D. M. The stepping patterns in tarantula spiders. *J. Exptl. Biol.*, **47**, 133–51 (1967)

323. Wilson, D. M. The flight control system of the locust. *Sci. Am.*, **218** (5), 83–90 (1968)

324. Wilson, D. M. Inherent asymmetry and reflex modulation of the locust flight motor pattern. *J. Exptl. Biol.*, **48**, 631–41 (1968)

325. Wilson, D. M., Davis, W. J. Nerve impulse patterns and reflex control in the motor system of the crayfish claw. *J. Exptl. Biol.*, **43**, 193–210 (1965)

326. Wilson, D. M., Gettrup, E. A stretch reflex controlling wing beat frequency in grasshoppers. *J. Exptl. Biol.*, **40**, 171–85 (1963)

327. Wilson, D. M., Weis-Fogh, T. Patterned activity of coordinated motor units, studied in flying locusts. *J. Exptl. Biol.*, **39**, 643–67 (1962)

328. Wilson, D. M., Wyman, R. J. Motor output patterns during random and rhythmic stimulation of locust thoracic ganglia. *Biophys. J.*, **5**, 121–43 (1965)

329. Wolbarsht, M. L., Yeandle, S. S. Visual processes in the *Limulus* eye. *Ann. Rev. Physiol.*, **29**, 513–42 (1967)

330. Wolfe, D. E., Nicholls, J. G. Uptake of radioactive glucose and its conversion to glycogen by neurons and glial cells in the leech central nervous system. *J. Neurophysiol.*, **30**, 1593–609 (1967)

331. Wood, F. D., Wood, H. E. Autotomy in decapod crustacea. *J. Exptl. Zool.*, **62**, 1–55 (1932)

332. Wyman, R. (Unpublished observations, 1969)

333. Yagi, K., Bern, H. A., Hagadorn,

I. R. Action potentials of neuro-secretory neurons in the leech, *Theromyzon rude. Gen. Comp. Endocrinol.,* **3,** 490–95 (1963)

334. Yasargil, G. M., Diamond, J. Startle-response in teleost fish: an elementary circuit for neural discrimination. *Nature,* **220,** 241–43 (1968)

335. Young, J. Z. Structure of nerve fibers in *Sepia. J. Physiol. (London),* **83,** 27P–28P (1934)

336. Young, J. Z. Fused neurons and synaptic contacts in the giant nerve fibers of cephalopods. *Phil. Trans. Roy. Soc. London,* **229,** 465–501 (1939)

337. Zawarzin, A. Zur Morphologie der Nervenzentren. Das Bauchmark der Insekten. Ein Beitrag zur vergleichenden Histologie (Histologishe Studien uber Insekten VI). *Z. Wiss. Zool.,* **124,** 118–212 (1925)

CENTRAL PATHWAYS OF VISION

G. S. BRINDLEY

Department of Physiology, Institute of Psychiatry
University of London

This review covers papers published in the principal periodicals from January 1968 to May 1969. I have made no systematic attempt to read the proceedings of symposia or other irregular publications.

EXTRAGENICULOSTRIATE PATHWAYS

Their functions in general.—Blindness, total with the exception of the ability to distinguish sudden lightening of a dark room from sudden darkening of a light one, has been shown to last at least $2\frac{1}{2}$ years after a lesion restricted to the occipital poles of the cerebral hemispheres in man (7). Optokinetic nystagmus remains absent. Such lasting blindness contrasts with the well-known substantial return of vision after similar lesions in monkeys and, still more, in nonprimate mammals. The extrastriate and presumably extrageniculate vision that does thus return has been found to be little affected by lesions of the superior colliculus in cats (83) and rats (36) but much affected in monkeys by lesions that destroy the 'accessory optic system', i.e. fibres that terminate in the nucleus paralemniscalis (65).

The visual "neglect" or lack of orienting reactions produced by lesions of the dorsal midbrain has been found to be conspicuous in hamsters (73) and slight in monkeys (2). It is accompanied by almost no defect in formal tests of pattern discrimination, but there is in monkeys a defect of discrimination of rates of movement (2). The controversy as to whether the significant parts of the causal lesions are collicular, tegmental, or both has not been satisfactorily resolved.

Their anatomy.—Sefton (74) has elegantly proved that the great majority of retinocollicular fibres in the rat are collaterals of retinogeniculate fibres.

The direct mapping of the retina on the colliculus in the cat has been reexamined by anatomical means (32), and its indirect mapping through the striate cortex by electrical recording (78). The two maps are at least roughly concordant, but it is not yet possible to say if they are exactly so.

Responses to electrical stimulation of the optic nerve have been recorded at various depths in the superior colliculus of cats (68) and rats (75). The results tell us nothing of function, but indicate the depths at which responding fibres and cells occur.

Collicular responses to visual stimuli.—These have attracted much attention (42, 52, 77–80, 87). The only strikingly new observations are those of Wickelgren & Sterling (87), who found that the visual sensitivity of collicular cells was abolished reversibly by cooling the ipsilateral visual cortex, and radically altered by removing the ipsilateral visual cortex a week or more before. Ordinarily, most collicular cells are binocularly driven, nearly unresponsive to stationary stimuli, and directionally selective in their responses to moving stimuli (78). After ipsilateral posteromedial neocorticectomy, they respond to stationary stimuli, are not directionally selective, and are driven only by the ipsilateral eye. Though ablation of striate cortex has so large an effect on responses of collicular cells to visual stimuli, it has none on the gross electrical response of the colliculus to an optic nerve volley (55).

Other extrageniculostriate responses to visual stimuli.—These have been recorded from the pretectal region (15), where their properties have been interestingly correlated with those to be expected in a pathway that controls the size of the pupils; and in other parts of the brainstem (6, 81) and nonstriate cerebral cortex (25, 51, 69), where no correlations of properties with likely functions have been made. Of all these extrageniculostriate responses, only the pretectal can be confidently attributed to pathways that do not go through the lateral geniculate nucleus. The brainstem responses may or may not depend on such pathways; there is no evidence. The collicular responses are shown by the observations of Wickelgren & Sterling (87) to depend mainly but not wholly on information relayed from the striate cortex, and the same is likely (though the evidence is thin) for extrastriate cortical responses.

Centrifugal fibres to the retina.—Cells of the isthmo-optic nucleus of the pigeon have been shown to be activated antidromically from the optic nerve (35). Strong earlier indications from anatomy that this nucleus (found in birds but not in mammals) is a source of centrifugal fibres to the retina are thus confirmed.

LATERAL GENICULATE NUCLEUS

Anatomy.—In young rats, deprivation of light decreases the number of axon terminals in the lateral geniculate nuclei, but increases their size (21).

The projection of the retina on its lateral geniculate nucleus has been examined in rats by electrical recording (60), and in cats by anatomical techniques (32); the results in cats agree closely with earlier inferences from electrical recording.

A claim that *Galago crassicaudatus* is anomalous among primates in the number of layers in its lateral geniculate nucleus has been convincingly contradicted (43).

The transynaptic cell atrophy after enucleation of an eye has been found to affect the large-celled layers more than the small-celled, and to be the same at a year as at two years in the squirrel monkey (44).

Responses of geniculate cells to visual stimulation.—Binocular interaction in the cat (18) and colour properties in monkeys (1) have been reexamined without great addition to knowledge. Some geniculate cells in the rat have been found to be directionally selective for moving stimuli (59). Ingenious and good arguments from experiments on geniculate responses (23) tend to show that all cones in the cat's retina are alike in spectral sensitivity, so that the inefficient but well-established colour discrimination of cats must depend on comparison of rod signals with cone signals. Off-centre optic nerve fibres and off-centre geniculate cells in the cat differ in the spatial organization of their receptive fields, though the corresponding on-centre units do not (31). Of geniculate cells in the cat, those that long survive ablation of the ipsilateral areas 17 and 18 are more often binocularly driven than the rest (17).

Responses to nonvisual stimulation.—In unanesthetized rabbits, the responses of geniculate cells to sound (pure tones of various frequencies), to diffuse light, and to combinations of sound and light have been compared (46).

Collateral influences on the sensitivity of geniculate cells.—Influences of sleep (61, 82), reticular stimulation (16, 62, 71), cooling the ipsilateral visual cortex (41), pentobarbital (72), and disuse achieved by poisoning the retinal receptors (10) have been examined. Of these, the effects of disuse are the most interesting; the effectiveness of the geniculate synapses is unchanged, but they are made less than normally susceptible to posttetanic depression. The fact that poisoning the retinal receptors does silence the optic nerve has an importance of its own, for it bears on the question whether the normal activity of optic nerve fibres in darkness depends on inescapable 'noise' arising in the rods and cones.

Events in the lateral geniculate nucleus during eye movements.—The electrical waves in the geniculate nucleus and elsewhere that accompany saccadic eye movements in the waking state and the rapid eye movements of desynchronized sleep have been further studied (9, 28). Presynaptic inhibition (on the criteria of enhanced excitability of optic tract terminals and depressed transmission through the nucleus), which was already known to occur during the rapid eye movements of desynchronized sleep, has now been shown to occur also during tracking eye movements (45).

GENICULOCALCARINE RADIATIONS

A careful examination of visual field changes after temporal lobectomy in man has shown that the variation between people in the anatomy of the radiations is great. The field defects in the two eyes usually differ; the larger field defect may with about equal frequency be found in the ipsilateral or contralateral eye (57).

VISUAL CORTEX

Anatomy.—Deprivation of light, besides causing loss of dendritic spines in layer IV of area 17 [as has lately been confirmed (29)], reduces the number of dendrites and the mean length of dendrites in stellate cells of layer IV (19). There is no such change in pyramidal cells of layer V. Deprivation of light also decreases by as much as 16 per cent the volume of the visual cortex, all layers being affected (30). The effects of enucleation of the contralateral eye (in a species with total chiasmal decussation) are similar to those of light deprivation, but probably more extensive (84, 85).

The cat's striate cortex contains some 500 metres of myelinated nerve fibre per cubic millimetre, the mean diameter being 0.6 μ and the maximum about 2 μ. About 300,000 fibres enter each square millimetre of it from the white matter, and about 80,000 leave each square millimetre (34).

Synaptic membrane differentiation in the cat's striate cortex is of two kinds, asymmetrical and symmetrical, roughly corresponding to Gray's types 1 and 2 (20). Asymmetrical membrane differentiation is generally associated with round synaptic vesicles, symmetrical with flattened. Nonspine synapses on stellate cells or their dendrites can be of either kind. Nonspine synapses on pyramidal cells always have symmetrical membrane differentiation, while spine synapses on pyramidal dendrites are usually asymmetrical.

The 'columnar' organization of area 17, already known by electrical recording in the cat, has been found anatomically in monkeys for ocular dominance (39), and by electrical recording in monkeys both for ocular dominance and for orientational specificity (38).

Responses of cortical cells to visual stimulation.—The spatial and spatiotemporal properties of cells of the visual cortex in monkeys have been found (38) to be very similar to properties already known for the cat. Only a minority of cells in the monkey's area 17 show specific colour sensitivities. Opportunities for examining cells of the human visual cortex are rare; however, some have been examined (56), and found to resemble the corresponding cells of monkeys.

Binocular interaction on cells of the cat's striate cortex has been examined in very great detail (11, 64, 67), and the well-known observations of Barlow, Blakemore & Pettigrew thereby confirmed and slightly extended.

The sensitivity of cells of the cat's striate cortex to moving lines (66) and gratings (14) has been explored.

A thorough but rather disappointing attempt has been made (22) to correlate the responses of single cells of the cat's visual cortex with the slow potentials produced by the same (diffuse flash) stimuli.

Responses to nonvisual stimulation.—It has been confirmed (4) that many cells of the striate cortex of unanesthetized cats respond to clicks.

Collateral influences on the sensitivity of cells of the visual cortex.—The most exciting recent paper on this subject is that of Horn & Hill (37), who found that the axis of the receptive field of some cells of the visual cortex of cats retains a constant relation to the external world when the animal is tilted through angles up to 18°. This finding, if correct (and the paper contains no internal reasons for doubting it), implies a compensating mechanism of evident utility but surprising complexity. The visual cortex was already known to receive vestibular afferents (on which the compensation of Horn & Hill must depend), but few neurophysiologists can have suspected that they were used to perform the formidable set of disconnexions and reconnexions necessary to alter the axes of receptive fields so as to compensate reversibly for tilting the head.

During saccadic eye movements in conscious monkeys, some cells of the striate cortex respond to visual stimuli in the same manner as they do when the eye is still, but others become unresponsive (89).

The effects of reticular, hypothalamic and limbic stimulation on cortical responses to diffuse flashes or shocks to various parts of the visual pathway have been further explored (16, 47, 62, 76), but no very striking new discoveries made thereby.

Electrical stimulation of the human visual cortex.—With the aim of developing a useful visual prosthesis, an array of radio receivers, connected to electrodes in contact with the occipital pole of one cerebral hemisphere, has been implanted into a blind patient (8). By giving appropriate radio signals, the patient can be caused to 'see' white spots of light at fixed points in one half of the visual field. The spots ('phosphenes') produced by electrodes 2.4 mm apart are always resolvable, and patterns can be built up predictably by simultaneous stimulation through several electrodes. The main importance of the work is clinical. I can report informally that it is being energetically developed, but that progress cannot be expected to be very fast. Physiologically, the least expected findings are the existence of a second mapping of the retina superimposed on the classical one, and lack of any flicker fusion frequency for cortical phosphenes.

Responses to visual stimuli recorded from the human scalp.—These have continued to be a fashionable subject for research, and without going beyond the principal European, American, and Japanese journals for the 17 months under review I have read 29 papers on them. The literature of the subject is very inbred, and at present has little influence on the rest of central visual neurophysiology, but I see little reason why this noninteraction should continue. Potentially interesting recent findings are that the scalp responses are depressed (perhaps abolished) when perception of the relevant stimulus is suppressed or altered in certain binocular rivalry situations (48, 53), in certain metacontrast situations (53, 86), and when the stimulus coincides with or just precedes a voluntary saccadic eye movement (26). Evidence has been given (3) that 'lambda responses', i.e. the scalp responses that accompany saccadic eye movements, are not wholly due to the shift of the retinal image; in particular, they include a component that precedes the eye movement by 150–200 msec. The distribution of responses over the scalp has been examined for stimuli restricted to half the visual field (50) and for stimuli to the left and right eyes of a subject with bitemporal hemianopia from a traumatic chiasmal lesion (49). These unsymmetrical stimuli give unsymmetrical scalp distributions which are rather accurately mirror images for the mirror-image modes of stimulation. To the well-known fact that responses to patterned and uniform stimuli differ in amplitude and time course can now be added (24, 54) that sudden movement of the retinal image produces a response with yet another time course. Changes during sleep in the scalp responses to a constant diffuse visual stimulus have been explored, and correlated with other electroencephalographic changes (70).

The unification of the visual cortex of the two hemispheres by means of fibres of the splenium of the corpus callosum.—The relevant connexions have been examined in the cat (88) and rabbit (40) by the Nauta technique. In the cat, the callosal projection from the boundary between visual II and visual III includes not only the approximate mirror region, but also the lateral half of the middle suprasylvian gyrus, which was already known to receive fibres from the ipsilateral visual land lateral geniculate nucleus.

Binocularly driven neurons have been detected in the visual cortex of cats in which the chiasma has been cut through. Their receptive fields, which are always within 10° of the vertical meridian, are very nearly congruent for the two eyes (5).

VISUAL FUNCTIONS OF OTHER PARTS OF THE CEREBRAL CORTEX

Clinical observations in man.—New evidence has appeared for a specific association of lesions of the right cerebral hemisphere (63), especially its temporal lobe (58), with poor performance in certain tests of interpretation and learning of visual patterns.

Left temporal lobectomy, but not right temporal lobectomy, has been found (33) to raise the flicker fusion frequency in the absence of any loss of visual field.

Inferior temporal lesions in monkeys.—In their effects on performance and relearning of a learned pattern discrimination, inferior temporal and preoccipital lesions potentiate one another (27).

It has been argued that inferior temporal lesions impair selective attention between one visual stimulus and another (13). It is clear (12) that though these lesions retard the learning of pattern discriminations (whether or not by an effect on selective attention), they do not affect their short-term retention when they have been learned.

LITERATURE CITED

1. Abramov, I. Further analysis of the responses of LGN cells. *J. Opt. Soc. Am.*, **58**, 574–79 (1968)
2. Anderson, K. V., Symmes, D. The superior colliculus and higher visual functions in the monkey. *Brain Res.*, **13**, 37–52 (1969)
3. Barlow, J. S., Ciganek, L. Lambda responses in relation to visual evoked responses in man. *Electroenceph. Clin. Neurophysiol.*, **26**, 183–92 (1969)
4. Bental, E., Dafny, N., Feldman, S. Convergence of auditory and visual stimuli on single cells in the primary visual cortex of unanesthetized unrestrained cats. *Exptl. Neurol.*, **20**, 341–51 (1968)
5. Berlucchi, G., Rizzolatti, G. Binocularly driven neurons in visual cortex of split-chiasm cats. *Science*, **159**, 308–10 (1968)
6. Bogacz, J., Wilson, E. Visual evoked potentials at hypothalamic and tegmental areas of the upper brainstem. *EEG Clin. Neurophysiol.*, **26**, 288–95 (1969)
7. Brindley, G. S., Gautier-Smith, P. C., Lewin, W. (1969) Cortical blindness and the functions of the nongeniculate fibres of the optic tracts. *J. Neurol. Neurosurg. Psychiat.*, **32**, 259–64 (1969)
8. Brindley, G. S., Lewin, W. S. The sensations produced by electrical stimulation of the visual cortex. *J. Physiol.*, **196**, 479–93 (1968)
9. Brooks, D. C. Waves associated with eye movement in the awake and sleeping cat. *Electroenceph. Clin. Neurophysiol.*, **24**, 532–41 (1968)
10. Burke, W., Hayhow, W. R. Disuse in the lateral geniculate nucleus of the cat. *J. Physiol.*, **194**, 495–519 (1968)
11. Burns, B. D., Pritchard, R. Cortical conditions for fused binocular vision. *J. Physiol.*, **197**, 149–71 (1968)
12. Butler, C. R. Is there a memory impairment in monkeys after inferior temporal lesions? *Brain Res.*, **13**, 383–93 (1969)
13. Butter, C. M. Impairments in selective attention to visual stimuli in monkeys with inferotemporal and lateral striate lesions. *Brain Res.*, **12**, 374–83 (1969)
14. Campbell, F. W., Cleland, B. G., Cooper, B. F., Enroth-Cugell, C.

The angular sensitivity of visual cortical cells to moving gratings. *J. Physiol.*, **198**, 237–50 (1968)
15. Cavaggioni, A., Madaràsz, I., Zampollo, A. Photic reflex and pretectal region. *Arch. Ital. Biol.*, **106**, 227–42 (1968)
16. Chi, C. C., Flynn, J. P. The effects of hypothalamic and reticular stimulation on evoked responses in the visual system of the cat. *Electroenceph. Clin. Neurophysiol.*, **24**, 343–56 (1968)
17. Chow, K. L., Lindsley, D. F. Microelectrode study of residual neurons in the degenerated lateral geniculate nucleus of the cat. *J. Neurophysiol.*, **32**, 116–26 (1969)
18. Chow, K. L., Lindsley, D. F., Gollender, M. Modifications of response patterns of lateral geniculate neurons after paired stimulation of contralateral and ipsilateral eyes. *J. Neurophysiol.*, **31**, 729–39 (1968)
19. Coleman, P. D., Riesen, A. H. Environmental effects on cortical dendritic fields: I. Rearing in the dark. *J. Anat.*, **102**, 363–74 (1968)
20. Colonnier, M. Synaptic patterns on different cell types in the different laminae of the cat visual cortex. An electron microscope study. *Brain Res.*, **9**, 268–87 (1968)
21. Cragg, B. G. The effects of vision and dark-rearing on the size and density of synapses in the lateral geniculate nucleus measured by electron microscopy. *Brain Res.*, **13**, 53–67 (1969)
22. Creutzfeldt, O., Rosina, A., Ito, M., Probst, W. Visual evoked response of single cells and of the EEG in primary visual area of the cat. *J. Neurophysiol.*, **32**, 127–39 (1969)
23. Daw, N. W., Pearlman, A. L. Cat colour vision: one cone process or several. *J. Physiol.*, **201**, 745–64 (1969)
24. Dawson, W. W., Perry, N. W., Childers, D. G. Flash and scan stimulation of retinal fields and evoked response production. *Electroenceph. Clin. Neurophysiol.*, **24**, 467–73 (1968)
25. Dubner, R., Brown, F. J. Responses of cells to restricted visual stimuli in an association area of cat cerebral cortex. *Exptl. Neurol.*, **20**, 70–86 (1968)

26. Duffy, F. H., Lombroso, C. T. Electrophysiological evidence for visual suppression prior to the onset of a voluntary saccadic eye movement. *Nature,* **218,** 1074–75 (1968)

27. Ettlinger, G., Iwai, E. Mishkin, M., Rosvold, H. E. Visual discrimination in the monkey following serial ablation of inferotemporal and preoccipital cortex. *J. Comp. Physiol. Psychol.,* **65,** 110–17 (1968)

28. Feldman, M., Cohen, B. Electrical activity in lateral geniculate body of the alert monkey associated with eye movements. *J. Neurophysiol.,* **31,** 455–66 (1968)

29. Fifková, E. Changes in the visual cortex of rats after unilateral deprivation. *Nature,* **220,** 379–81 (1968)

30. Fifková, E., Hassler, R. Quantitative morphological changes in visual centers in rats after unilateral deprivation. *J. Comp. Neurol.,* **135,** 167–78 (1969)

31. Freund, H.-J., Grünewald, G., Baumgartner, G. Räumliche Summation im receptiven Feldzentrum von Neuronen des Geniculatum laterale der Katze. *Exptl. Brain Res.,* **8,** 53–65 (1969)

32. Garey, L. J., Powell, T. P. S. The projection of the retina in the cat. *J. Anat.,* **102,** 189–222 (1968)

33. Goldman, P. S., Lodge, A., Hammer, L. R., Semmes, J., Mishkin, M. Critical flicker frequency after unilateral temporal lobectomy in man. *Neuropsychologia,* **6,** 355–63 (1968)

34. Haug, H. Quantitative elektronenmikroskopische Untersuchungen über den Markfaseraufbau in der Sehrinde der Katze. *Brain Res.,* **11,** 65–84 (1968)

35. Holden, A. L. Antidromic activation of the isthmo-optic nucleus. *J. Physiol.,* **197,** 183–98 (1968)

36. Horel, J. A. Effects of subcortical lesions on brightness discrimination acquired by rats without visual cortex. *J. Comp. Physiol. Psychol.,* **65,** 103–9 (1968)

37. Horn, G., Hill, R. M. Modifications of receptive fields of cells in the visual cortex occurring spontaneously and associated with bodily tilt. *Nature,* **221,** 186–88 (1969)

38. Hubel, D. H., Wiesel, T. N. Receptive fields and functional architecture of monkey striate cortex. *J. Physiol.,* **195,** 215–43 (1968)

39. Hubel, D. H., Wiesel, T. N. Anatomical demonstration of columns in the monkey striate cortex. *Nature,* **221,** 747–50 (1969)

40. Hughes, A., Wilson, M. E. Callosal terminations along the boundary between visual areas I and II in the rabbit. *Brain Res.,* **12,** 19–25 (1969)

41. Hull, E. M. Corticofugal influence in the macaque lateral geniculate nucleus. *Vision Res.,* **8,** 1285–98 (1968)

42. Humphrey, N. K. Responses to visual stimuli of units in the superior colliculus of rats and monkeys. *Exptl. Neurol.,* **20,** 312–40 (1968)

43. Ionescu, D. A., Hassler, R. Six cell layers in the lateral geniculate body in the night-active prosimian, *Galago crassicaudatus. Brain Res.,* **10,** 281–84 (1968)

44. Jacobs, G. H. Transneuronal changes in the lateral geniculate nucleus of the squirrel monkey. *J. Comp. Neurol.,* **135,** 81–84 (1969)

45. Kawamura, H., Marchiafava, P. L. Excitability changes along visual pathways during tracking eye movements. *Arch. Ital. Biol.,* **106,** 141–56 (1968)

46. Kuman, E. A., Skrebitski, V. G. The interaction of visual and auditory signals in the lateral geniculate body of the rabbit's brain (in Russian). *Zh. Vyssh. Nerv. Deyat.,* **18,** 507–13 (1968)

47. Langley, T. D., Siegel, J. Visual and auditory evoked potentials: specificity of reticular formation modulating influences. *Experientia,* **24,** 353–54 (1968)

48. Lehmann, D., Fender, D. H. Component analysis of human averaged evoked potentials: dichoptic stimuli using different target structure. *Electroenceph. Clin. Neurophysiol.,* **24,** 542–53 (1968)

49. Lehmann, D., Kavanagh, R. N., Fender, D. H. Field studies of averaged visually evoked EEG potentials in a patient with a split chiasma. *Electroenceph. Clin. Neurophysiol.,* **26,** 193–99 (1969)

50. Lesèvre, N., Rémond, A. Étude du champ visuel par les potentiels évoqués moyens. *Rev. Neurol.,* **118,** 419–30 (1968)

51. Loe, P. R., Venevento, L. A. Auditory-visual interaction in single units in the orbito-insular cortex of the

cat. *EEG Clin. Neurophysiol.*, **26**, 395–98 (1969)

52. McIlwain, J. T., Buser, P. Receptive fields of single cells in the cat's superior colliculus. *Exptl. Brain Res.*, **5**, 314–25 (1968)

53. Mackay, D. M. Evoked potentials reflecting interocular and monocular suppression. *Nature*, **217**, 81–83 (1968)

54. Mackay, D. M., Rietveld, W. J. Electroencephalogram potentials evoked by accelerated visual motion. *Nature*, **217**, 677–78 (1968)

55. Marchiafava, P. L., Rizzolatti, G., Sprague, J. M. Studies on corticotectal activity in the unanesthetized mid-pontine cat. *Arch. Ital. Biol.*, **106**, 21–41 (1968)

56. Marg, E., Adams, J. E., Rutkin, B. Receptive fields of cells in the human visual cortex. *Experientia*, **24**, 348 (1968)

57. Marino, R., Rasmussen, T. Visual field changes after temporal lobectomy in man. *Neurology*, **18**, 825–35 (1968)

58. Milner, B. Visual recognition and recall after right temporal-lobe excision in man. *Neuropsychologia*, **6**, 191–209 (1968)

59. Montero, V. M., Brugge, J. F. Direction of movement as the significant stimulus parameter for some lateral geniculate cells in the rat. *Vision Res.*, **9**, 71–88 (1969)

60. Montero, V. M., Brugge, J. F., Beitel, R. E. Relation of the visual field to the lateral geniculate body of the albino rat. *J. Neurophysiol.*, **31**, 221–36 (1968)

61. Mukhametov, L., Rizzolatti, G. Effect of sleep and waking on flash evoked discharges of lateral geniculate units in unrestrained cats. *Brain Res.*, **13**, 404–6 (1969)

62. Nakai, Y., Domino, E. F. Reticular facilitation of visually evoked responses by optic tract stimulation before and after enucleation. *Exptl. Neurol.*, **22**, 532–44 (1968)

63. Newcombe, F., Russell, W. R. Dissociated visual perceptual and spatial deficits in focal lesions of the right hemisphere. *J. Neurol. Neurosurg. Psychiat.*, **32**, 73–81 (1969)

64. Nikara, T., Bishop, P. O., Pettigrew, J. D. Analysis of retinal correspondence by studying receptive fields of binocular single units in

cat striate cortex. *Exptl. Brain Res.*, **6**, 353–72 (1968)

65. Pasik, P., Pasik, T. Further studies on extrageniculostriate vision in the monkey. *Trans. Am. Neurol. Assoc.*, **93**, 262–64 (1968)

66. Pettigrew, J. D., Nikara, T., Bishop, P. O. Responses to moving slits by single units in cat striate cortex. *Exptl. Brain Res.*, **6**, 373–90 (1968)

67. Pettigrew, J. D., Nikara, T., Bishop, P. O. Binocular interaction on single units in cat striate cortex: simultaneous stimulation by single moving slit with receptive fields in correspondence. *Exptl. Brain Res.*, **6**, 391–410 (1968)

68. Pickering, S. G., Freeman, W. J. Superior colliculus-evoked response in anesthetized cats: space-time characteristics. *Am. J. Physiol.*, **214**, 152–57 (1968)

69. Rutledge, L. T., Shellenberger, M. K. The influence of visual cortex upon non-primary area neurons. *Arch. Ital. Biol.*, **106**, 353–63 (1968)

70. Saier, J., Regis, H., Mano, T., Gastaut, H. Potentiels évoqués visuels et somesthetiques pendant le sommeil de l'homme. *Brain Res.*, **10**, 431–40 (1968)

71. Satinsky, D. Reticular influences on lateral geniculate neuron activity. *Electroenceph. Clin. Neurophysiol.*, **25**, 543–49 (1968)

72. Schmidt, R., Creutzfeld, O. D. Veränderungen von Spontanaktivität und Reizantwort retinaler und geniculärer Neurone der Katze bei fraktionierter Injektion von Pentobarbital-Na. *Pflügers Arch.*, **300**, 129–47 (1968)

73. Schneider, G. E. Two visual systems. *Science*, **163**, 895–902 (1969)

74. Sefton, A. J. The innervation of the lateral geniculate nucleus and anterior colliculus in the rat. *Vision Res.*, **8**, 867–81 (1968)

75. Sefton, A. J. The electrical activity of the anterior colliculus in the rat. *Vision Res.*, **9**, 207–22 (1969)

76. Sierra, G., Fuster, J. M. Facilitation of secondary visual evoked responses by stimulation of limbic structures. *Electroenceph. Clin. Neurophysiol.*, **25**, 274–78 (1968)

77. Sprague, J. M., Marchiafava, P. L., Rizzolatti, G. Unit responses to visual stimuli in the superior colliculus of the unanesthetized mid-

pontine cat. *Arch. Ital. Biol.*, **106**, 169-93 (1968)

78. Sterling, P., Wickelgren, B. G. Visual receptive fields in the superior colliculus of the cat. *J. Neurophysiol.*, **32**, 1–15 (1969)

79. Straschill, M., Hoffmann, K. P. Relationship between localization and functional properties of movement-sensitive neurons of the cat's tectum opticum. *Brain Res.*, **8**, 382–85 (1968)

80. Straschill, M., Hoffmann, K. P. Functional aspects of localization in the cat's opticum. *Brain Res.*, **13**, 274–83 (1969)

81. Suzuki, H., Kato, H. Neurons with visual properties in the posterior group of thalamic nuclei. *Exptl. Neurol.*, **23**, 353–65 (1969)

82. Thomas, J., Groves, P., Verzeano, M. The activity of neurons in the lateral geniculate body during wakefulness and natural sleep. *Experientia*, **24**, 360–62 (1968)

83. Urbaitis, J. C., Meikle, T. H. Relearning a dark-light discrimination by cats after cortical and collicular lesions. *Exptl. Neurol.*, **20**, 295–311 (1968)

84. Valverde, F. Structural changes in the area striata of the mouse after enucleation. *Exptl. Brain Res.*, **5**, 274–92 (1968)

85. Valverde, F., Esteban, M. E., Peristriate cortex of mouse: location and the effects of enucleation on the number of dendritic spines. *Brain Res.*, **9**, 145–48 (1968)

86. Vaughan, H. G., Silverstein, L. Metacontrast and evoked potentials: a reappraisal. *Science*, **160**, 207–8 (1968)

87. Wickelgren, B. G., Sterling, P. Influence of visual cortex on receptive fields in the superior colliculus of the cat. *J. Neurophysiol.*, **32**, 16–23 (1969)

88. Wilson, M. E. Cortico-cortical connexions of the cat visual areas. *J. Anat.*, **102**, 375–86 (1968)

89. Wurtz, R. H. Visual cortex neurons: response to stimuli during rapid eye movements. *Science*, **162**, 1148–50 (1968)

PAIN 1045

ROBERT K. S. LIM[1]

Medical Sciences Research Laboratory, Miles Laboratories, Inc., Elkhart, Indiana

This review deals with the author's concept of the physiology and pharmacology of pain based on the findings that the receptor for pain is chemosensitive rather than nocisensitive, since physiological concentrations of certain chemical agents (cations, some amines, and the bradykinin peptides) can evoke the same manifestations of pain as injury or nociception.

THE NATURE OF PAIN

Pain is felt by all humans except those who are comatose, unconscious, anesthetized, or congenitally analgesic, but may be suppressed or inhibited under certain circumstances. *Webster's 1966 International Dictionary* provides an adequate psychophysiological description of pain, without psychoanalytical considerations, viz. "Pain (Middle English, *peine;* Latin, *prena,* penalty, punishment), 1. originally penalty, 2. the sensations one feels[2] when hurt, mentally or physically, especially distress, suffering, great anxiety, anguish, grief, etc.: opposed to pleasure,[3] 3. a sensation of hurting, or strong discomfort, in some parts of the body, caused by an injury, disease, or functional disorder, and transmitted through the nervous system."

Definition 2 covers the feelings of pain modified, amplified, or distorted by central psychic and emotional influences, and 3 refers to the sensation of pain evoked in response to peripheral stimulation of the nerve endings concerned. The same central and peripheral mechanisms [including failure in coordination or imbalance between excitatory and inhibitory factors in the pain pathways (5, 107)] are probably involved in the more bizarre clinical states of central thalamic, phantom, and hysterical pain, in chronic pain, and in recurrent, spasmodic, or neuralgic types of pain, although the original stimulus may no longer be evident or operating.

Pain, a somesthetic modality.—Pain thus pertains to the body sensations which serve to inform the organism of the state of both the external and internal environment. Analysis of the types of stimuli which evoke somesthetic sensations according to classical concepts leads to the conclusion that

---

[1] Dr. Lim died on July 8, 1969, shortly after he wrote this chapter.

[2] Preferably "feelings one experience".

[3] More appropriate, "opposed to comfort".

269

there are three main groups of receptors: mechanoreceptors (for touch, pressure, and vibration); thermoreceptors (for cold and warmth); and no-ciceptors (for ache and pain). The last reflects the common association of any form of high-intensity stimulus (i.e. injury) with pain, disregarding the fact that the receptor is damaged and often fails to give a second response. Evidence will be presented later (pp. 273–76) to show that the majority of "nociceptors" will give a pain response when H and K ions, some amines, and the bradykinin peptides are applied in physiological concentrations; they are thus in fact somesthetic chemoreceptors, which will also respond to no-ciceptive stimulation of their axons or receptor terminals.

Somesthetic homeostasis.—Somesthetic information is not provided in pure or punctate form, but as a pattern which projects the image of the stimuli acting on all the receptors within the field of stimulation. Allowing for the adaptation of the mechanoreceptors, it is postulated that this infor-mation regulates a homeostatic function which tends to maintain the body in a condition of "feelinglessness" commonly called *comfort.* Any disturbance of somesthesis at the conscious level produces *uncomfort,* and triggers con-scious voluntary activity aimed at removing the organism from the disturb-ing environment, or restoring the environment to limits more compatible with normal function and the feelinglessness of comfort. More severe changes which affect the body produce *discomfort* and eventually pain (66).

Pain, whether cutaneous or visceral, forms part of the somesthetic image created by the contributions of the three basic somesthetic modalities: the mechano-, thermo-, and chemosensations. When injury strikes, all axons and receptors lying in the path of damage or destruction are stimulated by the supramaximal intensity of the injury stimulus to evoke their specific sensa-tion, and contribute to the somesthetic image of pain evoked. The terms used in describing pain, e.g. pricking, stabbing, cramping, throbbing, burn-ing, testify to the participation of all the basic somesthetic modalities in the characterization of pain. The degree of pain which pervades the image, how-ever, depends upon central factors of facilitation and inhibition; the sub-ject's personality, experiences, and memory; and his circumstances, attitude, composure of anxiety, etc., at the time of injury. Peripheral factors may also play a part in influencing pain (5, 9, 68, 96, 107).

Doubt regarding specificity of central "pain" pathways.—Recurrences of pain, after it has been abolished for various periods of time by surgical in-terruption of the ascending pain tracts in the spinal cord and brainstem, or by electrolytic lesions of the postulated pathways in the thalamus, have thrown considerable doubt on the existence of specific pathways for pain (83, 106), leading some clinicians to deny that there are "pure pain endings, pain fibers, or even pain neurons, in the mammalian nervous system. Yet most of us were taught to think of pain as a modality similar to vision, hearing, and especially touch." This expression of dissent against a basic

physiological mechanism for pain is refuted by the manner in which bradykinin evokes pain and aspirin blocks the bradykinin-evoked pain in animals
and man (30, 41, 74). It does point, however, to our lack of information
concerning central compensation of function, formation of new connections
by sprouting, etc., following injury or disease of the pain system.

The Nature of the "Pain" Receptor

The question of specificity at peripheral somesthetic receptors.—The finding that corneal nerve endings respond to more than one modality of stimulation led Weddell (111–113) to propose the pattern theory of body sensation. Although the sensations of touch and temperature could be detected besides pain, there was no assurance that the sensations were evoked by the
stimulation of a single receptor; or if several receptors were involved, that
they were served by the branches of the same axon. Mountcastle, in discussing this problem in the Ciba Symposium on Touch, Heat and Pain (82), had
this to say:

> The question of whether it is possible for a single afferent fiber to evoke, by
> different patterns of activity, different qualities of sensation is a problem com-
> pletely aside from the peripheral problem. From what I know of the central
> nervous system, I think this is very unlikely to be true. As many of you know,
> ten or twenty years ago there was another great debate on this subject, and Dr.
> Weddell did a great service in making us realize that this needed re-examination,
> and most first-order fibers have now been re-examined and found to be highly
> specific

[46, 54–56, 119]; cf. reports by same authors and others in the five symposia
on pain and skin senses].

Within each of the three main groups of somesthetic receptors there are
differences in specificity, especially among the mechanoreceptors, some of
which are distinguishable by morphological as well as physiological differences. The majority of the receptors, however, are not encapsulated or organized, being of the free-branching type. The thermoreceptors and "nocire-
ceptors" (or nociceptors) all appear to consist of free-branching nerve endings, unmyelinated at their terminals or for some distance along their
course.

Specificity in terms of stimulus modality holds for mechanoreceptors and
thermoreceptors, and human experience permits us to add that the sensations evoked by these receptors are stimulus related, i.e. mechanoreceptors
elicit sensations of touch and pressure, and the thermoreceptors, sensations
of cold and warmth. The nociceptors, however, are supposed to be excited
by injury, or any stimulus modality intense enough to constitute a supramaximal stimulus to an axon.

Sherringtonian nociception: terminal pain nerves equated with axons.—
Sherrington (96), who proposed nociception as the adequate stimulus for
pain, recognized the lack of stimulus specificity of the nerve endings for
pain. He noted that:

These pain endings in skin seem almost *equally excited by stimuli of such different modes as mechanical, thermal, chemical and electrical.*

But, these agents have all a *certain character in common,* in that they become adequate as excitants of pain, when *they are of such intensity as to threaten damage to the skin.*

And we may note, that *these excitants are all able to excite nerve when applied to naked nerve directly.*

He goes on to say,

a low threshold was not required because the stimuli were all intense, intensity constituting their harmfulness; but responses to a wide range of stimuli of different kinds were required, because harm might come in various forms. *That responsive range is supplied by naked nerve itself, and would be cramped by the specialization of an end-organ. Hence these nerve endings remained free.*

It is clear that Sherrington would not regard the pain nerve endings as a specialized "receptor", and so long as injury is accepted as the adequate stimulus for evoking pain, his position is logical, provided that the central connections of the pain pathways are specific, permitting the ascending signals to evoke the sensations and psychic manifestations of pain. The bimodal character of pain sensations is well known; the terms used in describing pain, e.g. pricking, stabbing, cramping, throbbing, burning, are readily explained by the simultaneous stimulation of pain nerve endings and adjacent mechanoreceptors or thermoreceptors (or their stem axons) to evoke a bimodal or multimodal pain response. Nevertheless, three types of receptors have been described as specific receptors for pain.

Evidence for specific "pain" receptors.—(*a*) *Thermosensitive nociceptor:* This receptor evokes pain when exposed to temperatures of 45° C or higher (43). It has been confirmed (19) that 45° heat applied to the skin of the rat's tail, or to the dog's visceral peritoneum [with thermode (30)], elicits responses usually associated with pain, but sufficient tissue damage had occurred to reduce or prevent responses to subsequent stimulation. The response may also be evoked by the application of the same heat stimulus to the axon.

(*b*) *Mechanosensitive nociceptor:* A "noxious deformation" skin receptor, which is believed to evoke pain, constitutes 20 to 25 per cent of the cutaneous receptors in the primate and cat respectively, and is supplied by fine myelinated afferent fibers conducting at 5–28 m/sec (in the primate) and 6–37 m/sec (in the cat). The adequate stimulus is noxious deformation of the skin, e.g. by a needle puncture caused by a 30 g weight, or by forcible pinching with a serrated tissue forceps (18, 85).

Perl (85) noted that damaging heat was without effect and never initiated more than one or two discharges (from the mechanosensitive nociceptor). Moreover, neither noxious concentrations of H_2SO_4 (1 N) applied to the surface, nor solutions (1 g/100 ml) of bradykinin injected into the skin at a mechanically sensitive spot elicited responses. The inability of the chemical agents to evoke a response, however, may well be due to failure to reach the nerve endings within the cutaneous epithelium. Perl's response was obtained by recording the action potentials from single fibers in a cutaneous nerve with microelectrodes. He admits that "unequivocal evidence for nociceptive afferent fibers in animals does not establish their causal relation to pain in man", but draws attention to Bishop's work (23, 45, 53) in humans, showing close correlation between activity in the small myelinated fibers to cutaneous stimulation and the first report of pain in conscious man.

Both of these examples fit Sherrington's stimuli "of such intensity as to threaten damage", and damage does occur. In both cases, the pain response may possibly be mediated by chemosensitive pain receptors (described below) with the addition of mechanical (prick or pinch) or thermal (burning) sensations elicited by the stimulation of the mechanosensitive and thermosensitive "nociceptors" respectively, or their stem axons.

(c) *Chemosensitive receptors (or chemoceptors) for pain:* The chemoceptors for pain are not classified as nociceptors because the chemical stimulus is not intense and evokes pain without causing injury. Experimental evidence that the intra-arterial injection of chemical agents such as hypertonic salts, acid (pH < 5.3) and alkaline (pH >9.2) solutions, specific cations (K+ >Na+), and organic anions (citrate>lactate) will evoke all the manifestations of pain in animals was furnished by R. M. Moore, R. E. Moore, and Singleton (cf. 81). The results could be produced repeatedly and did not involve nociception.

The pain response was similar to that obtained by Woodworth & Sherrington (117) by mechanical or electrical stimulation of nociceptive afferents in cutaneous, muscular, and visceral (splanchnic) nerves in the decerebrate cat. The response mimicked the behavioral effects of pain so closely, in spite of the lack of cortex and subcortex to mediate sensory perception, that Woodworth & Sherrington labeled them "pseudaffective" and used them to trace the pathways concerned in the production of pain. The intra-arterial injection of hypertonic solutions in man was already known to induce pain (70, 98). That close intra-arterial injections of such agents will cause centrifugal discharges in the sensory nerves of the area (16, 17) established the possibility of chemical stimulation of some cutaneous receptors by this mode of application and, thus, their chemosensitivity: when axons are stimulated, e.g. by KCl, discharges occur both centripetally and centrifugally to the locus of injection (29).

Using a vaccine-type pressure gun for intradermal injection of acid solutions in man, Lindahl (75) showed that pain is felt when the pH falls to 6.2 and is maximal at pH 3.2. Since the method is painless and permits instant application of known H ion concentration to the layer of skin desired, it is possible to estimate the H ion concentration which elicits pain. Potassium, which is released from tissue by injury, ischemia, etc., has long been known as a pain-producing agent (12). Benjamin (6, 7) has suggested that the release of intracellular K ions may be the actual physiological stimulus for pain and has shown that the application of K ions to the human skin by iontophoresis induces pain (8). According to Lindahl (75), potassium caused slight pain at 31.8 mM, and moderate pain at 98.8 mM, and was much less effective than acid solutions.

THE VARIETY OF CHEMICAL AGENTS THAT INDUCE PAIN

Keele and his group (3, 4) later demonstrated that some amines (acetylcholine, 5-hydroxytryptamine, and histamine); plasma activated by glass, serum, various inflammatory exudates; and the peptides angiotensin, substance P, and bradykinin applied to the denuded cantharidin blister base on human skin, all evoke cutaneous pain.

Guzman et al. (41) injected most of these agents intra-arterially into somatic, abdominal, thoracic, and cranial areas in the unanesthetized dog and cat, and elicited behavioral evidence of visceral pain after a latency of 12 to 15 sec. The response was identical with the "pseudaffective" response above mentioned, consisting of repeated vocalization, struggling, and biting behavior, lasting 30 to 45 sec from all sites tested. About 30 per cent of the dogs did not respond to chemical stimulation (usually with bradykinin), apparently because of inhibition, since they responded within minutes after receiving a dose (0.1 to 0.2 mg/kg i.v.) of the narcotic antagonist, nalorphine.

The bradykinin peptides.—The three known mammalian bradykinin peptides all have the same nonapeptide sequence:

Nonapeptide (bradykinin)	Arg-Pro-Pro-Gly-Phe-Ser-Pro-Phe-Arg	(34, 90)
Decapeptide (kallidin)	Lys-Arg-Pro-Pro-Gly-Phe-Ser-Pro-Phe-Arg	(86, 115)
Undecapeptide	Met-Lys-Arg-Pro-Pro-Gly-Phe-Ser-Pro-Phe-Arg	(36, 93)

and are among the most potent of the algesic agents known, being effective in a dose of 2 μg or less when given intra-arterially. The amino acid sequence of bradykinin was first described by Elliot et al. (34, 35), and both the nonapeptide and decapeptide were soon synthesized by Boissonnas et al. (11). The undecapeptide, synthesized by Schröder (93), appears to be the weakest of the peptides, which suggests that algesic activity depends upon the nonapeptide.

The peptides are formed by the action of specific kininogenases, liberated from tissue or leucocytes, on substrates in the α-2-globulin fraction of plasma, and are readily destroyed by kininases present in plasma, lymph, or circulating cells (33, 118). Besides shaking plasma with glass beads (3, 4), treatment with acids or trypsin (90) will produce some or all of the bradykinin peptides. Kininase activity depends upon carboxypeptidases in plasma or other peptidases in organs such as the pancreas or kidney (37). In addition to causing pain, the bradykinin peptides cause vasodilatation, increased capillary permeability, and edema—all the signs of inflammation (34). Bradykinin does not induce pain when injected intravenously, intramuscularly, or subcutaneously, because it is inactivated by kininase before it can reach the "pain" receptors. [In spite of the activity of kininase in plasma, sufficient quantities of all three bradykinin peptides are liberated in normal humans to allow the following quantities to appear in the urine: bradykinin 36 μg/liter, kallidin 7 μg/liter, met-lys-bradykinin 13 μg/liter (80).] The effectiveness of intra-arterial injections of bradykinin indicates that the "pain" receptors are situated close enough to the capillary area to permit bradykinin to reach the receptors before being eliminated by kininase. This relationship suggests that the paravascular sensory nerves which accompany blood vessels throughout the body to end in unmyelinated free-branching terminals in connective tissue spaces close to the capillaries and venules (73, 79, 114) are probably the chemoceptors for pain.

Introduction of bradykinin into the gastric or intestinal lumen of the dog does not cause pain, which indicates that it does not penetrate the mucosal epithelial barrier. On the other hand, application of bradykinin (4 μg) to either the visceral or parietal peritoneum in dog and man induces in 12–15 sec pain that lasts 30–40 sec (30, 74).

Appropriate dorsal root ganglionectomy resulted in the degeneration of the paravascular nerves and the failure of bradykinin to evoke pain when injected intra-arterially in the deafferented area, while sympathectomy had no effect on the pain response to bradykinin, or on the paravascular nerves, but was followed by degeneration of the perivascular vasomotor nerves (41, 73).

Ischemic sensitization of chemoceptors for pain.—Searching for an explanation for muscle cramp in man, Lewis et al. (62, 63) rediscovered the observation of MacWilliam & Webster (110) that making an arm ischemic by cutting off the blood supply with a blood pressure cuff did not in itself cause pain until the subject exercised the ischemic muscles. After a brief period of exercise, pain caused by each contraction became increasingly unbearable, compelling the subject to desist. The pain continued, but was relieved soon after the circulation was restored. It is apparent that ischemia, resulting in the development of local hypoxia and acidosis, sensitized the chemoceptors for pain in the muscle so that they now responded to mechanical stimulation exerted by the contracting muscles.

Bessou & Laporte (10), using Douglas & Ritchie's (32) antidromic collision technique, appeared to confirm Lewis et al. (63) when they showed that the unmyelinated afferent (pain ?) fibers of the cat's gastrocnemius-soleus muscle were activated when the muscle was made to contract for one minute under conditions of ischemia. Paintal (84) and Iggo (54, 55), however, recording from isolated small nerve fibers from muscle, failed to evoke any response while stretching or tetanizing the muscle during ischemia, although they obtained a response to pressure, and to intramuscular injection of hypertonic salt solution. Paintal suggested that "pressure pain" receptors (cf. Perl's "noxious deformation" nociceptor; pp. 272–73) were excited by both mechanical and chemical stimulation, but Iggo pointed out that the hypertonic salt stimulus were unspecific, "since all the other muscle afferent fibers tested were also excited, including muscle-spindle afferent fibers."

Another example of ischemic sensitization has been reported by Sicuteri (97), who found that the pain evoked by the intracarotid injection of brady-kinin in man is greatly increased when the injection is made after the common carotid artery is occluded by finger pressure upstream from the point of injection. Ischemic sensitization of the chemoceptors for pain (and their stem axons) in the spleen of the dog to mechanical (arterial distention with saline); electrical (splenic nerve stimulation near spleen); and chemical (intra-arterial bradykinin, acetylcholine) stimulation has been demonstrated by clamping the splenic artery (see Figure 1 in 66). After a few minutes of ischemia, previously subthreshold stimulation became effective in evoking pain responses.

The ischemic muscle-pain receptors of Lewis, which are also sensitive to squeezing of the muscle and to hypertonic salt, appear identical with the bradykinin-sensitive chemoceptors because the same pain responses are elicited by the intra-arterial injection of 0.5 M KCl, acetylcholine, and bradykinin into the vasoisolated gastrocnemius-soleus of the dog (41). Squeezing of the isolated muscle sometimes caused a pain response, but the lack of correlation between muscle contraction and the pain response indicated that the algesic agents do not evoke pain by stimulating the proprioceptors (73).

The adequate stimulus for pain.—From the variety of chemical agents (cations, some amines, and peptides) which can excite the "pain" receptor, it is unlikely that binding at receptor sites depends primarily upon specific chemical configuration. The nonspecific character of the chemoceptor and the nature of the algesic agents suggest that excitation may depend upon electrophilic attraction, with the assumption that the receptor sites are anionic or electron rich, and that algesic agents, or some part of their molecule, are cationic or electron deficient. Electrophilic attraction thus provides the *raison d'être* of the "pain" receptors, if it enables the chemoceptor to signal the increasing concentration of H ions in ischemia, or the accrual of algesic plasma peptides, which herald the onset of inflammation consequent to injury or disease. This concept is patterned after Amoore's (1) hypothesis governing the odor of pungent substances, which is attributed to radicals rendering part of the molecule strongly electrophilic.

STRUCTURAL ASPECTS OF NEURONS

Electronmicroscopic description of free-branching nerve endings.—Electronmicroscopic studies of unmyelinated peripheral nerve fibers by Gasser (39) showed them to consist of a number of axons enveloped in a train of contiguous satellite or Schwann cells. According to Robertson (89), unmyelinated axons change position within the Schwann cell, often following "a helical course in grooves in the surface of the Schwann cell." Using electron- and light microscopy, Weddell (112) has given further details: "When traced distally many of the nonmyelinated nerves (in the human forearm) gradually approached the surface of the Schwann cell cytoplasm ... We have tentatively assumed that they are readily available for stimulation." The reviewer (64) commented that the basis of this assumption was the apparent lack of a Schwann cell membrane (mesaxon) between the axonal membrane and the extracellular space when the axon comes to the surface, thus permitting chemical agents ready access to the axon. According to Cauna (21), this view is incorrect as a "basement membrane" always separates the end organ from the surrounding intercellular matrix. Even when the nerve fiber penetrates the epithelial layers of the skin, the epithelial basement membrane provides a complete covering for the axon in the same manner as the Schwann cell. The fiber grows as far as the cornified layer, where it appears to undergo fragmentation and regeneration. Terminal unmyelinated fibers may contain mitochondria (20) and possibly some dendrites are rich in microtubules (92).

The membrane of the Schwann cell.—The anionic receptor sites in pain terminals may be assumed to be located on the basement of plasma membrane which surrounds each Schwann cell and its contained axons. It is unclear what becomes of the axonal membrane, whether it is integrated with that of the Schwann cell or retains some part of its identity; the description here deals with both as a single membrane. The membrane is of high electrical resistance and capacitance and, in the electronmicroscope, appears as two electron-dense lines after $KMnO_4$ fixation, each 20 Å, separating a clear space of 35 Å. It is postulated to consist of a lipid bilayer apposed to form a continuous, nonpolar hydrocarbon phase sandwiched between monolayers of protein. The lipid bilayers comprise 40 to 50 per cent, and the outer protein layers 50 to 60 per cent of the mass of the membrane (26, 61, 88).

(*a*) *Outer coat:* There is usually a space of 150–200 Å between neurons, or neurons and glia, suggesting that there is an outer coat (sometimes seen as a fuzz in electronmicroscopic material) about 75 Å thick and of low electron density, which projects into the intercellular space from the dense lines of the plasma membrane. In addition to electronmicroscopy, it has been necessary to apply electrophoretic analysis and chromatography in combination with the action of specific enzymes, first to the erythrocyte, later to tissue cells to throw new light on the molecular structure of this membrane (24, 25, 59). Such methods have shown that the outer coat includes no collagen, chondroitin, or mucopolysaccharides usually found in the coats of other tissue cells, but contains glycolipids and glycoproteins (61).

(*b*) *Glycolipids:* Among the glycolipids are cerebrosides, which possess two long hydrocarbon chains and polar heads containing monosaccharides or oligosaccharides with no electrical charges and which are probably not concerned in the composition of anionic receptor sites.

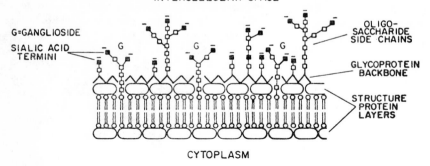

FIG. 1. A model of the plasma membrane and cell coat. From Lehninger (61).

According to Lehninger (61),

of far greater interest are the gangliosides, which are characteristic of neurons and are not found in glia [28, 77, 100] although they constitute <5 per cent of the neuronal lipids. The gangliosides, like other lipids, have two hydrocarbon tails and long branched polar head groups composed of oligosaccharides containing one or more residues of sialic acid, a generic term referring to N-acetyl or N-glycocol derivatives of the nine-carbon sugar derivative, neuraminic acid, which is negatively charged at pH 7.9. There are several classes of gangliosides containing one, two, three or more sialic acid residues. Mono-sialogangliosides predominate along the axon, whereas polysialogangliosides are more profuse at nerve endings [101]. . . . Gangliosides bind univalent cations such as Na⁺ and K⁺, divalent cations such as Ca⁺⁺, polycations such as protamine very strongly, presumably at the negatively charged carboxyl groups of the sialic acid residues.

(c) Glycoproteins:

The glycoproteins of cell coats share an important common denominator with the gangliosides; they also contain sialic acid residues. One class of glycoproteins contains 40 to 50 per cent carbohydrate, in the form of a small number of long branched oligosaccharide side chains containing sialic acid termini; these side chains are linked covalently to the amide group asparagine residues in the peptide chain backbone. The other type of glycoprotein contains a much larger number of short disaccharide side chains covalently linked to the hydroxyl groups of serine, threonine, and possibly hydroxylysine residues. Most of the side chains contain a terminal residue of sialic acid. Cell surfaces possess a net negative charge which in a number of cases has been shown to be contributed largely by sialic acid residues [cf. 108].

Figure 1 shows a hypothetical model of the cell coat and plasma membrane. It suggests that the negatively charged heads of the gangliosides may extend well outside the cell coat and into the intercellular space, like antennae. Their sialic acid groups are thus exposed to extracellular Na⁺ and Ca⁺⁺ ions. Changes in concentrations of these ions in the neighborhood of these antennae could cause conformational changes which might be transmitted mechanically to the hydrocarbon bi-layer and induce local changes in its packing arrangement. It is suggested that the glycoproteins are superimposed on the monolayer structure of protein [61].

The above model, in which sialic acid residues play an important role in binding Ca^{++} at rest and exchanging Ca^{++} for K^+ on electrical stimulation, is designed to explain excitation and conductions in axons. The exchange of di-valent and univalent cations at specific anionic sites is postulated to induce a conformational change resulting in increased membrane conductance and permitting Na^+ to diffuse in and K^+ to diffuse out in accord with Tasaki's hypothesis (102, 109). With the passing of the action potential, the mem-brane-bound K^+ is replaced by Ca^{++}, so that the membrane is restored to its original resting state (61).

A different distribution of sialic acid residues [e.g. polysialogangliosides (101)] at afferent nerve endings may provide the possibility of anionic sites which are excited by cations, some amines, and bradykinin peptides in the chemoceptors for pain. The concept of conformational changes resulting in rearrangement of the molecular state of the nerve membrane largely removes the distinction between the excitable properties of the receptor as an end organ and those of its axon in unmyelinated nerve fibers mediating pain.

ANALGESICS AND THEIR SITES OF ACTION

Analgesics were believed to relieve pain by blocking the pathways con-cerned in the central nervous system. Of the two types, narcotic and non-narcotic analgesics, the latter are considerably less potent and require about three times longer to develop analgesia against bradykinin-evoked pain (42). Furthermore, the nonnarcotic analgesics fail to block cutaneous pain evoked by nociceptive mechanical, electrical, and thermal stimulation in ro-dents (see 69, Table 1) but do so after inflammatory sensitization (87). The chemosensitive nature of the pain receptor suggests that besides attracting and binding algesic agents, it may attract their antagonists. For these rea-sons, it has been suspected that the nonnarcotic and the narcotic analgesics may act at different sites in the nervous system. Pain-producing intra-arte-rial injections of bradykinin have been used in three methods to determine whether analgesics act centrally or peripherally (70).

Blocking of splenic-splanchnic potentials evoked by bradykinin.—Brady-kinin was injected into the splenic artery of cats or dogs whose spinal cords had been transected at C-1. Action potentials were recorded in the splenic or splanchnic nerves after a latency of less than 5 sec, and continued for 20–30 sec. In naturally respiring postchloralose dogs, with neuraxis and splanchnic nerves intact, vocalization and struggling occurred in 12 to 15 sec, after in-tra-arterial injection of bradykinin while autonomic responses began earlier. Conduction velocity measurements of splanchnic potentials evoked electrically and by bradykinin indicated that group III and IV fibers were activated. Paccinian corpuscles did not respond to bradykinin.

Sodium acetylsalicylate given intravenously to cats and dogs in doses of 50–100 mg/kg blocked the bradykinin-evoked activity in the splanchnic nerve for 60–90 min. When morphine sulfate (1 mg/kg) was given intravenously following recovery from the aspirin block, there was no further interference of splanchnic activity. Aspirin, a nonnarcotic analgesic, blocks the generation of splenic potentials while morphine, a narcotic analgesic, does not do so. When aspirin was applied to 10–20 mm of desheathed splanchnic nerve in concentrations up to 10 mg/ml for 5 min (the usual duration of an intra-arterial injection of drugs into the spleen), no blockage occurred, while application of procaine solution to the nerve invariably blocked conduction in 1–2 min. On the other hand, analgesia occurred when the plasma total salicylate level reached 0.15 mg/ml after administration of aspirin into an intestinal fistula. Evidently aspirin acts on the nerve terminals (receptors) but not on the stem axons. The difference, however, may be due to the presence of more nerve sheaths surrounding the latter, hindering access of chemical agents to the receptor sites. In the epithelial layers of the skin, aspirin also fails to block the terminal receptors for pain (58, 65); in this case, the epithelial cells provide a closely fitting basement membrane for the free-branching "pain" fibers (21) which would seem to be less accessible to chemical agents from the subepithelial capillary supply areas.

Cross-perfused spleen experiments in dogs.—Cross-perfusion of the vasoisolated but innervated spleen of a recipient dog R by a donor dog D has shown that pain evoked in dog R (by bradykinin injections into the splenic artery of dog R) is blocked when any of the nonnarcotic antipyretic analgesics (aspirin, sodium salicylate, acetaminophen or APAP, aminopyrine, phenylbutazone) is injected intravenously into dog D. There is no block when the same nonnarcotic analgesics are injected intravenously into the circulation of dog R, where they would have access to dog R's brain and central nervous system. The opposite is true with the narcotic analgesics (morphine, meperidine, levorphan, ethoheptazine, d-propoxyphene) and the nonnarcotic antiappetite analgesics [amphetamine, 1-phenyl-4(2-oxocyclohexylmethyl) piperazine]; these block bradykinin-evoked pain only when given to dog R intravenously, i.e. centrally (70).

Deffenu, Pegrassi & Lumachi (27) applied our method (42, 70) of intra-arterial injection of bradykinin in dogs to the right carotid artery in rats weighing 280–320 g as a means for assessing analgesics. Bradykinin in doses of 0.125–0.500 μg per rat evoked dextrorotation of the head, flexion of the right forelimb, and occasionally vocalization.

The peripheral blocking of the receptors for pain by sodium salicylate has been confirmed by Hashimoto et al. (44) and Hirata et al. (49) in dogs with cross-perfused vasoisolated legs and nerves intact. RPP 201 (azaazepinophenothiazin) injected intra-arterially via the femoral circumflex was

TABLE I

CLASSIFICATION OF ANALGESICS ACCORDING TO POSTULATED MODE OF ACTION

	Median analgesic dose in dogs (mg/kg)		
	i.v.	SPA	BCA
Peripheral block of impulse generation at chemoceptors mediating pain:			
Aspirin (acetylsalicylic acid)	50	3.8	N.A.
Na-salicylate	195	17.8	N.A.
Acetaminophen (APAP)	1 08	14.7	N.A.
Aminopyrine	56	4.6	N.A.
Phenylbutazone	32	10.0	N.A.
Central block of synaptic transmissions (excitatory pathway):			
Morphine sulfate	1.	N.A.	0.56
Levorphan tartrate	0.65	N.A.	0.15
Ethoheptazine citrate	24.	11.0	N.A.
d-Propoxyphene hydrochloride	4.6	1.0	N.A.
Central block of synaptic transmission:			
Pentazocine	2.15	N.A.	0.68
Nalorphine hydrochloride (inhibitory pathway?)*	N.A.	N.A.	N.A.
Central inhibition:			
MA-1050 or 1-phenyl-4-(2-oxocylohexylmethyl) piperazine HCl	4.6	N.A.	1.47
dl-Amphetamine sulfate	0.068	N.A.	0.026

i.v., Intravenous; SPA, splenic artery injection; BCA, brachiocephalic artery injection; N.A., no analgesia at several multiples of the corresponding SPA (peripheral analgesic) or BCA (central analgesic) dose; *, applicable to narcotic antagonists such as nalorphine ?.

used to induce pain in pentobarbitalized and conscious animals. The authors reported that bradykinin caused tachyphylaxis while RPP 201 did not. Wiegerhausen & Reincke (116) repeated the pain-producing experiments in the cat's vasoisolated but innervated hindleg with bradykinin and kallidin but made no observations with analgesics.

Central and peripheral cannula experiments in dogs.—When aspirin is given directly into the spleen intra-arterially, through the same plastic tube as is used to inject bradykinin, less than 10 per cent of the intravenous dose of aspirin (3.8 mg/kg instead of 50 mg/kg) is sufficient to block the pain response to bradykinin (Table I), whereas eight times this dose (30 mg/kg) injected into the brain (central nervous system) via the brachiocephalic artery fails to block. Similar, but not so marked, differences are found with other nonnarcotic antipyretic analgesics. Less of the narcotic analgesics, of the narcotic antagonist pentazocine, and of the nonnarcotic antiappetite analgesics is required to block pain when given into the brain via the brachiocephalic artery than is needed when injected into the spleen via the splenic artery or intravenously, which indicates that they act centrally (Table I). Note that nalorphine is an analgesic in man (57, 60) but not in the dog, whereas pentazocine exhibits analgesic action in both man (2) and dog (70, 71).

(a) *Peritoneal (visceral and parietal) pain receptors:* Another example of the peripheral blocking action of aspirin is given by the analgesia produced when sodium aspirin is applied to the peritoneal surface through the same tube used for injecting bradykinin. The amount of aspirin required to cause a block equivalent in duration to that produced by an intravenous dose is only 10 to 20 per cent of the i.v. ED_{50} in both man and dog (30, 74).

(b) *Dentinal pain receptors:* Still another example of peripheral blockade by aspirin is given by Scott's (94, 95) demonstration that the local application of unhydrolyzed aspirin to the pain receptors lying in the cat's dentinal tubules prevented the generation of impulses to heat stimulation. On washing out, the response recovered in about 15 min.

Site of action of nonnarcotic analgesics.—Since the nonnarcotic analgesics are essentially acids, it is unlikely that they act at the same receptor sites on the "pain" receptor as bradykinin or other algesic agents which behave like cations. A cationic binding site may be involved, associated with an enzyme concerned in nerve function such as ATPase or one of the thiamine kinases. For more than a decade, Brody's (15) demonstration that both aspirin and sodium salicylate uncouple oxidative phosphorylation has been accepted (99). This has recently been denied by Thompkins & Lee (104), who found that the uncoupling activity of aspirin is due solely to the salicylic acid hydrolyzed during the experiment. Thompkins & Lee (103) also reported that the partition coefficients of salicylic acid were invariably higher than that of aspirin, which indicates that the latter is neither more soluble in lipid solvents nor more rapidly absorbed than the former; in fact, salicylates are absorbed more rapidly from the gastrointestinal tract than aspirin (51, 52). These findings, which require confirmation, suggest that, besides neural mitochondrial enzymes such as ATPase, other enzyme systems (e.g. thiamine kinase) in the nerve fiber may be the site of salicylate activity.

The presence of microtubules in dendrites and the fact that the afferent axon is a teledendron suggest that they may serve to transport a transmitter from the receptor the length of the neuron; there is, however, no evidence of a sensory cell capable of discharging a transmitter in the pain system or indeed of any need for such a mechanism. The long latency of the behavioral response to bradykinin (12 to 15 sec) suggests that bradykinin excites the liberation of a mediator of the pain receptor from some other cellular site. This explanation, however, does not tally with the discharge of action potentials in the splenic nerve within 5 sec of chemical stimulation (intra-arterial injection), and the appearance of autonomic responses within 5–10 sec. These various latencies are clearly occupied by processes occurring in the central nervous system.

LATENCY OF THE CHEMOCEPTORS (FOR ACHE AND PAIN) AND ASSOCIATED RESPONSES

By grouping the latencies and coordinating the associated responses, it is possible to correlate histological, physiological, pharmacological, and clinical findings as follows:

<5 sec latency: flexion reflexes and skeletal-cutaneous pain involving collaterals from ventrobasal to intralaminar pain neurones.

5–10 sec latency: autonomic reactions and visceral pain associated with intralaminar system.

12–15 sec latency: behavioral responses and central or psychic pain involving pathways anterior to the intralaminar.

With progressive transections of the cord and brainstem of rats, stronger electrical stimulation of the skin was required to evoke vocalization which ceased with the end of stimulation, until the plane of section passed the midbrain. Thereafter, still stronger stimulation was needed to evoke vocalization, which tended to "afterdischarge", continuing after stimulation had stopped (19). When the plane of section passed the midthalamus, the response became weakened or ceased, indicating that the afterdischarge invokes anterior thalamic and other centrencephalic neurons in the pain system. Later observers, using unrestrained rats (22, 47, 48, 50), extended the connections to the limbic system and the amygdala.

CENTRAL PAIN PATHWAY EXCITED BY BRADYKININ INJECTED INTRA-ARTERIALLY

Electrical activity of the cat's cortex and brainstem was explored, during and after either electrical stimulation of the skin or chemical stimulation by intra-arterial injection of bradykinin into one of the limb arteries (72). The greatest increase in unit discharges was encountered in the medial part of the thalamus; bradykinin also evoked activity from the candate nucleus to the mesencephalic and medullary reticular formation, but not in the cortex.

These results confirm the findings of previous workers [see Domino's excellent review (31)] on experimental (electrically evoked) pain regarding the intralaminar and posterior group systems in mediating pain. They show that chemical stimulation evokes activity in the same pathways. Ervin & Mark's (38) comprehensive review of the results of stereotaxic lesions in the relief of clinical (pathological) pain emphasizes the need to destroy the medial intralaminar group system bilaterally for the relief of pain, the role of the anterior thalamus in central or psychic pain, and the relative absence of effect on pain when lesions are placed in the sensory nuclei (ventrobasal complex). The Japanese surgeons Miyazaki (cited in 38) and Urabe et al. (105) have also added much support to the role of the parafasciculus centrum medianum nuclei in the mediation of pain.

Morphine blocks bradykinin-evoked central responses, while aspirin exaggerates the bradykinin-evoked impulses so that they may be very much greater than before, possibly by release from inhibitory control. Aspirin also inhibits the electrically evoked pain impulse although it does not block the bradykinin-evoked impulse. Morphine does not block the electrically evoked impulse, which suggests that the latter simulates primarily a mechanically evoked (or somatotopic) effect (72).

LITERATURE CITED

1. Amoore, J. E. The stereochemical theory of olfaction. *Proc. Sci. Sect. Toilet Goods Assoc., Suppl. 37*, 1–23 (1962)
2. Archer, S., Albertson, N. F., Harris, L. S., Pierson, A. K., Bird, J. G., Keats, A. S., Telford, J., Papadopoulos, C. N. Narcotic antagonists as analgesics. *Science,* **137,** 541–43 (1962)
3. Armstrong, D., Dry, R. M. L., Keele, C. A., Markham, J. W. Observations on chemical excitants of cutaneous pain in man. *J. Physiol. (London),* **120,** 326–51 (1953)
4. Armstrong, D., Jepson, J. B., Keele, C. A., Stewart, J. W. Pain producing substance in human inflammatory exudates and plasma. *J. Physiol. (London),* **135,** 350–70 (1957)
5. Beecher, H. K. *Measurement of Subjective Responses: Qualitative Effect of Drugs* (Oxford, New York, 494 pp., 1959)
6. Benjamin, F. B. Release of intracellular potassium as the physiological stimulus for pain. *J. Appl. Physiol.,* **14,** 643–46 (1959)
7. Benjamin, F. B. Release of intracellular potassium as a factor in pain production. In *The Skin Senses,* 466–79 (Kenshalo, D. R., Ed., Thomas, Springfield, Ill., 1968)
8. Benjamin, F. B., Helvey, W. M. Iontophoresis of potassium for experimental determination of pain endurance in man. *Proc. Soc. Exptl. Biol. Med.,* **113,** 566–68 (1963)
9. Beritoff, J. S. The spinal coordination of movements to the psychoneural integration of behavior. *Ann. Rev. Physiol.,* **28,** 1–16 (1966)
10. Bessou, P., Laporte, Y. Activation des fibres afférentes amyéliniques d'origine musculaire. *Compt. Rend. Soc. Biol.,* **152,** 1587–90 (1957)
11. Boissonnas, R. A., Guttmann, S., Jaquenoud, P. A. Synthèse de la L-arginyl-L-prolyl-L-prolyl-glycyl-L-phénylalanyl-L-séryl-L-phénylalanyl-L-arginine. Distinction entre cet octapeptide et la bradykinine. *Helv. Chim. Acta,* **43,** 1481–87 (1960)
12. Bommer, S. Neutralsalzreaktionen auf der Haut. *Klin. Wochschr., 3,* 1758–60 (1924)
13. Bowsher, D. Termination of the central pain pathway in man: The conscious appreciation of pain. *Brain, 80,* 606–22 (1957)
14. Bowsher, D., Albe-Fessard, D. Patterns of somato-sensory organization within the central nervous system. In *Assessment of Pain in Man and Animals* (UFAW Symp. 1961), 107 (Keele, C. A., Smith, R., Eds., Livingstone, Edinburgh, 1962)
15. Brody, T. M. Action of sodium salicylate and related compounds on tissue metabolism *in vitro. J. Pharmacol. Exptl. Therap.,* **117,** 39–51 (1956)
16. Brown, G. L., Gray, J. A. B. Some effects of nicotine-like substances and their relation to sensory nerve endings. *J. Physiol. (London),* **107,** 306–17 (1948)
17. Brown, G. L., MacIntosh, F. C. Discharges in nerve fibres produced by potassium ions. *J. Physiol. (London), 96,* 10P (1939)
18. Burgess, T. R., Perl, E. R. Myelinated afferent fibres responding specifically to noxious stimulation of the skin. *J. Physiol. (London),* **190,** 541–62 (1967)
19. Carroll, M. N., Lim, R. K. S. Observation of the neuropharmacol-

ogy of morphine and morphine-like analgesia. *Arch. Intern. Pharmacodyn.*, **125**, 383–403 (1960)

20. Cauna, N. Fine structure of the receptor organs and its probable functional significance. *Ciba Found. Symp. Touch, Heat and Pain,* 1965, 117–36 (De Reuck, A. V. S., Knight, J., Eds., Little, Brown, Boston, 1966)

21. Cauna, N. Light and electron-microscopical structure of sensory end-organs in human skin. In *The Skin Senses*, 15–37 (See Ref. 7)

22. Charpentier, J. Sur une nouvelle méthode psychophysiologique de mesure quantitative des réactions douloureuses chez le rat. *Compt. Rend. Soc. Biol.,* **155**, 727–31 (1961)

23. Collins, W. R., Jr., Nulsen, F. E., Randt, C. T. Relation of peripheral nerve fiber size and sensation in man. *Arch. Neurol. Psychiat. (Chicago),* **3**, 381–85 (1960)

24. Cook, G. M. W. Chemistry of membranes. *Biol. Med. Bull.,* **24**, 118–23 (1968)

25. Cook, G. M. W., Heard, D. H., Seaman, G. V. F. Sialic acids and the electrokinetic charge of the human erythrocyte. *Nature,* **188**, 1011–12 (1960)

26. Dannielli, J. F., Davson, H. The permeability of thin films. *J. Cellular Comp. Physiol.,* **5**, 495–508 (1935)

27. Deffenu, G., Pegrassi, L., Lumachi, B. The use of bradykinin-induced effects in rats as an assay for analgesic drugs. *J. Pharm. Pharmacol.,* **18**, 135 (1966)

28. Derry, D. M., Wolfe, L. S. Gangliosides in isolated neurons and glial cells. *Science,* **158**, 1450–52 (1967)

29. Diamond, J. The effects of injecting acetylcholine into normal and regenerating nerves. *J. Physiol. (London),* **145**, 611–29 (1959)

30. Dickerson, G. D., Engle, R. J., Guzman, F., Rodgers, D. W., Lim, R. K. S. The intraperitoneal bradykinin-evoked pain test for analgesia. *Life Sci.,* **4**, 2063–69 (1965)

31. Domino, E. F. Effects of narcotic analgesics on sensory input, activating system and motor output. In *The Addictive States, Res. Publ. Assoc. Res. Nervous Mental Disease,* **16**, 117–49 (1968)

32. Douglas, W. W., Ritchie, J. M. Non-medullated fibers in the saphenous nerve which signal touch. *J.*

Physiol. (London), **139**, 385–99 (1957)

33. Edery, H., Lewis, G. P. Inhibitions of plasma kininase activity at slightly acid pH. *Brit. J. Pharmacol.,* **19**, 299–305 (1962)

34. Elliott, D. F., Horton, E. W., Lewis, G. P. Actions of pure bradykinin. *J. Physiol. (London),* **153**, 473–80 (1960)

35. Elliott, D. F., Horton, E. W., Lewis, G. P. The isolation of bradykinin, a plasma kinin from ox blood. *Biochem. J.,* **78**, 60–65 (1961)

36. Elliott, D. F., Lewis, G. P., Smyth, D. G. A new kinin from ox blood. *Biochem. J.,* **87**, 21P (1963)

37. Erdos, E. G. Release and inactivation of kinins. *Gastroenterology,* **51**, 893–98 (1966)

38. Ervin, F., Mark, V. H. Relief of pain by stereotactic surgery. In *Pain and the Neurosurgeon, a Forty Years' Experience* (White, J. C., Sweet, W. H., Eds., in press)

39. Gasser, H. S. Conduction in nerves in relation to fiber types. *Res. Publ. Assoc. Res. Nervous Mental Disease,* **15**, 35–59 (1935)

40. Gasser, H. S. Properties of dorsal root unmedullated fibers on the two sides of the ganglion. *J. Gen. Physiol.,* **38**, 709–28 (1955)

41. Guzman, F., Braun, C., Lim, R. K. S. Visceral pain and the pseudaffective response to intra-arterial injection of bradykinin and other algesic agents. *Arch. Intern. Pharmacodyn.,* **136**, 353–84 (1962)

42. Guzman, F., Braun, C., Lim, R. K. S., Potter, G. D., Rodgers, D. W. Narcotic and non-narcotic analgesics which block visceral pain evoked by the intra-arterial injection of bradykinin and other algesic agents. *Arch. Intern. Pharmacodyn.,* **149**, 571–88 (1964)

43. Hardy, J. D., Stolwijk, J. A. J., Hoffman, D. Pain following step increase in skin temperature. In *The Skin Senses*, 444–57 (See Ref. 7)

44. Hashimoto, K., Kumakura, S., Taira, N. Vascular reflex responses induced by an intra-arterial injection of azaazepinophenothiazine andromedrotoxin, veratridine, bradykinin and kallikrein blocking action of sodium salicylate. *Japan. J. Physiol.,* **14**, 299–308 (1964)

45. Heinbecker, P., Bishop, G. H., O'Leary, J. Pain and touch fibers

in peripheral nerves. *Arch. Neurol. Psychiat.*, **29**, 771–89 (1933)

46. Hensel, H., Boman, K. K. A. Afferent impulses in cutaneous sensory nerves in human subjects. *J. Neurophysiol.*, **23**, 564–78 (1960)

47. Herold, M., Cahn, J. Rôle des médiateurs chimiques de la transmission nerveuse sur les réponses de comportement périphériques et centrales à la douleur. *Agressologie*, **6**, 525–44 (1965)

48. Herold, M., Cahn, J. The possible role of serotonin in affective component of pain behavioural reaction in the rat. In *Pharmacology of Pain* (Proc. 3rd Intern. Pharmacol. Mtg. 1966, Sao Paulo, **9**), 87–99 (Lim, R. K. S., Armstrong, D., Pardo, E. G., Eds., Pergamon, Oxford and New York, 1968)

49. Hirata, M., Tanaka, S., Taira, N., Hashimoto, K. Comparative studies on pseudaffective responses to different algesic substances in conscious dogs. The effect of sodium salicylate. *Arch. Intern. Pharmacodyn.*, **162**, 150–61 (1966)

50. Hoffmeister, F. Discussion working group 3. In *Neuropsychopharmacology*, **4**, 72 (Bente, D., Bradley, P. B., Eds., Elsevier, Amsterdam, 1966)

51. Hogben, C. A. M., Schanker, L. S., Tocco, D. J., Brodie, B. B. Absorption of drugs from the stomach. II. The human. *J. Pharmacol. Exptl. Therap.*, **120**, 540–45 (1957)

52. Hogben, C. A. M., Tocco, D. J., Schanker, L. S., Brodie, B. B. On the mechanism of intestinal absorption of drugs. *J. Pharmacol. Exptl. Therap.*, **125**, 275 (1959)

53. Hugon, M. *Réflexes polysynaptiques cutanéo et commandeo* volontaire (Thèse doctorate d'état et sci. nat. Fac. Sci. Paris, 1967)

54. Iggo, A. A single unit analysis of cutaneous receptors with C afferent fibers. In *Pain and Itch* (Ciba Found. Study Group No. 1), 41–59 (Wolstenholme, G. E. W., O'Connor, M., Eds., Little, Brown, Boston (1960)

55. Iggo, A. Nonmyelinated visceral, muscular and cutaneous afferent fibers and pain. In *Assessment of Pain in Man and Animals* (UFAW Symp. 1961), 74–87 (Keele, C. A., Smith, R., Eds., Livingstone, Edinburgh, 1962)

56. Iriuchijima, J., Zotterman, Y. The specificity of afferent cutaneous C fibers in mammals. *Acta Physiol. Scand.*, **49**, 267–78 (1960)

57. Keats, A. S., Telford, J. Nalorphine, a potent analgesic in man. *J. Pharmacol. Exptl. Therap.*, **117**, 190–96 (1956)

58. Keele, C. A., Armstrong, D. *Substances Producing Pain and Itch* (Williams & Wilkins, Baltimore, 399 pp., 1964)

59. Klenk, E. Discussion. In *Ciba Found. Symp. Chem. Biol. Mucopolysaccharides* (Wolstenholme, G. E. W., O'Connor, M., Eds., Churchill, London, 1958)

60. Lasagna, L., Beecher, H. K. The analgesic effectiveness of nalorphine and nalorphine-morphine combinations in man. *J. Pharmacol. Exptl. Therap.*, **112**, 356–63 (1954)

61. Lehninger, A. L. The neuronal membrane. *Proc. Natl. Acad. Sci. U.S.*, **60**, 1069–80 (1968)

62. Lewis, T. *Pain* (Macmillan, New York, 1942)

63. Lewis, T., Pickering, G. W., Rothschild, O. Observations upon muscular pain in intermittent claudication. *Heart*, **15**, 359–83 (1931); Centripetal paralysis arising out of arrested bloodflow to limb, including notes of form of tingling. *ibid.*, **16**, 1–32 (1931)

64. Lim, R. K. S. A revised concept of the mechanism of analgesia and pain. In *Pain* (Henry Ford Hosp. Intern. Symp., Detroit, 1964), 117–54 (Knighton, R. S., Dumke, P. R., Eds., Little, Brown, Boston, 1966)

65. Lim, R. K. S. Salicylate analgesia. In *The Salicylates*, 155–202 (Smith, M. J. H., Smith, P. K., Eds., Interscience, New York-London-Sydney, 1966)

66. Lim, R. K. S. Sites of action of narcotic and non-narcotic analgesics: mechanism of pain and analgesia. *Headache*, **7**, 103–21 (1967)

67. Lim, R. K. S. Cutaneous and visceral pain and somesthetic chemoreceptors. In *The Skin Senses* (See Ref. 7)

68. Lim, R. K. S. Neuropharmacology of pain and analgesia. In *Pharmacology of Pain*, 169–217 (See Ref. 48)

69. Lim, R. K. S., Guzman, F. Manifestations of pain in analgesic evaluation in animals and man. In *Pain*, 119–52 (Soulairac, A., Chan,

K., Chartentier, J., Eds., Academic London, 1968)

70. Lim, R. K. S., Guzman, F., Rodgers, D. W., Goto, K., Braun, C., Dickerson, G. D., Engle, R. J. Site of action of narcotic and nonnarcotic analgesics determined by blocking bradykinin-evoked visceral pain. *Arch. Intern. Pharmacodyn.,* **152,** 25–58 (1964)

71. Lim, R. K. S., Guzman, F., Rodgers, D. W., Goto, K., Braun, C., Dickerson, G. D., Engle, R. J., Potter, G. D., Guy, J. L., Rogers, R. W. Motion Picture Film: Mechanism of analgesia and pain. *Program 48th Ann. Mtg. Fed. Am. Soc. Exptl. Biol., Chicago, April 14–16, 1964*

72. Lim, R. K. S., Krauthamer, G., Guzman, F., Fulp, R. Central nervous system activity associated with pain evoked by bradykinin and its alteration by morphine and aspirin. *Proc. Natl. Acad. Sci. U.S.* (In press)

73. Lim, R. K. S., Liu, C. N., Guzman, F., Braun, C. Visceral receptors concerned in visceral pain and the pseudaffective response to intra-arterial injection of bradykinin and other algesic agents. *J. Comp. Neurol.,* **118,** 269–94 (1962)

74. Lim, R. K. S., Miller, D. G., Guzman, F., Rodgers, D. W., Rogers, R. W., Wang, S. K., Chao, P. Y., Shih, T. Y. Pain and analgesia evaluated by the intraperitoneal bradykinin-evoked pain method in man. *Clin. Pharmacol. Therap.,* **8,** 521–42 (1967)

75. Lindahl, O. Expermental skin pain induced by injection of water-soluble substances in humans (20 subjects). *Acta Physiol. Scand.,* **51,** *Suppl. 179,* 75–78 (1961)

76. Lloyd, D. P. C. Action of sodium acetylsalicylate upon sweat glands of the cat's food pad. *Proc. Natl. Acad. Sci. U.S.,* **60,** 1319–22 (1968)

77. Lowden, J. A., Wolfe, L. S. Studies on brain gangliosides. IV. The effect of hypercapnia on gangliosides in vivo. *Can. J. Biochem.,* **42,** 1703–10 (1964)

78. Mehler, W. R., Feferman, M. E., Nauta, W. J. H. Ascending axon degeneration following anterolateral cordotomy. An experimental study in the monkey. *Brain,* **83,** 718–50 (1960)

79. Millen, J. W. Observations on the innervation of blood vessels. *J. Anat.,* **82,** 68–80 (1948)

80. Miwa, I., Erdös, E. G., Seki, T. Presence of three peptides in urinary kinin (Substance Z) preparations. *Life Sci.,* **7,** 1339–43 (1968)

81. Moore, R. M. Some experimental observations relating to visceral pain. *Surgery,* **3,** 534–55 (1938)

82. Mountcastle, V. B. General discussion of Section II. *Ciba Found. Symp. Touch, Heat and Pain,* 137–44 (See Ref. 20)

83. Noordenbos, W. *Pain: Problems Pertaining to the Transmission of Nerve Impulses Which Give Rise to Pain* (Elsevier, Amsterdam, 1959)

84. Paintal, A. S. Functional analysis of Group III afferent fibres of mammalian muscles. *J. Physiol. (London),* **152,** 250–70 (1960)

85. Perl, E. R. Relation of cutaneous receptors to pain. *Proc. Intern. Union Physiol. Sci.,* **6,** 235–36 (1968)

86. Pierce, J. V., Webster, M. E. Human plasma kallidins—isolation and chemical studies. *Biochem. Biophys. Res. Commun.,* **5,** 353–57 (1961)

87. Randall, L. O., Selitto, J. J. A method for measurement of analgesic activity in inflamed tissue. *Arch. Intern. Pharmacodyn.,* **111,** 409–19 (1957)

88. Robertson, J. D. The ultrastructure of cell membranes and their derivatives. *Biochem. Soc. Symp. Cambridge, Engl.,* **16,** 3–43 (1959)

89. Robertson, J. D. The unit membrane of cells and mechanisms of myelin formation. *Res. Publ. Assoc. Res. Nervous Mental Disease,* **40,** 94–158 (1962)

90. Rocha e Silva, M., Beraldo, W. T., Rosenfeld, G. Bradykinin, a hypotensive and smooth muscle stimulating factor released from plasma globulin by snake venoms and by trypsin. *Am. J. Physiol.,* **156,** 261–73 (1949)

91. Rodgers, D. W., Engle, R. J. Guzman, F., Lim, R. K. S. (Unpublished observations)

92. Schmitt, F. O. Fibrous proteins—neuronal organelles. *Proc. Natl. Acad. Sci. U.S.,* **60,** 1092–11 (1968)

93. Schröder, E. Über Peptidsynthesen Synthese von methionyl-Lysyl-Bradykinin, einem Kinin aus Rinderblut. *Experientia,* **20,** 39 (1964)

94. Scott, D., Jr. Aspirin: Action on receptor in the tooth. *Science,* **181,** 180–81 (1968)

95. Scott, D., Jr., Stewart, G. Excitation of dentinal receptor of the cat by heat and chemical agents. *Oral Surg., Oral Med., Oral Pathol.,* **20,** 784–94 (1965)

96. Sherrington, C. S. *The Integrative Action of the Central Nervous System* (Constable, London, 1906)

97. Sicuteri, F. Vaso-neuroactive substances in migraine. *Headache,* **6,** 109–26 (1966)

98. Singleton, A. O. Use of intra-arterial injections of sodium iodide in determining condition of circulation in extremities; report of cases. *Arch. Surg.,* **16,** 1232–41 (1928)

99. Smith, G. M., Egbert, L. D., Markowitz, R. A., Mosteller, S., Beecher, H. K. An experimental pain method sensitive to morphine in man; the submaximum effort tourniquet technique. *J. Pharmacol. Exptl. Therap.,* **154,** 324–32 (1966)

100. Spence, M. W., Wolfe, L. S. Gangliosides in developing rat brain isolation and composition of subcellular membranes enriched in gangliosides. *Can. J. Biochem.,* **45,** 671–88 (1967)

101. Svennerholm, L. The gangliosides. *J. Lipid Res.,* **5,** 145–55 (1964)

102. Tasaki, I. *Nerve Excitation: A Macromolecular Approach* (Thomas, Springfield, Ill., 1964)

103. Thompkins, L., Lee, K. H. The mechanism of action of salicylate. 1. Partition coefficients of acetylsalicylic acid and salicylic acid. *Can. J. Pharm. Sci.,* **3,** 10–13 (1968)

104. Thompkins, L., Lee, K. H. Studies on the mechanism of action of salicylates. IV. Effect of salicylates on oxidative phosphorylation. *J. Pharm. Sci.,* **58,** 102–5 (1969)

105. Urabe, M., Tsubokawa, T., Watanabe, Y., Kadoya, S. Alteration of activity of the nucleus centrum medianum in the thalamus following the sensory stimulation. *Japan. J. Physiol.,* **15,** 28–41 (1965)

106. Wall, P. D., Melzack, R. A duplex theory of the mechanism of cutaneous sensation with special reference to pain. *Proc. 23rd Intern. Congr. Physiol. Sci., Tokyo,* 234–41 (1965)

107. Wall, P. D., Sweet, W. H. Temporary abolition of pain in man. *Science,* **155,** 108–9 (1967)

108. Wallach, D. F. H., Kamat, V. B. The contribution of sialic acid to the surface change of fragments of plasma membrane and endoplasmic reticulum. *J. Cell Biol.,* **30,** 660–63 (1966)

109. Watanabe, A., Tasaki, I., Lerman, L. Bi-conic action potentials in squid giant axons internally perfused with sodium salts. *Proc. Natl. Acad. Sci. U.S.,* **58,** 2246–52 (1967)

110. MacWilliam, J. A., Webster, W. J. Some applications of physiology to medicine; sensory phenomena associated with defective blood supply to working muscle. *Brit. Med. J.,* **1,** 51–53 (1923)

111. Weddell, G. Studies related to mechanism of common sensibility. *Advan. Biol. Skin,* **1,** 112–59 (1960)

112. Weddell, G. Observations on the anatomy of pain sensibility. In *The Assessment of Pain in Man and Animals.* 47 (See Ref. 14)

113. Weddell, G., Miller, S. Cutaneous sensibility. *Ann. Rev. Physiol.,* **24,** 199–222 (1962)

114. Weddel, G., Pallie, W., Palmer, E. The morphology of peripheral nerve terminations in the skin. *Quart. J. Microscop. Sci.,* **95,** 483–501 (1954)

115. Werle, E., Götze, W., Keppler, K. Über die Wirkung des Kallikreins auf den isolierten Darm und über eine neue darmkontrahierende Substanz. *Biochem. Z.,* **289,** 217–33 (1937)

116. Wiegerhausen, B., Reincke, A. Einfluss von synthetischen Bradykinin und Kallidin auf die Chemoreceptoren der Gefässe. *Experientia,* **22,** 90–91 (1966)

117. Woodworth, R. S., Sherrington, C. S. A pseudaffective reflex and its spinal path. *J. Physiol. (London),* **31,** 234–43 (1904)

118. Zachariae, H., Malmquist, J., Oates, J. A. Kininase in human polymorphonuclear leucocytes. *Life Sci.,* **5,** 2347–55 (1966)

119. Zotterman, Y. Nerve fibres mediating pain: a brief review with a discussion of the specificity of cutaneous afferent nerve fibres, 60–73 (See Ref. 14)

OVERALL REGULATION OF THE CIRCULATION   1046

J. ALAN HERD

Department of Physiology, Harvard Medical School, Boston, Massachusetts

INTRODUCTION

Blood circulates at a rate proportional to tissue metabolic requirements at a constant arterial pressure. Although this statement is an oversimplification, it is difficult to make one more elaborate that is more accurate. To be more precise, we must identify what is regulated and determine how specifically it is regulated. Complexity arises because there are many interacting control systems and many cardiovascular variables held within narrow ranges.

There is a vast amount of literature pertinent to cardiovascular regulation. Traditionally, various mechanisms which affect the circulation have been studied under separate subjects, such as (a) cardiac performance, (b) local regulation of blood flow, (c) regulation of blood volume, (d) renal function, (e) fluid and electrolyte balance, and (f) regulation of body temperature. Another subject, rapidly growing, is systems analysis, the creation of quantitative expressions for interactions between various components of the circulation.

The term "regulation" implies variables held within narrow ranges. We are interested not only in what is regulated, and how it is regulated, but also in the consequences of its regulation. For example, blood normally contains approximately 40 per cent erythrocytes. What are the consequences of higher and lower hematocrits? The red cell content of blood affects its viscosity, as well as its oxygen-carrying capacity. The greater the concentration of red cells, the greater is the work required to circulate the blood. However, the lower the concentration of red cells, the more blood must be circulated. In some way, the hematocrit is regulated so that the work of pumping blood and its oxygen-carrying capacity are optimally balanced (1). Another example is the regulation of blood pH and the partial pressures of gases in arterial blood. Because of the physicochemical properties of hemoglobin, optimal exchange of O_2 and CO_2 in lungs and tissue occurs at pH 7.4 with a P_{CO_2} of 40 mm Hg. Renal and respiratory control mechanisms regulate arterial blood gases and pH close to these optimal values (2).

For optimal cardiac performance, myocardial blood flow should keep pace with myocardial oxygen consumption. Since myocardial oxygen con-

289

sumption depends on both heart rate and heart size as well as intraventricular pressure, there is some optimal relation between stroke volume and heart rate. Since most of the coronary blood flows during diastole, the rate of coronary blood flow depends in part on arterial blood pressure during diastole which, in turn, depends on total peripheral vascular resistance, arterial capacitance, and stroke volume. Although the interactions of variables are complex, there is some optimal relation between heart rate, cardiac output, and peripheral vascular resistance for cardiac function under particular circumstances. These relations differ from animal to animal. For example, small animals tend to have high heart rates, probably because they have small arterial capacitance.

In the normal heart, right atrial pressure is close to atmospheric values, and peripheral venous pressure is always slightly higher. Since venous pressure and resistance affect capillary hydrostatic pressure, there are interactions between interstitial fluid volume, total blood volume, and venous capacitance. Because arterial pressure and arteriolar resistance affect fluid filtration, there are interactions between interstitial fluid volume, blood volume, and regional blood flow (3, 4). Although blood volume, right atrial pressure, and cardiac output are well-regulated variables, we are still unable to construct a quantitative description of the relations between them.

Ideal conditions for tissue metabolic activity include regional blood flows sufficient to meet metabolic requirements. In addition, the smaller the interstitial fluid volume the better the diffusion of gases, substrates, and metabolic products. In some organs, such as skin and kidney, blood circulates far in excess of metabolic requirements, with a small arteriovenous oxygen difference. The myocardium is at the other extreme. Coronary blood circulates at a rate closer to myocardial metabolic requirements with a large arteriovenous oxygen difference. Blood circulates through skeletal muscles in proportion to metabolic requirements but with small arteriovenous oxygen gradients at rest. Although much is known about local regulation of blood flow, we still do not know why blood flow through resting skeletal muscle is so high in proportion to its metabolic requirements or why blood flow through the myocardium is so low in proportion to myocardial requirements.

Other control systems are equally complex. In some way, extracellular fluid volume and composition affect fluid and electrolyte balance which, in turn, affects blood volume. The variables regulated are known but mechanisms for their regulation are poorly understood. Finally, the regulation of body temperature affects overall regulation of the circulation. In many ways, this system seems the one most specifically regulated; central hypothalamic and peripheral cutaneous temperatures both have strong influences on skin blood flow, sweating, and shivering. Any changes in heat production or heat loss have predictable effects on cardiovascular function.

Although many control systems affect cardiovascular function, and all could be discussed here, the review of literature for this chapter has been restricted to (*a*) effector mechanisms, both neurogenic and humoral, (*b*) sensory mechanisms, and (c) cardiovascular responses of intact subjects under various conditions. The majority of recent studies in circulatory physiology elaborate upon afferent pathways or efferent mechanisms. But after the current literature has been carefully studied, it is still not clear which variables are regulated by what mechanisms in intact, unanesthetized individuals under normal conditions.

The measurement of blood flow, blood pressure, and tissue metabolic requirements in unanesthetized subjects presents great challenges to our ingenuity. No one would deny the difficulties but the effort to overcome them is worth making. Anesthesia seriously affects many physiological processes, especially those involving the nervous system. For this reason modern respiratory physiologists have almost completely abandoned the use of anesthesia in the study of respiratory control mechanisms. Undoubtedly, cardiovascular control mechanisms are as seriously affected. Fortunately, many of the difficulties have been overcome. Barger (5), Gregg (6), and Rushmer (7) have pioneered the study of unanesthetized animals. Franklin, Van Citters, and co-workers (8) have shown many times that miniature strain-gauge pressure transducers and ultrasonic flowmeters can be permanently implanted in the circulation of animal subjects. Korner and co-workers (9) have shown versatility and ingenuity in studying the cardiovascular system of unanesthetized rabbits. Techniques used so successfully by these investigators permit reliable studies of unanesthetized subjects.

Although experiments in unanesthetized subjects require reliable equipment, they also demand good control of behavior. Any investigator who has studied unanesthetized subjects knows how readily they are disturbed. A poorly controlled environment may be as disruptive as anesthesia. As much attention should be paid to behavioral control as to any other part of the experiment. Some species and some individual subjects can be persuaded to rest quietly but many cannot. One of the reasons that unanesthetized human subjects have been studied so successfully is that they usually cooperate. Instead of selecting only those species or individuals that will rest quietly it is possible to train subjects by some simple procedure that has consistent effects on behavior (10). Also, a subject's learning and familiarization with experimental conditions may be as important in determining his cardiovascular response as acclimation to physical or chemical stress. Finally, behavioral techniques can induce persistent changes in cardiovascular function (10, 11). By careful attention to environmental events and behavioral procedures, it should be possible to make repeated measurements in unanesthetized subjects with consistent results.

EFFECTOR MECHANISMS
Autonomic Nervous System

Heart.—Electrical stimulation of sympathetic nerves to the heart caused increased heart rate and force of contraction and increased coronary blood flow (12, 13). Stimulation of vagal nerves to the heart caused decreased heart rate (14) and force of contraction (15). Beta-adrenergic blocking agents, such as propranolol, suppressed the effects of sympathetic stimulation on the heart (12, 13) and atropine blocked the effects of vagal stimulation. Interpretation of results can be difficult because of intermingling of adrenergic and cholinergic fibers. Also heart rate, end diastolic intraventricular pressure, arterial blood pressure (16), and coronary blood flow (17) affect cardiac contractility. The effects of sympathetic nerve stimulation are best seen if heart rate and arterial pressure are kept constant. Stimulation of individual cardiac nerves had localized effects on cardiac contractility (18). The effects of vagal nerve stimulation are seen less readily. The rate at which intraventricular pressure rises before and during vagal stimulation or infusion of acetylcholine must be related to changes in intraventricular end diastolic pressure. This is only possible if heart rate is kept constant. When the necessary precautions were taken, several studies showed decreased contractility of ventricles (15, 19–23) as well as atria (15, 24) during cholinergic stimulation. However, the effect of parasympathetic stimulation on ventricular contractility is much less dramatic than that of sympathetic stimulation.

Arterioles.—Direct electrical stimulation of peripheral sympathetic nerves usually increases arteriolar resistance. In a perfused limb, the increase was greater in skin than in skeletal muscles (25). Prior administration of alpha-adrenergic blocking agents reversed the effects of subsequent sympathetic stimulation, which then caused transient (26) and sometimes persistent vasodilatation (27). Reflex stimulation by carotid artery occlusion caused a rise in total peripheral vascular resistance (28) and a redistribution of cardiac output (29). Electrical stimulation in some sites of the hypothalamus (30–32), the mesencephalon (30), or the medulla (31) caused arteriolar vasodilatation and in others vasoconstriction. Although vasoconstrictor and vasodilator neurogenic influences have antagonistic effects on the total rate of blood flow through skeletal muscle, it is still not known whether adrenergic and cholinergic fibers innervate the same or different blood vessels. The results of most experiments suggest two sets of sympathetic fibers to blood vessels of skeletal muscles: one, adrenergic vasoconstrictor; the other, cholinergic vasodilator. It is possible that vasoconstrictor and vasodilator effects are elicited by efferent impulses occurring at different frequencies (33).

Veins.—Direct electrical stimulation of peripheral sympathetic nerves constricts intestinal veins (34) and superficial veins of the limb (35, 36) but not deep muscle veins or veins of the thigh (37). Both systemic and local peripheral heating also constricted the lateral saphenous veins (38). Prior administration of alpha-adrenergic blocking agents reduced the effects of subsequent direct electrical stimulation and the reflex venoconstriction caused by systemic or peripheral heating (39). Carotid occlusion (34) or reductions in systemic arterial blood pressure (40) caused only small changes in venous capacitance compared to changes in peripheral vascular resistance. However, venous tone did increase during vasovagal syncope (41, 42) at a time when heart rate and total peripheral vascular resistance were reduced. In intact anesthetized dogs, rapid expansion of blood volume caused an immediate increase in mean circulatory pressure (which is right atrial pressure 4 sec after onset of ventricular fibrillation) that gradually returned to normal even though blood volume was still elevated (43). This probably occurred because of a gradual decrease in venous capacitance mediated by neurogenic or humoral mechanisms. It seems likely there may be dissociation between the control of capacitance and resistance components of the circulation and dissociation between the reactions of veins in different regions. Surprisingly little is known about changes in venous tone elicited locally and directly in veins by changes in intraluminal pressure. A local mechanism of this sort could counteract the effects of gravity on venous pooling.

HUMORAL SUBSTANCES

Angiotensin.—Several reviews have recently summarized the effects of renin and angiotensin on the cardiovascular system (44–47). Renin released from the kidney in response to low blood volume, low serum Na concentrations, or a diet low in Na, initiates the conversion of an α-2-globulin to angiotensin I which is converted enzymatically to angiotensin II. Thus blood levels of angiotensin rise during hemorrhagic hypotension (48). Angiotensin constricts small vessels directly and also potentiates the effect of catecholamines. For example, infusions of phenylephrine facilitated the pressor effect of angiotensin and this facilitation was blocked by administration of dibenzyline (49). Angiotensin injected intravenously caused redistribution of cardiac output and increased total peripheral vascular resistance (50) that was overcome partially by exercise (51). Angiotensin also had an effect on the central nervous system, elevating systemic arterial blood pressure when injected into the lateral ventricles or into a vertebral artery (52). It had no effect on cardiac contractility if atrial and arterial pressures were kept constant (53). Its metabolic effects apparently were mediated by release of adrenal medullary catecholamines (54).

Prostaglandins.—Three reviews of the physiology and biochemistry of prostaglandins have appeared recently (55–57). When large amounts of prostaglandins were infused intra-arterially, some of these substances caused arteriolar dilatation, some arteriolar constriction, and some venous constriction (58). Those substances which decreased peripheral vascular resistance and increased limb volume were effective even after administration of alpha- or beta-adrenergic blocking agents (59) and they had no effect on the vascular actions of catecholamines. Prostaglandins had no direct effect on cardiac contractility. Any changes that occurred were a reflex response to peripheral vasodilatation and hypotension (60). Also, they have no apparent effect on capillary permeability. Although prostaglandins have been found in nearly all organs, it is uncertain whether these substances have a physiological role in normal cardiovascular function.

Plasma kinins.—Two reviews (45, 61) and the proceedings of a symposium (62) on vasoactive peptides have been published recently. The results of experiments published several years ago suggested that plasma kinins were important mediators of functional vasodilatation in exocrine glands (63) but the importance of that mechanism has been questioned recently (64). Bradykinin and related substances have definite vasodilator properties but their role in local control of blood flow is uncertain. These substances infused directly into the arterial circulation of an organ caused peripheral vasodilatation that was unaffected by prior administration of atropine or alpha- and beta-adrenergic blocking agents (65). Perhaps more important than their effect on vascular tone is the increase they cause in capillary permeability as part of the inflammatory response to injury (66).

SENSORY MECHANISMS
ARTERIAL BARORECEPTORS

Electrical stimulation of carotid sinus (67) and aortic depressor nerves (68) caused bradycardia and hypotension although the responses varied with the frequency and intensity of electrical stimulation. These variations in response suggest that large and small fibers do not have the same central connections. Chemoreceptor fibers also may be stimulated. High-intensity, low-frequency stimulation of aortic depressor nerves actually increased heart rate and blood pressure, possibly because afferent fibers from chemoreceptors were more effectively stimulated than those from baroreceptors (68). Perfusions of the carotid sinus and the aortic arch at increasing pressures produced the same changes in heart rate, which suggests that each set of baroreceptors had equal importance in the control of cardiac function (69). In studies on unanesthetized dogs (70), pressure in the carotid sinus fell when the animal's head was raised. Within a few seconds aortic pressure rose, bringing carotid sinus pressure halfway back to its original level. These results also suggested that baroreceptors in the aortic arch and carotid sinus had equal effects in the control of cardiovascular function. Techniques for quantifying impulse traffic in intact baroreceptor nerves (71–73) demonstrated that mechanical stimulation of aortic and carotid sinus baroreceptors produced comparable changes in impulse traffic (71). Both sets of baroreceptors responded more to pulsatile than to nonpulsatile pressures (72, 74, 75) especially at low levels; at high levels, there was less difference (75).

Bursts of sympathetic nerve impulse traffic during pulsatile perfusion of the carotid sinus occurred synchronously, but between bursts of impulse traffic in carotid sinus nerves (76). In turn, interactions between sympathetic nerve activity and carotid sinus sensitivity to pressure have also been described (77). Sympathetic nerve activity increased impulse traffic in carotid sinus nerves, effectively increasing the sensitivity of the carotid sinus to changes in arterial pressure. Histologic studies of systemic arteries demonstrated great numbers of adrenergic nerve fibers in the walls of carotid arteries but only a few fibers anywhere in the carotid sinus (78, 79). Although contraction of vascular smooth muscle in response to sympathetic stimulation might decrease the distensibility of the carotid sinus, the result would be a decrease in sensitivity of the carotid sinus to pressure. It is also possible that neurogenic connections exist between sympathetic efferent and carotid sinus afferent nerves. Single electrical pulses to cervical sympathetic nerves evoked action potentials in carotid sinus nerves (77).

Surprisingly few attempts have been made to apply neurophysiological techniques routinely used in the study of somatic mechanoreceptors to the study of arterial baroreceptors. For example, little is known about the rates at which baroreceptors adapt after a sudden change in pressure under various circumstances. Perhaps baroreceptors adapt more slowly in the presence of sympathetic stimulation of the carotid sinus and aortic arch.

ATRIAL RECEPTORS

Changes in atrial pressure affect sympathetic nervous system activity, secretion of antidiuretic hormone, and renal function. When left atrial pressure was increased by expansion of blood volume, vagal afferent activity increased and cardiac sympathetic nerve activity decreased (80). Distention of the left atrium caused by obstruction of the mitral valve caused diuresis that could be blocked by vagotomy (81). Vagotomy also prevented the secretion of antidiuretic hormone during hemorrhage in dogs with carotid sinus denervation (82). It has been suggested that changes in left atrial pressure during mild hemorrhage elicit reflex changes in autonomic nervous system activity that prevent any fall in systemic arterial blood pressure. After 10 per cent of the total blood volume had been rapidly removed from anesthetized dogs, arterial blood pressure initially remained constant and fell only after the vagus nerves had been sectioned (82). Apparently atrial receptors may be as important as arterial baroreceptors in the control of cardiovascular function during normal events.

CHEMORECEPTORS

Afferent impulses arise from carotid and aortic bodies in response to hypoxia and hypercapnia, travel to carotid sinus and aortic depressor nerves, and elicit increased heart rate and blood pressure. Perfusion of the carotid and aortic bodies with hypoxic, hypercapnic blood increased total peripheral vascular resistance (83). Here, again, interactions between sympathetic activity and receptor response were found. Electrical stimulation of the stellate ganglion caused increased chemoreceptor impulse traffic in the aortic nerves (84). Interactions with pulmonary stretch receptors also could be demonstrated. Increased systemic vascular resistance, produced by apnea, hypoxia, and hypercapnia, was reduced by reestablishing lung movements in the absence of any change in the composition of arterial blood (83).

PULMONARY STRETCH RECEPTORS

Inflation of the lungs causes a reduction in heart rate and blood pressure mediated by afferent impulses arising in the lungs and traveling in the vagus nerves. Passive inflation of the lungs in anesthetized dogs decreased heart rate and force of contraction (85) and decreased total peripheral vascular resistance (86). These reflex responses were abolished by cutting the cervical vagosympathetic trunk (85). Breath-holding in man caused bradycardia (87–89), perhaps associated with increased intrathoracic pressure. Deep inspiration caused increased venous tone (40, 42). In anesthetized dogs, the reflex effects of stimulating pulmonary stretch receptors overcame those elicited by stimulation of arterial chemoreceptors (83). Multiple interactions between baroreceptors, chemoreceptors, pulmonary stretch receptors, and sympathetic nervous system activity demonstrate the complexity of afferent mechanisms in overall regulation of the circulation.

SOMATIC MECHANORECEPTORS

Stimulation of somatic afferent nerve fibers increases heart rate and blood pressure and apparently influences the cardiovascular response to exercise. Electrical stimulation of afferent nerves increased heart rate and blood pressure (90). Intense electrical stimulation of the central end of the cut sciatic nerve caused not only increased heart rate and blood pressure but also increased cardiac output and redistribution of blood flow (91). Various types of exercise, involving different skeletal muscles but the same total oxygen consumption, had effects on heart rate and blood pressure that varied quantitatively (92–95), possibly because different somatic mechanoreceptors were stimulated.

CENTRAL INTEGRATIVE MECHANISMS

Connections of the autonomic nervous system exist throughout the brain. Central connections of the carotid sinus and aortic nerves have been located by antidromic stimulation (96) and evoked potential techniques (97) in the nucleus tractus solitarius and medial reticular formation. Central connections of vagal fibers have been found throughout the diencephalon as well as the medulla (98). These afferent nerves carry impulses from arterial baroreceptors and chemoreceptors while the vagus nerves also carry impulses from atrial baroreceptors and pulmonary stretch receptors. Interpretation of experimental results is often complicated by inadvertent activation of one afferent system while stimulating another. It is further complicated by cerebral ischemia, hypoxia, or hypercapnia when carotid or vertebral arterial blood supply is altered. Here, again, surprisingly few attempts have been made to apply neurophysiological techniques, such as the recording of extracellular action potentials at various levels of the sensory projection systems, to the study of baroreceptor and chemoreceptor mechanisms. Electrical stimulation of the motor cortex (99), hypothalamus (30–32), mesencephalon (30), or medulla (31, 100) induced various changes in cardiovascular function. Hypothalamic stimulation exerted its cardiovascular effects even after ablation of pressor regions in the medulla (32). Various psychic stimuli caused changes in heart rate and blood pressure (101–103), renal blood flow (103), and venous capacitance (40).

CARDIOVASCULAR RESPONSES

EXERCISE

Many control systems affect cardiovascular function during exercise: local regulation of blood flow, intrinsic regulation of cardiac function, regulation of blood volume, and regulation of body temperature. In addition, exercise has a unique effect on peripheral venous blood volume. External compression of veins by rhythmically contracting skeletal muscles in the presence of intact venous valves actively promotes the return of venous blood to the heart. During exercise, increased metabolic requirements markedly increase cardiac output. In well-trained athletes, oxygen consumption increased to an average of 5570 ml per min and cardiac output increased to 36 liters per min (104). In unanesthetized dogs (8), exercise elevated heart rates above 250 beats per min but affected systemic mean arterial blood pressure only slightly. Blood flow through the renal and mesenteric arteries remained unchanged even during severe exhaustive exercise, which suggests that little, if any, reflex arteriolar vasoconstriction occurred. Perhaps the stimulation of somatic afferent nerves elicits marked sympathetic stimulation of the heart but little arteriolar constriction. Perhaps increased venous return itself stimulates increased heart rate through some direct effect on the heart or through some indirect mechanism, such as the Bainbridge reflex.

Human subjects (105) exercising on a bicycle had not only increased heart rate and blood pressure but also increased venous tone in the forearm. At the same time, forearm arteriolar resistance decreased. Apparently changes in vascular tone of resistance and capacitance elements of the human forearm may be dissociated during exercise. Increased skin blood flow during exercise apparently occurred in response to increased body temperature (106). Changes in blood volume during exercise depend on renal function and intake of food and water as well as changes in capillary fluid filtration and reabsorption. Hikers with free access to food and water had increased plasma volumes of 7.3 per cent during an 8 to 10 hr period of exercise (107).

Some of the most intriguing effects of exercise on cardiovascular function are the bradycardia and increased stroke volume that develop after prolonged periods of physical training (108–111). Increased blood volume also occurred during physical training (112). Exercise and physical training produce many direct and reflex changes in cardiovascular function, so many that it is difficult to describe all the regulatory processes in quantitative terms. In qualitative terms, circulatory responses to exercise demonstrate the potential for dissociation between mechanisms controlling cardiac function, arteriolar resistance, and venous capacitance.

TEMPERATURE REGULATION

Changes in body temperature may directly affect local regulation of blood flow, intrinsic cardiac function, and venous capacitance but their chief effects apparently are mediated by the autonomic nervous system. Altered hypothalamic or cutaneous temperatures have reflex effects on heart rate, cardiac output, total peripheral vascular resistance, skin blood flow, and capacitance of superficial veins. The first effect of a hot, dry environment on the cardiovascular system of human subjects at rest was to increase heart rate (113). As environmental temperatures were increased, cardiac output increased and total arteriovenous oxygen difference decreased, both at rest and during exercise. Decreased extraction of oxygen from mixed venous blood probably occurred because of increased skin blood flow which occurs in a hot environment or during exercise (106). Localized heating of the anterior hypothalamus increased heart rate, cardiac output, and pulmonary arterial pressure and decreased total peripheral vascular resistance (114).

Both central and peripheral sensory mechanisms apparently elicit reflex changes in venous capacitance. In anesthetized dogs, cooling of systemic arterial blood, with reduction in esophageal temperature, constricted the superficial calf veins (38). Cooling of the blood perfusing the peripheral veins also caused venoconstriction except after administration of alpha-adrenergic blocking agents (39). Central and peripheral mechanisms had synergistic effects (38), and local cooling potentiated the constrictor effect of norepinephrine infused into the lateral saphenous vein (35). Deep muscle and thigh veins did not constrict in response to peripheral cooling and the venous capacitance of the spleen did not change (115). In intact subjects, changes in body temperture elicit direct and reflex changes in vascular tone of superficial arterioles and veins, which occur independently of changes in other resistance and capacitance vessels. It also is possible that reflex changes in heart rate occur in response to stimulation of peripheral temperature receptors.

POSTURE

Quiet standing, tilting, and the application of negative pressure around the legs and lower abdomen have been used to reduce the effective circulating blood volume and venous return. These procedures also decrease right atrial pressure which, in turn, directly affects cardiac function and reflexly elicits changes in activity of the autonomic nervous system. Unanesthetized human subjects exposed to lower body negative pressure developed tachycardia, decreased cardiac output, increased total peripheral vascular resistance, and decreased forearm blood flow, when right atrial pressure was reduced slightly (41). Human subjects, standing quietly, showed reduced active and reactive hyperemia (116). Prolonged tilting or application of negative pressure around the legs and lower abdomen eventually caused syncope (41, 42). Heart rate, cardiac output, blood pressure, and forearm vascular resistance fell abruptly, venous tone of the forearm increased, and right atrial pressure rose slightly. Decreased venous capacitance did not occur in the absence of syncope even when tachycardia and peripheral arteriolar vasoconstriction were evident (40). Decreased venous capacitance of the forearm apparently occurred only when systemic arterial blood pressure had fallen to levels low enough to cause vasovagal syncope. Perhaps capacitance of other venous beds decreased earlier.

HEMORRHAGE

Reductions in total blood volume by hemorrhage also have direct effects on cardiac function and reflex effects on the entire cardiovascular system. Some of the reflex changes tend to restore blood volume to normal and some cause redistribution of cardiac output. Decreased atrial pressure in anesthetized dogs reduced ventricular end diastolic volume and cardiac contractility and decreased cardiac output, in spite of increased sympathetic nervous system activity (117). Mild hemorrhage, insufficient to cause any reduction in cardiac output, increased heart rate and force of contraction, impeding the systolic phase of coronary blood flow (118). These reflex effects on cardiac function were abolished after administration of pronethalol. Severe hemorrhage in unanesthetized rabbits reduced cardiac output markedly but reduced systemic arterial blood pressure only slightly (119). Vascular resistance increased in skin, kidney, spleen, and lungs, and decreased in the cerebral, coronary, and hepatic circulations.

Replenishment of blood volume following hemorrhage is accomplished by mobilization of extravascular fluid and protein, and reduction in renal excretion of salt and water. Removal of blood from unanesthetized human subjects was followed by gradual decrease in venous hematocrit attributable to increased capillary reabsorption of interstitial fluid (120). Fractional reductions in total plasma protein concentration were much smaller than the reductions in hematocrit, which indicates that protein as well as water was restored to the blood. Most of this protein was mobilized from extravascular sources (121), although stimulation of plasma protein synthesis and depression of breakdown also contributed to the restoration of total plasma protein content (120). Reduction in renal excretion of water also tends to restore blood volume to normal. Decreased stimulation of atrial and arterial baroreceptors during hemorrhage induced secretion of antidiuretic hormone (82), and stimulation of renal sympathetic nerves caused redistribution of renal blood flow (122). Direct and reflex mechanisms, controlling cardiac function, blood volume, and regional blood flow, restore blood volume at the expense of interstitial fluid volume and maintain arterial blood pressure at the expense of blood flow through nonvital organs.

CAROTID OCCLUSION

Occlusion of the carotid arteries has often been used to study the influence of carotid sinus baroreceptors on cardiovascular function. Heart rate, blood pressure, and total peripheral vascular resistance invariably increase. However, carotid occlusion in the intact subject activates several mechanisms of circulatory regulation. As an immediate direct result of occluding both carotid arteries in anesthetized dogs, carotid sinus pressure fell to about 50 mm Hg and then gradually rose to almost normal values (103). In unanesthetized dogs, the immediate reflex effects were tachycardia, hypertension (123), and an increase in renal vascular resistance (103). In anesthetized dogs, arterial blood pressure and heart rate rose, while cardiac output remained unchanged (29). Skeletal muscle blood flow, renal blood flow, and mesenteric blood flow all decreased. Myocardial blood flow increased and coronary vascular resistance decreased (12). Prior administration of an alpha-adrenergic blocking agent decreased the pressor response by partially abolishing the change in peripheral vascular resistance (29). Prior administration of a beta-adrenergic blocking agent resulted in a fall in cardiac output and an increase in coronary vascular resistance during carotid occlusion (12).

Some of the cardiac responses to carotid occlusion apparently result from cerebral ischemia, and some apparently result from changes in left atrial and systemic arterial pressures. In anesthetized cats, pressure reduction in the entire brachiocephalic circulation increased ventricular contractility, whereas reduction in carotid sinus pressure alone produced tachycardia without any change in ventricular contractility (124). Left atrial and aortic pressures in anesthetized dogs both rise during carotid occlusion (28). Enhancement by vagotomy of the pressor response to carotid occlusion (29) can be attributed to interruption of atrial, aortic, and pulmonary sensory fibers, and of cardiac inhibitory fibers. Occlusion of the carotid arteries activates a whole chain of events that demonstrate multiple interactions between mechanisms controlling cardiovascular function. Apparently, the most prominent effects of decreased arterial baroreceptor stimulation are increased heart rate and increased peripheral vascular resistance, although changes in total venous capacitance probably occur as well.

HYPOXIA AND HYPERCAPNIA

Alterations in the partial pressures of gases in arterial blood have both direct effects on the heart and blood vessels and reflex effects through several sensory and effector mechanisms. In addition, the compensatory responses to the primary disturbance frequently elicit further adjustments in cardiovascular function. For example, hypoxia frequently elicits hyperventilation and hypocapnia. Stimulation of pulmonary stretch receptors during hyperventilation acts to decrease heart rate and force of contraction and to decrease peripheral vascular resistance.

In anesthetized rabbits (125), hypoxia with ventilation held at control values was accompanied by bradycardia, a rise in arterial pressure, and a fall in cardiac output. Hyperventilation during hypoxia caused heart rate and cardiac output to return to control values and allowed a peripheral vasodilatation that depressed arterial blood pressure. Hypocapnia itself had little effect on cardiovascular function. Various reflex effects of hypoxia were abolished in several ways. Hypoxia after administration of alpha-adrenergic blocking agents resulted in peripheral vasodilatation, with or without hyperventilation. After section of carotid and aortic nerves, hypoxia caused marked reductions in arterial pressure with little change in heart rate or cardiac output. After administration of propranolol and atropine, hypoxia caused little or no change in heart rate or cardiac output. In unanesthetized rabbits (9), a marked rise in right atrial pressure that occurred during severe hypoxia probably was caused by reflex reduction in systemic venous capacitance.

Although severe hypoxia in anesthetized and unanesthetized rabbits was associated with bradycardia, in anesthetized dogs it was associated with tachycardia (126). Hypercapnia with reflex hyperventilation in unanesthetized dogs initially was associated with increased right and left atrial pressures, increased pulmonary arterial pressure, decreased cardiac output, and decreased heart rate (127). Systemic mean arterial pressure was unchanged. All values except heart rate returned to normal levels within a 30 min period. Direct actions of hypoxia and hypercapnia on heart and blood vessels, stimulation of chemoreceptors, changes in cerebral interstitial fluid Po_2, Pco_2, and pH, and stimulation of pulmonary stretch receptors, all interact. However, ingenuity in the use of surgical, pharmacological, and physiological techniques for experiments in unanesthetized animals has separated many of the direct and reflex effects of hypoxia on overall regulation of the circulation.

ANESTHESIA

General surgical anesthetics have direct effects on the heart and blood vessels, and modify the reflex responses to physiological stimuli. In rabbits (128), general anesthesia, maintained by either sodium pentobarbital or chloralose and urethane, increased heart rate and decreased systemic arterial blood pressure but had little effect on cardiac output. Bilateral adrenalectomy, prolonged administration of guanethidine, and atropinization abolished the change in heart rate during anesthesia but potentiated the fall in peripheral vascular resistance. Since right atrial pressure was unaffected by general anesthesia, venous capacitance probably remained constant. Since cardiac output also remained unchanged, it is apparent that reflex adrenergic stimulation of the heart failed to overcome direct cardiac depressant actions of the anesthetic agents.

In human subjects, halothane-maintained anesthesia decreased right atrial and systemic arterial blood pressures and increased heart rate (129). Sodium pentobarbital-maintained anesthesia in dogs (130) increased heart rate without affecting cardiac output during spontaneous respiration. Positive-pressure ventilation caused a decrease in cardiac output. In rabbits (9), the respiratory and cardiovascular responses to severe hypoxia were attenuated during general anesthesia. In particular, right atrial pressure in unanesthetized rabbits rose markedly during hypoxia but rose very little during anesthesia. General anesthetic agents cause peripheral arteriolar dilatation and decreased cardiac contractility that are only partially overcome by neurogenically mediated adrenergic stimulation. Halothane apparently also has a venodilating effect. In addition, the cardiovascular responses to physiological stimuli are altered dramatically by general anesthesia.

SLEEP

The natural occurrence of sleep and wakefulness is an opportunity to study cardiovascular control mechanisms repeatedly during different states of central nervous system activity. In human subjects (131) and normal cats (132–134), sleep was associated with decreased heart rate and arterial blood pressure. Heart rate and blood pressure fell lower still when the cats entered the stage of sleep associated with desynchronization of the electroencephalogram, disappearance of muscle tone, and bursts of rapid eye movements. This fall was associated with decreased cardiac output, decreased peripheral vascular resistance, vasodilatation in the mesenteric vascular bed, and vasoconstriction in skeletal muscles supplied by the external iliac artery (134). Baroreceptor and chemoreceptor reflexes were still active during sleep. Human subjects had normal or augmented reflex bradycardia in response to small increases in blood pressure provoked by intravenous infusions of angiotensin (131). Cats with denervated carotid bodies and sectioned aortic nerves had profound depressions of arterial blood pressure (133) and cerebral ischemia (135), during desynchronized, rapid-eye-movement sleep. Less profound depressions of blood pressure occurred in cats with baroreceptor denervation. The results of these experiments suggest that the central nervous system continuously exerts an effect on the cardiovascular system independently of baroreceptor and chemoreceptor reflex activity. They also suggest that sensory impulses from tonically active skeletal muscles have reflex effects on heart rate, blood pressure, and peripheral vascular resistance. Perhaps stimulation of sensory receptors in muscles, tendons, and joints elicits reflex vasodilatation in skeletal muscles, and loss of skeletal muscle tone results in vasoconstriction.

BEHAVIORAL EVENTS

Of the many naturally occurring behavioral states, sleep is the one most readily defined and controlled. The behavior of subjects who are awake varies considerably and their patterns of cardiovascular activity change frequently. Perhaps the best index of the resting state is heart rate. Normal unanesthetized dogs had heart rates of 40 to 60 beats per min while sleeping, with increases to 80 to 100 beats per min when ambulatory, and further increases to 100 to 150 beats per min when the dogs were excited before a race (8). Unanesthetized dogs, startled by a loud noise, had an increase in heart rate from 60 to 160 beats per min, an increase in systemic arterial blood pressure from 95 to 110 mm Hg, and a 32 per cent reduction in renal blood flow (103). Unanesthetized dogs on a tilt table (136) had tachycardia even in a horizontal position, and tilting the animals caused no further change in heart rate or cardiac output. In contrast, when the dogs were anesthetized, tilting caused marked changes in heart rate and cardiac output.

Mental activity in human subjects was associated with increased heart rate, increased blood pressure, and increased urinary excretion of catecholamines (101, 102). Forearm venous capacitance was a sensitive indicator of change in a human subject's response to his environment (40, 42). Some subjects exposed to lower-body negative pressure had marked changes in venous tone, which occurred even before negative pressure was applied. Fighting behavior in unanesthetized cats (137, 138) was associated with increased heart rate and increased cardiac output. Mean arterial blood pressure remained unchanged and skeletal muscle blood flow increased only during actual muscle activity. Direct electrical stimulation of the hypothalamic defense region caused hypertension and increased skeletal muscle blood flow (139). These changes did not occur during natural fighting behavior.

Other experiments suggest that cardiovascular responses can be changed by repeated exposure of a subject to an experimental procedure. Repeated trials in which a human subject's face was immersed in water, initially caused bradycardia but after repeated immersions the heart rate no longer responded (140). Repeated trials in which curarized rats were reinforced according to a rise or fall in heart rate caused persistent tachycardia or bradycardia (141, 142). Similar experiments in which rate of urine formation was measured and small changes reinforced caused significant changes in renal blood flow (143). Animals trained to press a lever in the presence of a light, frequently associated with noxious stimuli, had marked elevations in systemic mean arterial blood pressure (10, 11). Some experimental procedures, such as exhaustive exercise, massive hemorrhage, or severe hypoxia, produce such dramatic physiological changes that all experimental subjects are forced into the same cardiovascular and behavioral patterns. Cardiovascular responses to less severe conditions can be controlled or exaggerated by behavioral procedures.

COMPARATIVE PHYSIOLOGY

Diving.—Several different species of birds and mammals have unusual patterns of behavior associated with profound changes in cardiovascular function. Diving birds and mammals have pronounced depressions in heart rate and cardiac output when submersed. Newborn seals responded to submersion with a marked bradycardia (144). Geese (145) showed bradycardia and decreased cardiac output with increased central venous pressure immediately after their heads were immersed in water. Systemic arterial blood pressure was unaffected. Marked bradycardia, induced in ducks by immersing their heads in water, was abolished by atropinization or vagotomy but was unaffected by the prior administration of propranolol (146). By comparison with the effects on diving birds and mammals, submersing human subjects had little effect on their cardiovascular function (87–89, 140, 147, 148). Immersion of the face caused slight bradycardia, minor reduction in cardiac output (87), and decreased volumes of forearm and finger (89). The diving reflex, as it occurs naturally in several species, demonstrates the profound effect vagal stimulation can have on heart rate. Apparently, cardiac parasympathetic and peripheral sympathetic vasoconstrictor mechanisms can be activated simultaneously without any demonstrable change in cardiac sympathetic stimulation.

Hibernation.—Many species of mammals are able to regulate their body temperature within far greater ranges than other homeothermic animals. Depressions and restorations of their body temperature are associated with marked changes in cardiovascular function. Hedgehogs (149), during arousal from hibernation, increased their heart rate from 20 to 250 beats per min. Cardiac output increased from less than 5 ml to more than 70 ml per min. Systemic arterial blood pressure rose from less than 50 mm to over 100 mm Hg. Part of the high total peripheral vascular resistance during hibernation was attributed to increased blood viscosity. Many of the changes in cardiovascular function during hibernation seem to be due to the direct effects of low temperature on the heart, blood, and blood vessels, but many are due to autonomic nervous system activity (150). Here, again, there is a dissociation between peripheral and cardiac sympathetic activity. Most homeothermic animals, including man, are unable to survive the extremely low body temperature achieved routinely by hibernating mammals. The ability to withstand severe hypothermia without serious cardiac arrhythmias has been attributed to an almost complete lack of sympathetic innervation of ventricular myocardial fibers (151).

CONCLUSIONS

Blood pressure, blood volume, interstitial fluid volume, cardiac output, and regional blood flows interact in complex but predictable patterns. Intrinsic control mechanisms in each component of the circulation are gently but continuously modulated by the autonomic nervous system. The end result for each cardiovascular parameter depends on this dynamic balance between various parts of the circulation. Marked changes in sensory or behavioral stimuli disrupt the normal relations, and multiple interactions evolve until a new balance is reached. The many patterns of cardiovascular response, elicited by varying physiological and behavioral stimuli, indicate an enormous capacity for diverse reactions. Cardiac output does vary according to tissue metabolic requirements and systemic arterial blood pressure is fairly constant, but it seems unlikely that any cardiovascular variable is specifically regulated by a single controlling mechanism. The physiological role of each sensory and effector mechanism in overall regulation of the circulation can best be determined from experiments using unanesthetized subjects whose behavior is carefully controlled.

LITERATURE CITED

1. Smith, E. E., Crowell, J. W. Influence of hematocrit ratio on survival of unacclimatized dogs at simulated high altitude. *Am. J. Physiol.*, **205**, 1172–74 (1963)

2. Priban, I. P., Fincham, W. F. Self-adaptive control and the respiratory system. *Nature*, **208**, 339–43 (1965)

3. Mason, D. T., Bartter, F. C. Autonomic regulation of blood volume. *Anesthesiology*, **29**, 681–92 (1968)

4. Mellander, S. Contribution of small vessel tone to the regulation of blood volume and formation of oedema. *Proc. Roy. Soc. Med.*, **61**, 55–61 (1968)

5. Herd, J. A., Hollenberg, M., Thorburn, G. D., Kopald, H. H., Barger, A. C. Myocardial blood flow determined with krypton 85 in unanesthetized dogs. *Am. J. Physiol.*, **203**, 122–24 (1962)

6. Pitt, B., Gregg, D. E. Coronary hemodynamic effects of increasing ventricular rate in the unanesthetized dog. *Circ. Res.*, **22**, 753–61 (1968)

7. Rushmer, R. F., Watson, N., Harding, D., Baker, D. Compensation to exsanguination hypotension in healthy conscious dogs. *Am. J. Physiol.*, **205**, 1000–4 (1963)

8. Van Citters, R. L., Franklin, D. L. Cardiovascular performance of Alaska sled dogs during exercise. *Circ. Res.*, **24**, 33–42 (1969)

9. Korner, P. I., Langsford, G., Starr, D., Uther, J. B., Ward, W., White, S. W. The effects of chloralose-urethane and sodium pentobarbitone anaesthesia on the local and autonomic components of the circulatory response to arterial hypoxia. *J. Physiol. (London)*, **199**, 283–302 (1968)

10. Herd, J. A., Morse, W. H., Kelleher, R. T., Jones, L. G. Arterial hypertension in the squirrel monkey during behavioral experiments. *Am. J. Physiol.*, **217**, 24–29 (1969)

11. Benson, H., Herd, J. A., Morse, W. H., Kelleher, R. T. Behavioral induction of arterial hypertension and its reversal. *Am. J. Physiol.*, **217**, 30–34 (1969)

12. Feigl, E. O. Carotid sinus reflex control of coronary blood flow. *Circ. Res.*, **23**, 223–37 (1968)

13. Ross, G., Mulder, D. G. Effects of right and left cardiosympathetic nerve stimulation on blood flow in the major coronary arteries of the anaesthetized dog. *Cardiov. Res.*, **3**, 22–29 (1969)

14. Hamlin, R. L., Smith, C. R. Effects of vagal stimulation on S-A and A-V nodes. *Am. J. Physiol.*, **215**, 560–68 (1968)

15. Harman, M. A., Reeves, T. J. Effects of efferent vagal stimulation on atrial and ventricular function. *Am. J. Physiol.*, **215**, 1210–17 (1968)

16. Mason, D. T. Usefulness and limitations of the rate of rise of intraventricular pressure (dp/dt) in the evaluation of myocardial contractility in man. *Am. J. Cardiol.*, **23**, 516–27 (1969)

17. Arnold, G., Kosche, F., Miessner, E., Neitzert, A., Lochner, W. The importance of the perfusion pressure in the coronary arteries for the contractility and the oxygen consumption of the heart. *Pflügers Arch.*, **299**, 339–56 (1968)

18. Randall, W. C., Szentivanyi, M., Pace, J. B., Wechsler, J. S., Kaye, M. P. Patterns of sympathetic nerve projections onto the canine heart. *Circ. Res.*, **22**, 315–23 (1968)

19. Randall, W. C., Wechsler, J. S., Pace, J. B., Szentivanyi, M. Alterations in myocardial contractility during stimulation of the cardiac nerves. *Am. J. Physiol.*, **214**, 1205–12 (1968)

20. Pace, J. B., Randall, W. C., Wechsler, J. S., Priola, D. V. Alterations in ventricular dynamics induced by stimulation of the cervical vagosympathetic trunk. *Am. J. Physiol.*, **214**, 1213–18 (1968)

21. Wildenthal, K., Mierzwiak, D. S., Wyatt, H. L., Mitchell, J. H. Influence of efferent vagal stimulation on left ventricular function in dogs. *Am. J. Physiol.*, **216**, 577–81 (1969)

22. Levy, M. N., Zieske, H. Comparison of the cardiac effects of vagus nerve stimulation and of acetylcholine infusions. *Am. J. Physiol.*, **216**, 890–97 (1969)

23. Levy, M. N., Zieske, H. Effect of enhanced contractility on the left

ventricular response to vagus nerve stimulation in dogs. *Circ. Res.,* **24,** 303–11 (1969)

24. Misu, Y., Kirpekar, S. M. Effects of vagal and sympathetic nerve stimulation on the isolated atria of the cat. *J. Pharmacol. Exptl. Therap.,* **163,** 330–42 (1968)

25. Davis, D. L., Hammond, M. C. Blood flow redistribution in the dog paw. *Am. J. Physiol.,* **215,** 496–501 (1968)

26. Djojosugito, A. M., Folkow, B., Lisander, B., Sparks, H. Mechanism of escape of skeletal muscle resistance vessels from the influence of sympathetic cholinergic vasodilator fibre activity. *Acta Physiol. Scand.,* **72,** 148–56 (1968)

27. Mauskopf, J. M., Gray, S. D., Renkin, E. M. Transient and persistent components of sympathetic cholinergic vasodilatation. *Am. J. Physiol.,* **216,** 92–97 (1969)

28. Iriuchijima, J., Soulsby, M. E., Wilson, M. F. Participation of cardiac sympathetics in carotid occlusion pressor reflex. *Am. J. Physiol.,* **215,** 111–14 (1968)

29. Bond, R. F., Green, H. D. Cardiac output redistribution during bilateral common carotid occlusion. *Am. J. Physiol.,* **216,** 393–403 (1969)

30. Bolme, P., Ngai, S. H., Rosell, S. Influence of vasoconstrictor nerve activity on the cholinergic vasodilator response in skeletal muscle in the dog. *Acta Physiol. Scand.,* **71,** 323–33 (1967)

31. Folkow, B., Lisander, B., Tuttle, R. S., Wang, S. C. Changes in cardiac output upon stimulation of the hypothalamic defence area and the medullary depressor area in the cat. *Acta Physiol. Scand.,* **72,** 220–33 (1968)

32. Chai, C. Y., Wang, S. C. Integration of sympathetic cardiovascular mechanisms in medulla oblongata of the cat. *Am. J. Physiol.,* **215,** 1310–15 (1968)

33. Tkachenko, B. I., Krasilnikov, V. G., Polenov, S. A., Chernjavskaja, G. V. Responses of resistance and capacitance vessels at various frequency electrical stimulation of sympathetic nerves. *Experientia,* **25,** 38–40 (1969)

34. Hadjiminas, J., Öberg, B. Effects of carotid baroreceptor reflexes on

venous tone in skeletal muscle and intestine of the cat. *Acta Physiol. Scand.,* **72,** 518–32 (1968)

35. Webb-Peploe, M. M., Shepherd, J. T. Peripheral mechanism involved in response of dogs' cutaneous veins to local temperature change. *Circ. Res.,* **23,** 701–8 (1968)

36. Abboud, F. M., Eckstein, J. W. Vascular responses after alpha adrenergic receptor blockade. II. Responses of venous and arterial segments to adrenergic stimulation in the forelimb of dog. *J. Clin. Invest.,* **47,** 10–19 (1968)

37. Webb-Peploe, M. M., Shepherd, J. T. Response of large hindlimb veins of the dog to sympathetic nerve stimulation. *Am. J. Physiol.,* **215,** 299–307 (1968)

38. Webb-Peploe, M. M., Shepherd, J. T. Response of dogs' cutaneous veins to local and central temperature changes. *Circ. Res.,* **23,** 693–99 (1968)

39. Webb-Peploe, M. M., Shepherd, J. T. Responses of the superficial limb veins of the dog to changes in temperature. *Circ. Res.,* **22,** 737–46 (1968)

40. Epstein, S. E., Beiser, G. D., Stampfer, M., Braunwald, E. Role of the venous system in baroreceptor-mediated reflexes in man. *J. Clin. Invest.,* **47,** 139–52 (1968)

41. Murray, R. H. Thompson, L. J., Bowers, J. A., Albright, C. D. Hemodynamic effects of graded hypovolemia and vasodepressor syncope induced by lower body negative pressure. *Am. Heart J.,* **76,** 799–811 (1968)

42. Epstein, S. E., Stampfer, M., Beiser, G. D. Role of the capacitance and resistance vessels in vasovagal syncope. *Circulation,* **37,** 524–33 (1968)

43. Prather, J. W., Taylor, A. E., Guyton, A. C. Effect of blood volume, mean circulatory pressure, and stress relaxation on cardiac output. *Am. J. Physiol.,* **216,** 467–82 (1969)

44. Zaimis, E. Vasopressor drugs and catecholamines. *Anesthesiology,* **29,** 732–62 (1968)

45. McGiff, J. C. Tissue hormones: angiotensin, bradykinin and the regulation of regional blood flows. *Med. Clin. N. Am.,* **52,** 263–81 (1968)

46. Whelan, R. F., Scroop, G. S., Walsh, J. A. Cardiovascular actions of angiotensin in man. *Am. Heart J.,* **77,** 546–65 (1969)

47. Sherwood, L. M., Parris, E. E. Recent developments in pathophysiologic studies of the renin-angiotensin system. *New Engl. J. Med.,* **280,** 148–55 (1969)

48. Finkielman, S., Worcel, M., Massani, Z. M., Nahmod, V. E., Paladini, A. C., Agrest, A. Angiotensin blood levels in hypovolemic shock during osmotic diuresis. *Am. J. Physiol.,* **215,** 308–13 (1968)

49. Pals, D. T., Fulton, R. W. Interrelationship between angiotensin and vascular alpha adrenergic receptors. *Am. J. Physiol.,* **214,** 506–12 (1968)

50. Kapitola, J., Küchel, O., Schreiberová, O., Jahoda, I. Blood flow through organs of the rat after an intravenous injection of angiotensin. *Physiol. Bohemoslov.,* **17,** 437–43 (1968)

51. Sannerstedt, R., Varnauskas, E. Influence of angiotensin on the hemodynamic response to exercise in normotensive subjects. *Circulation,* **38,** 1097–103 (1968)

52. Cranston, W. I., Lavery, H., Lowe, R. D., Rosendorff, C. The central pressor effect of angiotensin in the rabbit. *The Physiological Society, Oxford Mtg., England, June 1968. Proc., Commun. J. Physiol. (London),* **198,** 30–31P (1968)

53. Krasney, J. A. Effects of angiotensin on stroke volume and regional blood flow and resistance. *Am. J. Physiol.,* **215,** 1454–61 (1968)

54. Triner, L., Heully, M. C., Nahas, G. G. Metabolic effects of angiotensin. *Am. J. Physiol.,* **213,** 1545–51 (1967)

55. von Euler, U. S. Prostaglandins. *Clin. Pharmacol. Therap.,* **9,** 228–39 (1968)

56. Bergström, S., Carlson, L. A., Weeks, J. R. The prostaglandins: a family of biologically active lipids. *Pharmacol. Rev.,* **20,** 1–48 (1968)

57. Horton, E. W. Hypotheses on physiological roles of prostaglandins. *Physiol. Rev.,* **49,** 122–61 (1969)

58. Greenberg, R. A., Sparks, H. V. Prostaglandins and consecutive vascular segments of the canine hindlimb. *Am. J. Physiol.,* **216,** 567–71 (1969)

59. Davies, B. N., Withrington, P. G. The effects of prostaglandins E_1 and E_2 on the smooth muscle of the dog spleen and on its responses to catecholamines, angiotensin and nerve stimulation. *Brit. J. Pharmacol.,* **32,** 136–44 (1968)

60. Carlson, L. A. Ekelund, L.-G., Orö, L. Circulatory and respiratory effects of different doses of prostaglandin E_1 in man. *Acta Physiol. Scand.,* **75,** 161–69 (1969)

61. Kellermeyer, R. W., Graham, R. C., Jr. Kinins—possible physiologic and pathologic roles in man. *New Engl. J. Med.,* **279,** 754–59, 802–7, 859–66 (1968)

62. Schachter, M., Ed. *Physiological Soc. Symp. Peptides. 51st Annual Mtg. Fed. Am. Soc. Exptl. Biol., Chicago, April 1967. Fed. Proc.,* **27,** 49–99 (1968)

63. Hilton, S. M., Lewis, G. P. The cause of vasodilatation accompanying activity in the submandibular salivary gland. *J. Physiol. (London),* **128,** 235–48 (1955)

64. Schachter, M., Beilenson, S. Mediator of vasodilatation in the submaxillary gland, 73–75 (See Ref. 62)

65. Harrison, D. C., Henry, W. L., Paaso, B., Miller, H. A. Circulatory response to bradykinin before and after autonomic nervous system blockade. *Am. J. Physiol.,* **214,** 1035–40 (1968)

66. Greenbaum, L. M., Carrara, M. C., Freer, R. Inflammatory response and bradykinin, 90–91 (1968) (See Ref. 62)

67. Gleser, M. A., Grupp, G. Mathematical model of response to carotid sinus nerve stimulation. *Am. J. Physiol.,* **216,** 263–70 (1968)

68. Schmidt, E. M. Blood pressure response to aortic nerve stimulation in swine. *Am. J. Physiol.,* **215,** 1488–92 (1968)

69. Glick, G., Covell, J. W. Relative importance of the carotid and aortic baroreceptors in the reflex control of heart rate. *Am. J. Physiol.,* **214,** 955–61 (1968)

70. Lamberti, J. J., Jr., Urquhart, J., Siewers, R. D. Observations on the regulation of arterial blood pressure in unanesthetized dogs. *Circ. Res.,* **23,** 415–28 (1968)

71. Ninomiya, I., Irisawa, H. Aortic nervous activities in response to pulsatile and nonpulsatile pressure.

Am. J. Physiol., 213, 1504–11 (1967)

72. Koushanpour, E., McGee, J. P. Demodulation of electrical activity in the carotid sinus baroceptor nerve. J. Appl. Physiol., 24, 262–66 (1968)

73. Aars, H., Leraand, S. A method for quantitative analysis of aortic nerve activity. J. Appl. Physiol., 24, 416–18 (1968)

74. Katona, P. G., Poitras, J. W., Pantelakis, N., Jensen, E. V., Barnett, G. O. Deterministic nature of baroreceptor firing. Am. J. Physiol., 215, 1–7 (1968)

75. Koushanpour, E., McGee, J. P. Effect of mean pressure on carotid sinus baroceptor response to pulsatile pressure. Am. J. Physiol., 216, 599–603 (1969)

76. Green, J. H., Heffron, P. F. Studies upon the relationship between baroreceptor and sympathetic activity. Quart. J. Exptl. Physiol., 53, 23–32 (1968)

77. Koizumi, K., Sato, A. Influence of sympathetic innervation on carotid sinus baroreceptor activity. Am. J. Physiol., 216, 321–29 (1969)

78. Rees, P. M. The distribution of biogenic amines in the carotid bifurcation region. J. Physiol. (London), 193, 245–53 (1967)

79. Reis, D. J., Fuxe, K. Adrenergic innervation of the carotid sinus. Am. J. Physiol., 215, 1054–57 (1968)

80. Hakumaki, M. O. K. Effect of the left atrial pressure on vagal afferent discharge from the left atrium, and on the sympathetic postganglionic discharge to the heart. Acta Physiol. Scand., 74, 255–56 (1968)

81. Ledsome, J. R., Linden, R. J. The role of left atrial receptors in the diuretic response to left atrial distension. J. Physiol. (London), 198, 487–503 (1968)

82. Share, L. Control of plasma ADH titer in hemorrhage: role of atrial and arterial receptors. Am. J. Physiol., 215, 1384–89 (1968)

83. James, J. E. A., Daly, M. deB. Cardiovascular responses in apnoeic asphyxia: role of arterial chemoreceptors and the modification of their effects by a pulmonary vagal inflation reflex. J. Physiol. (London), 201, 87–104 (1969)

84. Mills, E. Activity of aortic chemo-

receptors during electrical stimulation of the stellate ganglion in the cat. J. Physiol. (London), 199, 103–14 (1968)

85. Glick, G., Wechsler, A. S., Epstein, S. E. Reflex cardiovascular depression produced by stimulation of pulmonary stretch receptors in the dog. J. Clin. Invest., 48, 467–73 (1969)

86. Daly, M. deB., Robinson, B. H. An analysis of the reflex systemic vasodilator response elicited by lung inflation in the dog. J. Physiol. (London), 195, 387–406 (1968)

87. Kawakami, Y., Natelson, B. H., DuBois. A. B. Cardiovascular effects of face immersion and factors affecting diving reflex in man. J. Appl. Physiol., 23, 964–70 (1967)

88. Paulev, P.-E. Cardiac rhythm during breath-holding and water immersion in man. Acta Physiol. Scand., 73, 139–50 (1968)

89. Heistad, D. D., Abboud, F. M., Eckstein, J. W. Vasoconstrictor response to simulated diving in man. J. Appl. Physiol., 25, 542–49 (1968)

90. Mitchell, J. H., Mierzwiak, D. S., Wildenthal, K., Willis, W. D., Jr., Smith, A. M. Effect on left ventricular performance of stimulation of an afferent nerve from muscle. Circ. Res., 22, 507–16 (1968)

91. Fell, C. Changes in blood flow distribution produced by central sciatic nerve stimulation. Am. J. Physiol., 214, 561–65 (1968)

92. Lind, A. A., McNicol, G. W. Cardiovascular responses to holding and carrying weights by hand and by shoulder harness. J. Appl. Physiol., 25, 261–67 (1968)

93. Freyschuss, U., Strandell, T. Circulatory adaptation to one- and two-leg exercise in supine position. J. Appl. Physiol., 25, 511–15 (1968)

94. Åstrand, I., Guharay, A., Wahren, J. Circulatory responses to arm exercise with different arm positions. J. Appl. Physiol., 25, 528–32 (1968)

95. Cotes, J. E., Allsopp, D., Sardi, F. Human cardiopulmonary responses to exercise: comparisons between progressive and steady state exercise, between arm and leg exercise, and between subjects differing in

body weight. *Quart. J. Exptl. Physiol.*, **54**, 211–22 (1969)

96. Crill, W. E., Reis, D. J. Distribution of carotid sinus and depressor nerves in cat brain stem. *Am. J. Physiol.*, **214**, 269–76 (1968)

97. Seller, H., Illert, M. The localization of the first synapse in the carotid sinus baroreceptor reflex pathway and its alteration of the afferent input. *Pflügers Arch.*, **306**, 1–19 (1969)

98. Urabe, M., Tsubokawa, T., Hamabe, N. Studies of the activities of vagal afferents in the medulla oblongata and thalamus with special reference to a central regulatory mechanism. *Physiol. Behav.*, **3**, 17–28 (1968)

99. Clarke, N. P., Smith, O. A., Shearn, D. W. Topographical representation of vascular smooth muscle of limbs in primate motor cortex. *Am. J. Physiol.*, **214**, 122–29 (1968)

100. Miranda, P. M. S., Gómez, B., Borison, H. L. Vasodilatation of brainstem origin suppressed by neuromuscular blockade in the cat. *J. Pharmacol. Exptl. Therap.*, **164**, 333–41 (1968)

101. Jones, M. T., Bridges, P. K., Leak, D. Relationship between the cardiovascular and sympathetic responses to the psychological stress of an examination. *Clin. Sci.*, **35**, 73–79 (1968)

102. Nestel, P. J. Blood-pressure and catecholamine excretion after mental stress in labile hypertension. *Lancet*, **1**, 692–94 (1969)

103. Kirchheim, H. Effect of common carotid occlusion on arterial blood pressure and on kidney blood flow in unanesthetized dogs. *Pflügers Arch.*, **306**, 119–34 (1969)

104. Ekblom, B. Cardiac output in athletes. *J. Appl. Physiol.*, **25**, 619–25 (1968)

105. Robinson, B. F., Wilson, A. G. Effect on forearm arteries and veins of attenuation of the cardiac response to leg exercise. *Clin. Sci.*, **35**, 143–52 (1968)

106. Kamon, E., Belding, H. S. Dermal blood flow in the resting arm during prolonged leg exercise. *J. Appl. Physiol.*, **26**, 317–20 (1969)

107. Pugh, L. G. C. E. Blood volume changes in outdoor exercise of 8–10 hour duration. *J. Physiol. (London)*, **200**, 345–51 (1969)

108. Frick, M. H. Coronary implications of hemodynamic changes caused by physical training. *Am. J. Cardiol.*, **22**, 417–25 (1968)

109. Leon, A. S., Bloor, C. M. Effects of exercise and its cessation on the heart and its blood supply. *J. Appl. Physiol.*, **24**, 485–90 (1968)

110. Ekblom, B., Åstrand, P.-O., Saltin, B., Stenberg, J., Wallström, B. Effect of training on circulatory response to exercise. *J. Appl. Physiol.*, **24**, 518–28 (1968)

111. Douglas, F. G. V., Becklake, M. R. Effect of seasonal training on maximal cardiac output. *J. Appl. Physiol.*, **25**, 600–5 (1968)

112. Oscai, L. B., Williams, B. T., Hertig, B. A. Effect of exercise on blood volume. *J. Appl. Physiol.*, **24**, 622–24 (1968)

113. Damato, A. N., Lau, S. H., Stein, E., Haft, J. I., Kosowsky, B., Cohen, S. I. Cardiovascular response to acute thermal stress (hot dry environment) in acclimatized normal subjects. *Am. Heart J.*, **76**, 769–74 (1968)

114. Whittow, G. C. Cardiovascular response to localized heating of the anterior hypothalamus. *J. Physiol. (London)*, **198**, 541–48 (1968)

115. Webb-Peploe, M. M. Effect of changes in central body temperature on capacity elements of limb and spleen. *Am. J. Physiol.*, **216**, 643–46 (1969)

116. Mosley, J. G. A reduction in some vasodilator responses in free-standing man. *Cardiov. Res.*, **3**, 14–21 (1969)

117. Nutter, D. O., Hurst, V. W. III, Murray, R. H. Ventricular performance during graded hypovolemia induced by lower body negative pressure. *J. Appl. Physiol.*, **26**, 23–30 (1969)

118. Entman, M. L., Martin, A. M., Jr., Mikat, E., Chang, J. H. T., Hackel, D. B. Phasic myocardial blood flow in hemorrhagic hypotension. Effect of beta sympathetic blockade. *Am. J. Cardiol.*, **21**, 881–85 (1968)

119. Neutze, J. M., Wyler, F., Rudolph, A. M. Changes in distribution of cardiac output after hemorrhage in rabbits. *Am. J. Physiol.*, **215**, 857–64 (1968)

120. Skillman, J. J., Awwad, H. K., Moore,

F. D. Plasma protein kinetics of the early transcapillary refill after hemorrhage in man. *Surg. Gynecol. Obstet.*, **125,** 983–96 (1967)

121. Adamson, J., Hillman, R. S. Blood volume and plasma protein replacement following acute blood loss in normal man. *J. Am. Med. Assoc.*, **205,** 609–12 (1968)

122. Pomeranz, B. H., Birtch, A. G., Barger, A. C. Neural control of intrarenal blood flow. *Am. J. Physiol.*, **215,** 1067–81 (1968)

123. Booker, W. M., Coffey, W. J., Fisher, E., Dutta, S. N. Carotid sinus responses in conscious intact and adrenalectomized dogs. *Arch. Intern. Pharmacol. Therap.*, **173,** 359–62 (1968)

124. Downing, S. E., Gardner, T. H. Cephalic and carotid reflex influences on cardiac function. *Am. J. Physiol.*, **215,** 1192–99 (1968)

125. Crocker, E. F., Johnson, R. O., Korner, P. I., Uther, J. B., White, S. W. Effects of hyperventilation on the circulatory response of the rabbit to arterial hypoxia. *J. Physiol. (London),* **199,** 267–82 (1968)

126. Krasney, J. A. Efferent components of the cardioaccelerator responses to oxygen lack and cyanide. *Am. J. Physiol.,* **213,** 1475–79 (1967)

127. Horwitz, L. D., Bishop, V. S., Stone, H. L. Effects of hypercapnia on the cardiovascular system of conscious dogs. *J. Appl. Physiol.,* **25,** 346–48 (1968)

128. Korner, P. I., Uther, J. B., White, S. W. Circulatory effects of chloralose-urethane and sodium pentobarbitone anaesthesia in the rabbit. *J. Physiol. (London),* **199,** 253–65 (1968)

129. Smith, N. T., Eger, E. I. II, Stoelting, R. K., Witcher, C. E. Cardiovascular effects of halothane in man. *J. Am. Med. Assoc.,* **206,** 1495–99 (1968)

130. Abel, F. L., Waldhausen, J. A. Effects of anesthesia and artificial ventilation on caval flow and cardiac output. *J. Appl. Physiol.,* **25,** 479–84 (1968)

131. Smyth, H. S., Sleight, P., Pickering, G. W. Reflex regulation of arterial pressure during sleep in man: a quantitative method of assessing baroreflex sensitivity. *Circ. Res.,* **24,** 109–21 (1969)

132. Kumazawa, T., Baccelli, G., Guazzi, M., Mancia, G., Zanchetti, A. Two different hemodynamic patterns underlying hypotension during desynchronized sleep. *Experientia,* **23,** 1021–22 (1967)

133. Guazzi, M., Baccelli, G., Zanchetti, A. Reflex chemoceptive regulation of arterial pressure during natural sleep in the cat. *Am. J. Physiol.,* **214,** 969–78 (1968)

134. Mancia, G., Adams, D. B., Baccelli, G., Zanchetti, A. Regional blood flows during desynchronized sleep in the cat. *Experientia,* **25,** 48–49 (1969)

135. Guazzi, M., Zanchetti, A. Carotid sinus and aortic reflexes in the regulation of circulation during sleep. *Science,* **148,** 397–99 (1965)

136. Abel, F. L., Waldhausen, J. A. Influence of posture and passive tilting on venous return and cardiac output. *Am. J. Physiol.,* **215,** 1058–66 (1968)

137. Baccelli, G., Mancia, G., Adams, D. B., Zanchetti, A. Hemodynamic patterns during fighting behaviour in the cat. *Experientia,* **24,** 1221–23 (1968)

138. Adams, D. B., Baccelli, G., Mancia, G., Zanchetti, A. Cardiovascular changes during naturally elicited fighting behaviour in the cat. *Am. J. Physiol.,* **216,** 1226–35 (1969)

139. Abrahams, V. C., Hilton, S. M., Zbrozyna, A. Active muscle vasodilatation produced by stimulation of the brain stem. Its significance in the defence reaction. *J. Physiol. (London),* **154,** 491–513 (1960)

140. Asmussen, E., Kristiansson, N.-G. The "diving bradycardia" in exercising man. *Acta Physiol. Scand.,* **73,** 527–35 (1968)

141. Miller, N. E., Banuazizi, A. Instrumental learning by curarized rats of a specific visceral response, intestinal or cardiac. *J. Comp. Physiol. Psychol.,* **65,** 1–7 (1968)

142. DiCara, L. V., Miller, N. E. Changes in heart rate instrumentally learned by curarized rats as avoidance responses. *J. Comp. Physiol. Psychol.,* **65,** 8–12 (1968)

143. Miller, N. E., DiCara, L. V. Instrumental learning of urine formation by rats; changes in renal blood flow. *Am. J. Physiol.,* **215,** 677–83 (1968)

144. Hammond, D. D., Elsner, R., Simi-

son, G., Hubbard, R. Submersion bradycardia in the newborn elephant seal *Mirounga angustirostris*. *Am. J. Physiol.*, **216,** 220–22 (1969)

145. Cohn, J. E., Krog, J., Shannon, R. Cardiopulmonary responses to head immersion in domestic geese. *J. Appl. Physiol.*, **25,** 36–41 (1968)

146. Butler, P. J., Jones, D. R. Onset of and recovery from diving bradycardia in ducks. *J. Physiol. (London)*, **196,** 255–72 (1968)

147. Bove, A. A., Lynch, P. R., Connell, J. V., Jr., Harding, J. M. Diving reflex after physical training. *J. Appl. Physiol.*, **25,** 70–72 (1968)

148. Craig, A. B., Jr., Medd, W. L. Man's responses to breath-hold exercise in air and in water. *J. Appl. Physiol.*, **24,** 773–77 (1968)

149. Kirkebö, A. Cardiovascular investigations on hedgehogs during arousal from the hibernating state. *Acta Physiol. Scand.*, **73,** 394–406 (1968)

150. Lyman, C. P., O'Brien, R. C. Autonomic control of circulation during the hibernating cycle in ground squirrels. *J. Physiol. (London)*, **168,** 477–99 (1963)

151. Nielsen, K. C., Owman, C. Difference in cardiac adrenergic innervation between hibernators and non-hibernating mammals. *Acta Physiol. Scand.*, **74,** *Suppl. 316*, 1–30 (1968)

SYSTEMIC CIRCULATION: LOCAL CONTROL[1] 1047

Stefan Mellander

Institute of Physiology, University of Lund, Lund, Sweden

Introduction

The regulation of the peripheral circulation implies adjustments of vascular smooth muscle tone by influences originating from sites within and outside the tissue. This permits distinction between "local" and "remote" control systems which by synergistic or antagonistic interactions determine the level of vascular tone. The remote control mechanisms are best defined in the sense that several of their specific mediators, the nerve transmitters and the blood-borne vasoactive hormones, have been unequivocally identified. Concepts of the final links in the local control system are, in general, more hypothetical.

Although many details of intergrated circulatory control remain to be elucidated, current experimental research has led to reasonably clear concepts of the modes of action of several of the regulatory mechanisms and to detailed descriptions of the patterns of vascular response elicited. This is evident from recent reviews which have dealt with various aspects of cardiovascular research. Chien (1) reviewed the sympathetic nervous control in hemorrhage; Haddy & Scott (2) the metabolic factors involved in local blood flow regulation; Mellander & Johansson (3) the local and remote control of resistance, exchange, and capacitance functions in the peripheral circulation; Bevegård & Shepherd (4) the regulation of the circulation during exercise in man; and Vane (5) the release and fate of vasoactive hormones in the circulation.

In this review an attempt is made to survey and analyze recent reports concerned with regional circulation and local vascular control. The major systemic vascular circuits will be considered with the exception of the coronary circulation which is dealt with in the chapter on cardiodynamics by Levy & Berne in this volume (6). Overall circulatory control, including the actions of the remote control systems on the peripheral circulation, is the topic of a special review by Herd (7). Nervous and humoral mechanisms involved in circulatory regulation will therefore only be considered in passing, and only to the extent that they may induce special regional flow patterns of apparent importance for local tissue function. Reports of mainly pathophysi-

[1] Supported in part by the Swedish Medical Research Council, grant B69-14X-2210-03A.

ological emphasis will not be included. Before the control of the regional vascular circuits is discussed, some general aspects of vascular smooth muscle physiology, of capillary exchange, and of the distribution of cardiac output will be considered. This article is not a comprehensive review, but the cited papers are representative of some current trends.

From the literature, some of which has been reviewed below, it may be inferred that local mechanisms in circulatory control are involved primarily in the establishment of an optimal capillary exchange function in the tissue. This, in turn, is achieved essentially by proper adaptation of regional blood supply and of capillary blood flow distribution. The resistance vessels and the precapillary "sphincters" in the vascular circuits are, therefore, important targets for the local control systems, whereas the tone in the postcapillary vessels is more the consequence of central nervous influence. Many details with regard to the functional significance of local vascular reactions are unexplained, but in some instances the picture seems relatively clear. There are local factors which promote nutritional flow to the region, for example, when tissue metabolism is increased. Further, there are local factors that tend to stabilize the blood supply during variations in perfusion pressure (autoregulation of flow). Capillary flow distribution in the tissue and occasional redistributions of flow between compartments of a composite organ may be intimately related to this type of control. Local mechanisms can also execute a protective function directed against deleterious circulatory effects in the tissue, such as gross edema formation in situations of increased hydrostatic load.

The fact that local myogenic mechanisms create a "basal" vascular tone, persisting after complete elimination of known extrinsic constrictor influences, is of great importance for our understanding of local circulatory regulation and of its sites of action in the vascular bed. Local inhibitory influences can act preferentially upon this basal tone to bring about vasodilatation, and excitatory influences of the local or remote control systems can be superimposed on the normal basal tone to elicit reinforced vasoconstriction. Since the level of basal tone is different in various circuits and sections of the peripheral circulation, differentiated vascular reactions can be anticipated and have, in fact, been observed frequently during involvement of the various control systems.

The factors responsible for local control are manifold and there is, at present, no consensus as to their relative importance. Much experimental evidence has accumulated to indicate that chemical factors associated with tissue metabolism, and myogenic reactions related to stretch, play major roles in local vascular control, but other mechanisms may be involved as well. There may be local control mechanisms that are common to all vascular beds, but there is much to indicate that the local factors, especially the dilator mechanisms, can vary in different vascular circuits. Myogenic mechanisms seem to operate in most circuits, but their quantitative significance in local vascular control may be different in the various vascular beds. The chemical factors involved in local regulation have been more clearly defined in some tissues, such as brain, myocardium, and skeletal muscle, than in others.

The importance of the interaction of local and remote systems in circulatory regulation both in normal and pathological states must be emphasized, although such aspects of control are beyond the scope of the present review. Synergistic action of local and remote influences on vascular smooth muscle does occur, but it appears that their interaction is more commonly characterized by antagonism. Normal reactivity of a vascular bed to these control systems may be deranged by an occasional imbalance between constrictor and dilator influences which can lead to functional disturbance of local tissue nutrition and of general cardiovascular homeostasis. Several studies on the interaction of local and remote control systems in various situations were recently reviewed (3).

An excellent review on the local control of the systemic circulation was presented in *Annual Review of Physiology* in 1968 by Sonnenschein & White (8).

REGIONAL DISTRIBUTION OF CARDIAC OUTPUT

Although vascular tone in the different circuits is changing continually as a result of the actions of local and remote control systems, there are two situations in which the level of tone can be reasonably well defined for a given tissue, i.e. "at rest" and during maximal dilatation. There is every reason to believe, although it has not been proved for all tissues as yet, that inhibitory control mechanisms are present *in vivo* which can bring the vascular smooth muscle to virtually complete relaxation, and hence increase regional flow to a maximum when tissue function so demands. Under such conditions, the organ recruits its "blood flow reserve", i.e. the difference between its maximal and resting flows. It is possible that in most organs such recruitment is caused mainly by local dilator factors related to tissue metabolism, but autonomic nervous mechanisms may contribute in some (e.g. salivary glands and external genital organs) and humoral factors in others (e.g. in those organs where circulating epinephrine can cause significant β-adrenergic vasodilatation). Maximal dilatation can be produced experimentally in the various circuits, for instance by pharmacological vasodilator agents. Comparison of flow values at rest and maximal dilatation between tissues provides some quantitative characterization of the vascular design of the regional resistance vessels. Such data collected from the current literature will be given below and may be used to illustrate the potential range of dilator effects from a resting level of tone, within which mainly local inhibitory mechanisms might act. To permit direct comparison between tissues, the flow values are expressed per unit tissue weight (ml/min·100 g) at a perfusion pressure of about 100 mm Hg (the first value refers to the "resting" state, the second to maximal dilatation): myocardium 70 and 400 (9); central nervous system 50 and 140 (10); skeletal muscle 3 and 60 (11); skin

10 and 180 (12); white adipose tissue 6 and 30 (13); salivary glands 40 and 500 (14); gastrointestinal tract 35 and 275 (15); liver, arterial supply, 30 and 150 (16); kidney 400 and 500 (17).

If we use these figures (mainly obtained from animal experiments) for a rough deduction of flows in the various organs of man, taking into consideration the weights of the respective organs, the flow values in liters/min "at rest" and during maximal dilatation would be: heart 0.2 and 1.2; CNS 0.8 and 2.1; skeletal muscle 0.9 and 18.0; skin 0.2 and 3.8; fat 0.6 and 3.0; salivary glands 0.02 and 0.25; gastrointestinal tract 0.7 and 5.5; liver, arterial supply, 0.5 and 3.0; kidney 1.2 and 1.5. These tissues, which together comprise some 70 per cent of total body weight, would thus require about 5 liters of blood/min at rest and almost 40 liters/min during maximal dilatation. It is evident from the latter figure that the cardiac pump cannot deliver, at unchanged pressure, an output equal to the sum of the regional blood flows pertaining to a state of maximal dilatation. Maintenance of tone in the resistance vessels above a given minimal level in some of the circuits is thus essential, in any situation, for adequate cardiovascular function.

The figures given above indicate a large flow reserve in some tissues, such as myocardium, brain, gastrointestinal tract, liver, skin, and glands, whereas the flow reserve is comparatively small in other tissues, such as skeletal muscle. It appears that the most vital organs, the myocardium and brain, have vascular beds that at maximal dilatation are large enough to satisfy their maximal metabolic demands reasonably well. Some other tissues, such as kidney and skin, have vascular dimensions far in excess of the local nutritional demands which can be attributed to their specific excretory and thermal regulatory functions. Skeletal muscle is a typical example in which circulation cannot cope with states of maximal metabolic activity. During strenuous exercise the acute high-energy demands must be supplied, to a great extent, via anaerobic metabolic pathways, and the consequent "oxygen debt" of the organism must be "repaid" in subsequent periods of rest.

It is clear that the data above which refer to total organ flows may not always reflect the details of the regional vascular design, or vascularization, since several of these organs contain different tissues, and an uneven flow distribution between the "parallel-coupled" vascular circuits within such organs is commonly present. In the brain, for example, grey matter is reported to receive maximal flows of up to 300 to 400 ml/min $\cdot$ 100 g tissue, whereas flow in white matter hardly exceeds 15 to 20 per cent of this figure (18). The situation is similar in the kidney (19, 20), the gastrointestinal tract (21), and skin (11), and, to some extent, even in skeletal muscle (22, 23), as will be discussed. It appears that with new techniques which permit reliable recordings of such compartmental flow patterns in the various organs, we will get information which can greatly contribute to a better understanding of regional vascular control and homeostatic regulation.

Another important trend in recent circulatory research is the more detailed study of the peripheral vascular bed which permits analyses not only of the resistance function but also of the exchange and the capacitance functions, as they are controlled by precapillary and postcapillary resistance vessels, precapillary sphincters, and capacitance vessels. This research field was reviewed in detail recently (3) and will not be recapitulated here.

VASCULAR SMOOTH MUSCLE AND VASCULAR TONE

An extensive review on the structure, biochemistry, and biophysics of vascular smooth muscle was presented recently by Somlyo & Somlyo (24) who give a detailed account of the basic contractile process, the characteristics of the contractile proteins, and the metabolism, mechanics, and electrophysiology of vascular smooth muscle. Those aspects of vascular smooth muscle physiology that are especially related to concepts of vascular tone and its modification by control systems were recently discussed (3). A few such ideas will be outlined briefly below, with references only to some of the more recent studies. For detailed information and references the reader is referred to the above-mentioned articles.

Vascular tone may be considered as the average level of contractility in the numerous smooth muscles in a region or section of the circulatory system, and there is evidence that, in many parts of the vascular tree, it is the integrated result of phasic smooth muscle twitches or tetani, initiated by action potentials. The resting membrane potential of the vascular smooth muscle cell is generally in the range of 30–65 mV (25–29). The action potentials are sometimes of the plateau type (25) but, more commonly, spikelike and they may appear singly, in bursts, or more continuously to produce phasic contractions or sustained tetani (26, 28–32). Rhythmic contractions of vascular smooth muscle are not only observed *in vitro,* but also *in vivo* in terms of "vasomotion" (33, 34), and it appears that changes of a tone in a vascular bed can be attributed, at least partly, to variations in the rate, duration, and amplitude of phasic constrictions in the numerous microvessels.

Electrophysiological studies indicate that phasic contractions are associated with propagated electrical activity and that the action potentials can be preceded by slow depolarizations, or "pacemaker potentials" (26, 28). Such conducted electrical activity from "pacemaker cells" to a population of neighboring muscles can explain the coordinated contractions observed *in vitro* and *in vivo.* Since activity of the nervous structures in the vascular wall is not essential for impulse generation or propagation, the muscle rhythmicity can be considered a result of myogenic mechanisms (35) and this vascular smooth muscle would belong to the single-unit type. It appears that "basal" vascular tone *in vivo* is related to such myogenic automaticity.

The multi-unit type of vascular smooth muscle seems to exist in several sections of the vascular system (cf. 3) where there is little or no automaticity or synchronized contraction of smooth muscles. Vasomotor nerve discharge to such muscle may be responsible for triggering action potentials that lead to asynchronous twitches, whose integrated effect results in establishment of vascular tone (e.g. 36). There is also some indication that a contracture type of smooth muscle exists in the vascular system and mechanical activity of this muscle is independent of spike discharge (37). The different mechanisms for establishing vascular tone may not be distinctly separated *in vivo*. They might operate simultaneously in the same vessel, and the smooth muscle possibly changes its behavior from one type to another depending, for instance, on the ionic or metabolic milieu (cf. 28, 30, 32).

Adjustments of vascular tone occur *in vivo* through the influence of numerous factors on smooth muscle activity. Many chemical and physical factors may interfere directly with the basic machinery of the muscle cell (24). Nerve transmitters and humoral vasoactive agents may exert their action by reacting with specific "receptor sites" on the effector. It appears that differentiated actions *in vivo* (3) might be expected in view of the apparent differentiation of the smooth muscle effector cells. The muscle characterized by automaticity and impulse propagation can be influenced by agents which affect dissimilarly the contractile response of the individual cell, the contraction frequency, and the intercellular conduction (30, 38). Differences among vessels in distribution of "receptors" for biogenic or exogenous agents may contribute to differentiated control within regions or sections of the vascular system *in vivo* (3).

Although *in vitro* studies strongly support the concept that changes in electrical activity are involved in many types of vascular smooth muscle adjustments, we must also be aware of the possibility that vasoactive agents can affect tension development by mechanisms unrelated to changes of electrical events (30, 32, 37). Attempts to get a detailed insight into the membrane characteristics of vascular smooth muscle and into the mechanisms responsible for its electrical activity are made difficult by the complex compartmental distribution of ions in the vascular wall (39–41).

It is evident that hypotheses on vascular smooth muscle regulation *in vivo*, derived from *in vitro* studies, can only be considered tentative, especially since most *in vitro* studies are performed on large blood vessels and not on those sections of the vascular tree considered most important for the control of peripheral vascular functions. A method was recently described for studying isolated resistance vessels of outside diameter down to 50 μ (42) and this approach promises to help to bridge the gap between interpretations from *in vitro* and *in vivo* experiments.

CAPILLARY EXCHANGE

Some important problems related to the capillary exchange function, approached in recent studies, are concerned with the the structural basis of capillary permeability, the permeability characteristics along the capillary pathway, the kinetics of capillary diffusion and filtration exchange, and its modification by vascular smooth muscle control mechanisms.

Karnovsky (43) reviewed his studies of capillary permeability in which he used peroxidase (mol wt 40,000) as an ultrastructural tracer. In capillaries with "continuous" endothelium (present, for instance, in heart, muscle, skin, and lung), intercellular junctions with gaps of about 40 Å were considered permeable to the tracer. These would correspond to the "small-pore system" for capillary transport. There was some evidence for vesicular transport, as well; this may be equivalent to the "large-pore system". Peroxidase did not traverse the brain capillaries, but passed "fenestrated" capillaries (present, for instance, in glomeruli and gastrointestinal tract) easily, apparently via the fenestrae, and even more readily through the intercellular gaps of capillaries with "discontinuous" endothelium (present, for instance, in hepatic and splenic sinusoids). The continuous basement membrane of continuous and fenestrated capillaries might serve as a coarse filter for large molecules. These and other electronmicroscopic studies [e.g. Casley-Smith (44)] indicate a generally good correlation between morphological and physiological observations of capillary permeability. It would be desirable, however, to find smaller ultrastructural tracers to permit more direct comparison between morphological and physiological experiments. A recent study by Vogel & Ströcker (45) confirms previous observations of regional differences of capillary permeability. The lymph/plasma ratio of polyvinylpyrrolidone (mol wt 38,000) was much lower in the hindlimbs than in kidney and liver.

In an interesting study of the permeability characteristics of capillaries in the omentum of the rabbit, Zweifach & Intaglietta (46) estimated the net flux of fluid through the walls of single capillaries from determinations of the movement of red cells after temporary capillary occlusion. Comparison of fluid movement before and during known colloid osmotic transients permitted an approximate calculation of the filtration constants which were found to be lowest in arterial capillaries (2 to $8 \cdot 10^{-3}$ μ^3/μ^2 sec·cm H_2O) and highest in venous capillaries (12 to $25 \cdot 10^{-3}$ μ/sec·cm H_2O). The majority of capillaries had filtration constants in the range of 3 to $10 \cdot 10^{-3}$ μ/sec·cm H_2O. The effective hydrostatic capillary pressure was estimated to vary between 22 and 28 cm H_2O, which was above the plasma colloid osmotic pressure. It was concluded that we might have to reconsider the precise application of the linear relationship governing transcapillary fluid movement as postulated by Starling.

It appears that the establishment of a Starling equilibrium need not necessarily be considered as a balance between filtration in the arterial end and absorption in the venous end of the capillary. Periods of predominating filtration may alternate with periods of absorption in a capillary loop because of spontaneous variations in vascular tone. Further, differences in hydrostatic capillary pressure may exist in various "parallel-coupled" exchange vessels because of varying capillary bore and length and precapillary sphincter activity, leading to filtration/absorption between adjacent channels. The gradient for absorption in the highly permeable venous capillaries need be only very small to assist effectively in the absorption process.

Zweifach & Intaglietta's finding that the effective hydrostatic capillary

pressure generally exceeded the plasma colloid osmotic pressure in the
omentum might indicate that in this tissue, lymph drainage plays an important role in local fluid balance and that the Starling principle in its restricted sense is less applicable in this tissue than in others. In skeletal muscle, for instance, there must normally be a balance between filtration and
absorption since lymph flow is negligible, at least at rest. It cannot a priori
be taken for granted that a "gradient of capillary permeability" to water
and certain dyes, that seems to exist in the omentum and also in the mesentery [Mori et al. (47), Wiederhielm (48)], is present in other tissues as
well. Furthermore, the general capillary permeability characteristics are
known to vary widely in different vascular beds. Therefore, deductions and
discussions of capillary filtration events in other tissues from observations
in the omentum (46) would seem to be invoked prematurely. Further, not
all substances may cross the capillary at the same sites along the pathway.
Thus, Mori et al. (47) showed that transcapillary leakage of highly diffusible dyes injected into the artery of the rabbit mesentery was first present
from arterial capillaries and only later, and to a smaller extent, from venous
capillaries and not at all from the venules, whereas poorly diffusible dyes
traversed the membrane mainly in venous capillaries and venules.

Yudilevich & Alvarez (49) studied transcapillary diffusion of sodium,
thiourea, and tritiated water in the dog heart by the multiple indicator-dilu-
tion technique. The fractional extractions of the diffusible tracers were
computed from the concentration ratio of the diffusible tracer to a nondiffusible reference tracer, extrapolated to zero time. The fractional extractions
for sodium and thiourea were of similar magnitude and lower than that for
water. Calculated values for the "permeability-surface area product", PS,
increased with flow and did not reach a constant level even at flows of 100
ml/min·100 g tissue, which indicates some flow limitation with regard to
transcapillary exchange. The PS ratio for sodium to water was lower
(0.26) than the ratio of their free diffusion constants (0.52); this indicated
restriction of sodium transfer compared to water. The authors concluded
that this was not due to "restricted diffusion" through capillary pores, since
in that case the pores could not be greater than 10 Å, and a more recent
study by these authors (50) suggests that they are, in fact, at least 80–100
Å. Instead, it was suggested that the capillary endothelial cells are permeable to water but not to sodium, whereas the gaps in the intercellular junctions are permeable to both. Since back diffusion may be a serious problem
when dealing with the exchange of these substances, the procedure of extrapolation to zero time was considered most important, but implies, of
course, some degree of approximation. The seemingly reasonable conclusion
from these studies that the capillary endothelial cells are permeable to some
extent to water (as are several other cells) might call for a reevaluation of
some previous concepts of capillary permeability, pore size, etc.

A comparative study was performed by Yudilevich, Renkin & their associates (51) in which the extraction fractions for various diffusible sub-

stances were determined by the multiple-tracer, slug-injection method and by the single-tracer, continuous-infusion method. Extraction was computed from ratios of diffusible to nondiffusible tracer concentrations in successive venous blood samples. Initial extraction was the same with both types of tracer administration, but decreased with time as a result of back diffusion. In skeletal muscle, initial extraction for sodium and rubidium was less than unity and decreased with increased flow perfusion, indicating diffusion limitation. With time, Rb extraction, but not Na extraction, reached a plateau level probably because of the large intracellular "sink" for Rb. Both initial and plateau extractions of Rb increased during exercise. Calculated PS values suggested that initial extraction reflects the diffusion capacity characteristics of the capillary membrane alone, but only for the capillaries of fastest arteriovenous transit. Plateau extraction reflects the diffusion capacity of the entire capillary bed and is also affected by extravascular "barriers". The problem of significant back diffusion seems to limit the number of test substances that can be used in this latter approach to a few, for example K and Rb.

Attempts have been made recently to develop methods which permit study of the exchange function in humans in normal and pathological states [Lassen & Trap-Jensen (52, 53), Appelgren & Lewis (54), Strandell & Shepherd (55)]. They are all based on the local clearance method with simultaneous measurements of the disappearance of hydrophilic tracers, such as Na or I, reflecting capillary diffusion capacity, and of a lipid-soluble tracer (xenon) reflecting blood flow. The calculation of capillary diffusion capacity is related to Renkin's (56) and Kety's (57) derivations of PS and clearance, although the processing of data was somewhat different in these studies (52–55). Lassen & Trap-Jensen estimated the capillary diffusion capacity in skeletal muscle during maximal vasodilatation, Appelgren & Lewis during normal and subnormal flows, and Strandell & Shepherd in the whole range from resting flow to maximal dilatation. Some problems may be encountered with this method. The transfer of the hydrophilic tracer may be flow limited to some extent and back diffusion may occur, especially in the low ranges of flow. It must further be assumed that no concentration gradients exist in the interstitial space, but recent studies, e.g. by Crone & Garlick (58), suggest that unstirred layers can be present in the interstitium (cf. also 59). Yet, the estimates, in different subjects or states, of capillary diffusion capacity with this method may be reasonably correct as long as the PS values are compared at the same flow or strictly correlated to the flow values (53, 54).

Studies dealing with the influence of changes of resistance vessel tone and of precapillary sphincter activity on the exchange function were reviewed by Renkin (60, 61) and Mellander & Johansson (3). So far, two methods have mainly been used for studies of relative changes in capillary exchange surface accomplished by adjustments of precapillary sphincter activity, i.e. measurement of changes of PS and of capillary hydrodynamic conductivity (capillary filtration coefficient). These two methods have given similar and reasonable results when precapillary sphincter activity is altered by physiological stimuli (3). Some vasodilator drugs, however, lead to an increase of the capillary filtration coefficient, but to decreased PS values (3, 61). This discrepancy might be explained if one assumes that the drugs relax the sphincters and, in addition, tend to produce a nonuniform capillary flow distribution. This could result in decreased extraction and decreased PS, due to changed flow distribution, but in an increased capillary filtration coefficient, since the latter is virtually independent of the magnitude of the flows in the individual capillaries that are patent. Under such special circumstances, the PS method would best describe the change of the exchange function with regard to solutes and the other method would more truly reflect the changes of activity in the precapillary sphincters.

SPECIAL REGIONS

Brain.—Cerebral vascular and metabolic effects of arterial hypocapnia and hypoxia have been analyzed in some detail recently. Wollman et al. (62) studied the effects on cerebral blood flow, during steady states, of extreme respiratory alkalosis produced by mechanical hyperventilation in lightly anesthetized man. Blood flow progressively decreased with decreasing Pa_{CO_2} and minimal values of less than 20 ml/min $\cdot$ 100 g tissue were observed at a Pa_{CO_2} of 10 mm Hg. Resistance was, however, maximal at about 20 mm Hg and the decrease of flow at lower Pa_{CO_2} values was due to concomitant fall in perfusion pressure. These data could indicate that a dilator stimulus related to flow reduction and tissue hypoxia competes with the cerebral constrictor response to hypocapnia. Such a mechanism might also be inferred from the studies of Plum et al. (63) who showed that the amounts of lactate in cerebral venous blood and cerebrospinal fluid were much less in dogs hyperventilated in a hyperbaric chamber with oxygen at 3 atm than in animals exposed to the same degree of hypocapnia by hyperventilation at sea-level oxygen pressure. Granholm et al. (64, 65) found increased lactate/pyruvate ratios in cerebral tissue and cerebrospinal fluid and increased tissue NADH levels during pronounced hyperventilation with air.

All these studies seem to support strongly the hypothesis that severe hypocapnia at normal oxygen pressure can lead to significant ischemic cerebral hypoxia. Metabolic alkalosis produced by sodium bicarbonate infusion at a controlled Pa_{CO_2} of 19 mm Hg, which raised arterial pH from 7.63 to 7.79, led to a slight dilator effect in cerebral vessels (62), probably by some indirect mechanism. Cohen et al. (66) studied cerebral vascular and metabolic effects of arterial hypoxia during normocarbia in man. When Pa_{O_2} was decreased from about 90 to 35 mm Hg, vascular resistance decreased by 45 per cent. The flow increase did not completely compensate for the reduced Pa_{O_2} but led to metabolic alterations, especially to increased cerebral glucose uptake and lactate production. It was concluded that the changes in the rate of glucose uptake, and in the relative amounts of glucose accounted for by lactate production, are the most sensitive indices of cerebral hypoxia. It must be assumed, then, that in these types of experiments alterations of arterial gas tensions produce no changes in the plasma concentrations of hormones, glucose, or other constituents that could lead to indirect interference with cerebral carbohydrate metabolism.

Metabolic and circulatory studies by Kjällquist et al. (67, 68) indicate that a marked reduction of cerebral perfusion pressure can lead to severe cerebral lactacidosis concomitant with decreased vascular resistance. This was followed by a reactive hyperemia upon restoration of pressure. Signs of slight hypoxic lactacidosis were also observed during moderate decreases of perfusion pressure within the range where flow autoregulation occurs, which might reflect a transient, or localized, cerebral underperfusion and hypoxia.

Betz & Heuser (69) studied the cerebral circulation in cats during respiratory and metabolic acidosis and alkalosis and during posthypoxic reactive hyperemia. Cortical vascular resistance was found to be correlated with cortical extracellular pH, but not always with cortical Pco_2 and Po_2, end-expiratory CO_2 content, arterial pH, and arterial blood pressure. This may indicate that extracellular pH is involved directly or indirectly in cerebral vascular control, although there seemed to be exceptions to this rule, for instance during the action of some vasodilator drugs.

A recent international symposium (70) was devoted to the regulation of cerebrovascular resistance with special reference to the role of pH of the cerebrospinal fluid. Much of the experimental evidence presented at this symposium, when taken together, indicates that cerebral extracellular pH phenomena not only are correlated with resistance changes in the brain, but may indeed play a causal role in some of the vascular reactions. Cerebral autoregulation was also dealt with and it appears that several factors are involved in the reaction, including metabolic and myogenic mechanisms, and under pathological situations perhaps also changes of tissue pressure. Apparently the local control factors normally interact and a physiological or experimental change of one factor may lead to interference with others. Cerebral autoregulation is abolished by a number of influences which ultimately might be related to cerebral anoxia and acidosis (70).

Baldy-Moulinier & Ingvar (71) showed that the "EEG frequency content" in cats was directly related to regional cortical blood flow. This occurred when EEG frequency content was changed either by the addition of anesthetics or by adequate sensory stimulation, strongly suggesting, as anticipated, the presence of a functional hyperemia in the brain.

Langfitt & Kassell (72) reported that cerebral blood flow increased in response to stimulation of the brainstem in cord-sectioned monkeys under circumstances when blood pressure was unchanged and concluded that this effect was most likely mediated by vasomotor nerves. Since, however, stimulation invariably affected the EEG pattern it cannot be entirely ruled out that the effect was linked to a change in tissue metabolism. Mchedlishvili &

Nikolaishvili (73) presented evidence that the pial vessels, besides metabolic and myogenic reactions, show cholinergic neurogenic vasodilatation.

Skeletal muscle.—Although skeletal muscle is a relatively homogeneous tissue compared to most other organs, its vascular bed may not be entirely uniform. The old morphological observation that "red" (tonic) muscle has a denser capillary network than "white" (phasic) muscle has been repeatedly confirmed. Romanul (74), using histochemical techniques, has recently studied the capillary supply of individual muscle fibers and showed a direct relationship between the density of the capillary network around each fiber and the cytochrome oxidase and succinic dehydrogenase activity of the fiber. Muscles with mainly white fibers, such as gastrocnemius, showed an uneven capillary distribution, whereas red muscles with high oxidative metabolism, such as soleus, had a more uniform capillary supply.

Studies of the circulatory dynamics in red muscle are now being pursued actively. Hilton & Vrbová (75, 76) observed that blood flow at rest in soleus greatly exceeded that known to exist in muscles with mainly white fibers and presented evidence that the regulation of flow can differ in some respects in the two types of muscle. Comparative studies by Reis et al. (22) and by Folkow & Halicka (23) have shown that resting blood flow in red muscle (soleus) is at least 20 to 30 ml/min·100 g tissue, more than twice that of gastrocnemius. Functional capillary surface area in soleus at rest determined by the method of capillary filtration coefficient was about twice as large as in gastrocnemius (23). During maximal vasodilatation soleus flow increased to about 115 ml/min·100 g at normal perfusion pressure and the functional capillary surface area increased about three times. This could provide an oxygen delivery and exchange in red muscle sufficient for maintaining a predominantly aerobic metabolism even in situations of high work loads, whereas in white muscle even quite low rates of contraction would lead to "oxygen debt" (23). Since most skeletal muscles seem to contain red fiber elements to some extent, the muscle vascular bed may be less uniform than commonly believed.

Haddy & Scott (2) recently surveyed the literature concerning metabolically linked chemicals in the control of the resistance function of various tissues, including muscle. Mellander & Johansson (3) also reviewed the subject of chemical factors involved in exercise hyperemia with special reference to their effects on the resistance, exchange, and capacitance functions in skeletal muscle. The latter authors also considered myogenic reactions related to stretch. It may be concluded from these papers that no single chemical factor is likely to be fully responsible for metabolic dilatation in muscle. Several factors appear to contribute to the exercise vasodilatation, such as increased hydrogen ion concentration, increased Pco_2, hypoxia, increased potassium ion concentration, and regional hyperosmolality. The last three factors seem to be of greatest quantitative importance. Autoregulation of blood flow seems to be established by interaction of metabolic and myogenic mechanisms on the tone of the resistance vessels. During increased perfusion pressure, constriction will ensue, and if the myogenic constrictor effect should tend to become too intense it would be balanced by metabolic dilator factors. Decreased pressure would result in dilatation due to the influence of "metabolites" and to partial elimination of the myogenic tone. The metabolic link in reactive hyperemia may be less well established and interference with the Bayliss response may contribute significantly to this vascular reaction. The local control in muscle will be considered below in relation to only a few recent studies and the reader is referred to the above-mentioned papers for a more detailed literature survey.

Kontos et al. (77, 78) have continued their studies of the reactions of the forearm blood vessels in man to increased Pco_2 and decreased pH. During local hypercapnic acidosis of increasing severity, forearm blood flow progressively increased as a result of decreased vascular tone. Blood flow at constant arterial pressure increased on the average from about 4 to 7 ml/min·100 g tissue when venous blood pH decreased from about 7.34 to 7.24 and blood Pco_2 rose from about 42 to 52 mm Hg. Hypercapnic acidosis produced by CO_2 breathing did not change the vascular resistance in the intact forearm, but led to some resistance decrease after adrenergic blockade. The vascular responses were not significantly different from those observed during hypercapnia without acidosis (CO_2 breathing + $NaHCO_3$ infusion), which indicates that the vascular effect was mediated by the increased blood Pco_2 rather than by the associated decrease in pH.

Daugherty et al. (79) observed moderate decreases of forelimb vascular resistance in the dog when Po_2 in the perfusate was decreased below 40 mm Hg, and when Pco_2 was increased, indicating that oxygen and carbon dioxide can contribute to, but far from entirely explain, metabolic vasodilatation. The importance of oxygen tension for vascular smooth muscle activity has also been demonstrated *in vitro* by Detar & Bohr (80). They showed that the contractile responses of aortic smooth muscle strips to epinephrine were closely depending on the Po_2 of the medium up to a partial pressure of 100 mm Hg. If, however, the isolated vessel was exposed to very low Po_2 for several hours, the contractile response during hypoxia was markedly improved and there was a reversal of the normal Po_2 contractile tension relationship in terms of a relaxation when Po_2 was raised back to 100 mm Hg (81). This interesting adaptation to hypoxia in vascular smooth muscle, which may be related to increased activity of enzymes allowing for greater anaerobic production of ATP, could be of importance in maintaining muscle contractility in states of low partial pressure of oxygen, e.g. chronic circulatory disorders. Honig (82) presented biochemical evidence to suggest that the oxygen-linked metabolites in smooth muscle are inorganic phosphate and 5'AMP which *in vitro* act synergistically to inhibit ATP utilization by the contraction-coupled ATPase of smooth muscle actomyosin. His observations were used for a theoretical discussion of the mechanism by which precapillary sphincters might adjust capillary surface in relation to local tissue metabolism. Martini & Honig's direct observation (83) that the intercapillary distances decrease significantly in the beating rat heart during hypoxia supports the hypothesis that oxygen is involved in some way in the control of precapillary sphincters.

The hypothesis that tissue hyperosmolality during work plays an important role in exercise hyperemia was proposed from studies performed on a "pure" calf muscle preparation in anesthetized cats, on the human forearm muscles, and on isolated vascular smooth muscle *in vitro* [Mellander et al. (84), Gray et al. (85), Lundvall et al. (86, 87)]. Muscle exercise in both cat and man was associated with a considerable increase of osmolality in muscle tissue as reflected in the venous effluent. During strenuous work osmolality increased by 30 to 40 mOsm/kg above venous control level. This change is apparently caused by release of osmotically active products from the contracting striated muscle cells. There was a direct relation between the degree of hyperosmolality and exercise hyperemia. Graded experimental hyperosmolality of magnitudes similar to those seen in exercise, produced in the resting muscle by intra-arterial infusions of various hypertonic solutions, evoked progressively increasing dilatation of the resistance vessels. Blood flow at normal pressure often increased to 30 ml/min·100 g, when osmolality was increased by 40 mOsm/kg, and at still greater hypertonicity maximal dilatation could be evoked. Furthermore, the pattern of response of the precapillary sphincters and the capacitance vessels resembled that during work. Intramuscular deposits of ^{133}Xe in resting muscle were cleared more rapidly when the tracer was dissolved in hypertonic than in isotonic medium, which indicates a hyperemic response also when the experimental hyperosmolality primarily involved the extravascular space. Increased osmolality caused a pronounced and sustained relaxation of spontaneously contracting vascular smooth muscle *in vitro,* mainly by inhibiting myogenic pacemaker activity. This effect could be ascribed to changes in transmembrane ionic concentration gradients, and in membrane permeability to ions, the latter change caused by osmotic reduction of smooth muscle cell volume [see (84) and Johansson & Jonsson (38)]. The hyperosmolality in the interstitial space ensuing during exercise might relax the vascular smooth muscle *in vivo* by the mechanisms discussed.

Boyd & Forrester (88) concluded from indirect evidence that ATP is released from exercising frog skeletal muscle *in vitro* and suggested a role for this agent in exercise vasodilatation. This interesting observation contrasts with the quite generally accepted view that ATP does not traverse the plasma membrane of intact mammalian skeletal muscle fibers. Another problem in this connection is that ATP does not seem to mimic the pattern of the dilator response in exercise. ATP elicits a pronounced active dilatation of the capacitance vessels of muscle, but such a reaction is not present during work (89).

Current experimental studies seem to support strongly the concept that myogenic reactions related to stretch play an important role in local vascu-

lar control (see e.g. 3). It can be inferred from *in vitro* and *in vivo* studies
that the smooth muscles of the precapillary vascular sections, which seem to
be of the "single-unit type", respond to increased transmural pressure by increasing the frequency of rhythmic contractions, which are initiated by "pacemakers" and propagated to a population of adjacent smooth muscle cells.
Such a train of events in the numerous microvessels would lead to reinforced vascular tone. This type of response is generally not much noted in
postcapillary vessels, which appear to have a "multi-unit type" of smooth
muscle (3). Basal tone in precapillary resistance vessels seems intimately
related to transmural pressure and is modified by pressure alterations. The
concept of local myogenic control has received strong support recently, for
instance, by studies on the umbilical artery [Shepherd (90)], on mesenteric
miscrovessels [Baez (91), Johnson (92)], and on terminal arterial vessels in
the bat wing [Wiedeman (34)], as will be discussed in the sections below.
Increased transmural pressure can lead to especially pronounced constrictions of precapillary sphincters (93, 94). This myogenic reaction helps to
establish an "autoregulation of transcapillary filtration" in situations of increased hydrostatic load on the vascular bed. This can be noted, for instance, in dependent regions in man during erect posture and seems to be a
mechanism by which gross edema formation is prevented (93). This reaction is fairly well maintained even during muscle exercise, despite the fact
that the sphincters are very sensitive to the chemical factors associated with
increased muscle metabolism (95).

Normal regulation of capillary flow distribution and capillary exchange
in muscle can perhaps in part be considered the result of an intimate interaction of myogenic and metabolic stimuli on the smallest precapillary vessels. Normal transmural pressure may contribute to the establishment of a
certain level of tone in the smallest precapillary resistance vessels and in the
precapillary sphincters which is balanced by the influence of local chemical
dilator factors so that the flow rates in the patent capillaries are adapted to
their individual exchange capacities. In Renkin's terminology this implies
that the ratio of flow to PS is roughly the same in all open capillaries (61)
which would yield optimum exchange. Such an optimal capillary flow distribution seems to prevail in most physiological situations (e.g. at rest, during
constriction, and during metabolic vasodilatation), but the regulation may
be deranged in pathological states (54), by "excessive" metabolic dilatation
noted in exercise during mechanical hindrance of blood flow, or by certain
vasodilator drugs (61).

The regulation of the resistance, exchange, and capacitance functions in
skeletal muscle executed by nervous and humoral control systems is beyond
the scope of the present paper, but was recently reviewed elsewhere (3).

Skin.—An important contribution to our understanding of the control in
precapillary vessels was made by Wiedeman (34) who studied, by vital microscopy, the changes of diameter of the series-coupled precapillary vessels

in the bat wing during denervation. Acute surgical denervation led to a pronounced dilatation of the large arterial vessels which showed an average increase of diameter of 38 per cent, whereas the smallest precapillary vessels decreased their average diameters by 24 per cent. The data support the hypothesis that loss of tone in the large arterial resistance vessels by sympathectomy leads to increased contractile activity and tone in the smaller, more distally located vessels and, hence, to a redistribution of the site of resistance control. There was much to indicate that the abruptly increased contractile activity in the smallest vessels was a myogenic reaction due to increased transmural pressure. These findings seem consonant with the above-discussed data from studies of circulatory dynamics in other organs suggesting that the local control mechanisms are of special importance for the precapillary resistance and sphincter vessels. In these a raised transmural pressure, for instance, will lead to increased tone, hence contributing to the autoregulation of flow and of transcapillary filtration.

The concept of critical closing pressure was reexamined by Hochberger & Zweifach (96) on the isolated rabbit ear perfused at low vascular tone with crystalloidal and colloidal solutions. The study gave no support for this concept, since perfusion was shown to continue until effective driving pressure was virtually zero.

Elkington (97) studied finger blood flow in people stationed for a year in Antarctica, and confirmed the concept that an important feature in acclimatization to cold is increased vasoconstrictor tone. In contrast to some previous reports, he found that finger blood flow decreased in the colder months of the year, both before and during immersion in ice water, and that the cold-induced vasodilatation became less as the year of cold exposure progressed. Gaskell & Long (98) studied the reactivity of the digital vessels in subjects exposed to repeated cold exposure of the hand in laboratory experiments, but this led to no detectable signs of local acclimatization to cold. *In vitro* studies by Sams & Winkelmann (99) on catecholamine-induced contraction of cutaneous artery strips during variation in temperature might have some bearing on the reactivity of skin vessels in cold and hot environments. The "slow component" of contraction was found to be maximal at about 30°C, but decreased if temperature was either raised or lowered. Webb-Peploe & Shepherd (100–103) studied in the dog the venomotor responses of the lateral saphenous vein perfused at constant flow during changes in the temperature of the perfusate and during central cooling and heating. Both central and local cooling elicited venoconstrictor responses which were dependent upon the integrity of the constrictor fibers. The reactivity of the vein to sympathetic stimulation was increased during local cooling (studied down to 17°C) and this effect was ascribed to increased sensitivity of the smooth muscle in the cold to arriving nerve impulses. One possible explanation of this somewhat surprising result is that cold interferes with the reuptake of the transmitter so that, at a given rate of discharge, the smooth muscle is exposed to greater norepinephrine concentrations in cold than in warm environment. Another possibility might be that cold interferes with some active process in the contractile system of the smooth muscle effector cell, for instance with the elimination of calcium, which could lead to augmented constriction. These results were taken to indicate that in the cold, cutaneous venous return is diverted preferentially to the deep veins for heat preservation through countercurrent exchange with the arteries.

Hyman & Wong (104) determined blood flow and capillary filtration coefficient in the human calf while changing the environmental temperature from 20 to 35° C. Flow increased by about 170 per cent and filtration coefficient by about 40 per cent when the temperature rose. This latter finding would indicate an increase of functional capillary surface area. Previous studies from the same laboratory had shown that clearance of iodide from cutaneous deposits was unchanged in these circumstances, which had been taken to indicate that no such increase occurs (see 104). This clearance method alone may, however, not permit valid conclusions to be drawn about changes of capillary surface (cf. section on capillary exchange). Although alterations in the capillary filtration coefficient seem to reflect adequately the relative changes in the perfused capillary surface area in "pure" tissue preparations, such as skeletal muscle (3), it is evident that the site for such an adjustment might be more difficult to define in a composite tissue, such as the intact calf. The above-mentioned increase of filtration coefficient in response to raised environmental temperature does not necessarily indicate a relative increase of capillary surface area in skin proper, but perhaps in more deeply located tissues.

Polster et al. (105) analyzed the temporal relation between electrical sympathetic stimulation and the resistance response in a cutaneous vascular bed and found that the shortest latency between stimulus and effector response was 230 msec. Hammond and co-workers (106, 107) showed in the dog paw that the resistance responses to nerve stimulation of the arterial and small vessels slightly preceded those of the venous segment and, further, that nerve excitation could elicit selective responses in arterial and venous segments of the vascular bed. Paessler et al. (108) showed an increased venomotor tone in dependent cutaneous vessels when the subject was tilted from the supine to the erect posture. This effect, most likely a reflex response, was largely abolished when the subjects were standing in a water-filled tank. Studies dealing with the effects on the resistance, exchange, and capacitance functions in the cutaneous circulation executed by various remote control systems were summarized elsewhere (3).

Sejrsen (109) analyzed the routes of disappearance of ^{133}Xe from intracutaneous depots in situations of arrested regional flow and found the diffusion through the intact epidermal barrier to be almost insignificant, whereas considerable loss of tracer could occur by sweating.

Adipose tissue.—Blood flow in adipose tissue of man was estimated from compartment analysis of the rate of uptake of ^{85}Kr from a closed breathing circuit by use of a perfusion-limited body compartment model [Lesser & Deutsch (110)]. The compartment with the slowest uptake was taken to represent adipose tissue. Total blood flow in adipose tissue averaged 0.4 liter/min in normal subjects corresponding to a mean flow of 2.12 ml/ min·100 g adipose tissue. Total adipose tissue blood flow increased in obesity but the flow per unit tissue weight decreased. Herd et al. (111) estimated the blood flows in various white and brown fat depots in the rat, during periods of activity and inactivity, from clearance measurements of intravenously injected tritium-labeled DDT. Flow in white fat was about 10, and in brown fat about 27 ml/min·100 g tissue in the morning when rats are inactive, and increased in all depots by about 50 per cent in the evening when they are active.

Öberg & Rosell (112) studied the effects of adrenergic nerve excitation on the series-coupled vascular sections in white fat in the dog and found evidence of α-adrenergic constrictor responses which were converted to β-adrenergic dilatation after α-receptor blockade. Fredholm & Rosell (113) showed that adrenergic nerve stimulation led to release of free fatty acids and glycerol into the venous blood and these effects were inhibited by β-adrenergic blocking agents. A special pattern of innervation in brown adipose tissue of the rat was found by Derry et al. (114) who, from histochemical studies before and after denervation, obtained evidence that the parenchymal cells are innervated via "short" adrenergic neurons from intrinsic ganglia, whereas the blood vessel innervation is separate and derived from the sympathetic chain via "long" adrenergic neurons. This raises the interesting question whether there is also a functional dissociation with regard to the adrenergic control of circulatory and of metabolic functions in this tissue.

Salivary glands.—Beilenson and co-workers (115) studied the vasodilator and secretory responses in the submaxillary gland in relation to the secretion of kallikrein. Saliva flow and blood flow increased rapidly in the low frequency range of chorda stimulation, whereas the rise in kallikrein output in saliva was much more gradual and reached a maximum only at about 20 imp/sec. There was poor correlation between vasodilatation and kallikrein concentration in saliva. These data per se may not necessarily speak against a role of the kallikrein-kinin system in chorda vasodilatation, since concentrations in saliva and in interstitial fluid may differ and there is probably not a simple linear relation between kallikrein-kinin formation and vascular effector response. However, the authors also reported that after depletion of kallikrein in the gland, chorda stimulation still produced a normal vasodilatation, and concluded that cholinergic dilator nerves are mainly responsible for chorda vasodilatation, although it is atropine-resistant. Hilton & Torres (116) showed, on the other hand, that in kallikrein-depleted glands the vascular sensitivity to bradykinin is increased so that this substance, even if produced in quite small amounts upon stimulation, still might elicit a marked dilatation.

Plasma and lymph contain kininogens for kinin-forming enzymes. One of these (substrate 2) is acted upon exclusively by glandular kallikrein [see Gautvik et al. (117)]. The concentration of this substrate in plasma drained from the submandibular salivary gland, when perfused at constant flow, was found to decrease by 20 to 60 per cent during supramaximal stimulation of the chordalingual nerve (117). These results indicate that glandular kallikrein released from the activated gland cells passes into the interstitial fluid on chorda stimulation, since the substrate for this enzyme is selectively consumed.

Skinner & Webster (118) showed that the chorda dilatation was unaffected after intravenous administration of carboxypeptidase B, whereas the dilator effect to close arterial bradykinin infusion was reduced or blocked. They concluded that the kinins are not involved in the regulation of salivary gland blood flow. It must be assumed, then, that this kinin inhibitory enzyme traversed the capillaries of the gland in sufficient amounts, in these experiments, to build up effective concentrations in the interstitium to inhibit entirely the action of endogenously formed kinin. These authors further reported that very large doses of propranolol and other β-blocking agents (up to 10 mg infused close arterially) could reduce the chorda vasodilatation and suggested that stimulation of β-adrenergic receptors is involved in the hyperemic response. Schachter & Beilenson (119) questioned this conclusion, since large doses of this β-blocking agent will reduce the action of acetylcholine as well. There might also have been interference with the nerve fibers in the chorda in these experiments since large doses of β-blocking agents are known to exert an effective local anesthetic action (120).

Garrett (121) showed by histochemical and electronmicroscopic studies that parasympathetic vascular nerves are present in salivary glands and this suggests that cholinergic vasodilator nerves do exist in the glands.

At the present state of knowledge it may be concluded that parasympathetic dilator nerves are engaged in the functional hyperemia of salivary glands during secretion, and that vasodilator factors other than acetylcholine can contribute to the pronounced increase in blood flow during increased cellular activity of the glands. The parasympathetic fibers have the additional function in the salivary glands of supplying the myoepithelial cells with motor nerves which cause them to contract [Emmelin et al. (122)].

An extensive review of the nervous control of salivary glands by Emmelin (123), and another one dealing with secretion and blood flow in the salivary glands and the gastrointestinal tract by Jacobson (124), were recently published.

Hilton & Jones (125) recently suggested a role of plasma kinin in functional hyperemia in still another gland, i.e. the pancreas. They showed that vagal stimulation and pancreozymin injection increased pancreatic blood flow, whereas it was unaffected by secretin. Kinin-forming enzyme was present in the venous effluent from the perfused gland at rest and enzyme activity increased fourfold when acetylcholine or pancreozymin, but not secretin, was added to the perfusate. Graham et al. (126) have claimed from electronmicroscopic studies that the vessels of the pancreas do not receive a cholinergic innervation.

Gastrointestinal tract.—Harper et al. (127) used the amidopyrin clearance technique for estimation of gastric mucosal blood flow in anesthetized cats in response to changes in H^+ secretion produced by histamine or gastrin. Total gastric flow, measured directly, and mucosal flow increased linearly with increase of H^+ secretion. The increase in total flow could be ascribed entirely to the increase in mucosal flow. They found no difference between the effects of gastrin and histamine on mucosal flow.

Johnson (92) analyzed the autoregulatory responses of cat mesenteric arterioles by observing changes in vessel diameter with the flying spot microscope technique in response to a sudden step change in large artery pressure. When pressure was reduced, the arterioles showed a biphasic response in the majority of the experiments: they narrowed for the first 5 to 15 sec and then widened again in the steady state, and then often assumed dimensions beyond their control diameters at normal pressure. Restoration of pressure led to an initial further dilatation followed by a constrictor response. These autoregulatory phenomena may be ascribed to myogenic as well as to metabolic mechanisms.

McGinn et al. (128) found no change in intestinal blood flow during wide variations in arterial blood pH produced by infusions of acid and alkali, but the sensitivity to norepinephrine was decreased during acidosis. However, gut flow increased during respiratory acidosis and in relation to the increase in end-tidal Pco_2. The dilator effect of CO_2 was also present after blockade with phentolamine, but some contribution to the response by β-receptor stimulation, produced for instance by reflex release of epinephrine from the adrenal medullas, was not ruled out. That β-receptor stimulation leads to pronounced dilatation of intestinal resistance vessels is well known, for instance, from studies by Greenway & Lawson (129). They observed a marked increase in superior mesenteric artery blood flow during intra-arterial infusion of epinephrine and this effect was blocked by propranolol.

Fronek & Stahlgren (130) recorded by electromagnetic flowmeters the flow distribution in some major systemic circuits during food intake and digestion in conscious dogs. During ingestion, cardiac output increased but the ratio of flow in the superior mesenteric artery to cardiac output decreased slightly. During digestion 1-3 hr after food intake, mesenteric artery flow increased as a result of regional dilatation, whereas, simultaneously, there was some constriction in the brachiocephalic and iliac vascular areas.

Prolonged excitation of the adrenergic nerves to the gut is known to cause a transient strong constrictor response of the intestinal resistance vessels, soon followed by a gradual recovery of flow towards the control level, attributed to an "autoregulatory escape from constrictor fibre influence" (see 3). This pattern of response is mimicked by intra-arterial infusion of norepinephrine, angiotensin II, and prostaglandin F_{2a}, as shown by Shehadeh and co-workers (131). For the last two agents this behavior may partly be related to tachyphylaxis. These authors further showed that dilator agents such as prostaglandin E_1, bradykinin, histamine, and acetylcholine produced large initial dilator responses which gradually faded away during continuous infusions. They were unable to confirm previous reports (132, 133) that changes in intestinal motility play an important role for vascular conductance in the gut.

The distribution of flow between the various intestinal tissue layers was estimated by Lundgren and co-workers (see 21) from γ-clearance curves for ^{85}Kr after intra-arterial administration. These curves could be resolved into four components, and corresponding tissue compartments were identified by radioautography and by recording β activity after local krypton injection into different tissue layers. At rest, mucosal flow was about 50, muscularis flow about 15, and submucosal flow in a region close to the intestinal crypts about 500 ml/min·100 g tissue. During maximal dilatation the corresponding figures were 200, 40, and 1000 ml, respectively. Circumstantial evidence obtained by several independent methods strongly suggested the possibility of an extravascular "shunt" mechanism, created by countercurrent exchange of material between the ascending and descending limbs of the vascular hairpin loops located in the intestinal villi. Such a countercurrent mechanism, it was postulated, creates a barrier hindering too rapid an absorption of solutes from intestinal lumen to blood and, conversely, limits oxygen diffusion in the opposite direction.

Jacobson (124, 134) recently reviewed the field of gastrointestinal circulation and another review considered the details of the control of resistance, exchange, and capacitance vessels in the gut (3).

Liver.—Lutz et al. (135) showed that a slight increase of pressure in the hepatic veins caused the hepatic artery vessels to constrict actively, whereas pressure in the portal vein was passively increased. Increase of portal vein pressure resulted in an even more pronounced constriction in the ramifications of the hepatic artery. Such a response, considered to be a myogenic reaction, may help to explain the reciprocity of flow between the arterial and venous supply of the liver. Chou & Emerson (136) studied the local effects of several cations on vascular resistances in the dog liver: Mg^{++} could lower hepatic artery resistance, while K^+ in high concentrations increased the resistance. The effects of Na^+ and Ca^{++} were insignificant.

Greenway and co-workers (137) studied the resistance to flow in the hepatic artery and the portal vein during graded stimulation of the hepatic nerves, infusion of norepinephrine, and occlusion of the carotid arteries. Both vascular beds constricted during these maneuvers. The resistance response was well maintained in the portal vein, but quite transient in the hepatic artery, and artery flow returned towards the control level in 1 to 2 min, apparently because of a counteraction by local control mechanisms. The responses were unaffected by previous administration of atropine and propranolol, but were blocked by phenoxybenzamine. The arterial vessels of the liver thus show a type of reaction similar to that of the intestinal vasculature in terms of an "autoregulatory escape from vasoconstrictor fibre influence". A review on the regulation of liver metabolism including aspects of the hepatic circulatory control was recently presented by Shoemaker & Elwyn (138).

Spleen.—The presence of both α- and β-adrenergic receptors in the spleen was revealed in studies by Ross (139) who recorded splenic inflow and outflow during intra-arterial injections of catecholamines and by Greenway et al. (140) who followed changes in arterial inflow and splenic weight during nerve stimulation. Small doses of epinephrine increased arterial inflow, whereas large doses of epinephrine and all doses of norepinephrine decreased inflow and simultaneously increased outflow. These latter effects were transient and were followed by prolonged increase of splenic flow. After β-adrenergic blockade the dilator response of epinephrine was changed to a constriction and the constrictor responses to norepinephrine were augmented. Graded nerve stimulation led to decreases in splenic flow and weight, and both the resistance and capacitance responses were maximal at about 3 imp/sec. Atropine and propranolol did not affect these responses but after α-adrenergic blockade, nerve stimulation resulted in a smaller decrease of weight and in an increased flow. This flow increase was blocked by propranolol. It appears from these studies that α-receptors are distributed to the smooth muscle structures that influence both the resistance and capacitance functions in the spleen, whereas the β-receptors, which seem to be affected to some extent by the adrenergic nerve transmitter, are mainly confined to the resistance vessels. This is an arrangement similar to that of skeletal muscle [see (3), and Viveros et al. (141)]. From pharmacological studies of the contractile activity of the isolated mouse spleen, Ignarro & Titus (142) obtained evidence for the presence of antagonistically acting α- and β-receptors in the splenic capsule.

In the first two studies mentioned above (139, 140), peculiar rhythmic oscillations in splenic flow were observed. This oscillatory behavior was much augmented after a period of temporary occlusion of the splenic artery or after administration of isoproterenol. This phenomenon could not be ascribed to extrinsic influences, but rather to interference with local, possibly myogenic, control mechanisms, which changed the spontaneous rhythmic behavior of the splenic smooth muscle.

Davies et al. (143, 144) presented evidence that excitation of the splenic nerves leads to local release of prostaglandin E_2. It has been suggested that prostaglandin (E_1) may inhibit norepinephrine release from the splenic nerves and also cause inhibition of the effector response to the released norepinephrine [Hedquist & Brundin (145)]. A review concerning the functional significance of the prostaglandins in the organism was published recently [Horton (146)].

Kidney.—Total renal resistance is relatively little influenced by moderate changes in arterial Po_2, but decreases in response to increased Pco_2 and vice versa [Daugherty et al. (79), Lockett (147)]. The effects of CO_2 are present also when arterial pH is kept constant and can be related to a local influence on the renal vessels, mainly on the preglomerular side (147).

Honda et al. (148) reinvestigated the postocclusive reactive hyperemic response in the rabbit kidney which consisted of an initial overshoot of flow and a secondary slowly developing flow increase. The length of the occlusion period influenced the duration, but not the magnitude, of the initial response. The reverse was true for the slowly developed hyperemia. Elevation of venous pressure suppressed the secondary response if produced by venous occlusion but not if produced by infusion of unoxygenated dextran into the renal vein. It was concluded that the initial overshoot of flow related mainly to myogenic mechanisms and the second hyperemic phase mainly to metabolic factors.

Basar & Weiss (149) analyzed the frequency characteristics of pressure-induced changes of flow resistance in the isolated artificially perfused rat kidney. At frequencies between 0.4 and 4 Hz there was a negative phase angle between pressure and flow, whereas at lower frequencies the phase angle was positive indicating an overshoot reaction upon the pressure stimulus. These results were compared with data on active tension development in isolated smooth muscle strips during rhythmic passive stretch and the authors concluded that autoregulation of renal flow is a purely myogenic response. It remains to be shown to what extent the reactions in the artificially perfused kidney reflect normal behavior of the renal vasculature *in vivo.*

From micropuncture studies and measurements of total GFR and renal blood flow in the dog kidney, Liebau et al. (150) obtained evidence to indicate a constancy of proximal tubular function during blood pressure variations within the autoregulatory range, supporting the concept of a preglomerular site for autoregulation.

Histochemical studies have revealed that adrenergic fibers innervate the arterial vessels out to the afferent arterioles in the cortex and the vasa recta in the outer medulla [McKenna & Angelakos (151)] and the walls of the parts of the juxtaglomerular arterioles that contain granulated cells [Wågermark et al. (152)]. No adrenergic fibers were detected in the glomeruli, the efferent arterioles, or the tubules (151). Acetylcholinesterase-containing fibers with a renal distribution similar to that of the adrenergic nerves have also been reported (153).

Studies of the intrarenal flow distribution during nerve activation and administration of vasoactive agents have given somewhat conflicting results. Pomeranz et al. (19) found by the use of ^{85}Kr clearance technique, autoradiography, and silicon rubber casts that stimulation of the renal nerves, which hardly affected total renal blood flow, led to a decrease of outer cortical blood flow and to an increase of outer medullary peritubular flow. It was suggested, but not proved, that this latter effect might be due to β-adrenergic or cholinergic dilatation of the descending vasa recta. It was postulated that neurogenic mechanisms via redistribution of intrarenal flow might lead to decreased urinary concentration and increased sodium retention. By the ^{85}Kr technique, Carrière (20) found intra-arterial infusion of norepinephrine to cause a constriction in the outer cortex and an increased flow rate in the medulla. He found no evidence for any β-adrenergic dilator effect of isoproterenol in cortical or medullary vessels.

The concept of a neurogenic redistribution of intrarenal blood flow has not received unanimous support. Aukland (154) and Aukland & Wolgast (155) used the local hydrogen clearance and the local ^{85}Kr clearance techniques supplemented by measurement of mean transit time of ^{32}P-labeled erythrocytes to estimate medullary blood flow. Cortical flow was estimated from cortical red cell transit time and from total renal blood flow measured by electromagnetic flowmeter. Intrarenal distribution of flow was studied in response to direct or reflex excitation of the renal nerves and to administration of catecholamines and angiotensin. In most of these experiments, total renal blood flow was significantly reduced. There was, however, no indication, in these studies, of selective hemodynamic responses in the juxtamedullary circulation, but flow resistance on the average increased proportionately in the cortical and outer medullary sections.

Some experimental differences between the studies of Pomeranz et al. and those of Aukland et al. might have contributed to their varying results. Aukland's data were obtained in an early phase of the renal nerve excitation or infusion (within 5 to 15 min) and when total renal blood flow was decreased significantly, whereas the data of Pomeranz et al. refer to a later stage of nerve excitation with no change of total flow. During prolonged nerve stimulation, total renal resistance is known to increase drastically at first, but the constrictor response tends to fade away with time [Feigl et al. (156)]. The pattern thus resembles that in the intestine where an "autoregulatory escape from vasoconstrictor fibre influence" is seen, which is believed to be due to a redistribution of flow from mucosal to submucosal layers (see 3). Possibly the gradual decline of total renal resistance seen during maintained nerve activation reflects a secondary dilatation of medullary vessels and hence a change of intrarenal flow distribution with time.

Aukland showed in another study (157) that intravenous administration of vasopressin had no effect on total renal perfusion or on medullary blood flow. This seems to refute the hypothesis that the rise in urine osmolality elicited by antidiuretic hormone is related to juxtamedullary constriction and reduction in medullary blood flow.

Current concepts of the control of renin release have been reviewed by Vander (158).

338 MELLANDER

LITERATURE CITED

1. Chien, S. Role of the sympathetic nervous system in hemorrhage. *Physiol. Rev., 47,* 214–88 (1967)
2. Haddy, F. J., Scott, J. B. Metabolically linked vasoactive chemicals in local regulation of blood flow. *Physiol. Rev., 48,* 688–707 (1968)
3. Mellander, S., Johansson, B. Control of resistance, exchange, and capacitance functions in the peripheral circulation. *Pharmacol. Rev., 20,* 117–96 (1968)
4. Bevegård, B. S., Shepherd, J. T. Regulation of the circulation during exercise in man. *Physiol. Rev., 47,* 178–213 (1967)
5. Vane, J. R. The release and fate of vaso-active hormones in the circulation. *Brit. J. Pharmacol., 35,* 209–42 (1969)
6. Levy, M. N., Berne, R. M. Heart: Cardiodynamics. *Ann. Rev. Physiol., 32,* 373–414 (1970)
7. Herd, J. A. Systemic circulation. Overall control. *Ann. Rev. Physiol., 32,* 289–312 (1970)
8. Sonnenschein, R. R., White, F. N. Systemic circulation: Local control. *Ann. Rev. Physiol., 30,* 147–70 (1968)
9. Gregg, D. E., Fischer, L. C. Blood supply to the heart. In *Handbook of Physiology,* II, Sect. 2, 1517–84 (Hamilton, W. F., Dow, P., Eds., Williams & Wilkins, Baltimore, Md., 1963)
10. Reivich, M. Arterial Pco_2 and cerebral hemodynamics. *Am. J. Physiol., 206,* 25–35 (1964)
11. Barcroft, H. Circulation in skeletal muscle. In *Handbook of Physiology,* II, Sect. 2, 1353–85 (See Ref. 9)
12. Greenfield, A. D. M. The circulation through the skin. In *Handbook of Physiology,* II, Sect. 2, 1325–51 (See Ref. 9)
13. Öberg, B., Rosell, S. Sympathetic control of consecutive vascular sections in canine subcutaneous adipose tissue. *Acta Physiol. Scand., 71,* 47–56 (1967)
14. Terroux, K. G., Sekelj, P., Burgen, A. S. V. Oxygen, consumption and blood flow in the submaxillary gland of the dog. *Can. J. Biochem. Physiol., 37,* 5–15 (1959)
15. Folkow, B., Lundgren, O., Wallentin, I. Studies on the relationship between flow resistance, capillary filtration coefficient and regional blood volume in the intestine of the cat. *Acta Physiol. Scand., 57,* 270–83 (1963)
16. Bradley, S. E. The hepatic circulation. In *Handbook of Physiology,* II, Sect. 2, 1387–438 (See Ref. 9)
17. Selkurt, E. E. The renal circulation. In *Handbook of Physiology,* II, Sect. 2, 1457–516 (See Ref. 9)
18. Häggendal, E., Nilsson, N. J., Norbäck, B. On the components of Kr^{85} clearance curves from the brain of the dog. *Acta Physiol. Scand., 66, Suppl. 258,* 5–25 (1966)
19. Pomeranz, B. H., Birtch, A. G., Barger, A. C. Neural control of intrarenal blood flow. *Am. J. Physiol., 215,* 1067–81 (1968)
20. Carrière, S. Effect of norepinephrine, isoproterenol, and adrenergic blockers upon the intrarenal distribution of blood flow. *Can. J. Physiol. Pharmacol., 47,* 199–208 (1969)
21. Lundgren, O. Studies on blood flow distribution and countercurrent exchange in the small intestine. *Acta Physiol. Scand., Suppl. 303,* 1–42 (1967)
22. Reis, D. J., Wooten, G. F., Hollenberg, M. Differences in nutrient blood flow of red and white skeletal music muscle in the cat. *Am. J. Physiol., 213,* 592–96 (1967)
23. Folkow, B., Halicka, H. D. A comparison between "red" and "white" muscle with respect to blood supply, capillary surface area and oxygen uptake during rest and exercise. *Microvasc. Res., 1,* 1–14 (1968)
24. Somlyo, A. P., Somlyo, A. V. Vascular smooth muscle. I. Normal structure, pathology, biochemistry, and biophysics. *Pharmacol. Rev., 20,* 197–272 (1968)
25. Roddie, I. C. The transmembrane potential changes associated with smooth muscle activity in turtle arteries and veins. *J. Physiol. (London), 163,* 138–50 (1962)
26. Funaki, S., Bohr, D. F. Electrical and mechanical activity of isolated vascular smooth muscle of the rat. *Nature, 203,* 192–94 (1964)
27. Steedman, W. M. Micro-electrode

studies on mammalian vascular muscle. *J. Physiol. (London)*, **186**, 382–400 (1966)

28. Axelsson, J., Wahlström, B., Johansson, B., Jonsson, O. Influence of the ionic environment on spontaneous electrical and mechanical activity of the rat portal vein. *Circ. Res.*, **21**, 609–18 (1967)

29. Nakajima, A., Horn, L. Electrical activity of single vascular smooth muscle fibers. *Am. J. Physiol.*, **213**, 25–30 (1967)

30. Johansson, B., Jonsson, O., Axelsson, J., Wahlström, B. Electrical and mechanical characteristics of vascular smooth muscle response to norepinephrine and isoproterenol. *Circ. Res.*, **21**, 619–33 (1967)

31. Keatinge, W. R. Ionic requirements for arterial action potential. *J. Physiol. (London)*, **194**, 169–82 (1968)

32. Somlyo, A. V., Somlyo, A. P. Electromechanical and pharmacomechanical coupling in vascular smooth muscle. *J. Pharmacol. Exptl. Therap.*, **159**, 129–45 (1968)

33. Wiedeman, M. P. Contractile activity of arterioles in the bat wing during intraluminal pressure changes. *Circ. Res.*, **19**, 559–63 (1966)

34. Wiedeman, M. P. Blood flow through terminal arterial vessels after denervation of the bat wing. *Circ. Res.*, **22**, 83–89 (1968)

35. Johansson, B., Ljung, B. Spread of excitation in the smooth muscle of the rat portal vein. *Acta Physiol. Scand.*, **70**, 312–22 (1967)

36. Keatinge, W. R. Electrical and mechanical response of arteries to stimulation of sympathetic nerves. *J. Physiol. (London)*, **185**, 701–15 (1966)

37. Su, C., Bevan, J. A., Ursillo, R. C. Electrical quiescence of pulmonary artery smooth muscle during sympathomimetic stimulation. *Circ. Res.*, **15**, 20–27 (1964)

38. Johansson, B., Jonsson, O. Cell volume as a factor influencing electrical and mechanical activity of vascular smooth muscle. *Acta Physiol. Scand.*, **72**, 456–68 (1968)

39. Villamil, M. F., Rettori, V., Barajas, L., Kleeman, C. R. Extracellular space and the ionic distribution in the isolated arterial wall. *Am. J. Physiol.*, **214**, 1104–12 (1968)

40. Villamil, M. F., Rettori, V., Yeyati, N., Kleeman, C. R. Chloride exchange and distribution in the isolated arterial wall. *Am. J. Physiol.*, **215**, 833–39 (1968)

41. Friedman, S. M., Gustafson, B., Hamilton, D., Friedman, C. L. Compartments of sodium in a small artery. *Can. J. Physiol. Pharmacol.*, **46**, 673–79 (1968)

42. Uchida, E., Bohr, D. F., Hoobler, S. W. A method for studying isolated resistance vessels from rabbit mesentery and brain and their responses to drugs. *Circ. Res.*, **21**, 525–36 (1967)

43. Karnovsky, M. J. The ultrastructural basis of transcapillary exchanges. *J. Gen. Physiol.*, **52**, 64–95 (1968)

44. Casley-Smith, J. R. An electron microscopical study of the passage of ions through the endothelium of lymphatic and blood capillaries, and through the mesothelium. *Quart. J. Exptl. Physiol.*, **52**, 105–13 (1967)

45. Vogel, G., Ströcker, H. Regionale Unterschiede der Capillarpermeabilität. Untersuchungen über die Penetration von Polyvinylpyrrolidon und endogenen Proteinen aus dem Plasma in die Lymphe von Kaninchen. *Pflügers Arch.*, **294**, 119–26 (1967)

46. Zweifach, B. W., Intaglietta, M. Mechanics of fluid movement across single capillaries in the rabbit. *Microvasc. Res.*, **1**, 83–101 (1968)

47. Mori, K., Yamada, S., Ohori, R., Takada, M., Naito, T. Observations *in vivo*, on the extravasation of various dye fluids from blood vessels into the connective tissue. *Okajimas Folia Anat. Japon.*, **39**, 277–99 (1964)

48. Wiederhielm, C. A. Analysis of small vessel function. In *Physical Bases of Circulatory Transport: Regulation and Exchange*, 313–26 (Reeve, E. B., Guyton, A. C., Eds., Saunders, Philadelphia, Pa., 381 pp., 1967)

49. Yudilevich, D. L., Alvarez, O. A. Water, sodium, and thiourea transcapillary diffusion in the dog heart. *Am. J. Physiol.*, **213**, 308–14 (1967)

50. Alvarez, O. A., Yudilevich, D. L. Heart capillary permeability to lipid-insoluble molecules. *J. Physiol. (London)*, **202**, 45–58 (1969)

51. Yudilevich, D. L., Renkin, E. M.,

Alvarez, O. A., Bravo, I. Fractional extraction and transcapillary exchange during continuous and instantaneous tracer administration. *Circ. Res.*, **23**, 325–36 (1968)

52. Lassen, N. A., Trap-Jensen, J. Theoretical considerations on measurement of capillary diffusion capacity in skeletal muscle by the local clearance method. *Scand. J. Clin. Lab. Invest.*, **21**, 108–15 (1968)

53. Trap-Jensen, J., Lassen, N. A. Increased capillary diffusion capacity for small ions in skeletal muscle in long-term diabetics. *Scand. J. Clin. Lab. Invest.*, **21**, 116–22 (1968)

54. Appelgren, L., Lewis, D. H. Capillary permeability-surface area product (PS) of Renkin in human skeletal muscle. *Acta Med. Scand.*, **184**, 281–82 (1968)

55. Strandell, T., Shepherd, J. T. The effect in humans of exercise on relationship between simultaneously measured ^{133}Xe and ^{24}Na clearances. *Scand. J. Clin. Lab. Invest.*, **21**, 99–107 (1968)

56. Renkin, E. M. Transport of potassium-42 from blood to tissue in isolated mammalian skeletal muscles. *Am. J. Physiol.*, **197**, 1205–10 (1959)

57. Kety, S. S. The theory and applications of the exchange of inert gas at the lungs and tissues. *Pharmacol. Rev.*, **3**, 1–41 (1951)

58. Crone, C., Garlick, D. A comparison of two methods of assessing capillary permeability in isolated perfused muscle based on single injection technique. *Acta Physiol. Scand.*, **76**, 7A–8A (1969)

59. Lundgren, O., Mellander, S. Augmentation of tissue-blood transfer of solutes by transcapillary filtration and absorption. *Acta Physiol. Scand.*, **70**, 26–41 (1967)

60. Renkin, E. M. Blood flow and transcapillary exchange in skeletal and cardiac muscle. *Intern. Symp. Coronary Circ. Energetics Myocardium, Milan*, 18–30 (Karger, Basel/New York, 1967)

61. Renkin., E. M. Transcapillary exchange in relation to capillary circulation. *J. Gen. Physiol.*, **52**, 96–108 (1968)

62. Wollman, H., Smith, T. C., Stephen, G. W., Colton, E. T. III, Gleaton, H. E., Alexander, S. C. Effects of extremes of respiratory and metabolic alkalosis on cerebral blood flow in man. *J. Appl. Physiol.*, **24**, 60–65 (1968)

63. Plum, F., Posner, J. B., Smith, W. W. Effect of hyperbaric-hyperoxic hyperventilation on blood, brain, and CSF lactate. *Am. J. Physiol.*, **215**, 1240–44 (1968)

64. Granholm, L., Siesjö, B. K. The effects of hypercapnia and hypocapnia upon the cerebrospinal fluid lactate and pyruvate concentrations and upon the lactate, pyruvate, ATP, ADP, phosphocreatine and creatine concentrations of cat brain tissue. *Acta Physiol. Scand.*, **75**, 257–66 (1969)

65. Granholm, L., Lukjanova, L., Siesjö, B. K. Tissue NADH levels in the rat brain during pronounced hyperventilation. *Acta Physiol. Scand.*, **72**, 533–34 (1968)

66. Cohen, P. J., Alexander, S. C., Smith, T. C., Reivich, M., Wollman, H. Effects of hypoxia and normocarbia on cerebral blood flow and metabolism in conscious man. *J. Appl. Physiol.*, **23**, 183–89 (1967)

67. Kjällquist, A., Siesjö, B. K., Zwetnow, N. Effects of increased intracranial pressure on cerebral blood flow and on cerebral venous pO_2 pCO_2, pH, lactate and pyruvate in dogs. *Acta Physiol. Scand.*, **75**, 267–75 (1969)

68. Kjällquist, A., Siesjö, B. K., Zwetnow, N. Effects of increased intracranial pressure on cerebral blood flow and on cerebrospinal fluid HCO_3, pH, lactate and pyruvate in dogs. *Acta Physiol. Scand.*, **75**, 345–52 (1969)

69. Betz, E., Heuser, D. Cerebral cortical blood flow during changes of acid-base equilibrium of the brain. *J. Appl. Physiol.*, **23**, 726–33 (1967)

70. Ingvar, D. H., Lassen, N. A., Siesjö, B. K., Skinhøj, E., Eds. CBF & CSF. IIIrd International Symposium on Cerebral Blood Flow and Cerebro-Spinal Fluid. Lund-Copenhagen, May 9-11, 1968. *Scand. J. Clin. Lab. Invest.*, 21–22, *Suppl. 102* (1968)

71. Baldy-Moulinier, M., Ingvar, D. H. EEG frequency content related to regional blood flow of cerebral cortex in cat. *Exptl. Brain Res.*, **5**, 55–60 (1968)

72. Langfitt, T. W., Kassell, N. F. Cerebral vasodilatation produced by brain-stem stimulation: neurogenic control vs. autoregulation. *Am. J. Physiol.*, **215**, 90–97 (1968)

73. Mchedlishvili, G. I., Nikolaishvili, L. S. Zum nervösen Mechanismus der funktionellen Dilatation der Piaarterien. *Pflügers Arch.*, **296**, 14–20 (1967)

74. Romanul, F. C. A. Capillary supply and metabolism of muscle fibers. *Arch. Neurol.*, **12**, 497–509 (1965)

75. Hilton, S. M. The search for the cause of functional hyperemia in skeletal muscle. In *Symp. Circ. Skeletal Muscle, Smolinice, 1966*, 137–44 (Hudlická, O., Ed., Pergamon, Oxford, 356 pp., 1968)

76. Hilton, S. M., Vrbová, G. Absence of functional hyperaemia in the soleus muscle of the cat. *J. Physiol. (London)*, **194**, 86P–87P (1968)

77. Kontos, H. A., Richardson, D. W., Patterson, J. L., Jr. Vasodilator effect of hypercapnic acidosis on human forearm blood vessels. *Am. J. Physiol.*, **215**, 1403–5 (1968)

78. Kontos, H. A., Richardson, D. W., Patterson, J. L., Jr. Roles of hypercapnia and acidosis in the vasodilator response to hypercapnic acidosis. *Am. J. Physiol.*, **215**, 1406–8 (1968)

79. Daugherty, R. M., Jr., Scott, J. B., Dabney, J. M., Haddy, F. J. Local effects of O_2 and CO_2 on limb, renal, and coronary vascular resistances. *Am. J. Physiol.*, **213**, 1102–10 (1967)

80. Detar, R., Bohr, D. F. Oxygen and vascular smooth muscle contraction. *Am. J. Physiol.*, **214**, 241–44 (1968)

81. Detar, R., Bohr, D. F. Adaptation to hypoxia in vascular smooth muscle. *Fed. Proc.*, **27**, 1416–19 (1968)

82. Honig, C. R. Control of smooth muscle actomyosin by phosphate and 5'AMP: Possible role in metabolic autoregulation. *Microvasc. Res.*, **1**, 133–46 (1968)

83. Martini, J., Honig, C. R. Direct measurement of intercapillary distance in beating rat heart *in situ* under various conditions of O_2 supply. *Microvasc. Res.*, **1**, 244–56 (1969)

84. Mellander, S., Johansson, B., Gray, S., Jonsson, O., Lundvall, J.,

Ljung, B. The effects of hyperosmolarity on intact and isolated vascular smooth muscle. Possible role in exercise hyperemia. *Angiologica*, **4**, 310–22 (1967)

85. Gray, S. D., Lundvall, J., Mellander, S. Regional hyperosmolarity in relation to exercise hyperemia. *Acta Physiol. Scand.*, **73**, 11A–12A (1968)

86. Lundvall, J., Mellander, S., White, T. Hyperosmolality and vasodilatation in human skeletal muscle. *Acta Physiol. Scand.*, **77**, 224–33 (1969)

87. Lundvall, J. Further studies on regional hyperosmolality in relation to exercise hyperemia. *Acta Physiol. Scand.*, *Suppl. 330*, 98 (1969)

88. Boyd, I. A., Forrester, T. The release of adenosine triphosphate from frog skeletal muscle *in vitro. J. Physiol. (London)*, **199**, 115–35 (1968)

89. Kjellmer, I., Odelram, H. The effect of some physiological vasodilators on the vascular bed of skeletal muscle. *Acta Physiol. Scand.*, **63**, 94–102 (1965)

90. Shepherd, J. T. Bayliss response in the umbilical artery. *Fed. Proc.*, **27**, 1408–9 (1968)

91. Baez, S. Bayliss response in the microcirculation. *Fed. Proc.*, **27**, 1410–15 (1968)

92. Johnson, P. C. Autoregulatory responses of cat mesenteric arterioles measured in vivo. *Circ. Res.*, **22**, 199–212 (1968)

93. Mellander, S., Öberg, B., Odelram, H. Vascular adjustments to increased transmural pressure in cat and man with special reference to shifts in capillary fluid transfer. *Acta Physiol. Scand.*, **61**, 34–48 (1964)

94. Johnson, P. C., Wayland, H. Regulation of blood flow in single capillaries. *Am. J. Physiol.*, **212**, 1405–15 (1967)

95. Lundvall, J., Mellander, S., Sparks, H. Myogenic response of resistance vessels and precapillary sphincters in skeletal muscle during exercise. *Acta Physiol. Scand.*, **70**, 257–68 (1967)

96. Hochberger, A. I., Zweifach, B. W. Analysis of critical closing pressure in the perfused rabbit ear. *Am. J. Physiol.*, **214**, 962–68 (1968)

97. Elkington, E. J. Finger blood flow in Antarctica. *J. Physiol. (London)*, **199**, 1–10 (1968)

98. Gaskell, P., Long, K. L. The effect of repeated cold exposure of the hand on the reactivity of digital vessels. *Can. J. Physiol. Pharmacol.*, **47**, 261–65 (1969)

99. Sams, W. M., Jr., Winkelmann, R. K. Temperature effects on isolated resistance vessels of skin and mesentery. *Am. J. Physiol.*, **216**, 112–16 (1969)

100. Webb-Peploe, M. M., Shepherd, J. T. Responses of the superficial limb veins of the dog to changes in temperature. *Circ. Res.*, **22**, 737–46 (1968)

101. Webb-Peploe, M. M., Shepherd, J. T. Response of dog's cutaneous veins to local and central temperature changes. *Circ. Res.*, **23**, 693–99 (1968)

102. Webb-Peploe, M. M., Shepherd, J. T. Peripheral mechanism involved in response of dogs' cutaneous veins to local temperature change. *Circ. Res.*, **23**, 701–8 (1968)

103. Webb-Peploe, M. M. Effect of changes in central body temperature on capacity elements of limb and spleen. *Am. J. Physiol.*, **216**, 643–46 (1969)

104. Hyman, C., Wong, W. H. Capillary filtration coefficient in the extremities of man in high environmental temperatures. *Circ. Res.*, **22**, 251–61 (1968)

105. Polster, J., Seller, H., Langhorst, P., Koepchen, H. P. Zeitliche Eigenschaften der Vasomotorik. I. Über den Verlauf von Widerstandsänderungen an Hautgefässen bei indirekter Reizung. *Pflügers Arch.*, **296**, 95–109 (1967)

106. Hammond, M. C., Davis, D. L., Dow, P. Rate of development of constrictor responses of the dog paw vasculature. *Am. J. Physiol.*, **216**, 414–20 (1969)

107. Hammond, M. C., Davis, D. L., Dow, P. Segmental responses of dog paw vasculature. *Circ. Res.*, **23**, 1–9 (1968)

108. Paessler, H., Schlepper, M., Westermann, K. W., Witzleb, E. Venentonusreaktionen in kapazitiven Hautgefässen bei passiver und aktiver Orthostase. *Pflügers Arch.*, **302**, 315–32 (1968)

109. Sejrsen, P. Epidermal diffusion bar-

rier to ^{133}Xe in man and studies of clearance of ^{133}Xe by sweat. *J. Appl. Physiol.*, **24**, 211–16 (1968)

110. Lesser, G. T., Deutsch, S. Measurement of adipose tissue blood flow and perfusion in man by uptake of ^{85}Kr. *J. Appl. Physiol.*, **23**, 621–30 (1967)

111. Herd, J. A., Goodman, H. M., Grose, S. A. Blood flow rates through adipose tissues of unanesthetized rats. *Am. J. Physiol.*, **214**, 263–68 (1968)

112. Öberg, B., Rosell, S. Sympathetic control of consecutive vascular sections in canine subcutaneous adipose tissue. *Acta Physiol. Scand.*, **71**, 47–56 (1967)

113. Fredholm, B., Rosell, S. Effects of adrenergic blocking agents on lipid mobilization from canine subcutaneous adipose tissue after sympathetic nerve stimulation. *J. Pharmacol. Exptl. Therap.*, **159**, 1–7 (1968)

114. Derry, D. M., Schönbaum, E., Steiner, G. Two sympathetic nerve supplies to brown adipose tissue of the rat. *Can. J. Physiol. Pharmacol.*, **47**, 57–63 (1969)

115. Beilenson, S., Schachter, M., Smaje, L. H. Secretion of kallikrein and its role in vasodilatation in the submaxillary gland. *J. Physiol. (London)*, **199**, 303–17 (1968)

116. Hilton, S. M., Torres, S. H. Bradykinin and functional vasodilatation in the submandibular salivary gland in the cat. *J. Physiol. (London)*, **189**, 69P–70P (1967)

117. Gautvik, K. M., Hilton, S. M., Torres, S. H. Consumption of the plasma substrate for glandular kallikrein on activation of the submandibular salivary gland. *J. Physiol. (London)*, **197**, 22P–23P (1968)

118. Skinner, N. S., Jr., Webster, M. E. Kinins, beta-adrenergic receptors and functional vasodilatation in the submaxillary gland of the cat. *J. Physiol. (London)*, **195**, 505–19 (1968)

119. Schachter, M., Beilenson, S. Mediator of vasodilatation in the submaxillary gland. *Fed. Proc.*, **27**, 73–75 (1968)

120. Ahlquist, R. P. Agents which block adrenergic β-receptors. *Ann. Rev. Pharmacol.*, **8**, 259–72 (1968)

121. Garrett, J. R. The innervation of salivary glands. IV. The effects

of certain experimental procedures on the ultra-structure of nerves in glands of the cat. *J. Roy. Microscop. Soc.*, **86**, 15–31 (1966)

122. Emmelin, N., Garrett, J. R., Ohlin, P. Neural control of salivary myoepithelial cells. *J. Physiol. (London)*, **196**, 381–96 (1968)

123. Emmelin, N. Nervous control of salivary glands. In *Handbook of Physiology*, **II**, Sect. 6, 595–632 (Code, C. F., Heidel, W., Eds., Williams & Wilkins, Baltimore, Md., 1967)

124. Jacobson, E. D. Secretion and blood flow in the gastrointestinal tract. In *Handbook of Physiology*, **II**, Sect. 6, 1043–62 (See Ref. 123)

125. Hilton, S. M., Jones, M. The role of plasma kinin in functional vasodilatation in the pancreas. *J. Physiol. (London)*, **195**, 521–33 (1968)

126. Graham, J. D. P., Lever, J. D., Spriggs, T. L. B. An examination of adrenergic axons around pancreatic arterioles of the cat for the presence of acetylcholinesterase by high resolution autoradiographic and histochemical methods. *Brit. J. Pharmacol.*, **33**, 15–20 (1968)

127. Harper, A. A., Reed, J. D., Smy, J. R. Gastric blood flow in anaesthetized cats. *J. Physiol. (London)*, **194**, 795–807 (1968)

128. McGinn, F. P., Mendel, D., Perry, P. M. The effects of alteration of CO_2 and pH on intestinal blood flow in the cat. *J. Physiol. (London)*, **192**, 669–80 (1967)

129. Greenway, C. V., Lawson, A. E. Effect of adrenaline and propranolol on the superior mesenteric artery blood flow. *Can. J. Physiol. Pharmacol.*, **46**, 906–8 (1968)

130. Fronek, K., Stahlgren, L. H. Systemic and regional hemodynamic changes during food intake and digestion in nonanesthetized dogs. *Circ. Res.*, **23**, 687–92 (1968)

131. Shehadeh, Z., Price, W. E., Jacobson, E. D. Effects of vasoactive agents on intestinal blood flow and motility in the dog. *Am. J. Physiol.*, **216**, 386–92 (1969)

132. Haddy, F. J., Chou, C. C., Scott, J. B., Dabney, J. M. Intestinal vascular responses to naturally occurring vasoactive substances. *Gastroenterology*, **52**, 444–51 (1967)

133. Scott, J. B., Dabney, J. M. Relation of gut motility to blood flow in the ileum of the dog. *Circ. Res.*, **14–15**, *Suppl. 1*, 235–39 (1964)

134. Jacobson, E. D. The gastrointestinal circulation. *Ann. Rev. Physiol.*, **30**, 133–46 (1968)

135. Lutz, J., Peiper, U., Bauereisen, E. Auftreten und Verhalten venovasomotorischer Reaktionen in der Leberstrombahn. *Pflügers Arch.* **299**, 311–25 (1968)

136. Chou, C. C., Emerson, T. E., Jr. Local effects of Na^+, K^+, Mg^{++}, and Ca^{++} on vascular resistances in the dog liver. *Am. J. Physiol.*, **215**, 1102–6 (1968)

137. Greenway, C. V., Lawson, A. E., Mellander, S. The effects of stimulation of the hepatic nerves, infusions of noradrenaline and occlusion of the carotid arteries on liver blood flow in the anaesthetized cat. *J. Physiol. (London)*, **192**, 21–41 (1967)

138. Shoemaker, W. C., Elwyn, D. H. Liver: Functional interactions within the intact animal. *Ann. Rev. Physiol.*, **31**, 227–68 (1969)

139. Ross, G. Effects of catecholamines on splenic blood flow in the cat. *Am. J. Physiol.*, **213**, 1079–83 (1967)

140. Greenway, C. V., Lawson, A. E., Stark, R. D. Vascular responses of the spleen to nerve stimulation during normal and reduced blood flow. *J. Physiol. (London)*, **194**, 421–33 (1968)

141. Viveros, O. H., Garlick, D. G., Renkin, E. M. Sympathetic beta adrenergic vasodilatation in skeletal muscle of the dog. *Am. J. Physiol.*, **215**, 1218–25 (1968)

142. Ignarro, L. J., Titus, E. The presence of antagonistically acting alpha and beta adrenergic receptors in the mouse spleen. *J. Pharmacol. Exptl. Therap.*, **160**, 72–80 (1968)

143. Davies, B. N., Horton, E. W., Withrington, P. G. The occurrence of prostaglandin E_2 in splenic venous blood of the dog following splenic nerve stimulation. *Brit. J. Pharmacol.*, **32**, 127–35 (1968)

144. Davies, B. N., Withrington, P. G. The effects of prostaglandins E_1 and E_2 on the smooth muscle of the dog spleen and on its re-

sponses to catecholamines, angiotensin and nerve stimulation. *Brit. J. Pharmacol.*, **32**, 136–44 (1968)

145. Hedquist, P., Brundin, J. Inhibition by prostaglandin E_1 of noradrenaline release and of effector response to nerve stimulation in the cat spleen. *Life Sci.*, **8**, Part I, 389–95 (1969)

146. Horton, E. W. Hypotheses on physiological roles of prostaglandins. *Physiol. Rev.*, **49**, 122–61 (1969)

147. Lockett, M. F. Effects of changes in Po_2, Pco_2 and pH on the total vascular resistance of perfused cat kidneys. *J. Physiol. (London)*, **193**, 671–78 (1967)

148. Honda, N., Aizawa, C., Yoshitoshi, Y. Postocclusive reactive hyperemia in the rabbit kidney. *Am. J. Physiol.*, **215**, 190–96 (1968)

149. Basar, E., Weiss, C. Analyse des Frequenzganges druckinduzierter Änderungen des Strömungswiderstandes isolierter Rattennieren. *Pflügers Arch.*, **304**, 121–35 (1968)

150. Liebau, G., Levine, D. Z., Thurau, K. Micropuncture studies on the dog kidney. I. The response of the proximal tubule to changes in systemic blood pressure within and below the autoregulatory range. *Pflügers Arch.*, **304**, 57–68 (1968)

151. McKenna, O. C., Angelakos, E. T. Adrenergic innervation of the canine kidney. *Circ. Res.*, **22**, 345–54 (1968)

152. Wågermark, J., Ungerstedt, U., Ljungqvist, A. Sympathetic innervation of the juxtaglomerular cells of the kidney. *Circ. Res.*, **22**, 149–53 (1968)

153. McKenna, O. C., Angelakos, E. T. Acetylcholinesterase-containing nerve fibers in the canine kidney. *Circ. Res.*, **23**, 645–51 (1968)

154. Aukland, K. Effect of adrenaline, noradrenaline, angiotensin and renal nerve stimulation on intrarenal distribution of blood flow in dogs. *Acta Physiol. Scand.*, **72**, 498–509 (1968)

155. Aukland, K., Wolgast, M. Effect of hemorrhage and retransfusion on intrarenal distribution of blood flow in dogs. *J. Clin. Invest.*, **47**, 488–501 (1968)

156. Feigl, E., Johansson, B., Löfving, B. Renal vasoconstriction and the "defence reaction". *Acta Physiol. Scand.*, **62**, 429–35 (1964)

157. Aukland, K. Vasopressin and intrarenal blood flow distribution. *Acta Physiol. Scand.*, **74**, 173–82 (1968)

158. Vander, A. J. Control of renin release. *Physiol. Rev.*, **47**, 359–82 (1967)

COMPARATIVE PHYSIOLOGY: CHROMATOPHORES[1] 1048

Milton Fingerman

Department of Biology, Tulane University
New Orleans, Louisiana

Introduction

The term chromatophore has sometimes been used to designate any pigment-containing cell found in animals. A more useful definition is that of Parker (1) and Prosser & Brown (2) which restricts it to cells and organs that effect color changes by the centripetal or centrifugal migration of the pigment they contain. If the restricted definition of the term were adopted by all investigators, a degree of ambiguity would be avoided in the literature. Fitzpatrick et al. (3) in revising the terminology of vertebrate melanin-containing cells also accepted the viewpoint that a chromatophore is a particular type of pigment cell by defining a melanocyte as "a cell which synthesizes a specialized melanin-containing organelle, the melanosome" (mature melanin granule) and a melanophore as "a type of melanocyte which participates with other chromatophores in the rapid color changes of animals by intracellular displacement (aggregation and dispersion) of melanosomes". However, the term melanophore has also been used for chromatophores of some invertebrates where the pigment has the appearance of melanin, but is not, as in the shrimp *Crangon crangon* which produces ommochromes instead [Goodwin (4)]. Because one of the definitions of "melano-" is black or dark, I propose that investigators feel free to use the term "melanophore" for all such dark (brown, brown-black, black) chromatophores, regardless of the chemical nature of the pigment. This proposal is in keeping with the suggestion of Bagnara (5) who in discussing nonmelanophore chromatophores of vertebrates recommended that they should be named according to their color or general pigmentary appearance and not according to the chemical nature of the pigment. Chromatophores which appear yellow would then be termed xanthophores or yellow chromatophores, and those appearing red, erythrophores or red chromatophores. The pigment of red and yellow chromatophores consists of pteridines in addition to the well-known carotenoids. Matsumoto (6) has found that in the swordtail *Xiphophorus helleri* the pteridines occur in membrane-bound granules which he

[1] The research of the author is supported by grant GB-7595X from the National Science Foundation.

345

called pterinosomes. Mature pterinosomes have a distinct internal lamellar structure in contrast to melanosomes where the matrix is obscured by the electron-dense melanin.

Several terms have been used for chromatophores with white pigment. These include, in addition to white chromatophore, leucophore, iridophore, iridocyte, iridoleucophore, and guanophore. The latter term was used because they contain guanine. Depending upon the size, shape, and intracellular distribution of the pigment granules, these cells impart different degrees of coloration and iridescence to the body surface. If the pigment can migrate, the effector is then a chromatophore as defined above, and I suggest that only the terms white chromatophore, leucophore, and iridophore be used. But if the pigment does not migrate, as in the case of the iridescent cells in the skin of the squid, iridocyte would be the proper term. Use of iridophore would imply that considerable iridescence is imparted to the skin of the chromatophore. The term guanophore should be discarded not only because these cells contain pigments in addition to guanine, but also in keeping with the suggestion of naming chromatophores by their appearance and not by the chemical nature of their contained pigment.

Earlier studies of chromatophores were more commonly of the organismic variety whereas increasingly these pigmentary effectors are being studied at the cellular level to elucidate the mechanism of pigment migration. The last general review of chromatophores and their control was by Fingerman (7). The present review is not intended to be an all-embracing treatment of chromatophores and their control. Rather, it will be devoted to a selective discussion of recent literature dealing with structure of chromatophores (especially recent ultrastructural observations), chromatophore control at the organismic level, electrophysiology of the multicellular chromatophores of cephalopods, substances controlling intermedin (MSH = melanocyte-stimulating hormone) release, and in a concluding section experiments designed to elucidate mechanisms of chromatophorotropin action at the cellular level.

STRUCTURE OF CHROMATOPHORES

Falk & Rhodin (8) published the first study of the ultrastructure of a chromatophore with the anticipation that its elucidation would provide insight into the mechanism of pigment movement. Using dermal melanophores of the guppy *Lebistes reticulatus,* they reported that each of these cells essentially has a thick cell membrane within which is a cytoplasmic sac, bounded by a thinner membrane, which contains the pigment granules and nucleus. Recent investigation, with refined techniques, failed to confirm their findings. Fujii (9) using the same species found no inner sac and concluded that the thick (about 1200 Å) outer membrane reported by Falk & Rhodin is the subepidermal basement membrane and that the membrane of the so-called inner sac is the true cell membrane. Falk & Rhodin had also reported the presence between the outer and inner membranes of fibrils that appeared to be contractile and involved in concentrating the melanin granules by compressing the inner sac. Fujii, on the other hand, identified these fibrils as collagen located outside the melanophores. Structures he observed within the melanophore, in addition to the melanin granules, included the nucleus, mitochondria, ribosomes, smooth-surfaced endoplasmic reticulum, and micropinocytotic vesicles, but no structure was found that could be directly (mechanically) involved in providing the motive force to the melanosomes. When the melanin was concentrated in the center of the melanophore the branches were devoid of pigment, which supports the conclusion of earlier investigators who worked at the light microscope level that such chromatophores are not ameboid but have a fixed cell outline. Fujii (10) also determined the ultrastructure of dermal melanophores in the tail fin of another fish, the goby *Chasmichthys gulosus,* and found them very similar to those in *Lebistes.*

Bikle, Tilney & Porter (11) have described the ultrastructure of dermal melanophores in a third fish, the killifish *Fundulus heteroclitus.* In addition to finding the structures that Fujii did, they observed in the branches of these melanophores microtubules, about 225 Å in diameter, aligned parallel to the direction of pigment movement. These microtubules, present in the branches whether the pigment is dispersed or concentrated, seem to define the channels along which the pigment granules move. Although it is not known how the motive force is applied to the melanin granules, it is tempting to consider the possibility that the microtubules are involved. In all of these fish melanophores the melanin granules are membrane bound and typically average about 0.5 μ in diameter. The observations of Bikle, Tilney & Porter have been confirmed on the same species by Novales & Novales (12). A question arises as to why Fujii did not observe microtubules in the melanophores of the two fishes he worked with. Either there is a fundamental difference in the ultrastructure of the melanophores in *Fundulus* as opposed to those in *Lebistes* and *Chasmichthys* or there is a difference in technique that could account for the disagreement. Fujii in his work on *Lebistes* stated that he fixed the tissue in osmium tetroxide (no mention of glutaraldehyde), but he used both fixatives in the work on *Chasmichthys* as did Bikle, Tilney & Porter with *Fundulus.* Without use of glutaraldehyde it is not at all certain that microtubules, if present, could have been detected. So, technique could account for the discrepancy in the case of *Lebistes,* but apparently not in the case of *Chasmichthys.*

Novales & Novales (12, 13) found that the ultrastructure of dermal melanophores in the adult frog *Rana pipiens,* fixed in glutaraldehyde and postfixed in osmium tetroxide, was similar to that seen in the two fishes by Fujii. Although Novales & Novales found microtubules in the melanophores of *Fundulus* they did not see them in adult *Rana* nor did they find any other cytoplasmic structure that might be involved in causing movement of the pigment granules. Jande (14) examined the ultrastructure of both epidermal and dermal melanophores of tadpoles of *R. pipiens* fixed with glutaraldehyde and osmium tetroxide. His description of tadpole dermal melanophores agrees with that of Novales & Novales (12, 13) for the adult melanophores. No microtubules were seen. With the epidermal melanophores, however, only after an intensive search did he find a single microtubule in one of these melanophores, but in the core of the branches of the epidermal melanophores were bundles of fine filaments that extended to the tip and appeared similar to the keratin filaments of the surrounding epidermal cells. These filaments were not seen in the dermal melanophores.

Erythrophores of the swordtail *X. helleri* [Matsumoto (6)] and the goldfish *Carassius auratus* [Matsumoto & Obika (15)] have ultrastructures similar to that of the melanophores described by Fujii (9, 10). The major difference between these erythrophores and these melanophores is the presence of pterinosomes in the former and melanosomes in the latter. The sizes of both granules are similar. No microtubules were reported.

Several ultrastructural studies have been done on iridescent pigment cells, but it is not always manifest whether these cells were true chromatophores. It seems that in some cases they were not, but instead were simply iridocytes that contribute to the general pigmentary pattern and color of the bearer. Taylor (16), however, has described the ultrastructure of the iridophores in larval *R. pipiens*. These cells are known to be capable of dispersing and concentrating their contained pigment. The pigment granules are reflecting plates, ranging in shape from squares to octagons approximately 1.9 μ wide and long, and 0.18 μ thick. Chemical analyses indicated they are composed of guanine, adenine, and hypoxanthine. Setoguti (17) reported a similar ultrastructure for iridophores of the tree frog *Hyla arborea*. The ultrastructural details described by both Taylor and Setoguti are similar to the earlier description of white pigment cells in the Japanese porgy *Chrysophrys major* by Kawaguti & Kamishima (18) where the reflecting plates are probably not capable of migrating, as far as can be interpreted from the description.

It has been known for many years that chromatophores of cephalopods are organs consisting of a pigment-containing cell to which are attached a number of muscle cells whose contraction enlarges the pigment cell. An important question concerning these chromatophores, how the pigment sac returns to its original size when the muscle cells relax, seems to have been resolved by the recent electronmicroscopic study of Cloney & Florey (19) who used the squid *Loligo opalescens*. The pigment-containing cell has a plasmalemma that is extensively folded when the muscle cells are relaxed; but when the muscle cells contract and the pigment cell spreads, the folds disappear. Proximal to the plasmalemma and containing the pigment granules is a previously undescribed cytoelastic sacculus which does not become folded, but instead the thickness of its wall decreases or increases depending upon the tension applied to it. The muscle cells are anchored to the plasmalemma which in turn at each region of attachment is joined on the opposite side to the sacculus. The plasmalemma, contrary to earlier reports, does not account for the elasticity of the pigment-containing cell. The cytoelastic sacculus would seem then to be responsible for retraction of the pigment cell. In addition to the muscle cells (which are not syncytial) and the pigment-containing cell, the chromatophore contains axons that innervate the muscle cells, processes of glial cells that accompany the axons, and sheath cells that surround the pigment cell and muscle cells. Myofilaments were found only in the periphery of the muscle cells which are obliquely striated in this species just as found earlier by Kinosita et al. (20) with the squid *L. edulis*. Weber (21) reported that each chromatophore muscle cell in *L. vulgaris* is innervated by two nerve fibers, one within the core of the muscle fiber and the other near the periphery. Experiments are needed to determine whether they have different functions.

PHYSIOLOGY OF CRUSTACEAN CHROMATOPHORES

Investigators of crustacean chromatophores routinely report the dosages of chromatophorotropins or chromatophorotropin-containing tissues they have injected on the basis of the weight of material or the number of organ equivalents. In contrast, a plethora of methods of assaying these substances and reporting the responses has been employed, with the result that comparison of data from different laboratories has been difficult. In an effort to resolve the difficulty Fingerman, Rao & Bartell (22) suggested that investigators of crustacean chromatophorotropins at least report their data in terms of what they called the Standard Integrated Response (SIR) whose method of calculation they described in detail. Each investigator could, of course, in addition to using the SIR continue to record and process data in any other manner that he considers best for his particular needs.

Chassard-Bouchaud (23) has a lengthy publication in which she discussed the pigmentary patterns of *C. crangon, Palaemon squilla, P. serratus, Hippolyte varians,* and *Athanas nitescens* and their chromatophore responses after transfer from a black to a white background. She found with specimens of the five species in intermolt that the ability of the chromatophores to respond to a white background by dispersion of their white pigment and concentration of their colored and black pigments is related to the sex of the individual, the stage of the intermolt period, the age of the individual, and among females their reproductive state. Juveniles exhibited a more precise response to the white background than did the adults. During intermolt the poorest background responses were exhibited just before ecdysis (stage D_2) and just after (stage A_1). The best responses to background occurred during stage D_1. These stages refer to the stages of the molt cycle as first defined by Drach (24). Adult males always responded more quickly and more nearly completely than did adult females. Furthermore, ovigerous females showed even further reduced ability as compared with nonbreeding adult females.

Brown & Ederstrom (25) had observed that although specimens of the shrimp *C. septemspinosus* are usually pale on a white background and dark on a black background, there were occasional exceptional individuals. Chassard-Bouchaud (23) was able to explain part of the anomalous behavior. If dark specimens of *C. crangon* were placed individually into different white containers they all blanched. But when several dark specimens were simultaneously placed on a white background, they remained dark for the 3-day period of observation, and when a pale individual was placed among these dark ones it darkened in spite of being on a white background. The adaptation of the chromatophores was no longer a function of the background but of the shade of the other specimens. She termed this interesting interaction *effet réciproque*. She did not observe this reciprocal group effect when specimens were placed into black containers.

Aoto (26) has considered the possibility that one portion of the neuroendocrine system of crustaceans contains a substance that normally stimulates release of chromatophorotropins from another portion of the system. Using the prawn *P. paucidens,* he (27) had earlier reported that substances which caused dispersion of the red pigment after injection into assay animals occurred in the brain and eyestalks. But he later found (26) that an extract of brains from prawns that had 2 hours previously received an injection of eyestalk extract evoked less than half the response obtained with an extract of brains from prawns that received an injection of only distilled water. Aoto suggested that at least some of the red pigment-dispersing substance in the eyestalk is a factor that causes the brain to release much of its own red pigment-dispersing hormone. Comparison of the responses to extracts assayed on intact animals and on chromatophores in isolated epidermis should be fruitful in determining the possible role of such releasing factors if present.

Brown & Sandeen (28) had found that at elevated temperatures the melanin of the fiddler crab *Uca pugilator,* from Woods Hole, Massachusetts, tended to concentrate and the white pigment to disperse, and interpreted these responses as thermoregulatory. Concentration of the melanin presumably diminished the area which absorbed heat, while dispersion of the white pigment would have increased the area which reflects it. Wilkens & Fingerman (29) tested and supported this thermoregulatory hypothesis by measuring body temperatures of pale and dark *U. pugilator* exposed to different temperatures after thermocouples had been implanted. Five minutes after crabs with maximally dispersed melanin were exposed to the heat-inducing rays of bright sunlight, their body temperatures were 2°C higher than those of similarly exposed crabs whose melanin was maximally concentrated whereas before exposure to sunlight their body temperatures were virtually the same. Furthermore, spectrophotometric determinations revealed that not only was more visible light reflected from the cephalothorax of a pale crab (its melanin was concentrated) than from a dark crab but that the difference in percentage of reflectance was more striking at longer wavelengths where the light has a greater heating capacity than do the rays at the violet end of the visible spectrum.

Barnwell (30) has recently determined the responses to elevated temperature of the melanophores and leucophores in three other species of *Uca*. He used a temperate species, *U. pugnax,* from the area of Woods Hole, Massachusetts, and two tropical species, *U. galapagensis herradurensis* and *U. zacae,* from Costa Rica. The tropical species showed little evidence of a thermoregulatory response on the part of their chromatophores whereas the responses of *U. pugnax* resembled those of *U. pugilator*. For example, when tropical crabs on a black background were exposed to elevated temperatures the melanin became more dispersed and the white pigment more concentrated. These responses were just the reverse of those expected if the responses were thermoregulatory. Only when the tropical species were maintained on a white background did the melanin concentrate at elevated temperatures but even on this background the white pigment became somewhat concentrated as the temperature was elevated. Barnwell suggested that the poor thermoregulatory behavior of the melanophores and leucophores in the two tropical species may be a reflection both of the narrower range of temperature variation on a tropical coast compared with that on a temperate coast, and of the higher thermal tolerance that tropical species of fiddler crabs are reported [Vernberg & Tashian (31)] to have, compared with temperate species.

The fiddler crab has, in addition to melanophores and leucophores, xanthophores and erythrophores. Because of technical difficulties in observing and staging the yellow chromatophores, very little has been done with them. But Stephens, Friedl & Guttman (32) reported the presence of yellow pigment-dispersing and -concentrating substances in the sinus gland of *U. pugilator*. Sandeen (33) found a white pigment-concentrating substance in *U. pugilator* from Woods Hole but she did not test for a white pigment-dispersing substance. Later the latter substance was found in the crabs *Carcinus maenas* [Powell (34)], *Ocypode platytarsis* [Nagabhushanam & Rao (35)], *U. annulipes* [Nagabhushanam & Rao (36)], *U. pugilator* [Rao, Fingerman & Bartell (37)], and *O. macrocera* [Rao (38)]. Rao, Fingerman & Bartell (37) used *U. pugilator* from the area of Panacea, Florida. In these crabs the white pigment becomes maximally concentrated when intact specimens are placed on a black background, which makes them ideal for use in assays for a white pigment-dispersing substance. Although the white pigment of Woods Hole *U. pugilator* is less dispersed in crabs on a black background then on a white one (28), it does not become maximally concentrated on a black background as it does in Panacea *U. pugilator*.

Extracts of tissues from Panacea *U. pugilator* prepared directly in saline produced either dispersion or concentration of the white pigment but not both (37). With the acetone fractionation technique of Nagabhushanam & Rao (35) it was found that the white pigment-concentrating substance from the crabs *O. platytarsis* (35), *U. annulipes* (36), *U. pugilator* (37), and *O. macrocera* (38) occurred in the acetone-soluble fraction, whereas the white pigment-dispersing substance was in the acetone-insoluble fraction. Sandeen

(33) had concluded from her experiments that a large quantity of melanin-dispersing hormone decreased the expression of the white pigment-concentrating substance. However, as noted above, she was unaware of the white pigment-dispersing hormone.

When Rao, Fingerman & Bartell (37) mixed an aqueous extract of the circumesophageal connectives which produced dispersion of the melanin and only concentration of the white pigment with an aqueous extract of the brain which produced only dispersion of both the melanin and the white pigment, the white pigment-dispersing activity of the latter extract was reduced as was the white pigment-concentrating activity of the former extract, but the response of the melanophores to the mixture increased slightly, presumably because of the additive effect of the melanin-dispersing substances in both extracts. This experiment revealed a mutual antagonism between the white pigment-dispersing and -concentrating substances while suggesting that the antagonism that Sandeen suspected between the melanin-dispersing and white pigment-concentrating substances was merely a coincidence arising because the tissues she used also contained the white pigment-dispersing substance. The white pigment-dispersing substance has now also been found in *U. pugilator* from Woods Hole [Rao & Fingerman (39)].

By means of filter-paper electrophoresis Fingerman (40) found a melanin-concentrating substance in the circumesophageal connectives of *U. pugilator*. The melanin-dispersing hormone has long been known [Carlson (41)]. With regard to the erythrophores of *U. pugilator* Brown (42) has found that this crab has substances with red pigment-dispersing and -concentrating potencies. In recapitulation then, pigment-dispersing and -concentrating substances have now been reported for the four types of chromatophores in *U. pugilator*. But an important question not yet fully answered is whether each type of chromatophore in the fiddler crab is controlled by different pigment-concentrating and -dispersing substances or whether a single chromatophorotropin can activate more than one type. In his publication Brown (42) noted that the melanin-dispersing and red pigment-dispersing substances might be the same substance. But Brown & Fingerman (43) using brains of *U. pugilator* later concluded, from differential solubilities in absolute isopropyl alcohol, that the melanin-dispersing material is different from the red pigment-dispersing substance. More recently, Fingerman & Couch (44) came to the same conclusion for the substances with corresponding actions found in the eyestalks of this crab, their experiments involving filtration of extracts through columns of Sephadex G-25. Although both substances peaked in the same fraction, other fractions were obtained that produced considerable dispersion of the melanin but almost no dispersion of the red pigment. Assays for red pigment-concentrating material in these same fractions did not show enough of it to account for the almost complete absence of a red pigment-dispersing response which might have been the result of antagonism of the red pigment-dispersing substance by a large quantity of the red pigment-concentrating substance. Rao, Fingerman & Bartell (37) considered the possibility that the melanin-dispersing and white pigment-dispersing substances were one and the same, and concluded it is highly unlikely that they are, because extracts of the circumesophageal connectives produced considerable dispersion of the melanin but never had a dispersing action on the white pigment. Furthermore, in eyestalkless *U. pugilator* from Panacea the melanin is fully concentrated while the white pigment is found in all stages ranging from maximally concentrated to maximally dispersed.

Stephens, Friedl & Guttman (32) and Fingerman (40) resolved the melanin-dispersing activity of fresh eyestalk extracts from *U. pugilator* into three peaks by means of filter-paper electrophoresis. By means of column chromatography Kleinholz (45) now has obtained three fractions with melanin-dispersing activity from the eyestalks of the shrimps *Pandalus borealis* and *Penaeus duorarum* after further purification of material that had been partially purified [Kleinholz & Kimball (46, 47)]. Kleinholz (45) also reported that the melanin-dispersing activity consistently accompanies the distal retinal pigment light-adapting activity and suggested that both effects may be due to the same substance.

In the past Kleinholz & Kimball (46) assayed for this retinal pigment hormone on the prawn *Palemonetes vulgaris* and used the melanophores of *U. pugilator*. Although Kleinholz (45) did not state what species of assay animals he used in his most recent publication, presumably they were the same two. *Palaemonetes* lacks melanophores. The same substance may have one effect in *Palemonetes* and another effect in *Uca*. A useful assay would be to test for both activities in *Uca*.

Fernlund & Josefsson (48) have also been purifying a red pigment-concentrating substance extracted from the eyestalks of *Pandalus borealis*. They found the hormone is a peptide, confirming the results of earlier investigators [Fingerman (7)], which contains eight amino acids, aspartic acid, glutamic acid, glycine, leucine, phenylalanine, proline, serine, and tryptophan, and concluded from ultraviolet absorption determinations that this hormone has a minimum molecular weight of about 1000. It is retained on Sephadex G-25, which retains substances having a molecular weight less than about 5000. Fingerman & Couch (49) had previously determined on the basis of retention on Sephadex gels that the red pigment-dispersing hormone from *P. vulgaris* has a molecular weight slightly less than 1500.

Bartell (50), using boiled extracts of eyestalks from *U. pugilator*, determined that the isoelectric point of one of the components having melanin-dispersing activity is about pH 5.15. Bartell & Fluke (51) suggested on the basis of their irradiation studies that this same component has a mass of 3750 daltons. Carlisle (52) found that thioglycollate partially inactivated the melanin-dispersing material from the eyestalks of the crab *C. maenas*, thereby indicating the presence of S–S bonds. Thioglycollate inactivates both oxytocin and vasopressin by reducing the S–S bonds which close the rings of these polypeptide hormones [Ames & van Dyke (53].

Carlisle also noted that the thioglycollate had no apparent effect on the red pigment-concentrating substance from the eyestalks of *Carcinus* which was tested on erythrophores of the prawn *P. serratus*. The latter observation correlates with the fact that Fernlund & Josefsson did not find a sulfur-containing amino acid in their analysis of the red pigment-concentrating substance they extracted from *Pandalus*. Kleinholz & Kimball (47) found that the red pigment-concentrating substance they extracted from eyestalks of *P. borealis* and *P. duorarum* is retained on Sephadex G-10. This gel normally only retains substances smaller than about 700 daltons, which implies that this substance is smaller than the one purified by Fernlund & Josefsson. In addition, Kleinholz & Kimball (47) found by a staining reaction that the active material was a sulfur-containing peptide.

Among the possible explanations for this apparent conflict are that Kleinholz & Kimball's material may have been an impure active fragment of a larger substance, or that more than one red pigment-concentrating substance is present in the eyestalks of these shrimps, and the two sets of investigators were each dealing with a different one. Support of the latter possibility comes from the data of Ōtsu (54) who obtained by means of paper electrophoresis of brain extracts from the crab *Eriocheir japonicus* two substances that concentrated the pigment in erythrophores of the prawn *P. paucidens*. Furthermore, amino acid analysis revealed the sulfur-containing amino acid cystine in both fractions although it is not certain from the description of his technique that Ōtsu had pure fractions. Similarly, Kapitza & Fischer (55) reported that the substances extracted from neuroendocrine tissues of *P. squilla,* one of which disperses the pigment in the large red chromatophores and concentrates the pigment in the small red chromatophores while the other concentrates the pigment in both types of red chromatophores, are peptides consisting in part of sulfur-containing amino acids.

Rao (38), using the crab *O. macrocera,* found that extracts of optic ganglia having a concentration of the ganglia from one eyestalk per dose, the only concentration tested, which were prepared by first gently extracting the eyestalks in ethanol, allowing the alcohol to evaporate, and then suspending the residue in saline, produced a much greater melanin-dispersing response than did a similar extract prepared directly in physiological saline. Rao, Bartell & Fingerman (56) found the same situation with eyestalks of *U. pugilator* at higher extract concentrations; but at lower concentrations, below 0.05 eyestalk per dose, the differences between the extracts were not marked, the material extracted with alcohol producing even somewhat less response than that extracted directly in saline. Extracts prepared directly in saline from freshly dissected, freeze-dried, and oven-dried eyestalks evoked nearly identical melanin-dispersing responses [Rao, Bartell & Fingerman (57)]. However, when such eyestalks were extracted first in ethanol, only the extract prepared from the fresh eyestalks produced the expected large response. Furthermore, the melanin-dispersing material extracted in ethanol is to a large extent destroyed by heat whereas the material in an extract prepared directly in saline is heat stable. These differences in extractability and heat stability between the material obtained with ethanol and that obtained by direct extraction in saline strongly suggest that some component of the melanin-dispersing material in each of these extracts is not the same in both extracts.

Shibley (58) found that the melanophores of large (>15 cm carapace width) male crabs (*Cancer magister*) showed a response to increased incident illumination that was not a direct effect on the melanophores but was mediated through the eyes; the melanin became more dispersed, presumably as a result of the release of melanin-dispersing hormone. No background response of the melanophores was detected. Surgical removal of the sinus glands and medulla terminalis X-organs did not abolish this response to incident illumination, but complete removal of the eyestalks did. Shibley concluded that because the medulla terminalis X-organ-sinus gland complex was dispensable so far as this reaction to increased illumination was concerned, it was most likely that the continued response to increased illumination after removal of the sinus glands and these X-organs was due to release of chromatophorotropins from extra-eyestalk sources (in the body proper) although some other neuroendocrine tissue still remained in the eyestalk. Fingerman & Lowe (59) have previously shown that chromatophorotropins from the body proper are normally involved in regulation of chromatophores in the dwarf crayfish *Cambarellus shufeldti*, and Fingerman & Yamamoto (60) found that upon occasion the melanophores of eyestalkless *U. pugilator* would continue to show rhythmical activity, their pigment being more dispersed by day than at night whereas the usual situation is for the melanin of eyestalkless crabs to become maximally concentrated permanently under normal laboratory conditions. The latter observation was interpreted as due to rhythmical release of chromatophorotropin from sources such as the postcommissural organs in the body proper.

PHYSIOLOGY OF CEPHALOPOD CHROMATOPHORES

A very small amount of research has been done on chromatophores of cephalopods in the past 35 years. Recently, however, Florey (61) provided some highly significant information concerning these chromatophores. Using the squid *L. opalescens,* he confirmed the presence of motor fibers innervating the radial muscles of these multicellular chromatophores, but contrary to the 1928 report of Bozler (62) he found no indication of inhibitory fibers. Electrical stimulation of the chromatophore nerves never resulted directly in relaxation of tonically contracted muscle cells, although sometimes relaxation occurred after partially contracted muscle cells were caused to contract further by stimulating their nerve supply. Acetylcholine caused tonic contraction of the muscle fibers. Tetrodotoxin, which prevents spike generation by at least partially blocking the passive influx of sodium ions, abolished all responses to nerve stimulation but not the effect of added acetylcholine. This showed that the effect of acetylcholine was directly on the muscle rather than indirectly through excitation of the nerve fibers. The drug 5-hydroxytryptamine antagonized the tonic effects of acetylcholine, allowing the muscle cells to return to their resting state. The salivary glands of some cephalopods appear to secrete into the blood 5-hydroxytrpytamine [Bacq & Ghiretti (63)], whose normal role may be assisting in the control of color changes by causing the chromatophores to return to their resting state in the absence of nerve activity. Kriebel & Florey (64) reported more recently as a result of their electrophysiological experiments that acetylcholine does not appear to function as a transmitter substance between the nerve fibers and muscle cells of these chromatophores. Cholinergic blocking agents did not alter neuromuscular transmission nor did acetylcholine affect the transmembrane potential or the membrane resistance of the muscle fibers.

Physiology of Chromatophores in Vertebrates

Fishes.—There is a unanimous agreement from experiments of many investigators that the melanophores of teleosts are innervated by melanin-concentrating axons belonging to the sympathetic nervous system. In support of the physiological evidence, Jacobowitz & Laties (65) found by use of a histochemical fluorescence technique that catecholamine-containing axons lie in close proximity to the melanophores of the cunner *Tautogolabrus adspersus*. The existence of melanin-dispersing nerve fibers still is being questioned by a few investigators, but in the opinion of this reviewer adequate although indirect evidence for such fibers has been provided by the elegant experiments of Parker and his associates (1) on *F. heteroclitus* and the catfish *Ameiurus nebulosus*. Direct proof awaits electrophysiological recording from such fibers. A European minnow, *Phoxinus phoxinus,* has also been investigated in detail with respect to the possible presence of melanin-dispersing fibers. Gray's results (66) cannot logically be explained by the presence of melanin-concentrating fibers alone. He was not able to give an adequate interpretation of his data other than dual innervation. Using a hypophysectomized fish he denervated a portion of the tail fin without interfering with the blood supply. When the fish, which had blanched completely because of having been maintained on a white background, was transferred to a black background the pigment in the normal melanophores dispersed, followed by the melanin in the denervated tail band with the dispersion clearly starting at the margins of the band and proceeding inwards. This sort of result had been interpreted by Parker (1) as due to diffusion inward of a pigment-dispersing transmitter substance from the melanin-dispersing axon terminals surrounding the denervated tail band. Waring (67) had considered Parker's evidence of innervation inconclusive and cited the possibility that the dispersion had been caused by intermedin. However, Gray's experiment with hypophysectomized fish eliminated that possibility.

In 1966 Healey & Ross (68) concluded from injections of a variety of pharmacological agents, "The experiments provided no evidence for the presence of pigment-dispersing fibres" in *P. phoxinus,* but in 1967 Healey (69), on the basis of experiments involving differential rates of regeneration of the severed pigmentomotor tract in the spinal cord, stated in the summary of his paper, "Such observations suggest, in addition to the familiar concept of a nervous aggregating system, the existence of an active pigment-dispersing nervous mechanism." However, in the text of the same publication he stated that on the basis of his experiments "there is good evidence in both directions for nervous action." Healey had subjected the fish to spinal section and then allowed time for regeneration of the chromatic nerves. In some of the fish the ability to darken rapidly was restored before the ability to blanch rapidly. The darkening response was faster than that which occurs in *Phoxinus* by hormonal action. The interpretation was that the melanin-dispersing fibers regenerated faster than did the pigment-concentrating fibers. Grove (70) recently obtained evidence consistent with the proposal that the melanin dispersion which occurs soon after lesioning the spinal chromatic tract in *P. phoxinus* maintained on a white background is an active process involving melanin-dispersing nerve fibers that were stimulated when severed. The melanophores with dispersed pigment in such a spinal-sectioned fish were less sensitive to melanin-aggregating catecholamines than were melanophores with dispersed pigment in intact speciments on a black background.

A cholinergic mechanism had been postulated by Parker (1) for the melanin-dispersing fibers (acetylcholine darkens, for example, *Ameiurus*). However, Watanabe, Kobayashi & Iwata (71) have postulated that at least in *Oryzias latipes* both the melanin-dispersing and -concentrating fibers are adrenergic. Applying epinephrine to the melanophores on isolated scales in saline resulted in melanin concentration. However, pretreatment of an isolated scale with a pharmacological agent such as caffeine, nicotine, or procaine caused a reversal of the action of epinephrine. That is, epinephrine then caused melanin dispersion. Healey & Ross (68) found that acetylcholine produced a very slight melanin-dispersing response in isolated pieces of skin from *Phoxinus,* but sublethal quantities injected into the fish had no darkening effect. Abbott (72), using *F. heteroclitus,* has recently also confirmed the adrenergic nature of its neuronal pigment-concentrating mechanism. However, with respect to the pigment-dispersing mechanism the use of a large number of autonomic blocking agents failed to confirm the cholinergic nature postulated by Parker. Acetylcholine did darken the fish, but only when injected at high concentrations (500 μg per fish). Abbott concluded that the response was a toxic effect. His results are very similar to those of Healey & Ross (68) with *P. phoxinus.*

Scott (73, 74) has continued his study of the melanophores of a flatfish, the sand dab or sand flounder *Scophthalmus aquosus.* There is no unequivocal evidence from Scott's experiments involving nerve sectioning and the formation of caudal bands for pigment-dispersing fibers in this species. Use of a wide range of pharmacological agents confirmed the adrenergic nature of the pigment-concentrating fibers. Propranolol and dihydroxyergotamine, adrenergic blockers, caused localized pigment dispersion after injection into pale fish. Pretreatment of the fish with pyrogallol which inhibits the enzyme catechol-o-methyl transferase whose role is to inactivate catecholamines strikingly potentiated the pigment-concentrating effects of epinephrine and norepinephrine. The effect of pyrogallol pretreatment supports the view that a catecholamine is the normal transmitter substance of the pigment-concentrating nerve fibers. Pure β-intermedin from hogs had no effect on the melanophores. The possibility of control of the melanophores by means of a bloodborne melanin-concentrating principle in addition to the melanin-concentrating nerve fibers has not been ruled out.

Amphibians.—Dermal melanophores have been the chromatophores observed in most investigations of color changes in amphibians. More recently, epidermal melanophores have been studied in some detail and interesting comparisons have been made. It is generally true of amphibians that the dermal melanophores contribute much more to the skin coloration than do the epidermal melanophores. Hadley & Quevedo (75) reported that just as in the dermal melanophores the melanin was more dispersed in the epidermal melanophores of adult frogs *R. pipiens* on a black background than on a white one. The light reflectance from white-adapted epidermis separated from the dermis was approximately 10 per cent greater than from black-adapted epidermis. McGuire & Möller (76) and McGuire (77) found that both types of melanophores in adult *R. pipiens* respond to intermedin. Whereas dermal melanophores with maximally dispersed pigment as a result of intermedin treatment responded to acetylcholine, melatonin, and norepinephrine by concentrating their pigment, these investigators (76, 77) reported that comparably treated epidermal melanophores showed no response to the latter three agents. However, Goldman & Hadley (78) reported more recently that acetylcholine does cause concentration of the pigment in the epidermal melanophores of *R. pipiens*. Hadley & Bagnara (79) confirmed the observation that intermedin disperses the pigment in both types of melanophores, and reported that acetylcholine caused melanin concentration in both types of melanophores. Of perhaps even greater significance is the conclusion of Hadley & Bagnara that contrary to considerable published data [see review of Lande & Lerner (80)], melatonin, which has been considered the most potent melanin-concentrator known for frog skin, had only a weak pigment-aggregating action on the dermal melanophores of adult *R. pipiens*, but was highly effective on the dermal melanophores of tadpoles. These investigators (79) reported that acetylcholine was a much more effective lightening agent of adult skin than either melatonin or norepinephrine.

That intermedin causes dispersion of the melanin in ranid frogs while at the same time causing concentration of the pigment in their iridophores is now well established [Bagnara (81)]. Bagnara (82) more recently compared the responses of the melanophores and iridophores in larvae of *R. pi-*

piens and *R. sylvatica* to a number of naturally occurring and synthetic peptides known to have melanophorotropic activity, to determine if the same portion of the intermedin molecule is required for a response by both types of chromatophore. The peptides tested included two pentapeptides, a hexapeptide, a heptapeptide, an octapeptide, two decapeptides, bovine α-intermedin, and bovine β-intermedin. The responses to the smaller peptides were much weaker than those induced by α-intermedin which contains 13 amino acids or bovine β-intermedin which contains 18 amino scids. The minimal effective doses in grams were the same with α- and β-intermedin for the corresponding type of chromatophore, but the melanophores were more sensitive to these hormones than were the iridophores. However, the strengths of the responses of the melanophores and iridophores to all of the peptides paralleled each other, strongly indicating thereby that common portions of the intermedin molecules were involved in the stimulation of both kinds of chromatophores.

When larvae of *Xenopus laevis,* commonly known as the clawed toad, are kept in darkness for about 30 min the pigment of the melanophores in the distal third of the tail becomes dispersed (tail-darkening reaction). Bagnara (83) postulated that this reaction is caused by an intramelanophore, photolabile melanin-dispersing agent. In contrast to the tail, the pigment in the body melanophores of larval *Xenopus* becomes concentrated when larvae are placed in darkness for 10–15 min (body-blanching reaction). The latter response, Bagnara hypothesized, is controlled by the pineal gland releasing a melanin-concentrating agent, supposedly melatonin which is the active agent in the mammalian pineal gland. Pinealectomized larvae fail to show the body-blanching reaction.

Van der Lek (84) has investigated in great detail the photosensitive dermal melanophores in the tail of larval *Xenopus.* He found that these melanophores are indeed independent effectors as postulated by Bagnara. Using very small beams of visible light, he showed that pigment concentration only occurred in illuminated tail melanophores. Stimulation of a small portion of a melanophore with weak radiation resulted in melanin concentration in the irradiated portion alone. But stimulation with higher intensities resulted first in pigment concentration in the irradiated portion followed by pigment concentration in the nonirradiated portion of the melanophore.

Using tissue-cultured melanophores from neural folds of neurulas of *Xenopus,* Kulemann (85) found that melanin dispersion occurred after the cells were exposed to illumination. More recently, Bagnara & Obika (86) confirmed Kulemann's observation not only with tissue-cultured explants from *Xenopus,* but from *R. pipiens* and *R. esculenia* as well. Direct dark-induced melanin aggregation may supplement the pineal-controlled body-blanching reaction, but the control via the pineal is the dominant one because whereas with tissue cultures the direct response to light (melanin dispersion) occurs very quickly while melanin concentration in darkness is slow, *in vivo* the body-blanching reaction occurs faster than it disappears.

Because of the strong interest in melatonin as a melanin-concentrating substance, Quay & Bagnara (87) determined the relative blanching potencies of 46 indolic and related compounds (including melatonin) on larval *Xenopus*. Five compounds produced a significant degree of blanching. Melatonin was effective at a minimum concentration of 0.0001 μg/ml of aquarium water, next was 6-methoxyindole at 0.1 μg/ml, and then 5-methoxytryptamine, N-acetyl serotonin, and 5-methoxyindole at 10μg/ml. Melatonin was obviously the most potent substance tested. The relatively high dosages, compared with melatonin, required for a significant response to the latter four substances raised some doubt that they had a direct, specific effect on the melanophores. Quay (88) later determined the responses to 37 additional compounds structurally related to melatonin. Of these compounds only 6-hydroxymelatonin produced a significant response at a low concentration (0.1 μg/ml) but it was still quite high compared with the minimum effective concentration (0.001 μg/ml) for melatonin. Quay concluded that there is "a very narrow chemical structure-biological activity relationship among indole derivatives" with respect to the blanching of larval *Xenopus*.

Charlton (89) not only confirmed Bagnara's observation that pinealectomy abolishes the body-blanching reaction of larval *Xenopus*, but he also reported that pinealectomy abolished the ability of larvae and adults to blanch on a white background and of adults to blanch in darkness. Earlier Bagnara (90), after investigating the body-blanching reaction of larval *H. arenicolor* and *R. pipiens*, the mechanisms being presumably the same as in *Xenopus*, had concluded that the body-blanching reaction is the result of direct pineal control of the melanophores and does not involve cessation of intermedin release from the pituitary gland. Charlton has now presented a theory that in larvae and adults darkness directly stimulates release of melatonin from the pineal which in turn both has a direct effect on the melanophores and either causes the release of an intermedin release-inhibiting factor by the hypothalamus or stimulates intermedin release-inhibiting neurons supplying the pars intermedia. The basis for Bagnara's conclusion that melatonin does not inhibit intermedin release was his observation that after melatonin treatment there was no change in the iridophores, only in the melanophores. If the blood titer of intermedin had decreased as a result of cessation of its release, then dispersion of the white pigment presumably would have occurred. Charlton postulated further that melatonin can displace intermedin from melanophores but not from iridophores and that in darkness not enough melatonin is released from the pineal gland to inhibit intermedin release from the pars intermedia sufficiently to be reflected in the state of the iridophores. Removal of the eyes eliminated background responses but not the larval body-blanching reaction or the blanching of the adult in darkness. Charlton then suggested that the response to a white background involves stimulation of the pineal gland via the eyes, but that in darkness the pineal is stimulated directly.

From time to time reports that amphibian chromatophores are innervated have appeared (1). The responses to nerve stimulation and cutting are at best very slight. Even if these chromatophores are innervated, the hormonal control is by far the dominant mechanism. Snell & Kulovich (91) recently found no physiological evidence for innervation of the melanophores in *R. pipiens*. Stimulation of the sciatic nerve did not cause dispersion of the pigment in either the epidermal or dermal melanophores of hypophysectomized frogs and did not inhibit or accentuate the action of intermedin.

Evidence for Intermedin Release-Inhibiting and Release-Stimulating Factors

Sectioning the hypothalamohypophyseal tract of an amphibian results in long-maintained darkening of the skin. The conclusion from this and other older experiments is that the pars intermedia is at least regulated by a release-inhibiting factor from the hypothalamus [Etkin & Rosenberg (92), Etkin (93)]. More recently Kastin & Ross (94) showed that the intermedin content of a pituitary gland from an adult *R. pipiens* whose hypothalamus had been surgically destroyed was less than that from an intact frog. In addition, the body fluids in lesioned frogs contained more melanin-dispersing activity than in the controls. Ito (95), using the frog *R. nigromaculata*, also found in a similar experiment that after the hypophyseal tract had been severed the intermedin content of the pars intermedia decreased markedly. Furthermore, using the electronmicroscope he saw that the number of secretory granules in the pars intermedia of these surgically treated frogs had decreased while the rough-surfaced endoplasmic reticulum was considerably more highly developed than in the controls. These experiments suggested that there was increased synthesis of the hormone as well as increased release after the hypothalamus was destroyed or the tract was severed. Ralph & Sampath (96) and Bercu & Brinkley (97) showed with *R. pipiens* that aqueous extracts of cerebral cortical and hypothalamic tissues contained a substance that inhibited the *in vitro* release of intermedin by the pars intermedia. Ralph & Sampath suggested that the inhibitor found outside the hypothalamus might well not be the same substance as that in the hypothalamus, and that the effect caused by the cerebral cortical tissue might have been due to a neurohumor that does not normally regulate the pars intermedia.

Ralph & Peyton (98) found that extracts prepared from the hypothalamus of adult *R. pipiens* contained a melanin-dispersing substance. A substance having the same effect was also present in the cerebrum in a lesser amount. They (98) concluded that the active material was not of hypophyseal origin because their experiments revealed that the quantity in the cerebrum at first decreased after hypophysectomy and then showed a resurgence about 6 days after the operation. In contrast, Bercu & Brinkley (97) using the same species reported that the adult hypothalamus but not the cerebral cortex contained a melanin-dispersing substance. The latter investigators, not having eliminated the possibility by hypophysectomy that they were dealing with a chromatophorotropic substance of hypophyseal origin, postulated that the activity was due to intermedin present in the hypothalamus through a feedback control loop involved in the inhibition of the secretion of intermedin.

Evidence that the amphibian hypothalamus does have a melanin-dispersing substance of endogenous origin comes from the recent work of Thurmond (99, 100) who not only homoplastically implanted hypothalami from embryos, larvae, and adults of the Pacific treefrog *H. regilla* and the tiger salamander *Ambystoma tigrinum* into hypophysectomized young larvae and obtained both melanin dispersion and concentration of the pigment in the iridophores, but also found that the hypothalami of these young larvae became chromatophorotropically active earlier in development than did their adenohypophyses. Consequently, it does not seem that the responses obtained with the hypothalami of the young tadpoles could have been due to a chromatophorotropin that originated in the adenohypophysis.

A steadily increasing literature shows the existence of a hypothalamic intermedin release-stimulating factor in addition to the release-inhibiting factor. Taleisnik & Orías (101) injected extracts of the median eminence of the rat, a neurohemal area receiving neurosecretory material from the hypothalamus, into rats. Twenty minutes later the pituitaries were removed and assayed for their intermedin content using the skin of the toad *Bufo arenarum*. The intermedin content of the glands had dropped by about 60 per cent with an injection of one fourth of a median eminence. The response was not detected with comparable extracts of the cerebral cortex. Although chromatophores are not found in mammals, they will be mentioned here for comparative purposes. Taleisnik & Tomatis (102) compared the effects of hypothalamic extracts from both rats and toads on the pituitaries of both species and found that the rat hypothalamic extracts induced intermedin depletion in both rats and toads, but they observed no significant intermedin-depleting effect with toad hypothalamic extracts in either species. However, in tests done only on rats, a toad hypothalamic extract was able to prevent the decrease in intermedin content that would have been caused by a rat hypothalamic extract if both extracts were injected together. On the other hand, a substance in the toad pars nervosa caused a decrease in the intermedin content of both the toad and rat pituitaries. It appears then that the toad has a pair of antagonistically acting factors, one intermedin release-inhibiting and the other release-stimulating. The toad hypothalamic substance completely lost its activity after trypsin digestion, which suggests that it is a peptide. Synthetic arginine vasopressin, arginine vasotocin, and oxytocin did not mimic the action of the toad hypothalamic extract. On the other hand, the extract did not inhibit the release of adrenocorticotropic hormone or luteinizing hormone; this supports a specific role for the factor. In further experiments Taleisnik & Tomatis (103) found that an extract of a rat's supraoptic nucleus had no depleting effect on the intermedin content of a rat's pituitary gland but could reduce the release-stimulating action of a median eminence extract, a situation comparable to that with the toad hypothalamic (102) extracts. Both the rat and toad then appear to have both factors. The intermedin release-stimulating factor from sheep seems to be a peptide also with a molecular weight between 1500 and 2000 [Dhariwal et al. (104)].

Etkin (93) has concluded that the inhibitory control of the pars intermedia in R. pipiens is by axons that go directly from the hypothalamus into the pars intermedia and not indirectly by way of the median eminence and the pituitary portal vessels. Knowles (105) has investigated the innervation of the pituitary gland of the dogfish Scylliorhinus stellaris with the electronmicroscope. In the pars intermedia he found two types of nerve fibers (termed A and B) both of which made intimate contact with the intermedin-secretings cells. The type A fibers appeared to be morphologically typical neurosecretory axons which would be expected to possess peptide-containing granules. Type B fibers are thought to possess catecholamine-containing vesicles and, therefore, to belong to what have been considered "ordinary" or nonneurosecretory neurons [e.g. Bercu & Brinkley (97)]. However, both types of fibers are referred to as neurosecretory by some authors [Knowles (106), Cohen (107)]. Type A fibers have vesicles greater than 1000 Å in diameter; type B, 1000 Å or less.

On the basis of his observations that the type A fibers innervated the secretory pole of the intrinsic cells whereas the type B fibers innervated these elongated secretory cells close to the point where they discharge their contents into the blood, Knowles suggested (105, 106) that the A fibers function to inhibit intermedin synthesis while the B fibers contain the release-inhibiting substance. On the other hand, Iturriza (108), also using the electronmicroscope, found only type B fibers in the pars intermedia of B. arenarum, and later (109) expressed the view that these fibers exert their inhibitory control over the pars intermedia by releasing catecholamines at their terminals and are not peptide neurosecretory axons. He had found that injection of monoamine-depleting drugs such as reserpine into B. arenarum resulted in melanin dispersion but had no effect on hypophysectomized toads. Indeed, fluorescence microscopy has revealed adrenergic nerves in the pars intermedia of R. temporaria [Enemar & Falck (110)] and B. arenarum [Enemar, Falck & Iturriza (111)]. On the other hand, Taleisnik & Tomatis (103) tested dopamine, norepinephrine, and serotonin on rats for their effect in inhibiting release of intermedin stimulated by median eminence extracts and found no effect. The latter two investigators, as stated above (102), expressed the view that the toad intermedin release-inhibiting factor is a peptide.

Cohen (107) using X. laevis and Saland (112) using R. pipiens and R. catesbeiana also have examined the ultrastructure of the pars intermedia. In contrast to the observations of Iturriza (110) with B. arenarum, both Cohen and Saland found peptide neurosecretory axon terminals (type A) in the pars intermedia but only near its border with the pars nervosa, whereas type B axons were seen throughout the pars intermedia. This situation also contrasts with that in *Scylliorhinus* (105) where both types of fibers penetrate deeply and make intimate contact with the secretory cells. Saland favored the view that the release-inhibiting substance is a catecholamine because of the restricted distribution of the peptide neurosecretory axons and doubted that there is the dual control of the secretory cells in these anurans that was described for *Scylliorhinus*, but Cohen stated that the possibility of dual control by type A and type B fibers as in the dogfish pituitary (105) could not be excluded on the basis of his observations alone.

PROPOSED MECHANISM OF CHROMATOPHOROTROPIN ACTION

Studies of the mechanism of action of chromatophorotropins at the cellular level have involved a number of different approaches. Fuchs & Lotz (113) and Fuchs (114), using isolated pieces of skin from *R. temporaria,* found that the oxygen consumption of the skin increased in the presence of melanin-dispersing substances (adrenocorticotropic hormone, caffeine, and a partially purified pituitary extract). Energy from oxidative metabolism was necessary for dispersion of the melanin and for maintenance of the dispersed state as well. However, oxygen was not required for melanin concentration to occur. Wright (115) had earlier postulated, on the basis of the results with various metabolic blocking agents, that the energy of glycolysis is necessary for blanching the skin from *R. pipiens* and *R. clamitans.* He had also suggested that intermedin might be exerting its melanin-dispersing effect by inhibiting the glycolysis necessary for melanin aggregation. It would now, however, seem that the energy from oxidative metabolism is necessary for melanin dispersion while the energy from glycolysis is needed for melanin concentration.

Although such metabolic studies yield extremely useful information, there still remains the problem of unraveling the earlier events that trigger the changes in chromatophore metabolism. One approach has been consideration of the possibility that the chromatophorotropins alter the permeability of the chromatophore membrane. Novales (116) demonstrated that sodium is absolutely required for the action of intermedin on the melanophores in frog skin (*R. pipiens*). Because melanin dispersion in the skin of *R. pipiens* can be induced in the absence of sodium by pharmacological agents such as caffeine and aminophylline (116), sodium ions are quite likely involved in the primary event or events whereby melanin dispersion is induced by intermedin. The most probable theory is that intermedin increases the permeability of the melanophore to sodium, although it is also possible that the hormone inhibits the extrusion of sodium [Novales (117)]. In either event the result would be a net accumulation of sodium in the cell, which presumably in some manner results in triggering melanin dispersion. In contrast to the situation in *R. pipiens,* in the fiddler crab *U. pugnax* sodium ions can be replaced by potassium or lithium with no significant change in the melanin-dispersing response to sinus gland extracts [Fingerman, Miyawaki & Oguro

(118)]. Melanophores of the spiny dogfish *Squalus acanthias* likewise do not have a specific sodium requirement for the action of intermedin. Novales & Novales (119) found that choline, potassium, lithium, and magnesium could replace sodium, and suggested that this difference in specificity between the melanophores of *Squalus* and *Rana* could reflect the more primitive nature of elasmobranchs compared with amphibians. The specificity may have increased during evolution.

Dikstein, Weller & Sulman (120) and Dikstein & Sulman (121), studying the tree frog *H. arborea,* have concluded that calcium ions are required for darkening of the skin and that calcium is the mediator of the action of intermedin in this species. Dikstein, Tal & Sulman (122) postulated on the basis of their results with a variety of drugs and metabolic inhibitors that in this hylid, at least, activation of melanin dispersion occurs because intermedin causes the loss of a high-energy compound connected with an ATPase structural protein complex of the melanophore membrane. This alteration in the state of the membrane is visualized as inducing the permeability changes which then trigger melanin dispersion.

Marsland (123) reported earlier that exposure of the melanophores on scales of *F. heteroclitus* to high pressures resulted in both solation of the peripheral cytoplasm and melanin dispersion and he suggested that as melanin dispersion occurs there is a progressive solation of the melanophore cytoplasm and that melanin concentration involves reestablishment of the gel state. Taking advantage of the fact that heavy water (D_2O) enhances gelation by fostering polymerization of protein subunits, Marsland & Meisner (124) using scale melanophores of the same species of fish have shown that for maximal melanin dispersion greater pressures were required, 14,000 and 16,000 psi in 50 and 70 per cent D_2O solutions respectively at 20°C, than in a regular aqueous medium where a pressure of 8,000–9,000 psi was sufficient. This observation is in harmony with Marsland's (123) hypothesis that melanin dispersion is closely associated with cytoplasmic solation. Entry of water in the chromatophore may normally also be involved in the process of melanin migration. Hypotonic media produce melanin dispersion and enhance the responses to melanin-dispersing substances [Kulemann (85); Novales (116); Fingerman, Miyawaki & Oguro (117); Novales & Novales (125)].

Bitensky & Burstein (126) and Novales & Davis (127) found that adenosine 3′, 5′-monophosphate (cyclic AMP) mimics the action of intermedin by darkening the skin of *R. pipiens in vitro.* Furthermore, Novales & Davis showed that the response to cyclic AMP is independent of the external sodium concentration. More recently Abe et al. (128) found not only that intermedin brought about an increase in the quantity of cyclic AMP in the skin of *R. pipiens,* but also that when the skin was exposed to a solution containing both norepinephrine and intermedin the norepinephrine almost completely prevented melanin dispersion and the cyclic AMP formation that would otherwise have occurred. Cyclic AMP would seem to be the intracellular mediator of the action of intermedin.

Fingerman & Connell (129) investigated the role of cations in the responses of the erythrophores of the prawn *P. vulgaris* to pigment-concentrating and -dispersing hormones. The red pigment-concentrating hormone was dependent upon sodium ions for a strong response to occur. The red pigment-dispersing hormone had a similar dependency on calcium. With both hormones the response to a constant amount of hormone was proportional to the quantity of the appropriate cation in the medium. This observation supports the theory that cations are involved early in the response to these hormones. Ouabain inhibited the response to the red pigment-concentrating hormone whereas tetrodotoxin enhanced it. Fingerman, Hammond & True (130) found that cyclic AMP caused dispersion of the red pigment in this prawn but had no pigment-concentrating effect, and that the pigment-dispersing response was independent of the external calcium concentration.

Freeman, Connell & Fingerman (131) reported a transmembrane potential of 55 ± 15 mV inside negative for erythrophores of *Palaemonetes* having maximally dispersed pigment. When the external potassium concentration was raised by isosmotic substitution for sodium above a potassium concentration of 20–30 meq/liter, the transmembrane potential decreased linearly with the logarithm of the external potassium concentration, but below 20–30 meq/liter there was a marked deviation from linearity. Therefore, although the transmembrane potential was predominantly a function of the transmembrane potassium gradient, other ions could have made a significant contribution to the potential. Evidence that this was a mixed electrode system comes from Freeman & Fingerman (132) who found that tetrodotoxin caused hyperpolarization of the transmembrane potential. With ten separate animals the potential was 56 ± 4 mV before application of the drug, a value very close to that reported earlier (131), and 63 ± 3 mV about 15 min later. The membrane was electrically inexcitable; an electric current did not trigger a membrane response that led to a nonlinear current-voltage relationship. The transmembrane potential hyperpolarized an average of 5 mV as the red pigment concentrated under the influence added chromatophorotropin. In contrast, Martin & Snell (133) found that intermedin did not cause a change in the transmembrane potential of melanophores in the skin of *R. pipiens* although, of course, pigment dispersion did occur.

With respect to the action of the chromatophorotropins in *Palaemonetes*, it is most likely according to Fingerman (134) that the primary action of the red pigment-concentrating hormone is stimulation of a pump which exchanges sodium ions from inside the erythrophore for potassium ions from the outside, whereas the red pigment-dispersing hormone quite likely stimulates entry of calcium ions into the chromatophore. The heightened internal calcium ion concentration would stimulate synthesis of cyclic AMP which in some manner would then trigger pigment dispersion. The amount of cyclic AMP synthesized is visualized as proportional to the amount of calcium that entered the chromatophore.

With respect to the red pigment-concentrating hormone, it is clear from the action of ouabain, which is to block the active efflux of sodium ions and the action of tetrodotoxin, that a large response to this hormone requires a low internal concentration of sodium ions while at the same time, because of the sodium dependency of this hormone, sodium ions must be outside. The necessity for a high external sodium concentration was postulated as a requirement for operation of the exchange pump. The exchange pump in the presence of red pigment-concentrating hormone presumably is stimulated into producing a high internal $K^+: Na^+$ ratio which results in hyperpolarization of the transmembrane potential while at the same time activating the pigment-concentrating mechanism. The passive fluxes tend to depolarize the membrane. When the red pigment-concentrating hormone is not able to activate the pump as when a high concentration of red pigment-dispersing hormone is present, the pump would operate at a low level resulting in a low internal $K^+: Na^+$ ratio and consequently partial depolarization of the transmembrane potential would occur.

LITERATURE CITED

1. Parker, G. H. *Animal Colour Changes and Their Neurohumours* (Cambridge, New York, 377 pp., 1948)
2. Prosser, C. L., Brown, F. A., Jr. *Comparative Animal Physiology* (Saunders, Philadelphia, 2nd ed., 688 pp., 1961)
3. Fitzpatrick, T. B., Quevedo, W. C., Jr., Levene, A. L., McGovern, V. J., Mishima, Y., Oettle, A. G. Terminology of vertebrate melanin-containing cells: 1965. *Science,* **152,** 88–89 (1966)
4. Goodwin, T. W. Biochemistry of pigments. In *The Physiology of Crustacea,* **I,** 101–40 (Waterman, T. H., Ed., Academic, New York, 670 pp., 1960)
5. Bagnara, J. T. Cytology and cytophysiology of non-melanophore pigment cells. *Intern. Rev. Cytol.,* **20,** 173–205 (1966)
6. Matsumoto, J. Studies on fine structure and cytochemical properties of erythrophores in swordtail, *Xiphophorus helleri,* with special reference to their pigment granules (pterinosomes). *J. Cell Biol.,* **27,** 493–504 (1965)
7. Fingerman, M. Chromatophores. *Physiol. Rev.,* **45,** 296–339 (1965)
8. Falk, S., Rhodin, J. Mechanism of pigment migration within teleost melanophores. In *Electron Microscopy: Proc. Stockholm Conference,* 213–15 (Academic, New York, 1957)
9. Fujii, R. A functional interpretation of the fine structure in the melano-phore of the guppy, *Lebistes reticulatus. Annotationes Zool. Japon.,* **39,** 185–92 (1966)
10. Fujii, R. Correlation between fine structure and activity in fish melanophore. In *Structure and Control of the Melanocyte,* 114–23 (Della Porta, G., Mühlbock, O., Eds., Springer-Verlag, New York, 374 pp., 1966)
11. Bikle, D., Tilney, L. G., Porter, K. R. Microtubules and pigment migration in the melanophores of *Fundulus heteroclitus* L. *Protoplasma,* **61,** 322–45 (1966)
12. Novales, R. R., Novales, B. J. Electron microscopic studies of pigment movements in melanophores. *Am. Zool.,* **6,** 576 (1966)
13. Novales, R. R., Novales, B. J. Cytological and ultrastructural aspects of amphibian melanophore control. In *Structure and Control of the Melanocyte,* 52–59 (See Ref. 10)
14. Jande, S. S. Fine structure of tadpole melanophores. *Anat. Record,* **154,** 533–44 (1966)
15. Matsumoto, J., Obika, M. Morphological and biochemical characterization of goldfish erythrophores and their pterinosomes. *J. Cell Biol.,* **39,** 233–50 (1968)
16. Taylor, J. D. Electron microscopy of iridophores in hypophysectomized *Rana pipiens* larvae. *Am. Zool.,* **6,** 587 (1966)
17. Setoguti, T. Ultrastructure of guanophores. *J. Ultrastruct. Res.,* **18,** 324–32 (1967)

18. Kawaguti, S., Kamishima, Y. Electron microscopic study on the iridophore of the Japanese porgy. *Biol. J. Okayama Univ.*, **10**, 75–81 (1964)

19. Cloney, R. A., Florey, E. Ultrastructure of cephalopod chromatophore organs. *Z. Zellforsch.*, **89**, 250–80 (1968)

20. Kinosita, H., Ueda, K., Takahashi, K., Murakami, A. Contraction of squid chromatophore muscle. *J. Fac. Sci., Univ. Tokyo, Sect. IV*, **10**, 409–19 (1965)

21. Weber, W. Multiple Innervation der Chromatophorenmuskelzellen von *Loligo vulgaris*. *Z. Zellforsch.*, **92**, 367–76 (1968)

22. Fingerman, M., Rao, K. R., Bartell, C. K. A proposed uniform method of reporting response values for crustacean chromatophorotropins: the Standard Integrated Response. *Experientia*, **23**, 962 (1967)

23. Chassard-Bouchaud, C. L'adaptation chromatique chez les Natantia (Crustacés Décapodes). *Cahiers Biol. Marine*, **6**, 469–576 (1965)

24. Drach, P. Mue et cycle d'intermue chez les Crustacés Décapodes. *Ann. Inst. Océanog. Monaco*, **19**, 103–391 (1939)

25. Brown, F. A., Jr., Ederstrom, H. E. Dual control of certain black chromatophores of *Crago*. *J. Exptl. Zool.*, **85**, 53–69 (1940)

26. Aoto, T. The releasing mechanism of chromatophorotropin in the supraesophageal ganglion of the prawn, *Palaemon paucidens*. *Annotationes Zool. Japon.*, **37**, 201–7 (1964)

27. Aoto, T. Chromatophorotropins in the prawn *Palaemon paucidens* and their relationship to long-term background adaptation. *J. Fac. Sci., Hokkaido Univ., Ser. VI* **14**, 544–60 (1961)

28. Brown, F. A., Jr., Sandeen, M. I. Responses of the chromatophores of the fiddler crab, *Uca*, to light and temperature. *Physiol. Zool.*, **21**, 361–71 (1948)

29. Wilkens, J. L., Fingerman, M. Heat tolerance and temperature relationships of the fiddler crab, *Uca pugilator*, with reference to body coloration. *Biol. Bull.*, **128**, 133–41 (1965)

30. Barnwell, F. H. Comparative aspects of the chromatophoric responses to light and temperature in fiddler crabs of the genus *Uca*. *Biol. Bull.*, **134**, 221–34 (1968)

31. Vernberg, F. J., Tashian, R. E. Studies on the physiological variation between tropical and temperate zone fiddler crabs of the genus *Uca*. I. Thermal death limits. *Ecology*, **40**, 589–93 (1959)

32. Stephens, G. C., Friedl, F., Guttman, B. Electrophoretic separation of chromatophorotropic principles of the fiddler crab, *Uca*. *Biol. Bull.*, **111**, 321 (1956)

33. Sandeen, M. I. Chromatophorotropins in the central nervous system of *Uca pugilator*, with special reference to their origins and actions. *Physiol. Zool.*, **23**, 337–52 (1950)

34. Powell, B. L. Chromatophorotropins in the central nervous system of *Carcinus maenas* (L.). *Crustaceana*, **4**, 143–50 (1962)

35. Nagabhushanam, R., Rao, K. R. The comparative physiology of the crustacean pigmentary effectors. XIII. Dual control of the white chromatophores of the crab, *Ocypode platytarsis*. *Am. Zool.*, **4**, 422 (1964)

36. Nagabhushanam, R., Rao, K. R. The endocrine control of white chromatophores of the crab, *Uca annulipes* (H. Milne Edwards). *Crustaceana*, **13**, 292–98 (1967)

37. Rao, K. R., Fingerman, M., Bartell, C. K. Physiology of the white chromatophores in the fiddler crab, *Uca pugilator*. *Biol. Bull.*, **133**, 606–17 (1967)

38. Rao, K. R. Studies on the differentiation of chromatophorotropins of the crab *Ocypode macrocera* H. Milne Edwards. *Physiol. Zool.*, **40**, 361–70 (1967)

39. Rao, K. R., Fingerman, M. A comparative analysis of the control of the white chromatophores in the fiddler crab, *Uca pugilator*, from Woods Hole, Massachusetts, and Panacea, Florida. *Biol. Bull.*, **135**, 432 (1968)

40. Fingerman, M. Neurosecretory control of pigmentary effectors in crustaceans. *Am. Zool.*, **6**, 169–79 (1966)

41. Carlson, S. P. The color changes in *Uca pugilator*. *Proc. Natl. Acad. Sci.*, **21**, 549–51 (1935)

42. Brown, F. A., Jr. Studies on the

physiology of *Uca* red chromatophores. *Biol. Bull.*, **98**, 218–26 (1950)

43. Brown, F. A., Jr., Fingerman, M. Differentiation of black- and red-dispersing factors from the brain of the fiddler crab, *Uca*. *Fed. Proc.*, **10**, 20–21 (1951)

44. Fingerman, M., Couch, E. F. Differentiation of chromatophorotropins from the prawn, *Palaemonetes vulgaris*, and the fiddler crab, *Uca pugilator*. *J. Exptl. Zool.*, **165**, 183–94 (1967)

45. Kleinholz, L. H. Crustacean pigmentary-effector isohormones. *Biol. Bull.*, **135**, 425–26 (1968)

46. Kleinholz, L. H., Kimball, F. Separation of neurosecretory pigmentary-effector hormones of the crustacean eyestalk. *Gen. Comp. Endocrinol.*, **5**, 336–41 (1965)

47. Kleinholz, L. H., Kimball, F. Further purification of a pigmentary-effector hormone from crustacean eyestalks. *Gen. Comp. Endocrinol.*, **9**, 464–65 (1967)

48. Fernlund, P., Josefsson, L. Chromactivating hormones of *Pandalus borealis*. Isolation and purification of the 'red-pigment-concentrating hormone'. *Biochim. Biophys. Acta*, **158**, 262–73 (1968)

49. Fingerman, M., Couch, E. F. The red pigment-dispersing hormone of the abdominal nerve cord and its contribution to the chromatic physiology of the prawn, *Palaemonetes vulgaris*. *Rev. Can. Biol.*, **26**, 109–17 (1967)

50. Bartell, C. K. Characterization of the melanin-dispersing hormone fraction of the eyestalks of *Uca pugilator* by electrophoresis. *Gen. Comp. Endocrinol.*, **8**, 208–13 (1967)

51. Bartell, C. K., Fluke, D. J. Temperature dependence of ionizing radiation effect on dry preparations of two melanophore-stimulating hormones. *Radiation Res.*, **30**, 811–24 (1967)

52. Carlisle, D. B. Partial inactivation of a crustacean chromactivator by thioglycollate. *J. Endocrinol.*, **34**, 503–5 (1966)

53. Ames, R. C., van Dyke, H. B. Thioglycollate inactivation of posterior pituitary antidiuretic principle as determined in the rat. *Proc. Soc.*

Exptl. Biol. Med., **76**, 576–78 (1951)

54. Ōtsu, T. Component amino acids of chromatophore concentrating hormones from Decapoda, Crustacea. *Naturwissenschaften*, **52**, 187–88 (1965)

55. Kapitza, W., Fischer, F. Gewinnung und Eigenschaften der Neurohormone aus den Augenstielen von *Leander adspersus*. *Z. Naturforsch.*, **21**, 712–13 (1966)

56. Rao, K. R., Bartell, C. K., Fingerman, M. Relationship between the response of melanophores in the fiddler crab, *Uca pugilator*, and the concentration of eyestalk extract. *Z. Vergleich. Physiol.*, **56**, 232–36 (1967)

57. Rao, K. R., Bartell, C. K., Fingerman, M. Solubility and stability properties of the melanin-dispersing substances from the eyestalks of the fiddler crab, *Uca pugilator*. *Z. Vergleich. Physiol.*, **60**, 1–13 (1968)

58. Shibley, G. A. Eyestalk function in chromatophore control in a crab, *Cancer magister*. *Physiol. Zool.*, **41**, 268–79 (1968)

59. Fingerman, M., Lowe, M. E. Influence of time on background upon the chromatophore systems of two crustaceans. *Physiol. Zool.*, **30**, 216–31 (1957)

60. Fingerman, M., Yamamoto, Y. Daily rhythm of melanophoric pigment migration in eyestalkless fiddler crabs, *Uca pugilator* (Bosc.). *Crustaceana*, **12**, 303–19 (1967)

61. Florey, E. Nervous control and spontaneous activity of the chromatophores of a cephalopod, *Loligo opalescens*. *Comp. Biochem. Physiol.*, **18**, 305–24 (1966)

62. Bozler, E. Über die Tätigkeit der einzelnen glatten Muskelfaser bei der Kontraktion. II. Mitteilung: Die Chromatophorenmuskeln der Cephalopoden. *Z. Vergleich. Physiol.*, **7**, 379–406 (1928)

63. Bacq, Z. M., Ghiretti, F. La sécrétion externe et interne des glandes salivaires postérieures des céphalopodes octopodes. *Arch. Intern. Physiol. Biochim.*, **60**, 165–71 (1952)

64. Kriebel, M. E., Florey, E. Electrical and mechanical responses of obliquely striated muscle fibers of

squid to ACH, 5-hydroxytrypta-
mine and nerve stimulation. *Fed.
Proc.*, **27**, 236 (1968)

65. Jacobowitz, D. M., Laties, A. M.
Direct adrenergic innervation of
a teleost melanophore. *Anat.
Record*, **162**, 501–4 (1968)

66. Gray, E. G. Control of the melanophores of the minnow (*Phoxinus
phoxinus* (L.)). *J. Exptl. Biol.*,
33, 448–59 (1956)

67. Waring, H. The co-ordination of
vertebrate melanophore responses.
Biol. Rev. Cambridge Phil. Soc.,
17, 120–50 (1942)

68. Healey, E. G., Ross, D. M. The
effects of drugs on the background
colour response of the minnow
Phoxinus phoxinus L. *Comp. Biochem. Physiol.*, **19**, 545–80 (1966)

69. Healey, E. G. Experimental evidence
for the regeneration of nerve fibres
controlling colour changes after
anterior spinal section in the minnow (*Phoxinus phoxinus* L.). *Proc.
Roy. Soc. (London), B*, **168**, 57–
81 (1967)

70. Grove, D. J. Melanophore dispersion
in the minnow *Phoxinus phoxinus*
(L.). *Comp. Biochem. Physiol.*, **28**,
55–65 (1969)

71. Watanabe, M., Kobayashi, M., Iwata,
K. S. The action of certain autonomic drugs on the fish melanophore. *Biol. J. Okayama Univ.*, **8**,
103–14 (1962)

72. Abbott, F. S. The effects of certain
drugs and biogenic substances on
the melanophores of *Fundulus
heteroclitus* L. *Can. J. Zool.*, **46**,
1149–61 (1968)

73. Scott, G. T. Physiology and pharmacology of color change in the sand
flounder *Scopthalmus aquosus*.
Limnol. Oceanog., Suppl. 10,
R230–46 (1965)

74. Scott, G. T. The action of pheno-
thiazines on pigment cells of the
flatfish *Scopthalmus aquosus*.
Agressologie, **9**, 231–38 (1968)

75. Hadley, M. E., Quevedo, W. C., Jr.
The role of epidermal melanocytes
in adaptive color changes in amphibians. *Advan. Biol. Skin*, **8**,
The Pigmentary System, 337–59
(1967)

76. McGuire, J., Möller, H. Differential
responsiveness of dermal and epidermal melanocytes of *Rana
pipiens* to hormones. *Endocrinology*, **78**, 367–72 (1966)

77. McGuire, J. S. The epidermal me-
lanocytes of the frog. *Advan.
Biol. Skin*, **8**, *The Pigmentary
System*, 329–36 (1967)

78. Goldman, I. P., Hadley, M. E.
Acetylcholine-induced aggregation
of melanin granules within epidermal (frog) melanocytes. *J. Invest.
Dermatol.*, **50**, 59–66 (1968)

79. Hadley, M. E., Bagnara, J. T. Integrated nature of chromatophore
responses in the *in vitro* frog skin
bioassay. *Endocrinology*, **84**, 69–82
(1969)

80. Lande, S., Lerner, A. B. The biochemistry of melanotropic agents.
Pharmacol. Rev., **19**, 1–20 (1967)

81. Bagnara, J. T. Hypophyseal control
of guanophores in anuran larvae.
J. Exptl. Zool., **137**, 265–84
(1958)

82. Bagnara, J. T. Stimulation of melanophores and guanophores by
melanophore-stimulating hormone
peptides. *Gen. Comp. Endocrinol.*,
4, 290–94 (1964)

83. Bagnara, J. T. Control of melanophores in amphibians. In *Structure and Control of the Melanocyte*, 16–28 (See Ref. 10)

84. Van der Lek, B. Photosensitive
melanophores : Some aspects of
the light-induced pigment migra-
tions in the tail fin melanophores
of the larvae of the clawed toad,
Xenopus laevis (Daud) (Bronder-
Offset, Rotterdam, 111 pp.,
1967)

85. Kulemann, H. Untersuchungen der
Pigmentbewegungen in embryo-
nalen Melanophoren von *Xenopus
laevis* in Gewebekulturen. *Zool.
Jahrb., Abt. Allgem. Zool. Physiol.
Tiere*, **69**, 169–97 (1960)

86. Bagnara, J. T., Obika, M. Light
sensitivity of melanophores in
neural crest explants. *Experientia*,
23, 155–57 (1967)

87. Quay, W. B., Bagnara, J. T. Relative potencies of indolic and related compounds in the body-
lightening reaction of larval *Xenopus. Arch. Intern. Pharmacodyn.*,
150, 137–43 (1964)

88. Quay, W. B. Specificity and struc-
ture-activity relationships in the
Xenopus larval melanophore assay
for melatonin. *Gen. Comp. Endocrinol.*, **11**, 253–54 (1968)

89. Charlton, H. M., The pineal gland
and color change in *Xenopus laevis*

Daudin. *Gen. Comp. Endocrinol.,* **7,** 384–97 (1966)

90. Bagnara, J. T. Independent actions of pineal and hypophysis in the regulation of chromatophores of anuran larvae. *Gen. Comp. Endocrinol.,* **4,** 299–303 (1964)

91. Snell, R. S., Kulovich, S. Nerve stimulation and the movement of melanin granules in the pigment cells of the frog's web. *J. Invest. Dermatol.,* **48,** 438–43 (1967)

92. Etkin, W., Rosenberg, L. Infundibular lesion and pars intermedia activity in the tadpole. *Proc. Soc. Exptl. Biol. Med.,* **39,** 332–34 (1938)

93. Etkin, W. Hypothalamic inhibition of pars intermedia activity in the frog. *Gen. Comp. Endocrinol., Suppl.,* **1,** 148–59 (1962)

94. Kastin, A. J., Ross, G. T. Melanocyte-stimulating hormone activity in pituitaries of frogs with hypothalamic lesions. *Endocrinology,* **77,** 45–48 (1965)

95. Ito, T. Experimental studies on the hypothalamic control of the pars intermedia activity of the frog, *Rana nigromaculata. Neuroendocrinology,* **3,** 25–33 (1968)

96. Ralph, C. L., Sampath, S. Inhibition by extracts of frog and rat brain of MSH release by frog pars intermedia. *Gen. Comp. Endocrinol.,* **7,** 730–74 (1966)

97. Bercu, B. B., Brinkley, H. J. Hypothalamic and cerebral inhibition of melanocyte-stimulating hormone secretion in the frog, *Rana pipiens. Endocrinology,* **80,** 399–403 (1967)

98. Ralph, C. L., Peyton, S. C. MSH-like substance in the brain of the frog, *Rana pipiens. Gen. Comp. Endocrinol.,* **7,** 363–69 (1966)

99. Thurmond, W. Hypothalamic chromatophore-stimulating activity in the amphibians *Hyla regilla* and *Ambystoma tigrinum. Gen. Comp. Endocrinol.,* **8,** 245–51 (1967)

100. Thurmond, W. Onset of chromatophore-stimulating activity by the hypothalamus and adenohypophysis in *Hyla regilla* and *Ambystoma tigrinum. Gen. Comp. Endocrinol.,* **8,** 252–57 (1967)

101. Taleisnik, S., Orías, R. A melanocyte-stimulating hormone-releasing factor in hypothalamic extracts. *Am. J. Physiol.,* **208,** 293–96 (1965)

102. Taleisnik, S., Tomatis, M. E. Antagonistic effect on melanocyte-stimulating hormone release of two neural tissue extracts. *Am. J. Physiol.,* **212,** 157–63 (1967)

103. Taleisnik, S., Tomatis, M. E. Melanocyte-stimulating hormone-releasing and inhibiting factors in two hypothalamic extracts. *Endocrinology,* **81,** 819–25 (1967)

104. Dhariwal, A. P. S., McCann, S. M., Taleisnik, S., Tomatis, M. E. Purification of hypothalamic melanocyte-stimulating hormone (MSH)-releasing factor with Sephadex. *Proc. Soc. Exptl. Biol. Med.,* **121,** 996–98 (1966)

105. Knowles, F. Evidence for a dual control, by neurosecretion, of hormone synthesis and hormone release in the pituitary of the dogfish *Scylliorhinus stellaris. Phil. Trans. Roy. Soc. London, B,* **249,** 435–56 (1965)

106. Knowles, F. Neuroendocrine correlations at the level of ultrastructure. *Arch. Anat. Microscop. Morphol. Exptl.,* **54,** 343–56 (1965)

107. Cohen, A. G. Observations on the pars intermedia of *Xenopus laevis. Nature,* **215,** 55–56 (1967)

108. Iturriza, F. C. Electron-microscopic study of the pars intermedia of the pituitary of the toad, *Bufo arenarum. Gen. Comp. Endocrinol.,* **4,** 492–502 (1964)

109. Iturriza, F. C. Monoamines and control of the pars intermedia of the toad pituitary. *Gen. Comp. Endocrinol.,* **6,** 19–25 (1966)

110. Enemar, A., Falck, B. On the presence of adrenergic nerves in the pars intermedia of the frog, *Rana temporaria. Gen. Comp. Endocrinol.,* **5,** 577–83 (1965)

111. Enemar, A., Falck, B., Iturriza, F. C. Adrenergic nerves in the pars intermedia of the pituitary in the toad, *Bufo arenarum. Z. Zellforsch.,* **77,** 325–30 (1967)

112. Saland, L. C. Ultrastructure of the frog pars intermedia in relation to hypothalamic control of hormone release. *Neuroendocrinology,* **3,** 72–88 (1968)

113. Fuchs, M. E. A., Lotz, R. G. A. Cell metabolism during melanophore activity. *Nature,* **212,** 39–40 (1966)

114. Fuchs, M. Eine Analyse des Melanophorenstoffwechsels Untersuchungen an *Rana temporaria. Z.*

Vergleich. Physiol., **53**, 449–74 (1966)

115. Wright, P. A. Physiological responses of frog melanophores *in vitro*. *Physiol. Zool.*, **28**, 204–18 (1955)

116. Novales, R. R. The effects of osmotic pressure and sodium concentration on the response of melanophores to intermedin. *Physiol. Zool.*, **32**, 15–28 (1959)

117. Novales, R. R. Melanocyte-stimulating hormone and the intermediate lobe of the pituitary: chemistry, effects, and mode of action. In *Neuroendocrinology*, **2**, 241–59 (Martini, L., Ganong, W. F., Eds., Academic, New York, 777 pp., 1967)

118. Fingerman, M., Miyawaki, M., Oguro, C. Effects of osmotic pressure and cations on the response of the melanophores in the fiddler crab, *Uca pugnax*, to the melanin-dispersing principle from the sinus gland. *Gen. Comp. Endocrinol.*, **3**, 496–504 (1963)

119. Novales, R. R., Novales, B. J. Factors influencing the response of isolated dogfish skin melanophores to melanocyte-stimulating hormone. *Biol. Bull.*, **131**, 470–78 (1966)

120. Dikstein, S., Weller, C. P., Sulman, F. G. Effect of calcium ions on melanophore dispersal. *Nature*, **200**, 1106 (1963)

121. Dikstein, S., Sulman, F. G. Mechanism of melanophore dispersion. *Biochem. Pharmacol.*, **13**, 819–26 (1964)

122. Dikstein, S., Tal, E., Sulman, F. G. Mechanism of melanophore dispersion. II. Stimulus-reaction-recovery and receptor problem. *Biochem. Pharmacol.*, **14**, 1151–59 (1965)

123. Marsland, D. Mechanism of pigment displacement in unicellular chromatophores. *Biol. Bull.*, **87**, 252–61 (1944)

124. Marsland, D., Meisner, D. Effects of D_2O on the mechanism of pigment dispersal in the melanocytes of *Fundulus heteroclitus:* a pressure-temperature analysis. *J. Cell. Physiol.*, **70**, 209–16 (1967)

125. Novales, R. R., Novales, B. J. The effects of osmotic pressure and calcium deficiency on the response of tissue-cultured melanophores to melanocyte-stimulating hormone. *Gen. Comp. Endocrinol.*, **5**, 568–76 (1965)

126. Bitensky, M. W., Burstein, S. R. Effects of cyclic adenosine monophosphate and melanocyte-stimulating hormone on frog skin *in vitro*. *Nature*, **208**, 1282–84 (1965)

127. Novales, R. R., Davis, W. J. Melanin-dispersing effect of adenosine 3′,5′-monophosphate on amphibian melanophores. *Endocrinology*, **81**, 283–90 (1967)

128. Abe, K., Butcher, R. W., Nicholson, W. E., Baird, C. E., Liddle, R. A., Liddle, G. W. Adenosine 3′,5′-monophosphate (cyclic AMP) as the mediator of the actions of melanocyte stimulating hormone (MSH) and norepinephrine on the frog skin. *Endocrinology*, **84**, 362–68 (1969)

129. Fingerman, M., Connell, P. M. The role of cations in the actions of the hormones controlling the red chromatophores of the prawn, *Palaemonetes vulgaris*. *Gen. Comp. Endocrinol.*, **10**, 392–98 (1968)

130. Fingerman, M., Hammond, R. D., True, R. S. The response of the red chromatophores of the prawn *Palaemonetes vulgaris* to cyclic 3′,5′-adenosine monophosphate. *Biol. Bull.*, **135**, 418 (1968)

131. Freeman, A. R., Connell, P. M., Fingerman, M. An electrophysiological study of the red chromatophore of the prawn, *Palaemonetes:* observations on the action of red pigment-concentrating hormone. *Comp. Biochem. Physiol.*, **26**, 1015–29 (1968)

132. Freeman, A. R., Fingerman, M. Action of tetrodotoxin and observations on the characteristics of the chromatophore membrane of the prawn, *Palaemonetes*. *Comp. Biochem. Physiol.*, **29**, 483–86 (1969)

133. Martin, A. R., Snell, R. S. A note on transmembrane potential in dermal melanophores of the frog and movement of melanin granules. *J. Physiol. (London)*, **195**, 755–59 (1968)

134. Fingerman, M. Cellular aspects of the control of physiological color changes in crustaceans. *Am. Zool.*, **9**, 443–52 (1969)

HEART   1049

Matthew N. Levy and Robert M. Berne

Department of Investigative Medicine
Mt. Sinai Hospital, Cleveland, Ohio, and
Department of Physiology
University of Virginia, Charlottesville, Virginia

In this review of the literature from June 1968 through May 1969, only certain aspects of cardiac physiology have been included: the mechanics of cardiac contraction, the regulation of cardiac contraction, the coronary circulation, and myocardial metabolism. Even within these categories, there has been no attempt to cover all articles published on these topics. Certain important areas have been excluded entirely: notably, the electrophysiology of the heart, excitation-contraction coupling, and the mechanics of the contraction of isolated strips of cardiac muscle. These and certain other aspects of the physiology of the heart will be incorporated in subsequent reviews.

Cardiac Mechanics

There has been a gradual evolution of our comprehension of the role played by the various components of the contractile machinery of the heart during cardiac contraction. Recently, this knowledge has been directed toward a quantitative appraisal of the contractile state of the myocardium in intact animals and man. Several noteworthy advances have been made in this effort within the past year.

The contractile state of the myocardium may be characterized in terms of changes in force, velocity, length, and time. Puri & Bing (1) assessed the velocity of myocardial fiber shortening in closed-chest, anesthetized dogs by means of a strain-gauge catheter assembly. Another catheter was introduced into the left ventricular cavity for pressure recording, which provided the data for the computation of force. The force-velocity relation was then determined at a specific reference length, referred to as the isolength point. Inverse changes in force and velocity were observed during alterations of afterload, whereas positive inotropic agents, such as the catecholamines, increased both force and velocity or augmented velocity without significantly affecting force.

The myocardial force-velocity relation in normal human subjects and in patients with various types of heart disease was evaluated by Frank & Levinson (2). A contractility index was computed by dividing the maximum

373

dP/dt by the maximum isovolumetric pressure, and then dividing this quotient by the circumferential fiber length in order to normalize for hearts of different sizes. The index so computed was found to be confined within a narrow range in normal subjects, and was independent of fiber length. It was not depressed in patients with left ventricular disease before the onset of failure, but was significantly depressed during failure. Smith & Schwede (3) devised an analog/hybrid computer program for deriving various critical indices of myocardial contractility.

Fallen & Gorlin (4) assessed the force-velocity relationship in patients with aortic stenosis by employing the narrowed valve as a natural orifice-flowmeter. Most of these patients showed a linear increase in the contractile element velocity and rate of fiber shortening for a fixed period of 110 msec after peak force. This interval was significantly longer than in normal subjects, both at rest and during isoproterenol infusions. At the end of this period, there was an abrupt deceleration of the contractile element and fiber, probably signaling the beginning of the decay of the maximum intensity of the active state.

In numerous investigations, including the above study by Frank & Levinson (2), the left ventricular dP/dt served as the basis for assessing the velocity of the contractile element. Hence, the maximum dP/dt has been widely used as an index of the inotropic state of the heart. In a study by Wildenthal et al. (5), it was emphasized that caution must be exercised in interpreting variations in maximum dP/dt, unless changes in aortic pressure and the time of aortic valve opening are taken into consideration. In open-chest, anesthetized dogs, at low or normal arterial pressures, the maximum dP/dt was appreciably limited by the time of aortic valve opening. However, this was not usually a significant factor when aortic pressure was elevated. Mason (6) also emphasized the limitations of the maximum dP/dt as an index of myocardial contractility. He advocated the use of the ratios of maximum dP/dt to certain other cardiovascular variables under conditions in which the preload and afterload vary independently or simultaneously.

In studies on closed-chest, sedated dogs, Taylor et al. (7) found that contraction in ejecting heart beats usually proceeded to a volume-tension relation at the end of ejection which closely approximated the relation at the peak of isovolumic contraction. Such ejecting beats began with much larger end diastolic volumes than obtained for the corresponding isovolumic contractions, and the equivalent tension was reached at a considerably later time after the onset of contraction. This suggests that increased ventricular volume, directly or indirectly, prolongs the duration of the active state.

Hood et al. (8) compared the left ventricular wall stresses in thin-walled and thick-walled ellipsoidal models. At the end of systole, the stresses in the thin-walled model consistently exceeded those in the thick-walled model, although the differences were only about 10 per cent. Estimates during the remainder of the cardiac cycle agreed even more closely. Mirsky (9) developed a thick-walled model for computing ventricular intramural stresses.

The results of his theoretical analysis agreed closely with experimental results during diastole, but there were significant discrepancies during systole. Therefore, the assumption of isotropy and homogeneity of the myocardial wall appear to be reasonable during diastole, but not during systole. When the mid-wall stresses derived from the thick-walled model were compared with the wall stresses computed on the basis of an infinitely thin shell (law of Laplace), the disparities were surprisingly small, i.e., within 15 per cent for ellipsoids, and within 5 per cent for spheres.

Using the simpler thin-walled model, Hood et al. (10) analyzed the changes in wall stress in normal and hypertrophied left ventricles. They found that in patients with compensated volume overload, peak systolic stress was not significantly different from normal. They concluded that the extent of hypertrophy was appropriate to the degree of overload, and that replication of sarcomeres must occur in parallel as well as in series. In patients with decompensated volume load, the extent of the hypertrophy was inadequate, so that peak systolic stress was significantly elevated.

Newman & Walton (11) measured directly the mural force in an ischemic region of the dog heart by suturing a strain-gauge arch to the left ventricle and making a deep transverse incision in the wall of the ventricle between the feet of the arch. After coronary artery ligation, there was a significant increase in maximum mural force without a concomitant increase in peak systolic pressure, which suggests that the increase in force was due to an increase in the radius of curvature or a flattening of the bulging ischemic zone. Mercury-in-rubber gauges were employed by Dieudonné & Jean (12) to record the changes in left ventricular epicardial strain in anesthetized dogs. Transverse and longitudinal strains were out of phase throughout the cardiac cycle, especially in the epicardium overlying the anterior papillary muscle. Also, there was stretch of all outer layers tested during isovolumic contraction.

By applying the most precise manometric technics currently available, Noble (13) demonstrated conclusively a significant, biphasic pressure gradient between the left ventricle and aorta. The gradient was positive during the acceleratory phase of ventricular ejection and negative during the deceleratory phase, thereby confirming the momentum concept propounded previously by Spencer & Greiss (14) The hypothesis that ventricular emptying during the terminal portion of the ejection phase of systole was dependent largely upon momentum was verified by Noble (13). He found that by occlusion of the aorta in late systole, left ventricular pressure fell considerably below the pressure which obtained at the corresponding time in the preceding beat.

Holt et al. (15) compared certain cardiovascular variables in nine species of mammals varying in size from the rat to the horse. They found that end diastolic and end systolic volumes of the ventricles varied linearly with body weight rather than with body surface area or metabolic rate. Ventricular volumes of anesthetized dogs were measured by a biplane videoangiographic technic by Tsakiris et al. (16). Under control conditions, the ejection fraction averaged 47 per cent of the left ventricular end diastolic volume. With a reduction in afterload the average ejection fraction increased to 73 per cent, though the resultant change in stroke volume was relatively small.

The mechanical properties of the left ventricle were assessed during diastole by Noble et al. (17). Ventricular volume was estimated in conscious dogs by means of biplane cineradiography. It was concluded that viscous and inertial, as well as elastic, properties were important determinants of left ventricular mechanics during diastole. Caution was urged in the assessment of changes in end diastolic volume and ventricular compliance on the basis of the end diastolic pressure.

NEURAL CONTROL OF THE HEART

Adrenergic factors.—Adrenergic receptors are present in the hearts of salamander larvae long before sympathetic fibers reach the heart, according to the studies of Adolph & Ferrari (18). In fetal lambs also, Friedman et al. (19) have found that cardiac beta-receptors appear before the complete development of an extrinsic nerve supply. They also observed that in developing rabbits, the myocardial content of norepinephrine closely paralleled histochemical evidence of sympathetic innervation, as measured by the monoamine fluorescence technic. Cardiac sympathetic innervation is sparse in rabbit embryos. However, innervation proceeds rapidly after birth, so that by 3 to 5 weeks, the density of sympathetic nerve fibers within the heart is about the same as in the adult. Monoamine oxidase is known to increase with age in developing rat hearts. However, the studies of De Champlain et al. (20) indicate that the myocardial content of monoamine oxidase parallels the change in cardiac mass during induced hypertrophy. Hence, the changes during development are probably ascribable to the concomitant alterations of heart size.

The technic of chemical epicardiectomy was employed by Geis & Kaye (21) to map the distribution of sympathetic fibers to the left ventricle of the adult dog. It was found that fibers from both the right and left stellate ganglia innervate both anterior and posterior surfaces of the left ventricle. The major sympathetic projections pass near the origins of the anterior descending and left marginal coronary arteries. The studies of Pace et al. (22) confirm the innervation of the right ventricular myocardium by sympathetic fibers from both the right and left stellate ganglia and from the vagosympathetic trunks as well. Increased sympathetic activity constricted the outflow tract, so that a pronounced pressure gradient developed between the sinus and conus regions of the right ventricle.

Complete A-V block was produced in dogs by Vassalle et al. (23), and the effects of cardiac sympathetic neural activity on idioventricular automaticity were determined. Isolation of the left stellate ganglion reduced the idioventricular frequency by about 5 beats/min, whereas stellate ganglion stimulation increased the frequency to a maximum of about 70 beats/min.

There was no significant difference between the effects of right and left sympathetic stimulation on the idioventricular rate.

Convincing evidence for the existence of adrenergic alpha-receptors in the canine sinoatrial node was furnished by the experiments of James et al. (24). Infusion of methoxamine, an alpha-adrenergic stimulant, directly into the sinus node artery produced bradycardia. This bradycardia was reversed with either phentolamine or phenoxybenzamine (Dibenzyline), which are alpha-adrenergic blocking agents. Evidence was also provided that sympathetic neural activity activates both alpha- and beta-adrenergic receptors in the S-A node, and that the overall effect is the resultant of the respective negative and positive chronotropic influences. Priola (25) observed negative chronotropic responses not infrequently in response to norepinephrine infusions, even in the absence of significant changes of arterial blood pressure. He also suggested the existence of inhibitory adrenergic receptors in addition to the usually accepted excitatory beta-receptors.

Priola (25) also found that after right-sided cardiac sympathectomy, the S-A node and atrial myocardium exhibited a tenfold increase in sensitivity to norepinephrine, whereas the ventricles showed no change. Conversely, after left-sided denervation the ventricles became two- to threefold more sensitive to norepinephrine, while the atria were unaffected and the S-A node became subsensitive. These results support previous evidence that the S-A node and atria are innervated primarily by the right cardiac sympathetic nerves, whereas the ventricles are supplied predominantly by the nerves from the left side.

The experiments of Ebert (26) also demonstrated a marked increase in the sensitivity of the denervated canine myocardium to norepinephrine. In control animals, high doses of norepinephrine produced large increases in total peripheral resistance, but only a slight augmentation of cardiac output. In cardiac denervated animals, however, the increase in cardiac output was pronounced, and as a consequence, total peripheral resistance actually diminished. Dempsey & Cooper (27) also found the denervated ventricular myocardium to be supersensitive to norepinephrine, but just normally responsive to calcium and actually subsensitive to isoproterenol. They concluded, therefore, that the supersensitivity to norepinephrine represents neither a nonspecific change in the myocardial cell membrane or its receptor sites nor a proliferation of postjunctional receptor sites. Furthermore, the studies by Sobel et al. (28) appear to rule out the possibility that changes in adenyl cyclase or phosphodiesterase activity are involved in myocardial denervation supersensitivity. Hence, the explanation for such supersensitivity may be related, at least in part, to a cocaine-like effect of denervation; i.e., a loss of binding sites in the postganglionic nerve fibers, and thus a greater availability of the catecholamine for action on the receptors.

Ebert et al. (29) showed that extrinsic cardiac denervation 3 weeks prior to ligation of the anterior descending coronary artery prevented ventricular fibrillation in response to the coronary occlusion. Associated with this was the absence of the myocardial potassium loss which characteristically supervenes in the normally innervated heart. Conversely, Nielsen et al. (30) observed that cardiac sympathectomy in cats did not reduce the incidence of ventricular fibrillation in response to hypothermia 2 to 3 days after denervation. These investigators attributed such results to the rapid development of supersensitivity to catecholamines.

It was found by LeLorier & Shideman (31) that the inotropic response to norepinephrine in perfused rat hearts was inversely related to the uptake of this catecholamine. They postulated a competition between the nerve endings and the adrenergic receptors for circulating norepinephrine; the greater the quantity taken up by the sympathetic nerve endings, the less the amount available for interaction with the receptors. There is an apparent defect in the myocardial storage of norepinephrine in rats made hypertensive by deoxycorticosterone acetate and NaCl (20) or given repeated doses of isoproterenol (32). In both conditions, the defect involves a rapid initial loss of norepinephrine from the microsomal fraction. Since the defect is readily reversible by ganglionic blockade, the mechanism underlying both conditions may be related to increased cardiac sympathetic neural activity. In rabbits made hypertensive by sinoaortic denervation, there was also observed an association between increased sympathetic neural activity and depletion of myocardial catecholamines (33). However, this was rapidly followed by a compensatory enhancement of neurotransmitter synthesis.

Gomez & Yard (34) investigated the acute tolerance to intravenous infusions of norepinephrine in anesthetized dogs. At lower dose levels, the gradual return in arterial blood pressure toward control after the initial peak could be ascribed almost exclusively to a progressive decrease in peripheral resistance. At higher doses, however, the fall in pressure depended upon reductions in both peripheral resistance and cardiac output.

Cholinergic factors.—There is general agreement concerning the directional changes in heart rate and coronary vascular resistance produced by acetylcholine (ACh), but its effects upon myocardial contractility are still not well understood. The myocardial response varies with dose, species, route of administration, region of the heart, intactness of the heart, contraction frequency, concentration of certain electrolytes, and a host of other experimental conditions.

Blumenthal et al. (35) introduced single injections of ACh into the coronary circulation of dogs over a wide range of doses. They found that the threshold doses required to produce coronary vasodilatation, the negative inotropic effect, and the negative chronotropic effect occurred in the ratio of 1:10:100. A positive inotropic effect was not observed after ACh alone, but was produced by ACh after preparation with neostigmine and atropine. This positive inotropic response could be abolished with beta-adrenergic blocking agents. Levy & Zieske (36) also reported differences in the responsiveness of the coronary circulation, the cardiac pacemaker, and the ventricular myocardium to ACh which were directionally similar to those described by Blumenthal et al. The nature of the ventricular response to ACh was considerably different in these two studies, however. Whereas Blumenthal et al. observed only a depression of ventricular contractility, Levy & Zieske obtained biphasic or triphasic responses. In the latter study, there was a characteristic negative inotropic effect during the infusion of ACh, followed by a pronounced postinfusion positive inotropic "rebound", almost identical with that reported previously by Hollenberg et al. (37). When the response was triphasic, there was a small, brief, positive inotropic phase as the initial change. The positive inotropic response to ACh observed by Blumenthal et al. after neostigmine and atropine was probably based upon a mechanism different from the rebound described by Hollenberg et al., since the response was blocked by beta-adrenergic blocking agents in the former, but not in the latter, study.

In the investigations of Levy & Zieske, the order of responsiveness of the various cardiac structures for vagal stimulation was entirely different than that for ACh infusions. With vagal stimulation, the pacemaker was most responsive, then the ventricular myocardium, and finally the coronary resistance vessels. The order of responsiveness undoubtedly depends upon the distribution of nerve fibers, capillaries, and cholinesterase, and probably upon many other factors as well. The myocardial response to vagus nerve stimulation was often biphasic or occasionally triphasic, just as with ACh infusions, although the positive inotropic components were usually less prominent than with ACh infusions.

The effects of the right and left vagosympathetic trunks on the cardiac pacemaker and on A-V impulse transmission in the dog were compared by Hamlin & Smith (38). The responses to right and left vagal stimulation were not significantly different. However, greater cardioacceleration was produced by right than by left vagotomy, indicating an unequal distribution of the physiological activity bilaterally. Also, second degree A-V block was caused preferentially by left-sided stimulation. Misu & Kirpekar (39) found that strong right vagal stimulation in the kitten completely abolished S-A nodal, but not A-V nodal, activity. Strong left vagal stimulation uniformly suppressed the activity of both nodes. Miller et al. (40) observed that the total duration of asystole following vagal stimulation in cats was dependent upon the frequency of stimulation. The maximum duration of asystole occurred at frequencies of 20 to 40 Hz. Furthermore, the peak occurrence of ventricular escape occurred over this same range of stimulation frequencies, whereas atrial escape supervened at higher and lower levels. High-frequency stimulation of the vagus nerves, at 50 pulses/sec for 15 sec, produced a posttetanic potentiation of transmitter release, according to the studies of Kötter et al. (41). After such a period of conditioning stimulation, test stimuli to the vagi evoked exaggerated reductions of heart rate for as long as 50 sec after cessation of the conditioning stimulation.

The negative inotropic effect on the ventricular myocardium mediated by the vagus nerves has been reconfirmed by several groups of investigators (36, 42–46). In general, the depressant effect was observed to be small to moderate, although in some experiments, large effects have been reported [viz., Fig. 6 in (36)]. The negative inotropic effect of vagal activity is critically dependent upon the experimental conditions, including the background level of cardiac sympathetic activity. Wildenthal et al. (45) have outlined the difficulties in assessing the role of parasympathetic inhibition of the ventricular myocardium in studies involving stimulation of the vagosympathetic trunks. In the absence of adrenergic blockade, such stimulation in the dog and certain other species involves the combined activation of fibers from both autonomic divisions, with consequent antagonistic results. However, adrenergic blockade abolishes the sympathetic-parasympathetic interaction, which also exerts a pronounced influence on the magnitude of the response.

Autonomic interactions.—Two major types of cardiac sympathetic-parasympathetic interactions have been identified. The first type involves the appearance of an adrenergic response during or following stimulation of the vagus nerves. This type of interaction is ascribable to the release of norepinephrine from storage sites in the heart as the result of parasympathetic neural activity (the Burn-Rand hypothesis). Furthermore, the possibility of activation of sympathetic fibers must always be considered in certain species, notably the dog, in which the vagosympathetic nerve trunk actually contains both sympathetic and parasympathetic components. The second type of interaction involves a change in cardiac responsiveness to stimulation of one division of the autonomic nervous system as a consequence of a change in the background level of activity in the other division.

Support for the operation of the Burn-Rand hypothesis in the heart was provided by the experiments of Copen et al. (47) and Haeusler et al. (48). Copen et al. observed that after cessation of vagal stimulation, tachycardia ensued even when the occurrence of increased sympathetic neural activity was effectively precluded. This postvagal tachycardia was prevented by pretreatment with reserpine, but reappeared after norepinephrine administration. Haeusler et al. recorded action potentials from cardiac sympathetic nerve fibers during ACh infusions in isolated cat hearts, and demonstrated the liberation of significant quantities of norepinephrine. Conversely, evidence for a significant adrenergic-cholinergic interaction could not be detected in the experiments of Misu & Kirpekar (39) or of Miller et al. (40). Hashimoto & Chiba (49) uncovered an inverse type of interaction. During perfusion of the sinus node artery in vagotomized dogs, injection of catecholamine produced the usual positive chronotropic response, and this was sometimes interrupted by a sudden reduction in heart rate. This negative chronotropic response was abolished by a minute amount of atropine, which suggested that ACh was released by the catecholamine injection.

The second type of autonomic interaction, which was defined at the beginning of this section, was first described in 1935 by Samaan (50). He noted that the response of the cardiac pacemaker to "'stimulation of the sympathetic fibers is attended . . . . by sensitization of the heart to vagal stimuli". This type of interaction has recently been confirmed by Warner & Russell (51) , and has been incorporated into the mathematical model which they have developed to describe the neural regulation of the activity of the sinoatrial node. In 1965, Hollenberg et al. (37) showed that this same type of interaction was involved in the regulation of myocardial contractility, and this has recently been confirmed (43, 46). Levy & Zieske (46) have demonstrated that the exaggerated vagal depression of myocardial contractility in the presence of an increased background of sympathetic activity probably represents a specific autonomic interaction. When myocardial contractility was enhanced by means other than increased sympathetic activity (such as paired pacing, calcium, aminophylline, and acetylstrophanthidin), then the characteristic increase in the depressant effect of a standard vagal stimulus was not observed. In fact, vagal stimulation was considerably less effective during paired pacing or after acetylstrophanthidin.

The studies of Hashimoto et al. (52) suggest that this adrenergic-cholinergic interaction is also involved in the induction of atrial fibrillation. Reserpine reduced the incidence of atrial fibrillation induced by the injection of ACh into the sinus node artery, but this effect was reversed by the administration of norepinephrine. Guanethidine, bretylium, and the beta-blocking agents also interfered with the induction of atrial fibrillation by ACh, whereas the alpha-blocking agents were ineffective.

Sinoaortic baroreceptors.—Numerous reports have previously been published which have demonstrated that the baroreceptor reflexes usually do not produce any appreciable or consistent changes in cardiac output. Yet, other studies have shown that the baroreceptor reflexes do evoke significant changes in myocardial contractility. This paradox is perhaps analogous to the apparent lack of efficacy of digitalis in normal animals and man, in that cardiac output is not appreciably affected, but appropriate technics reveal that myocardial contractility is indeed enhanced.

In their study of the redistribution of the cardiac output during bilateral common carotid artery occlusion, Bond & Green (53) confirmed the absence of any significant increase in cardiac output in anesthetized dogs. In fact, there was an initial reduction in cardiac output. Iriuchijima et al. (54) also failed to observe any significant increase in cardiac output in response to carotid artery occlusion in anesthetized dogs under control conditions. There was a marked increase in mean arterial pressure, but only a slight rise in left atrial pressure. After beta-adrenergic receptor blockade, however, the marked rise in arterial pressure in response to carotid occlusion was accompanied by a substantially elevated left atrial pressure and a reduction in cardiac output. Action potential recordings from the inferior cardiac nerve revealed augmented neural activity during carotid occlusion. It was concluded, therefore, that increased cardiac sympathetic activity does occur during carotid occlusion, and that the resultant positive inotropic effect prevents a reduction of cardiac output in the face of a severe increase in total peripheral resistance in the intact animal.

Downing & Gardner (55) challenged the importance of the carotid sinus baroreceptor system in the reflex regulation of ventricular contractility. In their studies in cats anesthetized with pentobarbital, they found that changes in cephalic perfusion pressure in the range of 75 to 150 mm Hg produced inverse changes in heart rate and ventricular contractility which were not appreciably different whether the carotid sinuses were intact or denervated. Vagotomy did not alter the responses, but they were abrogated by ganglionic blockade. It was concluded that the changes in cardiac sympathetic activity were related to the alterations in cephalic perfusion rather than to variations in carotid baroreceptor stimulation.

These results are contrary to those obtained previously by Sarnoff et al. (56) and De Geest et al. (57) in dogs anesthetized with morphine-chloralose-urethane. In at least some of the experiments in both of these studies, isolated carotid sinus preparations were employed, so that the reflex responses could not have been ascribable to changes in cephalic perfusion. Furthermore, in the experiments of Sarnoff et al., entirely different reflex responses were evoked by pulsatile and steady carotid artery pressures at the same mean value, which strongly suggests a baroreceptor response. De Geest et al. found that increases in cephalic perfusion pressure at pressure levels greater than 60 mm Hg had negligible effects in animals with denervated carotid sinuses. Perhaps the disparity in the results of Downing & Gardner relative to those of Sarnoff et al. and De Geest et al. is related to differences in species or anesthesia.

The precise manner in which the autonomic neural outflow to the heart is affected by changes in baroreceptor stimulation remains to be elucidated. Numerous studies have been conducted, but the subject remains controversial. The results in any given study undoubtedly depend upon the prevailing "autonomic tuning" (58) and other experimental conditions. For example, Fulton et al. (59) have shown that the cardiovascular responses to carotid artery occlusion may be modified during certain types of artificial circulation. Smyth et al. (60) have shown that sleep appears to alter the sensitivity of the baroreceptor reflex and the studies of Chai & Wang (61) reveal that ablation of certain regions of the brainstem modifies the cardioaccelerator responses to carotid occlusion.

In studies of the reflex regulation of ventricular performance in the dog, it was found by Martin et al. (62) that changes in pressure in the carotid sinus region produced responses in the two divisions of the autonomic nervous system which depended upon the direction of the intrasinusal pressure change. Increases in intrasinusal pressure above 150 mm Hg evoked predominantly parasympathetic reactions at the steady state, whereas reductions in pressure below that level elicited mainly sympathetic reactions. The results resembled those on heart rate reported previously by Glick & Braunwald (63), except that there appeared to be somewhat more overlap between the two autonomic divisions in the study of Martin et al., particularly during the transient period immediately after a carotid sinus pressure change.

Chai et al. (64) observed that cardiac arrhythmias were induced in cats by occlusion of the common carotid arteries. Production of these arrhythmias was not altered by atropine, and they were evoked more readily after vagotomy. The mediation of such arrhythmias, apparently exclusively by the sympathetic division, is consonant with the predominantly sympathetic response to carotid sinus hypotension alluded to above (62, 63).

In experiments on anesthetized dogs conducted by Berkowitz et al. (65), the cardiac effects of either bilateral carotid artery occlusion or electrical stimulation of the carotid sinus nerve appeared to be mediated almost exclusively by sympathetic pathways. Heart rate and atrioventricular conduction changes during such carotid sinus reflexes were not appreciably affected by vagotomy, but they were abrogated by upper thoracic sympathectomy or by propranolol. It is conceivable, however, that vagal activity could have been effectively suppressed by an indirect mechanism. In their Figure 1, for example, sympathetic denervation was accompanied by a pronounced reduction in arterial blood pressure to hypotensive levels. This in turn could have severely attentuated any parasympathetic response to baroreceptor stimulation.

Gleser & Grupp (66) concluded from their experiments on dogs that there was a significant vagal response to electrical stimulation of the carotid sinus nerve. In fact, their data were consistent with the hypothesis that there is a subgroup of carotid sinus fibers which affect only vagal centers. Whether there also existed an analogous subgroup influencing only sympathetic centers could not be ascertained from their data. They observed that high-voltage, low-frequency stimulation of the carotid sinus nerves primarily reduced heart rate and had little influence on blood pressure, whereas low-voltage, high-frequency stimulation evoked the opposite responses. The nonlinearity in the efferent vagal response to blood pressure alterations was investigated by Katona & Barnett (67). Cardiac vagal efferent activity increased considerably faster in response to a rise in arterial pressure than it diminished after a fall in pressure.

In his studies of the responses to electrical stimulation of the aortic nerves in swine, Schmidt (68) found that high-voltage, low-frequency stimulation accelerated the heart and raised the arterial blood pressure, whereas low-voltage, high-frequency stimulation decreased the heart rate and blood pressure. He concluded that the depressor responses were mediated by fibers originating in the aortic arch baroreceptors, whereas the pressor responses were mediated by fibers arising in the aortic bodies.

Other reflexes.—The release of K^+ from contracting skeletal muscle may play a role in evoking the characteristic cardiovascular changes observed during muscular exercise. Wildenthal et al. (69) infused small quantities of KCl into the vascularly isolated, innervated dog hindleg, and observed significant increases in heart rate, stroke volume, and certain indices of myocardial contractility. These effects were abolished by beta-adrenergic blockade, but were unaffected by vagotomy.

The reflex bradycardia associated with diving appears to depend upon different mechanisms in different species of animals. In contrast to the duck, in which the bradycardia is evoked from receptors in the beak, the studies of Cohn et al. (70) indicate that in the goose, bradycardia is initiated from proprioceptors in the thorax. The time course of the bradycardia also depends upon chemoreceptor stimulation associated with the concomitant period of apnea. In studies of the responses to immersion in man, Campbell et al. (71) inferred that face immersion is an essential predisposing factor for the diving response. Conversely, Asmussen & Kristiansson (72) concluded that in man, if face immersion elicits bradycardia on a reflex basis, the reflex is inconstant and evanescent. According to their data, the principal determinant of the bradycardia appears to be the associated cessation of respiration.

Afferent stimulation of the superior laryngeal nerve produces cardiovascular changes which resemble in certain respects the diving bradycardia. Iriuchijima & Kumada (73) reported that such stimulation produced bradycardia and a reduction in cardiac output. These cardiac effects were achieved virtually exclusively by increased vagal activity, in contrast to the responses to carotid sinus nerve stimulation, in which increased vagal activity was associated with reduced sympathetic activity. Glick et al. (74) have demonstrated a reflex negative inotropic and chronotropic response of the heart to stretch of the lungs. The afferent pathways are mediated predominantly by the vagus nerves.

Guazzi et al. (75) concluded that the bradycardia observed during natural sleep in the cat also appears to be mediated almost exclusively by vagal pathways. Powerful vagal discharges can apparently arise by purely central mechanisms, since similar changes in heart rate were observed in animals in which the sinoaortic baroreceptors were deafferented.

Submersion asphyxia and cephalic ischemia activate both divisions of the autonomic nervous system simultaneously. Ferrante & Opdyke (76) found that during submersion asphyxia in nutria, parasympathetic influences predominated at the pacemaker and ventricular myocardium, since a pronounced bradycardia and a negative inotropic response were produced. Vagal blockade unmasked the simultaneous increase in sympathetic activity, which in turn could be abolished with propranolol. In studies of the response of the dog heart to cephalic ischemia, Levy et al. (42) concluded that parasympathetic influences predominated at the cardiac pacemaker, whereas the sympathetic effects were prepotent on the ventricular myocardium. However, the vagal effects markedly attenuated the sympathetic enhancement of myocardial contractility, presumably on the basis of the adrenergic-cholinergic interaction described above. In studies on the cat conducted by Downing & Gardner (55), changes in cephalic perfusion pressure (even with the carotid sinus reflexes abrogated) produced significant inverse alterations in ventricular contractility, even in the perfusion pressure range between 75 and 150 mm Hg. These changes appeared to be mediated almost exclusively via sympathetic pathways; no significant role could be ascribed to the vagus nerves.

HUMORAL CONTROL OF THE HEART

Hormones.—In order to assess the role of the thyroid gland in the regulation of myocardial contractility, Taylor et al. (77) constructed tension-velocity curves from data obtained in anesthetized dogs. They concluded that there was a significant enhancement of contractility during hyperthyroid states, whereas contractility was depressed in hypothyroidism. Evidence for an increase in myocardial contractility in hyperthyroid cats was also provided by the experiments of Pannier (78). Interaction with adrenergic mechanisms was suggested by the observations that myocardial catecholamine depletion attenuated the positive inotropic state in hyperthyroidism and that the inotropic response to norepinephrine is much greater in cardiac muscle from hyperthyroid than from euthyroid animals. From measurements of cardiac ejection times and isovolumic contraction times, Amidi et al. (79) concluded that the myocardial contractility of hyperthyroid human subjects is enhanced, whereas that of hypothyroid patients is depressed. However, catecholamine depletion in the hyperthyroid patients did not abolish the improvement of myocardial contractility. Similarly, Murayama & Goodkind (80) observed an enhancement in the frequency-force curves of atria from hyperthyroid guinea pigs, and this was not altered by reserpine. Tipton et al. (81) found that thyroid hormones were not essential for the development of bradycardia in response to an exercise training program in rats, although the onset of bradycardia occurred significantly later in thyroidectomized than in normal animals. Zaimas et al. (82) have shown, however, that the chronic administration of small doses of thyroxine does increase the sensitivity of the S-A node of the cat to vagal stimulation.

The role of the adrenal corticosteroids in the regulation of myocardial contractility is not well understood, because the effect varies tremendously with experimental conditions. The studies of Davies et al. (83) provide further evidence of a salutary effect on the myocardium. They found that pretreatment with corticosteroid significantly reduced the degree of myocardial depression ordinarily produced by total cardiopulmonary bypass, and resulted in the maintenance of more normal levels of blood pH and total buffer base postoperatively.

The effects of glucagon on the heart will be considered below, in the section on myocardial metabolism.

Blood gases and pH.—Observations by Ng et al. (84) indicate that moderate degrees of hypoxia actually enhance myocardial contractility in the isolated heart. High oxygen tensions apparently have the opposite effect. Daniell & Bagwell (85) measured the changes in isometric systolic tension from a strain-gauge arch sutured to the left ventricle of open-chest dogs. They observed a significant decrease in systolic tension when the inspired oxygen concentration was increased from 25 to 100 per cent. Directionally similar changes in coronary blood flow were also observed, but the decrements in systolic tension were not significantly different even when coronary blood flow was held constant. Kioschos et al. (86) found that appreciable depressions of myocardial contractility were usually not obtained in anesthetized dogs until oxygen pressures exceeded 2 atm. At oxygen pressures above this level, there was a progressive reduction in left ventricular stroke volume and work at constant end diastolic pressures and afterloads. Reductions in maximum left ventricular dP/dt and in the ratio of dP/dt to integrated isometric tension and an increase in isometric contraction time were additional indices of impaired myocardial contractility during exposure to hyperbaric oxygen.

In studies on unanesthetized rabbits, Korner et al. (87) found that acute arterial hypoxia evoked a large increase in efferent vagal activity and in sympathoadrenal constrictor activity, but a diminution in cardiac sympathoadrenal activity. During the early phases of hypoxia, cardiac output was reduced, and there was a profound redistribution of systemic blood flow (88). During the later phases of acute hypoxia, blood flow was redistributed further, but cardiac output rose. During anesthesia with chloralose-urethane or pentobarbital, hypoxia evoked the same changes in sympathoadrenal activity as before anesthesia, but vagal efferent activity no longer increased in spontaneously breathing animals (87). Hyperventilation in anesthetized rabbits inhibited all the changes in autonomic activity to the heart and circulation evoked by hypoxic stimulation of the arterial chemoreceptors (89).

Souhrada et al. (90) found that respiratory alkalosis prolonged the ability of the heart to withstand hypoxia in rat heart-lung preparations and enhanced recovery after anoxia. The effects of chronic hypoxia on the myocardial resistance to anoxia were investigated by McGrath & Bullard (91). When ventricular muscle strips from acclimatized rats were subjected to an atmosphere of 95 per cent N_2, 5 per cent CO_2, the developed tension declined more gradually than did strips from control animals.

The effects of respiratory and metabolic acidosis on canine isovolumetric left ventricles were studied by Caress et al. (92). Total cardiopulmonary bypass was employed in order to control the effects of concomitant changes in the peripheral circulation. During respiratory acidosis, myocardial contractility was not depressed until the pH was diminished to below 7.0. This undoubtedly represents the combined effects of the increased Pco_2 acting directly upon the heart and indirectly via cardiac autonomic neural pathways. In hearts isolated from the nervous system, increased Pco_2 is significantly depressant to the myocardium with much smaller decrements in pH (93). Exposure of conscious dogs to an atmosphere containing a Pco_2 of 45 mm

Hg caused a significant depression of myocardial contractility, as shown by Horwitz et al. (94). In their experiments, the arterial blood pH decreased from 7.4 to 7.26. This was accompanied by a reduction in cardiac output, a rise in right and left atrial pressures, but no change in aortic pressure.

In anesthetized dogs (92, 95) and cats (96), metabolic acidosis produced by lactate infusions was found to impair myocardial contractility. In studies by Caress et al. (92) and by Wildenthal et al. (95), there was some residual depression even after correction of the acidemia, which suggests that the lactate ion itself may have a negative inotropic effect. In addition to direct effects upon the myocardium, the overall response to lactic acidosis was shown to depend upon catecholamine release and upon the altered myocardial sensitivity to circulating catecholamines (95). In studies on the cat conducted by Rocamora & Downing (96), it was found that animals with an intact sympathoadrenal system were resistant to metabolic acidosis down to pH levels of about 6.8. However, beta-adrenergic blockade with propranolol uncovered the direct myocardial depressant action of the acidemia.

Electrolytes.—Rat hearts were perfused by Page et al. (97) at rates of coronary vascular flow more than ten times normal. By this means, the transfer of K^+ became limited by the rate of transmembrane exchange, rather than by the rate of coronary vascular perfusion. Under these conditions, it was observed that a substantial fraction of what is generally considered to be cellular K^+ exchanges at a rate considerably faster than what had previously been reported.

Gerlings & Gilmore (98) developed an automated method for recording the net myocardial exchange of K^+ The method requires small volumes of blood, and provides continuous analysis for prolonged periods. These investigators (99) observed that when the contracting left ventricle was developing little tension, there was a net uptake of K^+, whereas during periods of relatively great tension development, a net loss of K^+ occurred. Catecholamines ordinarily result in a net uptake of K^+ by the myocardium (100–102). However, in the absence of an adequate supply of oxygen, such as may prevail in isolated, Tyrode-perfused hearts, catecholamines cause the net loss, rather than gain, of K^+ (102). During respiratory acidosis, the myocardium takes up K^+ (100). The net exchange of K^+ is dependent upon both the rise in Pco_2 and the concomitant sympathoadrenal discharge.

Concerning electrolyte effects upon cardiac performance, Logic et al. (103) found that the change in myocardial contractility evoked by K^+ infusions into the major coronary arteries of anesthetized dogs depended upon both the amount and the rate of the infusion. Hypernatremia, induced in dogs by means of peritoneal dialysis with 5 per cent saline solution, produced an increase in heart rate, a decrease in cardiac output, and consequently a marked reduction in stroke volume, according to the study by Maxwell (104). Increasing serum osmolality per se, however, apparently enhances myocardial contractility. In experiments conducted by Wildenthal et al. (105), hypertonic sucrose or urea was administered to anesthetized dogs. Moderate elevations of serum osmolality significantly increased the maximum dP/dt of the left ventricle, while end diastolic pressure remained constant or diminished slightly.

CORONARY BLOOD FLOW

Methods.—In recent years considerable effort has been expended in attempts to simplify the methods for the measurement of coronary blood flow and to enable the investigator to make accurate and repeated measurements in the intact and unanesthetized animal or subject. Most of these methods involve myocardial clearance of highly diffusible radioactive substances. The earlier studies used primarily Rb^{86} and Love et al. (106) have compared the myocardial clearance of this isotope from arterial blood with that of K^{42} and Cs^{131}. The myocardial uptake of K^{42} paralleled that of Rb^{86}, whereas cesium uptake was only about one-third the value of the other two isotopes and consequently is a less reliable index of coronary blood flow. Xenon and krypton are now used for estimating coronary blood flow in the intact animal and man. These inert gases are essentially removed in one passage through the lungs and their radioactivity is easily monitored over the precordium. A technique employing an occlusive balloon in the ascending aorta in dogs, with injection of Xe^{133} into the blood trapped between the aorta, and the right atrium. Only about 3 per cent of the right atrial H_2 was coronary vessels and monitor xenon washout without necessitating catheterization of the coronary arteries and the use of fluoroscopic equipment and contrast media (107). The 10-sec balloon inflation did not alter the subsequent isotope washout curve. In a comparison of lipid-soluble Xe^{133} and water-soluble antipyrine-I^{125} washout curves, Bassingthwaighte et al. (108) found greater tailing with xenon, suggesting longer retention of radioactivity in fat. At the apex, where there is little fat, the two curves which are described by a two-exponential equation and not by a single exponential, as has been often assumed, were almost identical and approximated 95 per cent of actual flow, whereas for the whole heart lower estimates of flow were obtained. Even after correction for fat content of the heart, both xenon and antipyrine gave flow values slightly lower than those measured directly. This may be due to inhomogeneity of flow in the myocardium, a problem studied by Klocke et al. (109) with washout of hydrogen gas and gas chromatography for detection of very small H_2 concentrations in blood. With this technique they clearly demonstrated, in dogs with coronary occlusion and patients with coronary artery disease, inhomogeneity of flow which might be overlooked by methods for gas analysis which cannot resolve venous-arterial differences of less than 5 per cent of the initial venous gas concentration. Of equal importance to detection of small differences in gas concentration is assurance that the gas tension in areas of low flow reaches equilibrium with that in the arterial blood. Hydrogen has an advantage over xenon and krypton in that it is much less soluble in blood and consequently is more completely eliminated in one passage through the lungs. However, nitrogen may be superior to foreign gases in that it is normally breathed and therefore even in low-flow areas it will be at the same partial pressure in myocardium and arterial blood (110). Desaturation would be started by having the subject breathe 21 per cent O_2 and 79 per cent of some inert gas other than nitrogen. The difficulty with the nitrogen washout technique is the ease of contamination of blood samples from the nitrogen in air.

In all studies where coronary sinus blood samples are required, it is essential that there not be admixture of right atrial blood with coronary sinus blood. Evidence that such admixture does not occur when the catheter is at least 1 or 2 cm into the coronary sinus of the closed-chest dog has been provided by Koberstein et al. (111). They injected H_2 in saline continually into the inferior vena cava and sampled blood from the coronary sinus, the aorta, and the right atrium. Only about 3 per cent of the right atrial H_2 was present in the aortic and coronary sinus blood, which indicated no admixture of right atrial and coronary sinus blood, even at coronary sinus blood withdrawal rates as high as 45 ml/min. Admixture was also absent with systemic hypotension, but did occur with pulmonary artery occlusion and elevated right ventricular pressures.

The coincidence counting technique using Rb^{84} has been employed: (a) to estimate effective capillary flow, by dividing myocardial uptake by the integrated arterial concentration; and (b) to measure total coronary flow, by dividing myocardial uptake by the integrated difference of arterial and coronary sinus concentrations of the isotope (112). Accurate measurements of myocardial uptake are essential and nonmyocardial sources of radioactivity must be eliminated if reasonable values for effective capillary flow and total coronary flow are to be obtained. The radioactivity present in blood becomes negligible between 90 and 270 sec (cleared by tissues but before substantial re-entrance into blood) and that present in the chest wall and lungs can be estimated by monitoring the right (noncardiac) side of the chest. Under control conditions and with isoproterenol administration, effective capillary flow and total flow were in good agreement. However, with norepinephrine and nicotine, total flow increased significantly more than did effective capillary flow. These results do not necessarily imply true shunting in the myocardium but may indicate that at high flow rates clearance by the tissue is less effective and, therefore, not proportional to the increase in perfusion. The difference between the responses to isoproterenol and norepinephrine is thought to be attributable to an effect of isoproterenol on precapillary sphincters, providing a large capillary surface area for isotope diffusion, in contradistinction to norepinephrine which acts primarily on arterioles. It also may be merely that isoproterenol, being a beta-receptor activator, elicits extensive resistance vessel dilation whereas norepinephrine produces vasoconstriction as its initial effect and dilation primarily as a result of its enhancement of myocardial metabolic activity.

Physical factors.—In recent studies on the regulation of coronary blood flow, attention has been chiefly directed toward neural and chemical mechanisms. Although these factors are of primary importance in the adjustment of flow to meet the changing requirements of the heart, the effects of such factors as perfusion pressure, heart rate, and extramyocardial pressure should not be overlooked. In a study on open-chest dogs with the systemic circulation supplied by a pump, Beneken et al. (113) investigated the effect of coronary perfusion pressure on ventricular function. When mean left atrial pressure was held constant and mean aortic pressure was changed, aortic flow became maximal at a certain aortic pressure which varied in different animals from 36 to 98 mm Hg. However, if coronary perfusion pressure was not permitted to vary with aortic pressure but was held at 115 mm Hg, aortic flow reached a plateau or increased slightly with aortic pressures below the previously established peak flow, whereas it still decreased when aortic pressure was elevated above this point. It is suggested that at low aortic pressures, oxygen supply to the myocardium is impaired. The balance between oxygen supply and demand is upset and can only be restored by a reduction in oxygen consumption, accomplished by a decrease in pumping activity (reduced aortic flow). The point where aortic flow starts to decrease as aortic pressure is reduced corresponds with the lower coronary perfusion pressures where autoregulation of coronary blood flow fails (the point where coronary resistance vessels become maximally dilated). With increase in aortic pressure above the point where peak aortic flow occurred, the greater left ventricular pressure load overrides any beneficial effects of enhanced coronary perfusion and accounts for the decrease in aortic flow. Hence, these studies are in agreement with the concept that coronary blood flow becomes pressure dependent outside the pressure range in which autoregulation occurs. At high coronary perfusion pressures, in the absence of increased aortic pressure and the associated increased cardiac work and vasodilator metabolite release, coronary vessel constriction is opposed by the high distending pressure and autoregulation disappears. Alterations in hematocrit and heart rate produced changes in the relationship of peak aortic flow and mean aortic pressure consistent with their effects on oxygen supply to the myocardium.

With respect to the effect of heart rate on coronary blood flow, Pitt & Gregg (114) have confirmed, in unanesthetized dogs, results previously obtained in anesthetized animals that increase in heart rate produces an increase in coronary blood flow. They used dogs with surgically induced atrioventricular block and found that with increases in heart rate from about 60 to about 150 beats/min, cardiac output, aortic pressure, and coronary flow increased and the results were not altered by beta-blockade with propranolol. However, at heart rates above 130–185 beats/min cardiac output and aortic pressure decreased but coronary blood flow continued to rise. Even at the highest heart rates studied (250–300), coronary blood flow did not decrease and the resistance vessels showed a reactive hyperemic response to 10-sec coronary occlusions, which indicates that they were not maximally dilated. These results show that with tachycardia in the unanesthetized dog, coronary blood flow responds to the oxygen demands of the myocardium despite enhanced extravascular compression (more time in systole) and that the coronary vessels are under metabolic rather than neurogenic control with electrically induced increases in heart rate.

Contraction of the myocardium is known to impede coronary blood flow, particularly in the left ventricle, and one might anticipate that systolic restriction of flow might be maximal in the endocardium where intramyocardial pressure is greatest. Griggs & Nakamura (115) studied this problem with injection of I^{131} iodoantipyrine into the coronary circulation of the open-chest dog and found that under control conditions or with slight constriction of the left coronary artery, the ratio of the isotope content of the inner half to that of the outer half of the left ventricle was essentially unity, but that with more severe coronary artery constriction the ratio fell as low as 0.28. These findings confirm earlier studies. Griggs & Nakamura concluded that under normal conditions flow to the inner and outer layers of the ventricular wall is determined by vasomotor tone but when the resistance vessels become maximally dilated, as occurs with severe coronary constriction, physical factors such as tissue pressure and perfusion pressure become the determinants of flow distribution in the myocardium.

Neural and neurohumoral factors.—Although knowledge of the effect of the cardiac nerves and of neurohumors on coronary resistance has significantly increased in the past few years, the picture is still somewhat clouded. This is due in large part to the difficulty in separating direct vasomotor effects from inotropic and chronotropic effects, but also to the difficulties encountered when extrapolating from isolated vessels or vessel segments to intact tissue, and to species differences.

In the dog, Ross & Mulder (116) confirmed the presence of alpha-receptors by means of cardiac sympathetic nerve stimulation after beta-blockade with propranolol. They also demonstrated that left cardiac sympathetic nerve stimulation elicited greater flow changes in the left circumflex than in the anterior descendens or right coronary arteries, whereas right cardiac sympathetic nerve stimulation produced approximately equal flow responses in all three vessels.

In an interesting study of responses of the coronary vessels of the cat to cardiac autonomic nerve stimulation and intracoronary injections of norepinephrine and acetylcholine, Brown (117) found no evidence of alpha-receptors. With constant pump perfusion of the left coronary artery sC fiber stimulation or norepinephrine administration elicited a reduction in coronary pressure associated with a rise in aortic pressure and a decrease in coronary sinus blood oxygen saturation. In the potassium-arrested heart sC fiber stimulation and norepinephrine produced coronary dilation without change in coronary sinus blood oxygen saturation. Stimulation of $A\delta$ and B fibers was without effect on coronary resistance. The beta-blocker propranolol abolished the effects of sympathetic nerve stimulation and norepineph-rine, but the alpha-adrenergic blocker dibenzylene had no effect on coro-nary resistance. It appears that the coronary circulation of the cat, unlike that of the dog (118), is devoid of alpha-adrenergic receptors. However, the data would be more convincing if there were an initial increase in coro-nary sinus blood oxygen saturation associated with the coronary dilation produced by adrenergic stimulation in the K-arrested heart. A pure coronary vasodilator like acetylcholine does produce a rise in coronary sinus blood oxygen tension and, if sympathetic stimulation and norepinephrine elicit pure dilation prior to their inotropic effects, then this should be reflected in the oxygen saturation of the coronary sinus blood. Apparently the coro-nary vessels of the cat in this preparation also did not show autoregulation, since changes in flow were accompanied by abrupt changes in pressure which remained steady and did not show the progressive alterations seen in an autoregulating preparation. Vagal stimulation and acetylcholine produced coronary dilation and an increase in oxygen saturation of the coronary sinus blood; both effects were blocked by atropine. These results confirm numer-ous earlier studies and are in agreement with those of Levy & Zieske (36), Blumenthal et al. (35), and Cobb et al. (119). Dopamine has been reported to elicit coronary dilation which is proportional to its inotropic effect and is probably secondary to the increased oxygen demand of the myocardium (120). The effect of angiotensin on coronary smooth muscle is thought to be due in part to a release of endogenous catecholamines by this polypeptide (121).

To what extent the coronary arterioles participate in the reflex altera-tions of resistance observed in other peripheral vascular beds is still uncer-tain. Incontrovertible evidence for reflex changes in coronary resistance elic-ited by stimuli originating in remote areas such as the gastrointestinal tract or even within the heart itself is lacking. However, recent studies by Feigl (122) indicate that the coronary vessels are responsive to baroreceptor acti-vation. In vagotomized open-chest dogs, bilateral common carotid artery oc-clusion produced an increase in aortic pressure, tachycardia, and a decrease in left circumflex coronary artery resistance. After beta-blockade with pro-pranolol, the same maneuver did not alter heart rate, increased aortic pres-sure, and resulted in an increase in coronary resistance, whereas after car-diac sympathectomy plus propranolol, carotid artery occlusion still elicited an increase in arterial pressure but did not change heart rate or coronary resistance. Thus, it is evident that there are alpha-receptors in the coronary vessels and that these can be activated reflexly from the carotid sinus baro-receptors, as demonstrated after beta-receptor blockade.

Beta-receptor blockade alone can produce an increase in coronary resis-tance (123, 124). This effect may be secondary to a reduction in myocardial oxygen consumption or possibly an unmasking of vasoconstrictor tone. Re-flex coronary constriction in the cat in response to oligemic hypotension has been reported by Ovsyannikov & Tkachenko (125) and was not affected by vagotomy, atropine, or denervation of the carotid sinuses. It is difficult to reconcile these results with those of Brown (117) or Feigl (122), but it is possible that the increased coronary resistance observed is of metabolic origin in response to the reduced cardiac work. In this regard, it would be of interest to determine whether increased coronary resistance in hypotension occurs following cardiac sympathectomy. Another possible reason for increased coronary resistance in hypotension is the intense positive inotropic stimulation of the heart with compression of the coronary vessels reflexly induced via the baroreceptors. This mechanism has been explored by Entman et al. (126) in anesthetized dogs made hypotensive by bleeding to aortic pressures of 45 mm Hg. Systolic coronary blood flow showed a greater percentage decrease than did diastolic coronary blood flow but was restored almost to control levels after pronethalol, whereas diastolic flow was unaffected by this beta-blocker. It is thought that the reduction of the extent of subendocardial hemorrhage and necrosis in hemorrhagic shock by pronethalol is due to (a) prevention of reflexly induced increases in metabolic activity of the myocardium under conditions of low coronary perfusion pressure and flow and (b) attenuation of the extravascular compression in systole, which increases systolic and total coronary blood flow.

Metabolic factors.—Among the various mechanisms that have been proposed for intrinsic regulation of blood flow has been the action of reduced P_{O_2} on the vascular smooth muscle. Most of the reports advocating a key role of P_{O_2} in local control of the circulation have dealt with the vascular bed of skeletal muscle or with isolated arterial segments. With the increase of interest in hyperbaric oxygenation, some attention has been focused on the coronary vessels. Support for the concept that oxygen tension of arterial blood can directly influence coronary resistance has been provided by Daniell and Bagwell (85), Lammerant et al. (127), and Weglicki et al. (128), confirming earlier studies. These three groups of investigators demonstrated that increasing Pa_{O_2} to supernormal levels resulted in a decrease in coronary blood flow. This effect also occurred after vagotomy, alpha- and beta-adrenergic receptor blockade (85, 127), or high spinal anesthesia (85) and, therefore, was not neurally mediated. The reduction in coronary blood flow produced by hyperoxia resulted in a decrease in myocardial oxygen consumption (85, 127, 128) a decrease in substrate uptake (128) but no impairment of substrate utilization (128). The evidence strongly favors a direct effect of high P_{O_2} on the coronary vascular smooth muscle. However, inhibition of a vasodilator substance or release of a constrictor substance from either the myocardium or the vasculature has not been eliminated. Additional evidence that Pa_{O_2} affects vascular smooth muscle, in this case precapillary sphincters, is that elevation of Pa_{O_2} increased the distance between visible functioning capillaries on the surface of the rat heart, whereas reduction of Pa_{O_2} produced the opposite effect (129).

Correlation between coronary blood flow and cardiac work has been recognized for many years and the studies of Pitt et al. (130), using Xe^{133} clearance as a measure of coronary flow, show that in man, as in the dog, flow per 100 g of myocardium is greater in the left than in the right coronary artery. Hence, even though the greater work load of the left ventricle is accomplished by a larger mass of muscle, a greater flow per unit of myocardium is required to do this work. What mediates the reduction in coronary resistance that is associated with increased cardiac work is still controversial. Adenosine has been proposed as a possible mediator. Studies by Rubio et al. (131) indicate that in reactive hyperemia following 30–60 sec of left coronary artery occlusion, the amount of adenosine calculated to be present in the interstitial fluid compartment of the heart is more than sufficient to account for the vasodilation observed in the period of reactive hyperemia. In an attempt to evaluate the adenosine hypothesis, Afonso (132) administered lidoflazine (a coronary vasodilator which potentiates the vasodilator action of adenosine) to dogs during hypoxia and induced tachycardia. Lidoflazine did not potentiate the vasodilation produced by these two interventions. However, as pointed out by Afonso, these results do not invalidate the adenosine hypothesis. Since the potentiation of adenosine dilation by lidoflazine is probably due to its adenosine-sparing effect in blood (decreased permeability of red cells to adenosine and inhibition of adenosine deaminase), one would not expect potentiation of endogenously produced adenosine. The latter originates in the myocardial cells and reaches the interstitial fluid, where it can elicit dilation of the resistance vessels and where there is no adenosine deaminase to protect against. Formation of adenosine in KCl-arrested ischemic rabbit hearts has been confirmed and its presence in similarly tested dog hearts reveals twice the concentration of that found in rabbit hearts (133).

Collateral circulation.—The mechanism involved in the formation and enlargement of collateral coronary vessels in response to gradual or abrupt occlusion of a coronary artery has not been elucidated. Nevertheless, useful information about the rate of collateral vessel development and the criteria for evaluation of the magnitude of collateral development is available. Khouri et al. (134) used hydraulic occlusive devices to occlude the left circumflex coronary artery of unanesthetized dogs gradually or acutely and measured aortic pressure, left ventricular pressure, and cardiac output and flow in both main branches of the left coronary artery. With progressive occlusion of the left circumflex coronary artery, reactive hyperemia decreased and became nil at the time that flow in the partially occluded artery began to decrease and myocardial contractility showed signs of impairment. Within 24 hr, flow in the anterior descendens artery increased and contractility returned to normal, which indicated enhancement of collateral flow to the partially ischemic area. With acute reduction of coronary flow to 25 per cent of control, flow in the unconstricted artery increased 34 per cent in an hour and 118 per cent by the seventh day, when the vessel was completely occluded. At this time, the flow in the unconstricted artery equaled 80 per cent of the combined control flows of the two arteries. In a study on miniature pigs, Howe & Winbury (135) observed that acute occlusion of the anterior descendens artery increased by 27 per cent the Rb^{86} uptake of the left ventricular muscle supplied by the unoccluded circumflex artery. No change was observed in Rb^{86} uptake of muscle supplied by the right coronary artery. These results are in agreement with earlier studies and suggest that the increased flow in the adjacent unoccluded artery is in part due to the increased work load of the nonischemic left ventricular muscle and not only to the presence of collateral vessels in the normal heart.

According to the results of clearance studies, collateral blood flow in the normal heart is considerably greater than that estimated by measurements of retrograde flow, and the high values given by the clearance technique may be artifactual. To what extent collateral blood flow following acute coronary occlusion is influenced by the cardiac nerves was investigated by Redding & Rees (136) in the dog, in an effort to reevaluate the claims of Grayson & Lapin (137) that collateral blood flow to the ischemic area fell progressively to zero over a 4-hr period after coronary occlusion and that this reduction in collateral flow as well as myocardial infarction could be prevented by sympathetic blockade. Redding & Rees (136) were unable to confirm the results of Grayson & Lapin (137) and they could provide no evidence that neurally mediated constriction was responsible for the infarction. A method for the study of collateral vessel development following coronary occlusion in the closed-chest dog has been described (138).

Since the presence of endomural or luminal vessels (those communicating between the coronary vessels and the cardiac chambers) has been known for many years, their role in providing collateral blood flow in the myocardium has come under consideration. Moir (139) investigated this problem in the open-chest dog by perfusing the coronary arteries with unlabeled blood and the cardiac chambers with I^{131}-labeled blood under control conditions, with myocardial ischemia during left and right ventricular hypertension and with coronary occlusion. The amount of labeled blood in the myocardium was small and was higher in the atria and right ventricle than in the left ventricle. Furthermore, of the various interventions performed, only coronary occlusion increased the myocardial content of labeled blood and in these experiments the epicardial half of the left ventricular wall contained more of the isotope than did the endocardial half. Hence, significant myocardial perfusion via the luminal vessels appears unlikely.

Myocardial Metabolism

High-energy phosphates.—The controversy about the biochemical defect in the failing heart continues, particularly with respect to energy production. Stoner et al. (140) observed no change in ADP/O ratios between mitochondria from control and those from chronically stressed dog hearts with either malate-pyruvate or succinate as substrate and found that oxidative

activity and respiratory control were unchanged or slightly greater in mitochondria from stressed than from unstressed hearts. The procedures used by
these investigators were (a) combined tricuspid insufficiency and pulmonary
artery stenosis, (b) pulmonic insufficiency, (c) aortic stenosis, (d) aortic
insufficiency, (e) anastomosis of the left pulmonary artery and the aorta,
and (f) induced thyrotoxicosis. The stress periods were from 332 to 608
days and those animals with the combined right heart valve lesions and
those with the pulmonary artery-aorta anastomoses showed signs of severe
myocardial failure. In contrast to these findings, Lindenmayer et al. (141)
confirmed their previous observation that oxidative phosphorylation, respiratory control, and oxidative activity are impaired in mitochondria from
failing guinea pig and rabbit hearts. The reason for these disparate results
is not clear but they may result from the difference in incubation media used
or possibly to the degree of heart failure in the two studies. In the experiments of Lindenmayer et al. (141) several different media were employed
and they observed that the use of proteinase impaired mitochondrial function. Since Stoner and colleagues used proteinase with succinate as substrate
and had lower ADP/O ratios in their control mitochondria than did Lindenmayer and associates, this may account for the divergent results. Of course,
other factors such as species differences, and degree of impairment of cardiac function must also be considered. In mitochondria from bovine fetal
hearts, oxidative phosphorylation is functionally efficient, although structural integration with myofibrils has not yet been achieved and there are
fewer mitochondria than in the mature heart (142). In mitochondria from
Syrian hamsters with hereditary myocardiopathy, oxidative phosphorylation
and respiratory control are depressed and this may be causally related to the
heart failure that occurs in these animals (143).

Concerning high-energy stores of the heart, Boerth et al. (144) found
that imposing an increased work load on the bypassed heart by distention of
a balloon in the left ventricle and by increasing heart rate had no effect on
ATP concentrations of the myocardium and slightly reduced the creatine
phosphate content of the outer half of the left ventricular wall. Under control and experimental conditions, the outer half of the left ventricular wall
had a higher concentration of creatine phosphate than did the inner half;
the ATP concentration was the same in the inner and outer halves. In hemorrhagic shock in the cat, Lefer et al. (145) observed no reduction in cardiac or skeletal muscle ATP or creatine phosphate, which constitutes evidence against the hypothesis that tissue ATP concentrations decline to critical levels in hemorrhagic shock. In rat atria suspended in artificial media
containing glucose, the absence of buffer led to a reduction in ATP content
which could be restored by the addition of bicarbonate but not by phosphate
or Tris buffers (146). No relationship between ATP levels and developed
tension were found. In cultured, spontaneously beating heart cells, beating
ceased when the ATP levels were reduced about 40 per cent by inhibition of
oxidative phosphorylation and glycolysis (147). However, the cells beat in

response to electrical stimulation and would do so until the ATP concentration was lowered to 85–90 per cent of the initial control level, which indicated no obvious impairment of contractile ability. Reduction in the ATP levels of isolated perfused rat hearts produced by substituting nitrogen for oxygen in the perfusion medium was frequently not associated with electrocardiographic changes (148), whereas reduction in the rate of perfusion elicited abnormalities in the electrocardiogram before ATP content of the myocardium declined (149, 150). No clear explanation of this strange dissociation of the electrical activity pattern and the myocardial ATP content is apparent. Electrocardiographic changes occurring without measurable decrease in ATP levels could possibly be due to depletion of small discrete ATP pools concerned with maintenance of normal electrical activity but the reverse situation cannot be accounted for by such a mechanism.

With myocardial ischemia produced by coronary occlusion in the dog, ATP and creatine phosphate levels decreased in the expected manner in the ischemic myocardium and were essentially unchanged in the nonischemic muscle (151). However, the concentration of several enzymes increased in the nonischemic muscle and this increase may represent metabolic changes associated with compensatory hyperfunction and increased energy requirement of the surviving muscle. The metabolism and changes in enzyme concentrations in infarcted myocardium in dogs during the early phases after coronary occlusions and during the reparative process have been examined by Gudbjarnason et al. (152). In myocardial infarction in dogs, acid phosphatase increased whereas alkaline phosphatase and potassium decreased (153). The intracoronary administration of ATP to the hypothermic, isolated nonperfused (ischemic) dog heart is reported to increase the myocardial adenine nucleotide and creatine phosphate content and decrease the rate of glycogen degradation (154). It is suggested that the nucleotides penetrate the myocardial cell membrane as a consequence of the concentration gradient across the cell wall and increased cell permeability to ATP resulting from the low pH and anoxia. Some of the metabolic changes occurring in the ischemic heart are reviewed by Wollenberger & Krause (155).

The question whether energy utilization and conversion of this energy to mechanical work is impaired in heart failure has been explored by Pool et al. (156). They found that right ventricular papillary muscles from cats in heart failure due to pulmonary artery constriction showed decreased mechanical performance, reduced high-energy phosphate stores, decreased rate of high-energy phosphate utilization but no defect in conversion of chemical energy to mechanical work. The reduction in energy utilization was commensurate with the reduction in contractile element work.

Consonant with the findings of reduced energy utilization by failing myocardium is the observation that myosin extracted from hearts of dogs with naturally occurring heart failure has a lower ATPase activity than does myosin from hearts of normal dogs (157). Hence, the impaired mechanical performance of the failing heart may be due, at least in part, to a reduced rate of energy liberation to the contractile machinery. These results support previous reports that myofibrillar ATPase is reduced in human hearts in congestive failure and in cat hearts made to fail by constriction of the pulmonary artery. Beta-adrenergic receptor blockade reduced tension development in the dog and rabbit papillary muscle but was without effect on myofibrillar ATPase activity or high-energy phosphate stores (158).

Oxygen consumption and substrate utilization.—In a review paper, Sonnenblick et al. (159) evaluated the various factors that influence myocardial oxygen consumption. Foremost among these factors are developed tension (internal contractile element work) and the contractile state of the myocardium (as judged by V_{max} in the force-velocity relationship). Basal testing myocardial oxygen consumption is low and the amount of oxygen required for activation is negligible. Finally, relatively little oxygen is utilized in performance of external work (external contractile element work), as exemplified by the large difference in myocardial oxygen consumption between a given amount of pressure work (tension development) and volume work. Studies on the isolated, perfused, isovolumetric rabbit heart in which perfusion pressure, ventricular volume, heart rate, and the contractile state of the heart (the latter by administration of catecholamines and calcium) were varied, gave results consistent with the view that ventricular tension development and contractile state are the chief determinants of myocardial oxygen consumption (160). In the intact anesthetized dog under control conditions and with catecholamine stimulation of the heart, stroke work showed a consistent correlation with oxygen consumption and stroke power or contractile element power did not show a significantly better correlation, which suggests that velocity of contraction had relatively little influence on myocardial oxygen consumption (161). When blood supply to the myocardium was restricted by coronary artery disease in man, an increase in cardiac oxygen requirement by induced tachycardia resulted in an increase in the coronary sinus blood lactate/pyruvate ratio in eight of twelve patients and a decrease in coronary sinus blood oxygen content in four patients (162). Nine patients experienced angina pectoris during the tachycardia but two showed spontaneous relief of symptoms associated with return of the venous blood lactate/pyruvate ratio toward normal, which indicated a delayed improvement of distribution of coronary blood flow.

The heart is capable of utilizing various substrates and in general, substrate utilization is proportional to the arterial blood concentration. Furthermore, the uptake of one substrate is influenced by the presence or the absence of a second substrate. In the isolated heart of the fasted rat, Vahouny et al. (163) found that the addition of unlabeled palmitate to the perfusion medium after 45 min of perfusion with Krebs bicarbonate buffer containing C^{14}-labeled glucose resulted in a reduction in glucose uptake and cessation of $C^{14}O_2$ production, without changes in tissue concentration of glucose 6-phosphate. When unlabeled glucose was added to the perfusion medium after 45 min of perfusion with C^{14}-palmitate, uptake of palmitate was unaltered, the rate of $C^{14}O_2$ formation increased, and the levels of glucose 6-phosphate and fructose 6-phosphate decreased. The authors propose that (*a*) the increased $C^{14}O_2$ from labeled palmitate, brought about by addition of glucose, represents depletion of acyl coenzyme A intermediates and (*b*) the release of inhibition of glycolysis by high levels of glucose was responsible for the decrease in the glucose and fructose phosphate and for the enhanced incorporation of C^{14} from palmitate into triglycerides by virtue of increase α-glycerol phosphate formation. When glucose uptake was increased in the isolated perfused cat heart by increasing left ventricular pressure development, the addition of palmitate to the medium reduced glucose utilization by as much as 85 per cent (164). The facts that in hearts with increased pressure development no free glucose was found in the myocardial cells and that palmitate, β-hydroxybutyrate, or acetate inhibited transport of the nonmetabolizable sugar 3-O-methylglucose indicate a direct effect on membrane transport. The enhanced glucose transport observed with severe hypoxia was not inhibited by fatty acid whereas that produced by insulin was inhibited. In this study by Neely et al. (164) the absence of exogenous substrate resulted in metabolism of endogenous glycogen and lipids and the rate of depletion of these endogenous substrates was accelerated by greater pressure development. Neither glucose nor palmitate alone could prevent some utilization of endogenous substrates but together the exogenous substrates were effective in maintaining constant tissue levels of glycogen and lipids. Finally, at either high or low levels of pressure development, exogenous palmitate was utilized in preference to glucose. However, Willebrands & Tasseron (165) found that epinephrine and prostaglandins E_1 and $F_1\alpha$ increased oxidation of glucose and palmitate but epinephrine shifted substrate preference toward glucose.

Fat in the form of chylomicrons disappears from the blood and the role of the heart and lungs in chylomicron uptake has been investigated by Simpson-Morgan (166) in a nonheparinized rat heart-lung preparation. Chylomicrons were removed from the circulation at a rate that would account for up to 10 per cent of the amount of chylomicrons oxidized in the intact rat. When the chylomicrons contained C^{14}-palmitic acid, the latter was readily oxidized to $C^{14}O_2$. Chylomicron fatty acid oxidation was not affected by the addition of glucose, whereas infusion of sufficient amounts of chylomicrons reduced glycogenolysis. Free fatty acid release from adipose tissue and its disappearance from plasma are inhibited by beta-adrenergic blockade. The question whether reduced uptake by the heart is a part of the decreased overall metabolic activity of the heart secondary to diminished cardiac work or is due to a direct effect on fatty acid uptake has been studied in the dog by Masters & Glaviano (167) and by Marchetti et al. (168). In one group of experiments (167), free fatty acid uptake decreased despite an increase in myocardial energy requirements by production of tachycardia after propranolol, and in the other study (168) fatty acid uptake was reduced considerably more by the beta-blocker butidrine than by an equivalent decrease in myocardial energy requirements induced by bleeding. In neither study was uptake of glucose, lactate, or pyruvate depressed by beta blockade. The nature of the mechanism of this reduced utilization of free fatty acids by beta-blockade is at present unknown.

An excellent up-to-date review of myocardial metabolism in the normal and diseased state has been written by Opie (169–171).

Hormonal effects.—Controversy exists as to whether or not the hypoglycemic hormone glucagon exerts its positive inotropic effect on the heart via stimulation of beta-receptors. In the isolated perfused rat heart LaRaia et al. (172) observed that propranolol blocked the positive inotropic effect of isoproterenol but was without effect on glucagon-induced increases in ventricular pressure in the isovolumetric heart. Alpha-blocking agents were ineffective in diminishing the positive inotropic actions of either isoproterenol or glucagon. In another study (173) the positive chronotropic as well as the inotropic effects of glucagon were found to be unaffected by beta-receptor blockade in the open-chest dog, and endogenous catecholamine depletion by reserpine did not alter the cardiac response to glucagon. Previously reported block by dicloroisoproterenol of the stimulatory effect of glucagon is thought by Lucchesi (173) to be due to a sympathomimetic action of this beta-blocker, since prior treatment with propranolol eliminated any blocking effect of dichloroisoproterenol of the positive inotropic and chronotropic effects of glucagon. Results consistent with those of LaRaia et al. (172) and of Lucchesi (173) have been obtained by Glick et al. (174) using cat papillary muscle, spontaneously beating cat atria, and intact dog hearts. The latter group did observe partial block of the chronotropic effect of glucagon by propranolol but found no effect of reserpine, insulin, or vagotomy on the inotropic and chronotropic actions of glucagon. Steiner at al. (175) also observed a chronotropic effect of glucagon as well as enhanced atrioventricular conduction without alteration of ventricular automaticity. The chronotropic and conduction responses to glucagon were not blocked by propranolol.

An increase in cyclic AMP in cardiac tissue associated with a positive inotropic effect in response to glucagon administration has been questioned by LaRaia et al. (172). In the isolated perfused rat heart, isoproterenol produced an increase in cyclic AMP whereas glucagon did not. Similarly, cyclic AMP levels in incubated rat heart slices increased with addition of norepinephrine, but were not significantly changed by glucagon (176). In contrast to these findings, Levey & Epstein (177) report that, in particulate fractions of cat and human heart, glucagon is as effective as norepinephrine in elevating cyclic-AMP levels, but only the effect of norepinephrine is blocked by propranolol. An increase in cyclic AMP in response to glucagon has also been observed in cell-free systems from rat heart by Murad (178) and in the perfused rat heart by Bowman et al. (unpublished data quoted by

Murad). These observations, in addition to those of Levey & Epstein that glucagon plus norepinephrine do not produce an additive effect on cyclic AMP formation, suggest that heart muscle contains only one adenyl cyclase which can be activated by beta-receptor stimulation with catecholamines and via another receptor by glucagon. In the failing heart, adenyl cyclase activity was significantly decreased whereas phosphodiesterase activity was normal (179). Thus, the failing heart not only has a reduced store of catecholamines but has less adenyl cyclase available to respond to catecholamine stimulation. Inhibition of phosphodiesterase by theophylline leads to increased levels of cyclic AMP. However, the large doses of theophylline required to enhance the phosphorylase-activating effect of norepinephrine were cardiodepressant and blocked the effect of norepinephrine on cardiac contractility (180). Hence, it appears that the positive inotropic effect of small doses of theophylline possibly accomplishes this action via endogenous catecholamine release and by increasing intracellular ionized calcium rather than by increasing myocardial levels of cyclic AMP (180).

In hypophysectomized rats, the rate of synthesis as well as the turnover of norepinephrine by the myocardium is increased and the effects appear to be mediated via increased sympathetic neuronal activity associated with the thyroid and adrenal insufficiency of hypophysectomy (181). The energy required for norepinephrine uptake and its incorporation into storage granules of the guinea pig heart can be adequately provided by glycolysis or by oxidation of endogenous or exogenous substrates (182). Actually, more norepinephrine uptake occurred under anaerobic than under aerobic conditions and this is presumably due to protection against degradation by monoamine oxidase by nitrogen. The uptake of labeled exogenous norepinephrine is inversely correlated with the inotropic response; the greater the norepinephrine uptake by the isolated perfused rat heart the smaller the increase in contractile force and vice versa (31). Furthermore, the initial inotropic action of epinephrine is not dependent upon high-energy phosphate synthesis since the isolated perfused rat heart exhibits increased contractile force with epinephrine when both glycolysis and oxidative phosphorylation are blocked by iodoacetate and oligomycin, respectively (183).

In rats made hypertensive by unilateral nephrectomy combined with administration of deoxycorticosterone and sodium chloride, norepinephrine storage in the heart is impaired but is restored to normal (along with disappearance of the hypertension) by withdrawal of sodium from the diet or by administration of a long-acting ganglionic blocking agent (184). Furthermore, similar effects on cardiac norepinephrine storage were obtained with sodium restriction and ganglionic blockade when impaired storage and hypotension were induced by repeated doses of isoproterenol given over a period of 4 days (32). These findings suggested that intraneuronal ionic imbalance and increased sympathetic nervous activity were responsible for the defect in myocardial norepinephrine storage; there is no evidence that increase in monoamine oxidase activity can be implicated (20).

In the failing heart, catecholamine stores are known to be depleted and Vogel et al. (185) have demonstrated correlation of the reduction in cardiac catecholamine content with loss of fluorescence in the terminal varicose nerve fibers in the hearts of calves in heart failure due to pulmonary artery constriction. The loss of catecholamines in the failing cat heart cannot be accounted for on the basis of increased activities of monoamine oxidase and catechol-O-methyltransferase, the enzymes primarily involved in catecholamine catabolism (186).

In skeletal muscle, catecholamines promote glycogenolysis by activation of phosphorylase and inhibition of the conversion of the glucose 6-phosphate dependent form or tranferase "D" (synthetase "D") or inactive form, to the independent or active form, transferase "I" (synthetase "I"). In cardiac muscle, the effects of catecholamines on transferase activity are controversial. It appears that in the intact animal the percentage of myocardial transferase in the independent form is increased by catecholamines (187), whereas in the isolated perfused heart no effect is observed (188). A similar difference in *in vivo* and *in vitro* effects of insulin on transferase I activity has been observed (188). The reason for this difference in behavior of *in situ* and isolated hearts is not apparent. Epinephrine also increases myocardial lipase activity in the isolated perfused rabbit heart (189).

Thyroxine and triiodothyronine uptake by the isolated perfused rat heart is inhibited, and release of these thyroid hormones is enhanced by the addition of serum to the perfusion medium (190). Consistent with the idea that this action of serum is due to its binding of thyroid hormones is the observation that the effects were greater with thyroxine than with triiodothyronine. Furthermore, oleic acid, which inhibits binding of thyroxine by albumin, increased its uptake in the presence of serum in the perfusion fluid (191). Thyroid hormone greatly increases the activity of α-glycerophosphate dehydrogenase and hence may increase the rate of operation of the α-glycerophosphate cycle and lower the NADH/NAD ratio in the extramitochondrial compartment by transfer of hydrogen from NADH across the mitochondrial membrane and, therefore, increase degradation of carbohydrate. Isaacs et al. (192) found that isolated perfused hearts from rats fed dessicated thyroid powder showed a 67 per cent increase in lactate uptake and they suggest that this effect is mediated by increased availability of NAD. However, in hearts from hypothyroid rats, lactate uptake was not reduced despite a marked reduction in α-glycerophosphate dehydrogenase activity, which suggests that another mechanism for oxidation of extramitochondrial NADH is operating in hypothyroid hearts. That glucose uptake was not altered in hyperthyroid hearts indicates that NAD was not rate limiting with respect to glucose degradation, as appears to be true for lactate oxidation.

Protein synthesis and hypertrophy.—As an outgrowth of many studies on protein synthesis at the subcellular level, interest has recently been focused on synthesis of protein in tissues such as myocardium, particularly under conditions leading to cardiac hypertrophy. Using tritiated leucine as a marker, McCallister & Brown (193) studied the incorporation of this amino acid into mitochondrial and myofibrillar protein of the rat heart by electron-microscopy autoradiography and protein fractionation techniques. Reasonably good correlation was found between the biochemical and morphological results and it appears that at 15 min and at 1 hr after intravenous administration of the tritiated leucine, protein synthesis occurred at about the same rate in mitochondria and myofibrils. Protein synthesis was not affected by actinomycin D in isolated beating rat atria in short-term experiments, which suggested that synthesis of new messenger RNA was not required for incorporation of C^{14} leucine into atrial protein (194). However, the need for available energy for protein synthesis was indicated by a diminished rate of leucine-C^{14} incorporation with reduced oxygen tension, or the addition of dinitrophenol or oligomycin (194). Similar conclusions with respect to messenger RNA were reached by McCarl & Shaler (195) who found that cultured heart cells continued to incorporate labeled leucine into protein following addition of actinomycin D.

In experimental cardiac hypertrophy induced in rats by aortic constriction, Fanburg & Posner (196) noted that the myocardial RNA concentration increased between 24 and 48 hr after constriction and then returned to normal values as heart weight increased to 50 per cent above control by about the seventh day. All the major species of RNA showed about the same increase in labeling with P^{32}, with labeling starting 4 hr after aortic constriction. Myocardial DNA concentration did not change as hypertrophy developed. Puromycin and actinomycin D inhibited P^{32} labeling of RNA in rats with aortic constriction but not in sham-operated animals (197). These observations suggest that in hypertrophy new RNA templates are synthesized, this effect leading to the myocardial protein synthesis that follows aortic constriction.

In another study employing aortic constriction in the rat, Nair et al. (198) had similar findings with respect to the changes in myocardial RNA concentration with hypertrophy. To determine whether the increased RNA concentration was due to increased synthesis of RNA, decreased degradation, or both, the activity of RNA polymerase, the enzyme responsible for RNA synthesis, was studied (198). Within 12 hr of aortic banding (constriction) the nuclear DNA-dependent RNA polymerase increased, reached a peak value at 2 days, and then declined to control levels (that of sham-operated rats) by about 7 days. These changes in polymerase represent one of the earliest manifestations of hypertrophy.

The rate of RNA synthesis in developing cardiac hypertrophy was also studied in the same laboratory (199) and was found to be fourfold greater than that of controls on the second day after aortic banding and two- to threefold greater on the fourth to fifth postoperative day, a pattern similar to that of RNA polymerase. The base composition of the RNA in the hypertrophied hearts was not different from that of the sham-operated controls. Associated with the increase in heart weight and synthesis was an increase in the uridine nucleotide pool. However, there was no change in the size of the adenine nucleotide pool and consequently a decrease in the concentration of the cardiac adenine nucleotides occurred.

Increased protein synthesis in overloaded hearts has been observed by Schreiber et al. (200) as early as an hour after an imposed work load. In these studies (200), isolated perfused guinea pig hearts were subjected to increased left ventricular outflow resistance for an hour and then the ability of microsomes obtained from control and overloaded hearts to incorporate labeled leucine or phenylalanine into protein was studied in the absence and presence of actinomycin D. In agreement with the observations mentioned above (194, 195), actinomycin D did not affect protein synthesis in control hearts but abolished the large increment in protein synthesis observed in the overloaded hearts. This observation, plus the facts that addition of polyuridilic acid enhanced phenylalanine incorporation by microsomes from control but not from overloaded hearts and that actinomycin pretreatment restored the stimulatory effect of polyuridilic acid to microsomes from overloaded hearts, suggests that the initial response to overload is increased formation of messenger RNA. What constitutes the transducer between the mechanical load and the increase in protein synthesis is not known. Wannemacher & McCoy (201) found increased concentrations of amino acids in hypertrophic hearts and suggest that this may stimulate polyribosomal aggregation and RNA polymerase activity via derepression of the DNA template.

With cardiac hypertrophy there is an increase in connective tissue as well as in muscle mass. Using hydroxyproline as an index of collagen, and hence connective tissue in heart, Buccino et al. (202) observed that in hearts of cats made hypertrophic by pulmonary artery constriction, the connective tissue increased proportionately more than did the muscle proteins. The reason for the increase in connective tissue in hypertrophic hearts and, particularly, for the increase in collagen of the nonstressed left ventricle in these studies remains to be clarified. Of interest is the observation that DNA synthesis, which is essentially unaltered in the myocardial fibers in cardiac hypertrophy, is markedly increased, as measured by thymidine-H^3 incorporation and radioautography, in connective tissue and endothelial cells between the second and seventh days after aortic coarctation in the rat (203). However, the relative growth of parenchymal versus connective tissue is influenced by the means employed in the production of the cardiomegaly (204).

The pattern of isoenzymes of lactic dehydrogenase is altered in right ventricular hypertrophy in the dog, with a shift from the heart type to the muscle type without a change in total enzyme activity, this phenomenon possibly reflecting altered control of protein synthesis (205). The increase in lactic dehydrogenase activity in rat plasma associated with acute severe exercise is reduced by training (4 hr of swimming per day for 10 weeks), whereas following cessation of training and regression of the cardiac hypertrophy, acute exercise results in marked elevations of plasma lactic dehydrogenase and alteration of the isoenzyme pattern (206). It is suggested that these high plasma enzyme levels indicate alterations in myocardial cell membrane permeability.

These studies on protein synthesis in cardiac hypertrophy and the possible mechanisms responsible for failure of the hypertrophied heart have been reviewed by Meerson et al. (207).

LITERATURE CITED

1. Puri, P. S., Bing, R. J. Evaluation of myocardial force-velocity relation in closed-chest dogs. *Am. J. Physiol.*, **214**, 1273–79 (1968)

2. Frank, M. J., Levinson, G. E. An index of the contractile state of the myocardium in man. *J. Clin. Invest.*, **47**, 1615–26 (1968)

3. Smith, N. T., Schwede, H. O. Rapid computation of myocardial contractility in intact animals. *J. Appl. Physiol.*, **26**, 241–47 (1969)

4. Fallen, E. L., Gorlin, R. Time dependence of myocardial contractility in the human left ventricle. *Cardiovasc. Res.*, **4**, 319–28 (1968)

5. Wildenthal, K., Mierzwiak, D. S., Mitchell, J. H. Effect of sudden changes in aortic pressure on left ventricular dp/dt. *Am. J. Physiol.*, **216**, 185–90 (1969)

6. Mason, D. T. Usefulness and limitations of the rate of rise of intraventricular pressure (dp/dt) in the evaluation of myocardial contractility in man. *Am. J. Cardiol.*, **23**, 516–27 (1969)

7. Taylor, R. R., Covell, J. W., Ross, J., Jr. Volume-tension diagrams of ejecting and isovolumic contractions in left ventricle. *Am. J. Physiol.*, **216**, 1097–1102 (1969)

8. Hood, W. P., Thomson, W. J., Rackley, C. E., Rolett, E. L. Comparison of calculations of left ventricular wall stress in man from thin-walled and thick-walled ellipsoidal models. *Circ. Res.*, **24**, 575–82 (1969)

9. Mirsky, I. Left ventricular stresses in the intact human heart. *Biophys. J.*, **9**, 189–208 (1969)

10. Hood, W. P., Jr., Rackley, C. E., Rolett, E. L. Wall stress in the normal and hypertrophied human left ventricle. *Am. J. Cardiol.*, **22**, 550–58 (1968)

11. Newman, W. H., Walton, R. P. Alterations in left ventricular dimensions and mural force following coronary occlusion. *Am. J. Physiol.*, **214**, 1388–91 (1968)

12. Dieudonné, J.-M., Jean, C.-F. Epicardial strains during left ventricular contraction cycle. *Am. J. Physiol.*, **216**, 1188–93 (1969)

13. Noble, M. I. M. The contribution of blood momentum to left ventricular ejection in the dog. *Circ. Res.*, **23**, 663–70 (1968)

14. Spencer, M. P., Greiss, F. C. Dynamics of ventricular ejection. *Circ. Res.*, **10**, 274–79 (1962)

15. Holt, J. P., Rhode, E. A., Kines, H. Ventricular volumes and body weight in mammals. *Am. J. Physiol.*, **215**, 704–15 (1968)

16. Tsakiris, A. G., Vandenberg, R. A., Banchero, N., Sturm, R. E., Wood, E. H. Variations of left ventricular end-diastolic pressure, volume, and ejection fraction with changes in outflow resistance in anesthetized intact dogs. *Circ. Res.*, **23**, 213–22 (1968)

17. Noble, M. I. M., Milne, E. N. C., Goerke, R. J., Carlsson, E., Domenech, R. J., Saunders, K. B., Hoffman, J. I. E. Left ventricular filling and diastolic pressure-volume relations in the conscious dog. *Circ. Res.*, **24**, 269–83 (1969)

18. Adolph, E. F., Ferrari, J. M. Regulation of heart rate before cardiac innervation in salamander larvae. *Am. J. Physiol.*, **215**, 753–56 (1968)

19. Friedman, W. F., Pool, P. E., Jacobowitz, D., Seagren, S. C., Braunwald, E. Sympathetic innervation of the developing rabbit heart. *Circ. Res.*, **23**, 25–32 (1968)

20. De Champlain, J., Krakoff, L. R., Axelrod, J. Increased monoamine oxidase activity during the development of cardiac hypertrophy in the rat. *Circ. Res.*, **23**, 361–69 (1968)

21. Geis, W. P., Kaye, M. P. Distribution of sympathetic fibers in the left ventricular epicardial plexus of the dog. *Circ. Res.*, **23**, 165–70 (1968)

22. Pace, J. B., Keefe, W. F., Armour, J. A., Randall, W. C. Influence of sympathetic nerve stimulation on right ventricular outflow-tract pressures in anesthetized dogs. *Circ. Res.*, **24**, 397–407 (1969)

23. Vassalle, M., Levine, M. J., Stuckey, J. H. On the sympathetic control of ventricular automaticity. *Circ. Res.*, **23**, 249–58 (1968)

24. James, T. N., Bear, E. S., Lang, K. F., Green, E. W. Evidence for adrenergic alpha receptor depres-

sant activity in the heart. *Am. J. Physiol.*, **215**, 1366–75 (1968)

25. Priola, D. V. Individual chamber sensitivity to norepinephrine after unilateral cardiac denervation. *Am. J. Physiol.*, **216**, 604–14 (1969)

26. Ebert, P. A. The effects of norepinephrine infusion on the denervated heart. *J. Cardiovasc. Surg.*, **9**, 414–19 (1968)

27. Dempsey, P. J., Cooper, T. Supersensitivity of the chronically denervated feline heart. *Am. J. Physiol.*, **215**, 1245–49 (1968)

28. Sobel, B. E., Dempsey, P. J., Cooper, T. Adenyl cyclase activity in the chronically denervated cat heart. *Biochem. Biophys. Res. Commun.*, **33**, 758–62 (1968)

29. Ebert, P. A., Allgood, R. J., Sabiston, D. C., Jr. The anti-arrhythmic effects of cardiac denervation. *Ann. Surg.*, **168**, 728–35 (1968)

30. Nielsen, K. C., Owman, C., Rosengren, E. Effect of cardiac catecholamine depletion through sympathectomy on spontaneous ventricular fibrillation during induced hypothermia in cats. *Experientia*, **24**, 1215–17 (1968)

31. LeLorier, J., Shideman, F. E. Uptake of norepineprhine as a determinant of the magnitude of the inotropic response. *Proc. Soc. Exptl. Biol. Med.*, **130**, 265–67 (1969)

32. Mueller, R. A., Axelrod, J. Abnormal cardiac norepinephrine storage in isoproterenol-treated rats. *Circ. Res.*, **23**, 771–78 (1968)

33. DeQuattro, V., Nagatsu, T., Maronde, R., Alexander, N. Catecholamine synthesis in rabbits with neurogenic hypertension. *Circ. Res.*, **24**, 545–55 (1969)

34. Gomez, H. J., Yard, A. C. Cardiac and vascular changes in acute tolerance to norepinephrine infusions. *J. Pharmacol. Exptl. Ther.*, **164**, 270–79 (1968)

35. Blumenthal, M. R., Wang, H.-H., Markee, S., Wang, S. C. Effects of acetylcholine on the heart. *Am. J. Physiol.*, **214**, 1280–87 (1968)

36. Levy, M. N., Zieske, H. Comparison of the cardiac effects of vagus nerve stimulation and of acetylcholine infusions. *Am. J. Physiol.*, **216**, 890–97 (1969)

37. Hollenberg, M., Carriere, S., Barger, A. C. Biphasic action of acetyl-choline on ventricular myocardium. *Circ. Res.*, **16**, 527–36 (1965)

38. Hamlin, R. L., Smith, C. R. Effects of vagal stimulation on S-A and A-V nodes. *Am. J. Physiol.*, **215**, 560–68 (1968)

39. Misu, Y., Kirpekar, S. M. Autonomic innervation of cat atria. *J. Pharmacol. Exptl. Ther.*, **163**, 343–52 (1968)

40. Miller, D. A., Pendleton, R. G., Richmond, A. T. Cardiac effects of vagal stimulation in the anaesthetized cat. *Brit. J. Pharmacol.*, **33**, 390–95 (1968)

41. Kötter, V., Pontzen, W., Kruckenberg, P. Posttetanische Potenzierung der Acetylcholinfreisetzung im Herzen unter Vagusreizung. *Pflügers Arch.*, **306**, 176–90 (1969)

42. Levy, M. N., Ng, M. L., Zieske, H. Cardiac response to cephalic ischemia. *Am. J. Physiol.*, **215**, 169–75 (1968)

43. Stanton, H. C., Vick, R. L. Cholinergic and adrenergic influences on right ventricular myocardial contractility in the dog. *Arch. Intern. Pharmacodyn.*, **176**, 233–48 (1968)

44. Harman, M. A., Reeves, T. J. Effects of efferent vagal stimulation on atrial and ventricular function. *Am. J. Physiol.*, **215**, 1210–17 (1968)

45. Wildenthal, K., Mierzwiak, D. S., Wyatt, H. L., Mitchell, J. H. Influence of efferent vagal stimulation on left ventricular function in dogs. *Am. J. Physiol.*, **216**, 577–81 (1969)

46. Levy, M. N., Zieske, H. Effect of enhanced contractility on the left ventricular response to vagus nerve stimulation in dogs. *Circ. Res.*, **24**, 303–11 (1969)

47. Copen, D. L., Cirillo, D. P., Vassalle, M. Tachycardia following vagal stimulation. *Am. J. Physiol.*, **215**, 696–703 (1968)

48. Haeusler, G., Thoenen, H., Haefely, W., Huerlimann, A. Electrical events in cardiac adrenergic nerves and noradrenaline release from the heart induced by acetylcholine and KCl. *Arch. Exptl. Pathol. Pharmakol.*, **261**, 389–411 (1968)

49. Hashimoto, K., Chiba, S. Blocking of adrenergic-cholinergic interaction by phenoxybenzamine. *Tohoku J. Exptl. Med.*, **94**, 431–32 (1968)

50. Samaan, A. The antagonistic cardiac nerves and heart rate. *J. Physiol. (London)*, **83**, 332–40 (1935)

51. Warner, H. R., Russell, R. O., Jr. Effect of combined sympathetic and vagal stimulation on heart rate in the dog. *Circ. Res.*, **24**, 567–73 (1969)

52. Hashimoto, K., Chiba, S., Tanaka, S., Hirata, M., Suzuki, Y. Adrenergic mechanism participating in induction of atrial fibrillation by ACh. *Am. J. Physiol.*, **215**, 1183–91 **(1968)**

53. Bond, R. F., Green, H. D. Cardiac output redistribution during bilateral common carotid occlusion. *Am. J. Physiol.*, **216**, 393–403 **(1969)**

54. Iriuchijima, J., Soulsby, M. E., Wilson, M. F. Participation of cardiac sympathetics in carotid occlusion pressor reflex. *Am. J. Physiol.*, **215**, 1111–14 (1968)

55. Downing, S. E., Gardner, T. H. Cephalic and carotid reflex influences on cardiac function. *Am. J. Physiol.*, **215**, 1192–99 (1968)

56. Sarnoff, S. J., Gilmore, J. P., Brockman, S. K., Mitchell, J. H., Linden, R. J. Regulation of ventricular contraction by the carotid sinus: Its effect on atrial and ventricular dynamics. *Circ. Res.*, **8**, 1123–36 (1960)

57. De Geest, H., Levy, M. N., Zieske, H., Jr. Carotid sinus baroreceptor reflex effects upon myocardial contractility. *Circ. Res.*, **15**, 327–42 (1964)

58. Gellhorn, E. The significance of the state of the central autonomic nervous system for quantitative and qualitative aspects of some cardiovascular reactions. *Am. Heart J.*, **67**, 106–20 (1964)

59. Fulton, R. L., Priola, D. V., Cooper, T. Alterations in cardiovascular reflexes during artificial circulation. *Am. J. Physiol.*, **214**, 1460–67 (1968)

60. Smyth, H. S., Sleight, P., Pickering, G. W. Reflex regulation of arterial pressure during sleep in man. *Circ. Res.*, **24**, 109–21 (1969)

61. Chai, C. Y., Wang, S. C. Integration of sympathetic cardiovascular mechanisms in medulla oblongata of the cat. *Am. J. Physiol.*, **215**, 1310–15 (1968)

62. Martin, P. J., Levy, M. N., Zieske, H. Bilateral carotid sinus control of ventricular performance in the dog. *Circ. Res.*, **24**, 321–37 (1969)

63. Glick, G., Braunwald, E. Relative roles of the sympathetic and parasympathetic nervous system in the reflex control of heart rate. *Circ. Res.*, **16**, 363–75 (1965)

64. Chai, C. Y., Huang, T. F., Wang, S. C. Mechanisms of cardiac arrhythmias induced by baroceptor reflexes in cats. *Am. J. Physiol.*, **215**, 1316–23 (1968)

65. Berkowitz, W. D., Scherlag, B. J., Stein, E., Damato, A. N. Relative roles of sympathetic and parasympathetic nervous systems in the carotid sinus reflex in dogs. *Circ. Res.*, **24**, 447–55 (1969)

66. Gleser, M. A., Grupp, G. Mathematical model of response to carotid sinus nerve stimulation. *Am. J. Physiol.*, **216**, 263–70 (1969)

67. Katona, P. G., Barnett, G. O. Central origin of asymmetry in the carotid sinus reflex. *Ann. N.Y. Acad. Sci.*, **156**, 779–86 (1969)

68. Schmidt, E. M. Blood pressure response to aortic nerve stimulation in swine. *Am. J. Physiol.*, **215**, 1488–92 (1968)

69. Wildenthal, K., Mierzwiak, D. S., Skinner, N. S., Jr., Mitchell, J. H. Potassium-induced cardiovascular and ventilatory reflexes from the dog hindlimb. *Am. J. Physiol.*, **215**, 542–48 (1968)

70. Cohn, J. E., Krog, J., Shannon, R. Cardiopulmonary responses to head immersion in domestic geese. *J. Appl. Physiol.*, **25**, 36–41 (1968)

71. Campbell, L. B., Gooden, B. A., Horowitz, J. D. Cardiovascular responses to partial and total immersion in man. *J. Physiol. (London)*, **202**, 239–50 (1969)

72. Asmussen, E., Kristiansson, N.-G. The "diving bradycardia" in exercising man. *Acta Physiol. Scand.*, **73**, 527–35 (1968)

73. Iriuchijima, J., Kumada, M. On the cardioinhibitory reflex originating from the superior laryngeal nerve. *Japan. J. Physiol.*, **18**, 453–61 (1968)

74. Glick, G., Wechsler, A. S., Epstein, S. E. Reflex cardiovascular depression produced by stimulation of pulmonary stretch receptors in the dog. *J. Clin. Invest.*, **48**, 467–73 (1969)

75. Guazzi, M., Mancia, G., Kumazawa, T., Baccelli, G., Zanchetti, A.

Effects of cardiac denervation on blood pressure and heart rate during natural sleep in the cat. *Cardiovasc. Res.*, **3**, 265–70 (1968)

76. Ferrante, F. L., Opdyke, D. F. Mammalian ventricular function during submersion asphyxia. *J. Appl. Physiol.*, **26**, 561–70 (1969)

77. Taylor, R. R., Covell, J. W., Ross, J., Jr. Influence of the thyroid state on left ventricular tension-velocity relations in the intact, sedated dog. *J. Clin. Invest.*, **48**, 775–84 (1969)

78. Pannier, J. L. The influence of thyroid hormone on myocardial contractility. *Arch. Intern. Physiol.*, **76**, 477–90 (1968)

79. Amidi, M., Leon, D. F., de Groot, W. J., Kroetz, F. W., Leonard, J. J. Effect of the thyroid state on myocardial contractility and ventricular ejection rate in man. *Circulation*, **38**, 229–39 (1968)

80. Murayama, M., Goodkind, M. J. Effect of thyroid hormone on the frequency-force relationship of atrial myocardium from the guinea pig. *Circ. Res.*, **23**, 743–51 (1968)

81. Tipton, C. M., Terjung, R. L., Barnard, R. J. Response of thyroidectomized rats to training. *Am. J. Physiol.*, **215**, 1137–42 (1968)

82. Zaimis, E., Papadaki, L., Ash, A. S. F., Larbi, E., Kakari, S., Matthew, M., Paradelis, A. Cardiovascular effects of thyroxine. *Cardiovasc. Res.*, **3**, 118–33 (1969)

83. Davies, A. L., Juca, E. R., Austen, W. G. Left ventricular function in steroid pretreated dogs following total cardiopulmonary bypass. *J. Cardiovasc. Surg.*, **9**, 273–77 (1968)

84. Ng, M. L., Levy, M. N., De Geest, H., Zieske, H. Effects of myocardial hypoxia on left ventricular performance. *Am. J. Physiol.*, **211**, 43–50 (1966)

85. Daniell, H. B., Bagwell, E. E. Effects of high oxygen on coronary flow and heart force. *Am. J. Physiol.*, **214**, 1454–59 (1968)

86. Kioschos, J. M., Behar, V. S., Saltzman, H. A., Thompson, H. K., Myers, N. E., Smith, W. W., McIntosh, H. D. Effect of hyperbaric oxygenation on left ventricular function. *Am. J. Physiol.*, **216**, 161–66 (1969)

87. Korner, P. I., Langsford, G., Starr, D., Uther, J. B., Ward, W., White, S. W. The effects of chloralose-urethane and sodium pentobarbitone anaesthesia on the local and autonomic components of the circulatory response to arterial hypoxia. *J. Physiol. (London)*, **199**, 283–302 (1968)

88. Korner, P. I., Uther, J. B. Dynamic characteristics of the cardiovascular autonomic effects during severe arterial hypoxia in the unanesthetized rabbit. *Circ. Res.*, **24**, 671–87 (1969)

89. Crocker, E. F., Johnson, R. O., Korner, P. I., Uther, J. B., White, S. W. Effects of hyperventilation on the circulatory response of the rabbit to arterial hypoxia. *J. Physiol. (London)*, **199**, 267–82 (1968)

90. Souhrada, J., Mrzena, B., Rakušan, K., Zajic, F., Poupa, O. Acute anoxia of heart muscle in a heart-lung preparation. The effect of pH and pCO_2 of the perfused blood. *Physiol. Bohem.*, **17**, 541–44 (1968)

91. McGrath, J. J., Bullard, R. W. Altered myocardial performance in response to anoxia after high-altitude exposure. *J. Appl. Physiol.*, **25**, 761–64 (1968)

92. Caress, D. L., Kissack, A. S., Slovin, A. J., Stuckey, J. H. The effect of respiratory and metabolic acidosis on myocardial contractility. *J. Thor. Cardiovasc. Surg.*, **56**, 571–77 (1968)

93. Ng, M. L., Levy, M. N., Zieske, H. A. Effects of changes of pH and of carbon dioxide tension on left ventricular performance. *Am. J. Physiol.*, **213**, 115–20 (1967)

94. Horwitz, L. D., Bishop, V. S., Stone, H. L. Effects of hypercapnia on the cardiovascular system of conscious dogs. *J. Appl. Physiol.*, **25**, 346–48 (1968)

95. Wildenthal, K., Mierzwiak, D. S., Myers, R. W., Mitchell, J. H. Effects of acute lactic acidosis on left ventricular performance. *Am. J. Physiol.*, **214**, 1352–59 (1968)

96. Rocamora, J. M., Downing, S. E. Preservation of ventricular function by adrenergic influences during metabolic acidosis in the cat. *Circ. Res.*, **24**, 373–81 (1969)

97. Page, E., Power, B., Borer, J. S., Klegerman, M. E. Rapid exchange of cellular or cell surface potas-

sium in the rat's heart. *Proc. Natl. Acad. Sci.*, **60**, 1323–29 (1968)

98. Gerlings, E. D., Gilmore, J. P. Continuous potassium-balance analysis in dog heart. *J. Appl. Physiol.*, **25**, 316–18 (1968)

99. Gilmore, J. P., Gerlings, E. D. Influence of developed tension on myocardial potassium balance in the dog heart. *Circ. Res.*, **22**, 769–75 (1968)

100. Mithoefer, J. C., Kazemi, H., Holford, F. D., Friedman, I. Myocardial potassium exchange during respiratory acidosis : The interaction of carbon dioxide and sympathoadrenal discharge. *Resp. Physiol.*, **5**, 91–107 (1968)

101. Cingolani, H. E., Marsiglia, J. C., Blesa, E. S., Garcia, R. Catecholamine-induced myocardial potassium uptake : Its relation to adrenergic α-receptors. *Arch. Intern. Pharmacodyn.*, **176**, 21–32 (1968)

102. Gerlings, E. D., Miller, D. T., Gilmore, J. P. Oxygen availability : a determinant of myocardial potassium balance. *Am. J. Physiol.*, **216**, 559–62 (1969)

103. Logic, J. R., Krotkiewski, A., Koppius, A., Surawicz, B. Negative inotropic effect of K+ : its modification by Ca++ and acetylstrophanthidin in dogs. *Am. J. Physiol.*, **215**, 14–22 (1968)

104. Maxwell, G. M. The effects of induced hypernatremia upon the general and coronary haemodynamics and metabolism in the intact animal. *Cardiologia*, **52**, 259–66 (1968)

105. Wildenthal, K., Mierzwiak, D. S., Mitchell, J. H. Acute effects of increased serum osmolality on left ventricular performance. *Am. J. Physiol.*, **216**, 898–904 (1969)

106. Love, W. D., Ishihara, Y., Lyon, L. D., Smith, R. O. Differences in the relationships between coronary blood flow and myocardial clearance of isotopes of potassium, rubidium, and cesium. *Am. Heart J.*, **76**, 353–55 (1969)

107. Dietzman, H., Nordberg, E. D., Loken, M. K., Lillehei, R. C. Xenon 133 myocardial blood flow determination : a simple new balloon technique. *J. Appl. Physiol.*, **24**, 840–43 (1968)

108. Bassingthwaighte, J. B., Strandell, T., Donald, D. E. Estimation of coronary blood flow by washout of diffusible indicators. *Circ. Res.*, **23**, 259–78 (1968)

109. Klocke, F. J., Koberstein, R. C., Pittman, D. E., Bunnell, I. L., Greene, D. G., Rosing, D. R. Effects of heterogeneous myocardial perfusion on coronary venous H_2 desaturation curves and calculations of coronary flow. *J. Clin. Invest.*, **47**, 2711–24 (1968)

110. Klocke, F. J., Rosing, D. R., Pittman, D. E. Inert gas measurements of coronary blood flow. *Am. J. Cardiol.*, **23**, 548–55 (1969)

111. Koberstein, R. D., Pittman, D. E., Klocke, F. J. Right atrial admixture in coronary venous blood. *Am. J. Physiol.*, **216**, 531–35 (1969)

112. Leb, G., Derntl, F., Goldschlager, N., Cowan, C., Bing, R. J. Determination of effective and total coronary blood flow using Rb⁸⁴. *Am. J. Med. Sci.*, **257**, 203–17 (1969)

113. Beneken, J. E. W., Guyton, A. C., Sagawa, K. Coronary perfusion pressure and left ventricular function. *Pflügers Arch.*, **305**, 76–95 (1969)

114. Pitt, B., Gregg, D. E. Coronary hemodynamic effects of increasing ventricular rate in the unanesthetized dog. *Circ. Res.*, **22**, 753–61 (1968)

115. Griggs, D. M., Jr., Nakamura, Y. Effect of coronary constriction on myocardial distribution of iodoantipyrine-I¹³¹. *Am. J. Physiol.*, **215**, 1082–88 (1968)

116. Ross, G., Mulder, D. G. Effects of right and left cardiosympathetic nerve stimulation on blood flow in the major coronary arteries of the anesthetized dog. *Cardiovasc. Res.*, **3**, 22–29 (1969)

117. Brown, A. M. Motor innervation of the coronary arteries of the cat. *J. Physiol. (London)*, **198**, 311–28 (1968)

118. Brandfonbrener, M., Gracey, D., Nice, R. Coronary pressure-blood flow relations. The effect of norepinephrine. *Am. J. Cardiol.*, **23**, 417–23 (1969)

119. Cobb, F. R., Wallace, A. G., Wagner, G. S. Cardiac inotropic and coronary vascular response to countershock. *Circ. Res.*, **23**, 731–42 (1968)

120. Brooks. H. L., Stein, P. D., Matson,

J. L., Hyland, J. W. Dopamine-induced alterations in coronary hemodynamics in dogs. *Circ.. Res.*, **24**, 699–704 (1969)

121. Drimal, J. Effects of angiotensin II on coronary smooth muscle. *European J. Pharmacol.*, **5**, 56–62 (1968)

122. Feigl, E. O. Carotid sinus reflex control of coronary blood flow. *Circ. Res.*, **23**, 223–37 (1968)

123. Nayler, W. G., McInnes, I., Swann, J. B., Race, D., Lowe, T. E. Effect of adrenergic beta receptor blocking drugs on blood flow in the coronary and other vascular fields. *Cardiovasc. Res.*, **2**, 371–78 (1968)

124. Nayler, W. G., McInnes, I., Carson, V., Swann, J., Lowe, T. E. The combined effect of atropine and beta adrenergic receptor antagonists on left ventricular function and coronary blood flow. *Am. Heart J.*, **77**, 246–58 (1969)

125. Ovsyannikov, V. I., Tkachenko, B. I. Changes in the lumen of coronary vessels under oligemic hypotension. *Experientia*, **25**, 501–03 (1969)

126. Entman, M. L., Martin, A. M., Jr., Mikat, E., Chang, J. H. T., Hackel, D. B. Phasic myocardial blood flow in hemorrhagic hypotension. *Am. J. Cardiol.*, **21**, 881–85 (1968)

127. Lammerant, J., DeSchryver, C., Becsei, I., Camphyn, M., Mertens-Strijthagen, J. Coronary circulation response to hyperoxia after vagotomy and combined alpha and beta adrenergic receptors blockade in the anesthetized intact dog. *Pflügers Arch.*, **308**, 185–96 (1969)

128. Weglicki, W. B., Rubenstein, C. J., Entman, M. L., Thompson, H. K., Jr., McIntosh, H. D. Effects of hyperbaric oxygenation on myocardial blood flow and myocardial metabolism in the dog. *Am. J. Physiol.*, **216**, 1219–25 (1969)

129. Martini, J., Honig, C. R. Direct measurement of intercapillary distance in beating rat heart in situ under various conditions of O_2 supply. *Microvasc. Res.*, **1**, 244–56 (1969)

130. Pitt, A., Friesinger, G. C., Ross, R. S. Measurement of blood flow in the right and left coronary artery beds in humans and dogs using the xenon[133] technique. *Cardiovasc. Res.*, **3**, 100–06 (1969)

131. Rubio, R., Berne, R. M., Katori, M. Release of adenosine in reactive hyperemia of the dog heart. *Am. J. Physiol.*, **216**, 56–62 (1969)

132. Afonso, S. Coronary vasodilator responses to hypoxia and induced tachycardia before and after lidoflazine. *Am. J. Physiol.*, **216**, 297–300 (1969)

133. Busch, E. W., Gercken, G. Abbau von Purinnucleotiden und Kohlenhydraten im KCl-stillgestellten kaninchen und ischämischen Hundherzen. *Z. Physiol. Chem.*, **350**, 105–10 (1969)

134. Khouri, E. M., Gregg, D. E., Lowensohn, H. S. Flow in the major branches of the left coronary artery during experimental coronary insufficiency in the unanesthetized dog. *Circ. Res.*, **23**, 99–109 (1968)

135. Howe, B. B., Winbury, M. M. Effect of acute coronary occlusion on myocardial nutritional circulation in swine. *Am. J. Physiol.*, **216**, 1069–74 (1969)

136. Redding, V. J., Rees, J. R. Early changes in collateral flow following coronary artery ligation: the role of sympathetic nervous system. *Cardiovasc. Res.*, **2**, 219–25 (1968)

137. Grayson, J., Lapin, B. A. Observations on the mechanisms of infarction in the dog after experimental occlusion of the coronary artery. *Lancet*, **I**, 1284–88 (1966)

138. Haft, J. I., Damato, A. N. Measurement of collateral blood flow after myocardial infarction in the closed-chest dog. *Am. Heart J.*, **77**, 641–48 (1969)

139. Moir, T. W. Study of luminal coronary collateral circulation in the beating canine heart. *Circ. Res.*, **24**, 735–44 (1969)

140. Stoner, C. D., Ressallat, M. M., Sirak, H. D. Oxidative phosphorylation in mitochondria isolated from chronically stressed dog hearts. *Circ. Res.*, **23**, 87–97 (1968)

141. Lindenmayer, G. E., Sordahl, L. A., Schwartz, A. Reevaluation of oxidative phosphorylation in cardiac mitochondria from normal animals and animals in heart failure. *Circ. Res.*, **23**, 439–50 (1968)

142. Warshaw, J. B. Cellular energy

metabolism during fetal development. I. Oxidative phosphorylation in the fetal heart. *J. Cell Biol.*, **41**, 651–57 (1969)

143. Lochner, A., Opie, L. H., Brink, A. J., Bosman, A. R. Defective oxidative phosphorylation in hereditary myocardiopathy in the Syrian hamster. *Cardiovasc. Res.*, **2**, 297–307 (1968)

144. Boerth, R. C., Covell, J. W., Seagren, S. C., Pool, P. E. High-energy phosphate concentrations in dog myocardium during stress. *Am. J. Physiol.*, **216**, 1103–06 (1969)

145. Lefer, A. M., Daw, J. C., Berne, R. M. Cardiac and skeletal muscle metabolic energy stores in hemorrhagic shock. *Am. J. Physiol.*, **216**, 483–86 (1969)

146. Ko, K. C., Gimeno, A. L., Berman, D. A. Effects of buffers on developed tension, membrane potentials and ATP levels of atria. *Am. J. Physiol.*, **216**, 853–59 (1969)

147. Seraydarian, M. W., Harary, I., Sato, E. In vitro studies of beating heart cells in culture. XI. The ATP level and contractions of the heart cells. *Biochim. Biophys. Acta*, **162**, 414–23 (1968)

148. Scheuer, J., Stezoski, S. W. Effects of high-energy phosphate depletion and repletion on the dynamics and electrocardiogram of isolated rat hearts. *Circ. Res.*, **23**, 519–30 (1968)

149. Scheuer, J., Stezoski, S. W. Relationship of ATP to the electrocardiogram in the isolated rat heart. *J. Lab. Clin. Med.*, **72**, 621–30 (1968)

150. Scheuer, J., Stezoski, S. W. Discordance between the electrocardiogram and ATP levels in the isolated rat heart. *Am. J. Med. Sci.*, **257**, 218–27 (1969)

151. Braasch, W., Gudbjarnason, S., Puri, P. S., Ravens, K. G., Bing, R. J. Early changes in energy metabolism in the myocardium following acute coronary artery occlusion in anesthetized dogs. *Circ. Res.*, **23**, 429–38 (1968)

152. Gudbjarnason, S., Braasch, W., Cowan, C., Bing, R. J. Metabolism of infarcted heart muscle during tissue repair. *Am. J. Cardiol.*, **22**, 360–69 (1968)

153. Manning, J. P., Pensinger, R. R., Fehn, P. A. Cardiac alkaline and acid phosphatase activity and potassium concentration in dogs with acute myocardial infarction. *Cardiovasc. Res.*, **2**, 308–13 (1968)

154. Fedelešová, M., Ziegelhöffer, A., Krause, E. G., Wollenberger, A. Effect of exogenous adenosine triphosphate on the metabolic state of the excised hypothermic dog heart. *Circ. Res.*, **24**, 617–27 (1969)

155. Wollenberger, A., Krause, E. G. Metabolic control characteristics of the acutely ischemic myocardium. *Am. J. Cardiol.*, **22**, 349–59 (1968)

156. Pool, P. E., Chandler, B. M., Spann, J. F., Jr., Sonnenblick, E. H., Braunwald, E. Mechanochemistry of cardiac muscle. IV. Utilization of high-energy phosphate in experimental heart failure in cats. *Circ. Res.*, **24**, 313–20 (1969)

157. Luchi, R. J., Kritcher, E. M., Thyrum, P. T. Reduced cardiac myosin adenosinetriphosphatase activity in dogs with spontaneously occurring heart failure. *Circ. Res.*, **24**, 513–19 (1969)

158. Nayler, W. G., Stone, J., Carson, V., McInnes, I., Mack, V., Lowe, T. E. The effect of beta adrenergic antagonists on cardiac contractions, myofibrillar ATPase activity, high-energy phosphate stores and lipid-facilitated transport of calcium ions. *J. Pharmacol. Exptl. Ther.*, **165**, 225–33 (1969)

159. Sonnenblick, E. H., Ross, J., Jr., Braunwald, E. Oxygen consumption of the heart; newer concepts of its multifactorial determination. *Am. J. Cardiol.*, **22**, 328–36 (1968)

160. Feinberg, H., Boyd, E., Tanzini, G. Mechanical performance and oxygen utilization of the isovolumic rabbit heart. *Am. J. Physiol.*, **215**, 132–39 (1968)

161. Krasnow, N. Effects of norepinephrine and phenylephrine on myocardial energetics. *Am. Heart J.*, **76**, 660–73 (1968)

162. Neill, W. A. Myocardial hypoxia and anaerobic metabolism in coronary heart disease. *Am. J. Cardiol.*, **22**, 507–15 (1968)

163. Vahouny, G. V., Liljenquist, J., Wilson, R., Liao, A., Rodis, S. L. Myocardial metabolism. III. Myocardial intermediates and substrate oxidation during in vitro

perfusion of palmitate and glucose. *Arch. Biochem. Biophys.,* **125,** 809–16 (1968)

164. Neely, J. R., Bowman, R. H., Morgan, H. E. Effects of ventricular pressure development and palmitate on glucose transport. *Am. J. Physiol.,* **216,** 804–11 (1969)

165. Willebrands, A. F., Tasseron, S. J. A. Effect of hormones on substrate preference in isolated rat heart. *Am. J. Physiol.,* **215,** 1089–95 (1968)

166. Simpson-Morgan, M. W. The metabolism of chylomicron fatty acids by isolated rat heart-lung preparations. *J. Physiol. (London),* **199,** 37–57 (1968)

167. Masters, T. N., Glaviano, V. V. Effects of dl-propranolol on myocardial free fatty acid and carbohydrate metabolism. *J. Pharmacol. Exptl. Ther.,* **167,** 187–93 (1969)

168. Marchetti, G., Merlo, L., Noseda, V. Myocardial uptake of free fatty acids and carbohydrates after beta adrenergic blockade. *Am. J. Cardiol.,* **22,** 370–74 (1968)

169. Opie, L. H. Metabolism of the heart in health and disease. Part 1. *Am. Heart J.,* **76,** 685–98 (1968)

170. Opie, L. H. Metabolism of the heart in health and disease. Part 2. *Am. Heart J.,* **77,** 100–22 (1969)

171. Opie, L. H. Metabolism of the heart in health and disease. Part 3. *Am. Heart J.,* **77,** 383–410 (1969)

172. LaRaia, P. J., Craig, R. J., Reddy, W. J. Glucagon: effect on adenosine 3′5′–monophosphate in the rat heart, *Am. J. Physiol.,* **215,** 968–70 (1968)

173. Lucchesi, B. R. Cardiac actions of glucagon. *Circ. Res.,* **22,** 777–87 (1968)

174. Glick, G., Parmley, W. W., Wechsler, A. S., Sonnenblick, E. H. Glucagon: Its enhancement of cardiac performance in the cat and dog and persistance of its inotropic action despite beta-receptor blockade with propranolol. *Circ. Res.,* **22,** 789–99 (1968)

175. Steiner, C., Wit, A. L., Damato, A. N. Effects of glucagon on atrioventricular conduction and ventricular automaticity in dogs. *Circ. Res.,* **24,** 167–77 (1969)

176. LaRaia, P. J., Reddy, W. J. Hormonal regulation of myocardial adenosine 3′5′–monophosphate. *Biochim. Biophys. Acta,* **177,** 189–95 (1969)

177. Levey, G. S., Epstein, S. E. Activation of adenyl cyclase by glycogen in cat and human heart. *Circ. Res.,* **24,** 151–56 (1969)

178. Murad, F. Effect of glucagon on heart. *New Engl. J. Med.,* **279,** 434–35 (1968)

179. Sobel, B. E., Henry, P. D., Robison, A., Bloor, C., Ross, J., Jr. Depressed adenyl cyclase activity in the failing guinea pig heart. *Circ. Res.,* **24,** 507–12 (1969)

180. McNeill, J. H., Nasser, M., Brody, T. M. The effect of theophylline on amine-induced cardiac phosphorylase activation and cardiac contractility. *J. Pharmacol. Exptl. Ther.,* **165,** 234–41 (1969)

181. Landsberg, L., De Champlain, J., Axelrod, J. Increased biosynthesis of cardiac norepinephrine after hypophysectomy. *J. Pharmacol. Exptl. Ther.,* **165,** 102–07 (1969)

182. Wakade, A. R., Furchgott, R. F. Metabolic requirements for the uptake and storage of norepinephrine by the isolated left atrium of the guinea pig. *J. Pharmacol. Exptl. Ther.,* **163,** 123–35 (1968)

183. Horn, R. S., Levin, R., Haugaard, N. The influence of oligomycin on the actions of epinephrine and theophylline upon the perfused rat heart. *Biochem. Pharmacol.,* **18,** 503–9 (1969)

184. De Champlain, J., Krakoff, L. R., Axelrod, J. Relationship between sodium intake and norepinephrine storage during the development of experimental hypertension. *Circ. Res.,* **23,** 479–91 (1968)

185. Vogel, J. H. K., Jacobowitz, D., Chidsey, C. A. Distribution of norepinephrine in the failing bovine heart. *Circ. Res.,* **24,** 71–84 (1969)

186. Krakoff, L. R., Buccino, R. A., Spann, J. F., Jr., De Champlain, J. Cardiac catechol O-methyltransferase and monoamine oxidase activity in congestive heart failure. *Am. J. Physiol.,* **215,** 549–52 (1968)

187. Belford, J., Cunningham, M. A. The effect of inotropic catecholamines, calcium and aminophylline on glycogen synthetase activity in the intact cat heart. *J. Pharmacol. Exptl. Ther.,* **162,** 134–38 (1968)

188. Huijing, F., Nuttall, F. Q., Villar-Palasi, C., Larner, J. UDP-glucose: α-1,4-glucan, α-4-gluco-syltransferase in heart regulation of the activity of the transferase in vivo and in vitro in rat. A dissociation in the action of insulin on transport and on transferase conversion. *Biochim. Biophys. Acta*, **177**, 204–12 (1969)

189. Mallov, S., Alousi, A. A. In vitro effect of epinephrine on lipase activity of heart. *Am. J. Physiol.*, **216**, 794–99 (1969)

190. Hillier, A. P. The uptake and release of thyroxine and triiodothyronine by the perfused rat heart. *J. Physiol. (London)*, **199**, 151–60 (1968)

191. Hillier, A. P. The effect of fatty acid on the uptake of thyroxine by the perfused rat heart. *J. Physiol. (London)*, **199**, 169–75 (1968)

192. Isaacs, G. H., Sacktor, B., Murphy, T. The role of the α-glycerophosphate cycle in the control of carbohydrate oxidation in heart and in the mechanism of action of thyroid hormone. *Biochim. Biophys. Acta*, **177**, 196–203 (1969)

193. McCallister, B. D., Brown, A. L., Jr. A biochemical and morphological study of protein synthesis in normal rat myocardium. *Cardiovasc. Res.*, **3**, 79–87 (1969)

194. Cohen, J., Feldman, R. E., Whitbeck, A. A. Effects of energy availability on protein synthesis in isolated rat atria. *Am. J. Physiol.*, **216**, 76–81 (1969)

195. McCarl, R. L., Shaler, R. C. The effects of actinomycin D on protein synthesis and beating in cultured rat heart cells. *J. Cell Biol.*, **40**, 850–54 (1969)

196. Fanburg, B. L., Posner, B. I. Ribonucleic acid synthesis in experimental cardiac hypertrophy in rats. I. Characterization and kinetics of labeling. *Circ. Res.*, **23**, 123–35 (1968)

197. Posner, B. I., Fanburg, B. L. Ribonucleic acid synthesis in experimental cardiac hypertrophy in rats. II. Aspects of regulation. *Circ. Res.*, **23**, 137–45 (1968)

198. Nair, K. G., Cutilletta, A. F., Zak, R., Koide, T., Rabinowitz, M. Bio-chemical correlates of cardiac hypertrophy. I. Experimental model; changes in heart weight, RNA content, and nuclear RNA polymerase activity. *Circ. Res.*, **23**, 451–62 (1968)

199. Koide, T., Rabinowitz, M. Biochemical correlates of cardiac hypertrophy. II. Increased rate of RNA synthesis in experimental cardiac hypertrophy in the rat. *Circ. Res.*, **24**, 9–18 (1969)

200. Schreiber, S. S., Oratz, M., Evans, C., Silver, E., Rothschild, M. A. Effect of acute overload on cardiac muscle mRNA. *Am. J. Physiol.*, **215**, 1250–59 (1968)

201. Wannemacher, R. W., Jr., McCoy, J. R. Regulation of protein synthesis in the ventricular myocardium of hypertrophic hearts. *Am. J. Physiol.*, **216**, 781–87 (1969)

202. Buccino, R. A., Harris, E., Spann, J. F., Jr., Sonnenblick, E. H. Response of myocardial connective tissue to development of experimental hypertrophy. *Am. J. Physiol.*, **216**, 425–28 (1969)

203. Morkin, E., Ashford, T. P. Myocardial DNA synthesis in experimental cardiac hypertrophy. *Am. J. Physiol.*, **215**, 1409–13 (1968)

204. Bartošová, D., Chvapil, M., Korecky, B., Poupa, O., Rakušan, K., Turek, Z., Vízek, M. The growth of the muscular and collagenous parts of the rat heart in various forms of cardiomegaly. *J. Physiol. (London)*, **200**, 285–95 (1969)

205. Fox, A. C., Reed, G. E. Changes in lactate dehydrogenase composition of hearts with right ventricular hypertrophy. *Am. J. Physiol.*, **216**, 1026–33 (1969)

206. Bloor, C. M., Papadopoulos, N. M. Plasma lactic dehydrogenase activity and myocardial cellular changes after cessation of training. *J. Appl. Physiol.*, **26**, 371–74 (1969)

207. Meerson, F. Z., Alekhina, G. M., Aleksandrov, P. N., Bazardjan, A. G. Dynamics of nucleic acid and protein synthesis of the myocardium in compensatory hyperfunction and hypertrophy of the heart. *Am. J. Cardiol.*, **22**, 337–47 (1968)

RESPIRATION

Robert A. Mitchell[1]

Department of Anesthesia and Cardiovascular Research Institute
University of California, San Francisco Medical Center
San Francisco, California

The present review will be devoted to a discussion of the regulation of respiration. Since this topic has not been reviewed in the *Annual Review of Physiology* in the last 2 years, I have selected work published between June 1966 and June 1969. In a few instances, I have included pertinent papers which appeared earlier or later than these dates and particularly important preliminary reports.

Peripheral Chemoreceptors

In terms of the total number of papers published, interest in regulation of respiration has been greatest in the area of arterial chemoreceptors. The Proceedings of the Wates Foundation Symposium on Arterial Chemoreceptors held in Oxford on 18–21 July 1966 (1) provide an excellent review of the field, especially the prolegomena by Torrance (2).

Ultrastructure of the carotid body.—Electronmicroscopic studies of the carotid body in recent years (3–6) have, in general, confirmed the observations of Ross (7). The parenchymal cell clusters are made up of two to ten type I and type II cells, bounded by a basement membrane and surrounded by connective tissue. The type I (chief, chemoreceptor, glomus, epithelioid, enclosed) cells contain a centrally located nucleus, dense granules, mitochondria, ribosomes, microtubules, and paired centrioles, one of which may serve as a basal body for a cilium. Of particular interest are the dense granules, 350–1900 Å diameter bounded by a unit membrane. These granules are distributed randomly and are occasionally seen budding from the sacs of the Golgi complex, but are not concentrated in the vicinity of nerve endings. Lall (6) describes a possible subtype of the type I cell. This subtype, type IA, is fixed poorly and contains granules which are larger and more numerous than those in type I cells.

[1] Recipient of a USPHS Research Career Development Award number 5-KO3-GM 19,411 from the National Institutes of Health.

The type I cells which are usually oval but often irregular in shape are covered by the processes of type II (sustentacular, enclosing) cells except at sites of contact with nerve endings, by other type I cells, or infrequently by the basement membrane of the parenchymal cell clusters. The type II cells are fewer and are usually located in the periphery of the parenchymal cell cluster. They have long, attenuated cytoplasmic processes which ramify within the cell clusters, and invest and separate type I cells and unmyelinated nerve fibers and nerve endings. There are no membrane-bound dense granules in the cytoplasm of the type II cells.

Myelinated and unmyelinated nerve fibers enclosed in Schwann cells course through the connective tissue. Before entering the parenchymal cell clusters the myelinated fibers lose their myelin sheath and thereafter are enclosed in type II cells. In perivascular areas there are unmyelinated fibers surrounded by Schwann cells.

The nerve endings on type I cells may be either round or elongated and contain numerous synaptic vesicles, 400–600 Å diameter, occasional dense-cored vesicles, and small mitochondria. The plasma membranes of the nerve endings and the type I cells are separated by 100–200 Å. Along their apposed surfaces are several electron-opaque zones which are characteristic of a synapse. The morphology of the nerve endings suggests a motor function for them. If these nerve endings were sensory, the part of the type I cell adjoining the nerve ending should be expected to contain synaptic vesicles; this is not so. Al-Lami & Murray (3) describe a basket-type ending which surrounds the type I cell in the carotid body of the cat. These endings contain fewer synaptic vesicles and mitochondria and have extensive contact with type I cells with many electron-dense thickenings of the plasma membranes at sites of apposition. However, they did not observe this type of ending in the carotid body of the monkey (8). They suggested that these basket-type endings might be afferent, whereas the round or elongated endings were efferent. No other investigator has described the basket endings. It appears that in morphology, the basket-type nerve ending is not sufficiently different from the round or club-shaped nerve ending to merit a separate function.

If the type I cells are chemoreceptor cells, the contents of the dense-cored vesicles might contain a transmitter substance. Tissue assays show the presence of high concentrations of dopamine and 5-hydroxytryptamine (5-HT) in the cat carotid body, and lesser concentrations of epinephrine and norepinephrine (9, 10). When radioactive precursors of catecholamines and indolamines were injected into hamsters, positive grains were located over the dense granules in type I cells (11). Chiocchio et al. (9) divided type I cells into three subtypes on the basis of histochemical staining and granule size. The first subtype contained large polymorphic granules believed to be norepinephrine. This cell is similar to the subtype I A described by Lall (6). The second, most numerous subtype had smaller granules and gave a positive reaction for 5-HT. The third subtype contained small granules which had the staining characteristics of epinephrine. All of these substances stimulate the carotid chemoreceptors; however, dopamine, which is as potent a stimulant of the dog carotid body as CN⁻, fails to stimulate the carotid body of the cat (12).

The nerve fibers supplying the blood vessels of the carotid body and walls of the carotid sinus contain norepinephrine (13) and degenerate after section of the superior cervical ganglion (13, 14). It might also be mentioned here that although the term sinusoids is still used to describe the vascular channels in the carotid body, electronmicroscopic studies have failed to show their presence. The vessels present either are fenestrated capillaries or are coated with pericytes or smooth muscle external to the endothelium (4, 6).

Although acetylcholine (ACh) is present in the carotid body in sufficient quantity to be considered a possible sensory transmitter, its precise location is not known. Cholinesterase, both true and pseudo, has been identified in the nerve plexuses surrounding the parenchymal cell clusters (15). Cholineacetylase (the enzyme required for synthesis of ACh) may be confined to cholinergic fibers in the sinus nerve. Hebb (16) compared the concentration of this enzyme in a number of neural structures and found its concentration in the carotid body significantly lower than that in the carotid sinus nerve and 1/20 of that in the cervical sympathetic ganglia. From their content of choline acetylase, she estimated that 30 per cent of the sinus fibers were cholinergic and, therefore, efferent since first-order cholinergic afferent nerves have not been demonstrated.

Attempts to decrease the number or density of the granules by physiological stimulation of the carotid body have been uniformly unsuccessful. Blümcke et al. (17) exposed rats to varying degrees of hypoxia and found no relationship between the associated hyperpnea and changes in dense granules in the type I cells. Whereas relative mild hypoxia caused hyperpnea, it did not affect either the number or the density of the granules in the type I cells. Inhalation of 2.5 per cent O_2, on the other hand, reduced the density and number of granules with apparent extracellular discharge of granules. They suggest that this cellular response is not related to the respiratory reflex. Chen et al. (18) subjected hamsters to 3–5 per cent O_2 for 20 min to 6 hr and found no abnormality in the appearance or in the number of granules. There was no evidence of movement of granules toward the cell membrane or subsequent exteriorization of granules. Al-Lami & Murray (3) exposed cats to 9.7 per cent inspired O_2 and observed that the cored vesicles of both type I and type II cells were increased in number as well as in density. None of the studies employed tissue assay or fluorescence microscopy of the carotid body to assess alterations in the catecholamine or 5-HT content.

Carotid body denervation.—Nerve degeneration following section of the nerves of the carotid body has been used to evaluate both the function and mode of innervation of the carotid body. Perivascular nerve endings degenerate following section of the postganglionic cervical sympathetic fibers (14). There is, however, disagreement about the time course and extent of degeneration following section of the carotid sinus nerve or the rootlets of the glossopharyngeal nerve. Section of the carotid sinus nerve should result in degeneration of both afferent and efferent nerve fibers. Hess (19) reported signs of degeneration in the first few days following nerve section and complete absence of nerve endings after 7 days. Likewise, de Castro & Rubio (20) observed signs of degeneration of the nerve endings on type I cells after 48 hr. These observations are quite different from those of Biscoe & Stehbens (14). On the 6th day after section of the sinus nerve, degeneration of nerve endings was patchy with normal endings remaining in many areas. After 3 months, a few normal nerve endings were still present; however, there was a marked reduction in the total number of endings and many of those remaining showed signs of degeneration. This observation is difficult to reconcile with the statement of Hess that no endings or synapses remained around the glomera after 7 days.

Similar difficulty arises in the interpretation of the reports on degeneration after section of the glossopharyngeal rootlets which should cause selective degeneration of efferent fibers in the carotid sinus nerve: de Castro & Rubio (20) report no change in nerve endings 30 days after section. However, quality of tissue fixation as evident from their published pictures was poor. Biscoe, Lall & Sampson (6, 21) sectioned the glossopharyngeal and rostral vagal rootlets and studied the ultrastructure of the carotid body as well as the functional integrity of the afferent chemoreceptor fibers. Signs of degeneration in nerve endings associated with type I cells were first apparent at 6 days. After 40 days, the number of endings was reduced to 35–40 per cent and remained relatively constant until 128 days. Electrophysiological studies demonstrated normal carotid chemoreceptor impulse traffic evoked by graded hypoxia or cyanide. On this evidence they conclude that the endings on type I cells are efferent. For the same duration of time that de Castro & Rubio studied the effect of denervation of the carotid body (30 days), Lall (6) reports only a 10 per cent reduction in nerve endings. This small reduction might have been overlooked by others.

The results of reinnervation of the distal cut end of the sinus nerve with the superior laryngeal nerve might be taken as evidence against a motor function of the endings on type I cells. The following assumptions made by the investigators are pertinent to the interpretation of the results (22). First, it was assumed that if reinnervation occurred it would be primarily sensory since the superior laryngeal nerve, although mixed, is primarily sensory. Secondly, if functional reinnervation occurred it would indicate again that the endings were sensory as it would be unique to have motor reinnervation by a sensory nerve. After 4 to 5 months, impulse activity in the nerve could be increased by N_2 and asphyxia, although these responses were significantly less than those in a normal nerve. However, baroreceptor activity was near normal. It is of interest that the authors used hexamethonium to depress blood pressure and reduce baroreceptor impulse traffic so that chemoreceptor activity could more readily be recorded. The electronmicroscopic studies were interpreted as showing reinnervation of parenchymal cell clusters; however, the endings were not normal. There were no elongated endings or electron-dense synaptic contacts with type I cells, and the vesicles were decreased in number. I think the mitochondria were abnormal in the sections illustrated, and the changes in some endings look much like those of degeneration. Only one normal synaptic-type ending was observed. Studies at frequent intervals after reinnervation of the carotid body would have been most helpful in interpreting the results. Since the endings lack the synaptic characteristics one cannot identify the reinnervating fibers as efferent or afferent, and one can only conclude that the carotid body and carotid sinus can be innervated by nonchemoreceptor sensory fibers, but I do not believe the chemosensitive nerve endings can be precisely identified in this way.

Although the interpretations placed on degeneration and reinnervation studies conflict, other studies yield evidence for efferent nerves to the carotid body. The presence of cholinergic fibers in the sinus nerve is suggestive of a motor function (16). Recording from the central end of the cut sinus nerve, Biscoe et al. (23) found two types of activity. One type, rhythmic in phase with either respiration or blood pressure, was shown to arise from fibers from the superior cervical ganglion. The second and more interesting type had a nonrhythmical pattern and a delayed response to large doses of epinephrine or vasopressin. Of particular interest was the relationship of the impulse traffic to Pa_{O_2} and Pa_{CO_2} which could be recorded even when all known peripheral chemoreceptors were denervated. Increased Pa_{CO_2} and decreased Pa_{O_2} raised the impulse frequency much as they do in the carotid chemoreceptor afferent fibers.

The possibility that these fibers form a negative feedback loop which modifies the chemoreceptor discharge is suggested by the report of Neil & O'Regan (24). They dissected out a small strand of the distal end of the cut sinus or aortic nerve for recording afferent chemoreceptor activity, and stimulated the remaining stump. Stimulation increased blood flow in the carotid body and depressed chemoreceptor impulse frequency. The inhibitory effect was still observed during stagnant hypoxia of the carotid body. Close intra-arterial injection of atropine reduced or blocked the vascular response without affecting the chemoreceptor response. What is obviously needed to assess the physiological importance of these efferent fibers upon the chemoreceptors is a study relating the chemoreceptor afferent response to graded hypoxia and hypercapnia in a small strand of sinus nerve with the main trunk intact, relating it to the response after cutting or blocking the efferent fibers. Also, if this efferent path is cholinergic the effect of hexamethonium upon these pathways would be of interest.

Lall (6) suggests that activation of the efferent nerves may cause the release of norepinephrine, epinephrine, 5-HT, and possibly dopamine from type I cells which may be of different types, each one containing a different amine. The selective release of these substances would then modulate the chemoreceptors. In keeping with this concept of efferent regulation of type I cells is the report that stimulation of the distal end of the cut carotid sinus nerve causes depletion of granules in some type I cells (25). This observation needs confirmation by tissue assay and fluorescent microscopic techniques.

Transmitter substance.—One of the bases for postulating a transmitter substance is that anemic anoxia (or CO breathing) does not stimulate the carotid body, whereas stagnant, anoxic, and histotoxic anoxia do. These observations, if true, suggest that the carotid body has a very small $(a-v)O_2$ difference and that chemoreceptor metabolism may be satisfied by O_2 in solution. That this argument is not correct is suggested by two recent investigations. Paintal (26) has challenged the necessity of postulating a transmitter substance and ACh in particular. He recorded impulse activity in medullated (A) and nonmedullated (C) fibers in the aortic nerve and found no difference in their responses to natural stimuli. Whereas the C fibers were stimulated by low doses of ACh, the A fibers were unaffected by doses three times larger. If both fibers serve the same function, why should the effect of ACh be different if it is the transmitter? Rising to the challenge, Sato et al. (27) and Fidone et al. (28) demonstrated that both A and C chemoreceptor fibers in the carotid sinus nerve could be stimulated by ACh.

Paintal (26) also reports that breathing 2 per cent CO in air, regularly and significantly stimulates the aortic chemoreceptors. One might challenge this observation since he failed to demonstrate that Pa_{O_2} did not fall during CO breathing. However, Mills & Edwards (29) confirmed the results of Paintal in an experiment where Pa_{O_2} was measured. The carotid chemoreceptor discharge increased when spontaneously breathing cats inhaled 1 per cent CO in air. The rise in discharge frequency when the saturation of hemoglobin with CO reached 18–40 per cent was comparable to the increase in frequency produced by reducing the Pa_{O_2} from a control level of 75-104 mm Hg to 62-70 mm Hg even though the Pa_{O_2} during CO breathing was 16-20 mm Hg higher. A few comparisons were done with equal blood pressure to exclude stimulation due to hypotension. The level of CO used would not be sufficient to have a direct effect on the cytochrome system. The authors suggest that the failure of CO to stimulate breathing is due to central anoxia as the venous and tissue Po_2 would be markedly reduced as a result of the shift in the O_2 dissociation curve for carbonylated blood. These studies suggest that the O_2 requirement of the chemoreceptors is not met by O_2 dissolved in blood alone and that the $(a-v)O_2$ difference across the carotid body may be significant. They also indicate that one need not postulate a transmitter substance to explain the response of the carotid chemoreceptors to the various types of anoxia and to changes in blood flow.

A second, but less convincing, argument against a transmitter results from the observation that the discharge frequency following circulatory arrest while a cat is breathing N_2 does not significantly increase (26). If a transmitter were involved, one might expect an increase in discharge frequency when the cat was switched from anoxic to stagnant hypoxia. However, this would seem true only if the discharge during anoxic anoxia were submaximal.

With respect to circulatory arrest, it has been generally thought that the chemoreceptor reflex was resistant to hypoxia. However, after 3 min of stagnant anoxia the impulse frequency in the chemoreceptor fibers was markedly diminished. Paintal suggests that this is adaptation, which should not occur if carotid chemoreceptor nerve impulses are mediated by a transmitter substance. However, the effect he observed with circulatory arrest could be due to substrate or transmitter exhaustion.

Of all the potential candidates for a transmitter, ACh has had the most press, but still fails to get all the votes. Eyzaguirre & Zapata (30) suggest that H^+ indirectly stimulates the chemoreceptor nerve endings either by increased release or by decreased destruction of ACh. They suggest that the direct effect of increased H^+ on chemoreceptor nerves is to stabilize the membrane, since increased H^+ decreased the frequency of chemoreceptor discharge evoked by the depolarizing effect of KCl. The *in vitro* response of the carotid chemoreceptors to ACh was increased by H^+. They suggest that H^+ potentiation of ACh is due to either inactivation of tissue cholinesterase or enhanced sensitivity of the nerve endings. Also, adding choline to the solution superperfusing of the carotid body prolonged its activity whereas hemocholinium-3, which blocks ACh synthesis, resulted in a progressive reduction in the chemoreceptor response to repeated periods of stimulation by hypoxia or H^+. Acetylcholine esterase, which might be expected to reduce the response to acid if it is ACh mediated, had no effect on discharge. This might result from its inability to reach the synaptic terminals. However, this explanation could not account for the failure of eserine to enhance the response since this agent is effective in Loewi-type experiments. The effect of cholinergic blocking agents was variable: mecamylamine and dihydro-β-erythroidine depressed the responses to hypoxia, H^+, and ACh, but it was difficult to reverse the inhibition. Hexamethonium, on the other hand, either enhanced or depressed the responses to ACh and H^+ but did not depress the response to hypoxia.

One major difficulty in accepting ACh as the transmitter substance is related to these last *in vitro* observations. *In vivo,* hexamethonium blocks the effect of ACh in the carotid chemoreceptors but does not block the effect of hypoxia. In an attempt to resolve this problem, Eyzaguirre & Zapata (31) studied the effects of ACh and cholinergic blocking agents by a Loewi-type experiment. A donor carotid body which could be stimulated electrically or by asphyxia was placed upstream in a channel containing flowing Locke solution. They recorded chemoreceptor activity in a second (detector) carotid body downstream. Stimulation of the donor increased chemoreceptor activity in the detector (Loewi effect). Eserine added to the Locke solution enhanced detector activity while acetylcholine esterase blocked the Loewi effect, which suggests that ACh is released from the donor cell. ACh and choline acetylase are present in the carotid body; however, the storage site of the former has not been identified, while the latter may be only in the nerves (16). Thus ACh may be released from the nerve endings and not the type I cells. However, donor organs denervated 4 days prior to study were effective in stimulating the detector carotid chemoreceptors. The conclusion that ACh must, therefore, come from the parenchymal cells cannot be fully accepted until the disagreement over the time course of nerve fiber degeneration is resolved.

The effect of cholinergic blocking agents on this preparation was again variable. Hexamethonium added to the superperfusing solution containing eserine decreased but did not block the response to asphyxia; mecamylamine did, but the effect was not readily reversible. Both drugs blocked the effect of ACh on the detector carotid body but the block could be overcome by increasing the dose of ACh. The authors suggest that this surmountable nature of cholinergic blocking agents may explain the relative inefficiency of these agents to block natural stimuli of the carotid body. They assume that the transmitter is released in abundance, is confined to the "synaptic region", is protected by type II cells from the effects of the blocking agents, and in itself does not desensitize the nerve endings (does not adapt). The increased efficiency of mecamylamine in blocking ACh may be due to its property of readily penetrating tissues.

Although the argument for release of ACh from the donor which excites the detector is convincing, there are still problems. First, the source of ACh is still in question; secondly, mecamylamine has not been tried *in vivo* to determine if it blocks natural stimuli and, lastly, in the reinnervation studies of Zapata et al. (22) the regenerated nerve endings did not have synaptic endings or an abundance of ACh, since they responded weakly to hypoxia. Despite this they were not affected by hexamethonium in concentrations sufficient to cause hypotension.

Transmitter release.—If one assumes no large diffusion barrier between carotid capillaries and chemoreceptor cells, then either the O_2 consumption of the carotid body may start to decrease as Po_2 falls below a critical O_2 tension or there may be a fall in ATP and a possible rise in H^+ before O_2 consumption diminishes. Both mechanisms have been suggested as possible causes of transmitter release (2).

The brief report of Purves (32) suggests the absence of a low critical Po_2 in the carotid body. He confirmed the high blood flow and high metabolic rate of the carotid body. With sympathetic nerves intact, the O_2 consumption of the carotid body was decreased by hypoxia, hypercapnia, and hypotension, and increased by hyperoxia and hypertension. When the mean arterial pressure was reduced, blood flow and O_2 consumption decreased proportionately but the $(a-v)O_2$ difference across the carotid body and presumably the tissue Po_2 remained constant suggesting no critical O_2 tension. Cutting the sympathetics increased blood flow and abolished the effect of hypercapnia, hypoxia and hypotension on metabolism. This regulation of carotid body O_2 consumption by sympathetic activity is difficult to reconcile with the observation that the activity in the sympathetic nerves to the carotid body is remarkably constant during chemoreceptor stimulation by hypoxia (33).

Chemoreceptor response to natural stimuli.—Integrated neurograms of the carotid sinus nerve show a hyperbolic relationship between Pa_{O_2} and impulse frequency (Pa_{CO_2} constant) (34). The position of the curve is shifted down by decreased Pa_{CO_2} and H^+ and up by opposite changes. In the range of normal Pa_{O_2} tensions the response curve is quite steep. It is unlikely that the hyperbolic nature of the response curve results from recruitment of fibers of increasing thresholds since the response of single fibers also had a hyperbolic form (35). Also, in single-fiber preparations, no threshold for O_2 was demonstrated: units discharged at a Pa_{O_2} of 650 mm Hg even when the arterial pH was increased to 7.6. The response curves to Pa_{CO_2}, derived from both single and multifiber preparations, showed an initial steep rise up to a Pa_{CO_2} of about 50 mm Hg and then tended to plateau. This type of curve was observed with Pa_{O_2} tensions up to 250 mm Hg.

The question whether Pa_{CO_2} has a direct effect other than by its acidifying properties is still unresolved. Biscoe et al. (35) report that Pco_2 has a specific effect on carotid chemoreceptor discharge. The Pa_{CO_2}-impulse response curves plotted from data derived from single fibers (Pa_{O_2} and pH constant) vary with pH, the slope being somewhat steeper at a low pH. Also, when the arterial pH was varied from 6.9 to 7.6 with Pa_{CO_2} and Pa_{O_2} kept constant, there was always an increase in chemoreceptor activity with a lowering of pH. Gray (36), perfusing carotid bodies of cats *in situ* with Locke solution of varying pH and Pco_2 and recording changes in the integrated activity in the whole carotid sinus nerve, observed no specific effect of CO_2. The effect of acidification was equal whether produced by a decrease in HCO_3^- or a rise in Pco_2. When Pco_2 and HCO_3^- were increased proportionately so that pH remained constant, chemoreceptor discharge transiently increased but returned to a common baseline in 20–30 sec. Gray interprets this response as indicating that the chemoreceptors are separated from the vascular space by a diffusion barrier more permeable to CO_2 than HCO_3^-. Thus, with increased P_{CO_2} at constant pH, there is an initial acidification of the extracellular fluid about the receptor which is subsequently restored to the control value on the arrival of the slower diffusing CHO_3^-. He concludes that the activity of the carotid chemoreceptors are uniquely determined by extracellular rather than intracellular pH as suggested by Hornbein & Roos (37).

Sympathetic innervation of the carotid body.—The carotid body is innervated by postganglionic fibers from the superior cervical ganglion which pass to the carotid body either directly or by way of the glossopharyngeal and carotid sinus nerve (23). Cutting the sympathetics increases blood flow through the carotid body and may also affect O_2 consumption (32). It also introduces irregular fluctuations in the chemoreceptor discharge (33). Electrical stimulation of the sympathetics to the aortic and carotid bodies increases the chemoreceptor discharge (38, 39). Mills & Sampson (40) report that stimulation of the sympathetics to the carotid body causes two- to threefold increase in ventilation in unanesthetized decerebrate cats. Anesthetic agents decreased the response but hyperoxia did not. This response to hyperoxia, which was not carefully studied, is surprising. If sympathetic stimulation causes a decrease in available O_2 to the chemoreceptors by reducing carotid blood flow, hyperoxia should offset this to some degree. That hyperoxia does suppress the stimulation of the carotid body because of reduction of its blood flow is suggested by the report of Joels & White (41) that the increases in ventilation and carotid body chemoreceptor discharges due to catecholamine infusions were suppressed by 100 per cent O_2 breathing in anesthetized cats.

Biscoe & Purves (33) report that postganglionic sympathetic fibers have a rhythmic pattern of discharge synchronous with either blood pressure or respiration. Their activity is not significantly altered by transient changes in Pa_{CO_2} or Pa_{O_2}, tracheal obstruction, or chest wall compression, which do significantly alter chemoreceptor activity. These observations suggest there is no rapidly acting feedback system to the carotid body via the sympathetic which is activated by the chemoreceptors themselves, but rather the sympathetics appear to provide a stable vasomotor tone to the carotid body. However, passive movement of the hindlimbs of anesthetized cats caused an impressive rise in sympathetic and chemoreceptor activity within 5 sec of the onset of movement (39). On cessation of movement, the activity in both nerves decreased rapidly. The response is too rapid to be mediated by blood gas changes or other humoral stimuli. The reflex nature of the fast response was demonstrated by section of either the postganglionic cervical sympathetics or the femoral and sciatic nerves. Both procedures eliminated the early rises in carotid chemoreceptor activity and ventilation. However, in these preparations, the ventilation did increase after a delay, and after 2 min was not significantly different from that before cutting the nerves. Cunningham et al. (42) have questioned the importance of this reflex in initiating the fast component of ventilation at the beginning of exercise since the increased Pa_{O_2}, which does not affect the magnitude of the fast component in man, should depress the effect of the sympathetics on the carotid body. Biscoe & Purves, unfortunately, did not test the effect of hyperoxia on their preparation.

The importance of this reflex is not striking in man (43). The steady-state level of ventilation achieved during exercise before and after bilateral stellate ganglion block was not siginficantly different. There was a delay in the onset of hyperpnea after the block, but it was not impressive.

Oscillatory stimuli.—Torrance (2) has reviewed the early literature on oscillatory stimuli and outlined the conditions under which a receptor will show a greater response to an oscillatory stimulus than to a steady-state stimulus: a portion of the oscillatory stimulus must fall below the threshold of the receptor, or the stimulus response curve must be nonlinear so that a decrease in stimulus below the mean will have less effect than that above the mean. The carotid receptor stimulus response curves for both Pa_{CO_2} and Pa_{O_2} are nonlinear (34, 35, 37). Even if there is no enhancement by an oscillatory stimulus at the receptor, an oscillating signal in the afferent nerves might be more effective than a steady signal of the same average activity. Both Pa_{O_2} and pH and, presumably, Pa_{CO_2} oscillate with a respiratory rhythm in carotid artery blood. These oscillations probably extend at least as far as the vertebral arteries (44). However, because of the relatively long time constant for the response to CO_2 of the central receptors, oscillations in CO_2 or pH would have little effect on these receptors. The oscillations of blood gases as well as those in chemoreceptor activity result from pulmonary gas exchange. Increased inspired CO_2 diminished oscillations in arterial pH and in chemoreceptor activity but intravenous CO_2, which might simulate increased CO_2 production of exercise, increased pH oscillations (44–46).

Hyperoxia decreases the amplitude of the oscillations in chemoreceptor activity (44). Also, the magnitude of these oscillations is directly related to tidal volume and inversely to the frequency of breathing (44, 45). In the cat, pH oscillations are detectable at respiratory frequencies up to 30–35/min. However, carotid chemoreceptors may respond to oscillatory stimuli at frequencies up to 70/min although the amplitude of the oscillations in chemoreceptor discharge is diminished (47).

Adaptation.—I doubt that chemoreceptors truly adapt to transient natural stimuli in the physiological range. McCloskey reports no adaptation in carotid chemoreceptor discharge following a step reduction in arterial P_{O_2} (48). However, when a sudden hypercapneic stimulus was delivered to the carotid body, there was a sudden burst of chemoreceptor activity which then decreased to a lower level. This effect was enhanced by hypoxemia. A sudden reduction in Pa_{CO_2} reduced chemoreceptor activity to a minimum and then the discharge returned to the control level. This might be adaptation, but another interpretation seems more plausible (36). The sudden burst of activity is due to the rapid diffusion of CO_2 into and subsequent acidification of the chemoreceptor extracellular fluid. The more slowly diffusing HCO_3^-, derived from blood buffers, would subsequently increase the pH and reduce the receptor discharge. This view is supported by the absence of an overshoot in chemoreceptor activity when the carotid body carbonic anhydrase was inhibited (48) ; and by the absence of a significant overshoot when the carotid body was perfused by Locke solutions which do not have the buffering capacity of blood (36).

Studies on the effect of patterned stimuli to the carotid body indicated that an oscillating stimulus is more effective than a steady one. Dutton et al. (49) measured the respiratory response to hypercapneic blood perfused bilaterally through the carotid bodies of anesthetized dogs. A step increase in Pa_{CO_2} caused an overshoot in ventilation as it did in chemoreceptor activity. However, step reductions in Pa_{CO_2} caused a gradual return to a control level without an undershoot. A ramp increase in Pa_{CO_2} also produced an excess of ventilation during the first few seconds but again no undershoot was observed when the Pa_{CO_2} was reduced (50). When an oscillating square wave of Pa_{CO_2} of 3 sec duration and at a rate of 10 cycles per sec was delivered to the carotid bodies, the increase in ventilation for a given mean increase in Pa_{CO_2} was about twice that for a step increase in Pa_{CO_2}. The respiratory response to this square-wave forcing function did not adapt (51).

There are no data to determine if an oscillatory stimulus is more effective than a steady one on the carotid body, but it would appear that an oscillatory signal in the carotid chemoreceptor afferents is more effective in increasing ventilation. This is suggested by the absence of an undershoot in ventilation at a time when an undershoot in chemoreceptor activity occurs as carotid artery P_{CO_2} is abruptly reduced.

That a central mechanism is involved in the respiratory response to an oscillatory stimulus is suggested by the work of Black & Torrance (52). They injected small volumes of Ringer's solution, equilibrated with 100 per cent CO_2, into the external carotid of anesthetized cats and measured the effect on ventilation. This stumulus, which caused a brief burst of activity in the carotid sinus nerve, increased tidal volume when delivered just before or during inspiration. If the stimulus was delivered during expiration, the next breath was delayed and tidal volume was only slightly increased. Dutton et al. (51) report a similar effect in anesthetized dogs. A step increase in Pa_{CO_2} delivered bilaterally to the carotid bodies was twice as effective in increasing ventilation when delivered during inspiration as when it arrived during expiration. However, when delivered during expiration it did significantly increase ventilation over a control produced by a steady stimulus of the same mean Pa_{CO_2}.

The central mechanism underlying these observations possibly involves the convergence of the chemoreceptor signal on neurons in the CNS that have rhythmic depolarization and possibly hyperpolarization, so that the generation of spike discharges in the postsynaptic element will be more likely if the input arrives during a wave of depolarization. Inspiratory neurons have this character (53) and antidromic spikes can be evoked more readily during inspiration than during expiration (54).

Tube breathing.—It has been suggested that the effect of tube breathing is related to an oscillatory stimulus. Fenner et al. (55) compared the effect of breathing through a tube of 1400 ml volume with the effect of breathing 4–6 per cent CO_2. They postulated that tube breathing would increase CO_2 oscillations in blood and CO_2 breathing would reduce them. At comparable end tidal CO_2, but not arterial tensions, the steady-state ventilation reached during tube breathing was greater than that during CO_2 breathing. They assumed that the slight fall in Pa_{O_2} during tube breathing could not account for the excess ventilation. Goode et al. (56) report that it does, and the tube effect is not observed in hyperoxia or during normoxia if the Pa_{O_2} of tube breathing is matched with that during CO_2 breathing. However, in the hypoxic range there was significant enhancement of the response to CO_2 during tube breathing. These authors predict that the amplitude of the oscillations of Pa_{CO_2} will not be increased by tube breathing, and suggest that a shift in the phase or shape of the oscillations or timing of arrival at the brain results in increased breathing.

Band et al. (46) report that tube breathing does not increase the amplitude of pH oscillations in the carotid artery in dogs. However, when the mean pH and respiratory pattern during tube breathing were similar to that during CO_2 breathing, the shape of the oscillations during tube breathing was different from air or CO_2 breathing. During tube breathing the rate of exchange pH during the decreasing and increasing phases of pH was more rapid than during air or CO_2 breathing. Also, the point of inflection was flatter during tube breathing so that the duration of maximum acidosis was prolonged. Theoretically this would increase the probability that the effect of peak acidosis would coincide with some phase of inspiration. However, this possibility needs further study.

Central chemoreceptors.—While investigations on the peripheral chemoreceptors have waxed, those on the central chemoreceptor have waned. Only two papers dealing directly with these receptors have appeared in the last few years. Cozine & Ngai (57), working with unanesthetized decerebrate cats with denervated peripheral chemoreceptors, confirmed the presence of a chemoreceptor zone on the ventrolateral surface of the medulla. Nicotine applied to this region stimulates ventilation. Topical application of 1 per cent procaine reduced ventilation to 72 per cent of control but produced apnea in only one of 32 cats. Procaine also decreased the slope of the CO_2 response curve. A repeat application of procaine after anesthetic doses of chloralose and urethane produced apnea. Hypotension following a reduction in blood volume made the unanesthetized animals more liable to apnea. The authors conclude that the surface chemoreceptors are only a part of an overall central chemosensitive mechanism.

In anesthetized cats, Schläfke & Loeschcke (58) have precisely mapped areas on the ventral medullary surface where cooling with a probe of 1 mm^2

area alters respiration. In an area rostramedial to the rootlets of the XII cranial nerve, cooling decreased tidal volume by 27–53 per cent. The effect was enhanced by section of the vagi and the carotid sinus nerves. When the contralateral thermosensitive area was coagulated, cooling caused apnea in 7 to 10 cats. The effect of cooling was present during hypercarbia but not during thermal polypnea, which suggests that the cooling does not directly block the "respiratory centers" or descending motor pathways. The authors conclude that since apnea occurs when the chemosensitive area is bilaterally inactivated there are no other important control chemoreceptors. In view of Cozine & Ngai's observations, this conclusion might be valid only if apnea occurred in unanesthetized cats.

Neural Regulation of Respiration

Primary afferents.—There has been increasing interest in the site of termination of the primary afferents of the carotid sinus nerve with respect to both the baro- and chemoreceptor afferents. As yet, there is no direct method of distinguishing between baro- and chemoreceptor responses evoked by stimulation of the carotid sinus nerve. Electrical stimulation of this nerve evokes a negative field potential in the ipsilateral nucleus tractus solitarius (NTS) in 0.2–2.0 msec (59–61). Smaller fields with a longer latent period are also evoked as far caudal as the commissural nucleus of Cajal, which suggests that fiber tracts may cross at many levels rather than solely at this nucleus (60). Humphrey (59) suggests that some of the secondary units may rejoin the tractus solitarius and later re-enter the NTS and add a polysynaptic component to the evoked field in the NTS. However, there is evidence that the early negative field is generated monosynaptically. The magnitudes of field potentials are attenuated by repetitive stimuli above about 30–50/sec and are depressed by hypoxia and barbiturates (61). Electrical stimulation at the site of the maximum field potential produces an antidromic action potential in the sinus nerve. Also, there is frequently a small low-threshold negative wave preceding the major deflection which is not suppressed by repetitive stimulation, suggesting presynaptic afferent fibers (61).

A secondary negative field has been reported in the region just ventral to the NTS (59, 60); this should be close to if not in areas rich in respiratory neurons. The field detected here has a short latency (2–3 msec) and high-frequency bursts of unit activity up to 1000/sec are frequently superimposed upon this field potential. Sampson & Biscoe (60) suggest that this field, because of its short latency, is disynaptic at most. More medially, these investigators found a positive field associated with inhibition of the spontaneous activity of some units in this area. The latency of 4–5 msec was compatible with the time course of an intracellular hyperpolarizing potential recorded in some cells in this region. They suggest that this hyperpolarizing field may be evoked by cells in the more lateral negative fields.

Miura & Reis (61) recorded a short-latency (0.7–1.4 msec) steeply rising negative wave, up to amplitudes of 20 mV, in the medial reticular formation, evoked by electrical stimulation of the sinus nerve. The amplitude of this potential, which has the characteristics of a monosynaptically evoked potential, is much larger than any recorded in the medulla by other investigators. Stimulation of this region of the medulla evoked antidromic compound action potentials in the aortic and sinus nerves. Also, repetitive stimulation at this site caused a drop in blood pressure and heart rate (62). These investigators conclude that some sinus nerve primary afferents, probably baroreceptor, terminate in the bulbar reticular formation.

Central interactions.—Relatively strong electrical stimulation of the sinus nerve evokes a burst of activity in the phrenic nerve and depolarizes motoneurons with a surprisingly short latency (about 6 and 4 msec respectively) especially in view of the latency of the mono- or disynaptic field near the tractus solitarius (63). The depolarization of the phrenic motoneuron probably is evoked by a relatively direct pathway from the chemoreceptor afferents. Low-intensity stimuli produce a hyperpolarizing potential in phrenic motor cells, especially when the central respiratory drive potential is suppressed by hyperventilation. At normal levels of Pa_{CO_2} the spontaneous activity in the phrenic motor units is suppressed during the wave of hyperpolarization. These effects are probably due to stimulation of low-threshold baroreceptor afferents. The fields evoked in the NTS by stimulation of the vagus and sinus nerves are quite similar and show considerable overlap (64).

The possibility that the primary afferents of one nerve may influence the monosynaptic transmission of another was investigated by Frankstein & Sergeeva (65). Using indirect methods they found no evidence or primary afferent depolarization in the region of the NTS following stimulation of the vagus nerve. However, their recording electrodes were on the surface of the medulla at some distance from the NTS. Rudomin (64), however, reports that electrical stimulation of the thoracic vagus or the aortic nerve decreased the amplitude of the potential monosynaptically evoked from stimulation of the superior laryngeal nerve. Stimulation of these nerves also increased the amplitude of the antidromic action potentials in the superior laryngeal nerve evoked by stimulation of the NTS. Lung inflation also caused primary afferent depolarization, which suggests that the effect of vagal stimulation was mediated by pulmonary stretch afferents. The effect from aortic nerve stimulation was mediated by low-threshold fibers probably baroreceptor. Thus it is possible that respiratory reflexes originating in the larynx may be modified by lung inflation and changes of blood pressure. Seller & Illert (66) found no evidence for primary afferent depolarization arising from the respiratory centers, as the fields evoked by sinus nerve stimulation did not vary with any phase of respiration. However, the vagi were cut so that any such depolarization arising from pulmonary stretch receptors would have been missed. The possibility that respiratory reflexes may be modified at the level of the primary afferents obviously merits further investigation.

Kahn & Wang (67) propose that the phenomenon of apneusis is a specific respiratory function and that the Hering-Breuer reflex acts via the apneustic center. They report that, in cats with midpontine sections of the brainstem, the expiratory-inspiratory phase spanning respiratory units in the caudal pons can be modulated by a smaller lung inflation than can inspiratory units in the medulla. This observation alone does not necessarily mean that the primary afferents of the vagus have a station in the apneustic center. This effect could be mediated equally well by an inspiratory inhibitory network arising from the medulla.

To those who believe that respiratory periodicity arises from two reciprocal neuronal networks the reports of Cohen (68, 69) will be of particular interest. He investigated the effect of hypocapnia and lung inflation on respiratory units in the medulla and pons. A striking finding, as in a similar study by Batsel (70) on the effect of hypocapnia, was that units with the same discharge pattern might have different responses to hypocapnia and to lung inflation. This was especially true in the medulla where most inspiratory and expiratory units were found. Cohen suggests that those units which respond in the same way as peripheral motor units contribute to the descending motor pathway and those having no counterpart in the periphery are members of a transmission network within the medulla and pons. He suggests that a pair of neuronal groups in the medulla made up of expiratory units which fire continuously and inspiratory units which become silent during hypocapnia would provide a tonic expiratory-facilitory system. Periodic breathing would result from increased CO_2 when inspiratory unit activity began which might periodically inhibit the expiratory units. The possibility of reciprocal neuronal pairs is much more striking in the pons where the expiratory-inspiratory (EI) units in the caudal pons and inspiratory-expiratory (IE) units in the rostral pons have a propensity for one type of response to hypocapnia and lung inflation. Lung inflation inhibits EI units and hypocapnia causes a continuous discharge in most. IE units, with one exception, stop discharging with hypocapnia. Cohen proposes that this neuronal pair would provide a tonic inspiratory-facilitory system whose basis would be the activity of the EI neurons. Periodicity returns when CO_2 is raised as a result of the return of activity in the IE units which inhibit the EI units. Since, under certain conditions, experimental animals may have patterns of respiration indicative of tonic inspiratory or expiratory facilitation, Cohen suggests that both systems are involved in the genesis of respiratory periodicity but does not speculate as to which may be dominant.

CEREBROSPINAL FLUID pH AND THE REGULATION OF RESPIRATION

The role of CSF pH in the regulation of respiration has been reviewed by Cameron (71). The regulation of CSF pH was a major topic for discussion in the International Symposium on CSF and CBF held in Lund and

Copenhagen in 1968 (72). Further evidence for the stability of CSF pH in metabolic acidosis and metabolic alkalosis has been reported by Ponten & Siesjö (73) and by Fencl et al. (74). Ponten & Siesjö injected NH_4Cl/NaCl or $NaHCO_3$ solutions intraperitoneally in rats and 6 hr later measured CSF pH. The pH in CSF changed in the direction of the arterial pH; however, this difference in pH between the acidotic and alkalotic groups was only 0.04 pH units in CSF for a change of 0.23 units in arterial blood. Fencl et al. (74) measured the CSF pH in man on the 5th day of metabolic acidosis and alkalosis induced by daily doses of NH_4Cl or $NaHCO_3$. The difference in arterial pH between the 5th day of acidosis and alkalosis was 0.171 pH units. However, the CSF pH difference was only 0.015 units. In both studies alkalosis had less effect on CSF pH than did acidosis. A number of mechanisms may contribute to the observed stability. The ventilatory response to central chemoreceptor stimulation by changes in CSF pH is obvious.

CSF/plasma electrical potential.—The potential difference between blood and CSF may be a major factor in the stability of CSF pH. Kjällquist & Siesjö (75) observed that the CSF/plasma potential in sustained metabolic acidosis and alkalosis in rats varied inversely, in a nonlinear fashion, with plasma pH. A plot of the potential versus arterial pH had a slope of 56.5 mV/pH unit in the alkaline range and 21 mV/pH unit in the acid range. This potential would act as a negative feedback system, apparently regulated by arterial pH, which would oppose the chemical potential for H^+. The steeper slope of the potential-pH curve in the alkaline range might then explain the greater stability of CSF pH in alkalemia than in acidemia where the slope is flatter. Kjällquist & Siesjö (76) calculated the single ion potential for H^+ concentrations (pmf) in rats with respiratory and metabolic acidosis and alkalosis. They found that the pmf varied between 0 and +7 mV, and had no consistent relationship with CSF or arterial pH. They take these observations as evidence against the concept that H^+ is actively transported between CSF and arterial blood. For example, the pmf value of +7 in respiratory acidosis would indicate than an H^+ pump would increase the acidity of CSF rather than transport H^+ out.

Cerebral blood flow.—Cerebral arterioles may contribute to the stability of extracellular fluid and CSF pH, in both metabolic and respiratory acidosis and alkalosis if CBF varies inversely with CSF pH. Fencl et al. (74) report that it does in man. Using the $C(a-v)O_2$ across the brain as an index of CBF, they measured the effect of CO_2 inhalation on changes in CBF in man with normal acid-base balance and with steady metabolic acidosis and alkalosis. The CBF varied inversely with Pa_{CO_2}; however, the CBF Pa_{CO_2} response curve was shifted to a lower Pa_{CO_2} than normal during acidosis and to a higher Pa_{CO_2} during alkalosis. When CBF was plotted against CSF pH, the data from the normal, acidotic, and alkalotic subjects described a single inverse relationship. The authors, therefore, propose that extracellular H^+ regulates CBF.

Lactic acid.—CSF is more acid than if H^+ were in electrochemical equilibrium between blood and CSF, which suggests continuous addition of H^+ to CSF. Normally there is a small efflux of lactic acid from brain cells which may be important in regulation of CSF pH. Also, Leusen et al. (77) report that lactate production by brain slices is increased in alkalosis under aerobic conditions. The addition of hypoxia may greatly increase lactate production. Cohen et al. (78) have demonstrated a Pasteur effect in the brain in awake man during transient reduction of Pa_{O_2} to 35 mm Hg. During hypoxia, oxygen consumption of the brain remained constant but glucose uptake increased 25 per cent. The lactate production increased fourfold while the fraction of total glucose related to O_2 consumption fell. No excess lactate appeared in either the arterial or venous blood. I think this paper is of special significance since it indicates that, in conscious man, moderate hypoxia may produce large increases in brain and presumably CSF lactate without measurably impairing the total energy production by glucose.

Increased lactate concentrations in brain and CSF have been reported in hyperventilated dogs. Both Plum & Posner (79) and Kazemi et al. (80) report significant elevations in CSF lactate in dogs artifically hyperventilated (Pa_{CO_2} 20–25 mm Hg) for 6 hr. With severe hyperventilation ($P_{CO_2} <$ 10 mm Hg) CSF lactate increased twofold and with added hypoxia, fivefold. Plum et al. (81) suggest that part of the increase in lactate in normoxic hyperventilation may be due to vasoconstriction and tissue hypoxia. When dogs were hyperventilated with O_2 at 3 atm, lactate still rose in the CSF but only half as much as with eupoxic hyperventilation. The rise in lactate unrelated to tissue hypoxia is unexplained. It might be expected that hypercapnia would decrease CSF and possibly brain lactate. Dogs breathing 10 per cent CO_2 in O_2 did show a decrease in lactate after 30 min but it returned to normal by 6 hr (80).

The increase in CSF lactate probably contributes to the stability of pH during chronic hypoxia. However, there is no stoichiometric relationship between the increase in lactate and the decrease in HCO_3^- in CSF, the rise in lactate being about ⅓–½ the fall in HCO_3^- in the studies by Plum et al. (79).

Respiration in metabolic acidosis and alkalosis.—Fencl et al. (74) also studied the respiratory response to inhaled CO_2 in man during normal acid-base balance and in maintained steady acidosis. They estimated CSF pH from the HCO_3^- in lumbar CSF, drawn immediately prior to the respiratory studies, and from the P_{CO_2} using the value of the jugular venous blood or estimated by the formula $1 + (Pa_{CO_2} - Pv_{CO_2})/2$. The respiratory response to inhaled CO_2 was shifted to the left of its normal position by acidosis and to the right by alkalosis. The magnitude of these shifts in terms of the Pa_{CO_2} was directly related to the CSF HCO_3^-. A change in CSF HCO_3^- of 1 meq/liter was associated with a shift in the CO_2 response curve of 1.7 mm Hg P_{CO_2}. When ventilation was plotted as a function of estimated CSF pH (calculated by either method), ventilation became a single function of estimated CSF pH during acidosis, alkalosis, and CO_2 breathing. The authors suggest that a unique relationship between CSF pH and ventilation and CBF provide regulatory loops which determine brain P_{CO_2} which in turn determines [H^+]. With respect to respiration they conclude that in the absence of a variable O_2 drive and in steady-state acid-base conditions, no significant role would be left for the peripheral chemoreceptors in the respiratory adaptation to chronic metabolic acidosis and alkalosis in humans. However, there is a defect in the study. Thirty per cent oxygen, to stabilize ventilation, was not given during the period of adaptation but was administered just before the respiratory studies and after the CSF sample for the estimation of HCO_3^- was drawn. Thus any suppression of peripheral chemoreceptors would be reflected by an acute acid shift in the estimated CSF pH and be interpreted as a central drive to respiration.

Goldring et al. (82) report an interesting observation on the respiratory depression due to metabolic alkalosis in normal humans. Metabolic alkalosis, induced by buffers or ethacrinic acid, produced hypoventilation whereas thiazide diuretics or aldosterone did not, despite equivalent changes in arterial pH and HCO_3^- concentration. Also, the pH and HCO_3^- of CSF were not significantly altered. But, on the basis of the differences in Pa_{CO_2} between the two groups, 45.5 versus 37.0, one would expect a difference in CSF HCO_3^- of about 4 meq/liter according to the results obtained by Fencl et al. (74). The only difference between the two groups was in the patterns of H^+ and K^+ balance during the development of alkalosis. The subjects who had no demonstrable external loss of H^+ but had a marked loss of K^+ (thiazides and aldosterone) did not hypoventilate. This study is of interest in that the results suggest that the intracellular concentration of K^+ and H^+ as well as the extracellular H^+ may be important in determining central chemoreceptor activity.

Acclimatization to altitude.—Eger et al. (83) attempted to separate the effects of hypoxia and hypocapnia on the respiratory acclimatization of humans. When the subjects were hyperventilated for 8 hr without hypoxia, the CO_2 responses shifted to the left 18 per cent of the reduction of Pa_{CO_2}. However, when hypoxia was added, the shift was doubled. In both studies. the shift in the CO_2 response curve was directly related to the reduction in Pa_{CO_2}. The authors suggest that the difference in acclimatization between nonhypoxic hyperventilation and hypoxic hyperventilation may be due to generation of lactic acid in the presence of hypoxia.

The fact that high-altitude natives have a Pa_{CO_2} 2–3 mm Hg higher than sea level natives residing at high altitude has been confirmed both in Andean natives (84, 85) and Sherpas (86–88). There is now good evidence from a number of investigators that the lower ventilation of high-altitude natives is due to decreased sensitivity of the peripheral chemoreceptors to hypoxia (84–92). The Pa_{CO_2} is related to the degree of insensitivity to hypoxia, being highest in subjects with chronic mountain sickness who have no response to hypoxia (84, 85.). It would appear that the insensitivity is acquired at birth or during the first few months of life. Lahiri et al. (89) report that the response to hypoxia was normal in sea level natives who had resided at altitude for $\frac{1}{2}$ to 35 years and their Pa_{CO_2} was no different from that of lowlanders residing for a short time at high altitude. The Pa_{CO_2}, however, was lower than high-altitude natives.

Sørensen & Severinghaus (84) observed that high-altitude natives failed to regain their sensitivity to hypoxia on going to sea level even when they left as early as 2 years of age or remained at sea level for up to 27 years. Velasquez et al. (92) and Lahiri et al. (89) report the persistence of insensitivity to hypoxia in high-altitude natives after residency at low altitude for 1 year and 10 months respectively. This insensitivity to hypoxia is not genetically determined. According to Sørensen & Severinghaus (93), five subjects, after correction of tetralogy of Fallot, all showed a marked insensitivity to hypoxia comparable to that of high-altitude natives. In these subjects and in high-altitude natives studied at sea level, the resting air breathing Pa_{CO_2} was normal as was the response curve to inhaled CO_2. This suggests that the loss of sensitivity to hypoxia may not be associated with a loss of sensitivity to CO_2 or H^+ in the peripheral chemoreceptors (or that the peripheral chemoreceptor continues to stimulate the respiratory center weakly but is incapable of strongly driving it). This suggestion assumes that the effect of denervating the peripheral chemoreceptors on ventilation is a rise of Pa_{CO_2} of 5–8 mm Hg.

These results pose the following problem: If high-altitude natives are insensitive to hypoxia why do they hyperventilate and acclimatize? It is probable that lactic acid generation is increased in high-altitude natives and contributes to the acidification of CSF. Lahiri & Milledge (88) report that the CSF pH is more acid and HCO_3^- is lower in Sherpas than in lowlanders studied at the same altitude. Lactate was not increased in the CSF of the Sherpas. Sørensen et al. (94) report that the CSF pH in Andean high-altitude natives was 7.29 compared to a sea level normal of 7.32. They measured jugular venous and arterial glucose, oxygen, and lactate in the subjects and report that the fraction of glucose metabolized to lactate was increased to about 25 per cent. It decreased when breathing O_2 to 5–10 per cent which indicated significant anaerobic brain metabolism at high altitude.

As yet, no experimental animal has been found which loses sensitivity to hypoxia with the same time relationship as man. Llamas born and raised at altitude have the same sensibility to hypoxia as second-generation sea level llamas (95). Also, native dogs at high altitude have a good chemoreflex response to oxygen (85). On the other hand, steers apparently lose their sensitivity to hypoxia after a few weeks (96).

LITERATURE CITED

1. *Arterial Chemoreceptors* (Torrance, R. W., Ed., Blackwell, Oxford, 402 pp., 1968)
2. Torrance, R. W. Prolegomena. In *Arterial Chemoreceptors*, 1–40 (See Ref. 1)
3. el-Lami, F., Murray, R. G. Fine structure of the carotid body of normal and anoxic cats. *Anat. Record*, 160, 697–718 (1968)
4. Biscoe, T. J., Stehbens, W. E. Ultrastructure of the carotid body. *J. Cell Biol.*, 30, 563–78 (1966)
5. Duncan, D., Yates, R. Ultrastructure of the carotid body of the cat as revealed by various fixatives and the use of reserpine. *Anat. Record*, 157, 667–82 (1967)
6. Lall, A. *Identification of efferent nerve endings on type I cells of the carotid body of the cat. An ultrastructural study* (Univ. California, San Francisco, Ph.D. thesis, 1969)
7. Ross, L. L. Electron microscopic observations of the carotid body of the cat. *J. Biophys. Biochem. Cytol.*, 6, 253–62 (1959)
8. Al-Lami, F., Murray, R. G. Fine structure of the carotid body of Macaca mulatta monkey. *J. Ultrastruct. Res.*, 24, 465–78 (1968)
9. Chiocchio, S. R., Biscardi, A. M., Tramezzani, J. H. 5-Hydroxytryptamine in the carotid body of the cat. *Science*, 158, 790–91 (1967)
10. Dearnaley, D. P., Fillenz, M., Woods, R. T. The identification of dopamine in the rabbit's carotid body. *Proc. Roy. Soc. (Biol.)*, 170, 195–203 (1968)
11. Chen, I., Yates, R. D. Electron microscopic radioautographic studies of the carotid body following injections of labeled biogenic amine precursors. *J. Cell Biol.*, 42, 794–803 (1969)
12. Jacobs, L., Comroe, J. H., Jr. Stimulation of the carotid chemoreceptors of the dog by dopamine. *Proc. Natl. Acad. Sci.*, 59, 1187–93 (1968)
13. Rees, P. M. The distribution of biogenic amines in the carotid bifurcation region. *J. Physiol. (London)*, 193, 245–53 (1967)
14. Biscoe, T. J., Stehbens, W. E. Ultrastructure of the denervated carotid body. *Quart. J. Exptl. Physiol.*, 52, 31–36 (1967)
15. Biscoe, T. J., Silver, A. The distribution of cholinesterases in the cat carotid body. *J. Physiol. (London)*, 183, 501–512 (1966)
16. Hebb, C. In *Arterial Chemoreceptors*, 138–39 (See Ref. 1)
17. Blumcke, S., Rode, J., Niedorf, H. R. The carotid body after oxygen deficiency. *Z. Zellforsch.*, 80, 52–77 (1967)
18. Chen, I., Yates, R. D., Duncan, D. The effects of reserpine and hypoxia on the amine-storing granules of the hamster carotid body. *J. Cell Biol.*, 42, 804–16 (1969)
19. Hess, A. Electron microscopic observations of normal and experimental cat carotid bodies. In *Arterial Chemoreceptors*, 51–56 (See Ref. 1)
20. de Castro, F., Rubio, M. The anatomy and innervation of the blood vessels of the carotid body and the role of chemoreceptive reactions in autoregulation of blood flow. In *Arterial Chemoreceptors*, 267–77 (See Ref. 1)
21. Biscoe, T. J., Lall, A., Sampson, S. R. On the nerve endings associated with the carotid body glomus cells of the cat. *J. Physiol. (London)*, 200, 131P (1969)
22. Zapata, P., Hess, A., Eyzaguirre, C. Reinnervation of carotid body and sinus with superior laryngeal nerve fibers. *J. Neurophysiol.*, 32, 215–28 (1969)
23. Biscoe, T. J., Sampson, S. R. Rhythmical spontaneous activity recorded from the central cut end of the sinus nerve. *J. Physiol. (London)*, 196, 327–38 (1968)
24. Neil, E., O'Regan, R. G. Effects of sinus and aortic nerve efferents on arterial chemoreceptor function. *J. Physiol. (London)*, 200, 69P (1969)
25. Chen, I., Yates, R. D., Duncan, D. The effects of nerve stimulation or transection on the glomus cells of the carotid body. *J. Cell Biol.*, 39, 24A (1968)
26. Paintal, A. S. Mechanism of stimulation of aortic chemoreceptors by

natural stimuli and chemical substances. *J. Physiol. (London)*, **189**, 63–84 (1967)

27. Sato, A., Fidone, S., Eyzaguirre, C. Presence of chemoreceptor and baroreceptor C-fibers in the carotid nerve of the cat. *Brain Res.*, **11**, 459–63 (1968)

28. Fidone, S., Sato, A., Eyzaguirre, C. Acetylcholine activation of carotid body chemoreceptor A fibers. *Brain Res.*, **9**, 374–76 (1968)

29. Mills, E., Edwards, M. W., Jr. Stimulation of aortic and carotid chemoreceptors during carbon monoxide inhalation. *J. Appl. Physiol.*, **25**, 494–502 (1968)

30. Eyzaguirre, C., Zapata, P. Pharmacology of pH effects on carotid body chemoreceptors in vitro. *J. Physiol. (London)*, **195**, 557–88 (1968)

31. Eyzaguirre, C., Zapata, P. The release of acetylcholine from carotid body tissues. Further study on the effects of acetylcholine and cholinergic blocking agents on the chemosensory discharge. *J. Physiol. (London)*, **195**, 589–608 (1968)

32. Purves, M. J. Changes in oxygen consumption of the carotid body of the cat. *J. Physiol. (London)*, **200**, 132P–133P (1969)

33. Biscoe, T. J., Purves, M. J. Observations on carotid body chemoreceptor activity and cervical sympathetic discharge in the cat. *J. Physiol. (London)*, **190**, 413–24 (1967)

34. Biscoe, T. J., Millar, R. A. Effects of inhalation anaesthetics on carotid body chemoreceptor activity. *Brit. J. Anaesth.*, **40**, 2–12 (1968)

35. Biscoe, T. J., Sampson, S. R., Purves, M. J. Stimulus response curves of single carotid body chemoreceptor afferent fibers. *Nature*, **215**, 654–55 (1967)

36. Gray, B. A. Response of the perfused carotid body to changes in pH and Pco_2. *Resp. Physiol.*, **4**, 229–45 (1968)

37. Hornbein, T. F., Roos, A. Specificity of H ion concentration as a carotid chemoreceptor stimulus. *J. Appl. Physiol.*, **18**, 580–84 (1963)

38. Mills, E. Activity of the aortic chemoreceptors during electrical stimulation of the stellate ganglion in the cat. *J. Physiol. (London)*, **199**, 103–14 (1968)

39. Biscoe, T. J., Purves, M. J. Factors affecting the cat carotid chemoreceptor and cervical sympathetic activity with special reference to passive hind limb movements. *J. Physiol. (London)*, **190**, 425–42 (1967)

40. Mills, E., Sampson, S. R. Respiratory response to electrical stimulation of the cervical sympathetic nerves in decerebrate, unanaesthetized cats. *J. Physiol. (London)*, **202**, 271–82 (1969)

41. Joels, N., White, H. The contribution of the arterial chemoreceptors to the stimulation of respiration by adrenaline and noradrenaline in the cat. *J. Physiol. (London)*, **197**, 1–24 (1968)

42. Cunningham, D. J. C. Regulation of breathing in exercise. *Circ. Res.*, **20**, *Suppl. 1*, 122–31 (1967)

43. Eisele, J. H., Ritchie, B. C., Severinghaus, J. W. Effect of stellate ganglion blockade on the hyperpnea of exercise. *J. Appl. Physiol.*, **22**, 966–69 (1967)

44. Biscoe, T. J., Purves, M. J. Observations on the rhythmic variations in the cat carotid body chemoreceptor activity which has the same period as respiration. *J. Physiol. (London)*, **190**, 389–412 (1967)

45. Band, D. M., Cameron, I. R., Semple, S. J. G. Oscillations in arterial pH with breathing in the cat. *J. Appl. Physiol.*, **26**, 261–67 (1969)

46. Band, D. M., Cameron, I. R., Semple, S. J. G. Effect of different methods of CO_2 administration on oscillations of arterial pH in the cat. *J. Appl. Physiol.*, **26**, 268–74 (1969)

47. Fitzgerald, R. S., Leitner, L.-M., Liaubet, M.-J., Carotid chemoreceptor response to intermittent or sustained stimulation in the cat. *Resp. Physiol.*, **6**, 395–402 (1969)

48. McCloskey, D. I. Carbon dioxide and the carotid body. In *Arterial Chemoreceptors*, 279–96 (See Ref. 1)

49. Dutton, R. E., Hodson, W. A., Davies, D. G., Chernick, V. Ventilatory adaptation to a step change in Pco_2 at the carotid bodies. *J. Appl. Physiol.*, **23**, 195–202 (1967)

50. Dutton, R. E., Hodson, W. A., Davies, D. G., Fenner, A. Effect of rate of rise of carotid body Pco_2 on the time course of ventilation. *Resp. Physiol.*, **3**, 367–79 (1967)

51. Dutton, R. E., Fitzgerald, R. S., Gross, N. Ventilatory response to square-wave forcing of carbon dioxide at the carotid bodies. *Resp. Physiol.*, **4**, 101–8 (1968)

52. Black, A. M. S., Torrance, R. W. Chemoreceptor effects in the respiratory cycle. *J. Physiol. (London)*, **189**, 59–61 (1967)

53. Salmoiraghi, G. C., Baumgarten, R. von. Intracellular potentials from respiratory neurones in brain stem of cat and mechanisms of rhythmic respiration. *J. Neurophysiol.*, **24**, 203–18 (1961)

54. Baumgarten, R. von, Nakayama, S. Spontane and reizbedingte Änderungen der antidromen Erregbarkeit von bulbären respiratorischen Nervenzellen der Katze. *Arch. Ges. Physiol.*, **281**, 245–58 (1964)

55. Fenner, A.., Jansson, E. H., Avery, M. E. Enhancement of the ventilatory response to carbon dioxide by tube breathing. *Resp. Physiol.*, **4**, 91–100 (1968)

56. Goode, R. C., Brown, E. B., Jr., Howson, M. G., Cunningham, D. J. C. Respiratory effects of breathing down a tube. *Resp. Physiol.*, **6**, 343–59 (1969)

57. Cozine, R. A., Ngai, S. H. Medullary surface chemoreceptors and regulation of respiration in the cat. *J. Appl. Physiol.*, **22**, 117–21 (1967)

58. Schläfke, M., Loeschcke, H. H. Lokalisation eines an der Regulation von Atmung und Kreisläuf beteiligten Gebietes an der ventralen Oberfläche der Medulla Oblongata durch Kälteblockade. *Arch. Ges. Physiol.*, **297**, 201–20 (1967)

59. Humphrey, D. R. Neuronal activity in the medulla oblongata of cat evoked by stimulation of the carotid sinus nerve. In *Baroreceptors and Hypertension*, 131–68 (Kezdi, P., Ed., Pergamon, Oxford, 460 pp., 1967)

60. Sampson, S. R., Biscoe, T. J. Electrical potentials evoked in the brain stem by stimulation of the sinus nerve. *Brain Res.*, **9**, 398–401 (1968)

61. Miura, M., Reis, D. J. Electrophysiological evidence for carotid sinus nerve fibers terminating in the bulbar reticular formation. *Brain Res.*, **9**, 394–97 (1968)

62. Crill, W. E., Reis, D. J. Distribution of carotid sinus and depressor nerves in cat brain stem. *Am. J. Physiol.*, **214**, 269–76 (1968)

63. Sampson, S. R., Biscoe, T. J., Campion, P. D. Effects of sinus nerve stimulation on activity of phrenic motoneurones. *Nature*, **218**, 680–81 (1968)

64. Rudomin, P. Presynaptic inhibition induced by vagal afferent volleys. *J. Neurophysiol.*, **30**, 964–81 (1967)

65. Frankstein, S. I., Sergeeva, Z. N. Presynaptic inhibition of the inhibitory Hering-Breuer reflex. *Exptl. Neurol.*, **19**, 232–35 (1967)

66. Seller, H., Illert, M. The localization of the first synapse in the carotid sinus baroreceptor reflex pathway and its alteration of afferent input. *Arch. Ges. Physiol.*, **306**, 1–19 (1969)

67. Kahn, N., Wang, S. C. Electrophysiologic basis for pontine apneustic center and its role in integration of the Hering-Breuer reflex. *J. Neurophysiol.*, **30**, 301–18 (1967)

68. Cohen, M. I. Discharge patterns of brain-stem respiratory neurons in relation to carbon dioxide tension. *J. Neurophysiol.*, **31**, 142–65 (1968)

69. Cohen, M. I. Discharge patterns of brain stem respiratory neurons during Hering-Breuer reflex evoked lung inflation. *J. Neurophysiol.*, **32**, 356–74 (1969)

70. Batsel, H. L. The activity of bulbar respiratory neurons during passive hyperventilation. *Exptl. Neurol.*, **19**, 357–74 (1967)

71. Cameron, I. R. Acid-base changes in cerebrospinal fluid. *Brit. J. Anaesth.* **41**, 213–21 (1969)

72. *Cerebral Blood Flow and Cerebrospinal Fluid. III International Symposium, Lund-Copenhagen, May 9–11, 1968* (Ingvar, D. H., Lassen, N. A., Siesjö, B. K., Skinhøj, E., Eds., *Scand. J. Clin. Lab. Invest., Suppl. 102*, 1969)

73. Ponten, U., Siesjö, B. K. Acid base relations in arterial blood and cerebrospinal fluid of the unanesthetized rat. *Acta Physiol. Scand.*, **71**, 89–95 (1967)

74. Fencl, V., Vale, J. R., Brock, J. A. Respiration and cerebral blood flow in metabolic acidosis and alkalosis in humans. *J. Appl. Physiol.*, **27**, 67–76 (1969)

75. Kjällquist, Á., Siesjö, B. K. The

CSF/blood potential in sustained acidosis and alkalosis in the rat. *Acta Physiol. Scand.*, **71**, 255–56 (1967)

76. Kjällquist, A., Siesjö, B. K. Regulation of CSF pH-influence of the CSF/plasma potential. *Scand. J. Lab. Clin. Invest., Suppl. 102*, 1:C (1968)

77. Leusen, I., Demeester, G., Lacroix, E. Lactate and pyruvate in the brain of rats during changes in acid-base balance. *Arch. Intern. Physiol. Biochem.*, **75**, 310–24 (1967)

78. Cohen, P. J., Alexander, S. C., Smith, T. C., Reivich, M., Wollman, H. Effects of hypoxia and normocarbia on cerebral blood flow and metabolism in conscious man. *J. Appl. Physiol.*, **23**, 183–89 (1967)

79. Plum, F., Posner, J. B. Blood and cerebrospinal fluid lactate during hyperventilation. *Am. J. Physiol.*, **212**, 864–70 (1967)

80. Kazemi, H., Valencia, L. M., Shannon, D. C. Brain and cerebrospinal fluid lactate concentrations in respiratory acidosis and alkalosis. *Resp. Physiol.*, **6**, 178–86 (1969)

81. Plum, F., Posner, J. B., Smith, W. W. Effect of hyperbaric-hyperoxic hyperventilation on blood, brain and CSF lactate. *Am. J. Physiol.*, **215**, 1240–44 (1968)

82. Goldring, R. M., Cannon, P. J., Heinemann, H. O., Fishman, A. P. Respiratory adjustment to chronic metabolic alkalosis in man. *J. Clin. Invest.*, **47**, 188–202 (1968)

83. Eger, E. I. II, Kellogg, R. H., Mines, A. H., Lima-Ostos, M., Morrill, C. G., Kent, D. W. Influence of CO_2 on ventilatory acclimatization to altitude. *J. Appl. Physiol.*, **24**, 607–15 (1968)

84. Sørensen, S. C., Severinghaus, J. W. Respiratory sensitivity to acute hypoxia in man born at sea level living at high altitude. *J. Appl. Physiol.*, **25**, 211–16 (1968)

85. Lefrançois, R., Gautier, H., Pasquis, P. Ventilatory oxygen drive in acute and chronic hypoxia. *Resp. Physiol.*, **4**, 217–28 (1968)

86. Lahiri, S., Edelman, N. H. Peripheral chemoreflexes in the regulation of breathing of high altitude natives. *Resp. Physiol.*, **6**, 375–85 (1969)

87. Lahiri, S., Milledge, J. S., Chattopadhyay, H. P., Bhattacharyya, A. K., Sinha, A. K. Respiration and heart rate of Sherpa highlanders during exercise. *J. Appl. Physiol.*, **23**, 545–54 (1967)

88. Lahiri, S., Milledge, J. S. Acid-base in Sherpa altitude residents and lowlanders at 4880 M. *Resp. Physiol.*, **2**, 323–34 (1967)

89. Lahiri, S., Kao, F. F., Velásquez, T., Martínez, C., Pezzia, W. Irreversible blunted respiratory sensitivity to hypoxia in high altitude natives. *Resp. Physiol.*, **6**, 360–74 (1969)

90. Milledge, J. S., Lahiri, S. Respiratory control in lowlanders and Sherpa highlanders at altitude. *Resp. Physiol.*, **2**, 310–22 (1967)

91. Sørensen, S. C., Severinghaus, J. W. Irreversible respiratory insensitivity to acute hypoxia in man born at high altitude. *J. Appl. Physiol.*, **25**, 217–20 (1968)

92. Velásquez, T., Martínez, C., Pezzia, W., Gallardo, N. Ventilatory effects of oxygen in high altitude natives. *Resp. Physiol.*, **5**, 211–20 (1968)

93. Sørensen, S. C., Severinghaus, J. W. Respiratory insensitivity to acute hypoxia persisting after correction of tetralogy of Fallot. *J. Appl. Physiol.*, **25**, 221–23 (1968)

94. Sørensen, S. C., Milledge, J. S., Severinghaus, J. W. Cerebral anaerobic metabolism and ventilatory acclimatization to chronic hypoxia. *Fed. Proc.*, **28**, 337 (1969)

95. Brooks, J. G. III, Tenney, S. M. Ventilatory response of llama to hypoxia at sea level and high altitude. *Resp. Physiol.*, **5**, 269–78 (1968)

96. Grover, R. F., Reeves, J. T., Will, D. H., Blount, S. G., Jr. Pulmonary vasoconstriction in steers at high altitude. *J. Appl. Physiol.*, **18**(3), 567–74 (1963)

REPRODUCTION

DAVID T. ARMSTRONG

Departments of Obstetrics and Gynecology and of Physiology
University of Western Ontario, London, Ontario, Canada

The enormous increase in research efforts directed toward all aspects of reproduction makes the preparation of a 30-page review more difficult with each succeeding year. If not yet providing solutions to the "population explosion", these efforts are certainly contributing to a "publication explosion" whose dimensions soon become apparent to anyone who undertakes to review this literature. There appear to be only two reasonable approaches to this undertaking: (*a*) restriction of coverage to a narrow area (presumably the research area in which the reviewer, himself, is actively engaged), which can then be treated in a cohesive and fairly thorough manner; or (*b*) selection of a few isolated topics, not necessarily bearing much relationship to one another, but including some of the highlights of the year's publications. Although there is undoubtedly considerable merit in the former approach, I have chosen the latter; the selection of topics has been essentially arbitrary, with greatest emphasis being placed on those subjects which have not been covered to a significant extent in recent years.

THE MALE

Androgen biosynthesis.—The search for alternate pathways of steroid hormone biosynthesis continues to occupy many investigators of steroid-producing tissues. An interesting development during the past year has been the demonstration by Jungmann (1, 2) of a new mode of cleavage of the cholesterol side chain, betwen carbon atoms numbers 17 and 20. This reaction, catalyzed by a bovine testicular enzyme system, and yielding dehydroepiandrosterone (DHEA) and 2-methyl heptan-6-one, provides a mechanism for bypassing both pregnenolone and progesterone, as well as 17-hydroxylated intermediates of these compounds, in the production of C-19 steroids.

Although it is not yet possible to ascertain the quantitative importance of this pathway under physiological conditions, it is of at least theoretical interest, in that it provides an additional branch point in the steroidogenic pathway, at which regulatory agents may act. It is difficult to explain the well-documented stimulatory role of ICSH on androgen production by a site of action solely upon the conversion of cholesterol to pregnenolone since such an action would be expected to increase intracellular levels of progesterone; yet progesterone has not been found to accumulate in testicular tissue (3), and if it did, it might be expected to *inhibit* the rate of formation of androgens by virtue of its demonstrated inhibitory action upon 17α-hydroxyprogesterone-C-17,20-lyase (3). This objection could be circumvented by postulating a Δ^5-pathway by which pregnenolone is converted to androgens via DHEA rather than via progesterone and 17α-hydroxyprogesterone; however, recent observations of Bell et al. (4) argue against such a pathway in the interstitial cells of the mouse testis. Therefore, it will be of considerable interest to determine whether ICSH may increase the rate of conversion of cholesterol directly to DHEA by this *alternate pathway* which bypasses *both* pregnenolone and progesterone.

The demonstration by Yamaji et al. (5) of increased amounts of DHEA and androstenediol in the spermatic vein of dogs in which secretion of testosterone and androstenedione has been stimulated *in vivo* with ICSH adds some support to a stimulatory action of this gonadotropin upon a pathway which includes DHEA. They further showed, by perfusion of various labeled precursors via the spermatic artery, that the sequence in this pathway was DHEA $\rightarrow$ androstenediol $\rightarrow$ testosterone, rather than androstenedione $\rightarrow$ testosterone $\rightarrow$ androstenediol, thus providing strong evidence for an intermediate role of androstenediol, as well as of DHEA, in the biosynthesis of testosterone.

According to a preliminary report, the direct conversion of cholesterol to DHEA also occurs in ovarian cells (6); this finding is particularly noteworthy, in that it provides at least a theoretical basis for the independent regulation of biosynthesis of progesterone and estrogens in the ovary.

The mechanism of another alternate pathway for testosterone biosynthesis has also been elucidated (7). In this pathway, which occurs in the bacteria *Cladosporium resinae,* progesterone is converted directly to testosterone acetate, by incorporation of molecular oxygen between carbon atoms 17 and 20. The acetate group is then removed by the action of an esterase. The possibility that this pathway may also operate in mammalian testes has been raised by Drosdowsky et al. (8), although they admit to other equally likely explanations for their observations that testosterone-^{3}H formed from progesterone-^{3}H had higher specific radioactivity than 17α-hydroxyprogesterone which they isolated as an intermediate. Nakano & Tamaoki have quite convincingly ruled out this pathway in the testis, at least as an obligatory pathway (9). They have observed that, while testis microsomes possess the esterase activity necessary for the final step in the reaction, inhibition of the esterase by diisopropyl fluorophosphate, which effectively prevented conversion of testosterone acetate to testosterone, was without inhibitory effect upon testosterone production from either progesterone or 17α-hydroxyprogesterone.

If pregnenolone and progesterone turn out not to be obligatory intermediates in the biosynthesis of testosterone, they may be essential as precursors of another class of testicular products of physiologic significance, the 16-

dehydro, C-19 steroids. These are volatile compounds, with a characteristic musklike odour, and since they are excreted in the urine, have been suggested as playing roles as pheromones in sexual attraction and territorial marking (10). They are produced in testes of boars (11, 12) and man (13) from pregnenolone and progesterone, but apparently not from testosterone, at least in boars (12). One member of this class, 5α-androst-16-en-3-one, has been isolated from the fat of intact, but not castrated, boars (14), in keeping with its demonstrated testicular source; it seems likely that this compound is responsible for the unsavoury odour and relative unpalatability of the meat of intact or cryptorchid male swine, as compared to that of barrows or gilts.

Numerous reports have dealt with alterations of steroidogenesis or general cellular metabolism in the testis under a variety of physiological and experimental conditions. Sandler & Hall (15), measuring *in vitro* conversion of cholesterol-7α-³H to testosterone and Δ⁴-androstenedione, have observed a much greater responsiveness to ICSH *in vitro* of testes obtained from 20-day-old rats than of testes from adult rats. They suggest that other pituitary hormones may be responsible for varying the tissue responsiveness to ICSH at different ages. That FSH may be one of these, at least in the rabbit, is suggested by the observation of Connell & Eik-Nes (16) that the amount of testosterone produced by testes slices *in vitro* under maximal stimulation with follicle-stimulating hormone (FSH) (contaminated with ICSH activity) is about four times the amount produced under maximal stimulation with purified ICSH. The latter is one of the few reports of *in vitro* measurements of actual mass of testosterone produced from endogenous precursors.

In another study of the influence of age upon androgen formation *in vitro*, Ficher & Steinberger have observed that teased testes preparations from newborn rats effectively convert progesterone to testosterone but produce very little of the (presumed) androgen metabolite, androsterone (17). In the course of development, a definite inverse relationship was found between the production of testosterone and androsterone, with the production of androsterone reaching maximal values at 20 days of age, then diminishing to practically undetectable levels at 90 days of age, when testosterone production again became elevated. The physiologic significance of these findings, if any, remains to be elucidated. They do, however, point to the value of measuring more than a single product in assessing alterations in steroidogenic capacity under different conditions. Although ICSH has become well accepted as an important regulator of testosterone biosynthesis, and testosterone as the androgen of greatest physiologic importance, other heretofore unexpected mechanisms may modulate the biologic activity of the testosterone produced, e.g. by increasing or decreasing the conversion of testosterone to metabolic products possessing increased or decreased biologic activity. A precedent for this type of control mechanism is operative in the ovary (18, 19).

Another factor in evaluating the above age difference is the variation in the amount or physiologic state of seminiferous tubular elements present at the different ages. That tubules may contribute to the steroid output by the testes has been demonstrated in a preliminary report by Bell et al. (20), employing a technique previously used by Christensen & Mason (21) for separating seminiferous tubules from interstitial elements of the rat testis. Conversion of both pregnenolone and progesterone to 17α-hydroxyprogesterone, $\triangle^4$-androstenedione, and testosterone was observed. In addition, two reduction products of progesterone, 20α-hydroxypregn-4-en-3-one, and 5α-pregnan-3β,20α-diol were identified in fairly high yield, but were not found upon incubation of interstitial tissue. The presence of the latter 5α-reduced products, combined with the observation that the total recovery of products was low (a finding which the authors attribute to binding by tubules), is of particular interest because seminiferous tubules are androgen "target" organs and because of the recent findings (discussed below) that testosterone first undergoes 5α-reduction in its target organs, before being bound to receptors involved in initiation of its biologic effects.

Several other approaches have been used, with varying degrees of success, to evaluate contributions of interstitial cells and tubules to certain aspects of testes metabolism. These include attempts to selectively damage spermatogenic components by X irradiation (22) or experimental cryptorchidism (23); isolation, by dissection, of clusters of interstitial cells for metabolic studies *in vitro* (24); and examination of androgen production, both *in vivo* and *in vitro,* by transplantable interstitial cell tumours (25, 26).

The demonstration that interstitial cells can be separated from tubules of normal testes for *in vitro* studies may inspire transplantation studies, to determine the *in vivo* secretory capabilities of these two testicular components, whether transplanted separately or together. Such approaches have been useful in demonstrating interactions between individual ovarian components (27–30), and may also help elucidate the mechanisms which regulate testicular steroid secretion and seminiferous tubular function *in vivo.*

Male accessory sex organs.—The concept that steroid hormones initiate their actions by becoming bound to specific "receptors" within their target cells, without undergoing any metabolic transformation, has been particularly useful in explaining the mode of action of estrogens (31). Testosterone has appeared to be an exception to this generalization, in that it is metabolized rapidly by male accessory sex glands, to a variety of reduction products (32 for references). One most significant advance in understanding the mechanism of action of androgens has been the demonstration that prostatic cell nuclei contain an active 3-ketosteroid 5α-reductase, which reduces testosterone to 17β-hydroxy-5α-androstan-3-one (dihydrotestosterone) (33), and that subsequent events characteristic of androgen action are preceded by (and likely initiated by) intranuclear binding of the latter compound, rather than of testosterone itself (34). This concept, which enables testosterone to conform to the above theory for estrogen action (with only the minor modification that it first is converted to the form in which it can be bound), has received ample support, with respect to both 5α-reduction (35, 36) and intranuclear binding (37–39) in ventral prostate tissue. The intranuclear binding substance appears, from the studies of Bruchovsky & Wilson (34), to be an acidic nuclear protein, although Mangan et al. (38) have reported binding of radioactivity derived from testosterone-³H directly to DNA preparations isolated from prostatic nuclei. That similar mechanisms probably also are involved in responses of other organs to androgens is suggested by the demonstration of selective uptake and retention of radioactivity by dorsal and lateral prostate lobes and coagulating glands (40) and by cell bodies in neurons of certain limbic and hypothalamic structures (41), as well as by the demonstration of steroid 5α-reductase activity in epididymides (42), seminiferous tubules (20), skeletal muscle (43), and human skin from perineal regions (but not other regions) (44).

Evidence continues to accumulate that increased RNA and protein synthesis occur early in the chain of events following administration of androgen, and ultimate expression of its actions (45–48). The previously reported (49) transient decrease in levels of ATP in prostate cells, following administration of testosterone to castrated rats, has been confirmed (50), and shown to be followed by increased activity of the nuclear enzyme nicotinamide mononucleotide (NMN) adenyltransferase. This enzyme in prostatic nuclei catalyzed the incorporation of ¹⁴C-ATP into acid-insoluble products believed to result from polymerization of the ADP-ribose moiety of NAD, and has been suggested to play a role in RNA transcription (50).

Evidence for a regulatory role of testosterone on a number of enzymes in androgen target organs has been presented. The decline in levels of hexokinase, glucose 6-phosphate dehydrogenase, and phosphofructokinase in seminal vesicles (51) and of phosphofructokinase in prostate glands (52) following castration is reversed by administration of testosterone. The reversal is prevented by actinomycin D, cycloheximide, or ethionine, which suggests that it is the result of hormone-induced synthesis of new proteins. From these observations, Singhal et al. (51, 52) have concluded that testosterone influences carbohydrate metabolism by "attacking receptor sites at the fountainhead of enzyme production" to switch on the biosynthetic action of "whole genic units governing the synthesis of key, rate-limiting enzymes".

In addition to regulating synthesis of general metabolic enzymes, testosterone influences the synthesis of more or less specific secretory products of androgen-dependent glands. One of the proteolytic enzymes of the rat submandibular salivary gland has been found to be induced by testosterone. This enzyme, given the trival name "glandulain," is present in greater amounts of salivary glands of males than of females from puberty on, is decreased to one-fifth the normal value as a result of castration, and is restored to normal following testosterone administration (53). The ability of prostate gland explants to secrete citric acid depends on the presence of testosterone or dihydrotestosterone in the culture medium; insulin is necessary for this response, and it is accompanied by increased protein synthesis, which suggests that the response depends upon the induction of new enzymes or other proteins (54).

The production of polyamines by prostate glands is also hormonally controlled. The pathway of biosynthesis of putrescine and spermidine in the rat prostate has been worked out by Pegg & Williams-Ashman (55–57). Two pyridoxal phosphate-dependent decarboxylating enzymes are involved, one which catalyzes the conversion of L-ornithine to putrescine, and a second which catalyzes the transfer of a methyl group from S-adenosyl methionine to putrescine, yielding spermidine. The activities of both these enzymes decreases markedly following castration, and restoration of their activities begins within a few hours after *in vivo* administration of testosterone.

Other factors influence the response of various target organs to androgens. As discussed above, insulin is required for regressed prostate gland explants to respond to testosterone with *in vitro* production of citrate (54). Testosterone-induced stimulation of growth, as well as of production of citrate by seminal vesicles and of fructose by coagulating glands, in castrate rats, is markedly enhanced by concomitant treatment with reserpine; this enhancement is attributed to increased prolactin secretion under the influence of reserpine (58), and confirms and extends previous observations of a synergism between prolactin and androgens in regulation of accessory sex glands (59 for references). Cortisol also increases the ability of testosterone propionate to increase weights of seminal vesicles and ventral prostates of castrate rats (60).

Androgens and sexual differentiation.—The role of androgens in sexual differentiation is well established. By gonadectomy at various stages of differentiation of fetal or neonatal rats, it has been shown that testicular hormonal agents are essential for the masculine differentiation and development of a number of structures, including the genital tract (61), and hypothalamic centres regulating gonadotropin secretion (62). To this list can now be added the liver. Sexual differences have been observed in the hepatic metabolism of corticosteroids in rats, first becoming evident at puberty. Reduction by Δ^4, 5α-reductase and 3α-hydroxysteroid dehydrogenase is characteristic of females of all ages. In males, commencing at puberty, 20β- and 3β-reduction become the major modes of catabolism (63). Neonatal castration of males prevents the development of the latter pattern, so that corticosteroid metabolism remains of the female type (64). Enzymes involved in testosterone metabolism in adult rats are also influenced by castration of male rats at birth, but not by castration at 2 weeks of age (64). Administration of testosterone on the first day of life to neonatally castrated rats of either sex resulted in the development and permanent maintenance of the male pattern in adult life (65). Thus, it appears that the rat liver is basically "feminine", and that the "masculine" pattern of enzymes first evident after puberty is organized by testicular factors present during immediate postnatal life.

Administration of the antiandrogenic steroid, 6-chloro-17-hydroxy-1α,2α-methylene-pregna-4,6-diene-3,20-dione acetate (cyproterone acetate) to pregnant rats from day 14 of gestation onwards prevented male sexual differentiation of the fetuses (66). In all rats, a vagina developed, ending blindly, anteriorly. Seminal vesicles were well developed, but small. Prostatic anlagen remained rudimentary, coagulating glands were absent, and testes were incompletely descended and sterile.

The syndrome of "testicular feminization" in the human is a form of hereditary male pseudohermaphroditism similar in many respects to this condition in rats induced by treatment with the androgen antagonist during embryonic development. Afflicted subjects, who appear quite feminine physically and psychologically and exhibit breast development at puberty, have testes (undescended) which produce both androgens and estrogens within the normal male range. These observations, together with the finding that administration of exogeneous androgens fails to produce any signs of masculinization, have led to the concept that the syndrome is caused by a genetic defect in the ability of all cells to respond to androgens (67). The recent demonstration that 5α-reduction of testosterone is a necessary prerequisite for the expression of its effects (discussed above) has suggested lack of the enzyme 5α-reductase as a possible metabolic defect which may be responsible for this end organ insensitivity. Preliminary evidence for this explanation has come from two laboratories. Jarvis et al. (68) compared patients with testicular feminization, and normal males, with respect to their abilities to convert radioactive testosterone to urinary 5α-androstanediol, when the testosterone was administered percutaneously versus intravenously. They concluded that subjects with testicular feminization possessed somewhat lower than normal ability to effect 5α-reduction of testosterone, thus suggesting an explanation for their relative insensitivity to androgens.

Northcutt et al. (69) came to a similar conclusion, on the basis of a more direct demonstration of decreased abilities of isolated abdominal skin, pubic hair follicles, epididymis, and vas deferens from two patients with testicular feminization to convert testosterone to 5α-dihydrotestosterone. Wilson & Walker (44), using a similar approach, found very low but equal rates of formation of dihydrotestosterone in abdominal skin of normal men and subjects with testicular feminization. Substantially higher rate of formation occurred in skin from perineal regions in all subjects, although conversion in subjects with testicular feminization was somewhat lower than in normal men. These authors have concluded, more cautiously, that there is insufficient evidence, as yet, to assign an important role to deficiency of 5α-reductase in the etiology of this syndrome. A hereditary syndrome of male pseudohermaphroditism in rats, identical in many respects to the syndrome in man, appears also not to be the result of deficiency of this enzyme (70).

The Female

Regulation of ovarian follicles.—The follicle is unquestionably the most essential functional component of the ovary, yet the component whose regulation is least understood. There seems to be general agreement that adenohypophyseal follicle-stimulating hormone (FSH) is important in this regulation, but much uncertainty as to what FSH can do *by itself* (most FSH preparations are contaminated with ICSH activity), and by what mechanisms. Progress in understanding the follicle has been hampered by many factors, one of the most important being its structural and functional complexity, combined with its small size. Under any set of experimental conditions, the responses must be considered of at least four different follicular cell types (oocytes, corona radiata, granulosa, and theca interna cells), and three noncellular components (basement membrane between thecal and granulosal layers, liquor folliculi, and zona pellucida); nor can interactions between follicular and extrafollicular ovarian components be ignored. Despite these difficulties, progress continues.

In several studies metabolic responses of prepubertal rat ovaries (in which no corpora lutea are present) to gonadotropic stimulation have been reported. These responses have included increased RNA polymerase activity (71), and increased incorporation of labeled precursors into RNA and protein (72, 73) within a few hours after treatment, *in vivo,* with pregnant-mare serum gonadotropin (PMS) or luteinizing hormone (LH); increased activity of aspartate aminotransferase following *in vivo* treatment with FSH preparations (74); increased glycolysis and increased membrane transport of monosaccharides, increased accumulation of fructose 1,6-diphosphate and pyruvate, and decreased ovarian content of ATP following action of LH *in vitro* (75, 76). Some attempts have been made to correlate these metabolic alterations with demonstrated increases in steroid secretion. While it is possible to exclude corpora lutea as the responding tissue in all these studies, it is impossible to distinguish between follicular and interstitial cell responses in any of them. Hamberger (77) has utilized a modified Cartesian diver technique for investigating metabolic responses of individual ovarian cell types to specific gonadotropins. In appying this technique to isolated granulosa cells, theca interna cells, and interstitial cells, evidence has been presented that respiration of granulosa cells, in the presence of succinate, is increased by the addition of LH *in vitro* or by pretreatment of rats with LH, but not with FSH *in vivo;* theca and interstitial cells exhibited responses opposite to this, with increased oxygen consumption in the presence of FSH, but not of LH (77).

Exactly how these findings are related, if indeed they are, to any of the metabolic or steroidogenic responses of whole, prepubertal rat ovaries discussed above is not clear. The hormone specificity is exactly opposite to what one might have predicted from present views as to the physiologic functions of FSH and LH and of the various ovarian cell types. Thus, LH

is widely regarded as the most important "steroidogenesis-stimulating" gonadotropin (78) and the theca interna cells and interstitial cells are the ones
which exhibit those cytologic characteristics generally attributed to cells engaged in steroid biosynthesis, viz. abundance of agranular endoplasmic reticulum, lipid droplets, histochemically detectable cholesterol (which undergoes
depletion in response to LH but not to FSH), and 3β-hydroxysteroid dehydrogenase (79–82). On the other hand, FSH is believed responsible for
stimulating follicular growth and has been shown to stimulate amino acid
uptake by ovarian cells (83), and the granulosa cells are the ones which,
prior to luteinization, possess cytologic features typical of cells engaged in
synthesis and export of proteins [viz. abundance of ribonucleoprotein particles and prominent golgi apparatus (81, 82, 84)].

Nevertheless, if Hamberger's observations (77) prove correct, it be-
hooves us to attempt to relate them to other physiologic processes within the
ovary under the influence of FSH and LH. Perhaps the most obvious physiologic implication of the increased metabolism of granulosa cells under the
influence of LH is its possible role in initiating "luteinization" of these cells.
Indeed, Channing (85–87) has provided evidence that granulosa cells will
undergo "luteinization" within a few days in culture, if removed from ovaries of mares in estrus or in the early luteal phase, but not from ovaries of
mares during the mid-luteal phase, which suggests that exposure *in vivo* to
hormonal conditions associated with estrus (LH?) is essential in initiating
luteinization of these cells. Granulosa cells obtained from mares during the
mid-luteal phase could be stimulated to produce progesterone (although in
amounts much smaller than those of granulosa cells obtained from estrous
mares in the absence of additional gonadotropin) by the addition to the culture medium of gonadotropic preparations possessing LH activity. The demonstration that the granulosa cells of rabbit follicles will undergo luteinization when follicles are transplanted under the kidney capsule, provided that
they either have been obtained from an estrous rabbit a few hours after coitus (30) or have been subjected to a brief exposure to LH (but not FSH)
in vitro (88), further supports the concept of an action of LH upon the
granulosa cells in initiating luteinization. That the luteinization which occurred in the latter experiments was of physiologic significance seems clear
since the "corpora lutea" so formed were able to maintain gestation in the
absence of normal corpora lutea *in situ* (30).

Another possible physiologic implication of a stimulatory action of LH
upon carbohydrate metabolism of granulosa cells is the role this may have in
induction of oocyte maturation. Under normal conditions, the follicular oocyte remains arrested in late prophase of the first meiotic division, until its
maturation is induced by a gonadotropic stimulus (presumably LH), resulting in completion of this division, shedding of the first polar body, and
progression to the metaphase of the second meiotic division. Recently it has
been reported that isolated mouse follicular oocytes will undergo the same
sequence of events leading to maturation *in vitro* in the absence of gonado-

tropins, if the medium in which they are incubated contains pyruvate or oxalacetate, but not glucose, as the sole exogenous energy source. However, when granulosa cells were incubated along with oocytes, glucose alone was an adequate substrate (89, 90). These findings suggest that granulosa cell glycolysis may play an important role in oocyte maturation *in vivo*. LH may initiate maturation by stimulating glycolysis in granulosa cells, thereby providing utilizable substrates for the oocyte; but it may act directly on the oocyte, perhaps altering its metabolism so that it can utilize other substrates.

Application of Hamberger's technique (77) for elucidation of the metabolic capabilities of isolated oocytes in the absence or presence of LH should prove particularly enlightening. An alternative, and equally intriguing possible explanation for the induction of oocyte maturation, also involving a granulosa cell-oocyte interaction, is that some steroid product of the follicular cells, under the influence of LH, initiates oocyte maturation. Evidence for such a possibility has been reported; frog oocytes, dissected from ovarian follicles, but still surrounded by follicular cells, can be induced to undergo physiological maturation by exposure *in vitro,* either to certain steroids (progesterone, deoxycorticosterone) or to a pituitary suspension (91). Activation by pituitary preparations never reached 100 per cent, exhibited considerable seasonal dependence, and was inhibited by actinomycin D (92, 93). It has been concluded from these studies that steroids act directly on the oocyte to induce maturation, whereas pituitary hormones act through the mediation of the follicular cells.

Evidence accumulates in numerous mammalian species that increased production of progesterone and related steroids occurs prior to ovulation and completion of oocyte maturation, most likely as a result of stimulation of steroid synthesis in follicular or interstitial cells (94–98), and most likely as a response to LH. Although other physiologic functions have been attributed to this preovulatory "progestin" secretion [viz. prolongation and enhancement of LH secretion via a positive feedback mechanism, initiation of mating behaviour, relaxation of cervices causing loss of uterine lumen fluid in rodents (19 for references)], the possibility that it may be involved in oocyte maturation may also be worth investigating.

The above evidence that the effect of LH on the oocyte may be secondary to its action(s) on the granulosa cells is, of course, only circumstantial. Recent experiments of El-Fouly & Cook have revealed another apparent interaction between the oocyte and granulosa cells (99). These authors have observed that the mere removal of the oocyte from large vesicular follicles of estrous rabbits is sufficient stimulus to initiate granulosa cell luteinization; "corpora lutea" formed as a result of this treatment were shown to secrete progesterone, although they appeared to have a considerably shorter lifespan than those which normally form as a consequence of ovulation. These observations suggest that the presence of the oocyte somehow inhibits luteinization of granulosa cells. Such an interpretation would be consistent with Channing's observations (85) (discussed above) that granulosa cells undergo spontaneous luteinization when removed from the follicle (and from the oocyte) and cultured *in vitro;* on the other hand, it seems at variance with the results of Keyes (88) who demonstrated that follicles, exposed to LH *in vitro,* underwent subsequent luteinization when autotransplanted back into their donors, *without removal or loss of the oocytes.* A hypothesis consistent with both these observations is that the supposed luteinization-inhibiting factor associated with the oocyte is inactivated during the process of oocyte maturation, so that when the latter is stimulated by the direct or indirect action of LH, the oocyte can no longer suppress luteinization, even though it has not been physically removed from proximity with the granulosa cells.

Concerning the physiologic functions of FSH, there is increasing evidence that this gonadotropin may play a role in ovulation over and above its ability to produce mature follicles, whose rupture is dependent upon LH. Measurements of plasma FSH during the human menstrual cycle have rather consistently revealed a sharp "mid-cycle peak" in FSH secretion coinciding fairly closely with the LH peak, the latter generally believed to be responsible for ovulation (100–102). In rats, a sharp drop in adenohypophyseal stores of FSH has been observed on the afternoon of proestrus, coinciding fairly closely with those of LH. During the same period, plasma levels of both FSH and LH increased (103–104). Stimulation of the amygdaloid region, which under certain conditions causes ovulation in rats, also elevated plasma levels of FSH as well as of LH (105).

In immunologic studies of Goldman & Mahesh (106), antiserum prepared against ovine LH (which effectively neutralized the biologic activities of both LH and FSH of the sheep and the hamster) blocked ovulation when administered to hamsters before 1:00 p.m. on the day of proestrus, but not after 3:00 p.m. This ovulation-blocking effect was greatly reduced following removal of most of the FSH antibodies by absorption with FSH, although this absorption caused very little reduction in the anti-LH activity of the antiserum.

In investigations with hypophysectomized rabbits designed to elucidate luteotropic mechanisms, Rennie (29) reported the incidental observation that treatment with LH, when begun shortly after pituitary removal, resulted several days later in the presence of two distinctly different types of follicles. Some were much larger than those normally present in estrous rabbits, but none of these follicles ovulated. Others were completely nonstimulated; there were no follicles of intermediate size, which suggests failure of growth of small follicles after hypophysectomy presumably due to lack of FSH, accompanied by continual development of the large follicles under the influence of the exogeneous LH. The failure of the latter to ovulate may have been due to lack of FSH, although these follicles continued to grow and secrete estrogen (29).

In prepubertal rats in which follicular growth has been stimulated with pregnant-mare serum gonadotropin (PMS), but ovulation blocked by administration of phenobarbital 53–54 hours later, ovulation has been produced by administration of *either* LH *or* FSH (103). Comparison of the minimal amount of LH required to induce ovulation under these conditions with the minimal amount of FSH required, excluded the possibility that the ovulation induced by FSH could have been due to contamination with LH. Two additional differences were also evident. On the morning of ovulation induced by LH, uterine distention with fluid was only rarely seen, a situation similar to that on the morning of ovulation in a normal estrous cycle and attributed to secretion of progesterone from nonluteal ovarian elements in response to LH (19). In contrast, all rats in which ovulation was induced by FSH still has distended uteri, indicating lack of the preovulatory elevation in progesterone secretion. Furthermore, the corpora lutea which formed following FSH were less well developed and less vascular than those found following LH. These observations indicate that while FSH may play a role in the ovulation process per se, LH appears necessary both for the preovulatory secretion of progresterone and for the development of normally functioning corpora lutea. It would be particularly interesting to know whether oocyte maturation and mating behaviour will occur when ovulation is induced by FSH rather than LH.

Little new information has been forthcoming on the actual intraovarian mechanisms which cause ovulation. However, Rodbard (107) has re-evaluated old information in light of a theoretical mathematical and physical model, which he has proposed; some reconciliation of previously opposed views has been claimed as to the relative importance of enzymatic processes versus intrafollicular pressure and volume changes in bringing about ovulation. On the basis of this model, in which the follicle is assumed to be a thin-walled elastic sphere composed of a semipermeable membrane and filled with an "ideal collodial solution", explanations have been offered for a number of observations regarding ovulation; these include how the stigma is formed, where rupture will occur, and why only those follicles "in a narrow critical region of pressure and radius" will be eligible for ovulation. While this seems to be the best single model proposed to explain mammalian ovulation, at least two facts seem not to be consistent with this model: follicles will rupture in ovaries grown in organ culture, without first undergoing significant preovulatory swelling (108), presumably because of lack of circulatory system necessary for follicular fluid accumulation (109); and stigma formation (and ovulation) may occur at the base of follicle (110), whereas the model predicts that it should occur in the "vulnerable region" on the apex of the follicle.

Evidence implicating DNA-dependent RNA synthesis in the process of ovulation has been provided with the observation that systemic administration of actinomycin D will block ovulation induced by PMS and human chorionic gonadotropin (HCG) in the hamster (111). Even though ovulation was prevented, signs of oocyte maturation were observed, and the hamsters exhibited estrous behaviour, indicating a measure of independence between mechanisms normally leading to ovulation and those leading to oocyte maturation and to secretion of those steroids responsible for induction of behavioural estrus.

Regulation of secretion of ovulatory hormones—Since this subject was considered at length by Everett (112) last year, only recent developments concerning the role of steroids in *stimulating* secretion of ovulatory hormones will be discussed.

Evidence provided in three species supports the "classic" (but previously not well-supported) concept that rising titers of estrogen may, indeed, play a causative role in initiating secretion of the gonadotropin(s) responsible for ovulation in the normal estrous or menstrual cycle.

In the normally cycling ewe, plasma LH levels, measured by radioimmunoassay, have been observed to rise sharply a short time after the onset of estrus (113–115), or perhaps actually shortly before (113). A peak of estrogen secretion has been reported on the day *before* estrus (116). Intramuscular administration of estradiol to ewes shortly before the onset of the breeding season was followed in a majority of instances by a sharp rise in the level of LH in jugular plasma within 8–12 hours (117); the elevation lasted for approximately 10 hours, reached levels equivalent to those reported by others during normal estrus (113–115), and resulted in ovulation as indicated by the presence of corpora lutea at laparotomy 11 days later. In ovariectomized ewes, administration of progesterone had no effect on plasma LH levels, but when estradiol was administered after progesterone withdrawal, plasma LH levels rose abruptly within 24–48 hours (118).

Measurements of estrogens in peripheral human plasma (119, 120) and in urine (121) throughout the menstrual cycle revealed gradual increases in levels of both estradiol and estrone beginning several days before the midcycle peak in plasma LH (measured in the same subjects). Maximal estrogen levels coincided with, or preceded slightly, the mid-cycle LH peaks.

In the rat, ovarian venous plasma levels of estrogens have been measured (by bioassay) throughout the estrous cycle (122). Estrogens rose sharply on the afternoon of the second day of diestrus, increased further on the day of proestrus to reach maximum levels before noon, remained elevated for several hours, and then declined sharply in the early evening of proestrus to remain low until the second day of diestrus of the next cycle. Concomitant measurements of plasma LH made in the same laboratory under the same conditions showed the critical time for LH release to be between 5:00 and 7:00 p.m. on the day of proestrus, i.e. approximately 6 hours *after* the maximum secretion of estrogen (123). In fact, the decline in plasma estrogen levels occurred during the period of greatest increase in plasma LH levels. It therefore seems likely that the high estrogen levels initiated the LH release, rather than vice vrsa.

Evidence implicates progesterone, in addition to estrogen, in the stimulation of secretion of LH. In postmenopausal women treated with estrogen, progesterone administration was followed by marked elevation of plasma LH levels, reminiscent of the mid-cycle peak in the normal menstrual cycle (124). Ovarian venous levels, and secretion rates, of progesterone rose in rats on the afternoon of proestrus, reaching maximal values *after* the proestrous peak in plasma LH (123, 125), but perhaps beginning to rise before the LH peak (125). The elevation in progesterone secretion (123) coincided closely with the precipitous decline in plasma estrogen levels discussed above (122), which suggests cause-effect relationship; a mechanism whereby progesterone and related steroids may inhibit estrogen biosynthesis, by exerting a feedback inhibitory action upon steroid-$C_{17,20}$-lyase, has been proposed previously (126 for references). An interplay between estrogen and progesterone in induction of ovulatory hormone secretion seems probable, and is supported by Grayburn & Brown-Grant's (127) recent observations that PMS or FSH preparations were relatively ineffectual in inducing "spontaneous" ovulation (i.e. without subsequent treatment with HCG) when administered to prepubertal rats in doses insufficient to cause maximum uterine weight stimulation. Neither estrogen alone nor progesterone alone induced ovulation following treatment with such subthreshold doses of FSH; however, administration of estradiol and progesterone together was followed by ovulation in the majority of animals.

This requirement for progesterone, in addition to estrogen, taken together with the observations that progesterone rises *before* ovulation but *after* LH secretion (or injection) in several species including the human (94–98), may indicate that both estrogen and progesterone regulate, in a stimulatory manner, the secretion of the pattern of gonadotropins essential for ovulation in all these species. An explanation which seems consistent with all these observations is that rising estrogen levels stimulate the secretion of initial amounts of LH; this LH then stimulates progesterone secretion which in turn exerts a positive feedback effect to augment or prolong the secretion of LH and perhaps FSH, in amounts sufficient to cause ovulation. The latter effect of progesterone may be mediated in part by its postulated ability either to decrease the secretion of estrogens, or to remove an inhibitory action of excessive estrogens upon ovulatory hormone secretion (128). In the rabbit, 20α-hydroxypregn-4-en-3-one, rather than progesterone, may be the steroid responsible for the positive feedback action (129); arguments supporting a similar, although probably not obligatory role for 20α-hydroxypregn-4-en-3-one in the rat have also been advanced (19).

The physiologic factors which control the secretion of the estrogen responsible for the initiation of this chain of events are unknown, and will undoubtedly remain so until still more refined methods for the assay of gonadotropins enable the detection of small fluctuations in basal levels of gonadotropins present in the plasma during the diestrous interval, i.e. between the more marked preovulatory peaks.

Corpus luteum.—Several extensive reviews of corpus luteum regulatory mechanisms, considered from a variety of standpoints, have appeared recently (126, 130–135). Because of this saturation coverage and because few really significant new developments have occurred in this area during the past year, only minimal treatment of the topic will be given here.

Some of the factors involved in the process of "luteinization", or transformation of follicles into corpora lutea, have been discussed under follicles. The physiologic (hormonal) factors necessary for maintaining the corpus luteum, once formed, in a "functional" state (usually defined as capable of secreting progesterone) continue to undergo much scrutiny. The concept which appears to be emerging, championed primarily by Greenwald and by Rothchild (130), is that a luteotropic complex rather than a single luteotropic hormone seems to operate in many species, although the individual components of the complex (including prolactin, LH, FSH and estrogens) appear to differ somewhat from species to species (19, 136–143). The factor common to most appears to be prolactin, but it is becoming increasingly obvious that even in the rat, prolactin is only one of the luteotropic hormones to be reckoned with. For this reason, it no longer seems appropriate to use the terms "luteotropic hormone" ("LTH") and "prolactin" interchangeably. This terminology is an injustice, both to the corpus luteum (whose regulation involves other tropic agents) and (especially) to prolactin (which possesses biologic activities and physiologic functions of far greater scope) (144, 145). The name prolactin, assigned to the protein when originally isolated and identified (144 for references), still seems perfectly adequate; it is not difficult to spell or pronounce, or susceptible to misinterpretation, and is sufficiently short to need no abbreviation.

The quest to identify the components of the luteotropic complex in many different species continues to yield occasional apparently conflicting reports even within a given species, undoubtedly because of different approaches and different end points. For example, infusing LH into the arterial supply of the ovary transplanted into the neck of the otherwise intact sheep resulted in an increased rate of appearance of progesterone in the venous output of the ovary, accompanied by a markedly increased rate of blood flow through the ovary (146). Prolactin did not affect either parameter. In apparent conflict, prolactin has been reported to be as effective as LH in partially restoring the decline in blood flow through, and rate of secretion of progesterone by the corpus luteum, which otherwise results immediately following acute hypophysectomy (147).

Another important factor in evaluating the luteotropic requirements of a given species is the stage of development of the corpus luteum during experimentation. While prolactin and FSH may be the minimum luteotropic requirements in the hamster after 4 days (148), an additional hypophyseal factor seems essential before this time (138). On the other hand, requirements of other species may become more rigorous at later stages of luteal development; the rat corpus luteum may not require prolactin (or indeed any hypophyseal support) until the fourth day after its formation (19, 149).

The requirement of the rabbit corpus luteum for estrogen (or at least for some follicular product), may not become established until several days after its formation (88, 99). It therefore becomes increasingly apparent that in any discussion of luteotropic hormones, not only must the species be identified, but also the experimental conditions and the end point examined must be carefully spelled out to avoid confusion and misinterpretation.

An important new development concerning the mechanism of luteolysis has been the demonstration, by Pharriss & Wyngarden, of a luteolytic action of prostaglandin F2α (PGF 2α) in the rat (150); this has been confirmed in the guinea pig (151) and the rabbit (152). These observations are of particular significance in that they have provided for the first time a clearly stated hypothesis to explain the well-established local luteolytic effects of the uteri upon adjacent corpora lutea under a variety of circumstances (131). The hypothesis advanced by Pharriss & Wyngarden (150) is that the endometrium, under the appropriate conditions, secretes a venoconstrictive substance which restricts the common venous drainage of the ovary and uterus, thereby causing corpora lutea to succumb to conditions such as ischemia, limited substrate availability, or accumulation of products. That prostaglandin F2α may be this substance is supported by its presence in endometrial tissue (153) and by its potent and selective venoconstrictive activity (154).

Whether or not prostaglandin F2α turns out to be the heretofore elusive uterine "luteolysin", it may well be important as an intraovarian regulatory agent, mediating some of the ovarian responses to LH. It shares at least two activities with LH: the ability to stimulate progesterone biosynthesis in ovarian tissue *in vitro* (126, 155) and the ability to induce luteolysis in the pseudopregnant rabbit (152, 156). Arachidonic acid is probably the physiologic precursor of PGF2α (157 for references), and this is one of the polyunsaturated fatty acids esterified with cholesterol in rabbit ovarian interstitial tissue (158). The well-known ability of LH to "mobilize" cholesterol esters in this tissue (126 for references), perhaps by increasing the activity of cholesterol esterase (as it does in the rat ovary) (159), may result in increased availability not only of free cholesterol as substrate for progesterone biosynthesis (126), but also of increased arachidonic acid as substrate for PGF2α production. The latter compound may then act within the interstitial cells to stimulate further the formation of progesterone from the released cholesterol, and may diffuse through the ovary to the adjacent corpora lutea, whose circulation it disrupts via its venoconstrictive activity, thereby precipitating luteolysis.

Another intriguing possibility is that venoconstriction, resulting from increased intraovarian levels of PGF2α, acting in conjunction with the increased permeability of capillaries and of the "blood-follicular barrier" which occurs in response to LH (160), may lead to increased capillary filtration, thereby playing an important role in the rapid accumulation of follicular fluid, preovulatory swelling, and rupture of follicles. Experimental restriction of ovarian venous drainage has been shown previously to enhance follicular swelling and hasten ovulation in mated rabbits, apparently because of increased rate of production, by filtration, of extravascular fluid more rapidly than it can be removed by the ovarian lymphatic vessels (109).

It may even be possibile that the luteolytic responses to both LH and PGF2α are secondary to actions of these agents upon the follicles. Considerable circumstantial evidence suggests an association between the processes leading to luteolysis, and those leading to follicular maturation and rupture (161 for references). The recent observations that follicular destruction by irradiation of rat (162) and human (163) ovaries leads to prolongation of luteal life or increased progesterone synthetic activity provide more direct support for such an hypothesis.[1] It will be of interest to determine whether the luteolytic effects of PGF2α and LH can still be demonstrated when follicles have been eliminated by this means.

Actions of female sex hormones on their target organs.—The literature continues to be inundated with reports dealing with details of estrogen binding to "receptor" proteins, and with the sequence of biochemical events which follows this initial interaction. Despite this deluge, the basic tenets of the hypotheses of Jensen (31) (that estradiol-17β is bound in a metabolically unaltered form to a receptor protein in the uterus and other target organs, as a first and necessary event in initiation of its physiologic effects) and of Mueller et al. (164) (that hormones control the production of templates composed of nucleic acids) remain intact. Whether the initial binding is directly to the nuclear chromatin (165), or to a protein in the cytosol fraction which may function to transport the steroid into the nucleus (166) where it is then bound, is not certain. However, there seems general agreement, as reviewed by Hamilton (165), that the binding of the hormone to a protein in the nucleus is followed by stimulation of synthesis of ribosomal RNA; acceleration of the rate of formation of ribosomal precursor particles, and of transport of these particles with attached messenger RNA to the cytoplasm; and accumulation of new polyribosomes in the cytoplasm having different amino acid incoporation properties compared to those present before estrogen treatment.

Progress in understanding the mode of action of progesterone upon mammalian target organs has been somewhat slower. In contrast to estradiol, progesterone appears to be readily metabolized by at least three of its target tissues, the endometrium (167–169), the myometrium (170), and the vaginal mucosa (171). In light of the recent demonstration (discussed above) that conversion of testosterone in target organs to 5α-reduced metabolites is a prerequisite for its binding and exertion of its biologic effects,

[1] Similar prolongation of the luteal phase in sheep and swine following destruction of ovarian follicles by X irradiation has been reported recently (Karsch, F. J., Noveroske, J. W., Roche, J. F., Nalbandov, A. V., Program Soc. Study of Reproduction. Davis. 1969: Noveroske, J. W., Karsch, F. J., Nalbandov, A. V. *Ibid.* 1969).

it will be of great interest to find out whether 5α-reduction of progesterone may have similar consequences in its target organs. The few existing reports would support such a concept. Endometrial, myometrial, and vaginal tissues, as well as skin, have been observed to convert progesterone both *in vivo* and *in vitro* to 5α-reduced metabolites (167–171); some evidence for the selective retention of these compounds by rat decidual tissue has also been presented, although its physiologic significance was not emphasized (167).

In contrast to the deficiency of information concerning mode of action of progesterone in target organs of mammals, very substantial progress has been made in understanding its actions upon the avian oviduct. This organ in the newly hatched chick is lined by undifferentiated epithelial cells: estrogen stimulates these cells to proliferate, and three distinct cell types differentiate, two of which have the capacity to synthesize cell-specific proteins: The first, the tubular gland cells, secrete ovalbumin (172) and lysozyme (173) under the influence of estrogens. Progesterone, if administered concomitantly with estradiol, prevents proliferation of those cells destined to become tubular gland cells; however, if administered after such cells have proliferated in response to estrogen, subsequent cytodifferentiation and lysozyme synthesis are not prevented by progesterone (173). The second, the goblet cell, has the potential to synthesize the protein, avidin; but it is only induced to do so by administration of progesterone (174). The studies of O'Malley and colleagues (175–180), and of Hahn et al. (181) suggest that progesterone, like other sex hormones, male and female, acts upon the nucleus at the transcription level of protein synthesis, and that this results in new gene transcriptions and ultimately in synthesis of new protein (avidin).

The physiologic implications of the interactions of the female sex hormones with their target organs are manifold. Under the influence of specific variations in their secretion, conditions within the reproductive tract undergo continual shifts, presumably to accommodate the ever-changing requirements of the gametes, zygotes, and preimplantation and postimplantation embryos from insemination to parturition. Some of these will now be discussed.

The hormonal requirements for transport of spermatozoa from their usual site of deposition in the vagina, through the mucus within cervical canal into the uterus appear to be rather rigorous. In the human, this mucus is believed to act as a physiologic barrier to sperm entry at all times other than during the mid-cycle fertile period of the menstrual cycle. Evidence has been reviewed suggesting that certain contraceptive drugs owe their antifertility effects to actions at this site (182). On the basis of extensive studies of the physical and chemical characteristics of this mucus, Odeblad (183 for references) has proposed an ingenious theory to explain sperm transport at mid-cycle, in which sperm are envisioned as being carried, in a "surfing fashion", on propagating waves within the micellar lattice of the mucus. It is suggested that the "surfing" mechanism, believed to result from a type of mechanical resonance between sperm tail frequency and thermal oscillations of the molecular lattice, may exclude morphologically or "hydrodynamically" abnormal sperm from transport through the cervix. Only at mid-cycle are the physical characteristics of the cervical mucus compatible with the operation of this mechanism.

A different mechanism operates in the rat (184), involving a complex interaction between the glans penis, cervical os, copulation plug, and uterine contractions; oxytocin seems to play no essential role in this process, as sperm have been observed to reach the oviduct as soon after coitus in rats deficient in oxytocin (as a result of neurohypophyseal lesions which produce diabetes insipidus) as in intact rats (185).

Evidence implicating prostaglandins of seminal plasma in sperm transport within the uterus has been reviewed by Horton (186). Prostaglandin E_1 inhibited the constriction of the isthmus of the oviduct which normally follows hypogastric nerve stimulation or norepinephrine administration (187), a result suggesting that this compound in seminal plasma plays a physiologic role in facilitating passage of sperm into the oviduct by relaxing this sphincter-like region of the isthmus.

Spermatazoa capacitation.—Some progress in understanding the mechanism of capacitation appears to have been made. In the rabbit, the species in which the need for capacitation is best established, evidence indicates the necessity for intimate contact between the sperm and the epithelial lining of the oviduct or uterus (188). Capacitation failed to occur in oviduct or uterine fluid *in vitro,* or when sperm were placed in millipore filter tubes within the uterine lumen, and was substantially reduced when they were placed in uteri which were ligated, causing distention of the lumen with fluid and thereby decreasing the chances for contact with the endometrium. These observations are consistent with the hypothesis of Ericsson (189) that eosinophils within the endometrium, through contact with the sperm, are involved in capacitation, perhaps by removing an antigenic, or other protein coat from the sperm head. This coat is believed to exert a stabilizing effect on the plasma membrane of the sperm, and its removal, during capacitation, would have a destabilizing effect on the membrane, allowing the "'acrosome reaction" (discussed below), a prerequisite for fertilization, to occur (190). Rabbit spermatozoa can be capacitated by incubation with eosinophils (obtained from mules) (189) and eosinophils can remove material (tetracycline) bound to the sperm heads (191). That capacitation occurs best in uteri under the influence of estrogenic stimulation, and that it is under these conditions that eosinophil infiltration of the endometrium occurs (192), provide further circumstantial evidence for this hypothesis. Other authors, however, continue to emphasize the role of the uterine fluid in the capacitation process (193, 194). In the hamster, evidence has been presented that the fallopian tube is the site of capacitation (195) and that it is the follicular fluid released into the tube at the time of ovulation which contains the active factor(s) (196).

Fertilization.—Evidence of *in vitro* fertilization of oocytes from five mammalian species has been reported within the past year, and in three of these, the rhesus monkey (197), the human (198) and the rabbit (199), the oocytes were collected from unovulated follicles; mouse (200, 201) and rat (202) ova were recovered from the oviducts. In only one of these reports (201) was fertilization confirmed by transfer into pseudopregnant or pregnant hosts (with genetic markers) followed by examination of live fetuses. The sperm used in the latter experiment were recovered from the uteri of previously mated sperm donors, so were presumably capacitated. Whether this was actually necessary in the mouse is not certain, as higher fertilization rates *in vivo* reported in mice inseminated at the time of ovulation than in mice inseminated at varying intervals before insemination (203) suggest that capacitation may not be essential in this species. In the rat, where capacitation apparently is necessary, treatment of eggs with chymotrypsin resulted in dissolution of the zonae pellucidae; this was followed by sperm penetration and apparent fertilization. Epididymal sperm were as effective as capacitated sperm (202). These observations suggest either that capacitation can be achieved in a short time *in vitro* in the presence of chymotrypsin, or that capacitation is necessary only for penetration of the zona pellucida, but not for fertilization per se. The latter interpretation is supported by the demonstration of proteolytic enzymes extractable from sperm heads (204) and from detached acrosomes (205), which caused rapid dispersal of the cumulus cells and disintegration of the zona pellucida of freshly ovulated eggs.

Bedford has described the ultrastructural changes which occur in the acrosome during fertilization (190). This "acrosome reaction" involves fusion of the plasma membrane of the sperm head in numerous places with the underlying outer membrane of the acrosome, followed by local breakdown of the membrane, vesicle formation, and release of the acrosomal contents in the vicinity of the egg, where they presumably act to digest the zona pellucida. The ovum or the cumulus cells or both are believed somehow to initiate the "acrosome reaction", and it is suggested that capacitation involves destabilization of the plasma membrane, making it susceptible to those factors which initiate the reaction. Although acrosomal enzymes can disperse the cumulus and corona radiata cells, they are not absolutely essential for this, as dispersal occurs in oviduct fluid *in vitro* in the absence of spermatozoa. The oviduct factor responsible for this dispersal in the rabbit has been identified as bicarbonate ion (206).

Egg transport.—The oviducts of the rat, rabbit, and human possess a rich sympathetic innervation, particularly in the region of the isthmus (187,

207, 208). These nerves are believed to play a role in maintenance of tone of the isthmic sphincter, causing retention of fertilized ova in the oviducts. The constrictor response of the oviduct smooth muscle to stimulation of these nerves, or to exogenous catecholamines, is depressed or changed to relaxation by α-adrenergic blocking agents in the human (208) and the rabbit (209). In the rat, which has fewer adrenergic terminals in the isthmus, abundant terminals innervate both blood vessels and extravascular smooth muscle within the mesotubarium. The latter may provide an additional means of occluding the extensive coiled oviduct in this species, by causing kinks in the coils (207). The ability of the adrenergic nerves (and autonomic drugs) to influence the rate of ovum transport may be modified by estrogens and progesterone (210). Other humoral substances, including prostaglandins (187, 211), tachykinin peptides (211), and kininlike peptides, present in follicular fluid (212) have been observed to influence oviduct contractions in several species. Whether these compounds play physiologic roles in regulation of ovum transport remains uncertain, although treatment with exogenous prostaglandin E_2 delayed the time of arrival of blastocysts in the uteri of rats, contributing to a reduction in fertility (213).

Implantation.—The "diapausing" blastocyst from animals in which implantation delay has occurred spontaneously, or resulted from experimental manipulation, continues to be the target of numerous investigations of the mechanism of nidation, and its hormonal control. Markedly decreased rates of synthesis of DNA and RNA have been observed in blastocysts of several mammals during delayed implantation (214–216). Induction of implantation in rats with estrogen enhances synthesis of DNA, RNA, and protein in blastocysts, and RNA and protein synthsis in the adjacent uterine epithelium (216). The sequence of events which occurs in blastocysts of lactating mice following removal of litters or estrogen treatment include: appearance of W-bodies (believed to represent epithelial cell nuclei in the process of being engulfed by trophoblastic cell processes) in the neighbourhood of the blastocysts; disappearance of zonae pellucidae (which are shed during implantation delay, but remain in the uterine lumen; appearance of the "Pontamine Blue" reaction; edema of the uterine stroma; formation of the primary decidual zone (216).

Investigations with specific inhibitors of FSH and LH point to the latter as the gonadotropin most likely responsible for induction of implantation in the rat (217). Administration of anti-LH serum to rats early on the fourth day of gestation prevented implantation; this inhibition could be overridden by administration of estradiol. Administration of an FSH inhibitor isolated from monkey urine (which neutralizes the biologic activity of FSH, but not of LH) failed to prevent implantation. Some uncertainty still exists as to whether the follicles or the corpora lutea are the principal source of the estrogen responsible for implantation. Transplantation experiments, in which follicles or corpora lutea were transplanted to the kidney capsules of ovariectomized, pregnant, progesterone-treated rats, revealed that either structure could induce implantation (28).

Using another experimental approach, Macdonald et al. (218) observed that implantation did not occur in hypophysectomized, pregnant rats bearing autografted pituitary tissue under their kidney capsules, if follicles had been destroyed by X irradiation before attempted induction of implantation with LH. Since exogenous estradiol induced implantation in these circumstances, it was concluded that the follicles are essential as a source of estrogen for induction of implantation. The failure of corpora lutea to produce adequate amounts of estrogen to induce implantation in these experiments may indicate that the X irradiation destroyed the ability of the copora lutea to produce estrogen, since in the experiments of Schlough & Meyer (28) transplanted, nonirradiated corpora lutea were able to induce implantation in the absence of follicles or other ovarian components.

That the steroids, or other ovarian factors necessary for implantation may reach the uterus via a local mechanism of some sort, rather than solely via the general circulation, has been demonstrated in both the mouse (219) and the rat (220). Unilateral ovariectomy in both species, after ovulation but before implantation, resulted in interference with pregnancy only in the uterine horn on the operated side. Unimplanted blastocysts recovered from the uteri on the operated side suggest that implantation, rather than ovum transport, was impaired (219).

Parturition.—New evidence suggests a need to re-evaulate some of our ideas concerning the regulation of myometrial contractility and of parturition. The concept that estrogens are activators of uterine motility has been challenged by the results of recent experiments of Coutinho & de Mattos in which myometrial atrophy following castration was prevented by inserting fluid-filled balloons in the uteri of rabbits (221). By varying the amount of fluid in the balloons, thereby varying the extent of stretching of the myomerial fibres following castration, the growth of the myometrium and its working potential could be closely controlled. These experiments demonstrated that the contractile activity of the nonatrophic myometrium actually *increased* markedly after castration, rather than decreasing. This rise in contractility was *prevented* by administration of estrogen. The authors have concluded that estrogens contribute to suppression of uterine activity and that the most favourable condition for development of uterine activity is that which results from *estrogen withdrawal.*

The physiologic role of oxytocin in initiation of uterine contraction at parturition has been difficult to establish. Evidence discussed by Theobald et al. (222, 223) indicates that myometrial sensitivity to oxytocin increases before labour begins in the human. This increased sensitivity, which may be either gradual or abrupt, is believed to be more important than increased circulating levels of oxytocin, in the initiation of parturition (222). There is evidence that increased uptake, by the myometrium, of 5-hydroxytryptamine (5-HT) of fetal origin, may be involved in regulation of parturition (224,

225). Fetal 5-HT increases, and placental monoamine oxidase (the enzyme which inactivates 5-HT) decreases steadily up to term, and selective uptake of 5-HT by the myometrium, varying with hormonal state, has been demonstrated.

Compelling evidence implicates prostaglandin F2α as directly responsible for initiating labour in the human (226, 227). Marked fluctuations in levels of this prostaglandin have been observed in peripheral venous blood of women in various stages of labour. During the first stage of labour, when uterine contractions were occurring every 4 to 6 minutes, levels rose markedly during the minute immediately preceding each contraction, remained elevated during the contraction, and declined in the minute immediately following the contraction. Levels were almost undetectable in the interval between contractions. Levels were also elevated during the second (expulsion of the fetus) and third (explusion of the placenta) stages, and had returned to undetectable levels by 3 hours postpartum (226). In another series of ten women, labour was successfully induced in every instance by intravenous infusion of prostaglandin F2α (227). In every instance, labour started within 20 minutes after the onset of infusion [in contrast to studies with oxytocin infusion, in which the lag time between onset of infusion and initiation of labour is frequently much longer (222)]. In no instance was there any increase in the resting tone of the myometrium, and complete relaxation between contractions was observed. These findings support the hypothesis that prostaglandin F2α has a physiologic role in the initiation of parturition; it seems likely that the prostaglandin itself is responsible for the myometrial contractions, although it also may play a role in development of the increased sensitivity to oxytocin, discussed above. The exact source of the prostaglandin involved, and the endocrine or other physiologic mechanisms which bring about its release in effective amounts, remain unknown.

Lactation.—A resurgence of interest in the mammary gland within recent years has led to considerable progress in our understanding of mechanisms which regulate lactation, the last event in the complex sequence leading to reproduction in mammals, and the event which distinguishes them from all "'lower" forms. A variety of experimental approaches has led to advances on several fronts. *In vitro* studies with mammary gland explants, pioneered by Elias (228), continue to be most fruitful in elucidating the hormonal requirements for various facets of mammary gland function. The concept which seems to be emerging rather clearly, at least for mouse mammary tissue, is that the development in culture of new differentiated function depends on the production of new cells. DNA synthesis and cell proliferation will occur in the presence of insulin as the only hormone but under these conditions, the new cells remain undifferentiated. For differentiation of cells capable of synthesis of specific milk protein (casein) to occur in response to subsequent stimulation by prolactin, cortisol is required in the medium along with insulin during cell division (229). In the absence of other hormones, insulin will increase the activity of RNA polymerase, which suggests an early effect of insulin on nuclear transcription (230). Prolactin will further stimulate RNA polymerase activity and RNA synthesis, provided that cortisol has been present during the preceding period of insulin-stimulated cell proliferation. Since these latter effects of prolactin are evident before induction of specific milk protein, an early effect of prolactin on nuclear transcription is suggested also.

The hormonal requirements for development of lobule-alveolar structure with visible evidence of secretion in mouse mammary explants appear to be the same as those for differentiation of synthesis of milk proteins (i.e. insulin, corticosteroids, and prolactin) (231, 232). Rat mammary gland explants, by contrast, developed small lobules of alveoli in chemically defined medium lacking steroids but containing insulin and prolactin (233), although the degree of lobule-alveolar development could be increased by adding estradiol, progesterone, and aldosterone.

Many, although not all, aspects of these *in vitro* studies have been confirmed *in vivo*. Both prolactin and cortisol stimulated RNA synthesis in mammary glands of rats hypophysectomized during lactation under conditons in which they also effected reasonably satisfactory maintenance of the mammary glands, and milk synthesis (234, 235). The activities of a number of general metabolic enzymes increased at parturition (236) and declined following hypophysectomy; an essentially normal pattern of these enzymes could be restored by treatment of hypophysectomized rats with prolactin and cortisol together, but not separately (237, 238).

That the hormone-induced increases in the activities of these enzymes may be due to stimulation of nuclear transcription is suggested by several lines of evidence. The RNA synthesized by nuclei isolated from mammary glands stimulated with prolactin and cortisol corresponded in base composition to DNA-like RNA, with sedimentation values between 10S and 15S (234); such mammary gland RNA fractions have been reported to have high template activity, and may represent the messenger RNA required to specify the synthesis of mammary gland enzymes as well as milk proteins (234, 239). The ability of prolactin, when administered intraductally to pseudopregnant rabbits, to increase mammary gland lipoprotein lipase activity, was abolished by prior intraductal administration of actinomycin D or cycloheximide (240). Addition of prolactin to mouse mammary glands in organ culture led to an early increase in phosphorylation of acidic nuclear proteins and specific histone fractions, only under conditions in which the hormone also induced synthesis of specific milk proteins (241), suggesting a role of nuclear protein phosphorylation in hormonal activation of genes. However, another attempt to implicate histones in regulation of genetic expression by hormones involved in initiation of lactation has been unsuccessful; the patterns of three major classes of histones did not change significantly from late pregnancy to early lactation, and only slightly during mammary gland involution (242).

Investigations of the hormonal control of lactose synthesis have uncovered an apparently new concept in biological regulation which may well have important implications beyond the mammary gland. Lactose is virtually undetectable in rat and rabbit mammary glands during pregnancy, but increases dramatically at parturition (243 for references). Lactose synthetase (UDP-D-galactose-D-glucose-1-D-galactosyltransferase, EC2.4.1C), the enzyme which catalyzes the reaction:

$$\text{UDP-D-galactose} + \text{D-glucose} \rightarrow \text{UDP} + \text{lactose}$$

appears to be the rate-limiting step in lactose synthesis; its activity begins to appear during the last day of pregnancy, in rats, simultaneously with the appearance of tissue lactose (243). This enzyme consists of two subunits, a particulate enzyme referred to as the "A" protein, and a "B" protein, loosely associated with the "A" protein and easily solubilized as one of the whey proteins of milk (244–247). The "'B" protein has been identified as α-lactalbumin (248) and snown to possess a unique activity. In its absence, the "A" protein possesses galactosyl tansferase activity, but has different *substrate* (acceptor) *specificity*; it catalyzes the reaction:

$$\text{UDP-D-galactose} + \text{N-acetyl-D-glucosamine} \rightarrow$$
$$\text{UDP} + \text{N-acetyl lactosamine}$$

Addition of the "B" protein, α-lactalbumin, modifies the substrate specificity so that D-glucose is the acceptor and lactose, the product. The term *specifier* protein has been coined to describe this type of activity, i.e. the ability to bind to an enzyme and alter its substrate specificity (247). In mouse mammary glands grown in organ culture, the hormonal requirements for synthesis of both the "A" and "B" proteins are the same as those for synthesis of milk proteins, viz. insulin, cortisol, and prolactin (244). *In vivo*, mammary gland levels of the "A" protein begin to rise around day 10 of pregnancy, whereas levels of α-lactalbumin, the "B" protein, are very low during pregnancy, but rise dramatically just before parturition (249). The kinetics of the induction of the two proteins in response to prolactin and cortisol in the presence of insulin as determined in the *in vitro* studies do not adequately explain the asynchronous appearance of the two proteins *in vivo* during pregnancy, which suggests that another physiologic mechanism must prevent the induction of α-lactalbumin. Progesterone appears to be the agent responsible for this repression in both the mouse (249) and the rat (250). The induction, by prolactin, of α-lactalbumin in mouse mammary gland explants is specifically inhibited by addition of progesterone in physiologic concentrations to the culture medium. Under the same conditions, progesterone decreased the rate of RNA synthesis, but did not prevent the induction of casein synthesis. The administration of progesterone, *in vivo*, during the last 1 to 2 days of gestation prevented the normal elevation of α-lactalbumin at parturition, without altering the galactosyltransferase ("A"-protein) activity (249) Further evidence for progesterone as the hormone that suppresses α-lactalbumin synthesis is provided by the observations that lactose appears in the mammary glands of rats concomitantly with the decline in plasma levels of progesterone which results from ovariectomy or hysterectomy during the latter part of gestation; lactose appearance was prevented by progesterone in both instances, and by prolactin in hysterectomized rats (the latter effect presumably due to the "luteotropic" rather than the "lactogenic" effects of prolactin) (250). The marked decline of plasma levels of progesterone on the day before parturition in the rat, because of increased ovarian levels of 20α-hydroxysteroid dehydrogenase which converts progesterone to its progestationally inactive reduction product (251), provides further circumstantial evidence for this action of progesterone.

Attractive as this hypothesis is, it seems on the surface not to be entirely consistent with certain observations in rabbits; intraductal administration of prolactin into the mammary glands of rabbits on day 10 of pseudopregnancy [at which time corpora lutea are actively secreting progesterone (252)] leads to increased lactose formation observed on day 15. In fact, this response has been used as a bioassay method for prolactin (253). However, progesterone secretion rate at day 15 of pseudopregnancy is considerably lower than at a comparable stage of pregnancy (252) and may be sufficiently low to be unable to suppress α-lactalbumin synthesis.

If progesterone levels do play a critical role in regulating the initiation of lactation, it becomes difficult to explain the ability of exogenous cortisol or ACTH to initiate lactation during pregnancy in the rabbit (254), unless one proposes that this treatment causes an inhibition of progesterone secretion. Some circumstantial evidence suggests such an action of ACTH. Suckling stimuli, or other exteroceptive stimuli associated with suckling, well known to be capable of initiation and maintenance of mammary gland secretory activity (255, 256), have been found effective in increasing ACTH and corticosteroid secretion in rats (257, 258) and cows (259, 260). In the latter species, exogenous oxytocin exerts a similar elevation of cortisol secretion (260). Perhaps increased ACTH and corticosteroid levels somehow mediate the suppression of corpus luteum activity which results from suckling or oxytocin administration in certain species including the rabbit (261–263); if so, it could offer an explanation for the induction of lactation by ACTH consistent with the above hypothesis that initiation of lactose synthesis (and of lactation) is dependent upon, and triggered by, progesterone withdrawal.

There is increasing evidence that stimuli arising from, or associated with, suckling can produce other forms of ovarian quiescence in addition to corpus luteum suppression, in several species (263–269). Although an adequate explanation for this phenomenon is still lacking, it may be attributed, at least in part, to an "antigonadotropic" action of prolactin; it is well established that such stimuli promote prolactin secretion (268, 270–272) and that prolactin possesses antigonadotropic capabilities, at least in birds (144). In light of the recent evidence that similar stimuli also evoke increased secretion of ACTH (discussed above), and the demonstrations that administration of exogenous ACTH or corticosteroids, or both, interferes with LH secretion in rats (273) and swine (274), it may be worthwhile to consider a possible role of ACTH as a mediator of the ovarian inactivity associated with suckling.

The elucidation of the basic mechanisms by which stimuli associated with suckling and lactation suppress ovarian function could well have important practical consequences. It seems likely that these mechanisms have evolved to protect the maternal mammal against her own procreative potential, by enabling spacing of offspring consistent with the well-being of both mother and young. If the fundamental processes underlying this most natural form of contraception could be better understood, they might be exploited to enable the development of more acceptable (and therefore more effective) methods of fertility control at a critical time in the evolution of *Homo sapiens*.

ACKNOWLEDGMENTS

The preparation of this review was aided, in part, by grants from the Medical Research Council of Canada (No. MA-3392) and from the National Institutes of Health, USPHS (No. HD04169). I am grateful to Dr. James E. Hixon for reading the manuscript and for offering a number of helpful suggestions, and to Mrs. Kathleen Dickson for typing the manuscript.

LITERATURE CITED

1. Jungmann, R. A. *Biochim. Biophys. Acta*, **164**, 110–23 (1968)
2. Jungmann, R. A. *Steroids*, **12**, 205–14 (1968)
3. Huseby, R. A., Dominguez, O. V., Samuels, L. T. *Recent Progr. Hormone Res.*, **17**, 1–51 (1961)
4. Bell, J. B. G., Vinson, G. P., Hopkins, D. J., Lacy, D. *Biochim. Biophys. Acta*, **164**, 412–20 (1968)
5. Yamaji, T., Motohashi, K., Tanioka, T., Ibayashi, H. *Endocrinology*, **83**, 992–98 (1968)
6. Jungmann, R. A., Schweppe, J. S. *Program 51st Meeting Endocrine Soc., New York*, 74 (1969)
7. Nakano, H., Sato, H., Tamaoki, B. *Steroids*, **12**, 291–98 (1968)
8. Drosdowsky, M. A., Forchielli, E., Dorfman, R. I. *European J. Steroids*, **2**, 515–37 (1968)
9. Nakano, H., Tamaoki, B. I. *Arch. Biochem. Biophys.*, **129**, 771–73 (1969)
10. Sink, J. D. *J. Theoret. Biol.*, **17**, 174–80 (1967)
11. Katkov, T., Gower, D. B. *Biochim. Biophys. Acta*, **164**, 134–36 (1968)
12. Ahmad, N., Gower, D. B. *Biochem. J.*, **108**, 233–42 (1968)
13. Brooksbank, B. W. L., Cunningham, A. E., Wilson, D. A. *Steroids*, **13**, 29–50 (1969)
14. Patterson, R. L. S. *J. Sci. Food Agr.*, **19**, 30–38 (1968)
15. Sandler, R., Hall, P. F. *Biochim. Biophys. Acta*, **164**, 445–47 (1968)
16. Connell, G. M., Eik-Nes, K. B. *Steroids*, **12**, 507–16 (1968)
17. Ficher, M., Steinberger, E. *Steroids*, **12**, 491–506 (1968)
18. Hashimoto, I., Wiest, W. G. *Endocrinology*, **84**, 886–92 (1969)
19. Armstrong, D. T. In *Progress in Endocrinology, Proc. Intern. Congr. Endocrinol., 3rd, Mexico City, Mexico, 1968* (In press)
20. Bell, J. B. G., Vinson, G. P., Lacy, D. *Biochem. J.*, **110**, 58P (1968)
21. Christensen, A. K., Mason, N. R. *Endocrinology*, **76**, 646–56 (1965)
22. Inano, H., Tamaoki, B. I. *Endocrinol. Japon.*, **15**, 197–207 (1968)
23. Inano, H., Tamaoki, B. I., *Endocrinology*, **83**, 1074–82 (1968)
24. Hamberger, L. A., Steward, V. W. *Endocrinology*, **83**, 855–61 (1968)
25. Inano, H., Machino, A., Tamaoki, B. I., Tsubura, Y. *Endocrinology*, **83**, 659–70 (1968)
26. Inano, H., Tamaoki, B. I. *Endocrinology*, **84**, 123–31 (1969)
27. Falck, B. *Acta Physiol. Scand., Suppl.* **163**, 1–101 (1959)
28. Schlough, J. S., Meyer, R. K. *Endocrinology*, **82**, 1179–82 (1968)

29. Rennie, P. *Endocrinology*, **83**, 323–28 (1968)
30. Keyes, P. L., Armstrong, D. T. *Endocrinology*, **85**, 423–27 (1969)
31. Jensen, E. V., Jacobson, H. I. *Recent Progr. Hormone Res.*, **18**, 387–414 (1962)
32. Ofner, P., *Vitamins Hormones*, **26**, 237–91 (1968)
33. Bruchovsky, N., Wilson, J. D. *J. Biol. Chem.*, **243**, 2012–21 (1968)
34. Bruchovsky, N., Wilson, J. D. *Ibid.*, **243**, 5953–60 (1968)
35. Baulieu, E. E., Lasnitski, I., Robel, P. *Nature*, **219**, 1155–56 (1968)
36. Belham, J. E., Neal, G. E., Williams, D. C. *Biochem. J.*, **109**, 33P (1968)
37. Anderson, K. M., Liao, S. *Nature*, **219**, 277–78 (1968)
38. Mangan, G. E., Neal, G. E., Williams, D. C. *Arch. Biochem. Biophys.*, **124**, 27–40 (1968)
39. Unhjem, O., Tveter, K. J. *Acta Endocrinol.*, **60**, 571–78 (1969)
40. Tveter, K. J. *Acta Endocrinol.*, **60**, 60–68 (1969)
41. Pfaff, D. W. *Science*, **161**, 1355–56 (1968)
42. Inano, H., Machino, A., Tamaoki, B. I. *Endocrinology*, **84**, 997–1003 (1969)
43. Thomas, P. Z. *J. Biol. Chem.*, **243**, 6110–14 (1968)
44. Wilson, J. D., Walker, J. D. *J. Clin. Invest.*, **48**, 371–79 (1969)
45. Liao, S., Stumpf, W. E. *Endocrinology*, **83**, 629–32 (1968)
46. Fujii, T., Villee, C. A. *Endocrinology*, **82**, 463–67 (1968)
47. Fujii, T., Villee, C. A. *Acta Endocrinol.*, **60**, 527–36 (1969)
48. Dirscherl, W., Henrichs, H. R., Caspari, R. *Acta Endocrinol.*, **59**, 433–41 (1968)
49. Ritter, C. *Mol. Pharmacol.*, **2**, 125–33 (1966)
50. Coffey, D. S., Ichinose, R. R., Shimazaki, J., Williams-Ashman, H. G. *Mol. Pharmacol.*, **4**, 580–90 (1968)
51. Singhal, R. L., Ling, G. M. *Can. J. Physiol. Pharmacol.*, **47**, 233–39 (1969)
52. Singhal, R. L., Valadares, J. R. E. *Biochem. J.*, **110**, 703–12 (1968)
53. Riekkinen, P. J., Niemi, M. *Endocrinology*, **83**, 1224–31 (1968)
54. Lostroh, A. J. *Proc. Natl. Acad. Sci.*, **60**, 1312–18 (1968)
55. Pegg, A. E., Williams-Ashman, H. G. *Biochem. J.*, **108**, 533–40 (1968)
56. Pegg, A. E., Williams-Ashman, H. G.
57. Pegg, A. E., Williams-Ashman, H. G. *J. Biol. Chem.*, **244**, 682–93 (1969)
58. Peyre, A., Ravault, J. P., Laporte, P. *Compt. Rend. Soc. Biol.*, **162**, 1592–95 (1968)
59. Apostolakis, M. *Vitamins Hormones*, **26**, 197–235 (1968)
60. Klaiber, E. L., Lloyd, C., Solomon, A., Broverman, D. M. *Endocrinology*, **83**, 387–89 (1968)
61. Jost, A. *Recent Progr. Hormone Res.*, **8**, 379–418 (1953)
62. Harris, G. W. *Endocrinology*, **75**, 627–48 (1964)
63. DeMoor, P., Denef, C. *Endocrinology*, **82**, 480–92 (1968)
64. Kraulis, I., Clayton, R. B. *J. Biol. Chem.*, **243**, 3546–47 (1968)
65. Denef, C., DeMoor, P. *Endocrinology*, **83**, 791–98 (1968)
66. Forsberg, J. G., Jacobsohn, D., Norgren, A. *Z. Anat. Entwicklungsgeschichte*, **127**, 175–86 (1968)
67. Morris, J. M., Mahesh, V. B. *Am. J. Obstet. Gynecol.*, **87**, 731–48 (1963)
68. Jarvis, P., Bercovici, J. P., Gauthier, F. *J. Clin. Endocrinol. Metab.*, **29**, 417–22 (1969)
69. Northcutt, R. C., Island, D. P., Liddle, G. W. *J. Clin. Endocrinol. Metab.*, **29**, 422–25 (1969)
70. Bardin, C. W., Bullock, L., Gram, T. E., Schroeder, D. H., Gillette, J. R. *Program 51st Meeting Endocrine Soc., New York*, 40 (1969)
71. Van Dyke, K., Katzman, P. A. *Endocrinology*, **83**, 107–12 (1968)
72. Reel, J. R., Gorski, J. *Endocrinology*, **83**, 1083–91 (1968)
73. Reel, J. R., Gorski, J. *Ibid.*, **83**, 1092–100 (1968)
74. Eckstein, B., Hochman, J. *Biochim. Biophys. Acta*, **177**, 50–58 (1969)
75. Ahrén, K., Beviz, A., Hamberger, L., Lundholm, L. *Acta Physiol. Scand.*, **73**, 23A–24A (1968)
76. Ahrén, K., Hamberger, L., Rubinstein, L. *Acta Physiol. Scand.*, **74**, 79–90 (1968)
77. Hamberger, L. A. *Acta Physiol. Scand.*, **74**, 410–25 (1968)
78. Savard, K., Marsh, J. M., Rice, B. F. *Recent Progr. Hormone Res.*, **21**, 285–365 (1965)
79. Rubin, B. L., Deane, H. W., Hamilton, J. A., Driks, E. C. *Endocrinology*, **72**, 924–30 (1963)
80. Claesson, L., Hillarp, N. *Acta*
Ibid., **109**, 32P (1968)

Physiol. Scand., **14,** 102–19 (1947)
81. Blanchette, E. J. *J. Cell Biol.,* **31,** 501–16 (1966)
82. Christensen, A. K., Gillim, S. W. *The Gonads,* 415 (McKerns, K. W., Ed., Appleton - Century - Crofts, New York, 1969)
83. Ahrén, K., Kostyo, J. L. *Endocrinology,* **73,** 81–91 (1963)
84. Bjorkman, N. *Acta Anat.,* **51,** 125–47 (1962)
85. Channing, C. P. *J. Endocrinol.,* **43,** 381–90 (1969)
86. Channing, C. P. *Ibid.,* **43,** 415–25 (1969)
87. Channing, C. P., Grieves, S. A. *J. Endocrinol.,* **43,** 391–402 (1969)
88. Keyes, P. L. *Science,* **164,** 846–47 (1969)
89. Biggers, J. D., Whittingham, D. G., Donahue, R. P. *Proc. Natl. Acad. Sci.,* **58,** 560–67 (1967)
90. Donahue, R. P., Stern, S. *J. Reprod. Fertility,* **17,** 395–98 (1968)
91. Smith, L. D., Ecker, R. E., Subtelny, S. *Develop. Biol.,* **17,** 627–43 (1968)
92. Dettlaff, T. A. *J. Embryol. Exptl. Morphol.,* **16,** 183–95 (1966)
93. Schuetz, A. W. *J. Cell Biol.,* **35,** 123A (1967)
94. Hilliard, J., Archibald, D., Sawyer, C. H. *Endocrinology,* **72,** 59–66 (1963)
95. Feder, H. H., Resko, J. A., Goy, R. W. *J. Endocrinol.,* **41,** 563–69 (1968)
96. Hashimoto, I., Wiest, W. G. *Endocrinology,* **84,** 873–85 (1969)
97. Feder, H. H., Resko, J. A., Goy, R. W. *J. Endocrinol.,* **40,** 505–13 (1968)
98. Neill, J. D., Johansson, E. D. B., Knobil, E. *Endocrinology,* **84,** 45–48 (1969)
99. El-Fouly, M. A., Cook, B. *Program 51st Meeting Endocrine Soc., New York,* 54 (1969)
100. Midgley, A. R., Jaffe, R. B. *J. Clin. Endocrinol. Metab.,* **28,** 1699–703 (1968)
101. Cargille, C. M., Ross, G. T., Yoshimi, T. *J. Clin. Endocrinol. Metab.,* **29,** 12–19 (1969)
102. Taymor, M. L., Aono, T., Pheteplace, C. *Acta Endocrinol.* **59,** 298–306 (1968)
103. Goldman, B. D., Mahesh, V. B. *Endocrinology,* **83,** 97–106 (1968)
104. McClintock, J. A., Schwartz, N. B. *Endocrinology,* **83,** 433–41 (1968)
105. Velasco, M. E., Taleisnik, S. *Endocrinology,* **84,** 132–39 (1969)
106. Goldman, B. D., Mahesh, V. B. *Endocrinology,* **84,** 236–43 (1969)
107. Rodbard, D. *J. Clin. Endocrinol. Metab.,* **28,** 849–60 (1968)
108. Fritz, H. I., Cho, W. K., Biggers, J. D. *J. Cell Biol.,* **27,** 31A (1965)
109. Burr, J. H., Davies, J. I. *Anat. Rec.,* **111,** 273–97 (1951)
110. Blandau, R. J. *Fertility Sterility,* **6,** 391–404 (1955)
111. Barros, C., Austin, C. R. *Endocrinology,* **83,** 177–79 (1968)
112. Everett, J. W. *Ann. Rev. Physiol.,* **31,** 383–416 (1969)
113. Pelletier, J., Kann, G., Dolais, J., Rosselin, G. *Compt. Rend.,* **266,** 2352–54 (1968)
114. Geschwind, I. I., Dewey, R. *Proc. Soc. Exptl. Biol. Med.,* **129,** 451–55 (1968)
115. Niswender, G. D., Roche, J. F., Foster, D. L., Midgley, A. R. *Proc. Soc. Exptl. Biol. Med.,* **129,** 901–4 (1968)
116. Moore, N. W., Barrett, S., Brown, J. B., Schindler, I., Smith, M. A., Smyth, B. *J. Endocrinol.,* **44,** 55–62 (1969)
117. Brown, J. M., Catt, K. J., Cumming, I. A., Goding, J. R., Kaltenbach, C. C., Mole, B. J. *J. Physiol.,* **201,** 98P–100P (1969)
118. Radford, H. M., Wheatley, I. S., Wallace, A. L. C. *J. Endocrinol.,* **44,** 135–36 (1969)
119. Baird, D. T., Guevara, A. *J. Clin. Endocrinol. Metab.,* **29,** 149–56 (1969)
120. Corker, C. S., Naftolin, F., Exley, D. *Nature,* **222,** 1063 (1969)
121. Burger, H. G., Catt, K. J., Brown, J. B. *J. Clin. Endocrinol. Metab.,* **28,** 1508–12 (1968)
122. Hori, T., Ide, M., Miyake, T. *Endocrinol. Japon.,* **15,** 215–22 (1968)
123. Kobayashi, F., Hara, K., Miyake, T. *Endocrinol. Japon.,* **15,** 313–19 (1968)
124. O'Dell, W. D., Swerdloff, R. S. *Proc. Natl. Acad. Sci.,* **61,** 529–36 (1968)
125. Goldman, B. D., Kamberi, I. A., Siiteri, P. K., Porter, J. C. *Endocrinology* (Submitted for publication) (1969)
126. Armstrong, D. T. *Recent Progr. Hormone Res.,* **24,** 255–319 (1968)
127. Grayburn, J. A., Brown-Grant, K. *J. Endocrinol.,* **42,** 409–16 (1968)
128. Ying, S. Y., Meyer, R. K. *Proc. Soc.*

Exptl. Biol. Med., **130,** 40–54 (1969)

129. Hilliard, J., Penardi, R., Sawyer, C. H. *Endocrinology,* **80,** 901–9 (1967)

130. Greenwald, G. S., Rothchild, I. *J. Animal Sci.,* **27,** Suppl. *I,* 139–62 (1968)

131. Melampy, R. M., Anderson, L. L. *J. Animal Sci.,* **27,** Suppl. *I,* 77–96 (1968)

132. Armstrong, D. T. *J. Animal Sci.,* **27,** Suppl. *I,* 181–203 (1968)

133. Moor, R. M. *Proc. Roy. Soc. Med.,* **61,** 1217–26 (1968)

134. Short, R. V. *Ann. Rev. Physiol.,* **29,** 373–400 (1967)

135. Nalbandov, A. V., Cook, B. *Ann. Rev. Physiol.,* **30,** 245–78 (1968)

136. Spies, H. G., Hilliard, J., Sawyer, C. H. *Endocrinology,* **83,** 354–67 (1968)

137. Choudary, J. B., Greenwald, G. S. *Anat. Rec.,* **163,** 373–88 (1969)

138. Grady, K. L., Greenwald, G. S. *Endocrinology,* **83,** 1173–80 (1968)

139. Moudgal, N. R., Madhwa Raj, H. G., Rao, A. J., Sairam, M. R. *Indian J. Exptl. Biol.,* **7,** 45–46 (1969)

140. Laurence, K. A., Ichikawa, S. *Intern. J. Fertility,* **14,** 8–15 (1969)

141. Loewit, K., Badawy, S., Laurence, K. A. *Endocrinology,* **84,** 244–51 (1969)

142. Moudgal, N. R. *Nature,* **222,** 286–87 (1969)

143. Greenwald, G. S., Johnson, D. C. *Endocrinology,* **83,** 1052–64 (1968)

144. Riddle, O. *J. Natl. Cancer Inst.,* **31,** 1039–109 (1963)

145. Bern, H. A., Nicoll, C. S. *Recent Progr. Hormone Res.,* **24,** 681–712 (1968)

146. Baird, D. T., Uno, A., McCracken, J. A. *J. Endocrinol.,* **43,** xviii–xix (1969)

147. Hixon, J. E., Clegg, M. T. *Endocrinology,* **84,** 828–34 (1969)

148. Greenwald, G. S. *Endocrinology,* **80,** 118–29 (1967)

149. Acker, G., Alloiteau, J. J. *Compt. Rend. Soc. Biol.,* **162,** 29–33 (1968)

150. Pharriss, B. B., Wyngarden, L. J. *Proc. Soc. Exptl. Biol. Med.,* **130,** 92–94 (1969)

151. Blatchley, F. R., Donovan, B. T. *Nature,* **221,** 1065–66 (1969)

152. Gutknecht, G. D., Cornette, J. C., Pharriss, B. B. *Biol. Reprod.* (In press, 1969)

153. Pickles, V. R. *J. Physiol.,* **183,** 69P (1966)

154. Du Charme, D. W., Weeks, J. R., Montgomery, R. G. *J. Pharmacol. Exptl. Therap.,* **160,** 1–10 (1968)

155. Pharriss, B. B., Wyngarden, L. J., Gutknecht, G. D. *Gonadotropins 1968,* Proc. Workshop Conf., Vista Hermosa, Mexico, 121–29 (Rosemberg, E., Ed., Geron-X, Inc., Los Altos, Calif., 1968)

156. Stormshak, F., Casida, L. E. *Endocrinology,* **75,** 321–25 (1964)

157. Bergström, S., Carlson, L. A., Weeks, J. R. *Pharmacol. Rev.,* **20,** 1–48 (1968)

158. Armstrong, D. T. (Unpublished observations)

159. Behrman, H. R., Armstrong, D. T. *Endocrinology,* **85,** 474–80 (1969)

160. Zachariae, F. *Acta Endocrinol.,* **27,** 339–42 (1958)

161. Rothchild, I. *Vitamins Hormones,* **23,** 209–327 (1965)

162. Christiansen, J. M., Keyes, P. L., Armstrong, D. T. *Biol. Reprod.* (Submitted for publication)

163. Rivera, A., Sherman, A. I. *Am. J. Obstet. Gynecol.,* **103,** 986–93 (1969)

164. Mueller, G. C., Herranen, A. M., Jervell, K. F. *Recent Progr. Hormone Res.,* **14,** 95–139 (1958)

165. Hamilton, T. H. *Science,* **161,** 649–61 (1968)

166. Gorski, J., Toft, D., Shyamala, G., Smith, D., Notides, A. *Recent Progr. Hormone Res.,* **24,** 45–71 (1968)

167. Wiest, W. G. *J. Biol. Chem.,* **238,** 94–99 (1963)

168. Wiest, W. G. *Endocrinology,* **73,** 310–16 (1963)

169. Bryson, M. J., Sweat, M. L. *Endocrinology,* **81,** 729–34 (1967)

170. Bryson, M. J., Sweat, M. L. *Endocrinology,* **84,** 1071–75 (1969)

171. Frost, P., Gomez, E. C., Weinstein, G. D., Lamas, J., Hsia, S. L. *Biochemistry,* **8,** 948–52 (1969)

172. Kohler, P. O., Grimley, P. M., O'Malley, B. W. *J. Cell Biol.,* **40,** 8–27 (1969)

173. Oka, T., Schimke, R. T. *Science,* **163,** 83–85 (1969)

174. Korenman, S. G., O'Malley, B. W. *Endocrinology,* **83,** 11–17 (1968)

175. O'Malley, B. W., Aronow, A., Peacock, A. C., Dingman, C. W. *Science,* **162,** 567–68 (1968)

176. O'Malley, B. W., McGuire, W. L. *Proc. Natl. Acad. Sci.,* **60,** 1527–34 (1968)

177. O'Malley, B. W., McGuire, W. L.,

Middleton, P. A. *Nature*, **218**, 1249–50 (1968)

178. O'Malley, B. W., McGuire, W. L. *Endocrinology*, **84**, 63–68 (1969)

179. Dingman, C. W., Aronow, A., Bunting, S. L., Peacock, A. C., O'Malley, B. W. *Biochemistry*, **8**, 489–94 (1969)

180. O'Malley, B. W. *Trans. N.Y. Acad. Sci., Ser. II*, **31**, 478–503 (1969)

181. Hahn, W. E., Church, R. B., Gorbman, A., Wilmot, L. *Gen. Comp. Endocrinol.*, **10**, 438–42 (1968)

182. Diczfalusy, E. *Am. J. Obstet. Gynecol.*, **100**, 136–63 (1968)

183. Odeblad, E. *Acta Obstet. Gynecol. Scand.*, **47**, *Suppl. 1*, 57–79 (1968)

184. Blandau, R. J. *Am. J. Anat.*, **77**, 253–72 (1945)

185. Manabe, Y. *J. Reprod. Fertility*, **18**, 371–73 (1969)

186. Horton, E. W. *Physiol. Rev.*, **49**, 112–61 (1969)

187. Brundin, J. *Acta Physiol. Scand.*, **73**, 54–57 (1968)

188. Hamner, C. E., Sojka, N. J. *Nature*, **220**, 1042–43 (1968)

189. Ericsson, R. J. *Nature*, **221**, 568–69 (1969)

190. Bedford, J. M. *Am. J. Anat.*, **123**, 329–58 (1968)

191. Ericsson, R. J. *Proc. Brook Lodge Conf. Prob. Reprod. Biol., 4th, Augusta, Mich., 1969*

192. Bjersing, L., Borglin, N. E. *Acta Pathol. Microbiol. Scand.*, **60**, 27–35 (1964)

193. Murdoch, R. N., White, I. G. *J. Endocrinol.*, **43**, 167–74 (1969)

194. Murdoch, R. N., White, I. G. *Australian J. Biol. Sci.*, **21**, 961–72 (1968)

195. Barros, C. *J. Reprod. Fertility*, **17**, 203–6 (1968)

196. Yanagimachi, R. *J. Reprod. Fertility*, **18**, 275–86 (1969)

197. Suzuki, S., Mastroianni, L. *Fertility Sterility*, **19**, 500–8 (1968)

198. Edwards, R. G., Bavister, B. D., Steptoe, P. C. *Nature*, **221**, 632–35 (1969)

199. Suzuki, S., Mastroianni, L. *Fertility Sterility*, **19**, 716–25 (1968)

200. Pavlok, A. *J. Reprod. Fertility*, **16**, 401–8 (1968)

201. Whittingham, D. G. *Nature*, **220**, 592–93 (1968)

202. Toyoda, Y., Chang, M. C., *Nature*, **220**, 589–90 (1968)

203. McGaughey, M. W., Marston, J. H., Chang, M. C. *J. Reprod. Fertility*, **16**, 147–50 (1968)

204. Stambaugh, R., Buckley, J. *Science*, **161**, 585–86 (1968)

205. Allison, A. C., Hartree, E. F. *Biochem. J.*, **111**, 35P (1969)

206. Stambaugh, R., Noriega, C., Mastroianni, L., *J. Reprod. Fertility*, **18**, 51–58 (1969)

207. Brundin, J., Fredricsson, B., Norberg, K. A., Swedin, G. *Acta Physiol. Scand.*, **75**, 69–72 (1969)

208. Nakanishi, H., Wood, C. *J. Reprod. Fertility*, **16**, 21–28 (1968)

209. Longley, W. J., Black, D. L., Currie, G. N. *J. Reprod. Fertility*, **17**, 95–100 (1968)

210. Longley, W. J., Black, D. L., Currie, G. N. *J. Reprod. Fertility*, **17**, 579–81 (1968)

211. Zetler, G., Mönkemeier, D., Wiechell, H. *J. Reprod. Fertility*, **18**, 147–49 (1969)

212. Ramwell, P. W., Shaw, J. E., Jessup, S. J. *Endocrinology*, **84**, 931–36 (1969)

213. Nutting, E. F., Cammarata, P. S. *Nature*, **222**, 287–88 (1968)

214. Gulyas, B. J., Daniels, J. C. *Biol. Reprod.*, **1**, 11–20 (1969)

215. Prasad, M. R. N., Dass, C. M. S., Mohla, S. *J. Reprod. Fertility*, **16**, 97–104 (1968)

216. McLaren, A. *J. Endocrinol.*, **42**, 453–63 (1968)

217. Madhwa Raj, H. G., Sairam, M. R., Moudgal, N. R. *J. Reprod. Fertility*, **17**, 335–41 (1968)

218. Macdonald, G. J., Keyes, P. L., Greep, R. O. *Endocrinology*, **84**, 1004–8 (1969)

219. Bruce, H. M., Renwick, A. G. C., Finn, C. A. *Nature*, **219**, 733–34 (1968)

220. Lamming, G. E., Little, S. L. *J. Physiol.*, **196**, 14P–15P (1968)

221. Coutinho, E. M., de Mattos, C. E. R. *Endocrinology*, **83**, 422–32 (1968)

222. Theobald, G. W., Robards, M. F., Suter, P. E. N. *J. Obstet. Gynaecol. Brit. Commonwealth*, **76**, 385–93 (1969)

223. Caldeyro-Barcia, R., Theobald, G. W. *Am. J. Obstet. Gynecol.*, **102**, 1181 (1968)

224. Koren, E., Pfeifer, Y., Sulman, F. G. *J. Endocrinol.*, **43**, 465–69 (1969)

225. Koren, E., Pfeifer, Y., Sulman, F. G. *J. Endocrinol.*, **43**, 471–75 (1969)

226. Karim, S. M. M. *Brit. Med. J.*, **5631**, 618–20 (1968)

227. Karim, S. M. M., Trussell, R. R., Patel, R. C., Hillier, K. *Brit. Med. J.*, **5631**, 621–22 (1968)

228. Elias, J. J. *Science,* **126,** 842–43 (1957)
229. Turkington, R. W. *Endocrinology,* **82,** 540–46 (1968)
230. Turkington, R. W., Ward, O. T. *Biochim. Biophys. Acta,* **174,** 291–301 (1969)
231. Gadkari, S. V., Chapekar, T. N., Ranadive, K. J. *Indian J. Exptl. Biol.,* **6,** 75–79 (1968)
232. Mayne, R., Forsyth, I. A., Barry, J. M. *J. Endocrinol.,* **41,** 247–53 (1968)
233. Dilley, W. G., Nandi, S. *Science,* **161,** 59–60 (1968)
234. Baldwin, R. L., Korsrud, G. O., Martin, R. J., Cheng, W., Schober, N. A. *Biol. Reprod.,* **1,** 31–40 (1969)
235. Baldwin, R. L., Martin, R. J. *Endocrinology,* **82,** 1209–16 (1968)
236. Gul, B., Dils, R. *Biochem. J.,* **112,** 293–301 (1969)
237. Baldwin, R. L., Martin, R. J. *J. Dairy Sci.,* **51,** 748–53 (1968)
238. Korsrud, G. O., Baldwin, R. L. *Biol. Reprod.,* **1,** 21–30 (1969)
239. Sirakov, L., Rychlik, I., Sorm, F. *Collection Czech. Chem. Commun.,* **33,** 951–59 (1968) (cited in Ref. 234)
240. Falconer, I. R., Fiddler, T. J. *Biochem. J.,* **110,** 56P (1968)
241. Turkington, R. W. *Program 41st Meeting Endocrine Soc., New York,* 49 (1969)
242. Stellwagen, R. H., Cole, R. D. *J. Biol. Chem.,* **243,** 4456–62 (1968)
243. Kuhn, N. J. *Biochem. J.,* **106,** 743–48 (1968)
244. Turkington, R. W., Brew, K., Vanaman, T. C., Hill, R. L. *J. Biol. Chem.,* **243,** 3382–87 (1968)
245. Coffey, R. G., Reithel, F. J. *Biochem. J.,* **109,** 169–76 (1968)
246. Coffey, R. G., Reithel, F. J. *Biochem. J.,* **109,** 177–84 (1968)
247. Brew, K., Vanaman, T. C., Hill, R. L. *Proc. Natl. Acad. Sci.,* **59,** 491–97 (1968)
248. Brodbeck, U., Denton, W. L., Tanahashi, N., Ebner, K. E. *J. Biol. Chem.,* **242,** 1391–97 (1967)
249. Turkington, R. W., Hill, R. L. *Science,* **163,** 1458–60 (1969)
250. Kuhn, N. J. *J. Endocrinol.,* **44,** 39–54 (1969)

251. Wiest, W. G., Kidwell, W. R., Balogh, K. *Endocrinology,* **82,** 844–59 (1968)
252. Hilliard, J., Spies, H. G., Sawyer, C. H. *Endocrinology,* **82,** 157–65 (1968)
253. Chadwick, A. *Biochem. J.,* **85,** 554–58 (1962)
254. Meites, J., Hopkins, T. E., Talwalker, P. K. *Endocrinology,* **73,** 261–64 (1963)
255. Thatcher, W. W., Tucker, H. A. *Proc. Soc. Exptl. Biol. Med.,* **128,** 46–48 (1968)
256. Gachev, E. P. *Endokrinologie,* **53,** 352–54 (1968)
257. Voogt, J. L., Sar, M., Meites, J. *Am. J. Physiol.,* **216,** 655–58 (1969)
258. Kamoun, A., Haberey, P. *Pathol. Biol.,* **17,** 159–64 (1969)
259. Wagner, W. C. *J. Am. Vet. Med. Assoc.,* **154,** 1395 (1969)
260. Wagner, W. C., Oxenreider, S. L. *Proc. Biennial Symp. Animal Reprod., 9th, Lafayette, Ind., 1969*
261. Sharman, G. B. *Excerpta Med. Intern. Congr. Ser. 83,* 669–74 (1964)
262. Armstrong, D. T., Hansel, W. *J. Dairy Sci.,* **42,** 533–42 (1959)
263. Hammond, J. *Reproduction in the Rabbit,* 122 (Oliver & Boyd, Edinburgh, 1925)
264. Greenwald, G. S. *Endocrinology,* **77,** 641–50 (1965)
265. Peters, J. B., First, N. L., Casida, L. E. *J. Animal Sci.,* **28,** 537–41 (1969)
266. Wagner, W. C., Hansel, W. *J. Reprod. Fertility,* **18,** 493–500 (1969)
267. Cyonin, T. J. *Lancet,* **II,** 422–24 (1968)
268. Moltz, H., Levin, R., Leon, M. *Science,* **163,** 1083–84 (1969)
269. Crighton, D. B., Lamming, G. E. *J. Endocrinol.,* **43,** 507–19 (1969)
270. Sar, M., Meites, J. *Neuroendocrinology,* **4,** 25–31 (1969)
271. Brumby, H. I., Forsyth, I. A. *J. Endocrinol.,* **43,** xxiii–xxiv (1969)
272. Bryant, G. D., Greenwood, F. C. *Biochem. J.,* **109,** 831–40 (1968)
273. Hagino, N., Watanabe, M., Goldzieher, J. W. *Endocrinology,* **84,** 308–14 (1969)
274. Liptrap, R. M., Raeside, J. I. *J. Endocrinol.,* **42,** 33–43 (1968)

COMPARATIVE PHYSIOLOGY: ELECTRIC ORGANS[1] 1052

Michael V. L. Bennett[2]

Albert Einstein College of Medicine of Yeshiva University
New York, N.Y.

INTRODUCTION

In this review I shall discuss some recent findings concerning electric organs and electrosensory systems. I will emphasize aspects that have general physiological and biological relevance and indicate areas where I think future research is likely to give results of general value. Electric organs have evolved six or possibly seven different times. Representative forms are shown in Figure 1 and the different groups are listed in Table I. The diversity of electric fish makes it difficult to remember which is which, but it is this diversity that is one of their more interesting features. Detailed descriptions of electric organs and electroreceptors—with pictures—are in preparation (23).

Electric fish have been divided into two types, weakly and strongly electric. This is somewhat arbitrary and determination that a fish is strongly electric depends largely on whether the experimenter regards the organ discharge as a deterrent to handling the fish. It is remarkable how ineffective strongly electric fish are at stunning small fish, and careful studies of the effectiveness of the organs in predation are necessary. The electric eel and at least one torpedinid (*Narcine*) have both strongly and weakly electric organs (27, 110). A number of weakly electric gymnotids have small or accessory electric organs in the head region (23).

A strongly electric organ is presumably used to capture prey or resist predators. The primary role of weakly electric organs in freshwater species is presumed to be in "electrolocation", which is a process whereby the fish gains knowledge of its immediate environment by detecting distortions in the field set up by its electric organ. In freshwater species, weakly electric organs, and probably strongly electric organs as well, can also function in

[1] The following symbols are used: PSP (postsynaptic potential), ACh (acetylcholine), CCh (carbamylcholine), and ATPase (adenosine triphosphatase.)

[2] This work was supported in part by grants from the National Institutes of Health (NB-07512 and HD-04248), the National Science Foundation (GB-6880), and the Air Force Office of Scientific Research (AF-AFOSR-550). Some of the data described were obtained on the Rio Negro expedition of the R. V. Alpha-Helix.

STRONGLY ELECTRIC

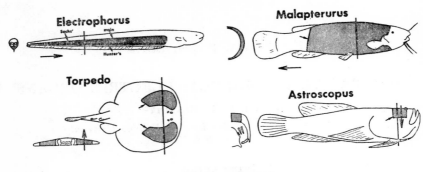

WEAKLY ELECTRIC

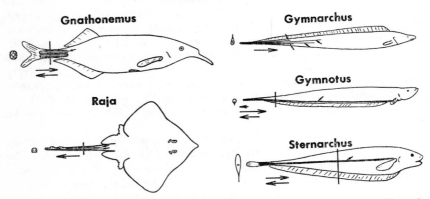

FIG. 1. Representative electric fish. All are shown from the side except *Torpedo* and *Raja*, which are shown from the top. Electric organs are stippled or solid and indicated by small arrows. Cross-sectional views through the organs are also shown at the levels indicated by the solid lines. The large arrows indicate the direction of active current flow through the organs; where there is more than one arrow, they indicate successive phases of activity and the relative lengths are proportional to relative amplitudes of the phases. *Gnathonemus* is a mormyrid; other groups can be determined from family names in Table I. (Taken from Ref. 21.)

communication between species, both intra- and interspecifically (42, 107). The role of weakly electric organs in marine species has not been established. The discharge pattern and pulse shape are generally species specific, although there are suggestions of polymorphism in some mormyrids (26, 70). Different species may also have organ discharges that are indistinguishable.

Strongly electric fish can discharge their electric organs only intermittently because of the large power outputs, e.g., about 1 kW peak pulse

TABLE I

GROUPS OF ELECTRIC FISH[a]

Common name	Family	Genera and species	Strength of organ discharge	Distribution
Skates, ordinary rays	Rajidae	*Raja*, many species, a number of other genera not known to be electric	Weak	Marine, cosmopolitan
Electric rays, torpedos	Torpedinidae	A number of genera, many species	Strong, up to 60 V or 1 kW, some perhaps weak[b]	Marine, cosmopolitan
Mormyrids, elephant-nosed fish (many lack enlarged chin or snout)	Mormyridae	A number of genera, several with many species	Weak	Freshwater, Africa
Gymnarchus	Gymnarchidae	1 species, *G. niloticus*	Weak	Freshwater, Africa
Gymnotid eels; electric eel and knifefish	Electrophoridae	1 species, *Electrophorus electricus*	Strong, more than 500 V[c]	Freshwater, South America
	Gymnotidae	1 species, *Gymnotus carapo*	Weak	Freshwater, South America
	Sternopygidae	4 or 5 genera, a number of species	Weak	Freshwater, South America
	Rhamphichthyidae	2 monospecific genera	Weak	Freshwater, South America
	Sternarchidae	About 9 genera, a number of species	Weak	Freshwater, South America
Electric catfish	Malapteruridae	1 species, *Malapterurus electricus*	Strong, more than 300 V[d]	
Stargazers	Uranoscopidae	1 electric genus, *Astroscopus*; several species	Strong? about 5 V in air from small animals[e]	Marine, Western Atlantic

[a] Detailed classifications will be given in (23).
[b] From (36).
[c] From D. Albe-Fessard, *Arch. Sci. Physiol.*, **4**, 413–34 (1950).
[d] From W. Remmler, *Beitr. Physiol.*, **4**, 151–78 (1930).
[e] From (28).

power in *Torpedo* (36). Skates also discharge their electric organs intermittently (14). All known weakly electric fish living in freshwater discharge their organs continuously, or cease discharging only briefly under conditions where the cessation has clear biological significance in communication or avoiding detection.

The patterns of discharge in freshwater weakly electric fish can be divided into two types which may be termed variable frequency and constant frequency or, somewhat slangily, buzzers and hummers (references in 21). The buzzers emit brief pulses separated by intervals much longer than the pulse duration and the sound is a buzz when pulses are amplified and fed into a loud speaker. Buzzers generally increase their discharge rate markedly when stimulated in any of a variety of ways, a response which appears to represent an increased rate of "probing" the environment. Hummers emit pulses that are separated by intervals about equal to the pulse duration and when converted into sound the result is a relatively pure tone. Hummers alter their discharge rates very little, although small and transient changes in gymnotids probably function in communication and *Gymnarchus* can cease discharging. Gymnotids also change their frequencies when presented with a frequency close to their own, a response which apparently represents an attempt to avoid interference with the sensory system (42, 97, 148).

The freshwater weakly electric fish have what may be considered an active sensory system, that is, a sensory system in which the energy detected is provided by the organism itself (105). A more familiar example is the echolocation system of bats. Obviously an active sensory system operates passively when the appropriate energy is provided by an extrinsic source. The electroreceptors are modified lateral-line receptors. Some fish are very sensitive to electric fields and have morphologically similar receptors but lack electric organs (57, 58, 101). These species have passive electrosensory systems. It is interesting that the passive electrosensory systems were not discovered until after the active systems. Although the receptors had been characterized morphologically, their function was unknown. Both large groups of freshwater weakly electric fish have particular receptors that are sensitive to lower frequencies than are present in their electric organ discharges. These receptors apparently operate passively under all conditions, and the fish have both active and passive sensory systems.

PHYSIOLOGY OF THE GENERATING CELLS, ELECTROCYTES[3]

The fact that some electric fish could generate large voltages made them

[3] The terms electroplaque(s), or what I find less satisfactory, electroplax(es) and electroplate(s), were originally used to describe generating cells that were markedly flattened. In some weakly electric fish the generating cells may be drum-shaped to tubular or may even be spinal neurons sending a U-shaped process from the spinal cord into the electric organ. In others the main part of the cells may be flat, but from one face there may be a more or less complex system of processes or stalks on which the innervation occurs. I propose the more general term, electrocyte, to denote the generating cells of electric organs.

an obvious target for physiological study. Aside from curiosity as to how the discharge was developed, it was hoped that the evolutionary specializations would lead to a greater understanding of physiology of excitable cells. This hope has not I think been borne out to a very great extent, in that considerably more has been learned from nerve and muscle. Nonetheless, a number of important generalizations have been clarified through the study of electrocytes. The large voltages and currents generated by electric organs turn out not to be a result of membrane properties very different from those of nerve and muscle; rather they are the result of modification of the single cells to maximize external current and of arrangement of many cells in series and parallel.

Microelectrode studies showed that for many electric organs the early suggestion of Bernstein (37) as to mode of operation was essentially correct. He proposed that at rest each face of the generating cell generates the same resting potential, and as two equal potentials are opposed, no external current flows. During activity the innervated face of each electroplaque generates an action potential while the resting potential of the uninnervated face remains unchanged. Thus, during activity the potentials of the two faces are no longer equal and opposite, and external current flows. The potential recorded across the cell by external electrodes is a monophasic pulse, positive outside the uninnervated face.

By now every known type of electric organ has been studied sufficiently to explain its voltage output in terms of membrane potentials of the individual electrocytes. Not only the form but the amplitude of the organ discharges can be accounted for in terms of the responses of the single cells. Although a variety of pulse shapes are produced, the basic operation is always similar to that of the Bernstein mechanism, that is the cell has what may be considered as two faces whose membranes develop different potentials to generate external currents (14). The individual faces can have a number of combinations of different types of membrane: (a) spike-generating membrane alone, presumably involving Na and K activation and anomalous rectification; (b) spike-generating membrane mixed with PSP-generating (endplate) membrane, the spike-generating membrane sometimes without delayed rectification but with anomalous rectification; (c) PSP-generating membrane only; (d) membrane exhibiting delayed rectification only; (e) PSP-generating membrane with membrane exhibiting delayed rectification; (f) membrane having a high capacity and high resistance so that most of the current through it is capacitative; (g) membrane exhibiting what is apparently a polarization capacity, possibly due to accumulation of potassium in the extracellular space; and (h) low resistance and inexcitable membrane, that is membrane having a fixed (low) resistance and capacitance. These different kinds of faces are combined in a number of ways as described below.

Types of discharge.—The simplest electroplaques are those of the strongly electric marine fish (Figure 2A, 27, 28, 36). One face is diffusely innervated and generates only a PSP. The uninnervated face is inexcitable and of low resistance. The externally recorded response is a monophasic pulse, positive outside the uninnervated face. The cells themselves are electrically inexcitable and give no response to depolarization. The response obtained by electrical stimulation externally is mediated through the efferent nerve fibers, as is shown by its irreducible delay, a characteristic of chemically mediated PSPs, and by its being blocked following denervation or treatment with cholinergic blocking agents such as curare. Because fibers in the muscles of origin of these electroplaques generate spikes it appears that in evolution from muscle the electroplaques lost their spike-generating membrane and greatly enlarged the amount of PSP-generating membrane.

In one group of skates, which are weakly electric marine fish, the electrocytes are "cup-shaped" and the response resembles that of electroplaques in the strongly electric marine fish except that the uninnervated face exhibits delayed rectification (Figure 2B, 14). The resting resistance of the uninnervated face is high, but when this face is depolarized by PSPs generated in the innervated face, the resistance decreases and the external current flow increases. The response across the cell is entirely positive external to the innervated face, but the shape depends on the condition of the cell. In the resting cell, there is an initial peak of external current before the delayed rectification is turned on; this is due to discharge of the membrane capacity of the uninnervated face. Turning-on of the rectification results in a second peak. The return of the resistance to its resting value requires several hundred milliseconds and a second stimulus just after a conditioning stimulus produces an external potential with only a single peak because the relative contribution of the capacitative current is reduced. The segregation of delayed rectification to the innervated face is not complete, although for maximum efficiency it should be; in some cells the degree of rectification in the two faces is about the same. In "disc-shaped" electroplaques found in a different group of skates, there is less or in some species perhaps no rectification and the responses are the same as those of the strongly electric marine fish (14, 41).

The electroplaques of the eel are only slightly more complex than those of the strongly electric marine fish (Figure 2C, 94, 112, 119). In this type one could include the electrocytes of the main organ of one weakly electric gymnotid and of the cranial accessory organs of several others (15, 23). In these cells the innervated face generates in addition to a PSP a spike that overshoots the zero potential. The uninnervated face is inexcitable and of low resistance. The externally recorded response is like that in the strongly electric marine fish but larger (at least in the absence of electrical loading). In several of the weakly electric fish with electrocytes of this kind the innervation occurs on short stalks and the impulse is conducted along the stalk to involve the main part of the electrocyte.

In many electrocytes both faces generate spikes (Figure 1D). However, the spike-generating membranes have different properties to a greater or lesser degree. In the gymnotid *Gymnotus* one face is diffusely innervated (25). This face is of lower threshold and fires first when the cell is depolarized by PSPs or intracellular electrodes. This activity causes more current to flow outward through the uninnervated face, which then fires causing current to flow in the opposite direction. The resulting external potential is diphasic and initially positive outside the uninnervated face; the two phases are of about the same size. The initial phase of current through the uninnervated face may be largely capacitative (not shown in Figure 2). The resistance of the innervated face remains low while the uninnervated face fires. (The organ discharge in *Gymnotus* is triphasic because two groups of electrocytes are oppositely oriented and fire at slightly different times. The second phase generated by the earlier firing cells sums with the first phase generated by the later firing cells.)

Other electrocytes with two faces that generate spikes are innervated on stalks. In several weakly electric gymnotids and the electric catfish there are one or a few unbranched stalks from one face of the cell (14, 15, 23, 93). Alternatively in the mormyrids there are many stalks profusely arising from one face that fuse to form one or several larger stalks on which the innervation is located (26, 140). The two faces of the electrocytes produce externally recorded phases of about equal amplitude in most gymnotids and mormyrids. In the mormyrid genus, *Mormyrus,* the second phase predominates because the action potential of the uninnervated face is larger and longer lasting (26).

In the electric catfish there is a single small stalk arising from the center of the caudal face of the body of the electrocyte, and the impulse propagates down the stalk to excite the body of the cell (93). Both faces of the cell generate a spike (that of the stalk face may be only a graded response), but that of the nonstalk face is larger and longer lasting (Figure 2E). The external potential is entirely negative over most of the nonstalk face. Close to the junction of stalk and body of the cell a small positivity can be recorded outside of the nonstalk face when the stalk excites the nonstalk face (23). But no sign of the initial positivity on the nonstalk side of the cell has been recorded at some distance from a single cell or in the organ discharge as a whole.

In many mormyrids the stalks lie entirely on the side of the cell from which they arise. In others, some of the ones in which the two faces generate potentials of about equal amplitude, the stalk system is more complex (26, 140). The stalks, after fusing a variable number of times, turn around and come to lie external to the other face by passing through channels penetrating the body of the cell. It is on this side opposite to the side of origin that the stalks fuse to form one or several stalks on which the innervation occurs. The propagation of the action potential in the penetrating stalks produces in the external potential an initial phase of positivity outside the stalk face; thus, the overall discharge is triphasic. The size of the stalk potential is related to the number of penetrations, which is a function of the relative amount of fusion of stalks that occurs on the two sides of the cell. Propagation of activity in stalks that lie exclusively to one side of the cell may also contribute slightly to organ discharge.

In all electrocytes where the spike in the stalk has been recorded, its duration is longer than that of the spike in the stalk face. Although geometrical factors might contribute to the difference, it is probable that the kinetics of spike generation can differ in the stalk from that in the faces just as it can differ between the faces.

In *Gymnarchus* the cells are similar to those in the electric eel except that the uninnervated face is of very high resistance and has a large capacity (Figure 2F, 29). The external current that flows is entirely capacitative (to the degree of accuracy of the measurements). The external potential associated with the monophasic spike of the innervated face is diphasic, and the amplitude-time integral of the initial phase is equal to that of the second phase. The time constant of decay of the second phase is severalfold longer than the period between single organ discharges and the organ discharge appears as a series of pulses on a level baseline. However, there is no dc component in the discharge (no net current flow integrated over one complete discharge cycle). The zero dc baseline lies midway between the pulse peaks and the "inactive" periods between pulses.

The same form of organ discharge is seen in *Sternopygus* and the closely related genus *Eigenmannia* (14). Pulses appear to be superimposed on a steady or dc level, so that there is no net dc component in the organ discharge. In *Sternopygus* the steady component declines with a time constant of about 20 sec when the organ discharge is stopped by spinal section and recovers with a similar time constant, if discharge is resumed artificially by spinal stimulation. These changes are due to changes in the potential developed by the uninnervated faces of the cells, and may represent accumulation and depletion of K^+ external to the membranes. The long time constant of the phenomenon indicates that it is not a true membrane capacity and that it results instead from a process akin to electrode polarization. Although the form of organ discharge in *Eigenmannia* is like that in *Sternopygus,* the discharge frequency is much higher. It is not clear whether the mechanism in *Eigenmannia* is like that in *Gymnarchus* or *Sternopygus*.

The same kind of discharge is seen in one sternarchid, *Sternarchorhamphus* (35). In this form as in other sternarchids the electrocytes are spinal neurons. The generating part is an axonal process that leaves the spinal cord and enters the longitudinally running electric organ, which lies just ventral to the vertebral column. The axon runs caudally for several segments and then ends blindly. [Apparently the myogenic electrocyte has been lost in this and other sternarchids. The electric organ is located where there is a longitudinal nerve plexus in several other gymnotids (23).] Microelectrode studies have not been carried out in this species, but by comparison to *Sternarchus* (see below) it can be concluded that the anterior part of the axonal process generates a spike while the caudal part is inactive. The absence of a dc component in the organ discharge suggests that the caudal part of the process acts as a series capacity, as does the uninnervated face in *Gymnarchus*.

In *Sternarchus* and some other sternarchids the organ discharge consists of biphasic pulses separated by a brief more or less level phase (18). Sometimes the two parts of the biphasic pulse are separated by a distinct inflection. The axon comprising the generating part of the electrocyte leaves the spinal cord to enter the longitudinally running electric organ (122). The fiber passes anteriorly in the organ for several segments and then returns caudally to end blindly at about the level that it entered the organ (23). Intracellularly recorded spikes are larger near the posterior end of the anteriorly running part than they are near the anterior end. Similarly spikes are larger near the anterior end of the posteriorly running part. The timing indicates that the anteriorly running parts fire first and contribute the initial phase of the organ pulse; the impulse propagates around the turning part of the fiber and excites the posteriorly running part which generates the second phase. Apparently one end of each part of the electrocytes generates a spike and the other end is inactive. The inactive end probably acts as a series capacity, because if propagation into the caudally running parts of the electrocytes is blocked by anoxia the organ discharge still does not develop a dc component. This conclusion is supported by comparison to the monophasic sternarchid *Sternarchorhamphus*. Furthermore, in other sternarchids (one of which we believe to be *Adontosternarchus*) the initial head-positive phase is much smaller than the head-negative phase, but the level between pulses is such that there is still no dc component in the overall organ discharge (35). Presumably, morphological studies will show that the anteriorly running part of the electrocyte is smaller than the posteriorly running part, presenting an intermediate condition between *Sternarchus* and *Sternarchorhamphus*.

The size of the nodes of Ranvier differs along the electrocytes in a manner correlating with the proposed function (23). As the fiber leaves the spinal cord it is about 20 μ in diameter and the nodes are of normal size. Just inside the organ the nodes are somewhat enlarged. In its anterior course, the fiber is dilated to be 100 μ or more in diameter and the nodes are very narrow (although area is difficult to estimate because of the dilation). At the anterior end as the fiber tapers, the nodes are very large, 20–50 μ long. The nodes become reduced to normal size as the fiber tapers to a diameter of 10–20 μ and then turns around. The nodes then become somewhat enlarged again as just after entry into the organ. They become narrow as the fiber runs caudally and again dilates to be about 100 μ in diameter. They are very large where the fiber tapers to end blindly. Presumably the medium-sized nodes do the active pulse generation, while the enlarged nodes act as series capacitors. The narrow nodes in the enlarged parts of the fiber may well be sealed off to increase the length constant of the fiber and maximize current flow along the organ. The increase in diameter would also increase the length constant.

In *Adontosternarchus* there is an accessory organ in the chin region which is derived from sensory fibers (35). These fibers end in what appear to be modified electroreceptor cells in the epidermis. The remarkable thing is that the terminal portion of the fiber is greatly expanded and has the same characterisitc nodal structure found in the main electric organ. In the chin organ, the impulse frequency is set in the organ itself (as would be expected from its origin in sensory fibers) and this organ can fire at a frequency somewhat different from that of the main organ. The cells are autoactive, but because they are all aligned with each other in a single parallel array, they tend to excite each other and discharge synchronously. Afferent impulses run centrally in these previously sensory fibers, but the effects of this activity, if any, have not been studied. Although some electroreceptors generate oscillatory external potentials when the skin is dried (see below), one can conclude that the modified fibers of the chin are an electric and not a receptor organ because (a) the nerve fibers are very similar morphologically to fibers of the main organ and very different from electroreceptor afferent fibers; (b) the external potential is generated by the nerve fibers and not by the modified receptor cells, whereas receptor cells generate the external potential of electroreceptors, and (c) the chin organ frequency is very insensitive to changes in conductivity of the external milieu, from air to physiological saline, whereas high-frequency firing of the electroreceptors is easily blocked by covering with water of normal (low) conductivity. It has not been shown that the chin organ excites the cranial electroreceptors to an extent that is affected by the presence of insulators and conductors nearby, but the magnitude of the potential is sufficient for it to do so.

Functional aspects of physiology and morphology.—From the preceding description of types of electrocytes, it is seen that the same form of organ discharge can be achieved in a number of ways. The significance of the particular specializations is often unknown, although sometimes the properties of the organs or the individual cells can be understood in terms of maximizing the efficiency of power generation. For example, it was appreciated very early that the shape of strongly electric organs is correlated with environmental conductivity. In freshwater the organs are long and slender in the axis of current flow in order to give a high-voltage, low-current output; in saltwater the organs are flattened in the axis of current flow for low-voltage, high-current output. A principle of frequent applicability to electrocytes is a kind of impedance matching between the faces (14). The lower the membrane resistance the greater the cell output, but also the greater the leakage at rest, and the greater the exchange between Na^+ and K^+ across spike-generating membrane during activity. It would thus be inefficient to have one face of much lower resistance than the other (or of much lower resistance than the series resistances of the external medium and cytoplasm). One finds that an inexcitable face acting as a series battery with a fixed resistance is generally of lower resistance than the opposed, excitable face at rest (Figures 2A, C). The excitable face reduces its resistance during activity so that under these conditions the resistance of the two faces is more closely matched.

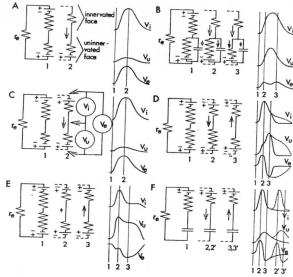

Fig. 2. Activity of different kinds of electroplaques and their equivalent circuits. The upper part of each circuit, labeled only in A, represents the innervated or stalk face; the lower part represents the uninnervated or nonstalk face. The resistance of the extracellular current pathway is represented by r_e. The potentials that are recorded differentially across the two faces (V_i and V_u) and across the entire cell (V_e) are drawn to the right of each circuit (intracellular positivity and positivity outside the uninnervated face shown upwards; note that $V_i - V_u = V_e$). Placement of electrodes for recording these potentials is indicated in C. The successive changes in the membrane properties are shown by the numbered branches of the equivalent circuits, and their times of occurrence are indicated on the potentials. A lower membrane resistance is indicated by fewer zigzags in the symbol. Return to resting condition is omitted. (A) Electroplaques of strongly electric marine fish and cup-shaped electroplaques of rajids. The innervated face generates only a PSP. (B) Disc-shaped electroplaques of rajids. The innervated face generates a PSP and the uninnervated face exhibits delayed rectification. (C) Electrocytes of the electric eel and a few other gymnotids. The innervated face generates an overshooting spike. (D) Electrocytes of mormyrids and some gymnotids. Both faces generate a spike and V_e is diphasic. In some the spike across the uninnervated face is longer lasting and the second phase of V_e predominates. These potentials are shown by dotted lines. (E) Electrocytes of the electric catfish. The stalk face is of higher threshold and generates a smaller spike (indicated by a smaller battery symbol) and the external potential is entirely negative on the nonstalk side distant from the stalk. (F) Electrocytes of *Gymnarchus* and probably of one sternarchid, *Sternarchorhamphus*. The uninnervated face acts as a series capacity and the external response has no net current flow. The summation of a second response (2′, 3′) on the first is shown by the dotted lines.

Many electrocytes have highly convoluted surfaces, and there may also be an extensive system of straight or interconnecting canaliculi. In general the relative resistances of the two faces of a cell correlate with their relative surfaces. In electroplaques of torpedinids and the eel the uninnervated, low-resistance faces have surfaces that are greatly increased by canaliculi in torpedinids and by both convolutions and canaliculi in the eel (39, 103, 104, 111, 133). The uninnervated face of *Gymnarchus* electrocytes is highly convoluted; this membrane is of high resistance, and the increased surface must represent a modification to increase capacity (132). In the disc-shaped electroplaques of rajids the resting resistances of the two faces are about equal and the degree of surface convolution of the two faces does not differ greatly (111). In electrocytes where both faces generate spikes, the surfaces also tend to be fairly similar (104, 111, 132). It is a little disappointing that electronmicroscopical techniques have not to date enabled one to distinguish between membranes of markedly different electrical properties to a greater extent.

Another generalization concerns the presence of a dc component in the organ discharge. All strongly electric fish emit dc pulses; perhaps this leads to more effective shocking of prey or predator. A few weakly electric fish that fire at low frequencies also emit pulses that are dc or have a large dc component, but in most weakly electric fish including all high-frequency species, the organ discharge has no dc component. The significance of an organ discharge without net current flow may be to conserve ions. It also allows the fish to have a dual electrosensory system in which one set of receptors is sensitive to low-frequency signals arising in the environment and the other set detects distortions in the high-frequency field produced by the electric organ.

A long recognized difference between the electric eel and *Torpedo* is now known to be universal: electrocytes of freshwater fish have spike-generating membrane; those of marine fish do not (14, 73). The significance would seem to be related to the need to deliver maximum power to environments of high vs. low resistivity, but it is difficult to see why (14). The subsynaptic membrane of electroplaques, being electrically inexcitable, would be activated to an extent determined by the amount of ACh released presynaptically, whatever the degree of loading. Thus, this membrane might seem better adapted to marine environments. However, the degree of activation of the eel and *Malapterurus* organs has been shown to be independent of loading (9, 51, 92). Probably in most freshwater fish the internal resistance of the organs provided by cytoplasm, extracellular space, and inactive membranes is so great that loading does not prevent maximum activation of the electrocytes whatever the conductivity of the medium. Furthermore, most electric organs have many elements arranged in series-parallel and whichever kind of electrocyte was more efficient energetically would seem better adapted to both environments. We do not understand this difference between marine and freshwater forms.

Some quantitative considerations.—The amplitudes of responses of individual electrocytes of several of the strongly electric fish tend to be somewhat larger than responses of other excitable cells. The PSPs in electroplaques of marine strongly electric fish are up to 90 mV in amplitude, which is near zero resting potential in *Astroscopus* (28). In *Torpedo* the PSPs appeared to overshoot, but in view of the thinness of the cells, it is unlikely that the full resting potential was measured (36). In the electric eel the spike amplitude is about 150 mV. The Na equilibrium potential appears to be about +70 mV (7, 119). Voltage amplitudes of membrane responses are otherwise unexceptional. Of course the externally recorded responses of the individual cells of even weakly electric organs are generally much larger than those of ordinary nerve and muscle cells.

The values of membrane resistance in electroplaques are far below the values for muscle and correspondingly the current outputs are much greater. In eel electroplaques the resting resistance of the innervated face is about 2–5 Ωcm^2 (119; values of 7 and 19 Ωcm^2 are reported in 49 and 94). The resistance of the uninnervated face is about 0.3 Ωcm^2 (94). During activity the resistance of the innervated face decreases to about 1 Ωcm^2 (calculated from 119), and the peak inward current is about 60 mA/cm^2. These values approach the resistance of the extracellular fluid and cytoplasm in series with the innervated face. A 0.1 mm layer of cytoplasm—about the thickness of electroplaques of the main organ—with volume resistivity of 50 Ωcm would have an areal resistivity of 0.5 Ωcm^2; a value of 3 Ωcm^2 for series resistance is given in (49). Decrease of the resistance of the innervated membrane to much below the series resistance would make the cells less efficient.

In *Torpedo* the resting resistance across an entire cell is 5–30 Ωcm^2 (3, 36). The peak current during activity is about 75 mA/cm^2 (36) which, assuming a driving force for each cell of about 90 mV, would give a resistance of 1.2 Ωcm^2 during activity (which would include the series resistance of the cell).

Although the resting and active resistances of the electroplaques are far below those of muscle membranes, the values are comparable to those of the node of Ranvier [resting resistance, 30 Ωcm^2; active resistance, 2 Ωcm^2 (66); peak inward current, 10 mA/cm^2 (59)]. Furthermore, the figures for electroplaques were calculated from macroscopic areas, disregarding the considerable surface convolutions, and a more realistic comparison would be referred to actual areas of plasma membrane. On the reasonable assumption that the plasma membranes of the electroplaques have a capacity of 1 $\mu F/cm^2$ one may estimate the true membrane area from the capacities measured per macroscopic area, which in the eel is about 15 $\mu F/cm^2$ (49, 94) and in *Torpedo* is about 5 $\mu F/cm^2$ (3). Thus, the actual membrane parameters probably differ by factors of 5 to 15 from the reported ones [factors which appear consistent with the increases in surfaces seen morphologically (39, 103, 104, 111, 133)]. Weakly electric organs tend to have somewhat higher membrane resistances, several tens to several hundred Ωcm^2 referred to macroscopic surface. Insufficient data are available for an accurate comparison among weakly electric organs in terms of area of plasma membrane, but the membranes with the exception of membranes acting as a series capacity all have a shorter time constant than muscle and presumably are of lower resistivity.

The property of electrocytes that is most outstanding is frequency of firing. The electric organs of sternarchids discharge constantly at frequencies from 600–2000/sec, *Eigenmannia* operates at 300–600/sec, and *Gymnarchus* at about 250/sec (23). *Sternopygus* discharges at 50–100/sec, but it is like *Eigenmannia* on a 50 per cent duty cycle where the interval between pulses is about equal to the pulse duration (14). The higher values set a record for maintained spike frequency in muscle or nerve. In the fish other than the sternarchids the nerve-electroplaque junction is chemically transmitting (and cholinergic) so that chemically mediated transmission can also operate at high frequencies. However, the synapses between the controlling neurons, which fire at the full organ frequency, may well all be electrically transmitting.

The high frequency of maintained activity suggests that there could be a considerable power output. As yet no satisfactory data are available on these organs, but many of the cells contain large numbers of mitochondria, which suggests a high metabolic rate (132). The peak pulse power of the strongly electric organs is very large, but the pulses can be emitted at a high rate only for short times, and the energy output presumably represents ions running down pre-existing concentration gradients. The strongly electric electrocytes do not have very large numbers of mitochondria, and it would be predicted that the power output per gram of cell that they could maintain would be lower than that of the high-frequency cells.

In marine electroplaques the site of production of electric energy is somewhat paradoxically the innervated face which is inexcitable in the strongly electric fish. It is across this face that the potential is found during organ discharge. In the eel the contribution of the two faces is about equal, as it is in many of the cells where both faces generate spikes. In *Gymnarchus*, where the uninnervated face acts as a capacity, the energy is produced entirely across the innervated face (and similarly in other electrocytes in which one face acts as a capacity).

Ionic mechanisms of electrically excitable membrane.—The ionic basis of the action potential in electroplaques has been carefully studied only in the eel. Inward current is dependent on external Na^+ ions, and Na activation and inactivation occur in the usual time relations during the action potential. The resting potential depends on external K^+ (79) and there is little permeability to Cl^- (83, 119). K activation or delayed rectification is absent in these cells, but there is a rectification phenomenon that appears to correspond to anomalous rectification in muscle fibers (1). This process involves a decrease in K conductance when outward current is passed through the membrane and has been termed K inactivation (30, 119), but it should be distinguished from the K inactivation that is the turning-off of activated K conductance analogous to Na inactivation (2, 117, 118). The voltage-current relation of the anomalously rectifying membrane has a negative slope region, and when Na activation is blocked (by depolarization, tetrodotoxin, or Na$^+$ removal) the cells can exhibit bi-stable behavior under current-clamp conditions (119). When the innervated face is polarized by a constant outward current, it can be stable at either of two potentials and transition between them [inactivation responses (30)] can be evoked by small pulses of the appropriate direction.

Transition to the high-resistance state can be thought of in terms of a regenerative increase in resistance. The applied current depolarizes the cell and decreases K conductance which causes a further depolarization and further decrease of K conductance. Return to the low-resistance condition involves the converse changes. The voltage threshold for transition in either direction is the point of unstable equilibrium at which the current through the membrane resistance at that potential just equals the applied current. If the membrane is poised at this point, a small change in either direction initiates a further change in the same direction.

The significance of lack of K activation and presence of anomalous rectification appears to be to maximize external current flow by limiting exchange of Na$^+$ and K$^+$ across the innervated face (112, 119). At the peak of the spike not only is there no K activation, but the K conductance is decreased severalfold below its resting value. Just after the peak of the spike, the conductance decreases below the resting level to reach a minimum on the falling phase. The sequence of changes during the spike is: depolarization causes Na activation and increased conductance and further depolarization; depolarization also decreases K conductance by anomalous rectification and therefore causes a larger depolarization for a given Na conductance; as Na inactivation ensues, membrane potential falls and the total conductance decreases to below the resting level; at a sufficiently low potential, anomalous rectification reverses and conductance rises to its resting level.

The termination of the action potential is due to Na inactivation without contribution from K activation. The time constant of the electroplaque is sufficiently short that K activation is not required, and also it would seem more useful for the fish to discharge its electroplaques through the external environment as much as possible. The time constant of the node of Ranvier is also very short and the degree of K activation during spikes is considerably less than in the squid axon, where the time constant is much longer (66, 81).

The spike-generating membrane in electrocytes of *Sternopygus* and *Eigenmannia* resembles that in the eel (14). The resistance at the spike peak is actually slightly greater than that at rest. This property can be explained by there being more of the cell conductance in anomalously rectifying membrane and less in membrane showing Na activation. The conductance on the falling phase is somewhat greater than that on the rising phase; the falling phase may involve some degree of delayed rectification.

The spike-generating membrane in electrocytes of several weakly electric gymnotids has delayed rectification, presumably as a result of K activation (14, 25, 30). This response is inactivated, that is the resistance returns to near its initial valve, when the cell is subjected to maintained depolarization, either by immersion in high-K^+ solutions or by applied currents. In these circumstances the anomalous rectification becomes apparent and the cells exhibit bi-stable phenomena under current clamp, as do the eel electroplaques (30).

It is useful to summarize the differences between membrane showing K activation and then inactivation, and anomalously rectifying membrane showing K inactivation only. Activatable membrane is not blocked by Rb^+ or Cs^+, to judge from the normal shape of the spike in skeletal muscle fiber immersed in solutions containing these ions (1). Anomalously rectifying membrane is converted to its high-resistance condition by Rb^+ or Cs^+, presumably because Rb^+ and Cs^+ plug up sites of K^+ passage (1, 119). In membrane showing K activation, K inactivation occurs slowly with a time constant of the order of seconds (2, 30). Anomalous rectification is very rapid; the time constant has not been measured, but is less than about 0.1 msec (30, 112, 119). Membrane showing K activation remains inactivated in the face of continued depolarization by high-potassium solutions. Anomalous rectification follows the potassium equilibrium potential; the current-voltage relation has the same shape starting from whatever the resting potential is (1, 30, 119).

This list of different properties leads one to conclude that the two types of rectification arise from two distinct kinds of sites in the membrane where ions enter or leave the cell (loosely speaking, "channels"). These sites are presumably scattered over the cell surface, intermixed with each other to a variable extent. A further indication of separability is provided by the separate occurrence of the two types in different kinds of cells.

Another type of response, the hyperpolarizing (inactivation) response, has been characterized in electrocytes of several weakly electric gymnotids (30). This response occurs in physiological saline when large currents are passed inward through the cell membrane. It involves a threshold phenomenon due to an increase in resistance like the depolarizing inactivation responses of anomalously rectifying membrane in the same cells. Correspondingly voltage clamping shows that the current-voltage relation has a negative slope region in the hyperpolarizing quadrant. The increased resistance must largely represent decrease in K conductance. Hyperpolarizing responses are unlike depolarizing inactivation responses in that they are not well maintained; the conductance gradually increases again in the face of the large membrane potential, which more or less gradually returns to a value approximately corresponding to its resistance for small currents. The nature of the secondary conductance increase that terminates the response is unknown. Recovery from the secondary conductance increase requires many seconds, and it may represent some kind of breakdown of the membrane caused by the large potentials. Hyperpolarizing responses occur in a number of other tissues (for references see 30), but appear to have no physiological significance, and the mechanisms are as yet undisclosed.

Although responses of freshwater electroplaques appear to involve the same ions as those of muscle in other vertebrates, the delayed rectification in skate electroplaques is possibly different (14, 72, 80). The equilibrium or reversal potential of this process is altered in the depolarizing direction when external Cl^- is replaced by impermeant anions. This result suggests that the rectification might involve increased permeability to Cl^-. The reversal potential can be altered sufficiently to lie above the range where the rectification is turned on. Thus, the effect of Cl^- replacement can be the dramatic one of transforming a graded activation tending to restore the normal resting potential into a regenerative all-or-none response. (The turning-off of the all-to-none response is due to inactivation of the activatable membrane.) The response does not require external Na^+, and is not affected by tetrodotoxin (80). Cl^- activation remains an attractive explanation of the phenomenon. However, Cl^- fluxes during rectification have not been demonstrated, nor are there adequate quantitative data concerning the effects of internal and external concentrations of Cl^- on the reversal potential. A similar response has been seen in muscle fibers of the frog exposed to Na_2SO_4 solutions made hypertonic with sucrose and containing tetrodotoxin to block the normal spike-generating mechanism (117). It seems likely that the mechanism is the same in these fibers and the electroplaques. In other Na-independent responses, Ca^{++} has been implicated (89), although it is difficult to see how Ca^+ could be involved here.

Synaptic mechanisms.—Few specific data on ionic mechanisms of synaptic processes are available for electrocytes. Where it has been measured the PSP reversal potential is near zero potential or at least below the spike peak, which indicates similarity to other excitatory synapses. All neuroelectrocyte synapses are cholinergic as indicated by curarization; a number of electroplaques have been shown to be depolarized by ACh and related drugs and to have their PSPs prolonged by cholinesterase inhibitors (28, 36, 41). There is some evidence from impedance measurements on columns of marine electroplaques that the conductance of synaptic membrane depends to a small degree on membrane potential and that the synaptic membrane is not in the strictest sense electrically inexcitable (16). The direction of the effect allows it to be due to iontophoresis of transmitter, but it is difficult to make this mechanism quantitatively reasonable.

The relation between depolarizing action and concentration of carbamylcholine (CCh) has been studied using the isolated eel electroplaque. The relationship between resulting potential and concentration was found to be sigmoidal (45). (Conductance should have been used as a measure of receptor activation instead of depolarization; saturation at high concentrations could result from approach to the reversal potential for the PSP, but the curve would have the correct shape at low concentrations where the depolarization was small.) Although not much can be made from the upper part of the sigmoidal relation as measured, the lower portion with a positive upward curvature does suggest interaction between activator molecules at sites on the receptor (or receptors). A further observation confirming this conclusion is the alteration of the shape of the dose-effect relation for CCh in the presence of decamethonium, a different activator substance. The upward positive curvature of the relation is largely lost and the shape is changed which indicates that the two activators do not act in exactly the same way. A much earlier iontophoretic study suggested interactions of activator molecules at receptor sites (90).

Some very interesting data on the ACh receptor, presumably localized to the subsynaptic membrane, has been obtained using eel electroplaques (84). There is evidence of a disulfide bond close to the receptor. The reducing agent dithiothreitol largely blocks the effect of depolarizing drugs such as ACh but augments the effect of decamethonium and converts hexamethonium, normally a blocker, into a weak activator. Gentle reoxidation restores sensitivity to ACh and the other drugs unless the cell has been treated with n-ethylmaleimide, which would alkylate an exposed –SH group. Much more rapid action is obtained if one uses several quaternary derivatives of n-methylmaleimide. The increased rate is believed to be due to binding of the quaternary nitrogen of these substances to the site where the quaternary ammonium of ACh binds to the receptor, and this binding holds the alkylating part of the molecule close to the –SH group, increasing the probability of reaction. This class of procedure is termed affinity labeling (134).

Another affinity label for the ACh receptor is p-(trimethyl ammonium) benzene diazonium fluoroborate, a compound which is not an activator, although one end of it is made up of phenyl trimethylammonium, a potent activator (47). This label does not require prior treatment with reducing agents and may be less specific, because the reactive group is more reactive.

Other alkylating agents have been found that activate the receptor as well as form a covalent bond with the –SH group (84). Bromoacetylcholine has a bromide atom on the α carbon of the acetyl group that can be replaced by nucleophiles. It also activates the receptor of the normal electroplaques in the same manner as ACh. When applied after dithiothreitol treatment, it still depolarizes, but the depolarization is only slightly reversed by washout. Curare, however, largely reverses the depolarization. It appears, therefore, that bromoacetylcholine reacts with the exposed –SH group, but that the acetylcholine part of the molecule can still reach the receptor to bind with and activate it. Furthermore, attachment to the receptor is reversible and the covalent –S– bond is flexible enough for curare to displace the activating part of the molecule.

The p-nitrophenylester of (p-carboxyphenyl) trimethylammonium iodide (NPTMB) can acylate nucleophiles which replace the p-nitrophenyl group. NPTMB has a potent curare-like action on the normal electroplaque. After dithiothreitol treatment it appears to bind close to the receptor and bound molecules become activators. Since excess agent blocks the receptor, the maximum depolarization is not reached until unreacted material is washed out. Again this depolarization is reversed by curare as well as by readdition of NMPTB. [It is not clear whether the change from blocker to activator depends on change in the receptor or change in the (p-carboxyphenyl) trimethylammonium moiety.] These results greatly strengthen the case for a disulfide group close to the receptor. Curiously, depolarizing action is restored to the reduced receptor by reaction with the two nucleophiles, bromoacetylcholine and NPTMB, whereas reaction with n-ethylmaleimide and its derivatives does not restore sensitivity to ACh or other activators.

Similar studies could be carried out on muscle fibers with moderately increased difficulty. Particularly where it is important to measure time courses of action, as by iontophoretic techniques, will it be necessary to shift to muscle fibers or at least to small electroplaques. Nevertheless, the great mass of tissue obtainable from the eel should make it useful in isolation of the protein with which ACh is believed to act. The affinity labeling that has now been carried out appears to be a major step towards isolation and characterization of the receptor macromolecules.

Related studies show a number of similarities between acetylcholinesterase and the ACh receptor, as might be expected since each binds ACh (46). Although receptor and esterase activity are clearly separable, the subunits responsible for ACh binding may be very similar in the two cases.

Biophysical studies.—Particularly in strongly electric organs, the work done by the tissue can be controlled by altering the resistance in the external circuit, an experimental variable that one cannot manipulate using nerve trunks. By choice of *Torpedo* or catfish organ the active membrane can be largely limited to PSP or spike-generating membrane. When a piece of organ is carefully isolated, the resistance of shunt paths around and through the tissue can be quite small, and controlled electrical loading can be carried out between electrodes at either end of the tissue (9, 92). As loading of a slice of eel or catfish organ is changed, the tissue behaves in respect to energy output like a battery with constant emf and internal resistance. Although in the eel the shape of the action potential is affected (9), the changes are probably in the passive falling phase (112) and have little effect on the time course and magnitude of Na conductance.

This controlled loading of the tissue has been used in studies of heat production and optical properties. It was suggested by Bernstein & Tschermak (38) that if ions moving down their concentration gradients provided the energy for electric organ discharge, the electric organ should lose heat energy approximately equivalent to the energy expended in the external circuit. This suggestion has been confirmed in that increased loading causes increased cooling, but there is another substantial component of cooling that is more or less independent of loading (9, 92). No satisfactory explanation of the cooling has been achieved. Aubert & Keynes elaborate Hodgkin's suggestion that during the action potential the Na pump in the innervated face is coupled to K^+ efflux and runs backwards to regenerate ATP. This explanation seems quantitatively unsatisfactory in that about half the work done by inward-flowing Na^+ would have to regenerate ATP. It is also difficult to understand how backward driving of the Na pump of this magnitude can be squared with the current-voltage relations (112, 119).

A light scattering change in the electroplaques, related to the total amount of current flowing through the organ (48), is ascribed to alteration in the size of tubules in one or the other face as a result of accumulation or depletion of ions. If a tubule is selectively permeable to cations, current entering the tubule from cytoplasm is carried entirely by cations while current leaving the tubule is carried about half by cations leaving the tubule and half by anions entering it. Thus, the tubules accumulate ions and become hyperosmotic; and water tends to enter the tubule, making it swell [the water movement being relatively fast, cf. (69)]. Birefringence changes were also observed in the eel electroplaque. These changes closely parallel the action potential, but with a slight time lag (although less than that of the light scattering). What is almost certainly the same phenomenon was also observed in the squid axon, which is probably a better tissue for study since its geometry is much simpler (49). In the eel, because of the surface convolutions, it was not possible to determine the direction of the birefringence change for a given direction of polarization of the membrane.

A late optical event in the electroplaques is the change in fluorescence ascribed to oxidation and reduction of diphosphopyridine nucleotide (8). These changes have been related to energy utilization by the cells, and are again affected by loading of the cells.

Electrocytes as experimental material.—In this section I will describe what I see as the experimental advantages and disadvantages of electrocytes, what kind of problems they are particularly useful for, and what they are not useful for.

An advantage of many electrocytes is that they are very large cells that are of low resistance and easily accessible for microelectrode studies. Unlike muscle they do not move when stimulated. Yet the large size and low resistance are often a disadvantage, because the membrane potential may not remain uniform over the cell when it is stimulated by a single intracellular microelectrode, that is, the cells are not "space-clamped". Thus, qualitative results can be obtained using microelectrodes, but quantitative characterization of membranes in terms of Hodgkin-Huxley parameters such as has been done for squid axon (50, 81) and node of Ranvier (66) may not be possible. For example in voltage-clamp studies of electrocytes of weakly electric gymnotids, the normal cells did not remain space-clamped during depolarizations that increased membrane conductance (30). Voltage clamping during decreases in membrane conductance was more successful in that stable currents were obtained at potentials on the negative slope region of the voltage-current relation. The exact shape of the relation in these regions is open to some question, but the data are adequate to predict the responses to current pulses. Better results including characterization of normal excitation could probably be obtained by using very small fish. Spike-generating membrane in electrocytes of *Sternopygus* and *Eigenmannia* apparently can be space-clamped, and the unusual impedance changes during activity should be studied by voltage-clamp techniques (14).

Because electrocytes have a uniform orientation, it is sometimes feasible to use external electrodes on columns of cells, or even on the entire electric organ. This kind of preparation allows satisfactory impedance measurements that can be referred to the single cell (3, 14, 36), and crude but useful current-clamp measurements are also possible where the properties of the individual cells are sufficiently alike that the current density through them can be taken or shown to be uniform (7, 14). It is difficult to study threshold phenomena in this way, because current density must then be non-uniform over a particular cell's surface because of non-uniform activation of other cells in series with it.

Electrocytes are not suited to use of low-resistance axial electrodes for space clamping. However, single eel electroplaques can be isolated (131) and current can be applied more or less uniformly by external electrodes (112, 119). This procedure is possible because the uninnervated face is inexcitable and of low resistance. The single cell is placed between two baths, and transcellular current is restricted to a small area by pressing the innervated face of the cell against a plastic sheet with a small hole through it. This preparation has been used in voltage-clamp and impedance measurements, although it is not clear that space clamping is possible even under these conditions. As shown in respect to the squid axon, space clamping may fail if access resistance through the surrounding solution is too large compared to membrane resistance (50). It is difficult or impossible to clamp the squid axons showing the largest inward currents, and eel electroplaques pass considerably larger currents. Although current density in the node of Ranvier is high, the area is so small that space clamping is not a problem.

In the electroplaque preparation the effects of membrane outside the edges of the window should also be evaluated. If one neglects curvature, the space constant for spread between plastic and innervated face would be given by $\lambda = (R_m l/\rho)^{1/2} \simeq 0.3$ mm where $R_m \simeq 5$ Ωcm^2 is membrane resistance, $\rho \simeq 50$ Ωcm is volume resistivity of the solution, and $l \simeq 0.1$ mm is separation of the plastic and innervated face of the cell. As windows about 1 mm wide were used, this calculation suggests that a significant fraction of the current may cross the innervated membrane at regions where the membrane potential is not clamped. Even if the estimate of l is high, the membrane resistance during activity is less than 5 Ωcm^2. Another question is whether the small stalks on the eel cells (103) like those of several weakly electric gymnotids protrude from the innervated face far enough to be non-isopotential with neighboring membrane. All of these factors require careful analysis (as did voltage clamp of the squid giant axon, 50) and it will be necessary to use exploring microelectrodes to verify space clamping. In spite of these possible or real shortcomings, gymnotid electroplaques allow voltage clamping superior in respect to temporal resolution to what has been possible with skeletal muscle fibers (2). One important measurement that has not been obtainable from muscle fibers is the high speed of onset and reversal of anomalous rectification (30, 112, 119). The primary factor is that the time constant of the excitable membrane is much lower in electroplaques, and capacitative currents consequently are less important.

Another area in which the isolated eel electroplaque can be of value is in flux measurements (79, 131). The spatial uniformity of concentration as well as potential becomes important and the conductances are so large that intracellular concentrations can change rapidly (83). Still the large amounts of synaptic as well as spike-generating membrane and the possibility of controlling transmembrane potential during drug application and flux measurements are features not readily available in muscle. To date drug studies on the eel have involved changes of solutions over minutes, but an improvement of speed of application by two orders of magnitude should be practical.

The electroplaques of the eel are the most suitable for isolation as single cells and mounting across a window so that applied current is transcellular. Two other approaches might be possible: some weakly electric gymnotid electroplaques lie in a connective tissue tube that has some insulating properties and that might be isolated in air or other insulator to prevent current flow around the cell (14, 25); alternatively current might be applied through an electrode pressed against the cell surface, perhaps also using a surrounding guard electrode.

It is not very interesting to voltage-clamp electroplaques of strongly electric marine fish, because they are electrically inexcitable, but an isolated preparation would be useful for pharmacological studies and flux measurements. The electroplaques of *Torpedo* are roughly circular and larger in area than those of the eel, but they are much thinner and would be difficult to obtain in a viable condition. The electroplaques of *Astroscopus* might be suitable, although it would probably be necessary to cut through the edges of the cells in some regions and it is not known how well they tolerate such treatment.

Electroplaques do not appear to be as good as muscle for electrophysiological study of many aspects of synaptic transmission. The presynaptic fibers are no larger than those in muscle and usually do not end in a localized but accessible region. The low-input resistance of the cells makes them less useful for study of miniature PSPs and actions of a restricted synaptic area. The low-input resistance and wide distribution of synaptic membrane also impede experiments using iontophoretic application of drugs, which remains the best method for study of kinetics of drug action. Nonetheless, through experimental simplicity, electrocytes have been and should continue to be useful in studies involving relatively gross application of drugs and intracellular polarization and recording of PSPs. Facilitation of PSPs is a phenomenon of much greater prominence in many electrocytes than in muscle fibers, and might well be usefully studied there, although anatomical complexities are considerable.

Electrocytes are likely to be particularly useful in biochemical studies. The organs are a rich source of acetylcholine esterase (98) and much of the work characterizing the enzyme has been done on material of this origin. The electric organ of the eel is probably the richest known source of the Na-K transport ATPase (6), and has been used in biochemical characterization of this enzyme (6, 126). The eel electric organ is not particularly rich in mitochondria compared to a number of muscles, which suggests that its mean metabolic rate is not particularly high. Nevertheless, the only work it does is generation of electricity. So, it is reasonable that its Na-K ATPase levels should be very high. From the much greater concentration of mitochondria in electrocytes of repetitively active weakly electric fish (132), one would expect considerably higher levels of the transport ATPase. Of course the weight of organ available is measured in grams rather than kilograms. When macromolecules of excitable membranes are to be isolated, electric organs are probably a good place to start. The ability to choose by choice of organ the type of excitability present in terms of PSP or spike-generating membrane may be helpful in the future isolation procedures.

The electric organ of *Torpedo* is now being used for the isolation of vesicles containing acetylcholine (82). Electric organs seem to be much better tissues than guinea pig brain in which to look for cholinergic vesicles when only a very small fraction of interneuronal synapses can involve this transmitter. Another probably useful tissue for vesicle isolation is the electromotor lobe of the *Torpedo* brain. Available evidence indicates that synapses on the electromotor neurons are chemically transmitting, but the transmitter is unlikely to be acetylcholine (23, 130). The electromotor lobes provide a tissue sample of up to a gram of what appear to be neurons of a single type with a single class of synaptic ending on them. While the weight of tissue is small compared to the kilograms of electric organ, the size is very large compared to other neuronal groups of comparable homogeneity.

One important disadvantage of electric fish is difficulty in obtaining them. In the United States supplies of electric eels are reasonably assured (one supplier is Paramount Aquarium, P.O. Box 627, Ardsley, N.Y. 10502) and the gulf torpedinid *Narcine* and *Raja texana* may be obtained somewhat irregularly (Gulf Specimen Co., Inc., P.O. Box 236, Panacea, Fla. 32346). Freshwater weakly electric fish of many kinds and small electric catfish are likely to appear in any tropical fish store. (Suppliers are Paramount Aquarium, Inc., address above, Tropical Distributors, Inc., 29-20 Hoyt Ave. So., Queens, N.Y. 11102; and Aquarium Stock, Inc., 31 Warren St., New York,

N.Y. 10007. Any of the above will ship by air with a good probability of the fish's surviving.)

Neural Control of Electric Organs

How an electric fish manages to discharge its electric organ is a problem that attracted interest even before the operation of the single generating cells was understood. A number of different species have been studied and the basic picture is this (21) : A small group of cells in the medulla, higher spinal cord, or perhaps midbrain fire synchronously which constitutes initiation of the "command signal" to discharge the electric organ. This activity is then transmitted to the electroplaques directly or through one or more neural relays. The necessity for a central control system arises from the fact that activity of electrocytes tends to prevent firing of cells in series with them, and synchronous activity, which is necessary for the largest output, could not be achieved by a peripheral mechanism. The only exception to central control is the chin organ of *Adontosternarchus* where all the electrocytes are in parallel and the activity of each tends to excite the others (34).

The command neurons are probably autoactive in the continually discharging forms, and they receive excitatory inputs in those species that are active only intermittently. In the latter case the command cells "decide" when there are adequate inputs to call for an organ discharge. The most significant feature of these pacemaker or command cells is that they are coupled to each other by means of "electrotonic synapses" (33). The coupling causes them all to fire highly synchronously and prevents autoactive cells from getting out of step with each other. The coupling mediates rapid-acting positive feedback between cells; a relatively more depolarized cell tends to excite its less depolarized neighbors and is itself made less depolarized and inhibited by them. Thus, these synapses are both excitatory and inhibitory, and it seems reasonable to term them synchronizing synapses (22). One may ask whether mutually excitatory chemically transmitting synapses could also mediate the observed degree of synchronization. The synchronization in many of these systems is so precise that the negligible delay of electrically mediated transmission is required; chemically mediated transmission would be too slow.

Synchronous activity of an electric organ leads to a larger output in terms of both voltage and power, because inactive cells prevent maximum effectiveness of active ones. Synchronization is particularly important if diphasic pulses are produced because slightly out of phase addition causes cancellation. How synchronous activity of the command cells leads to synchronous activity of electrocytes will be discussed after consideration of central mechanisms.

Anatomical correlates of electrotonic coupling.—The morphological basis of electrotonic coupling has been investigated in a number of synchronized systems (31–33, 123). In every case close membrane appositions occur that are rare or absent in neighboring regions and that do not occur at synapses for which there is evidence that transmission is chemically mediated. These close appositions are believed to be the site of current passage between cells. They are probably what are now termed "gap junctions" (40, 128). This name arises from the appearance of a 20–30 Å gap between membranes in sections perpendicular to the membrane surface. This gap is penetrable by marker substances applied in the extracellular space. However, there is now evidence that the gap is crossed by channels interconnecting the cell cytoplasms, but separated from the extracellular space (124). The channels continuous with extracellular space form a more or less hexagonal lattice in whose centers the intercytoplasmic channels are probably located. Gap junctions are distinct from "tight junctions", appositions where there is neither gap nor any hexagonal structure (40, 128). (Both types were formerly called tight junctions.) Tight junctions generally occur in epithelia where they form complete rings around cells (*zonulae occludentes*) that prevent transepithelial leakage through intercellular clefts (64). There is no evidence that tight junctions form low-resistance channels between cell cytoplasms, because no cells are known to be both electrotonically coupled and joined exclusively by tight junctions.

Coupling between cells of the same kind may be mediated by electrotonic synapses between dendrites (32). Alternatively cells may be coupled by way of presynaptic fibers that form electrotonic synapses on the cells; current then spreads from one postsynaptic cell to another through the presynaptic fibers (31, 33). (As activity can normally be conducted in either direction across some of these synapses, pre- and postsynaptic connote the usual morphological relations rather than the direction of impulse propagation.) Coupling may also be mediated by both presynaptic fibers and dendrodendritic synapses in the same nucleus (123).

Pathways and patterns of neural activity.—The circuitry of electric organ command systems in teleosts that have been studied physiologically is diagramed in Figure 3. The simplest system is in the electric catfish (31). Two neurons lie in the first spinal segment, one on either side. Each neuron innervates all the electrocytes on its side and each impulse fires the electrocytes once. The two neurons are closely coupled electrotonically, and an impulse initiated in one cell propagates into the other. Excitatory inputs gradedly depolarize the cells, and when one cell is excited, the other must fire also.

In the weakly electric gymnotids more than one neural level is involved (33). The pacemaker cells, of which there may be 20 to 50 or more, are located in the medulla. These cells activate a relay nucleus also in the medulla. The axons of the relay cells descend the spinal cord to innervate the electromotor neurons that innervate the electroplaques. A single impulse in the pacemaker is relayed as a single impulse to the electric organ which is discharged once per pacemaker impulse. In the Sherringtonian sense the final

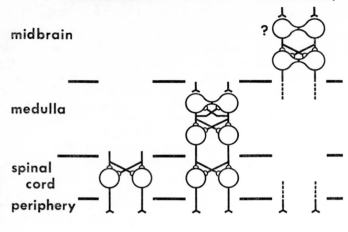

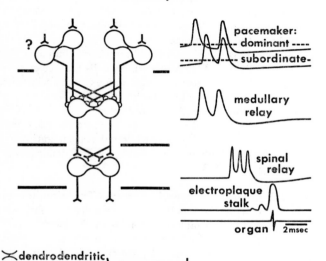

FIG. 3. Neural circuitry controlling electric organs. The modes of transmission are diagramed as shown in the key below. Where axosomatic junctions are indicated, axodendritic junctions are also found. The mode of transmission to the command nucleus is known only in the electric catfish *Malapterurus,* although it is indicated as chemically mediated in the others. Where there is a question mark, the cells have not been definitely localized, but several of their properties can be inferred. The command nucleus of the stargazer *Astroscopus* is now known to be in the medulla, not the midbrain. In *Malapterurus,* the gymnotids, and *Astroscopus,* a single command volley at each level precedes each organ discharge. In the mormyrids, the activity is more complex and is diagramed for each level. The dotted lines indicate the thresholds of the cells in the two pacemaker nuclei. The dominant pacemaker at any given time is the one receiving more excitatory inputs and firing before the other. (Taken from Ref. 21.)

common path for electric organ discharge extends three neurons back into the nervous system. At both medullary and spinal relays the neurons may be electrotonically coupled to each other. Here the coupling tends to synchronize cell firing, although it may not be necessary to fire the cells, since every cell always fires when a command signal is received from the higher-level neurons.

In the stargazer the command signal is initiated in what is probably a midline nucleus in the medulla, and is relayed in the oculomotor nucleus (21, 23). At least under the experimental conditions, synchronization of the command nucleus was not very precise and the oculomotor neurons did not simply relay the signal, but also served the function of "deciding" whether a sufficiently large command volley was present.

In the mormyrids the situation is more complex (21, 32). There is some evidence that the pacemaker nucleus is bilateral, and that an organ discharge can be initiated by a command signal arising on either side (Figure 3). This activity is relayed through a midline nucleus in the medulla to the spinal neurons and thence to the electric organ. The pacemaker activity on the two sides is coordinated, because an impulse arising on one side propagates from the medullary relay "antidromically" into the nucleus on the other side and so resets its rhythm. A bilateral command nucleus apparently also occurs in *Torpedo* (65). No data are available as to interaction between the two sides. The adductor muscles of the pectoral fins of the hatchet fish are caused to contract by activity of the Mauthner cell on either side (11). These cells are then bilateral command cells rather than nuclei for contraction of the muscles. There is evidence for crossed inhibition between the two cells (10) like that demonstrated between the Mauthner fibers of the goldfish (67). Inhibition rather than resetting by excitation is required functionally, because the Mauthner fibers also innervate the axial musculature that flips the tail to either side.

There is another interesting aspect of the mormyrid electric organ control system (Figure 3). What is presumably a single spike in either pacemaker nucleus initiates a two-spike discharge in the medullary relay. The second spike propagates to the pacemaker that initiated the command (the dominant pacemaker), and both spikes propagate to the other (subordinate) pacemaker. Firing in "doublets" appears to be a property intrinsic to the relay cell membrane because the cells give a two-spike discharge in response to a brief stimulus. The two medullary relay volleys descend the spinal cord, and cause two PSPs in spinal neurons that innervate the electroplaques. The first PSP initiates a three-spike discharge. Triplet firing appears to be intrinsic to the cell membrane of the spinal cells as does the doublet firing of the medullary cells. However, the third spike is somewhat labile and the second PSP from the medullary relay guarantees its occurrence. The three electromotor neuron spikes are propagated out to the synapses on the stalks of the electroplaques, but only a single postsynaptic spike is produced. The first PSP is very small, the second is greatly facilitated but still subthreshold, and the third is facilitated sufficiently to reach threshold. The PSPs are not recorded external to the fish, because the synapses are on stalks far from the main body of the cells and there is little or no longitudinal current associated with them. (A similar firing pattern would be detected externally if the cells were diffusely innervated over one face.) The significance of this peculiar sequence of signal transformations is unknown.

A different kind of control is found in the electric eel (21, 24). The circuitry of the control system appears to be identical to that of the weakly electric gymnotids (although it should be admitted that the pacemaker nucleus has not yet been localized). However, the eel has two electric organs to be discharged, the weakly electric (Sachs') organ and the main organ. (Hunter's organ has two parts; the caudal part resembles Sachs' organ and the rostral part resembles the main organ.) Each command impulse from the medulla is relayed at every spinal electromotor neuron and transmitted out to each electroplaque (24). At all frequencies the PSPs in the organ of Sachs are large and adequate to excite the cells (4). At low frequencies the PSPs in the main organ are small and far below threshold. Only when the command signals are separated by several milliseconds are the PSPs in the main organ facilitated enough to cause firing. In the eel then a single neural system controls two organs. Whether one or both organs are discharged is coded in terms of frequency. A considerable simplicity of the control system is achieved at the expense of increased latency of discharge in the main organ.

Synchronization of electrocyte activity.—Given that the command nucleus has reached a decision to fire the electric organ, that is, it has itself fired, the individual electroplaques must be excited synchronously. This is a significant problem, because the different parts of the electric organ may be sufficiently separated that even rapidly conducting nerve tracts could not fire the cells synchronously if they ran directly to the organ.

Two basic mechanisms are known to contribute to synchronization; both involve using conduction time in nerve fibers (or electroplaque stalks) to equalize overall latency of the command signal in reaching the electroplaques. In one mechanism the nerve fibers run directly to the more distant part of the organ, but take a more devious path to the nearer parts, thus tending to equalize pathlength and thereby conduction time. In the second the shorter paths to the nearer parts of the electric organ are of lower conduction velocity, again tending to equalize conduction time. Equalization of pathlength is an obvious feature of a number of electric organs where the different nerves enter the electric organ and run for some distance before giving off branches that return to end near the point of entry. Compensatory differences in conduction velocity apparently occur in the stalk system of mormyrid electroplaques where differences in conduction distance are easily visualized and where synchronization between different parts of the body of the cell is very precise (26). As would be expected, the shorter paths involve stalks that are smaller in diameter. Probably most systems use a combination of the two mechanisms.

In the electric eel differences in conduction time down the spinal cord are compensated for in two ways. At more rostral regions of the electric organ there are both increased delay at the spinal relays and increased latency from activity in ventral roots to spike initiation in the electroplaques (5). The compensatory delay at the spinal relay is due to conduction time in branches of the descending axons. Presumably these collaterals are longer and thinner (or both) at the anterior region of the spinal relay nucleus. The evidence for this conclusion is that transmission from descending fibers to electromotor neurons is electrotonic and the PSPs are sufficiently rapidly rising that they can be delayed very little (19). It is also possible to record from collaterals of the descending fibers and find action potentials at intermediate delays.

At chemically transmitting synapses such as on electroplaques, compensatory delays could in principle arise in "synaptic delay" [which at the neuromuscular junction at least is due to time required for release of transmitter (85)]. Several chemically transmitting relays are known where compensatory delays occur (and they may be found at the nerve-electroplaque synapse in the eel), but it is not known whether the delays are in terminal conduction or in synaptic processes. If morphological investigations reveal that terminals are longer and thinner where delays are greater, one will be less inclined to consider synaptic delay as a factor in the compensatory mechanism.

The demonstration of compensatory delays by differential conduction times provides a mechanism for precise timing that may be applicable to a number of sites in the nervous system. The auditory system for example is exquisitely sensitive to differences in latency of sounds presented to the two ears, although phase-sensitive cells need not lie in the midline at equal distances from the two cochleas (113).

Organizational principles.—Two properties are common to the organization of electric organ control systems. First, where a group of neurons act together, there is likely to be positive feedback between the cells. In command nuclei where a highly synchronous volley arises, the feedback must be present and it must be electrically mediated because chemically mediated transmission is too slow. In relay nuclei there is no absolute requirement for feedback, but cells are often coupled electrotonically, presumably to increase synchronization.

The second property of electric organ control systems is the tendency towards reduced numbers of cells at higher levels. The decision to fire the electric organ is probably always reached in cells that are few in number compared to the final generating cells. The electric catfish is the most striking example, where two neurons control the several million electrocytes. This aspect of neural organization may be termed the committee principle by analogy with decision making in committees, where the smaller the group the better.

One might propose that there be a command "nucleus" containing a single cell, a committee of one. The Mauthner cells can be considered single-cell command systems for the axial musculature on either side (11, 67). In the electric organ systems the controlling nuclei are very effectively synchronized in spite of the number of cells, and one could propose a number of reasons for their containing more than one cell, such as protection against loss of neurons and production of enzymes for chemically mediated synaptic transmission.

Recognition of the requirement for speed of transmission in synchronized systems has been useful in predicting sites where electrically mediated transmission has subsequently been found including neurons controlling sonic muscles (123) and oculomotor neurons (95). In mediating activity which is not very precisely synchronized, the speed of electrotonic synapses might not be required. Examples are the bursting behavior of respiratory neurons and various invertebrate cardiac ganglia. The discharge of skate electric organs may also be quite asynchronous (14). The extent to which synchronization of slow systems is mediated by positive feedback and the degree to which the positive feedback is mediated electrically remain to be worked out. Electrotonic coupling appears to provide a simpler and perhaps more efficient means of positive feedback between cells, particularly where they lie in a compact group (22).

The pathways going to command nuclei in the variable-frequency and intermittently discharging forms are by and large unknown, although most if not all sensory modalities can be excitatory. The slight modifications of frequency in some high-frequency species and the complete inhibition of discharge in others normally repetitive also involve pathways that have not been worked out. But as far as the highly rhythmic discharges are concerned, the analysis of electric organ control achieved to date is reasonably complete, provided one can accept the proposition that the pacemaker cells are autoactive. Certainly one would like to know the ionic basis of the pacemaker activity, but in terms of impulse traffic, the origins and pathways are well defined. However, one does not understand all about the control of an intermittently firing organ when one knows the final common path. Although the decision to fire the organ can be considered firing of the command nucleus, it can also be considered activity of any subset of excitatory and inhibitory inputs to the nucleus that causes it to fire.

ELECTRORECEPTION

Behavioral thresholds to electric stimuli were measured before receptor function was investigated at the cellular level. *Gymnarchus* was found by conditioning experiments to be able to detect voltage gradients as small as 0.15 μV/cm (106). This is a remarkable evolutionary achievement that must be respected (and tends to be suspected) by the electrophysiologist. The nature of the responses of the receptors and of the specializations that lead to their electric sensitivity will be described in this section. While membrane phenomena in receptor function are not understood in any detail, electroreceptors are probably not very different from other acoustico-lateralis receptors.

The electroreceptors are specialized receptors of the lateral-line system. They are usually widely distributed over the fish's surface, but may be concentrated in the head region to a greater or lesser degree. Spatial separation of receptors is necessary if they are to detect the distribution of an electric field, as is required for object location. Possession of electroreceptors does not exclude possession of ordinary mechanosensitive lateral-line receptors (21, 139).

The morphology of electroreceptors has been studied at both light- and fine-structural levels in many species (13, 54, 102, 114, 141, 144–147). The basic organization is that a receptor cell lies in the epidermis. The cell is protected by being at the base of an invagination of the surface, but its outer face is in contact with fluid connected to the external medium by a channel of greater or lesser length. The inner face is exposed to subepidermal space and is innervated by the afferent fiber or fibers (efferent synapes have not been observed on electroreceptors). Generally, a single fiber innervates a group of receptor cells, and a cluster of cells may be innervated by more than one fiber. The receptor cells are sensitive to the potential across the epithelium, and may electrically filter or amplify the signal before it is transmitted to the innervating fiber. The mode of operation of electroreceptors thus is like that of many other receptors where the initial transduction of stimulus energy is carried out by a receptor cell (e.g. 53). On the basis of an ingenious functional argument Lissmann & Machin proposed that the receptors were sensitive to the second spatial derivative of the potential along the skin (100). This hypothesis is contradicted by the experimental results.

At the receptor synapses there is a presynaptic ribbon or dark body as found at receptors of the acoustico-lateralis system (149) and at rod, cone, and bipolar cell synapses in the retina (60). The outer face of the receptor cell may have numerous microvilli or be more or less smooth, but with the exception of ampullae of Lorenzini (147), it lacks the kinocilium of mechanoreceptors (149). The receptor cells are joined to supporting cells by circumferential tight junctions [*zonulae occludentes* (65)] that must tend to prevent leakage of current between cells and channel current through the receptor cells (102, 144). Generally, there is an epithelial layer in the epidermis that is or appears to be modified to have a high electrical resistance. It may have few layers or many. Multiple layers may be important in reducing capacity, as in myelin sheaths.

Receptors have been characterized physiologically both by recording impulses in the afferent nerve and by recording responses external to the receptor opening. The externally recorded responses are best studied when the overlying water is removed, because the water acts as a shunt and reduces response amplitude. Receptors may be excited by very small stimuli applied directly to the receptor; when the fish is immersed in water, they may be excited by gradients set up along the entire fish. They may also be excited by the electric organ discharge to a degree depending on the presence of conductors or insulators close to the receptor.

The receptors require their innervation for maintenance of structure and function (20). The effects of denervation are reported to appear in as little as 24 hr (54).

Receptors have been studied physiologically as well as morphologically in mormyrids, gymnotids, and elasmobranchs, and they fit for the most part into two classes, the tonic receptors, which are sensitive to lower frequencies and are of the "ampullary" type, and the phasic receptors, which are sensitive to higher frequencies and are of the "tuberous" type. Tonic receptors are found in both mormyrids and gymnotids and include the ampullae of Lorenzini insofar as they have been studied. Two classes of phasic receptors occur in mormyrids, the large and medium receptors in my terminology (20). Only one class of phasic receptor has been identified physiologically in weakly electric gymnotids, although there are morphological indications of a second type (141).

In ampullary receptors (Figure 4) an obvious canal connects the receptor or ampulla lumen to the exterior. The receptor cells are largely embedded in the wall of the ampulla and only a small part of their total surface is in contact with the lumen. In tuberous receptors (Figure 4) the passage from the lumen of the receptor cavity to the exterior is occluded by loose epithelial tissue. However, intercellular clefts can be readily observed by electronmicroscopy (102, 146) and a connection to the exterior is required by the physiological data. The receptor cells generally protrude from the receptor epithelium into the lumen of the cavity and most of their surface is in contact with the lumen. Often the lumenal surface of the receptor cells is greatly increased by microvilli.

Tonic receptors.—The tonic receptors in the weakly electric mormyrids and gymnotids are very similar (17, 20). There is a resting discharge in the innervating nerve fiber that is accelerated or retarded by appropriate stimuli (Figure 4 inset). The resting discharge acts as a carrier frequency which is modulated by stimulation. The mode of operation appears to be as follows: Although activity of the innervating fiber can be recorded external to the receptor, the receptor cell itself is linear electrically and does not change its electrical properties in the face of moderate voltages. In the absence of stimuli the receptor cell continuously secretes transmitter that depolarizes the postsynaptic nerve fiber and causes it to fire continuously (Figure 5). If an anodal stimulus is applied to the exterior of the receptor, the inner (presynaptic or secretory) face of the receptor cell is depolarized. The rate of transmitter release is increased and the postsynaptic fiber fires more rapidly. A cathodal stimulus applied externally hyperpolarizes the inner face of the

Tonic, Ampullary Receptor

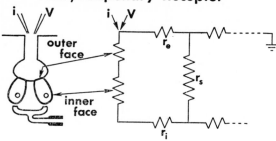

Phasic, Tuberous Receptor

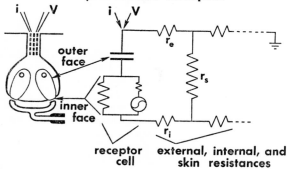

FIG. 4. Anatomical diagrams and equivalent circuits of electroreceptors. Cross sections through the receptors are shown with the external medium to the top. The skin and walls of the receptor cavities are represented by lines; innervation of the receptor cells is indicated. The opening to the exterior of the phasic receptor is shown as occluded by a porous mass. Resistances of external medium (r_e), skin (r_s), and internal tissue (r_i) are included in the circuits; resistances of receptor cell cytoplasm and canals are presumably small and are omitted. Electrodes for stimulating and recording with respect to a distant elecrode are shown at the receptor opening. (Taken from Ref. 20.)

receptor cell and decreases the rate of transmitter release; the nerve fiber fires at a lower rate.

Simple response analysis (by ear) indicates that the receptors in freshwater species are sensitive to signals of the order of a tenth of a millivolt. Since the receptors are tonically active, they probably do not have a sharp threshold and effects of much smaller stimuli should be detectable by signal averaging.

The response to a brief excitatory stimulus is a transient acceleration followed by deceleration. The acceleration phase can long outlast the stimulus. The converse sequence, deceleration followed by acceleration, is evoked

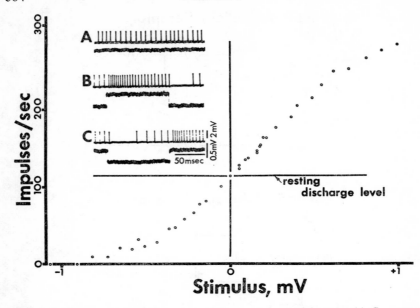

Fig. 5. Input-output relation at a tonic receptor of the gymnotid *Gymnotus*. Inset: upper trace, impulses in afferent nerve; lower trace, stimulating potential applied externally at the receptor. (A) Spontaneous discharge. (B) Excitation by an anodal stimulus. (C) Inhibition by a cathodal stimulus. Graph: For the same receptor, average impulse frequency during a stimulus of about 100 msec duration is plotted against stimulating voltage, anodal stimuli to the right, cathodal to the left. For small stimuli of either sign the input-output relation is linear. (Taken from Ref. 22.)

by a brief inhibitory stimulus. Maintained stimuli cause accommodation, and the sensitivity to very low-frequency sinusoidal stimuli is reduced. The sensitivity to sinusoidal stimuli is also reduced at high frequencies, and there is a maximum of sensitivity at intermediate frequencies (125).

To achieve maximum sensitivity a large fraction of the potential across the skin should appear across the inner face of the receptor cells. The sensitivity of the receptors is great enough to make one think that this condition is met, although no direct measurements of membrane potentials of the receptor cells have been made. For maximum potential to be developed across the inner face, its resistance should be large compared to that of the outer face, which would require that the inner face be of higher resistivity since its area is greater. (As noted above, some electrocytes have surfaces greatly differing in resistivity.) High resistivity implies a long time constant, and the time constant of the inner membrane may be one factor limiting the high-frequency response of the receptors. The impulse frequency evoked by a step excitatory stimulus of moderate strength usually accelerates gradually over several impulses, which could represent gradual changing of the membrane capacity of the inner face.

The ampullae of Lorenzini of the skate, and presumably other elasmobranchs, operate differently from the tonic receptors of mormyrids and gymnotids (115, 116, 121). These receptors are also tonically active but are affected oppositely from gymnotid and mormyrid tonic receptors by stimuli of a given polarity, that is, they are excited by stimuli of a direction that should hyperpolarize the inner (secretory) face of the receptor cells. One explanation of this behavior is that hyperpolarization of the inner face causes release of transmitter. However, there is an alternative that involves ordinary mechanisms. These receptor cells do not behave linearly, but cathodal stimuli can evoke an all-or-none impulse that is negative-going recorded in the lumen; it appears that the outer faces of the receptor cells can generate an impulse of conventional polarity (121). Thus, a cathodal stimulus excites an impulse in the outer face of the receptor cells, and this activity counteracts the effect of the stimulus on the inner faces and depolarizes them, thus causing secretion of transmitter that excites the nerve. The tonic activity of the nerve fibers is ascribable to asynchronous tonic firing of the receptor cells which is accelerated or decelerated by cathodal or anodal stimuli respectively. The inward current through the excited outer face of a receptor cell tends to make the receptor lumen more negative and thus excite other receptor cells. The synchronous activity of many cells evoked by relatively strong stimuli apparently provides a large enough negativity in the receptor lumen that other cells are excited and the response becomes sufficiently regenerative for an all-or-none impulse to occur.

The ampullae of Lorenzini are more sensitive than freshwater tonic receptors that have been studied; they have been observed to respond unequivocally to stimuli of 1–10 μV (115). Perhaps, the impulse-generating capability of the receptor cells provides a stage of amplification that helps to achieve this great sensitivity. Occasionally all the fibers in the innervating nerve fire together in repetitive bursts, suggesting that the interaction between receptor cells of neighboring ampullae can become excessive. Similar oscillations are sometimes observed in phasic receptors as will be described below.

Several lines of evidence indicate that transmission at the receptor synapses of tonic receptors is chemically mediated. Morphologically, the synapses appear to be chemically transmitting, that is pre- and postsynaptic membranes are separated by a distinct gap and the receptor cells contain many presynaptic vesicles (13, 102, 144, 147). There is an irreducible synaptic delay of about 1 msec as is characteristic of chemically mediated transmission (20). [The delay is considerably longer in the ampulla of Lorenzini, which is ascribable to the indirect means by which excitatory stimuli depolarize the inner faces of the receptor cells (121).] If a strong brief stimulus is given, the nerve response long outlasts the stimulus. An inhibitory stimulus cannot block this maintained response, a result that is difficult or impossible to explain by electrically mediated transmission (17, 20, 121). It is tempting to suppose that the maintained discharge is due to secreted transmitter remaining in the synaptic gap. This explanation seems unlikely, however, because at the end of a long-lasting stimulus where the nerve is still firing rapidly, termination of the stimulus causes an immediate cessation of nerve activity. It is more likely therefore that during a brief excitatory stimulus, transmitter is "committed" to be secreted as might for example be caused by an accumulation of Ca^{++} inside the receptor cells (cf. 89).

Since effects of stimulation on transmitter release are inferred from nerve impulse frequency, the response patterns of tonic receptors can be explained in alternative but more complex ways than the ones set forth here. For example, excitation and inhibition could be caused by separate transmitters released by opposite polarities of stimulation and acting on a level of spontaneous activity in the nerve. It is difficult to accept a two-transmitter hypothesis because of the symmetry of the response to small stimuli of either sign (Figure 5). In the ampulla of Lorenzini it should be possible to obtain direct evidence for the kind of transmitter action, because it is possible to record intracellularly from the afferent fibers (121). At this synapse excitation is due to a PSP involving increased conductance as indicated by decrease in height of antidromic spikes during the PSP. In a few instances inhibitory stimuli were accompanied by hyperpolarization of the nerve, but we have not yet been able to measure the predicted decrease in conductance during this hyperpolarization. The problem is that the experimental manipulations tend to cause failure of the resting discharge; we believe that they do so by blocking the resting release of transmitter.

A number of species of nonelectric catfish as well as a few other fish have receptors morphologically very similar to tonic receptors (56, 99, 114, 145). No physiological data are available as to receptor function, although there is behavioral evidence that some of these receptors operate in a passive electrosensory system (57, 101). It would be very interesting to know to what extent the receptors are like those of weakly electric species. A particularly favorable preparation may be the receptors in the transparent catfish *Kryptopterus* (145). In this form the receptor cells are very close to the receptor opening and probably could be reached by microelectrodes without passing through connective tissue. Also important is the transparency of the fish which should allow visualization of electrode placement. [Note added in proof: It is indeed possible to record intracellularly from the receptor cells in *Kryptopterus*. As expected the receptors are tonic electroreceptors and the properties of the receptor cells are like those demonstrated or inferred for tonic receptors in gymnotids and mormyrids.]

Phasic receptors.—The defining characteristic of phasic receptors is the absence of maintained response to maintained stimuli. A rectangular stimulus can evoke one or several impulses in the nerve at its onset or termination or both, but the response does not last throughout the stimulus (17, 20, 138). Spontaneous activity is usually absent except in the large receptors of mormyrids; when present it is irregular, unlike the steady discharge of tonic receptors. The evidence indicates that the response pattern results from electrical differentiation of the applied signal. The outer faces of the receptor cells act as a series capacity and thus prevent any maintained effect of long-lasting stimuli (17, 20). The morphological correlary of this role of the outer faces is the protruding nature of the receptor cells. In these receptors the outer faces have a much greater area than the inner faces, even if we ignore the large multiplication of area due to microvilli (20, 55, 102, 141, 146). Phasic receptors are "tuberous" and the receptor cells seem well protected from the external medium, perhaps because the large lumenal surface requires the receptor cell to be in contact with solutions approximating physiological saline.

A second response characteristic of phasic receptors is that the receptor cells respond electrically to a stimulus (17, 20). The response may be an all-or-none impulse, a regenerative but graded response, or possibly delayed rectification. (A possible exception is presented by phasic receptors of the eel in which the receptor cells were not observed to give an electrical response in isolated preparations.) The regenerative responses provide a moderate degree of amplification; all the electrically excitable responses do some signal shaping. The receptor cells that respond regeneratively often exhibit damped or maintained oscillations if the overlying water is removed, which has the effect of increasing r_e in Figure 4 (20). Under these circumstances the electrical loading of the receptor cells is reduced and apparently the feedback of the regeneratively responding membrane becomes excessive. That the oscillations are merely due to absence of loading is shown by the immediate onset and termination of the oscillations when the receptor is electrically disconnected and connected to a loading resistance (20). In mormyrid large receptors the oscillations can be at a frequency of 1000 or 2000 impulses per second. In various gymnotids the frequency of oscillation correlates with the duration of the electric organ discharge. The nerve response need not follow at the frequency of the receptor oscillations; afferent impulses may totally cease or continue irregularly at a lower frequency but in a fixed phase relation to the oscillations.

The presence of the blocking capacity at phasic receptors leads to a number of properties (or more logically, the series capacity was inferred from these properties). The response to a long-lasting rectangular stimulus is not maintained and after the initial transient the excitability to a brief stimulus returns to its resting value. The response to the onset of a rectangular anodal pulse is identical to the response to the termination of a long-lasting cathodal stimulus of equal amplitude. This is because each change in stimulus changes the charge on the capacity of the outer face by the same amount and therefore causes the same current to flow through the inner face of the receptor cell (Figure 6A, B). The same equality of response holds for onset

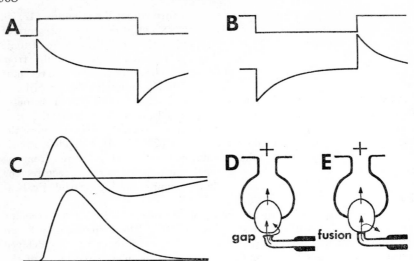

FIG. 6. External potentials and potentials across the inner face of the receptor cells of phasic receptors. Effect of the blocking capacity of the outer face (circuit in Fig. 4). Upper trace in (A-C), potential at the receptor opening, positivity upwards; lower trace, potential that would be recorded across the inner face of the receptor cell, intracellular positivity upwards. (A) If a rectangular anodal voltage pulse is applied at the receptor opening, the inner face is depolarized at the onset of the stimulus, but the membrane potential then returns to its resting level. At the termination of the stimulus, the inner face is transiently hyperpolarized. (B) If a rectangular cathodal voltage pulse is applied, the converse sequence is observed. Excitability of the receptor cell is neglected here. Also, the potential across the inner face would be smaller than the applied potential but is shown as larger, as if recorded at higher gain. (C) If the inner face generated a spike of the form shown on the lower trace, the external potential would be diphasic as indicated on the upper trace, the areas under the two phases being equal. Shown as if recorded at the same gain. (D) Where the synapse between receptor cell is chemically transmitting and there is a gap, nerve action currents (arrows) that make the exterior positive will tend to hyperpolarize the inner, excitable face of the receptor cell. (E) Where there is an electrotonic synapse between receptor cell and nerve fiber, action currents (arrows) making the exterior positive will also depolarize nonjunctional membrane of the inner face. (Taken from Ref. 20.)

of cathodal stimuli and termination of long-lasting anodal stimuli. The onset of cathodal and termination of long-lasting anodal stimuli both transiently hyperpolarize the inner face of the receptor cell. In large receptors of mormyrids and phasic receptors of gymnotids, responses to these stimuli are delayed as if they represented anode break responses following the hyperpolarization.

The responses generated by the inner face of receptor cells are, when recorded externally, transmitted through the capacity of the outer face. Since the potential across the inner face of the receptor will return to its initial value at the end of a response, no net current can flow through the capacitor. Thus, a monophasic impulse generated by the inner face of the receptor cell causes a diphasic potential to be developed across the external resistance—the first, positive phase representing discharge of the capacity and the second, negative phase representing recharging to the initial potential (Figure 6C). The positive and negative phases have equal integrals of amplitude over time, thus in the photographic records the areas under the positive and negative phases are equal.

The equivalence of onset and termination of equal but opposite stimuli has been observed at all phasic receptors studied. The lack of effect on excitability of maintained stimuli is a closely related property that has been checked less frequently. The absence of net current flow during a receptor cell response has been demonstrated only in large receptors of mormyrids and phasic receptors of *Gymnotus*, because only in these are the responses sufficiently large and separated from the stimulus required to evoke them.

Transmission at synapses of phasic receptors of gymnotids and (phasic) medium receptors of mormyrids is indicated to be chemically mediated by the same kind of evidence as obtained for tonic receptors. In brief, the morphology is right, there is an irreducible synaptic delay, and a brief excitatory stimulus produces a long-lasting nerve discharge that cannot be blocked by an inhibitory stimulus. However, at the large receptors of mormyrids, transmission is apparently electrically mediated.[4] This conclusion depends on three principal lines of evidence. Most simply, the time required for an impulse to propagate across the synapse is small, about 0.3 msec at room temperature (17, 20, 137). This value is less than synaptic delay at chemically transmitting synapses at this temperature (86). A second reason for believing that there is electrically mediated transmission at the receptor synapse is the way in which antidromic impulses invade the receptor cells. The antidromic spike in the receptor cells arises when the externally recorded nerve impulse is positive-going. This would occur if there were an electro-

[4] In earlier studies I reported that the externally recorded response at large receptors lasted for at least 1 month after denervation, and that it could be concluded that the response was generated in the receptor cells (17, 20). The observations were in error because I had sectioned only the dorsal sensory nerve and some of the dorsal receptors are innervated by small branches that run up from the branch of the lateral-line nerve that passes posteriorly at the level of the spinal cord (78). Derbin et al. (54) state that decline of externally recorded responses and degeneration of receptor cells proceed in parallel and that both responses and cells are gone after 2 weeks. The conclusion is still that the externally recorded response is generated by the receptor cells. The site of origin is of some importance to the question of synaptic transmission, because the response must be generated by the receptor cells and not the nerve fiber in order that there is a synapse for activity to cross. Other less direct evidence for the existence of the synapse is discussed in the earlier students (17, 20).

tonic synapse connecting the two, but not if they were separated by a synaptic gap (Figure 6E). At phasic receptors in gymnotids where transmission is chemically mediated, antidromic impulses can excite the receptor cells, but the relations between nerve and receptor cell activity are quite different. Because of separation of nerve and receptor cell, nerve activity causing positivity outside the receptor is equivalent to a cathodal stimulus applied at the receptor opening (Figure 6D). A final factor indicating electrically mediated transmission at large receptors is that high-Mg^{++} solutions have little effect on the response at concentrations that markedly reduce excitability of medium receptors (137).

Morphological investigations of large receptors have so far only disclosed synapes typical of chemically mediated transmission, but electrotonic synapses may well have been missed (55). The presence of synaptic characteristics of chemically mediated transmission does not preclude electrically mediated transmission, for all known axosomatic and axodendritic electrotonic synapses have, in addition to regions of close apposition, presynaptic vesicles and desmosome-like structures, yet at several of these synapses the evidence indicates that there is little or no chemically mediated component of the PSPs (31, 33).

The synapses of the large receptors are probably not unique among receptors in transmitting electrically. It has been apparent for some time that transmission should be electrically mediated at the calyx synapses of the vestibular system, for the form of the synapse would greatly impede postsynaptic currents through chemically sensitive membrane on the inner surface of the calyx (16). Recently, close appositions between receptor cell and afferent nerve fiber have been found that provide a morphological basis for electrical transmission (136).

Input-output relations.—Accepting that impulse frequency in the afferent fiber reflects release of an excitatory transmitter, one can infer important features of the input-output relations at electroreceptor synapses. In tonic receptors of mormyrids and gymnotids, the impulse frequency–stimulus strength relation is sigmoidal in shape (Figure 5), and the relation between transmitter release and presynaptic potential would be expected to have the same form. The actual potential-secretion relation should extend a little below the level at which impulse frequency stops, and it should rise somewhat more rapidly and not level off so soon as the impulse relation, because refractoriness would reduce impulse frequency. This sigmoidal relation differs in several important respects from the sigmoidal relation between pre- and postsynaptic potentials at the squid giant synapse (88, 96) which is probably representative of neuromuscular (87) and many other synapses. At the squid synapse there is no detectable release for presynaptic depolarizations below about 25 mV, and PSP amplitude reaches its maximum for depolarizations of about 75 mV. In contrast, the receptor cell releases transmitter in the absence of applied depolarization and nearly the full range of release is produced by only a few millivolts change in presynaptic potential.

The input-output relation of synaptic membrane of phasic receptor cells differs from that of tonic receptor cells in that there is little resting release of transmitter. It is difficult to be confident of the shape of the potential-secretion relation because of active processes in the receptor cells. In some phasic receptors the number of impulses in response to a brief stimulus rises sharply after a certain threshold is reached and then saturates (74, 75). As these receptors are activated by the electric organ and presumably operate in active electroreception, it makes biological sense for them to have a high threshold close to the minimum size of stimulus provided by the organ and to be very sensitive to changes above this threshold, which would then signal influences of objects distorting the field. However, other phasic receptors do not appear to have such rapidly rising input-output relations (138).

The input-output relations at synapses of tonic electroreceptors may be typical of other receptor synapses. In mechanically sensitive receptors of the acoustico-lateralis system, the basic morphology of the synapse is the same (149). Only the outer face of the receptor cells is different in being mechanically sensitive. Very probably, excitation of these receptors involves altered permeability of the outer face such that current flows inward through this face depolarizing the presynaptic face and causing it to release transmitter (53, 68). Although the possibility of electric excitability of receptor cells is generally not considered, the electroreceptors indicate that anything from spike generation to delayed rectification may occur. Intracellular recording from certain hair cells in the goldfish did not reveal any signs of electric excitability (68). Some vestibular receptors are tonically active like tonic electroreceptors (68, 136).

It would be expected that low-threshold auditory and other receptors would have the same requirement for sensitivity of the secretory membrane as do sensitive electroreceptors. The cochlear microphonic that results from activity of hair cells has been calculated to be about 0.01 μV at auditory threshold (106). Since this externally recorded response is probably 1 per cent or less of the actual transmembrane potential across the presynaptic face of the hair cells, the actual stimulus for transmitter secretion is 1 μV or more. One concludes that electroreceptors probably do not have a sensitivity very different from that of hair cells. [The opposite conclusion was drawn by Machin & Lissmann (106) at a time when there was little information about receptor function.]

The sensitive input-output relation of electroreceptor synapses might be found in short axon cells such as the bipolar cells of the retina (60) and at reciprocal synapses such as those of the olfactory bulb (127). In these cases the propagated action potential probably is not required to transmit potentials between receptive and output parts of the cells, and slow graded PSPs generated at one site could cause release of transmitter at a site that is nearby in terms of electrotonic decrement. In this connection it is interesting that the bipolar cell synapses have presynaptic ribbons like those otherwise found only in receptor cells.

The virtue of the tonic electroreceptors of freshwater fish is that they are specialized to detect low-frequency electric fields across the skin. The specializations that channel current through the receptor cells and the electrical linearity of the cells allow the experimenter to have considerable control over the size and shape of the presynaptic potential.

Chemistry of transmission.—It has been suggested that release of transmitter at interneuronal and neuromuscular synapses involves entry of Ca^{++} (89). Mg^{++} antagonizes Ca^{++} and can block release of transmitter at many synapses, presumably by competing with Ca^{++} at some stage of the release process. The effects of Ca^{++} and Mg^{++} on the synapse of medium electroreceptors of mormrids have been studied in an isolated preparation (137). Antagonism between the two divalent cations is not nearly so clear cut as at other synapses. The most dramatic result is that even 30 mM Mg^{++} does not block transmission, although sensory threshold is markedly raised and the maximum number of impulses is reduced to one from the usual four to six. The tentative conclusion is that either the Ca^{++} site is less affected by Mg^{++} than at ordinary synapses or Mg^{++} can to a small degree substitute for Ca^{++}.

Some preliminary experiments have been done on the nature of the transmitter at these receptors. Cholinergic drugs are without effect, but L-glutamate and L-aspartate (but not D-glutamate) in millimolar concentrations excite and then block the receptors. Direct stimulation of the nerve close to the receptor fails shortly after electrical stimulation of the receptor cells fails to excite the nerve fiber, but subsequently the directly evoked nerve response recovers. This sequence of changes is ascribable to depolarization of the nerve terminal by glutamate producing first excitation and then cathodal block; later desensitization to glutamate and the transmitter occurs; and finally the terminal recovers its normal resting potential and direct excitability.

Little work of this kind has been done on other receptor synapses with the exception of the carotid body where the effects of divalent ions are also complex and where the transmitter has been identified as acetylcholine (62, 63). Possibly pharmacology of transmission would be better investigated at a mechanoreceptor where substances could be iontophoretically applied with much less fear of electrical stimulation of the receptor cells. Intracranial receptors, being in a protected location, may also be less enveloped in connective tissue, an advantage for microelectrode studies (68).

Effect of electric organ discharge on electroreceptors.—Unfortunately most studies of afferent inpulses evoked by organ discharge have not involved identification of receptor type (43, 74–77, 138, 143). Usually, however, it is possible to infer from the response what kind of receptor was being studied. Because tonic receptors have low sensitivity to higher-frequency (sinusoidal) stimuli, they probably do not respond to the electric organ discharge in species where the discharge has little dc component. This lack of interaction has been directly demonstrated only in *Gymnotus* (138) and *Sternopygus* (43) but should hold for mormyrids as well (20). It appears then that in most electric fish tonic receptors act largely passively and detect low-frequency signals of extrinsic origin. What are probably tonic receptors in the eel do respond to discharges of the weakly (43) electric organ (76); these are monophasic pulses that therefore have a significant low-frequency component. There may be some stimulation of tonic receptors by muscle action potentials and dc potentials such as those due to injuries of the skin, and conceivably changes in these responses could signal the presence of objects (43, 58).

Phasic receptors are excited by the organ discharge. Changes in afferent responses can be evoked by the presence of insulators or conductors. A variety of coding mechanisms have been described (43). For lower-frequency organ discharges there may be several nerve impulses following each discharge; changes in the field may alter the number of impulses per discharge and/or their latency. Particularly for higher-frequency discharges, the impulses may fail to follow the organ discharge frequency one to one, and changes in the field may alter the probability of an impulse's occurrence as well as its latency (77). Phasic receptors generally continue to give an altered response in the presence of a stationary stimulating object, although there may be some adaptation. The continued responding has sometimes been called tonic even though it is not due to a maintained electrical stimulus, but rather to repeated stimulation of the receptor by an organ discharge of altered size (77).

Sensitivity of the receptors and behavioral thresholds.—An important factor in the sensitivity of electric fish to electric fields is the accessory structures to the receptors. The most straightforward example of the effect of accessory structures is found at the ampulla of Lorenzini (147). This receptor lies deep beneath the surface and is connected to it by a canal that may run more than half the length of the body in the skates. The canal wall has a very high surface resistivity, about 5 $M\Omega$-cm^2, and the space constant of a canal can be up to a meter. Thus, the receptor cells detect most of the difference in potential between the canal opening and body interior just external to the inner face of the receptor cell. A potential gradient in the seawater appears in the animal with little change, which indicates that the skin resistance is not very great compared to the resistance of the interior (116). (Some distortion of the applied field must be produced because the fish's tissue has a conductance well below that of seawater.) Thus each receptor provides information about external fields in terms of the potential difference between two points. The fish is equipped with a large number of receptors with canals of different lengths oriented in different directions. Receptors with long canals should be sensitive to smaller overall gradients, but provide less spatial resolution. Because of the capacity of the canal walls, receptors with long canals should also be less sensitive to higher frequencies (147).

In freshwater weakly electric fish the arrangement of accessory structures is somewhat different (17, 20). The skin of the fish is of very high resistance and the potential gradient inside the fish is much smaller than the external gradient. Each receptor detects the difference in potential between its external opening and the interior of the animal, the latter being an average of the potential over the whole fish.

A question that arises is whether the observed sensitivities of the electroreceptors explain the behavioral thresholds. From the foregoing considerations it is clear that comparison of behavioral thresholds measured in terms of uniform gradient along the fish and threshold of receptors measured as transepithelial potentials can be misleading. For ampullae of Lorenzini the actual stimulus is the gradient times the length of the receptor canal oriented in the direction of the stimulus; for freshwater species the stimulus is about half the total voltage difference across the fish (assuming the skin resistance is equal on opposite surfaces).

A difficulty also arises from the use of longitudinally oriented stimuli while recording from single afferent fibers. Receptors in the middle of the fish where current flow is largely tangential to the surface are much less affected by longitudinal fields than are receptors at the ends of the fish where most of the current enters and leaves the body, even though the sensitivity of the receptors to transepithelial stimulation is uniform along the fish (17).

In the skate the lowest behavioral threshold observed was about 0.01 μV/cm while the lowest receptor threshold was about 1 μV (58, 115). Since the longest ampullary canal in the behavioral experiments must have been about 20 or more cm in length, the total voltage across these receptors would have been 0.2 μV, which brings sensitivities of receptor and organism into reasonable agreement.

The sensitivity of *Gymnarchus* was about 0.15 μV/cm, which in the 50 cm animal used would correspond to a stimulus of about 5 μV to the receptors (25 cm times 0.15 μV/cm, 106). The receptors in *Gymnarchus* have not yet been studied physiologically, but the required sensitivity is only 20 times greater than that readily observed in tonic receptors of mormyrids. For high frequencies the threshold to pulsed stimuli was given by the dc component of the stimuli, which indicates that the phasic receptors were not more sensitive to the ac component of the stimulus than the tonic receptors were to the dc component.

Thresholds measured in *Eigenmannia* for the unconditioned interference avoidance response were of the order of 10 μV/cm (148). These thresholds would correspond to voltages across the receptors that ranged from about 5 or 10 μV or up to 5 or 10 times larger, depending on the orientation of the fish. It should be kept in mind that detection of high-frequency ac signals involves the phasic receptors. The relevant factor in high-frequency fish is the incremental sensitivity of the receptors, which would give the change in response for a small externally applied stimulus superimposed on the larger organ discharge. Behaviorally the sensitivity of *Gymnarchus* to applied fields is about the same as that calculated from detection of objects distorting the field produced by its electric organ (100). Insufficient data are available for comparison of incremental thresholds of phasic receptors to behavioral thresholds. It will be recalled that phasic receptors need not have particularly low thresholds, but that the change in response may be very rapid just above threshold (75). In pulsing species, the incremental thresholds may also be relevant to detection of extrinsic signals. In *Hypopomus* the unconditioned response of acceleration of organ discharge rate is evoked by a much weaker electric pulse if the pulse is superimposed on organ discharge rather than presented between discharges (97). Presumably this difference is a result of differences in stimulation of the receptors.

Much of the work on sensory inputs has been concerned with the effects of objects, insulating and conducting (74–77). While these studies are important in establishing that electroreceptors can actively sense objects, the actual change in the potential that the organ discharge develops across the receptors has not been measured. This aspect of the sensory process badly needs exploration.

The electric fish are sensitive to voltage gradients some 10^5 times smaller than the reported sensitivities of fish without an electrosensory system (100, 106). Tonic receptors in *Gymnotus* at least are more than 100 times more sensitive to electric fields than are mechanoreceptors of its own lateral line (139). Conversely phasic receptors are quite insensitive to touch or other types of stimuli. Tonic receptors are moderately sensitive to other modalities such as touch, temperature, and salinity changes; the latter are apparently due to diffusion potentials (116). The specializations of accessory structures leading to increased electrical sensitivity suggest that the touch and temperature responses are nonspecific, as are our own visual or auditory responses to mechanical stimulation. In ampullae of Lorenzini the location of the receptors deep in the body makes any function other than electroreception extremely unlikely. Evaluation of the degree to which nonelectric excitation of the receptors gives the animal information about its environment would require extensive conditioning experiments.

I think the tentative conclusion is that there is a factor no worse than 10 between observed behavioral and receptor thresholds, although the comparison is difficult to make accurately because of methodological differences in the two types of measurement. The resolution of the discrepancy may well lie in the difficulties of single-unit techniques, namely, finding the lowest-threshold receptors and keeping the animal in good condition so that the receptors operate at their greatest sensitivity. Further studies are required that utilize current knowledge of receptor function. Of course an additional factor in behavioral sensitivity may be averaging over a number of receptors in the CNS. Another problem in sensory physiology is whether, and if so how, the CNS makes the same discriminations of changes in afferent volleys that the experimenter does.

Central processing of electrosensory inputs.—The remarkable thing about the brain of fish with electrosensory systems is the large size of the cerebellum. This hypertrophy reaches an extreme in mormyrids in which the cerebellum constitutes most of the brain (cf. 34). One infers from as yet little experimental evidence that the cerebellum is involved with processing of electrosensory inputs. Physiological data show that these inputs project to the cerebellum in mormyrids (34), to the eminentia granulosa in gymnotids (61), and to the lateral lobes in gymnotids (61) and elasmobranchs (120). In gymnotids maintained responses to the presence of objects could be evoked that must have been mediated by the electrosensory system. Often responses adapted rapidly to maintained stimuli and required movement of the object to be detected. Some were excited by movement of the object in a particular direction. These movement responses were evoked in units that were sensitive to electric stimuli, but may have involved convergence of electric and mechanical inputs on the same neuron. The adaptation to stationary objects of many of the fish's central sensory neurons was thought to reflect the relative biological importance of moving and stationary objects. Since ordinary lateral-line and electrosensory inputs run in separate nerves in gymnotids, it should be possible to separate influences of electro- and mechanoreceptors (20, 138, 139).

An interesting aspect of the mormyrid electrosensory system is the fact that the neural command signal to fire the organ is relayed to many parts of the cerebellum and hindbrain (34). This signal presumably prepares the central sensory neurons for processing incoming information. By using the knowledge of when it is going to discharge the electric organ, the fish can calculate absolute latency of the sensory response. Only relative latencies can be obtained in a passive sensory system. The initial experiments have only shown inhibitory action of the command associated signal on an incoming sensory volley. It has been suggested that for a similar reference signal, gymnotids use an afferent volley from particularly sensitive and rapidly conducting inputs (142).

The electrosensory systems may well provide convenient subjects for the study of central processing of sensory data. A problem for the experimenter is failure of his intuition; we do not have an electrosensory system and what the perception of an object involves is not immediately obvious. This difficulty is probably compensated for by the ease of working with fish and the simplicity of applying electric stimuli.

EVOLUTION

Electric fish provide remarkable examples of convergent evolution. Not merely the production of electricity, but many of the properties of the individual electrocytes and of their activity patterns show convergences. There are also equally dramatic convergences in the properties of the electroreceptors.

The demonstration of electrosensory systems in weakly electric fish provided an important intermediate for the evolution of strongly electric organs. Darwin recognized that gradual evolution of strongly electric organs seemed impossible because the intermediate steps would have no value as weapons (52). The existence of the highly specialized but weakly electric organ of the skates also was a problem in the absence of any apparent function. Lissmann provided a resolution of this difficulty by suggesting that the weakly electric organs functioned in electrosensory systems (99). The sequence of evolutionary development was presumed to be that receptors of the lateral-line system were somewhat sensitive to the electric fields set up by ordinary muscle contractions, and under selection for improved electrolocation the receptor's electrical sensitivity increased and in parallel certain muscles lost contractility and became specialized for electricity production. Once a weakly electric organ was evolved, increasing the size of the discharge could increase its value as an electrosensory organ until it achieved some limited usefulness as a weapon, and further increase in strength would be selected for by increasing value in this function. A question raised by the existence of the then not clearly recognized passive electrosensory systems is the degree to which specialization of receptors for electric sensitivity preceded development of electric organs. The existence of generalized elasmobranchs with an electrosensory system (58) suggests that in this group electrosensitivity preceded electric organs, and the same argument probably applies to catfish. (It is a little surprising that there is one strongly electric catfish and no known weakly electric catfish.) In both gymnotids and mormyrids all known species are electric and no known close nonelectric relative has a passive electrosensory system. In these groups specialization of receptors and generating tissue might have occurred simultaneously, although their possession of a passive system mediated by the tonic receptors is consistent with the passive system preceding the active one.

An important problem is the development of passive sensory systems. Did they arise from ordinary lateral-line receptors in the sensing of the animal's own muscle or skin potentials or were the primitive responses to extrinsic signals of biological or physical origin? Study of sensitivity of ordinary lateral-line receptors and electroreceptors to muscle action potentials would be useful in this respect. Characterization of signals present in the aqueous environment is also required. Synchronously discharging muscle groups generate larger potentials; sonic muscles produce external potentials of tens of millivolts (unpublished data). Somewhat smaller potentials are generated by the less synchronous activity initiated by Mauthner fibers; Lissman recorded external potentials from ordinary eels that probably had this origin. Signals of this kind might have been the ones providing the initial step in electroreception. Many catfish have sonic muscles, and the electric organ of the electric catfish (31, 93) has innervation similar to that of a sonic muscle which it lacks (123); perhaps this electric organ was evolved from a sonic muscle. The osteology of the skull of mormyrids and *Gymnarchus* indicates the close affinities between the two families (129), and the body shape of *Gymnarchus* could be evolved from that of *Mormyrus*. The similarities of the receptors of mormyrids and *Gymnarchus* (141) suggest that *Gymnarchus* probably had an active sensory system and therefore its electric organ before it separated from the mormyrid line.

The chin organ of *Adontosternarchus* suggests the existence of what is as far as I know a previously unrecognized evolutionary mechanism. It could be considered a kind of pre-evolution but without the connotation of gradual change towards a structure that has survival value only at some later time (the antithesis of Darwinism). A probable first step was maintained oscillatory activity of a group of electroreceptors that served as a weakly electric organ for other receptors. (The independent evolution of rostral accessory organs in other gymnotids attests to the value of these organs.)

But are we then to suppose that the sensory fibers of the primitive accessory organ gradually enlarged over many generations to repeat the evolutionary sequence followed in the main organ? I think not. I find it much more likely that having evolved the developmental mechanism to make large generating nerve fibers in its main organ, all the fish did was to evolve the ability to apply the same mechanism to the chin fibers. In molecular terms, DNA-coded information required to make the main organ fibers was also present in the DNA of the sensory neurons; what was required was a way of derepressing the same operons at the different site or of duplicating the operon with a different repressor. The precise molecular biology doesn't really matter. The point is that evolution of a mechanism of turning-on a previously evolved very complex developmental mechanism in a new part of the organism seems more probable than convergent evolution of the same complex mechanism all over again.

The evolution of a structure in one part of the body and then the sudden appearance of a very similar structure in a quite different part of the body may be of not infrequent occurrence (in geologic time). Apparently the primitive vertebrate limb appeared initially at the pectoral level only (44, 150). The pelvic girdle was a later appearing structure and probably utilized the same genetic material at the second site. Some early fish had more than two pairs of appendages, suggesting repetitive utilization of the same material. The common genetic basis of anterior and posterior limbs is evidenced by similar structure as well as by such mutations as those leading to polydactyly, which involves both fingers and toes. Another example from electric fish is Hunter's organ of the eel, which appears to be evolved from a different muscle group than the main and Sachs' organs, but which has very similar electroplaques (Figure 1, 4, 103). [In accessory electric organs of other gymnotids and *Narcine* the innervation suggests that the organs developed by migration of electrocytes from the main organ rather than development from a different and local muscle group (23, 110).]

This concept of pre-evolution also raises the possibility that electric organs may have evolved only once in elasmobranchs. The argument for separate evolution is based on the muscles of origin being different in torpedinids and rajids. The organs could have originated in one muscle type in a common ancestor and then "jumped" to a second muscle type by evolution of depression at the second site and then evolution of repression at the first site. The skates seem the more generalized of the two and a hypothetical electric common ancestor would probably have been rajidlike. The same argument does not seem applicable to separate evolution of electric organs in teleost groups because of their much wider evolutionary separation.

To extend the argument, if repeated structures utilize the same operons, limits are imposed on evolution of these structures. Mutations of the operons must affect each structure and independent changes in them can be evolved only through changes in the mechanisms controlling expression of the operons. Independence might be achieved by duplication of the genetic material with the pre-existing separate control mechanisms for separate sites. Such duplication could allow a sudden increase in the rate of evolutionary divergence of members of a repeated structure.

CONCLUSIONS AND PROSPECTS

The study of electric organs and electrocytes has illuminated many aspects of membrane physiology. For example, electrical inexcitability of synaptic membrane is most clearly demonstrated in marine electroplaques (16, 71, 73). Also, the concept of separability of a number of different kinds of membrane sites that pass different ions is strongly supported by the occurrence of membranes of different properties in different regions of the same or different cells (14, 72). The macroscopic separation in these cells suggests microscopic separation within the normal membrane, in which the separation may only be inferred from function or pharmacological data. The course of evolution has led to exaggeration of different aspects of membrane function in different cells. This diversity may not yet have had great value for electrophysiology beyond the fact that it exists. But as new morphological and biochemical methods of analyzing membrane function are proposed, electrocytes may be among the best tissues on which to try them out. As far as histochemical procedures are concerned, the surface differences in some electrocytes provide these single cells with built-in controls. The selection of different kinds of cell allows selection of membranes of different kinds with varying degrees of purity. While it may violate some kind of uncertainty principle to propose separability of Na^+ and K^+ channels from purely electrophysiological data, it is now quite reasonable to consider isolation of the macromolecules that make up the different kinds of site. Electric organs may provide the material of choice in some of these procedures, just as they have proved useful in characterization of cholinesterase and Na-K ATPase.

Electric organs are effectors with neural control systems that are simple in function and readily amenable to microelectrode experimentation. Electrically mediated transmission, as is generally found in these systems, meets the functional requirement for fast communication between cells.

These systems have also revealed that electrotonic synapses can have a diversity of properties including some often thought to be exclusively within the province of chemically mediated transmission (22). Combined morphological and physiological studies have greatly strengthened identification of the close appositions termed gap junctions as sites of electrotonic transmission. These results tend to validate electronmicroscopy as a technique for finding electrotonic synapses at sites where electrophysiological experiments are more difficult such as neuropil or the mammalian brain (12, 60, 135).

The electric organ control systems may be too simplified to serve as models for higher functions, but they set a kind of lower limit for simplicity of decision processes, and also show a few elaborations on this lowest level. The control systems are good examples of small systems of neurons like those that have been much studied in invertebrates (91). The functional requirement for electrically mediated transmission in synchronization, as first recognized in the electric organs, has proved to have predictive value for other kinds of synchronous systems (95) and may apply to less synchronous activity as well.

The next level of analysis of electric organ control systems requires exploration of brain structure and function that may be no easier than in other, relatively unspecialized systems of more general interest. One must question whether this will be a sufficiently rewarding line of research. Some knowledge is being gained of the afferent paths of electroreceptors, paths which are themselves of interest and which include important connections to the control system. Furthermore, both operant and respondant conditioning of electric organ discharge is possible and conditioned response latency can be very short (108, 109). Analysis of pathways of learned responses in these animals is conceivable. Finally it should be recalled that in most species, electric organ discharge is a unidimensional behavior that varies only in frequency, and thus the output at least is readily quantified.

Electroreceptors are essentially eighth nerve receptors out on the skin where they can be easily studied. Their specialization for electrosensitivity allows a number of experiments that would be more difficult with either ordinary lateral-line receptors or eighth nerve receptors within the cranium. Of particular importance is the input-output relation of the tonic receptors which is likely to have some general relevance. The electric excitability of phasic receptor cells also suggests that similar properties may be found at other receptors. No other receptor seems to have a blocking capacity like that of the phasic receptors, but it remains a nice adaptation to a particular functional need. The same adaptation has been utilized by some electrocytes to control output rather than input.

Although the astonishing sensitivity of electric fish measured behaviorally has been made more reasonable by analysis of receptor function, the sensitivity is still very great. I note with some relief that the sensitivity is not below the level one would expect for electrical noise (17,100) but the membrane properties required for this sensitivity are still unclear. The role of the CNS in electroreception is largely unexplored, and again may be no easier to analyze than in other systems of more general relevance. Still, the feasibility of controlling inputs from known numbers of individual receptors gives the preparation some advantages. Also, the extraordinary patterned complexity of the brain structures involved (references in 34) invites experimentation.

It is unlikely that many people thought that the theory of evolution was threatened by the existence of electric fish, yet the demonstration of electrosensory systems removed a rather annoying apparent exception. Many things remain unclear about the evolution of electric fish, some of which will be clarified as further knowledge is gained of the role of the electrosensory system in each fish's ecological niche. Intra- and interspecific communication are likely to be important but have been little studied as yet. The extent to which electric fish may contribute to evolutionary theory remains to be evaluated. There are by now many data from the electrosensory systems that must be considered in their taxonomy and that are likely to require revision of existing taxa.

In this review I have followed the concept that one does not understand the physiology of an organ until one knows its function in the organism as a whole, and, in addition, how it evolved. At this stage one can define the electroreceptor activity going into the nervous system, and one can also follow electric organ activity several synapses antidromically. The loop is far from closed; but the prospects are good for further progress.

LITERATURE CITED

1. Adrian, R. H. The rubium and potassium permeability of frog muscle membrane. *J. Physiol.*, **175**, 134–59 (1964)
2. Adrian, R. H., Chandler, W. K., Hodgkin, A. L. Voltage clamp experiments in skeletal muscle fibers. *J. Physiol.*, **186**, 51P–52P (1966)
3. Albe-Fessard, D. Propriétés électriques passives du tissue électrogène des poissons électriques. *Arch. Sci. Physiol.*, **4**, 413–34 (1950)
4. Albe-Fessard, D., Chagas, C. Étude de la sommation à la junction nerf-électroplaque chez le gymnote (*Electrophorus electricus*). *J. Physiol. (Paris)*, **46**, 823–40 (1954)
5. Albe-Fessard, D., Martins-Ferreira, H. Rôle de la commande nerveuse dans la synchronization du fonctionnement des éléments de l'organe électrique du gymnote *Electrophorus electricus* L. *J. Physiol. (Paris)*, **45**, 533–46 (1953)
6. Albers, R. W. Biochemical aspects of active transport. *Ann. Rev. Biochem.*, **36**, 727–56 (1967)
7. Altamirano, M. Electrical properties of the innervated membrane of the electroplax of electric eel. *J. Cellular Comp. Physiol.*, **46**, 249–78 (1955)
8. Aubert, X., Chance, B., Keynes, R. D. Optical studies of biochemical events in the electric organ of *Electrophorus*. *Proc. Roy. Soc. (London), B*, **160**, 211–45 (1964)
9. Aubert, X., Keynes, R. D. The temperature changes during and after the discharge of the electric organ in *Electrophorus electricus*. *Proc. Roy. Soc. (London), B*, **169**, 241–63 (1968)
10. Auerbach, A. A. (Unpublished observations)
11. Auerbach, A. A., Bennett, M. V. L. Chemically mediated transmission at a giant fiber synapse in the central nervous system of a vertebrate. *J. Gen. Physiol.*, **53**, 183–210 (1969)
12. Baker, R., Llinás, R. Electrotonic coupling between cells in the rat mesencephalic nucleus (Submitted to *Nature*)
13. Barets, A., Szabo, T. Ultrastructure des cellules sensorielles des mormyromastes de *Gnathonemus* et leur appareil synaptique. *J. Microscop.*, **3**, 85–90 (1964)
14. Bennett, M. V. L. Modes of operation of electric organs. *Ann. N.Y. Acad. Sci.*, **94**, 458–509 (1961)
15. Bennett, M. V. L. Electric organs of the knifefish *Steatogenys*. *J. Gen. Physiol.*, **45**, 590A (1961)
16. Bennett, M. V. L. Nervous function at the cellular level. *Ann. Rev. Physiol.*, **26**, 289–340 (1964)
17. Bennett, M. V. L. Electroreceptors in Mormyrids. *Cold Spring Harbor Symp. Quant. Biol.*, **30**, 245–62 (1965)
18. Bennett, M. V. L. An electric organ of neural origin. *Fed. Proc.*, **25**, 569 (1966)
19. Bennett, M. V. L. Physiology of electrotonic junctions. *Ann. N.Y. Acad. Sci.*, **137**, 509–39 (1966)
20. Bennett, M. V. L. Mechanisms of electroreception. In *Lateral Line Detectors*, 313–93 (Cahn, P., Ed., Univ. Indiana, Bloomington, Ind., 1967)
21. Bennett, M. V. L. Neural control of electric organs. In *The Central Nervous System and Fish Behavior*, 147–69 (Ingle, D., Ed., Univ. Chicago, 1968)
22. Bennett, M. V. L. Similarities between electrically and chemically mediated transmission. In *Physiological and Biophysical Aspects of Nervous Integration*, 73–128 (Carlson, F. D., Ed., Prentice-Hall, Englewood Cliffs, N.J., 1968)
23. Bennett, M. V. L. Electric organs. Electroreception (In preparation for *Fish Physiology*, Hoar, W. S., Randall, D. S., Eds., Academic, New York)
24. Bennett, M. V. L., Giménez, M., Nakajima, Y., Pappas, G. D. Spinal and medullary nuclei controlling electric organ in the eel, *Electrophorus. Biol. Bull.*, **127**, 362 (1964)
25. Bennett, M. V. L., Grundfest, H. Electrophysiology of electric organ in *Gymnotus carapo*. *J. Gen. Physiol.*, **42**, 1067–104 (1959)
26. Bennett, M. V. L., Grundfest, H. Studies on morphology and electrophysiology of electric organs.

III. Electrophysiology of electric organs in Mormyrids. *Bioelectrogenesis*, 113–35 (Chagas, C., Paes de Carvalho, A., Eds., Elsevier, Amsterdam, 1961)

27. Bennett, M. V. L., Grundfest, H. The electrophysiology of electric organs of marine electric fishes. II. The electroplaques of main and accessory organs of *Narcine brasiliensis*. *J. Gen. Physiol.*, **44**, 805–18 (1961)

28. Bennett, M. V. L., Grundfest, H. The electrophysiology of electric organs of marine electric fishes. III. The electroplaques of the star-gazer, *Astroscopus y-graecum*. *J. Gen. Physiol.*, **44**, 819–43 (1961)

29. Bennett, M. V. L., Grundfest, H. Electric organ discharge in the weakly electric fish, *Gymnarchus niloticus*. *Abstr. 9th Mtg. Biophys. Soc.*, 18 (1965)

30. Bennett, M. V. L., Grundfest, H. Analysis of depolarizing and hyperpolarizing inactivation responses in Gymnotid electroplaques. *J. Gen. Physiol.*, **50**, 141–69 (1966)

31. Bennett, M. V. L., Nakajima, Y., Pappas, G. D. Physiology and ultrastructure of electrotonic junctions. III. Giant electromotor neurons of *Malapterurus electricus*. *J. Neurophysiol.*, **30**, 209–35 (1967)

32. Bennett, M. V. L., Pappas, G. D., Aljure, E., Nakajima, Y. Physiology and ultrastructure of electrotonic junctions. II. Spinal and medullary electromotor nuclei in Mormyrid fish. *J. Neurophysiol.*, **30**, 180–208 (1967)

33. Bennett, M. V. L., Pappas, G. D., Giménez, M., Nakajima, Y. Physiology and ultrastructure of electrotonic junctions. IV. Medullary electromotor nuclei in Gymnotid fish. *J. Neurophysiol.*, **30**, 236–300 (1967)

34. Bennett, M. V. L., Steinbach, A. B. Influence of electric organ control system on electrosensory afferent pathways. In *Neurobiology of cerebellar evolution and development*, 207–14 (Llinás, R., Ed., AMA Educ. Res. Found., Chicago, Ill., 1969)

35. Bennett, M. V. L., Steinbach, A. B. (Unpublished observations)

36. Bennett, M. V. L., Würzel, M.,

Grundfest, H. The electrophysiology of electric organs of marine electric fishes. I. Properties of electroplaques of *Torpedo nobiliana*. *J. Gen. Physiol.*, **44**, 757–804 (1961)

37. Bernstein, J. *Electrobiologie* (Braunschweig, Fr. Vieweg, 1912)

38. Bernstein, J., Tschermak, A. Untersuchungen zur Thermodynamik der bioelektrischen Ströme. Zweiter Teil. Über die Natur der Kette des elektrischen Organs bei *Torpedo*. *Pflügers Arch.*, **112**, 439–521 (1906)

39. Bloom, F. E., Barrnett, R. Fine structural localization of acetylcholinesterase in electroplaque of the electric eel. *J. Cell Biol.*, **29**, 475–95 (1966)

40. Brightman, M. W., Reese, T. S. Junctions between intimately apposed cell membranes in the vertebrate brain. *J. Cell Biol.*, **40**, 648–77 (1969)

41. Brock, L. G., Eccles, R. M. The membrane potentials during rest and activity of the ray electroplate. *J. Physiol.*, **142**, 251–74 (1958)

42. Bullock, T. H. Species differences in effect of electroreceptor input on electric organ pacemakers and other aspects of behavior in gymnotid fish. *Brain Behav. Evol.* (In press)

43. Bullock, T. H., Chichibu, S. Further analysis of sensory coding in electroreceptors of electric fish. *Proc. Natl. Acad. Sci.*, **54**, 422–29 (1965)

44. Carter, G. S. *Structure and habit in vertebrate evolution* (Univ. Washington, Seattle, 1967)

45. Changeux, J. P., Podleski, T. R. On the excitability and cooperativity of the electroplax membrane. *Proc. Natl. Acad. Sci.*, **59**, 944–50 (1968)

46. Changeux, J. P., Podleski, T. R., Meunier, J. C. On some structural analogies between acetylcholinesterase and the macromolecular receptor of acetylcholine. *J. Gen. Physiol.*, **54**, 225s–44s (1969)

47. Changeux, J. P., Podleski, T. R., Wofsy, L. Affinity labeling of the acetylcholine-receptor. *Proc. Natl. Acad. Sci.*, **58**, 2063–70 (1967)

48. Cohen, L. B., Hille, B., Keynes, R. D. Light scattering and birefringence changes during activity in the elec-

tric organ of *Electrophorus electricus. J. Physiol.,* **203,** 489–509 (1969)

49. Cohen, L. B., Keynes, R. D., Hille, B. Light scattering and birefringence changes during nerve activity. *Nature,* **218,** 438–41 (1968)

50. Cole, K. S. *Membranes, Ions and Impulses* (Univ. California, Berkeley, 1968)

51. Cox, R. T., Coates, C. W., Brown, M. V. Relations between the structure, electrical characteristics and chemical processes of electric tissue. *J. Gen. Physiol.,* **28,** 187–212 (1945)

52. Darwin, C. *The Origin of Species and the Decent of Man* (Modern Library Ed., Random House, New York, 1959)

53. Davis, H. A model for transducer action in the cochlea. *Cold Spring Harbor Symp. Quart. Biol.,* **30,** 181–89 (1965)

54. Derbin, C., Roth, A., Szabo, T. Lieu d'origine du potentiel récepteur des organes bulbeux déterminés par des méthodes de dégénérescence et d'électrophysiologie. *J. Physiol. (Paris),* **59,** 390 (1967)

55. Derbin, C., Szabo, T. Ultrastructure of an electroreceptor (Knollenorgan) in the Mormyrid fish *Gnathonemus petersii. J. Ultrastruct. Res.,* **22,** 469–84 (1968)

56. Dijkgraaf, S. The functioning and significance of the lateral-line organs. *Biol. Rev.,* **38,** 51–105 (1963)

57. Dijkgraaf, S. Electroreception in the catfish, *Amiurus nebulosus. Experientia,* **24,** 187–88 (1968)

58. Dijkgraaf, S., Kalmijn, A. J. Versuche der biologischen Bedeutung der Lorenzinischen Ampullen bei den Elasmobranchiern. *Z. Vergleich. Physiol.,* **53,** 187–94 (1966)

59. Dodge, F. A., Frankenhaeuser, B. Sodium currents of the myelinated nerve fibre of *Xenopus laevis* investigated with the voltage clamp technique. *J. Physiol.,* **148,** 188–200 (1959)

60. Dowling, J. E., Boycott, B. B. Neural connections in the retina: fine structure of inner plexiform layer. *Cold Spring Harbor Symp. Quant. Biol.,* **30,** 393–402 (1965)

61. Enger, P. S., Szabo, T. Activity of

central neurons involved in electroreception in some weakly electric fish (Gymnotidae). *J. Neurophysiol.,* **28,** 800–18 (1965)

62. Eyzaguirre, C., Koyano, H., Taylor, J. R. Presence of acetylcholine and transmitter release from carotid body chemoreceptors. *J. Physiol.,* **178,** 463–76 (1965)

63. Eyzaguirre, C., Zapata, P. Pharmacology of pH effects on carotid body chemoreceptors *in vitro. J. Physiol.,* **195,** 557–88 (1968)

64. Farquhar, M. G., Palade, G. E. Junctional complexes in various epithelia. *J. Cell Biol.,* **17,** 375–412 (1963)

65. Fessard, A., Szabô, T. Sur l'organisation anatomo-fonctionnelle des lobes électriques de la Torpille. *J. Physiol. (Paris),* **45,** 114–17 (1953)

66. Frankenhaeuser, B., Huxley, A. F. The action potential in the myelinated nerve fibre of *Xenopus laevis* as computed on the basis of voltage clamp data. *J. Physiol.,* **171,** 302–15 (1964)

67. Furukawa, T., Furshpan, E. J. Two inhibitory mechanisms in the Mauthner neurons of goldfish. *J. Neurophysiol.,* **26,** 140–76 (1963)

68. Furukawa, T., Ishi, Y. Neurophysiological studies on hearing in goldfish. *J. Neurophysiol.,* **30,** 1377–403 (1967)

69. Girardier, L., Reuben, J. P., Brandt, P. W., Grundfest, H. Evidence for anion-permselective membrane in crayfish muscle fibers and its possible role in excitation-contraction coupling. *J. Gen. Physiol.,* **47,** 189–214 (1963)

70. Gosse, J. P., Szabo, T. Variation morphologique et fonctionelle de l'organe électrique dans une méme espèce de Mormyrides (*Mormyrops deliciosus* Leach). *C. R. Acad. Sci.,* **251D,** 2791–93 (1960)

71. Grundfest, H. The mechanisms of discharge of the electric organs in relation to general and comparative electrophysiology. *Progr. Biophys. Biophys. Chem.,* **7,** 1–85 (1957)

72. Grundfest, H. Comparative electrobiology of excitable membranes. *Advan. Comp. Physiol. Biochem.,* **2,** 1–116 (1966)

73. Grundfest, H., Bennett, M. V. L. Studies on the morphology and electrophysiology of electric organs. In *Electrophysiology of marine electric fishes. Bioelectrogenesis*, 57–95 (See Ref. 26)

74. Hagiwara, S., Kusano, K., Negishi, K. Physiological properties of electroreceptors of some gymnotids. *J. Neurophysiol.*, **25**, 430–49 (1962)

75. Hagiwara, S., Morita, H. Coding mechanisms of electroreceptor fibers in some electric fish. *J. Neurophysiol.*, **26**, 551–67 (1963)

76. Hagiwara, S., Szabo, T., Enger, P. S. Physiological properties of electroreceptors in the electric eel, *Electrophorus electricus*. *J. Neurophysiol.*, **28**, 775–83 (1965)

77. Hagiwara, S., Szabo, T., Enger, P. S. Electroreceptor mechanisms in a high frequency weakly electric fish. *J. Neurophysiol.*, **28**, 784–99 (1965)

78. Harder, W. Die Beziehungen zwischen Elektrorezeptoren, elektrischem Organ, Seitenlinienorganen und Nervensystem bei den Mormyridae (Teleostei, Pisces). *Z. Vergleich. Physiol.*, **59**, 272–318 (1968)

79. Higman, H. B., Podleski, T. R., Bartels, B. Correlation of membrane potential and potassium flux in the electroplax of *Electrophorus*. *Biochem. Biophys. Acta*, **79**, 138–50 (1964)

80. Hille, B., Bennett, M. V. L., Grundfest, H. Voltage clamp measurements of the Cl-conductance changes in skate electroplaques. *Biol. Bull.*, **129**, 407–8 (1965)

81. Hodgkin, A. L., Huxley, A. F. A quantitative description of membrane current and its application to conductance and excitation in nerve. *J. Physiol.*, **117**, 500–44 (1952)

82. Israel, M., Gautron, J., Lesbats, B. Isolement des vésicules synaptiques de l'organe électrique de la Torpille et localisation de l'acétylcholine à leur niveau. *C. R. Acad. Sci.*, **D266**, 273–75 (1968)

83. Karlin, A. Permeability and internal concentration of ions during depolarization of the electroplax. *Proc. Natl. Acad. Sci.*, **58**, 1162–67 (1967)

84. Karlin, A. Chemical modification of the active site of the acetylcholine receptor. *J. Gen. Physiol.*, **54**, 245s–64s (1969)

85. Katz, B., Miledi, R. The measurement of synaptic delay, and the time course of acetylcholine release at the neuro-muscular junction. *Proc. Roy. Soc. (London), B*, **161**, 483–95 (1965)

86. Katz, B., Miledi, R. The effect of temperature on the synaptic delay at the neuromuscular junction. *J. Physiol.*, **181**, 656–70 (1965)

87. Katz, B., Miledi, R. The release of acetylcholine from nerve endings by graded electric pulses. *Proc. Roy. Soc. (London), B*, **167**, 23–38 (1967)

88. Katz, B. Miledi, R. A study of synaptic transmission in the absence of impulses. *J. Physiol.*, **192**, 407–36 (1967)

89. Katz, B., Miledi, R. Tetrodotoxin-resistant electric activity in presynaptic terminals. *J. Physiol.*, **203**, 459–87 (1969)

90. Katz, B., Thesleff, S. A study of the "desensitization" produced by acetylcholine at the motor end-plate. *J. Physiol.*, **138**, 63–80 (1967)

91. Kennedy, D., Selverston, A. I., Remler, M. P. Analysis of restricted neural networks. *Science*, **164**, 1488–96 (1969)

92. Keynes, R. D. The temperature changes during and after the discharge of the electric organ in *Malapterurus electricus*. *Proc. Roy. Soc. (London), B*, **169**, 265–74 (1968)

93. Keynes, R. D., Bennett, M. V. L., Grundfest, H. Studies on morphology and electrophysiology of electric organs. II. Electrophysiology of electric organ of *Malapterurus electricus*. In *Bioelectrogenesis*, 102–12 (See Ref. 26)

94. Keynes, R. D., Martins-Ferreira, H. Membrane potentials in the electroplates of the electric eel. *J. Physiol.*, **119**, 315–51 (1953)

95. Kriebel, M. E., Bennett, M. V. L., Waxman, S. G., Pappas, G. D. Oculomotor neurons in fish: electrotonic coupling and multiple sites of impulse initiation. *Science*, **166**, 520–24 (1969)

96. Kusano, K. Further study of the relationship between pre- and postsynaptic potentials in the squid giant synapse. *J. Gen. Physiol.*, **52**, 326–45 (1968)

97. Larimer, J. L., MacDonald, J. A. Sensory feedback from electroreceptors to electromotor pacemaker centers in gymnotids. *Am. J. Physiol.*, **214**, 1253–61 (1968)

98. Leuzinger, W., Baker, A. L. Acetylcholinesterase, I. Large-scale purification, homogeneity, and amino acid analysis. *Proc. Natl. Acad. Sci.*, **57**, 446–51 (1967)

99. Lissmann, H. W. On the function and evolution of electric organs in fish. *J. Exptl. Biol.*, **35**, 156–91 (1958)

100. Lissmann, H. W., Machin, K. E. The mechanism of object location in *Gymnarchus niloticus* and similar fish. *J. Exptl. Biol.*, **35**, 451–86 (1958)

101. Lissmann, H. W., Machin, K. E. Electric receptors in a non-electric fish (*Clarias*). *Nature*, **199**, 88–89 (1963)

102. Lissmann, H. W., Mullinger, A. M. Organization of ampullary electric receptors in Gymnotidae (Pisces). *Proc. Roy. Soc. (London), B,* **169**, 345–78 (1968)

103. Luft, J. H. The histology and cytology of the electric organ of the electric eel (*Electrophorus electricus*, L.). *J. Morphol.*, **100**, 113–40 (1957)

104. Luft, J. H. The fine structure of electric tissue. *Exptl. Cell Res. Suppl. 5*, 168–82 (1958)

105. Machin, K. E. Electric receptors. *Symp. Soc. Exptl. Biol.*, **16**, 227–44 (1962)

106. Machin, K. E., Lissmann, H. W. The mode of operation of the electric receptors in *Gymnarchus niloticus*. *J. Exptl. Biol.*, **37**, 801–11 (1960)

107. Mandriota, F. M. (Personal communication)

108. Mandriota, F. M., Thompson, R. L., Bennett, M. V. L. Classical conditioning of electric organ discharge rate in Mormyrids. *Science*, **150**, 1740–42 (1965)

109. Mandriota, F. M., Thompson, R. L., Bennett, M. V. L. Avoidance conditioning of the rate of electric organ discharge in mormyrid fish.

Anim. Behav., **16**, 448–55 (1968)

110. Mathewson, R., Mauro, A., Amatniek, E., Grundfest, H. Morphology of main and accessory electric organs of *Narcine brasiliensis* (Olfers) and some correlations with their electrophysiological properties. *Biol. Bull.*, **115**, 126–35 (1958)

111. Mathewson, R., Wachtel, A., Grundfest, H. Fine structure of electroplaques. In *Bioelectrogenesis*, 25–53 (See Ref. 26)

112. Morlock, N. L., Benamy, D. A., Grundfest, H. Analysis of spike electrogenesis of eel electroplaques with phase plane and impedance measurements. *J. Gen. Physiol.*, **52**, 22–45 (1969)

113. Moushegian, G., Rupert, A. L., Langford, T. L. Stimulus coding by medial superior olivary neurons. *J. Neurophysiol.*, **30**, 1239–61 (1967)

114. Mullinger, A. M. The fine structure of ampullary electric receptors in *Amiurus*. *Proc. Roy. Soc. (London), B,* **160**, 345–59 (1964)

115. Murray, R. W. The response of the ampullae of Lorenzini of elasmobranchs to electrical stimulation. *J. Exptl. Biol.*, **39**, 119–28 (1962)

116. Murray, R. W. The function of the ampullae of Lorenzini of elasmobranchs. In *Lateral Line Detectors*, 277–93 (Cahn, P., Ed., Univ. Indiana, Bloomington, Ind., 1967)

117. Nakajima, S., Iwasaki, S., Obata, K. Delayed rectification and anomalous rectification in frog's skeletal muscle membrane. *J. Gen. Physiol.*, **46**, 97–115 (1962)

118. Nakajima, S., Kusano, K. Analysis of K inactivation and TEA action in the supramedullary cells of the puffer. *J. Gen. Physiol.*, **49**, 629–40 (1966)

119. Nakamura, Y., Nakajima, S., Grundfest, H. Analysis of spike electrogenesis and depolarizing K inactivation in electroplaques of *Electrophorus electricus*, L. *J. Gen. Physiol.*, **49**, 321–49 (1965)

120. Nicholson, C., Llinás, R., Precht, W. Neural elements of the cerebellum in elasmobranch fishes: structural and functional characteristics. In *Neurobiology of Cerebellar Evolution and Development*, 215–43 (See Ref. 34)

121. Obara, S., Bennett, M. V. L. Receptor and generator potentials of ampulla of Lorenzini in the skate. *Biol. Bull.*, **135**, 430–31 (1968)
122. Oliveira Castro, G. de. Differentiated nervous fibers that constitute the electric organ of *Sternachus albifrons* Linn. *Acad. Brasileira Ciências*, **27**, 557–60 (1955)
123. Pappas, G. D., Bennett, M. V. L. Specialized sites involved in electrical transmission between neurons. *Ann. N.Y. Acad. Sci.*, **137**, 495–508 (1966)
124. Payton, B. W., Bennett, M. V. L., Pappas, G. D. Permeability and structure of junctional membranes at an electrotonic synapse. *Science* (In press)
125. Poppele, R. E., Bennett, M. V. L. (Unpublished observations)
126. Post, R. L., Kume, S., Tobin, T., Orcutt, B., Sen, A. K. Flexibility of an active center in sodium-plus-potassium adenosine triphosphatase. *J. Gen. Physiol.*, **54**, 306s–26s (1969)
127. Rall, W., Shepherd, G. M., Reese, T. S., Brighton, M. W. Dendro-dendritic synaptic pathway for inhibition in the olfactory bulb. *Exptl. Neurol.*, **14**, 44–56 (1966)
128. Revel, J. P., Karnovsky, M. J. Hexagonal array of subunits in intercellular junctions of the mouse heart and liver. *J. Cell Biol.*, **33**, C7–C12 (1967)
129. Ridgewood, W. G. On the cranial osteology of the families Mormyridae, Notopteridae, and Hyodontidae. *J. Linnean Soc. London, Zool.*, **29**, 188–217 (1904)
130. Saito, N. Spike potentials of the electromotoneuron of the electric skate, *Narka japonica. Japan. J. Physiol.*, **16**, 509–18 (1966)
131. Schoffeniels, E. Ion movements studied with single isolated elextroplax. *Ann. N.Y. Acad. Sci.*, **81**, 285–306 (1959)
132. Schwartz, I. R., Pappas, G. D., Bennett, M. V. L. Fine structure of electroplaques of weakly electric teleosts (In preparation)
133. Sheridan, M. N. The fine structure of the electric organ of *Torpedo marmorata. J. Cell Biol.*, **24**, 129–41 (1965)
134. Singer, S. J. Covalent labeling of active sites. *Advan. Protein Chem.*, **22**, 1–54 (1967)
135. Sotelo, C. Ultrastructural aspects of the cerebellar cortex of the frog. In *Neurobiology of Cerebellar Evolution and Development* (See Ref. 34)
136. Spoendlin, H. Some morphofunctional and pathological aspects of the vestibular sensory epithelia. In *2nd Symposium on the role of vestibular organs in space exploration*, 99–115 (NASA, Washington, D.C., 1966)
137. Steinbach, A. B., Bennett, M. V. L. (In preparation)
138. Suga, N. Coding in tuberous and ampullary organs of a gymnotid electric fish. *J. Comp. Neurol.*, **131**, 437–52 (1967)
139. Suga, N. Electrosensitivity of canal and free neuromast organs in a gymnotid electric fish. *J. Comp. Neurol.*, **131**, 453–58 (1967)
140. Szabo, T. Les organes électriques des Mormyrides. In *Bioelectrogenesis*, 20–23 (See Ref. 26)
141. Szabo, T. Sense organs of the lateral line system in some electric fish of the Gymnotidae, Mormyridae, and Gymnarchidae. *J. Morphol.*, **117**, 229–50 (1965)
142. Szabo, T. Activity in peripheral and central neurons involved in electroreception. In *Lateral Line Detectors*, 295–312 (See Ref. 116)
143. Szabo, T., Fessard, A. Le fonctionnement des électrorécepteurs étudié chez les Mormyres. *J. Physiol. (Paris)*, **57**, 343–60 (1965)
144. Szamier, R. B., Wachtel, A. W. Special cutaneous receptor organs of fish: III. The ampullary organs of Eigenmannia. *J. Morphol.*, **128**, 261–90 (1969)
145. Wachtel, A. W., Szamier, R. B. Special cutaneous receptor organs of fish: IV. Ampullary organs of the non electric catfish, *Kryptopterus. J. Morphol.*, **128**, 291–308 (1969)
146. Wachtel, A. W., Szamier, R. B. Special cutaneous receptor organs of fish: The tuberous organs of *Eigenmannia. J. Morphol.*, **119**, 51–80 (1966)
147. Waltman, B. Electrical properties and fine structure of the ampullary canals of Lorenzini. *Acta*

Physiol. Scand., **66,** *Suppl. 264,* 1–60 (1966)

148. Watanabe, A., Takeda, K. The change of discharge frequency by A. C. stimulus in a weak electric fish. *J. Exptl. Biol.*, **40,** 57–66 (1963)

149. Wersäll, J., Flock, A., Lundquist, P. G. Structural basis for directional sensitivity in cochlear and vestibular sensory receptors. *Cold Spring Harbor Symp. Quant. Biol.*, **30,** 115–32 (1965)

150. Westoll, T. S. The paired fins of placoderms. *Trans. Roy. Soc. (Edinburgh),* **61,** 381–98 (1945)

THE LYMPHOID SYSTEM[1,2] 1053

R. A. GATTI,[3] O. STUTMAN,[4] AND R. A. GOOD[5]

In the three years that have elapsed since Allen reviewed the lymphoid system for this journal (1), many new concepts regarding its function have come into clearer focus. Largely through animal experimentation as well as from experience gained in organ transplantation and in the care of patients with immunologic deficiency diseases and lymphoid malignancies, the anatomy of the lymphoid system can now be redefined from several new perspectives. If we consider the three main functions of this network to be: (*a*) antibody and immunoglobulin production, (*b*) cell-mediated graft rejection and delayed hypersensitivity, and (*c*) chyle transport and lymphocyte circulation, we must then include the following anatomical structures as intrinsic parts of the lymphoid system: thymus, gut-associated lymphoid tissue (GALT), lymph nodes, spleen, thoracic and other main lymphatic ducts, lacteals of the intestinal villi, and the ubiquitous network of microscopic lymphatic channels throughout the body. Within this structural framework, the lymphoid cells differentiate, proliferate, and respond immunologically to various antigenic stimuli.

Ontogenetic studies.—Because these new perspectives of lymphoid physiology have been gleaned mainly from phylogenetic and ontogenetic studies, let us begin with a brief overview of the experimental work that has been done in this area over the past decade. In 1956, Glick and his co-workers (2) found that in chickens if the bursa of Fabricius, a small lymphoid organ located at the end of the gastrointestinal tract just anterior to the cloaca, was extirpated soon after hatching, antibody response was markedly decreased. When this approach was extended to neonatal extirpation of the

[1] From the Pediatric Research Laboratories of the Variety Club Heart Hospital, Departments of Microbiology, Pediatrics and Laboratory Medicine, University of Minnesota, Minneapolis, Minnesota 55455.

[2] Original work reported here was aided by grants from The National Foundation —March of Dimes, American Cancer Society, the United States Public Health Service (AI-08677, AI-00798, CA-10445 and NB-02042), and the American Heart Association.

[3] United States Public Health Service Special Fellow.

[4] Assistant Professor of Laboratory Medicine.

[5] American Legion Memorial Heart Research Professor of Pediatrics and Microbiology.

thymus in rabbits (3) and mice (4, 5), homograft rejection responses were found to be consistently and severely impaired while antibody production was compromised only to certain antigens (6). Further experiments in mice, rats, and hamsters showed that neonatal thymectomy depleted small lymphocytes and thereby depressed cell-mediated immune responses, but left the plasma cell population intact (7, 8). This dissociation of immunologic responsiveness between thymic-dependent homograft immunity and bursal-dependent antibody formation in the chicken was also encountered by Warner & Szenberg (9, 10) as a result of their studies in which inhibition of development by hormonal treatment instead of surgical extirpation was used to inhibit respectively thymic and bursal development. However, this hormonal model created certain incongruities regarding the affiliations of delayed hypersensitivity, antibody production, homograft immunity, and graft-versus-host reactions which were in disagreement with abundant clinical and experimental data. These relationships were only brought into proper perspective when Cooper et al. (11) extended this work and used surgical extirpation of either thymus or bursa in newly hatched, near lethally irradiated chicks. At 7 weeks of age, the thymectomized chicks had low lymphocyte counts, depletion of small lymphocytes in the splenic white pulp, lack of skin homograft rejection, absent delayed allergic responses, and inability of their lymphocytes to initiate graft-versus-host reactions. These animals had normal immunoglobulin concentrations and only slightly diminished antibody responses to several antigens after challenge. Plasma cells and germinal centers were present in normal numbers. Bursectomized chicks, on the other hand, showed normal numbers of small lymphocytes in the peripheral blood and spleen and rejected skin homografts with normal vigor. They, instead, completely lacked plasma cells, immunoglobulins (both IgM and IgG types), and germinal centers in the spleen. Even after repeated antigenic stimulation, these chickens could not make circulating antibodies.

More recently Cooper et al. (12), Van Alten et al. (13), and Cain et al. (14) have extended this analysis by utilizing the technique of bursectomy *in ovo*. In these studies, without the interjection of noninterpretable influences such as those contributed by irradiation or 19-nortestosterone, it was possible to produce by sufficiently early bursal extirpation alone a model of agammaglobulinemia. When chickens were subjected to bursectomy prior to the 17th day of embryonation, many failed to develop germinal centers, plasma cells, and immunoglobulins IgM and IgG and they could not be stimulated to produce antibodies even by repeated antigenic stimulation. When bursectomy was carried out on the 18th or 19th day of embryonation, the chickens grew up often possessing plasma cells, having ability to produce both antibodies and immunoglobulins of the IgM class, but lacking germinal centers and ability to produce antibodies and immunoglobulins of the IgG class.

In still more recent studies, Cain et al. (15) have found that removal of the bursa at different times, even after hatching, selectively inhibits certain types of immune response but not others. Thus, the bursal influence on immunologic maturation appears to be an influence that can be dissected into several components. Initially, this influence renders lymphoid cells capable of responsiveness to antigen and sequential development into plasma cells with ability to produce IgM immunoglobulins; more prolonged bursal influence renders lymphoid cells capable of developing into IgG producers, probably through an intermediate developmental step involving the germinal centers of peripheral lymphoid tissue. Finally, still more prolonged influence, not yet fully analyzed, makes possible a full range of antibody responses to a wide variety of antigenic stimuli not possible without bursal influence extending into the first week of posthatching life.

Recently, Weidanz et al. (16) have created another most interesting and useful model of immunologic deficiency in chickens by injecting an alkylating agent, cyclosphosphamide, intravenously in newly hatched chickens. Linna et al. (17) have found that this treatment results in production of agammaglobulinemia in a high percentage of chickens, prevents development of ability to form antibodies and both IgM and IgG immunoglobulins, and prevents development of germinal centers and plasma cells while leaving small lymphocytes and cell-mediated immunities relatively intact.

Phylogenetic studies.—Running concurrently to the above studies, a phylogenetic survey of immunologic adaptive responses was undertaken in our laboratories. Invertebrates, it was found, possess neither humoral nor cellular types of immune responses. In our original studies we could not demonstrate immune responses in a variety of invertebrates or in two species of hagfishes, another and separate line of agnathans (18). More recently, using what must be much better conditions of husbandry, Hildemann et al. (19) have observed very feeble and delayed homograft rejection and immunological memory to be demonstrable in these cyclostomes as well. They have attributed the very slow rejection of homografts to weakness of the transplantation antigens, but Finstad's failure to demonstrate lymphocyte characteristics of a significant cell population in myxine suggests the alternative that the slowness and feebleness of this response may be consequent to the small proportion of cells possessing immunological competence and other characteristics of lymphocytes.

Adaptive immune responses involving both humoral and cell-mediated immunity, on the other hand, were demonstrated in modern derivatives of the ancient ostrachoderms, the sea lamprey. The lamprey responds to strong antigenic stimuli, rejects homografts of skin, manifests delayed hypersensitivity, and exhibits immunologic memory. This development seemed to coincide phylogenetically with the appearance of true lymphoid cells having numerous characteristics similar to those of mammalian lymphoid cells and with what we interpret to be a primitive protothymus (20). These animals possess no real thymus, but within the epithelium of the pharyngeal gutter during the ammocete phase of their life cycle, small foci of lymphoid cells occur in clusters of 5–25 cells. These clusters lie in intimate contact with the epithelium of the foregut and may represent a forerunner of the lympho-epithelial thymus of later species. These animals also lack a definite spleen but possess an invagination extending along the spiral valve in the anterior portion of the mid-gut region which contains a distinct concentration of hematopoietic tissue. Although plasma cells have not been seen, cells resembling plasmablasts have been identified by ultrastructural analysis.

In all the fishes, elasmobranchii, holosteans, chondrosteans, and marine and freshwater teleosts, a well-defined thymus is seen with corticomedullary organization and even epithelial whorls having the appearance of primitive Hassal's corpuscles. Lymphocytes have numerous characteristics very similar to those of mammalian lymphocytes. True Marschalko plasma cells are not recognized in some of the primitive forms, but all have pyroninophilic cells. in the paddlefish *Polydon spathula,* a chondrostean, one can define by both light and electronmicroscopy a cell line with the characteristic eccentric, cartwheel nucleus and clear Hof area. Ultrastructurally, these cells are easily distinguished from lymphocytes by their well-organized endoplasmic reticulum. None of the fishes possess lymph nodes, Peyer's patches, or a bursa. Although they produce antibodies of both 19-S and 7-S type, these antibodies have, by immunochemical analysis, a single heavy-chain type.

In the amphibian one sees tiny collections of lymphoid cells along the blood vessels that respond to antigenic stimulation. Within these tiny "lymph nodes" both plasma cells and small lymphocytes are seen and structures resembling germinal centers may be present. Both 19-S and 7-S immunoglobulins are produced in response to repeated antigenic stimulation. The possibility of a correlation between phylogenetic appearance of two immunoglobulin classes and germinal centers is intriguing (21, 22).

The bursa and Peyer's patches as such are absent in both amphibians and reptiles, although recent work in our laboratories has indicated a variety of gut-associated lymphoid accumulations, any of which might represent the bursal equivalent. Sidky & Auerbach (23) have described a bursalike structure in turtles and we have found similar lymphoid accumulations in the derivatives of the proctodeal plate in amphibians (24). Whether either of these exerts the kind of influence on development of antibody-producing cells exerted by the bursa of Fabricius in birds can only be established by extirpative studies carried out sufficiently early in development.

Studies on a representative marsupial, the opossum, have shown a lymphoid structure and immunologic responses identical with those of mammals. Tonsils, Peyer's patches, and lymph nodes with well-defined germinal centers are present. Both lymphocytes and plasma cells are in abundance. Both cell-mediated and humoral immune responses are now present (25, 26).

A mammalian bursa?—The search for a bursal equivalent in mammals continues. We have recently demonstrated in rabbits that extirpation of the sacculus rotundus, appendix, and Peyer's patches in near-lethally irradiated rabbits severely compromises the immunoglobulin-producing capacity while leaving cell-mediated immune responses intact (27).

In what seem to be crucial studies, Perey et al. (28) used supralethal irradiation in animals previously subjected to either thymectomy or extirpation of the GALT. They then salvaged the animals from death due to irradiation by giving fetal liver cells taken from 19- or 20-day-old rabbit fetuses prior to development in that species of immunoglobulin-producing cells. Only those animals which lacked the entire GALT failed to develop a system of cells capable of responding to *Brucella* in a primary immune response. Morphologically, an interesting correlate was obtained. Animals which had been subjected to extirpation of GALT developed a good population of small lymphocytes and abundant lymphocytes in the deep cortical areas. By contrast, the thymus-independent far-cortical populations of lymphocytes failed to develop. A precursor of immunoglobulin-producing cells present in the hematopoietic liver of the fetal mouse is also thymus-independent (29).

Although a number of studies suggested that in central lymphoid organs, such as the thymus and bursa of Fabricius, the lymphoid cells might develop from epithelial precursors (30, 31), this view seems no longer tenable (32). In the mouse, a traffic pattern from marrow to thymus and then from thymus to peripheral lymphoid tissues has been established (33, 34). Further, in the chicken, analysis of the derivation of replicating lymphoid cells in both thymus and bursa excludes the epithelium and implicates stem cells from circulation and embryonic sites (32). On the other hand, Silverstein (35) has observed no significant influence following removal of virtually the entire colon in fetal lambs.

Development and differentiation of the lymphoid system.—On the basis of the above studies considered together with our experience in immunological reconstitution of mice and humans (36–38), it has been possible to construct a scheme of lymphoid system development (Figure 1) which has striking parallels to that already forthcoming from studies of erythropoietic differentiation and development (39, 40). Multipotential, undifferentiated stem cells, from sources such as fetal liver or bone marrow, are induced to differentiate by passing through specific microenvironments. These microenvironments are provided by the *central lymphoid organs,* thymus and bursa. Depending then upon a cell's past history, its new microenvironment will have varying differentiative influence. Specifically, if a stem cell traffics to the thymus it differentiates there into a small lymphocyte. Such fully differentiated cells then leave the thymus via the blood and never return to it. In contrast, were the same stem cell to have come under the differentiative microenvironment provided by the bursa or its equivalent (bone marrow in some mammals), it would have differentiated ultimately into an antibody-producing plasma cell.

THYMUS SYSTEM DEVELOPMENT

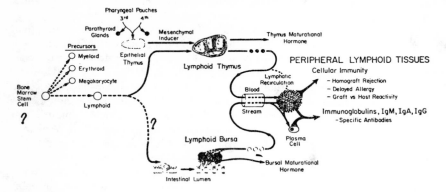

BURSAL SYSTEM DEVELOPMENT

Fig. 1. The developmental scheme of the lymphoid system.

The similarity of lymphoid cell differentiation and hematopoiesis goes perhaps even further with regard to poietins. In much the same manner that erythropoietin expands the red cell population, there is mounting evidence that the thymus produces an immunopoietin to expand the lymphoid cell populations (41–44). Whether this substance also provokes further cell differentiation is not yet clear. The *central lymphoid tissues,* then, are sites where precursor cells appear to become committed by differentiative events to particular lines having functional specialization. After receiving these maturation influences, some of the lymphoid cells leave the central tissues and migrate to *peripheral lymphoid tissues* such as lymph nodes and spleen. Further maturation may take place in the periphery and part of this process, including expansion, seems to be fostered by humoral substances derived from the thymus. However these influences are exerted, it seems clear that the *central lymphoid organs* are essential for specialization of function of the lymphoid cells.

In the mouse, thymic influence is exerted in two ways which may or may not be mutually exclusive. The thymus acts both as a differentiative site for cells of hematopoietic origin and to produce an indirect expander of the differentiated thymus-dependent population of peripheral lymphoid cells. With the aid of functional thymomas (45), it has been shown that stem cells originating from embryonic hematopoietic liver are capable of trafficking to the thymus and require viable thymic stroma in order to develop into immunocompetent cells in peripheral lymphoid tissue (44). This latter migratory population of postthymic cells can be expanded by humoral products of thymic origin, i.e., thymomas or thymus in cell-impermeable diffusion chambers (43). In the adult mouse, this differentiated migratory population, although in some degree autonomous, is not completely self-sustaining in the absence of the thymus and requires both the presence of the thymus and thymus traffic of bone marrow stem cells for constant replacement (46).

Immunologic deficiency dieseases.—Once the dichotomy of the lymphoid system had been placed in clear focus, clinical correlates were readily recognized. Bruton-type agammaglobulinemia had been known to be featured by absence of what now could be considered to be the bursa-dependent or thymus-independent lymphoid system (47). Such patients lacked plasma cells and germinal centers but possessed normal numbers of small lymphocytes and had splendid populations of lymphocytes in the thymus-dependent areas of the spleen and lymph nodes (48, 49). By contrast, DiGeorge (50, 51) had recognized that certain children lacking parathyroid glands and exhibiting neonatal tetany lacked the thymus and the thymus-dependent lymphoid system as well. Such children have been found to have normal levels of all the immunoglobulins and to form antibodies to many antigens normally (52). They lack small lymphocytes and are deficient in lymphocyte populations in the thymus-dependent deep-cortical regions of the lymph nodes and spleen. By contrast, they have normal far-cortical regions and develop germinal centers and plasma cells normally. These patients cannot survive without treatment because they are prone to develop lethal infections with fungi, viruses, and bacteria.

Another form of immunological deficiency which illustrates these relationships is the lymphopenic agammaglobulinemia originally described by the Swiss investigators (53, 54). Children with Swiss-type agammaglobulinemia lack both plasma cells and germinal centers as well as the thymus-dependent small lymphocytes (55). Thus, because of these developmental anomalies these patients lack both cell-mediated and humoral immunities. Based on experimental results in both mouse and chicken, recent therapeutic successes in children with these developmental defects contribute further to analysis of the relation of structure and function in the lymphoid system. For example, Cleveland et al. (56, 57) and then August et al. (58) have treated children with the DiGeorge syndrome successfully by transplantation of fetal thymus. Reconstitution of the cell-mediated immunities and the missing lymphoid cells was the consequence of this treatment.

Further, on three separate occasions children with dual-system lymphopenic immunological deficiency have been fully reconstituted immunologically and morphologically by administration of bone marrow containing stem cells from matched donors (37, 38, 59, 60). Such reconstitution replenishes both the thymus-dependent lymphoid cells responsible for cell-mediated immunity and the plasma cells responsible for antibody and immunoglobulin synthesis. Thus, providing a suitable stem cell source for these children permits correction of the dual-system immunological deficiency and providing a thymus corrects the isolated thymus-dependent system deficit of DiGeorge syndrome.

Another group of patients, those with intestinal lymphangiectasia, seems pertinent to a review of the lymphoid system. These patients may present varying degrees of immunologic and lymphoid system inadequacies ranging from a mild protein-losing enteropathy with concomitant loss of immunoglobulins, to severe chyloperitoneum with hypocalcemic tetany and lymphopenia (61–63). Such patients with lymphopenia often have markedly prolonged homograft rejection times and closely resemble experimental models in which thoracic duct drainage has been used to deplete the lymphoid systems of the long-lived recirculating lymphocyte pool. Although dilatation to the lacteals of intestinal villi and lymphatic fistulae into the lumen of the small bowel (62) have been demonstrated in some patients, the pathogenesis of intestinal lymphangiectasia is incompletely understood.

Lymphoid cell populations.—The cells of the lymphoid system represent a heterogeneous population with varying life-spans and cell cycles. These populations are continually maintained in spite of constant loss of cells through differentiation, utilization, or both. Although this dividing transitory population is in a constant state of flux, it is not completely self-maintaining and depends on the input of precursor stem cells (64). Varying degrees of maturity for each cell type are present and traffic patterns seem closely related not only to function but to differentiation and progressive functional maturation. One of the major obstacles in the study of these cell populations lies in controlling precursor cell input and cell loss from the peripheral lymphoid system.

On the basis of morphology and size, lymphocytes in the periphery have been subdivided into "large, medium, and small". This classification is arbitrary since studies of the frequency distribution of these cells have never been shown to be trimodal (65). The pitfall of this type of classification is that it suggests similarities of origin or of function which do not seem to exist.

A more useful classification, based on ontogenetic origins, divides lymphoid cells into thymus-derived and thymus-independent populations. Another equally helpful concept has been the division of peripheral lymphocytes by life-span, as determined by labeling experiments. Finally, a third classification is possible, based on mobilization as demonstrated by studies of lymphocyte recirculation and the effects of antilymphocyte serum: one population constantly circulating through lymph and blood stream, percolating through tissues, and then recirculating, while another more sessile population tends to remain *in situ*. It must be kept clearly in mind, however, that even these more recent categorizations of lymphoid cell populations are grossly inadequate, are based only on scanty evidence in some respects, and most likely are not completely exclusive of one another.

Thymus-derived cells, primarily involved in cell-mediated responses, are now known to be required for at least some types of humoral responses, i.e., formation of antibody to sheep red cells and bovine serum albumin (66, 67), but their need in this respect is probably as antigen handlers (68, 69) rather than as precursors of antibody-secreting cells (70, 71). This type of thymus bone marrow interaction is not necessary for immune responses of the cell-mediated type such as graft-versus-host reactions or for antibody formation to antigens such as *Brucella abortus* (72). The role of the thymus-derived cells in the immune response to sheep red cells *in vitro* has not been clarified. Cell cooperation or interaction seems to be needed in these systems just as it is in the intact animals since populations of cells can be isolated from the mouse spleen, by gradient centrifugation, or by surface adherence that are ineffective by themselves. These populations have to be combined and aggregated to obtain a full response *in vitro* (73, 74). The helper population which facilitates response to certain antigens may involve different populations of cells under different circumstances. For example, thymus-dependent cells, in one situation, or macrophages, in another, may abet antigenic stimulation of the thymus-independent cell population.

Several aspects of production and traffic patterns of the lymphocyte help to distinguish differences among them. In contrast to their apparent morphological homogeneity under light microscopy, ultrastructural analysis provides evidence to suggest the existence of at least two distinct types of cells. One of these possesses aggregated ribosomal granules in the cytoplasm resembling pancreatic acinar cells and in the other, the ribosomal granules are dispersed (75). This ultrastructural distinction correlates well in ontogenetic studies with populations derived from bursa and thymus, respectively (76).

Lymphocyte circulation and recirculation.—Traffic patterns also fall into two categories: (a) recirculation of small lymphocytes from the blood into the lymphoid tissues and back to the blood with a cycling time of several hours and involving a population of nondividing small lymphocytes with an average life-span of several weeks (77–79); and (b) traffic of a dividing population of cells from bone marrow, and hemopoietic liver in the young animal, to the thymus and from there to the peripheral lymph nodes. The duration of this latter cycle is unknown but can be estimated to be from several days to weeks and this probably represents the maturational sequence leading to immunologically competent cells (33, 34, 44). Both traffic patterns are modified by antigenic stimulation and by procedures that depress immune functions, e.g., thymectomy, thoracic duct drainage, irradiation, or chemical agents.

Although these traffic patterns, particularly the recirculation pattern, have been defined and their functional significance in the immune process suggested, many questions remain (77). Perhaps the most crucial involves definition of the traffic "signals" employed to govern this system. Histocompatibility surface antigens seem to play a role since traffic of bone marrow cells to the thymus differs when syngeneic or allogeneic stem cells are compared. It is obvious, however, that such signals do not play a role under physiological conditions. Special surface antigens have been described in thymus and lymphoid cells but their *in vivo* role in cell traffic is still unknown (80). Surface sugars (81) may represent the ideal type of simple signal, and treatment of lymphoid cells with different enzymes including neuraminidase can alter traffic patterns as demonstrated by intravenous injections of labeled, enzyme-treated cells (82, 83). This effect does not seem to be related to changes in viability of the cells injected. In this context it is interesting that the only free extracellular sugar, i.e., glucose, is conspicuously absent from the membranes of all cells. Conversely, none of the sugars predominant in cell membranes, i.e., disaccharides, are present in significant amounts in plasma or extracellular fluids.

The first evidence of recirculation of lymphocytes was provided by an observation indicating marked and progressive decrease of the lymphocyte output in the rat's thoracic duct after chronic drainage (84, 85). The curve defining this decline can be divided into two exponential components: (a) initial rapid decrease due to the depletion of a readily mobilizable pool of lymphocytes, mainly small lymphocytes; and (b) progressive depletion of a heterogeneous pool of lymphocytes containing the less mobilizable, fixed small lymphocytes and medium- and large-size lymphocytes capable of DNA synthesis. The magnitude of output is from 2×10^9 to 1×10^{10} cells per kg body weight per 24 hours for mice, rats, dogs, sheep, calves, and humans. The pig seems to be an exception that deserves further study since its thoracic duct lymph apparently lacks small lymphocytes (86). With an extracorporeal circulation and continuous injection of thoracic duct lymphocytes into the jugular vein, it was demonstrated in sheep that the cellular flow rate per day remains constant for prolonged periods of time if the animals can be maintained in good general condition (87, 88). There is a constant relation between the daily cellular output and the size of the recirculating lymphocyte pool. Steroids, pyrogens, and histamine markedly reduce the output cellular flow rate for several hours, the rate returning to former levels after 2 or 3 days. The actions of steroids are interesting since they suggest that besides its known capacity to kill lymphocytes, the drug may prevent the release of lymphocytes into the efferent lymph. The administration of cortisone was followed by a sharp fall in the thoracic duct output of lymphocytes which lasted a few hours: the size of the recirculation pool of small lymphocytes was not reduced (88). Interestingly, pertussis antigen which produces fantastic accumulation of lymphocytes in the peripheral blood of both man and several experimental animals seems to exert its influence by a similar alteration of the traffic pattern: lymphocyte recirculation is inhibited by interfering with return of lymphocytes from blood to lymphatic tissue and hence to lymph. This influence is strikingly reflected in the rapid decline of lymphocytes in the thoracic duct lymph following administration of pertussis antigen (89).

The route of recirculation for the small lymphocyte includes transit across the cytoplasm of the endothelial cells in the postcapillary venules of the nodes (90). It is of interest that a similar cytoplasmic transit through the endothelial cell has been described in delayed hypersensitivity reactions, in which the mononuclear cells that infiltrate the lesion pass from the lumen of venules to the extravascular space via this transit and not between the endothelial cells themselves, as suggested by light microscopy (91, 92). By contrast, in antibody-mediated allergic reactions the transport of cells and fluid to the extracirculatory site of inflammation goes by way of intercellular channels.

Life-span of lymphocytes.—Estimates of lymphocyte life-span based on the fall of labeled cells after discontinuing the administration of 3H-thymidine are complicated by the reutilization of the radioactive precursors. On the other hand, the estimates based on the presence and persistence of unlabeled cells during periods of continuous administration of the radioactive precursor are quite significant. By this latter method, it has been demonstrated that at least 10 per cent of the small lymphocytes in the blood of rats have a life-span in excess of 220 days (93). Several studies indicate that peripheral small lymphocytes can be divided into at least two populations on the basis of life-span, a short-lived minority having a life-span of 2 weeks or less and a long-lived majority having a life-span of many months or even years. One estimate, in humans, places the average life-span of this long-lived population at 4.4 years (94).

The functional significance of these two populations has not yet been clarified. The long-lived lymphocytes seem to be the most likely candidates for the storage and transport of immunological memory and can probably be equated with the thymus-dependent populations (see below). Problems such as range of life-spans within populations and correlation between life-span uniformity and homogeneity of origin or function are still open to analysis. The study of different lymphoid organs and bone marrow shows different proportions of these two populations. Thymus and bone marrow contain mainly short-lived cells while thoracic duct, blood, and lymph nodes contain mainly long-lived cells; spleen contains approximately equal numbers of both types. It is clear that the second type of traffic described initially above may complicate such estimates since the movement of labeled cells from one compartment to another is difficult to determine and could drastically influence these estimates. It seems fairly clear, however, that the recirculating pool of small lymphocytes is composed mainly of long-lived cells and the proportion of "recirculating" lymphocytes in different organs closely parallels the respective proportions of "long-lived" lymphocytes in those organs.

Lymphocytes in the regional nodes and lymphatics.—Recent studies on the output of lymphocytes from individual lymph nodes in sheep suggest that recirculation may play an important functional role. On the average, 1 gram of lymph node will discharge 3×10^7 lymphocytes per hour into the efferent lymph; 90 per cent of these are small lymphocytes (95). The contribution of both afferent lymphatics or endogenous production within the lymph node indicates that only a small proportion of the lymphocyte output is derived from these sources (96). It follows that most of the lymphocytes in the efferent lymph must derive from recirculation of lymphocytes in the blood flowing through the vasculature of the node. Measurement of the venous outflow from individual nodes permits calculations which suggest that in order to populate the efferent lymph about 10 per cent of the blood lymphocytes must leave the blood with each passage through the node (97).

Antigenic stimulation drastically changes the numbers and cell types in the efferent lymph (98). Antigen injected into the drainage area of a sheep lymph node arrests the output of cells into the efferent lymphatics for about 6 hours, then over the following 72 hours the flux of cells in the efferent lymph is greatly increased. During this time, there is little evidence of cellular proliferation within the node, so the increase must be accounted for by an increased rate of lymphocyte recirculation (98). This "recruitment" phase is followed by a proliferative phase which lasts about 50 hours and is characterized by the appearance of many large, rapidly dividing basophilic cells in the efferent lymph—the immunologic display (98). These cells have been followed to other lymph nodes and there is evidence that at least some of them can actually develop into classical antibody-producing plasma cells. It is of interest that this response of the regional node to antigenic stimulation is inhibited when a methylcholanthrene-induced tumor is transplanted to a site draining into the regional node (99).

Local irradiation of the node with 2000 R does not modify substantially the immune response after antigenic challenge, which again indicates that the functional capacity of the lymphoid components in a lymph node depends mainly on the entry of recirculating lymphocytes derived from the pool of peripheral lymphocytes, rather than on the primary production of lymphocytes within the node (100). Comparable results have been obtained by local irradiation of the spleen in rats (101).

Although the labeling experiments would seem to suggest the contrary, the thymus appears to be of major importance in the production of the recirculating small lymphocyte population. Neonatal thymectomy in mice leads to a 99 per cent deficit in the thoracic duct output of small lymphocytes (102). In rats, on the other hand, the deficit in lymphocyte output after neonatal thymectomy is less marked (103, 104). The actual magnitude of the thoracic duct output spared after neonatal thymectomy may not reflect accurately the true proportion of cells normally contributed from extra thymic sources, since thymus ablation may remove both a source of humoral factors capable of influencing lymphopoiesis in the periphery and a supply of precursor cells derived from the thymus that, although thymus-dependent, establishes an autonomous, replicating, relatively thymus-independent population in the periphery. Thus, these cells may be visualized as differentiating under thymus influence but proliferating autonomously in the peripheral lymphoid tissues.

Extracorporeal irradiation of circulating blood[6] in calves produces a severe depletion of small lymphocytes within the body. It is interesting that the germinal centers in the lymphoid tissues are left intact albeit depleted of small lymphocytes. The number of peripheral small lymphocytes drops markedly to a low constant level after the first 12 hours and is maintained up to 48 hours after extracorporeal irradiation. On the other hand, the lymphoid tissues continue to lose lymphocytes between 12 to 48 hours after irradiation. This suggests that the apparent steady-state lymphocyte level in blood is maintained by a nonsteady-state process in the lymphoid organs where the new production of lymphocytes is insufficient to replace the cells leaving these tissues (105).

It is striking that depletion of the recirculating lymphoid pool by extracorporeal irradiation and by thoracic duct drainage depletes selectively the same broad areas in lymphoid tissues which are depleted in neonatally thymectomized or thymectomized and irradiated rodents. Similar depletion may be accomplished by administration of antilymphocyte globulins or antithymocyte globulin. All of these influences, depleting the recirculating lymphoid pool, interfere selectively with capacity to develop and exercise the cell-mediated thymus-dependent immune responses, while sparing the production of immunoglobulins and antibody responses to most antigens (106, 107).

Germinal centers.—Another component of the lymphoid system receiving much attention in the current literature is that comprising the germinal centers. These structures, heretofore erroneously considered to be a site of production of the small lymphocytes, can now be linked to the antibody-producing system of cells. Indeed, much evidence associates these structures with capacity to achieve secondary responses of antibody synthesis, but their exact role in exercising this influence has not been fully elucidated. In the genetic defects of immunoglobulin synthesis in man, germinal centers, like plasma cells, were found to be lacking. For the most part, germinal centers develop following antigenic stimulation in the regions of the peripheral lymphatic organs where the more sessile lymphocyte populations abound. Germinal center formation in the chicken can clearly be shown to be prevented by removal of the bursa of Fabricius in the newly hatched chicken given near-lethal irradiation. Recent studies show that as in the thymus, proliferation of cells in the germinal centers involves continuous division of cells, the great majority of which are destroyed in the germinal centers without ever leaving this site (108). In the germinal center these proliferating lymphoid cells associate intimately with dendritic reticulum cells which have capacity to trap certain antigens, often when the latter are combined with antibody and complement (109, 110).

[6] With a flow of approximately 300 ml per minute, the circulating blood in the shunt receives a transit dose of approximately 900 R.

Incisive studies involving bursectomy carried out *in ovo* during the late stages of embryonation in the chick provide new information of the association of germinal centers with development of ability to produce the 7-S IgG immunoglobulins. If, as discussed earlier, the bursa of Fabricius is extirpated prior to the 17th day of embryonation in the chick, capacity for production of both IgM and IgG type immunoglobulins, germinal centers, and plasma cells fails to develop. If, on the other hand, bursectomy is delayed until the 18th or 19th day of embryonation, plasma cells and IgM production develop normally, whereas germinal centers, IgG-synthesizing plasma cells, and capacity to produce IgG type immunoglobulin fail to develop.

A final line of evidence seems revealing. In studies of phylogenetic developement, the elasmobranchii, holosteans, chondrosteans, and teleosts have been shown to be capable of producing only a single type of immunoglobulin, probably most closely related to IgM. Even though they can produce both large (19-S) and small (7-S) immunoglobulins, both of these molecular types have immunologically identical H-chains. Beginning with amphibians and perhaps also reflected as early as the dipnoid fishes, capacity to produce both 19-S IgM and 7-S IgG type immunoglobulins and antibodies has been demonstrated. The first appearance of structures reminiscent of the germinal centers of mammals has been described in the amphibians and these structures have been consistently found in the lymphoid tissues of birds, monotreans, marsupials, and true eutherians. Taken together, these associations suggest that germinal centers are linked to the thymus-independent lymphoid system and may function as a site of proliferation of lymphoid cells, permitting their further differentiation from immunocompetent cells to cells capable of synthesis and secretion of the IgG type of immunoglobulins and antibodies.

Role of the lymphoid system in bodily defense.—The mechanisms by which the cell-mediated and humoral immune systems exercise influences mediated by the immune response are complex. The interaction in the complement system of a series of protein factors and enzymes mediating cell destruction, inflammation, and phagocythosis lies beyond the scope of this review. Nonetheless, it is clear that this rather complex system represents one means of amplification of the humoral immunities which are functions of the thymus-independent lymphoid cells. Perhaps more pertinent to this review are the means of amplification or execution of the functions of the thymus-dependent, long-lived population of lymphocytes. Interaction of sensitized lymphocytes of this population with antigen apparently leads to production and release of a factor or factors which can exercise cytotoxicity, chemotaxis, and both inhibition of macrophage migration *in vitro* and activation of macrophages *in vivo*.

The role of cellular immunity in the bodily defense against facultative, intracellular, pyogenic bacterial pathogens and fungi can be attributed to the nonspecific activation of macrophages by products of lymphoid cells stimulated by antigens to which the host has been sensitized. These "angry" macrophages seem appropriate candidates to be considered a major means of amplification of cellular immunity. They, however, are certainly not the only means of amplifying these responses (111, 112). It is clear that in hypersensitivity reactions involving cellular immunity only a small number of reacting cells are specifically sensitized. Subsequent studies are essential to assess the role of cellular immunity and the "angry" macrophage in resistance to fungus infection, certain viral infections, participation in graft-versus-host reactions, and even cancer immunity and solid tissue homograft rejections which represent major functions attributable to the thymus-dependent system of lymphocytes.

To realize, however, that the lymphoid system can be compartmentalized vertically, so to speak, into central (differentiative) lymphoid organs and peripheral lymphoid organs and horizontally into thymus-dependent, long-lived mobile lymphoid cells, on the one hand, and thymus-independent antibody-producing cells, on the other, offers a most useful point of departure for consideration of classification and analysis of the interrelationships of the lymphoid cells, the perturbation of lymphoid systems in disease, and hopefully, ultimately, both positive and negative control of lymphoid functions.

LITERATURE CITED

1. Allen, L. *Ann. Rev. Physiol.,* **29,** 197–224 (1967)
2. Glick, B., Chang, T. S., Jaap, R. G. *Poultry Sci.,* **35,** 224–25 (1956)
3. Archer, O., Pierce, J. C. *Fed. Proc. (Abstr.),* **20,** 26 (1961)
4. Martinez, C., Kersey, J., Papermaster, B. W., Good, R. A. *Proc. Soc. Exptl. Biol. Med.,* **109,** 193–96 (1962)
5. Miller, J. F. A. P. *Lancet,* **ii,** 748–49 (1961)
6. Humphrey, J. H., Parrott, D. M. V., East, J. *Immunology,* **7,** 419–39 (1964)
7. Arnason, B. G., Jankovic, B. D., Waksman, B. H., Wennerstein, C. *J. Exptl. Med.,* **116,** 177–86 (1962)
8. Sherman, J. D., Adner, M. M., Dameshek, W. *Blood,* **23,** 375–88 (1964)
9. Warner, N. L., Szenberg, A., Burnett, F. M. *Aust. J. Exptl. Biol.,* **40,** 373–88 (1962)
10. Warner, N. L., Szenberg, A. Immunologic studies on hormonally bursectomized and surgically thymectomized chickens, dissociation of immunologic responsiveness. In *The Thymus in Immunobiology,* 395–411 (Good, R. A., Gabrielsen,

A. E., Eds., Harper & Row, New York, 1964)
11. Cooper, M. D., Peterson, R. D. A., Good, R. A. *Nature,* **205,** 143–46 (1965)
12. Cooper, M. D., Cain, W. A., Van Alten, P. J., Good, R. A. *Intern. Arch. Allergy,* **35,** 242–52 (1969)
13. Van Alten, P. J., Cain, W. A., Good, R. A., Cooper, M. D. *Nature,* **217,** 358–60 (1968)
14. Cain, W. A., Cooper, M. D., Van Alten, P. J., Good, R. A. *J. Immunol.,* **102,** 671–78 (1969)
15. Cain, W. A., Cooper, M. D., Good, R. A. *Fed. Proc. (Abstr.),* **28,** 432 (1969)
16. Lerman, S. P., Weidanz, W. P. Antibody deficiency syndrome resulting from cyclophosphamide treatment of bursectomized chickens. *Proc. 69th Ann. Meeting Am. Soc. Microbiol. (Abstr.)* (To be published in *Bacteriol. Proc.*)
17. Linna, T. J., Frommel, D., Good, R. A. (Manuscript in preparation)
18. Papermaster, B. W., Condie, R. M., Finstad, J., Good, R. A. *J. Exptl. Med.,* **119,** 105–30 (1964)
19. Hildemann, W. H., Thoenes, G. H. *Transplantation,* **7,** 506–21 (1969)

20. Finstad, J., Papermaster, B. W., Good, R. A. *Lab. Invest.*, **13**, 490–512 (1964)

21. Thorbecke, G. J., Cohen, M. W., Jacobson, E. B., Wakefield, J. D. The production of memory cells by the white pulp of the spleen in rabbits. In *Germinal Centers in Immune Responses*, 259–69 (Cottier, H., Odartchenko, N., Schindler, R., Congdon, C. C., Eds., Springer-Verlag, Berlin, 1967)

22. Pollara, B., Finstad, J., Good, R. A. Specific immunoglobulin synthesis in lower vertebrates lacking germinal centers. In *Lymphatic Tissue in Germinal Centers in Immune Response*, 1–8 (Fiore-Donati, L., Hanna, M. G., Eds., Plenum Press, New York, 1969)

23. Sidky, Y. A., Auerbach, R. *J. Exptl. Zool.*, **167**, 187–96 (1968)

24. Track, E., Good, R. A. Phylogenetic study: The lymphoid organs of the bullfrog, *Rana catesbeiana:* A bursa? (Manuscript in preparation)

25. La Plante, E. S., Taylor, D. L., Burrell, R. G. *Fed. Proc. (Abstr.)*, **25**, 232 (1966)

26. Sutherland, D. E. R., Finstad, J., Good, R. A. (Unpublished observations)

27. Cooper, M. D., Perey, D. Y., Gabrielsen, A. E., Sutherland, D. E. R., McKneally, M. F., Good, R. A. *Intern. Arch. Allergy*, **33**, 65–88 (1968)

28. Perey, D. Y. E., Cooper, M. D., Good, R. A. *Science,* **161**, 265–66 (1968)

29. Tyan, M. L., Herzenberg, L. A. *Proc. Soc. Exptl. Biol. Med.*, **128**, 952–54 (1968)

30. Auerbach, R. *Develop. Biol.*, **3**, 336–54 (1961)

31. Ackerman, G. A., Knouff, R. A. *Anat. Record*, **149**, 191–216 (1964)

32. Moore, M. A. S., Owen, J. J. T. *J. Exptl. Med.*, **126**, 715–26 (1967)

33. Ford, C. E., Micklem, H. S. *Lancet,* **i**, 359–62 (1963)

34. Harris, J. E., Ford, C. E. *Nature,* **201**, 884–85 (1964)

35. Silverstein, A. Development of antibody production in fetal lambs subjected to complete extirpation of the bowel (In preparation)

36. Good, R. A., Martinez, C., Gabrielsen, A. E. *Advan. Pediat.*, **13**, 93–127 (1964)

37. Gatti, R. A., Meuwissen, H. J., Allen, H. D., Hong, R., Good, R. A. *Lancet*, **ii**, 1366–69 (1968)

38. Meuwissen, H. J., Gatti, R. A., Terasaki, P. I., Hong, R., Good, R. A. *New Engl. J. Med.*, **281**, 691–96 (1969)

39. Bennett, J. C., Owen, R. D. *J. Cell Physiol.*, **67** *(Suppl. 1)*, 207–15 (1966)

40. Curry, J. L., Trentin, J. J. *Develop. Biol.*, **15**, 395–413 (1967)

41. Osoba, D., Miller, J. F. A. P. *Nature,* **199**, 653–54 (1963)

42. Osoba, D. *J. Exptl. Med.*, **122**, 633–50 (1965)

43. Stutman, O., Yunis, E. J., Good, R. A. *J. Natl. Cancer Inst.*, **43**, 499–508 (1969)

44. Stutman, O., Yunis, E. J., Good, R. A. *Transplant. Proc.*, **1**, 614–15 (1969)

45. Stutman, O., Yunis, E. J., Good, R. A. *J. Natl. Cancer Inst.*, **41**, 1431–52 (1968)

46. Stutman, O., Yunis, E. J., Good, R. A. *J. Exptl. Med.*, **130**, 809–19 (1969)

47. Bruton, O. C. *Pediatrics,* **9**, 722–28 (1952)

48. Good, R. A., Varco, R. L. *J. Lancet,* **75**, 245–71 (1955)

49. Good, R. A., Kelly, W. D., Rotstein, J., Varco, R. L. *Progr. Allergy,* **6**, 187–319 (1962)

50. DiGeorge, A. M., Discussion of Cooper et al. *J. Pediat.*, **67**, 908 (1965)

51. DiGeorge, A. M. Congenital absence of the thymus and its immunological consequences. Concurrence with congenital hypoparathyroidism. In *Proc. 3rd Develop. Immunobiol. Workshop: Immunologic Deficiency Diseases in Man, 4, Birth Defects, Original Article Ser.,* 116–21 (Natl. Found. Press, New York, 1968)

52. Kretschmer, R., Say, B., Brown, D., Rosen, F. S. *New Engl. J. Med.,* **279**, 1295–1301 (1968)

53. Glanzmann, E., Riniker, P. *Ann. Paediat. (Basel)*, **175**, 1–32 (1950)

54. Hitzig, W. H. Swiss type of agammaglobulinemia (See Ref. 51), 82–87

55. Hoyer, J. R., Cooper, M. D., Gabrielsen, A. E., Good, R. A. *Medicine*, **47**, 201–26 (1968)

56. Cleveland, W. W., Fogel, B. J., Kay,

H. E. M. *J. Clin. Invest. (Abstr.)*, **47,** 20a–21a (1968)

57. Cleveland, W. W., Fogel, B., Brown, W. T., Kay, H. E. M. *Lancet*, **ii,** 1211–14 (1968)

58. August, C. S., Rosen, F. S., Filler, R. M., Janeway, C. A., Markowski, B., Kay, H. E. M. *Lancet*, **ii,** 1210–11 (1968)

59. De Koning, J., Dooren, L. J., Van Bekkum, D. W., Van Rood, J. J., Dicke, K. A., Radl, J. *Lancet*, **i,** 1223–27 (1969)

60. Ammann, A. J., Meuwissen, H. J., Good, R. A., Hong, R. Successful bone marrow transplantation in a patient with thymic hypoplasia, deficient cellular immunity and IgA deficiency. *New Engl. J. Med.* (Submitted)

61. Milhaud, G., Vesin, P. *Nature*, **191,** 872–74 (1961)

62. Poley, J. R., Hitzig, W. H. Congenital lymphedema and chyloperitoneum. In *Proc. 3rd Symp. Physiol. and Pathophysiol. of Plasma Protein Metabolism*, 186–90 (Koblet, H., Vesin, P., Diggelmann, H., Barandum, S., Eds., Grune & Stratton, New York, 1965)

63. Strober, W., Wochner, R. D., Carbone, P. P., Waldmann, T. A. *J. Clin. Invest.*, **46,** 1643–56 (1967)

64. Lajtha, L. G. *Radiation Res.*, **33,** 659–69 (1968)

65. Sipe, C. R., Chanana, A. D., Cronkite, E. P., Joel, D. D., Schiffer, L. M. *Proc. Soc. Exptl. Biol. Med.*, **123,** 158–61 (1966)

66. MacLean, L. D., Zak, S. J., Varco, R. L., Good, R. A. *Transplant. Bull.*, **4,** 21–22 (1957)

67. Taylor, R. B. *Nature*, **208,** 1334–35 (1965)

68. Claman, H. N., Chaperson, G. A., Triplett, R. F. *Proc. Soc. Exptl. Biol. Med.*, **122,** 1167–71 (1966)

69. Miller, J. F. A. P., Mitchell, G. F. *Nature*, **216,** 659–63 (1967)

70. Mitchell, G. F., Miller, J. F. A. P. *J. Exptl. Med.*, **128,** 821–37 (1968)

71. Doria, G., Agarossi, G. *Transplantation*, **6,** 218–29 (1968)

72. Stutman, O., Good, R. A. *Proc. Soc. Exptl. Biol. Med.*, **130,** 848–52 (1969)

73. Raidt, D. J., Mishell, R. I., *Dutton*, R. W. *J. Exptl. Med.*, **128,** 681–98 (1968)

74. Mosier, D. E., Coppleson, L. W. *Proc.*

Natl. Acad. Sci., **61,** 542–47 (1968)

75. Johnson, H. A., Schnappauf, H., Chanana, A. D., Cronkite, E. P. *Nature*, **211,** 420 (1966)

76. Clawson, C. C., Cooper, M. D., Good, R. A. *Lab. Invest.*, **16,** 407–21 (1967)

77. Gowans, J. L., McGregor, D. D. *Progr. Allergy*, **9,** 1–78 (1965)

78. Gowans, J. L. *J. Physiol.*, **146,** 54–69 (1959)

79. Ford, W. L., Gowans, J. L. *Seminars Hematol.*, **6,** 67–83 (1969)

80. Boyse, E. A., Miyazawa, M., Aoki, T., Old, L. J. *Proc. Roy. Soc. B*, **170,** 175–93 (1968)

81. Gesner, B. M. *Ann. N.Y. Acad. Sci.*, **129,** 758–66 (1966)

82. Gesner, B. M., Ginsburg, V. *Proc. Natl. Acad. Sci.*, **52,** 750–55 (1964)

83. Woodruff, J. J., Gesner, B. M. *J. Exptl. Med.*, **129,** 551–67 (1969)

84. Mann, J. D., Higgins, G. M. *Blood*, **5,** 177–90 (1950)

85. Gowans, J. L. *Brit. J. Exptl. Pathol.*, **38,** 67–78 (1957)

86. Binns, R. M., Hall, J. G. *Brit. J. Exptl. Pathol.*, **47,** 275–80 (1966)

87. Schnappauf, H., Schnappauf, U. *Blut*, **16,** 209–20 (1968)

88. Schnappauf, H., Schnappauf, U. *Nouv. Rev. Franc. Hematol.*, **8,** 555–64 (1968)

89. Morse, S. I., Riester, S. K. *J. Exptl. Med.*, **125,** 619–28 (1967)

90. Marchesi, V. T., Gowans, J. L. *Proc. Roy. Soc. B*, **159,** 283–90 (1964)

91. Astrom, K. E., Webster, H. de F., Arnason, B. G. *J. Exptl. Med.*, **128,** 469–95 (1968)

92. Willms-Kretschmer, K., Flax, M. H., Cotran, R. S. *Lab. Invest.*, **17,** 334–49 (1967)

93. Robinson, S. H., Brecher, G., Lourie, I. S., Haley, J. E. *Blood*, **26,** 281–95 (1965)

94. Buckton, K. E., Court-Brown, W. M., Smith, P. G. *Nature*, **214,** 470–73 (1967)

95. Hall, J. G., Morris, B. *Quart. J. Exptl. Physiol.*, **48,** 235–47 (1963)

96. Hall, J. G., Morris, B. *Brit. J. Exptl. Pathol.*, **46,** 450–54 (1965)

97. Hall, J. G. *Quart. J. Exptl. Physiol.*, **52,** 76–85 (1967)

98. Hall, J. G., Morris, B. *J. Exptl. Med.*, **121,** 901–10 (1965)

99. Alexander, P. *Progr. Exptl. Tumor Res.*, **10,** 22–71 (1968)

100. Hall, J. G., Morris, B. *Lancet*, **i,**

546   GATTI, STUTMAN & GOOD

1077–80 (1964)
101. Simic, M. M., Petrovic, M. Z. Effects of local irradiation of the spleen on the primary response in rats. In *Germinal Centers in Immune Responses*, 240–49 (Cottier, H., Odartchenko, N., Schindler, R., Congdon, C. C., Eds., Springer-Verlag, Berlin, New York, 1967)
102. Miller, J. F. A. P., Mitchell, G. F., Weiss, N. S. *Nature, 214,* 992–97 (1967)
103. Goldschneider, I., McGregor, D. D. *J. Exptl. Med., 127,* 155–68 (1968)
104. Rieke, W. O. *Anat. Record (Abstr.), 148,* 327 (1964)
105. Cottier, H., Cronkite, E. P., Jansen, C. R., Rai, K. R., Singer, S., Sipe, C. R. *Blood, 24,* 241–53 (1964)
106. Martin, W. J., Miller, J. F. A. P. *J. Exptl. Med., 128,* 855–74 (1968)
107. Lance, E. M. *Advan. Transplant.,* 107–16 (Munskgaard, Copenhagen, 1968)
108. Fliendner, T. M., Kesse, M., Cronkite, E. P., Robertson, J. *Ann. N.Y. Acad. Sci., 113,* 578–94 (1964)
109. Nossal, G. J. V., Ada, G. L., Austin, C. M. *Aust. J. Exptl. Biol. Med., Sci., 42,* 311–30 (1964)
110. Williams, G. M., Nossal, G. J. V. *J. Exptl. Med., 124,* 47–56 (1966)
111. Mackaness, G. B. *J. Exptl. Med., 129,* 973–92 (1969)
112. Mackaness, G. B., Hill, W. C. *J. Exptl. Med., 129,* 993–1012 (1969)

THE REGULATION OF EXTRACELLULAR FLUID VOLUME   1054

Otto H. Gauer, James P. Henry, and Claus Behn

Departments of Physiology
of the
Freien Universität Berlin and University of Southern California

INTRODUCTION

A complete review of the above topic would be formidable indeed since it would comprise a good part of circulatory physiology, plus the physiology of salt and water balance and, last but not least, the physiology of fluid exchange through cell membranes (cell metabolism). Although the latter subject has been almost entirely excluded, more than a thousand papers were studied—one out of four of which were selected for references. Encouraged by the editors, we have chosen to develop certain delimited aspects of the problem of fluid volume control rather than to present an annotated bibliography.

In essence, the work updates a previous review on the circulatory aspects of fluid volume control (1), and for older literature, the reader is referred to this article. The focus will be on the regulation of plasma volume; but, because this volume is an integral part of extracellular fluid volume, the regulation of extracellular volume and factors controlling its compartmentation into the intravascular and interstitial sections must also be considered. The problem has a Janus head, facing into circulatory physiology on the one side, and into the physiology of body fluids and kidney function on the other. Recently Guyton & Coleman have presented a bold theoretical analysis of the long-term regulation of the circulation and its interrelationships with body fluid volumes (2). Those of their viewpoints to which we would subscribe and our differences concerning the way in which central venous pressure plays its crucial role will appear as we proceed.

DEFINITION OF BLOOD VOLUME CONTROL

The control of plasma volume or blood volume centers about the need for a mechanism for the reciprocal adjustment of two variables, the blood volume and the size of the total vascular bed. The size of the vascular bed or its potential capacity is given by: the dimensions attained by the struc-

547

tural elements of the capacitance vessels and their elastic properties; and the tone of the vascular smooth muscles.

As Guyton points out, the various aspects of the long-term adaptation of the size of the vascular tree to the needs of the body are scarcely recognized as basic physiological problems (2). Yet Sjöstrand (3, 4) has shown that blood volume is a function of body type, body size, age, climate, and, of particular importance, physical activity. From the viewpoint of blood volume control, we believe that the increased blood volume in response to greater metabolic demands is a two-step operation in which the dimensions of the heart and vascular bed are first increased, while the ensuing demand for a greater filling volume is satisfied in a second step. Observations of newborn infants held in an incubator speak in favor of this concept: Upon exposure to high oxygen tension the vessels already present in the immature retinal tissues shrink within hours, and if the high oxygen tension is maintained, they will fail to grow in sufficient number and size. The secondary pathological changes lead to the blindness of retrolental fibroplasia (5).

But metabolic demand is not the only factor inducing increased size of a vascular bed. When a high regional blood flow is enforced without an increase in oxygen consumption as, for instance, in long-standing arteriovenous fistulas, anastomoses open up and the dimensions of the afferent and efferent vessels may increase grotesquely (6). A pertinent and very interesting observation is the development of wide anastomoses in the coronary circulation of dogs which have been treated with high dosages of a coronary dilator drug for several weeks. So effective is the collateralization, that they may not show coronary infarction following ligation of a major vessel as do controls (7). The mechanism by which these changes in the dimensions of the vascular bed are controlled is obscure.

A clear-cut example involving an adjustment of volume secondary to a change in vascular capacity is the observation that patients with gross varicose veins and, therefore, an oversized capacity of the vascular beds of the dependent legs exhibit an abnormally large blood volume (8). The increased blood volume often found in patients with idiopathic postural hypotension (9) may be explained on a similar basis (10).

To summarize: If we speak in this article of blood volume control, we do not mean homeostatic control of volume, but the continuous adaptation of plasma volume to the everchanging size of the heart and the vascular bed.

PRESSURE-VOLUME DIAGRAM OF THE CIRCULATION

It has long been known that the veins can constrict and thereby acutely change the caliber of the peripheral vascular bed (11). The emphasis has been on the established fact that quite small reductions in vascular circumference will shift considerable amounts of blood into the central veins, thereby increasing the filling pressure of the heart. This phenomenon was too readily accepted as a facile explanation for moment-to-moment control of cardiac output through "venous return". But, in point of fact, the experiments from which these conclusions were drawn usually involved strong stimuli in stressed animals. The concept of an unfailing homeostatic control of venous return is furthermore strictly at odds with the simple observation that in healthy man, assumption of the upright position leads to a considerable reduction in cardiac filling. The obvious explanation is that the peripheral veins do not constrict adequately and that 400–600 ml of blood pool in the dependent vessels (10). The absence of a noteworthy increase in tone of the vascular bed of the extremities during changes in posture and moderate changes in blood volume has been directly demonstrated by several independent groups (10–14). These results have been repeatedly confirmed. The recent data of Walsh et al. (15) who tilted subjects to 60° using a saddle and found a decrease in forearm venous distensibility are no contradiction, for such a procedure is a strong stimulus equivalent to the loss of 20 to 25 per cent of the blood volume. This is the figure that Sears (14) has found to be the critical point for increase of venomotor tone in his lucid analysis of the question of blood volume loss and venous distensibility.

The absence of any noteworthy venomotor response to moderate fluid volume changes leads to the conclusion that in the reciprocal adjustment of vascular capacity and blood volume to achieve a normal measure of J. P. Peter's "fullness of the blood stream", blood volume must be considered as the prime variable (1).

The degree of filling of a container with rigid walls can easily be given in percent of its total capacity. The most expedient way to define the fullness of a container with elastic walls is to establish the pressure-volume diagram and indicate on it the actual filling pressure.

The analysis of the overall function of the circulation with regard to volume changes is greatly facilitated when we divide it into two functionally different compartments: the distributing arterial system and the low-pressure system. The latter comprises the capacitance vessels of the systemic circulation, the right heart, the pulmonary vascular bed, and the left heart during diastole (1). When the heart is stopped, the pressures throughout the whole circulation equalize and the static pressure is obtained (1). This static pressure is a function of the compliance of the vascular bed and total blood volume. Since the volume elasticity of the arterial system is about 200 times higher than that of the total circulation, the compliance of the vascular bed is practically identical with the compliance of the low-pressure system which holds approximately 80 per cent of the total blood volume (1, 16). When the heart starts to beat again, only a relatively small volume of blood is transferred from the low-pressure system into the arterial tree. Because of the very different compliances of the two systems, there is a great rise in arterial pressure, while the pressures in the low-pressure system fall a few cm H_2O below the static pressure. A well-defined pressure-volume relationship similar to that found in the static circulation is maintained in the low-pressure system of an active circulation operating under steady-state conditions. Changes in cardiac output due to an altered filling pressure of

TABLE I

CHANGE IN PRESSURES (cm H_2O) FOR $\pm 10\%$
BLOOD VOLUME CHANGE

Ref.	Animal	N	Right atrial pressure		Left atrial pressure		Pulmonary arterial pressure	
			Inf	Hem	Inf	Hem	Inf	Hem
Henry et al. (18)	Dog$_c$	12–15	+2.5	−1.8	+3.0	−2.0	+1.5	−1.5
Gupta et al. (19)	Dog$_c$	15	+2.0	−1.8	—		—	
Pabst & Gauer (20)	Dog$_u$*	4	+2.0	−1.4	—		—	
Pabst & Gauer (20)	Dog$_u$**	6	+1.4	−2.0	—		—	
Arndt (21)	Cat$_c$	6	+1.8	−2.0	+2.3	−2.2	—	
	Man		3.0				(7.0)	

* 20 ml H_2O/kg by stomach tube.
** 20 ml saline/kg by stomach tube.
c = Chloralose anesthesia.
u = Unanesthetized.
Inf = Infusion.
Hem = Hemorrhage.

the heart may slightly change the distribution of blood volume between the arterial and low-pressure systems or they may cause additional dynamic pressure in the low-pressure system. However, in view of the very low flow resistance in the low-pressure system, the latter effect is insignificant and as the actual measurements show (see below), the possible transfer of blood out of and into the low-pressure system is too small to disturb the basic pressure-volume relationship.

Data were presented in Table 1 of Gauer & Henry's earlier review (1) which showed that in man any change in blood volume induced by hemorrhage or transfusion results in long-lasting rises or falls in central venous pressure of the order of 3 cm H_2O for a change of blood volume of 10 per cent. Confirming data comes from some of the many clinical observations in which central venous pressure has been followed during blood volume expansion for therapeutic reasons. Thus Thomasson (17) simultaneously measured central venous pressure and pulmonary arterial pressure. A 10 per cent increase in blood volume raised central venous pressure by 3.5 cm H_2O, while pulmonary arterial pressure rose by 7 cm H_2O. It is noteworthy that cardiac output did not change significantly with a transfusion of 17 per cent blood volume.

Similar results are obtained with animals; however, as Table I of the present paper shows, the compliance of the circulation of dogs and cats is about 50 to 100 per cent greater than that of man. This appears to be independent of anesthesia.

With a rapid hemorrhage or transfusion (up to 15 per cent blood volume change in 10 sec) a comparatively large pressure change is obtained which is attenuated after cessation of the procedure. About 5 to 15 min later, the pressures in the low-pressure system stabilize at a new level (18–21). The readjustment of the pressures is probably due to a combination of rapid blood volume redistribution and, most importantly, in the context of this review, inward or outward filtration. The so-called "delayed compliance" may also play a part.

It is relevant to point out that a blood volume change of 10 per cent in either direction does not change the arterial blood pressure significantly and that the volume loss must usually exceed 25–30 percent before there is a fall in mean arterial pressure (18, 19). This is why arterial pressure is of little value as a guideline for shock therapy. On the other hand, as numerous recent publications attest, the recently introduced continuous recording of central venous pressure is proving an invaluable tool for the monitoring of intravenous fluid therapy (22–32).

VOLUME AND COMPLIANCE OF THE INTERSTITIAL FLUID SPACE

SIZE OF THE EXTRACELLULAR FLUID SPACE

Ever since the days of Starling, much effort has been expended on the physiology of transcapillary exchange of fluid and solutes. There are a number of outstanding review articles and monographs which deal with the multifaceted aspects of this difficult and important field (33–42).

There is a small group of physiologists whose principal field of concern is with the factors controlling the absolute size of the extracellular fluid (ECF) volume and the way in which it is distributed between the interstitial fluid space (IF) and plasma volume (PV). It is important to determine the laws which govern the transfer of fluid and protein through the capillary wall and in the lymphatic system. However, it is also critical to know the distensibility or compliance of the extravascular space, for it is this factor that finally determines the fluid distribution between the intra- and extravascular compartments.

The size of the ECF space can conveniently be determined by the use of ^{35}S or inulin. The interstitial fluid volume is obtained after subtraction of PV. It has been found that it varies much more than the PV. In nine subjects in whom ECF, PV, and red cell volume were measured with a multi-tracer technique, the extreme values for ECF ranged between 21 and 11 liters. The range for PV was between 2.8 and 2.1 liters (43).

Reinhardt & Behrenbeck (44) investigated the effect of altered sodium intake on the inulin, i.e., the ECF space, in chronic experiments in the dog. With high salt intake (1.7 to 14 meq/kg per day) salt was retained and the ECF went up. A new equilibrium was struck when the ECF reached 22 per cent body weight. With a sodium-poor diet (0.5 meq/kg per day), the ECF went down to 16 per cent of the body weight within 4 months. On the other hand, in the postprandial state, that is, after the ingestion of fluid and salt the ECF will increase by as much as 12.7 to 25.5 per cent (45). These experiments demonstrate the dependence of the ECF on salt metabolism, but an explanation of the factors that determine these changes and set a limit to the ECF ceiling is not available (46).

In general the IF is determined by the rate of capillary filtration and reabsorption. Of great importance is the permeability of the capillaries for protein and the rate at which protein is removed by the lymph. With a slow lymph flow, interstitial protein concentration and hence interstitial fluid volume must increase.

The important role which the protein content of the interstitial fluid plays in the determination of the interstitial fluid volume as well as of the effective colloid osmotic pressure across the capillary wall is well recognized. The mechanisms which regulate its transfer through the capillary wall have been the objects of intensive study (33–42).

It is not always appreciated that half of the extracellular protein is found in the interstitial spaces; but it is an important fact to remember when making exchange transfusions or therapeutic replacements of plasma proteins (36). The average concentration of this protein is 2 per cent; however, an average figure is inadequate since the tissues of every organ have specialized capillary networks, interstitial space, and lymphatic draining systems. Unfortunately, very little is known about the factors which relate plasma protein synthesis and distribution to fluid volume control.

COMPLIANCE OF THE INTERSTITIAL SPACE

The compliance of the interstitial space determines the final extent and rate of interstitial volume change when the balance between inflow and outflow has been upset. By and large, the problem of tissue space compliance has received almost no attention, partly because the methods for the measurement of interstitial pressure (IFP) were considered unreliable. Wiederhielm (38) in his computer model assumes a value of 60 per cent/mm Hg. This corresponds to the current concept that the IF space is a large and distensible reservoir from which the PV can easily be replenished. It is often considered that the only limiting factor is the change in the oncotic pressure of the plasma due to protein concentration or dilution. Two arguments against this concept of great distensibility come to mind. (1) If there were such a large reservoir communicating freely with the circulation, then it would have been difficult to establish a well-defined compliance for the low pressure system (see above). (2) In a paragraph on "fluid priming —an antihemorrhagic shock measure", Ingraham & Wiggers (47) observe that surviving animals (which were primed with saline infusion before the experiment) revealed a common tendency to undergo continuous hemodilution for 60–90 min of the hypotension period. However in those which succumbed, the hemodilution processes were arrested early and "hemoconcentration usually set in."

In the well-hydrated animals there were considerable resources for auto-transfusion, and more fluid was available for a given change in tissue pressure. In the language of the physicist, this means that in dogs with a greater than normal interstitial fluid content there is an increase in the compliance of the interstitial compartment.

GUYTON'S OBSERVATION OF NEGATIVE INTERSTITIAL PRESSURE

By implanting perforated capsules in various tissues, Guyton (48–50) tried a new approach to the problem of interstitial pressure measurement. Using a needle to measure the pressure in the fluid which had accumulated in the lumen during the 2–4 week healing process, he found a subatmospheric pressure of the order of −7 mm Hg. This Guyton took to be the true value of the interstitial pressure because there was convincing evidence of a free communication between the interstitial fluid and the fluid in the capsule. He explained the fact that this pressure was negative by marshaling evidence that the mean capillary hydrostatic pressure may be as low as 12 mm Hg. If we use this value in the classical formula of Starling for the forces acting across the capillary wall, then we find that tissue pressure may well be of the order of −10 mm Hg.

In support of this viewpoint, it seems appropriate to point out that negative pressures in serous spaces are by no means unusual. Subcutaneous fluid tension, the peritoneal fluid tension, and the negative pressures in the joint cavities as well as in the intrapleural space all range between −5 and −10 cm H_2O—a fact which suggests that they have the same origin.

To use an analogy: we may compare the interstitium with that type of X-ray technician's splint which consists of a rubber bag filled with sand. Such a bag is very pliable. However, it can be "frozen" in any desired form into which it has been shaped by sucking the air out of it: for then the pressure from without tightly packs the grains, leaving only minute channels between them. The force packing the tissue cells is, as was explained above, the colloidal osmotic pressure of the blood. The spaces between the cells are filled with ground substance (50a) which is entrapped in a fine meshwork of polymerized hyaluronic acid and mucopolysaccharides. The fluid within the ground substance has an extremely low mobility. Dye-injection studies (33) reveal few channels of very small diameter. Only when the force packing the tissue cells together is reduced, can confluent fluid pools be formed and edema occur (50).

The finding of a negative pressure in the interstitial space caused considerable bewilderment, and the reviewers admit that their enthusiasm for the concept of a low compliance of the interstitial space does not prevent them from realizing that this matter is far from being settled. However, several other investigators have now found a negative pressure when using Guyton's capsules (51–53); and Scholander (54) fully confirmed the concept of a negative pressure in interstitial spaces of animal and plant tissue using a completely different technique. His value for muscle and skin was −10 cm H_2O: plants revealed amazingly high negative pressures ranging up to 60 atm in the desert flora!

The rate of partial recovery of central venous pressure from the low value that it attains immediately after a nonhypotensive hemorrhage (55) corresponds to the expected rate of inflow of protein-poor fluid into the capillary bed from the interstitial spaces (33). A new equilibrium is attained when after 15–20 min some 40 per cent of the blood loss has been replaced (64). Hopkinson et al. (51) showed that these fluid shifts are also mirrored in the changes of IFP measured with implanted capsules. In their experiments with a modified shock model devised by Wiggers, a blood loss of 35 per cent with uncomplicated recovery was accompanied by a drop of IFP by 3 mm Hg which reverted to normal after retransfusion. With more severe shock, the IFP stayed low after retransfusion of the blood volume taken and an infusion of an extra volume of lactate Ringer's solution was necessary to bring it back to normal (51). However, survival of the animal had no relation to the reestablishment of control IFP. Their findings suggest that the gravely reduced blood flow impairs cell metabolism, leading to an uptake of extracellular fluid into the cells. This concept is supported by the work of Shires et al. (56). In this context, the all-important objective in the treatment of shock is the restoration of an adequate blood flow in order to permit recovery of normal cell metabolism. Without this, the replacement of interstitial fluid remains without benefit.

It has been pointed out that this review will not be concerned with the regulation of intracellular fluid. However, the experiments of Hopkinson (51) and Shires (56) seem to indicate that intracellular volume does not complicate the regulation of extracellular fluid unless grave deviations from normal cell metabolism are induced. Another complication could arise from abnormal osmotic pressures, but it appears that cell volume is actively controlled and is not susceptible to these effects (57, 58).

QUESTIONS CONCERNING NEGATIVE PRESSURE

Kjellmer (59) working with an indirect method and Wiederhielm (38, 39) with ultrafine micropipettes, which do not seriously injure the tissue, were both unable to find negative pressures in the tissue. Stromberg & Wiederhielm (53) question free communication between tissue space and capsule lumen. They come to the conclusion that scar tissue forming around the capsule and acting as a semipermeable membrane was responsible for low intracapsular pressures.

The observation of Landis & Pappenheimer (cf. 33) that an increased IFP limits the effect of raised capillary pressure on filtration speaks against the concept of an increased compliance with increasing interstitial volume. There are great variations in the tissue structure of organs, and their capillary supply differs in respect to permeability, to arrangement of precapillary sphincters, vasomotion, etc. so it is not possible to select a tissue which would be representative for all the rest (33, 37, 40). All encapsulated tissues such as the eye, the kidney, and to some extent the muscles (60) require special consideration. The fact that the IFP in the leg of a giraffe, which is encapsulated in an extremely tough hide, may be well over 200 mm Hg is no argument against Guyton's concept, and no one will deny the negative pressure in the intrapleural space and its biological significance, despite the fact that high positive pressures will be recorded when the subject is breathing against a high resistance. The important factor is not the absolute pressure, but the tightness with which the tissue cells are packed—that is, the low compliance of the interstitial space.

The assumption of a negative IFP demands that there be mechanisms capable of pumping the lymph uphill. However, this problem does not seem to present insuperable difficulties (34, 41). As a result of the great pliability of the lymph vessels together with their valves, unidirectional flow can be maintained when the tissue is massaged either by external forces or arterial pulsation. In loose tissue, like the mesentery of the guinea pig, Horstmann (61) has demonstrated in a beautiful motion picture the function of actively contractile areas in the vessels with inlet and outlet valves which act like peripheral hearts.

MATCHING COMPLIANCES OF INTERSTITIAL FLUID SPACE AND INTRAVASCULAR SPACE

With the availability of a method for recording the IFP, it was possible to establish the pressure-volume relationship of the interstitial space (49). This is of considerable consequence for the concept of fluid volume control (2). Under normal conditions the IFP is −7 mm Hg. It rises by 1 mm Hg for a volume increase of about 4 ml/kg body weight. As the IFP increases, the compliance increases considerably; and at an IFP slightly above atmospheric, it is about 100 ml/kg for 1 mm Hg pressure change. Thereafter, the state of edema prevails—a condition in which the interstitial fluid is freely movable, while in the normally "dry" interstitium, the resistance to flow is very high (50).

For the problem of volume control, it is of particular interest to compare the compliance of the interstitial space with that of the vascular bed. As Table I indicates, central venous pressure in animals changes by approximately 2 cm H_2O for a 10 per cent change in blood volume (8 ml/kg), or 0.7 mm Hg for a volume change of 4 ml/kg. For man, Gauer, Henry & Sieker (55) found a pressure change of 0.5 ± 0.1 cm H_2O for a volume change of 1 ml/kg. This means the compliance of the interstitial space of dogs (4 ml/kg · 1 mm Hg) lies between the compliance of the vascular bed of dogs and cats (4 ml/kg · 0.7 mm Hg) and man (4 ml/kg · 65 mm Hg). In other words, we find that for all practical purposes, the compliances of the vascular bed and the interstitial space are identical.

For any physiologist who has convinced himself that the regulation of the total extracellular fluid volume is primarily handled through mechanisms located in the circulation regardless of their nature (1, 2), the recognition of such an unexpectedly tight coupling of the mechanics of the interstitial space and blood volume comes as a welcome surprise. Should this concept of Guyton's stand the test of time, it will become a mere matter of taste whether we speak of the control of blood volume or the control of the extracellular fluid space.

VOLUME CONTROL BY PHYSICAL AND AUTOREGULATORY MECHANISMS

The existence of a quantitative relationship between the pressures in the low-pressure system and total blood volume lies at the basis of the generally considered possibilities for the control of plasma volume, i.e., control either by physical or by neuroendocrine regulatory mechanisms, respectively. The following is concerned with the first of these alternatives.

The maintenance of an adequate cardiac output is the prime task of the regulatory mechanisms of the circulation. Provided the inotropic setting of the heart and the arterial flow resistance does not change, cardiac output and hence arterial blood pressure become (nonlinear) functions of the filling pressure of the heart. If we further assume that the arterial pressure directly affects the excretory function of the kidney, then, it is possible to construct an analog model of the circulation in which cardiac output is regulated through a change in extracellular volume without the help of any neural or hormonal mechanisms. This idea, which was first stated by Borst (62), was recently meticulously worked out by Guyton & Coleman (2). They have opted for the first alternative mentioned above and have developed an elaborate analog model of the whole circulation which illustrates the dependence of circulatory homeostasis on fluid volume control (2). This model is based entirely on the physical and autoregulatory properties of its components. Provided all the assumptions made are correct, i.e., that the real mechanisms react like the various paradigms fed into an analog computer, it explains the pertinent physiological observations without resorting to any nervous or hormonal reflex mechanisms. The salient point of this hypothesis is the assumption that there is a close relationship between the height of the arterial blood pressure and the excretory function of the kidney. It is assumed that when the blood volume is reduced by hemorrhage or a loss of extracellular fluid, the central venous pressure is reduced. Since, according to Guyton, this pressure is the major determinant of cardiac output, therefore arterial pressure must fall. The ensuing fluid retention by the kidney will bring ECF back to normal and blood volume will simultaneously increase.

In the next step, the increasing blood volume will raise the atrial pressure in accordance with the known pressure-volume relationship of the whole circulation. As a consequence, cardiac output and arterial pressure will rise until the normal value is again reached and the negative feedback loop is closed.

To obtain a better agreement between the performance of the analog model and that of the real circulation, Guyton & Coleman increased the operational steps from the original 8 of the basic loop to 28. There are a number of points at which one might take issue with this elaborate work. One obvious difficulty is to accept diuresis with high arterial pressure, and anuria with low pressure, as seen in isolated kidneys as the basis for the regulation of the excretory function of the kidney in everyday life. It is almost universally believed that the autoregulation of the kidney preserves constancy of renal function in spite of accidental changes of arterial blood pressure (63). One can, of course, interpret the anuria which occurs when the blood pressure falls below 60 mm Hg as an expression of volume regulation, but such a regulation would be coarse, showing great oscillations about the normal mean value. On the other hand, the mechanism to be discussed later permits the sensing of the filling pressure of the heart and a reflex and direct monitoring of kidney function instead of relying on the Starling mechanism to change, first cardiac output, then arterial pressure, and finally urine excretion. Such a reflex based on the filling pressure permits the independent control of blood volume while maintaining cardiac output at any desired level. There is no doubt that with the ablation of the neurohumoral reflexes controlling fluid volume, more basic mechanisms would take over. However, although the various components of the hydraulic system mesh remarkably well, they would form a solution which would seriously degrade the delicate homeostatic equilibrium on which the organism depends.

VOLUME CONTROL BY NEUROENDOCRINE MECHANISMS

Since changes of pressure within the low-pressure system directly result from changes in blood volume, stretch receptors incorporated in the walls could signal changes of blood volume to the central nervous system and thereby evoke adaptive reflexes.

There is a dense population of such receptors in both atria. Although they are not different in their basic morphology from similar receptors in the arterial system, nevertheless because of their subendocardial location, they are highly sensitive to moderate changes of blood volume. The long-term rise or fall of venous pressure which accompanies such changes will influence capillary filtration pressure and automatically lead to a partial return of plasma volume toward the control value (64). The evidence furthermore is suggestive that these vascular receptors reflexly reset the pre- and postcapillary resistance ratio so that filtration pressure is actively modified in the direction appropriate for restoring the plasma volume to normal (65, 66).

The arterial receptors can only respond to changes in mean arterial pressure and pulse pressure—that is to changes in cardiac output and stroke volume. Depending on the filling of the central reservoir, such changes in arterial hemodynamics may lag considerably behind the alteration of blood volume. Experimental observations which support the concept of a reflex control of the kidney in response to changes of intrathoracic blood volume were presented several years ago (1). Today much new evidence is available and the various research groups that have provided this evidence have made evaluations of the diuretic reflex within the framework of their own differing experimental viewpoints. A discussion of these various data will occupy the next portion of this review.

PATTERNS OF RECEPTOR DISCHARGE

Johnston (67) has amplified knowledge of subendocardial receptors making studies on human hearts. He has confirmed that man has the same type of unencapsulated branching terminal fibers that Nonidez described at the entrances of the venae cavae and pulmonary veins of other mammals (68). Johnston further describes them at the orifice of the coronary sinus. Comparing them to tendon and fascial stretch receptors, Johnston refers to them as "the baroreceptors of which the physiologists speak which are stimulated by deformation of the subendocardial tissue of the atrial walls." In this connection, Hakumäki et al. (69) have recently confirmed Paintal's classical observation of a linear relationship between left atrial volume and average firing frequency of B-type atrial afferents. Johnston reports on the recent finding of unrelated further networks of repeatedly branching and anastomosing fine-beaded fibers. Despite their small caliber, they originate from myelinated fibers. They are present all over the endocardium including the surface of the atrioventricular valves (67). If they are indeed sensory as most workers think, then perhaps they record heart chamber size and could as Williams (70) has suggested give some indication of rates of blood movement.

The termination of some of the heart's baroreceptors in the upper thoracic spinal cord has been reported by Semenov (71). Ellison & Williams (72) find that in humans the sympathetic pathways of the heart are extremely variable, frequently extending to the fifth thoracic ganglion. There is evidence of collateral sprouting following denervation, so that attempts to eradicate these nerves can be nugatory, resulting in hyperstimulation via a new network.

The effect of atrial receptors upon cardiovascular responses has been studied by Ledsome & Linden (73–75) in a series of observations in which they report a modest increase of heart rate and often of arterial pressure. Their technique was to distend the pulmonary vein-atrial junctions with a balloon. They determined that the afferent path of the effect was vagal and the efferent was sympathetic. Recently, Edis & Shepherd (76) have performed the same distention both with and without intact high-pressure baroreceptors. They only noted the cardioacceleration of Ledsome & Linden if the initial pulse rate was below 160/min. In general they report a depressor effect with relaxation of splanchnic capacity vessels, but no effect on cutaneous veins. Atrial stretch led to a sharp decrease in aortic pressure and also a decrease in hindlimb resistance sufficient to drop perfusion pressure by 40 mm Hg at constant flow. Carswell, Hainsworth & Ledsome (77) have made similar limb blood flow measurements. They, too, observed a fall in vascular resistance. In their hands however the effect was not statistically significant.

With the opposite maneuver of gently distending a special pericardial pouch, Goetz, Hermreck & Trank (78) prevented the stretch of the atrium that would normally follow a volume expansion by isotonic fluid. Under these circumstances, despite the increase of blood volume, they report a virtual elimination of the diuresis. In addition, they report that sodium output fell with pouch distention (personal communication). All this occurred without significant change in arterial pressure.

Observations by Dieudonné (79) of ventricular myocardial pressure changes using implanted gauges showed that pressure differences in the wall change with different time rates of compression in early systole. Great increases in ventricular activity after sympathetic stimulation will change the shape of the pressure response from a single to a double curve. The results of Kolatat et al. (80), whose patient analysis of some 2000 vagus fibers yielded equal numbers of atrial and aortic fibers and only 15 ventricular afferents, support Dieudonné for they report that normally there are two bursts of ventricular action potentials in a single cardiac cycle. If, however, hypotension is induced by a chemical infarction, only one single higher-frequency burst remains. Brown (81) studying afferent impulses from receptors located near coronary arteries found that they decreased their impulse frequency with occlusion. The discharge increased with increasing pressure. He, too, confirms that ventricular receptors may have a double spike.

In ingenious experiments designed to demonstrate the relation of atrial receptors to urine flow changes, Thomas (82) working in Paintal's laboratory has injected veratridine into the venous side, the left ventricle, and the aorta. The drug stimulates the mechanoreceptors chemically. Only when it was introduced into the circulation before the blood reached the coronary orifice did it induce a renal response. This took the form of a rise in urine flow which took 20–30 min to peak, suggesting the action of a humoral factor.

Paintal (83) has recently reported nonmedullated vagal fibers arising from endings near the pulmonary capillaries. He suggests that they affect the tone of the skeletal muscles and that they are stimulated by a rise in pressure as occurs during exercise.

Henry et al. (84) have been studying the response of atrial receptors to acute changes in central venous pressure during chronic experimental and spontaneous heart failure in dogs. In a preliminary report, they state that in normal dogs mean atrial firing rate per unit time is quadrupled for a 20 cm increase of venous pressure, whereas in chronic heart failure with a mean central venous pressure of 10 cm H_2O, it is only doubled by the same rise in pressure. When the vascular bed is acutely distended by dextran infusion and the pressures exceed 20 cm H_2O, Gupta (unpublished observations) reports little further increment of atrial firing rate (84). Pericardial resistance to stretching of the heart was not believed to be responsible for this flattening-out effect as it was also found in pericardectomized animals. The data confirm the earlier work of Eliahou, Clarke & Bull (85) and the recent observations of Payne, Stone & Engelken (86) who used an ultrasonic device to measure atrial size. They, too, found decreased atrial movement at higher filling pressures.

The fact that the central venous pressure reached heart failure levels of 20 cm H_2O when Wright et al. (87) used blood volume expansion, whereas only 10 cm H_2O was attained when using saline, may partially explain why they did not obtain as significant a natriuresis with blood as they did with saline; for the greater pressure could lead to the above-mentioned failure of the distended atria to pulsate freely and hence to inadequate baroreceptor function. The other aspect of the problem would be the sharp difference between the effects of blood and saline in terms of their reduction of oncotic pressure in the peritubular capillary network with consequent vigorous natriuresis (88, 89).

Gupta et al. (19) compared the activity of aortic and atrial type-B receptors when the blood volume was altered. Moderate nonhypotensive hemorrhage resulted in a sharp fall in the activity of atrial receptors, i.e., an 80 per cent decrease with a 20 per cent blood volume loss. At the same time, when the alteration in pulse frequency was taken into account, the drive from the aortic receptors remained essentially constant. This disparity between changing atrial and constant sinoaortic receptor drives may then trigger changes in sympathoadrenal drive with appropriate responses in the peripheral vascular bed, i.e., in renal blood flow redistribution and renin-angiotensin levels (see Figure 1). Recent work with the high-pressure baroreceptors by Kumada et al. (90) suggests that, as Share (91) also has shown, the moderate decrease of pulse pressure in a 20 per cent nonhypotensive hemorrhage does not significantly change the drive from the carotid sinus.

The foregoing observations increasingly point to a significant physiological regulatory role for the impulse patterns that derive from various receptors in the heart and open the way for the demonstration of the effects of even more complex patterns of receptor response from this highly innervated region.

AFFERENT PATHWAYS

The fact that a mechanical stimulation of the atria leads to an unequivocal diuretic response has again been demonstrated, this time by Godley, Myers & Rosenbaum (92) using negative pressure breathing. Elimination of the response by cooling or sectioning of the vagus has been confirmed in the case of atrial balloon inflation by Shu'ayb, Moran & Zimmerman (93), by Johnson, Moore & Segar (94), and by Ledsome & Linden (75); in the case of atrial distention by a mitral snare by Lydtin & Hamilton (95), by

Lydtin (162), and by Shu'ayb et al. (93); and in atrial pacing by Kilburn (96).

The question of the renal response to infusion of iso-oncotic dextran, of artificial blood and of saline is exceedingly complex. Saline is particularly confusing because of the inevitable changes which it induces in plasma oncotic pressure with consequent direct effects on kidney function (88, 89).

The response of the kidney to stellate stimulation was investigated by Gilmore (97) who established that the diuresis which occurs is secondary to withdrawal of renal sympathetic vasoconstrictor nerve discharge. In more recent work, Michaelis & Gilmore (98) have shown that in hydropenia, despite the fall in blood pressure, acute carotid sinus nerve stimulation has no effect on urine flow or sodium excretion. However, in water diuresis, it resulted in a fall in free water excretion. Sodium excretion and glomerular filtration rate remained constant. They suggested that circulatory antidiuretic hormone levels had increased due to stimulation of the accompanying carotid body nerve. Gilmore & Weisfeldt (99) observed the responses of the kidney to isotonic iso-oncotic intravascular volume expansion in normal, vagotomized, and carotid sinus denervated dogs. They concluded from the moderate attenuation of the diuretic response that carotid sinus receptors and receptors with vagal afferents contribute to the control of free water excretion. Perlmutt (100) has made an elegant related study of vagal and carotid afferents, and found that in dogs undergoing a water diuresis in whom the vagus nerve was interrupted, there was a reduced free water clearance.

Pearce & Lichardus (101) infusing anesthetized dogs with "artificial" blood induced an initial natriuresis with increased glomerular filtration together with a solute diuresis. This natriuresis persisted despite vagotomy or renal denervation. Their results suggested an increase in glomerular filtration together with inhibition of tubular sodium reabsorption. They doubted the need to postulate separate effector mechanisms to account for the diuresis and natriuresis.

In a discussion of the contribution of cardiac nerves to the control of body salt and water, Gilmore (102) proposes that atrial distention is associated with increased sodium excretion due to reflex diminution of renal sympathetic nerve discharge. Certainly in acute volume-loading, vagal pathways appear to do little to modulate sodium excretion. Since chronic cardiac denervation attenuates natriuresis, this raises the question of the role of the cardiac sympathetic nerves in the control of sodium excretion.

The technique of Cooper et al. (103) of cardiac denervation by extensive ablation of autonomic structures in the mediastinum has been used by Gilmore & Daggett (104) to demonstrate attenuation of both the diuretic and the natriuretic responses to dextran infusions totaling 3 per cent of body weight. Their results thus differed from the effects of vagotomy which only influenced free water excretion (99, 100).

Knox, Davis & Berliner (105) found similar results. Instead of dextran, they used saline, infusing up to 4 per cent of the body weight. The percent-

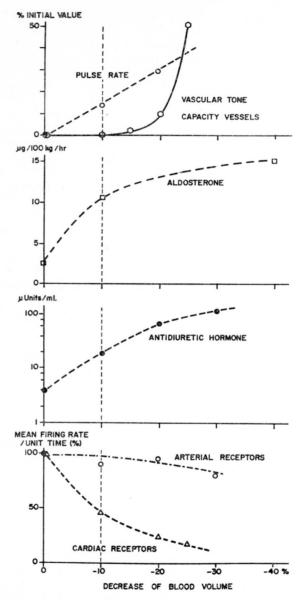

FIG. 1. Data showing from above downwards the measured responses to a graded hemorrhage in terms of: The increase in autonomic (sympathetic) drive as the measured change in pulse rate. Note the sharp inflection in the response curve for the vascular tone of the capacitance vessels. Volume-regulating are hormones expressed

age of filtered sodium was less in denervated dogs, but depression of sodium reabsorption by the proximal tubule still occurred, and it was concluded that the extrinsic cardiac nerves play some, albeit "only a minor, role in the regulation of sodium excretion by the kidneys."

The response of the autotransplanted heart to blood volume expansion has been studied by Willman et al. (106). They note that their technique invaded the atrial receptor areas. When the controls were given blood, their urinary response was somewhat greater. They considered that the troublesome fluid retention observed in many of their cases might have been related to a loss of afferent stimuli because atrial receptor areas had been amputated.

Lower (107) has commented on the results of the Stanford group's (108) technique of heart transplantation which differs from Willman's (106) in leaving the entire posterior atrial wall intact with all of its receptors. He concludes that preservation of the volume receptor afferent nerve supply might explain why few evidences of fluid retention have been encountered with this operation.

Michaelis & Gilmore (109) have cut the spinal cord at C8, leaving the vagus intact. They studied the renal response to intravascular volume expansion. In almost two out of three acute experiments, 30 cc/kg of 6 per cent dextran induced an attenuated, but still significant, increase in sodium and water excretion. In earlier chronic experiments, Pearce & Sonnenberg (110) had obtained no response to 20 cc/kg of artificial blood. They discussed whether the difference was due to the nature of the infusion, to a diminution of the body fluids, or to changes in hormonal levels in the chronically paralyzed animals (110a).

---

as μ of aldosterone released into the plasma and μ units/ml ADH. Receptor activity is expressed in percent of resting value: receptor drive is an inverse function of mean firing rate.

With loss of the first 10% of the blood volume, the drive from baroreceptors in the low-pressure system increases sharply as the firing rate of the cardiac (atrial) receptors falls to one-half. As the loss exceeds 20%, there is an increasing influence from the arterial system. Meanwhile, the plasma aldosterone and antidiuretic hormone concentrations increase, effecting water and salt retention. The pulse rate shows a steady acceleration up to the point of impending syncope, i.e., the loss of some 20–30% of the blood volume. There is no appreciable change of the tone of the capacity vessels until collapse threatens. At this point it increases, effectively moving blood towards the central region.

Data sources: Pulse rate changes in men from Murray et al. (224). The vascular tone in the capacity vessels measured as ml of blood pooled per 100 ml human arm tissue at 50 mm Hg [Sears (14)]. Both studies used lower body negative pressure to displace blood from the central region. Aldosterone from Fabre et al. (173) in anesthetized dogs. Antidiuretic hormone from Henry et al. (131) in unanesthetized dogs (typical curve) (note the logarithmic scale). Atrial and aortic fiber firing rates from Gupta et al. (19) in anesthetized dogs.

These various observations of cardiac receptors and their afferent pathways firmly establish the significance of the vagus trunks in the excretion of free water by the kidney. Some evidence from studies with denervated hearts suggests that cardiac sympathetic pathways have an additional influence on sodium excretion.

CENTRAL NERVOUS SYSTEM

The hypothalamus and related regions certainly play an important role in the integration of various parameters of importance to the cardiovascular system such as osmotic pressure, blood pressure, and extravascular fluid volume (111). However, as Chai & Wang (112) point out, there are major stations of the various baroreceptor reflexes in the medulla. Here the afferent impulses enter, pass through the midline, and run on to the lateral pressor or sympathetic areas, and the regulation of arterial pressure by carotid baroreceptor afferents will remain relatively unaffected, despite removal of structures rostral to the midbrain. Furthermore, Ueda, Yasuda & Takabatake et al. (113) have shown that sympathetic and renal pressor responses giving renin release can be elicited by midbrain stimulation.

Bargainer & Woods (114) have shown that measures such as the inferior vena caval constriction which reduces central blood volume still continue to cause antidiuresis despite mesencephalic decerebration. Their dogs retained intact an island of hypothalamic tissue, including the supraoptico-hypophysial apparatus, completely severed from the medulla. Such a preparation will still respond with appropriate changes of ADH to osmotic stimuli carried in the blood. Because the medulla is intact, it will also respond to baroreceptors in the high- and low-pressure system with a change of sympathetic outflow and concurrent changes of kidney function. The authors find a depression of renal function with hemorrhage, inferior vena caval ligature, and positive pressure breathing. They do not record cardiovascular parameters; nevertheless, it is reasonable to assume that all these measures, by decreasing thoracic filling, affected the baroreceptor outflow which in turn changed the medullary sympathetic outflow.

The elegant work of Bisset, Hilton & Poisner (115) has established a differentiation between the exclusively vasopressin-releasing supraoptic nucleus and the paraventricular nucleus which, in addition, is involved in oxytocin production. Clark & Rocha e Silva (116) working in the same laboratory point out that, since no oxytocin is released during baroreceptor stimulation, the selective release of vasopressin in response to changes in blood pressure and volume primarily involves neurons of the supraoptic nucleus as the efferent limb of an arc, whose afferent component consists of inhibitory fibers arising from the high- and low-pressure system baroreceptors.

The route taken by the impulses from the baroreceptors in getting to the supraoptic and paraventricular nuclei is becoming clearer. The ascending pathway of the oxytocin-driven milk-ejection reflex has been studied recently by Tindal, Knaggs & Turvey (117). Since the paraventricular nucleus is concerned with secretion of vasopressin as well as with that of the closely related oxytocin, this information is of potential significance to those concerned with volume-regulating reflexes. Woods, Holland & Powell (118) have made related observations using evoked potentials. The work of the two groups has shown that the mesencephalic central gray, the medial lemniscus, the lateral reticular formation of the lower brainstem, the subthalamus, and the posterior hypothalamus are intimately involved in neurohypophysial hormone release.

Hayward & Baker (119) have found that abrupt bilateral midpreoptic cooling in the monkey can inhibit the release of vasopressin. They speculate that this cooling may induce peripheral vasoconstriction, causing an increase in central blood volume which, in turn, induces a reflex fall in vasopressin levels. Certainly, Segar & Moore (120) have shown a fall in antidiuretic hormone levels on chilling a man. Stricker (121) has suggested that the regulation of body fluid by drinking activity is determined not only by osmoreceptor dehydration but also by an interaction with a volume-regulatory system. Drinking elicited by intravascular dehydration ceases when body osmolality has fallen low enough to activate a "thirst satiety center." He has speculated that an additional mechanism controlling sodium intake might exist.

In this vein, Houpt & Epstein (122) found that systemic renin and intracranial angiotensin restore drinking activity to nephrectomized rats. They point out that hypovolemia and hypotension are potent releasers of renin-angiotensin which, in turn, may function as a dipsogen with direct action on the brain. In line with this is the recent report of Daniels, Ogden & Vernikos-Danellis (123) who noted the effect of the cerebral intraventricular injection of angiotensin into conscious rats. Water consumption was immediately increased, and plasma and adrenal cortiscosterone were doubled within an hour.

On the obverse side of the coin, Dorn et al. (124) have shown that the injection of 5 per cent sodium chloride into the third ventricle of anesthetized dogs induces a natriuresis. This is not related to alteration in renal plasma flow, glomerular filtration rate, or the filtered load of sodium. They regard their findings as implicating this area of the brain with an as yet unidentified control mechanism regulating urinary sodium excretion.

Mouw & Vander (125) using ventriculocisternal perfusion of iso-osmotic low-sodium solutions showed decreased sodium excretion. They postulate that brain sodium receptors control renin secretion and renal electrolytes. Their conclusions relate further to those of Andersson, Olsson & Warner (126) who note that thirst may be induced by nervous elements specifically sensitive to an elevated sodium concentration. They differentiate osmoreceptors controlling ADH release from elements eliciting thirst.

Many cases of the recently described "inappropriate antidiuretic hormone syndrome" (IAHS) suffer from central nervous system lesions (127). Wise (128) has described two which were due to the development of obstructions in ventriculoatrial shunts. The malfunction caused acute enlargement of the third ventricle which, in turn, it was suggested interfered with the hypothalamic osmoreceptors and so induced the IAHS. Carter, Rector & Seldin (129) have described cases suggesting that under these circumstances antidiuretic hormone secretion is regulated by extracellular volume changes. Further study is needed, for Segar & Moore (120) point out that during coma blood may pool in the abdomen, and they suggest that under these conditions ADH levels may merely be elevated on the basis of inadequate filling of thoracic capacitance vessels rather than as a result of the central nervous system dysfunction per se.

ANTIDIURETIC HORMONE RESPONSES

A number of questions concerning the effectiveness of the functional connection between the baroreceptors and the hypothalamic neuroeffectors have been answered by the work of Share. In two reviews summarizing recent work (91, 130), he discusses the effects of changing extracellular fluid volume (ECF) on the plasma concentration of arginine vasopressin. In trained, conscious dogs (131) and in anesthetized dogs (132) and rats (133) which had been subjected to a nonhypotensive hemorrhage of 10 to 20 per cent of blood volume, there was a significant increase in vasopressin levels from the basal resting values of the order of 2–4 μU/ml. If the input from the baroreceptors in both the high- and low-pressure systems was eliminated by sectioning the vagi and perfusing the carotid sinuses at constant pressure, then despite the loss of as much as 40 per cent of the blood volume, there was no significant change in vasopressin level.

The precise work of Segar & Moore (120) has demonstrated that quiet standing raised antidiuretic hormone (ADH) levels from the supine resting value of 0.4 $\pm$ 0.6 μU/ml to 3.1 $\pm$ 1.5 μU/ml. When sitting, the level was 1.65 $\pm$ 0.63 μU/ml. As stated above, there was some fall when sitting in the cold, presumably as thoracic filling increased because of the peripheral vasoconstriction; and there was a rise to 3.1 $\pm$ .08 μU/ml in the seated, sweating, vasodilated subject.

This work shows that the system connecting the baroreceptors with the neurosecretory cells responds to the minor physiological blood shifts accompanying changes in posture. The data may be considered in conjunction with the studies of Johnson, Moore & Segar (134) who subjected the left atrium to the minor pressure rises of 2, 4, or 8 cm H_2O by gentle inflation of a balloon. Low values were deliberately used to simulate normal physiological stimuli. They obtained a highly significant (P < 0.005) negative linear relationship between changes in left atrial transmural pressure and plasma ADH concentration, the slope being 0.45 $\pm$ 0.1 μU/ml · cm H_2O increase in left atrial transmural pressure.

These shifts in ADH values with minute changes in atrial pressure indicate that a reduction in carotid sinus pressure is not the necessary stimulus for increased vasopressin release. Clark & Rocha e Silva (116) indirectly support this, for they find the vagus of greater importance for vasopressin release than the sinus nerve.

On the other hand, Share (91) shows that once the vagi have been cut, eliminating afferents from both the atria and the aortic arch, then reduction of the pulse pressure, the mean arterial pressure, or both, in the carotid sinus leads to a great increase in ADH secretion.

In an important series of observations, Shu'ayb, Moran & Zimmerman (93) have demonstrated that the ADH concentration in the serum is reduced by distention of the atrium with a balloon, only to be followed by a dramatic increase in the blood level when the engorgement is released.

The various observations described above have established that vasopressin secretion reliably responds to minor disturbances in central blood volume. In dogs the ADH response to hemorrhage was markedly attenuated when cervical vagus nerves were sectioned in contrast to that observed in animals with divided abdominal vagus nerves (134a.)

OSMOCONTROL VERSUS VOLUME CONTROL

The interplay of these two regulatory mechanisms is of interest since they both use ADH as an effector, although they are concerned with physiological parameters of different physical dimensions (135).

As long as the store of osmotically active material remains constant and volume changes are due to loss or gain of water, then osmotic control will automatically regulate volume. However, if, as is usually the case, osmotically active material has been lost or gained, then restoration to the original condition demands that some measure of the actual volume change be available. According to current opinion, volume changes first induce changes in salt, and then, secondly, through a readjustment of the osmotic pressure, the appropriate change in volume. In this review, evidence has been presented which shows that the need for volume control may be directly met by the regulation of water metabolism. Certain observation shows that small isotonic changes of fluid volume will induce rapid changes in water excretion, while the mechanism influencing salt excretion remains undisturbed (135). Using an appropriate modification of Verney's technique, Arndt (136) investigated what happened when osmotic and volume stimuli of near-threshold intensity competed for the control of antidiuretic hormone. Infusion of water at different rates into the carotid loop of anesthetized dogs produced a graded diuresis, but infusion in a peripheral vein was without effect. However, when intracarotid water infusion was combined with a slight hemorrhage (6 per cent blood volume), the expected diuresis was abolished. If the blood which had been removed was then retransfused, a considerable water diuresis ensued. It must be stressed that the blood volume changes (150 ml in a 22-kg dog resting on his side) were too small to cause measurable disturbances of arterial pressure or heart rate. This experiment shows that the slightest impingement on the working capacity of the heart will result in retention of the needed amount of water regardless of any minor osmotic pressure changes that may be involved (135).

Evidence of Osmoreception in the Portal Circulation

The group of Haberich (137, 138) has produced evidence that the primary mechanism for the control of osmotic pressure resides in the portal hepatic circulation. Here, the osmotic pressure of the blood changes considerably when water is given by direct infusion into the duodenum. When similar changes of osmotic pressure are induced by minute water infusions into the portal vein of unanethetized rats, urine flow increases rapidly. This diuresis does not occur when the same amount of water is administered into the vena cava. Enteral hydration to the extent of 1 per cent of body weight leads to a rapid fall of osmotic pressure in the portal vein, while osmolarity in the aorta remains constant (139). Measurements of the water content of the liver showed that water was being stored during this period. Only when the liver "spilled over" did the osmolarity of the aortic blood decrease. Attempts to demonstrate a hormonal transmittal of the diuretic effect were not successful; however, sectioning of a small afferent branch of the vagus in the hepatogastric ligament abolished the response (140).

This mechanism can secure control of osmotic pressure in the arterial blood long before the Verney mechanism is activated. There is evidence that it is also active in man (141), and results similar to those of Haberich have been obtained in the dog by Lydtin (142). He has contrasted the effects of infusing 0.45 per cent saline solution at identical rate and in the same amount into a peripheral vein, into the portal vein, or via the mouth into the alimentary canal of the unanesthetized animal. The diuretic response was greatest with oral infusion, insignificant with the intravenous route, and intermediate when the fluid was infused into the portal vein. Lydtin also confirmed Haberich's findings in man (143). When infusing 0.45 per cent saline in the stomach, he found the diuretic response was significantly larger and faster than when the fluid was given by vein. With isotonic saline or in cirrhosis of the liver, no difference was seen.

From the point of view of volume replacement in disease states, it is interesting that in dehydrated animals the diuretic response is reversed. In the rat, 62 per cent of the volume was retained with infusion into the portal vein. With intravenous infusion the gain was only 34 per cent, while the remainder was lost in the urine (139).

In a preliminary report, Schneider et al. (144) have failed to confirm these results despite repeating Haberich's original experiments in the dog. Further work in this important area is clearly indicated.

Changes in Autonomic Outflow to the Viscera

In addition to the well-documented effects upon the secretion of vasopressin, the baroreceptors in the low-pressure system have been implicated in a number of other responses. A convenient device for detecting such changes in the cardiovascular system is to observe responses during nonhypotensive hemorrhage. As noted above, with a moderate hemorrhage

of 20 per cent of the blood volume, the drive from the aortic receptors remains essentially constant, despite the fall in central venous pressure and a
sulting 80 per cent decrease in atrial firing rate (19).

Hakumäki (145) reports that a rise in the number of atrial-B impulses,
such as occurs during an increase of blood volume, was followed by inhibition of the postganglionic sympathetic discharge to the heart. The reverse
effect, i.e., a rise in sympathetic discharge, would account for the heart rate
increase in moderate hemorrhage.

Webb-Peploe (146) has recently suggested that the spleen is a useful
index of reflex changes in splanchnic vascular capacity. Henry et al. (147)
have visualized the perimeter of the spleen with wire sutures. In preliminary studies, they report that in the dog under chloralose, the organ starts
to contract perceptibly with a loss of 5–10 per cent of the blood volume, and
in other preliminary studies, Hinderleider et al. (148) report that this response can be weakened by cardiac denervation. After such denervation,
more than 20 per cent of the blood volume must be removed to induce a response, which suggests that the splenic nerve outflow responds to atrial receptor drive.

Gill & Bartter (149) have shown that when normal men are deprived of
sodium, adrenergic blockade by guanethidine impairs the capacity to conserve sodium. Further, in dogs with constriction of the thoracic inferior
vena cava (a procedure that produces a sustained filling deficiency of the
low pressure system in the thorax), Gill et al. (150) demonstrated that
blockade of the autonomic ganglia increased mean sodium excretion. They
concluded that a sustained increase of autonomic activity is responsible for retention of sodium in these states.

Further evidence of renal participation in states of altered visceral sympathetic drive is provided by Dieter's (151) experiments with the frog. He
showed that atrial distension led to decreased impulse traffic in the renal
nerves.

In an ingenious application of the cross-perfusion technique, Gill & Casper (152) have recently used a deoxycorticosterone-treated donor dog to
perfuse the still innervated kidney of a recipient which was also treated
with deoxycorticosterone. The donor was then infused with albumin in saline; and when the expected natriuresis had developed in both donor and
recipient kidneys, the recipient was bled until the urine flow from its perfused kidney decreased. Thus the recipient kidney experienced no change in
cardiovascular parameters. One out of three donors showed no significant
change in arterial pressure; nonetheless, sodium excretion in the kidney fell
to one-third the control value. This fall did not occur if the kidney was denervated. These important experiments add to the growing evidence that
moderate volume changes induce alterations in sympathetic outflow to the
kidney which, in turn, affect sodium excretion.

Berne et al. (153) have shown that the denervated kidney will eventually
develop an increased sensitivity to epinephrine and norepinephrine; and

Vander (154) has shown that catecholamines in physiological dosage can be substituted for renal nerve stimulation to induce renin release. Thus the absence of the renal nerves does not preclude a normal response to sympathetic stimulation nor is the secretion of antidiuretic hormone the sole effector pathway by which changes in atrial receptor drive can influence renal function.

REDISTRIBUTION OF INTRARENAL BLOOD FLOW

Research during World War II into renal lesions developing during the crush syndrome led Trueta et al. (155) into postulating that the organ has two potential circulations, and that under conditions of enhanced sympathetic drive there may be a diversion of blood flow from cortex to medulla. With the development of new techniques, important observations have recently been made in relation to renal blood flow distribution during the state of sympathetic arousal and sodium deficit.

Tuttle & Sadler (156) have implanted thermistors to observe the rate of return of renal tissue to baseline temperature after the rapid injection of 0.5 cc iced saline. Their data indicated that the sodium retention during increased sympathetic tonus was associated with low outer-cortical high juxtamedullary flow and vice versa.

Applying their expertise in micropuncture technique to this problem, Horster & Thurau (157) also found great differences between the superficial cortical and juxtamedullary nephron filtration rates, depending on the salt intake. They suggested that the changeover between the cortical and juxtamedullary nephron predominance might depend on extrarenal nervous regulation.

Carriere et al. (158) of Barger's laboratory have used Kr^{85} autoradiographs in a study of the effects of hemorrhage on renal blood flow distribution. They presented data to show that nonhypotensive hemorrhage will initiate a decrease of blood flow through subcapsular peritubular capillaries. In such cases there could be observable subcapsular ischemia, despite an undiminished total renal blood flow. Later Pomeranz, Birtch & Barger (159) activated the renal nerves gently by splanchnic nerve stimulation and by a phrenic-to-splanchnic nerve transfer. This mild stimulation, which fell short of altering total renal blood flow, decreased perfusion of the outer cortical peritubular capillaries and increased that of the medulla.

The above evidence for redistribution correlates well with sodium excretion results, and Barger's group speculated on the as yet not clearly established intrarenal mechanisms that may underlie the changes in sodium reabsorption that they observed. Thus the increased medullary blood flow might lower sodium concentration in the medulla. Alternatively, arteriolar constriction in the outer cortex may decrease hydrostatic pressure in peritubular capillaries, increasing the capillary uptake of salts from the interstitial space (159).

Hollenberg et al. (160), from Merrill's laboratory, using the above techniques have shown that a preferential renal cortical ischemia characterizes acute renal failure in man. They recognized the possible role of constriction of the intralobular and even of the arcuate and interlobar vessels in inducing the selective cortical ischemia. The possible initiating role of the sympathetic nervous outflow and the sustaining function of the renin-angiotensin system were also discussed.

Evidence that atrial distention may induce a significant decrease in the level of sympathetic stimulation to the kidney comes from the work of Arndt, Reineck & Gauer (161) who found that distention of a balloon will cause an increase in renal blood flow as measured by renal clearance techniques. Lydtin (162), using an adjustable purse string around the mitral annulus, increased left atrial pressure in unanesthetized dogs, a maneuver that lowers blood ADH levels. The resultant diuresis of left atrial distention was accompanied by electromagnetic flowmeter evidence of increased renal blood flow. In possibly related results, Fisher, Grunfeld & Barger (163) using the Kr^{85} method on unanesthetized dogs showed that in the absence of antidiuretic hormone, outer-cortical blood flow was increased and juxtamedullary flow decreased, and vice versa. This result seems to be a direct effect of ADH on efferent renal vascular tone.

If the above changes in renal blood flow distribution with altered sympathetic drive will override the effects of antidiuretic hormone, then it could explain the observations of Ledsome, Linden & O'Connor (164) who obtained a diuresis on inflation of a balloon in the atrium despite giving large doses of ADH. If atrial distention were to reduce sympathetic outflow and change the ratio of cortical to medullary blood flow, then a diuresis could be expected despite the raised ADH levels due to the injection. In this connection, reference should also be made to the results of Baïsset & Montastruc (165). They agree with Ledsome, Linden & O'Connor (164) that when ADH is given during anesthesia, the balloon diuresis cannot be blocked. However, they report that if the ADH is injected before anesthesia is given, then the diuretic response is eliminated. The mechanism of these interesting effects needs further investigation.

RENIN-ALDOSTERONE RESPONSES

The interesting response of the independent perfused kidney to its own remaining sympathetic innervation, which was observed by Gill & Casper (152), occurred despite the blocking of the aldosterone mechanism by adrenal cortical hormone. Wågermark, Ungerstedt & Ljungquist (166) have shown in the rat that there are sympathetic nerve terminals in the walls of those parts of the arterioles that contain granulated intraglomerular cells. This gives a morphological basis for direct sympathetic influence in the liberation of renin.

In experiments with dogs, Vander & Luciano (167) found that fluid loss by a diuretic will lead to renin release. Although mean arterial pressure and plasma sodium do not change, pulse pressure and renal plasma flow fall.

When they replaced the fluid lost by isotonic saline infusion, the circulatory effects disappeared, together with the increase in renin levels. Their interpretation that receptors in the low-pressure system might be involved seems probable, but remains unproven because central venous pressure was not measured. In a further study, Vander & Luciano (168) showed that the release of renin during mercurial diuresis was diminished in a denervated kidney. They concluded that, though not essential, the sympathetic nervous system was involved in renin release.

As noted above, Goetz, Hermreck & Trank (78) have observed an increase in sodium in the urine upon slightly compressing the atria by local tamponade. Korz, Fischer & Behn (169) have observed a decrease in reninlike activity in humans in whom central blood volume was increased by water immersion. In animals, Bunag, Page & McCubbin (170) observed increases in renin levels with nonhypotensive hemorrhage. The release was dependent on sympathetic discharge, for it was blocked by anesthesia of the renal nerves. Hodge, Lowe & Vane (171) found a similar nerve-dependent increase in angiotensin level with minor blood loss. Observing a progressive fall in central venous pressure, Hodge et al. (172) undertook further work and found that blocking of the transmission of afferent impulses in the vagus caused an increase in angiotensin II levels in the circulation. Equating the drop in afferent impulses from atrial receptors with the effects of vagal interruption, they concluded that vagal afferent fibers played a part in adjusting the activity of sympathetic nerves to the kidney—thereby causing changes in renin secretion.

The control of aldosterone secretion has been shown by Fabre et al. (173) to be dependent on complex functions of blood volume as well as blood pressure. Demonstrating a biphasic response with steadily progressive hemorrhage, they report a rise from a control rate of 2.6 μU/100 kg $\cdot$ hr to a first peak of 13.25 μU with a nonhypotensive loss of 10 per cent of the blood volume. With further progressive hemorrhage and the development of severe hypotension, a second peak of some 15 μU was eventually reached. They attribute the first increase during the steadily progressing bleeding to the transient depletion of adrenal stores and discussed the need to consider regulation by a hierarchy of receptor mechanisms. They suggested that the first of these receptors to be triggered are those in the low-pressure system.

QUESTION OF A NATRIURETIC HORMONE

In 1961, De Wardener et al. (174, 175) initiated a series of studies which suggested that saline diuresis was due to the action on the tubules of a humoral agent other than aldosterone. They reported that the efferent mechanism did not depend upon the renal nerves and did not involve a decrease in aldosterone secretion. Division of the vagi in the neck did not eliminate the diuresis. Their work was based upon the injection of antidiuretic and adrenocortical hormones in doses high enough to eliminate responses of the kidney that are due to these parameters.

Shortly thereafter, Davis et al. (176) demonstrated that neither renal venous hypertension nor renal nerves were necessary for the sodium retention accompanying constriction of the thoracic inferior vena cava. Davis et al. (177) later concluded that a humoral sodium-excreting factor might contribute to the natriuresis of saline loading. Cirksena, Dirks & Berliner (178) showed by micropuncture technique that there was decreased fractional proximal reabsorption of fluid during saline loading, and Knox et al. (179) also showed that blood volume expansion can depress sodium reabsorption by the proximal tubule. Levinsky (180) confirmed that the evidence suggested that most of the natriuresis accompanying saline loading is due to a decreased sodium absorption by the proximal tubule. With the exception of the studies of Knox et al. (179), the above work used animals pretreated with hormones.

These interesting new concepts culminated in an intensive search for a hormonal inhibitor of renal tubular reabsorption. It appeared to have succeeded when Rector et al. (181) announced that plasma from saline-loaded animals inhibited the reabsorptive capacity of the proximal tubule. However, Wright et al. (182), in a striking international effort with double blind studies carried out independently in Bethesda, London, and Cologne, were unable to detect the inhibitor in natriuretic plasma. In a review of the problem, Pearce et al. (183) reported that a prolonged series of cross-circulation studies of salt-loaded and salt-deficient rats had failed, in their hands, to yield evidence of a humoral natriuretic factor. They concluded that the prime effector mechanism of the natriuresis accompanying fluid volume expansion in ADH and aldosterone-treated animals was not a hormone, but seemed to rest with local factors in the kidney. Evidence was also cited indicating that changes of extracellular fluid volume may activate complex extrarenal reflex systems involving both neural and humoral pathways.

Some evidence however remains of a humoral factor, possibly of central nervous origin, which may modify the renal response to vascular expansion. Cort and his associates (184, 185) continuing their long-sustained and arduous search have recently described the natriuretic effect of a polypeptide derived from the hypothalamus (186). Their latest report is concerned with an oxytocin-like polypeptide extracted from the plasma of volume-expanded cows. The material appears to release yet another agent from the brain which in turn affects tubular sodium rejection.

Linkenbach, Eckert & Gauer (187) have described a diuretic effect of human serum following expansion of intrathoracic blood volume. This work recalls the earlier results of Jahn, Stephan & Stahl (188). Finally, Krück (189) has recently reported preparation of a dialyzable fraction from the urine of orally hydrated persons which induces an increase in renal sodium excretion in sodium-depleted rats. Thus the question of hitherto unrecognized humoral agents affecting the kidney awaits the results of further investigation.

INTRARENAL MECHANISMS: THE ROLE OF COLLOID OSMOTIC PRESSURE

Earley & Daugharty (88) in their review of the problem of sodium metabolism have emphasized the influence of hemodynamic effects on tubular reabsorption. While they accepted the possibility that these effects might be mediated by extrarenal factors such as the sympathetic nerves or by changes in circulating catecholamines or other vasoactive substances, nevertheless, they stress the significance of local changes within the organ. They point out that saline infusion brings out these effects with particular force. This is because a fall in postglomerular oncotic pressure is added to the factors present, when iso-oncotic fluids are used to expand volume, i.e., to the fall in postglomerular vascular resistance and to the rise in postglomerular hydrostatic pressure. When saline is administered intravenously, the rise in postglomerular pressure has added to it a fall in oncotic pressure; these together combine to decrease peritubular capillary uptake and with it sodium reabsorption. Thus experiments using saline infusion lead to natriuresis for powerful passive intrarenal hemodynamic and physical causes.

The effectiveness of these physical intrarenal causes is attested by the data of Nizet (89) who added serum albumin to a saline load which was being imposed on isolated, perfused dog kidneys. When he administered 150 ml saline containing 6 per cent of albumin, he reduced the output of sodium very sharply, while the oncotic pressure of the plasma increased by 6 mm Hg. Claiming an advantage for the isolated organ technique due to the elimination of extrarenal influences, he concluded that increased reabsorption was occurring due to the changed oncotic gradient in the kidney. He suggested that the natriuresis that develops with saline was due to the reverse effect of decreased peritubular oncotic pressure.

In the same context, Kessler et al. (190) made paired studies to determine whether saline infusion produced an effect different from that of iso-oncotic albumin in saline. Their work with dogs supports Nizet's conclusion with the isolated kidney, that for equal volumes of infusion at identical rates, saline proves to be a greater stimulus than saline plus albumin.

Vereerstraeten & Toussaint (191) reduced plasma protein concentration by plasmapheresis without changing plasma volume, glomerular filtration rate, or plasma sodium concentration. The increase of sodium excretion which occurred as protein fell in the plasma was attributed by them to intrarenal changes, i.e., to the fall in peritubular oncotic pressure. Since plasma volume expansion did not occur, it was not, in their opinion, necessary to postulate changed secretion of a hypothetical natriuretic hormone to explain changes in tubular sodium reabsorption. They see the transtubular oncotic gradient as a basic elementary mechanism leading to rapid automatic adjustments of tubular sodium reabsorption. Lewy & Windhager (192), using a micropuncture technique, arrived at the same determination, i.e., that the rate of proximal tubular reabsorption is in part controlled by the oncotic pressure of peritubular blood.

Finally, Pomeranz, Birtch & Barger (159) suggest that the active redistribution of filtration among nephrons of different reabsorptive capacity, i.e., the shift from long juxtamedullary nephrons of high capacity to short cortical ones of low capacity, will account for the changes in reabsorption by individual nephrons that occur during volume expansion in the normal animal. The reverse effect would occur during pathological states such as heart failure when there is increased sympathetic drive. While deferring judgment pending the development of more evidence on the distribution of filtration among the nephron population, both Pearce et al. (183) and Earley & Daugharty (88) in their respective, recent reviews acknowledge the possible quantitative importance of such an intrarenal redistribution in determining the amount of sodium excreted or retained.

INTRATHORACIC BLOOD VOLUME AND THE KIDNEY: WATER IMMERSION IN MAN

During simple head-out immersion in a thermoindifferent bath, the hydrostatic pressures affecting the body produce a shift of blood into the intrathoracic circulation. This redistribution of the blood volume is similar to that of continuous negative pressure breathing (NPB). As in any procedure which causes engorgement of the intrathoracic circulation diuresis follows. This phenomenon has been interpreted as an expression of a volume regulatory mechanism having receptors within the intrathoracic circulation (1).

Following Graveline's (193, 194) introduction of long-term water immersion as a means of simulating the state of weightlessness, a great number of publications have appeared in this field representing a powerful revival of Bazett's (195, 196) early work in this area. An extensive survey by McCally (197) presented at a symposium at French Lick (Indiana) in 1969 on *Hypogravic and Hypodynamic Environments* gives a complete bibliography. Other comprehensive reviews by Piemme (198) and by Wunder (199) are to be found in a recent monograph on *Hypodynamics and Hypogravics: The Physiology of Inactivity and Weightlessness*. The following paragraphs will be limited to the discussion of phenomena directly related to volume control. The technique of whole-body immersion has fundamental advantages over the use of NPB which becomes very uncomfortable after about an hour: it can be maintained for hours and even days. This advantage must not be underestimated when it comes to the analysis of reflex mechanisms which have considerable inertia and require time to take effect.

The mild engorgement of the intrathoracic circulation has been directly demonstrated with an X-ray technique (200). The results of the pressure measurements that have been made in the right atrium are somewhat difficult to interpret since pressure breathing equipment was used (201). Depending on the pressure used, positive pressure breathing can actually eliminate the effects of immersion (202).

RENAL FUNCTION

There has been some hesitation in interpreting the diuretic response to NPB as a blood volume regulatory mechanism, for the most part for two reasons (203). First of all, the diuresis almost always subsides spontaneously after 45–60 min of NPB. Moreover, it is in most cases a pure water diuresis, and renal physiologists have been reluctant to accept a change in free water clearance as an expression of volume control.

This difficulty vanishes with immersion, for the changes of kidney function are sustained throughout the whole period which usually lasts 6–8 hr and may even go on for days. Subjects prepared for this type of experiment in the normal way (in most cases this means a slight overhydration) usually develop a water diuresis both with negative pressure breathing and with immersion. There is, however, always more or less of an increase in osmotic clearance depending on the intensity of the diuresis and the state of hydration (194–196, 204, 205).

Behn et al. (204) compared the effect of water immersion in two groups of subjects in which salt and water intake had been controlled for several days. To avoid the further influence of diurnal changes, the experiments were always performed at the same time of day. All subjects received 100 meq Na^+ per diem. One group was slightly overhydrated with water, receiving 3.1 per cent of body weight per day. The other was on the verge of thirst, receiving only 1.7 per cent. In the well-hydrated subjects a water diuresis was evoked (with the washout of some salt) while the "dry" subjects achieved fluid elimination by an increase in osmolar clearance only. In other words, volume elimination appeared as the all-important factor regardless of the composition of the urine.

In one of two exceptionally sensitive subjects, a weight reduction of 5 kg with a salt loss of 40 g, and a reduction of central venous pressure by 7 cm H_2O occurred during a 48 hr immersion period (206). It appears that the constant bombardment of the hypothalamus with depressor impulses can lead to a condition the very opposite of congestive heart failure, i.e., one characterized by a wasting of salt and water (135). Two more cases of this relatively rare condition have been described by Graveline & Jackson (194) and by Graybiel (207), respectively. It is the impression of the experimenters that these subjects are tense and tend to be more wakeful than the "normals" during the immersion period.

PLASMA VOLUME

The proposition that the diuretic reflex effectively achieves blood volume control demands the demonstration that engorgement of the intrathoracic blood compartments for several hours will lead to a reduction in blood volume. Several investigators (169, 204, 208–211) have demonstrated significant decrease of plasma volume after 6–8 hr of immersion (Table II). Interestingly, the final reduction of plasma volume is preceded by an increase during the first half-hour of immersion, probably due to inward filtration of interstitial fluid caused by the general tissue compression in the bath (209).

DISTRIBUTION OF EXTRACELLULAR FLUID VOLUME

The observation that there is no water uptake in a thermoindifferent bath nor is there any water loss through the skin (204) has greatly facilitated the quantitative assessment of fluid balance in these experiments. Furthermore, the subjects breathe only 5 cm above the surface of the water at 34°C; therefore, the difference in water vapor saturation between inhaled and exhaled air is small and respiratory water loss is minimal. As a result, a correlation of nearly 1:1 between weight loss (i.e., loss of body fluid) and urine volume is found.

Assuming that the fluid compartments contribute to urine volume during immersion in proportion to their original volume, then reduction of plasma volume should be about 7.5 per cent of urine volume. Instead in a group of well-hydrated subjects, plasma volume shrinkage accounted for 20 per cent of urine volume, a value which one may expect if urine volume were primarily derived from the extracellular fluid space. In subjects who were poorly hydrated, plasma volume reduction may account for the total fluid loss and in some cases may even exceed it. This can only be explained by a shift of plasma fluid into the interstitial space. It is suggested that the same stimulus which induces fluid elimination through the kidney may, at the same time, favor movement of fluid from the intravascular compartment into the interstitium. This explanation is in agreement with Öberg's (65, 66) experiments; he found that in cats mild hemorrhage, with consequent decreased stimulation of the baroreceptors in the arterial system and the heart, leads to a resetting of the post- and precapillary resistances and a decrease of fluid filtration pressure. On the other hand, stimulation of heart receptors

TABLE II

CHANGES IN PLASMA VOLUME (%) DURING WHOLE-BODY IMMERSION

Author	Ref.	6–8 hr	5–10 days	n subjects
Behn et al.	204	−9.7	—	7
Behn et al.	204	−15.3	—	6
Kaiser et al.	208	−14.0	—	17
Korz et al.	169	−14.1	—	8
McCally	209	−11.0*	—	5
McCally	210	−7.9	—	6
White et al.	211	—	−23	10
White et al.	211	—	−10**	10

* 9% transitory increase after 25 min immersion.
** 10 days immersion.

with veratridine led to net outward filtration. In keeping with this, "dry" subjects lost fluid more easily into the interstitium than hydrated ones, while their diuretic response was less (204).

<h2>EFFECTOR MECHANISMS IN IMMERSION DIURESIS</h2>

In order of discovery and solid experimental foundation, vasopressin comes first. Indirect evidence of its influence comes from the following observations. In many cases, a clear-cut water diuresis is found with a great increase in free water clearance and an insignificant change in osmotic clearance. If there has been an excessive prehydration and a profuse water diuresis in the control period, then the urine flow cannot be further increased by immersion (205). An immersion diuresis amounting to 6 ml/min can be reduced to 1 ml/min for 1 hr with a single injection of 0.5 mU/kg of vasopressin, or it can be prevented by the continuous i.v. infusion of 0.24 mU/kg · 30 hr (212). The prevention of immersion diuresis prevented the development of postimmersion orthostatic hypotension (213). McCally, Pohl & Samson (210) and Hunt (214) observed the same effect of ADH on urine flow; however, McCally's subjects showed no improvement with regard to postinfusion orthostatic tolerance.

Goodall, McCally & Graveline (215) found a significant reduction in urinary excretion of norepinephrine. This goes hand-in-hand with a slight renal vascular dilation which is probably in part due to a reduction in nervous sympathetic tone (1, 205). Behn et al. (204) and Hunt (214) found that a considerable increase in the Na/K quotient developed during a 6–8 hr immersion. This argues in favor of a reduced aldosterone secretion. Using the method of Boucher, Korz et al. (169) demonstrated a highly significant fall in the plasma concentration of reninlike activity, thus supporting the above-mentioned observation (204, 214).

Other factors may play a role in the increased urine flow. Thus as has been mentioned in the discussion of natriuresis, rats prepared for a bioassay of ADH showed a small increase in urine output when receiving 0.2 ml serum obtained from a recumbent or immersed subject. This response was significantly different from that to the serum of sitting subjects (187).

In the course of investigations on the renal clearance of phenolsulfonphthalein, Korz et al. (216) found a significant decrease of the plasma albumin fraction by 6.8 per cent. This reduction is of the same order of magnitude that of as the reduction of plasma volume and it is tempting to speculate that it is inseparably linked to regulation during immersion. Furthermore, evidence is accumulating that the colloid osmotic pressure of the blood has a distinct influence on sodium reabsorption by the kidney (88, 89, 190–192).

Finally the tone of the capacitance vessels of the forearm measured with a Whitney plethysmograph is reduced during immersion (217). This increased compliance may be maintained for several hours after leaving the water tank. It is suggested that it is in part responsible for the orthostatic weakness after immersion (217, 218). A severe reduction in working capacity, particularly in well-trained athletes, after immersion should be mentioned. It may or may not be related to the increased compliance of the capacitance vessels (219).

GRAVITY, BED REST, AND WEIGHTLESSNESS

GRAVITY

The principles of plasma volume control and body fluid metabolism as exemplified by the stimulus of water immersion seem to be applicable to many conditions in which blood volume is redistributed by gravity or related means. The response of the kidney to posture has been the subject of numerous investigations (1). The effects are augmented when an increased force of gravity is simulated on the human centrifuge. As a rule, urine flow falls when the forces act in a direction which leads to a reduced intrathoracic blood volume ($+ G_z$) (1). Under this condition plasma ADH is increased (220). When central blood volume is increased with transverse G, ($+ G_x$) reduced plasma ADH (220), and diuresis are observed (221).

Increased urine flow, decreased ADH, and dehydration were found by Bengele (222, 223) with the constant centrifugation of rats at 1.7 G for many days. The author was unable to record central venous pressure; however, he reports that the thorax of his animals was the lowermost part of the body mass during centrifugation (223). If we attribute his findings to the diuretic reflex, the importance of his results would lie in the demonstration that this response to atrial distension shows no signs of adaptation, even after 2 weeks of exposure.

Gravitational shifts of blood volume in man can be simulated by exposing the lower half of the body to subatmospheric pressure, i.e., LBNP. The application of LBNP with an intensity of −30 cm H_2O dropped central venous pressure (CVP) by approximately 6 cm H_2O; the increase of the negative pressure still further to −40 to −60 cm H_2O reduced CVP by approximately 7 cm H_2O (14, 224). This latter value corresponds to a reduction of effective blood volume by about 25 per cent. These changes are paralleled by significant increases in the ADH levels during a 30 min exposure to −30 to −40 mm Hg, but not with 20 mm Hg LBNP. In this connection, it is interesting that application of LBNP proved to be an effective means to combat the dehydration observed in bed rest studies (225).

BED REST

In six subjects, Miller, Johnson & Lamb (226) found the following changes in plasma volume and red cell volume during a 28 day bed rest study. (See Table III.)

If we accept that the upright posture is an important factor in the deter-

TABLE III
Time Course of Blood Volume Changes in Bed Rest (226)

	Δ Blood volume	Δ Plasma volume	Δ Red cell volume
2 days	− 528 ml	−418 ml	− 47 ml
28 days	−1048 ml	−672 ml	−408 ml

mination of man's blood volume and its distribution (227), the following explanation can be offered. With assumption of the supine posture for several hours, about 400 ml of blood augmented by some interstitial fluid is poured into the central circulation, leading to an increased cardiac output. The hyperactivity of the circulation, and a rise in blood pressure, is attenuated by an instantaneous reflex reduction in heart rate and peripheral arterial resistance. In a further volumetric adjustment to the acutely reduced capacity of the vascular bed, the plasma volume decreases by 400–500 ml during the first 6–8 hr of recumbency while no significant change in red cell mass is seen. The continued reduction of blood volume in the following 4 weeks is mainly due to a considerable diminution of red cell mass which is probably related to the reduction in activity and hence in the metabolic needs of the organism. The final decrease in blood volume may reflect the reduction of the dimensions of the structural elements of the heart and the circulatory bed in accommodation to the diminished demands upon the cardiovascular system.

WEIGHTLESSNESS

With the knowledge already available at the end of World War II on the effects of high G, it was safe to assume that neither the accelerations to be encountered in the brief period of takeoff nor the state of weightlessness in orbit would lead to serious disturbances of respiration or arterial hemodynamics. However, it could be foreseen that long-term weightlessness would lead to a deterioration of the circulation similar to that seen in long-term bed rest (228). This has proved to be the case, and, in fact, it has been the advent of space travel that has stimulated most of the work on bed rest and immersion just discussed.

It is interesting that practically all the symptoms described in these simulations are found in space pilots. One may therefore speculate that they are due to the same basic physiological mechanisms. In terms of the extent of blood redistribution and the relative degree of engorgement of the intrathoracic circulation, weightlessness appears to lie between bed rest on the one hand and water immersion on the other (197, 227). The crucial information on the change of central venous pressure on entry into the weightless state is not available in man; however, the animal in the long-term primate satellite showed a rise of 2 cm H_2O (229).

Fluid balance.—There is as yet no balance sheet of human fluid intake versus fluid loss. However, prolonged weightlessness is associated with a lack of desire to drink and a reduction of plasma volume of about 500 cc. The exception to this was a crew on a strict metabolic regime, who maintained their water intake to comply with the requirements of the study (230). Most of the sometimes considerable weight loss (231) of several kilograms is regained within 2–3 days, which indicates that it was due to simple water deficit.

In the studies of Lutwak et al. (232) on the mineral balance of the 14 day orbiting Gemini crew, both men showed a moderate natriuresis during flight and a significant retention of sodium in the early postflight period. These results may be related to those of Behn et al. (204) who observed an increase in sodium excretion which was only significant in the less hydrated of their two groups of immersed subjects.

In the remarkable studies of Lutwak, Whedon, LaChance et al. (232) on the mineral balance of the 14 day orbiting Gemini crew, both men showed a moderate natriuresis during flight with significant retention in the early postflight period. These important first results may be related to those of Behn et al. (204) who observed an increase in osmolar clearance in the less hydrated of their two groups of immersion-bath subjects.

In the satellite monkey, the fluid uptake and loss were recorded (229). His condition deteriorated rapidly when the fluid deficit reached 20% of his body weight. In the Soviet Cosmos 110 flight with two dogs, within 3 days the animals had lost 26 and 29 per cent of their body weight, respectively. Half of this was regained after 10 days. It was suggested that this was primarily loss of body fluid (233).

These observations, which have to be taken as preliminary, and the experience with a small group of subjects who (probably because of their particular psychic texture) showed poor adaptation to immersion (206), together with the results in chronically centrifuged rats (222, 223) demonstrate that under certain circumstances the mechanisms involved in fluid control may fail to accommodate leading to disturbances of fluid balance.

Plasma volume.—The material on the changes in plasma volume in space pilots does not yet permit definitive conclusions. One variable is the amount of exercise engaged in by the subjects and another the fluid uptake. However, in general, the results show a moderate decrease in plasma volume as would be expected in view of the fluid loss experienced by most of these men (234).

Orthostatic tolerance and maximal work capacity.—The significant deterioration of these two parameters (234, 235) after long-term exposure to the weightless state is of the same order of magnitude as that experienced after 6–8 hr of water immersion (219).

STATES OF CLINICAL INTEREST

HEART FAILURE

Chronic heart failure raises questions as to the action of the mechanoreceptors in the low-pressure system. How is it that, in spite of the increased atrial stretch accompanying the elevated venous pressure, there is not a diuresis, but water and sodium retention?

As noted above, Eliahou, Clarke & Bull (85) have reported a decreased atrial pulsation in hearts distended by overtransfusion, and Henry et al. (84) have made preliminary observations of the response of atrial stretch receptors in animals with heart failure. They report a greatly diminished change in atrial firing rate per unit change of venous pressure. It remains to be seen whether this loss of sensitivity is sufficient to account for the increase of sympathetic drive reported in heart failure (236, 244).

POSTCOMMISSUROTOMY HYPONATREMIC SYNDROME

Shu'ayb, Moran & Zimmerman (93) have shown in the above context that when the chronic obstruction and atrial distention of mitral stenosis is relieved by commissurotomy, there is a rise in ADH levels which persists for days and is accompanied by water retention. Perhaps the previously overstretched atria may for varying periods fail to provide the subendocardial baroreceptor network with sufficient stimulation. It is also possible that especially in longstanding cases the atria may have developed morphological changes in the walls which impair the functioning of the delicate network. A prolonged period of more normal pressure may be required before the sensors eventually return to normal function. There is evidence that by overtransfusing the postoperative patient and so sustaining high levels of central venous pressure, water balance can be restored (M. L. Pearce, personal communication). Perhaps the higher pressures provide a stimulus which is more effective to the receptors in the still-damaged atria.

PAROXYSMAL TACHYCARDIA

In acute paroxysmal tachycardia the conditions are reversed. The event strikes a previously normally functioning heart and circulation and with its onset, as Wood (237) has demonstrated, there may be an abrupt increase in atrial mean pressure and pulse pressure to double the resting state, together with a pulse rate up to 200 and more per minute. Kilburn (96) reports that electrical pacing of the normal dog's left atrium to 200/min or more produces a diuresis within 30 min. The response failed, if cardiac output dropped by more than 50 per cent. Kilburn's preliminary report concludes that increases in atrial volume or amplitude of pulsation lead to a diuresis readily inhibited by infusion of ADH or by vagal cooling, and he attributed these responses to receptors in the left atrium. There was some evidence that direct stimulation with a catheter electrode produced a diuresis when it was located in the left atrium and not when in the right (96). Further work is needed in this interesting area.

Mersch & Arndt (238) made similar pacing observations, showing an increase in left atrial circumference as the pressure rises and heart failure impends. In their discussion of the "urina spastica" of paroxysmal tachycardia, Haynal & Matsch (239) report that approximately four out of five patients discharge abundant dilute urine during or immediately after the attacks. Their observation that the antidiuretic hormone level in the blood decreases in these cases is further evidence of an increased atrial receptor drive as the mechanism underlying this renal response to the paroxysms. It is significant that in a discussion of the renal response that occurs during or after paroxysmal tachycardia, Ghose, Joekes & Kyriacou (240) note that there is not always an increase in free water clearance, but that a raised osmolar clearance will often occur. They recognize that the factors involved may include both stimulation of the atrial receptors and influences associated with the emotions that accompany the attack and recovery from it. Also as Kilburn (96) has noted in dogs and Wood (238) in patients, if heart failure supervenes, then a diuresis can no longer be expected in view of the likelihood of a decreased pulsation and of changes in neuroendocrine state.

In a review of ADH control in relation to the surgical patient, Moran & Zimmermann (241) point to four mechanisms involved in the regulation of ADH secretion. Each overrides the preceding one, starting with the osmoreceptors which control ADH levels up to the 6 μU/ml range. The osmoreceptors are superseded by the baroreceptors in the low-pressure system whose influences will raise ADH levels to 60 μU. Overriding both the foregoing are the arterial receptors which are primarily activated by circulatory collapse. Their excitation can lead to enormous blood levels ranging to 900 μU. At such concentrations, the vascular effects of the hormone will presumably play an important role. The fourth and final mechanism depends on the effect of visceral and cutaneous pain fibers which, when activated, lead to gross elevations of ADH levels overriding the osmo and baroreceptors.

CONCLUSION

We will end by citing reviews which furnish excellent surveys of various aspects of the foregoing areas. They include developments in kidney physiology by Windhager (242) and the question of circulatory regulation which has been assessed both by Sagawa (243) and by Guyton & Coleman (2). Mason & Bartter (244) summarize important evidence on the autonomic regulation of blood volume and the review by Houdas (245) covers similar ground.

Concerning neurohumoral mechanisms, Riecker (246) discusses recent advances in kidney physiology, while Vander (247) has lucidly summarized the pros and cons of renin release mechanisms. Frazier (248) has reviewed the renal regulation of sodium balance, especially with regard to clinical aspects of renal function. Earley & Daugharty (88) have paid particular attention to the question of intrarenal mechanisms and Pearce et al. (183) weigh the evidence on the important question of the natriuretic hormone. They also present some views on the matter of the intrarenal redistribution of blood flow.

It was pointed out in the introduction that this paper is an updating of a review summarizing the evidence that the basic mechanical properties of the vascular bed are appropriate for a neurohumoral mechanism regulating fluid volume via baroreceptors, especially those located in the low-pressure system (1). In the present discussion on mechanics, this approach is extended by drawing conclusions from Guyton's (48–50) new work on the compliance of the interstitial fluid space. It is suggested that this compliance is of the same order as that of the low-pressure compartment of the cardiovascular system. Since the two are so closely linked, they will, in effect, share the same mechanism of neurohumoral control of volume. It was concluded that it may well become a matter of taste whether we speak of the control of blood volume or the control of the extracellular fluid space.

In the above-mentioned earlier paper (1), an attempt was made to summarize schematically the way in which a hypothetical change of drive by stretch receptors in the low- and high-pressure systems might lead to changes in the neurohormonal effectors [Figure 2 (1)]. Various groups have now produced sufficient quantitative data to permit the conversion of this schema into a diagram more closely depicting physiologic behavior (Figure 1).

ACKNOWLEDGMENTS

It is a pleasure to record our debt to Mrs. Anneliese Eggebrecht, Miss Jo Kolsum, Mrs. Beverly Rhue, and Mrs. Patricia Stephens for their excellent support and to Dr. John P. Meehan, for his encouragement and valuable criticism.

That portion of this work which was done at the Physiologisches Institut der Freien Universität Berlin was supported in part by contract F 61052-68-C-0069 of the USAF School of Aerospace Medicine, European Office of Aerospace Research (OAR) United States Air Force. The portion done by the Department of Physiology, University of Southern California was supported in part by the United States Air Force Office of Scientific Research through contract 49(638)-1531.

LITERATURE CITED

1. Gauer, O. H., Henry, J. P. Circulatory basis of fluid volume control. *Physiol. Rev.*, **43**, 423–81 (1963)
2. Guyton, A. C., Coleman, T. G. Long-term regulation of the circulation: Interrelationships with body fluid volumes. In *Physical Bases of* *Circulatory Transport: Regulation and Exchange*, 179–201 (Reeve, E. B., Guyton, A. C., Eds., Saunders, Philadelphia-London, 1967)
3. Sjöstrand, T. Volume and distribution of blood and their significance in regulating the circulation.

Physiol. Rev., **33**, 202–28 (1953)
4. Sjöstrand, T. Blood Volume. *Circulation*, **I**, 51–62 (Am. Physiol. Soc., Washington, D.C., 1962)
5. Patz, A. The effect of oxygen on immature retinal vessels. *Invest. Ophthal.*, **4**, 988–99 (1965)
6. Vollmar, I., *Rekonstruktive Chirurgie der Arterien* (Thieme, Stuttgart, 1967)
7. Schmidt, H. D., Schmier, J. Erhöhte Toleranz gegen Coronarverschluß durch ein pharmakologisch vermehrtes Gefässnetz. *Arzneim.-Forsch.*, **16**, 1058–64 (1966)
8. Chapman, E. M., Asmussen, E. On the occurrence of dyspnea, dizziness and precordial distress occasioned by the pooling of blood in varicose veins. *J. Clin. Invest.*, **21**, 393–99 (1942)
9. Bevegård, S., Jonsson, B., Karlöf, I. Circulatory response to recumbent exercise and head-up tilting in patients with disturbed sympathetic cardiovascular control (postural hypotension). *Acta Med. Scand.*, **172**, 623–36 (1962)
10. Gauer, O. H., Thron, H. L. Postural changes in the circulation. *Circulation*, **III**, 2409–39 (1965) (See Ref. 4)
11. Franklin, K. J. *A monograph on veins* (Thomas, Springfield, Ill., 1937)
12. Gauer, O. H., Thron, H. L. Properties of veins in vivo: integrated effects of their smooth muscle. *Physiol. Rev.*, **42**, *Suppl. 5*, 283–303 (1962)
13. Epstein, S. E., Beiser, G. D., Stampfer, M., Braunwald, E. Role of the venous system in baroreceptor mediated reflexes in man. *J. Clin. Invest.*, **47**, 139–52 (1968)
14. Sears, W. J. *Effects of lower body negative pressure on venous tone, atrial and central venous pressures and heart rate* (M. S. thesis, USC Dept. Physiol., 1966)
15. Walsh, J. A., Hyman, C., Maronde, R. F. Venous distensibility in essential hypertension. *Cardiov. Res.*, **3**, 338–49 (1969)
16. Wiedeman, M. P. Dimensions of blood vessels from distributing artery to collecting vein. *Circ. Res.*, **12**, 375–78 (1963)
17. Thomasson, B. A study in right heart performance in man with special reference to the effect of experimentally induced acute hyper-

volemia. *Scand. J. Clin. Lab. Invest.*, **11**, *Suppl. 40*, 1–76 (1959)
18. Henry, J. P., Gauer, O. H. Sieker, H. O. The effect of moderate changes in blood volume on left and right atrial pressures. *Circ. Res.*, **4**, 91–4 (1956)
19. Gupta, P. D., Henry, J. P., Sinclair, R., von Baumgarten, R., Responses of atrial and aortic baroreceptors to nonhypotensive hemorrhage and to transfusion. *Am. J. Physiol.*, **211**, 1429–37 (1966)
20. Pabst, K., Gauer, O. H. Nierenhämodynamik und Ausscheidungsfunktion der Niere unter definierten Änderungen des Blutvolumens. *Pflügers Arch.*, **274**, 213–26 (1961)
21. Arndt, J. O. Die Beziehungen zwischen Umfang der Vorhöfe und Vorhofdrucken bei Volumenänderungen an narkotisierten Katzen. *Pflügers Arch.*, **292**, 343–55 (1966)
22. Borow, M., Escaro, R. The reliability of central venous pressure monitoring and errors in its interpretation. *Surg. Gynecol. Obstet.*, **127**, 1288–94 (1968)
23. Brisman, R., Parks, L. C., Benson, D. W. Pitfalls in the clinical use of central venous pressure. *Arch. Surg.*, **95**, 902–7 (1967)
24. Wilson, F., Nelson, J. H., Jr., Moltz, A. Methods and indications for central venous pressure monitoring. *Am. J. Obstet. Gynecol.*, **101**, 137–51 (1968)
25. Andersen, D., Klebe, J. G. Measurement of central venous pressure. *Am. J. Gastrenterol.*, **3**, 113–22 (1968)
26. Burri, C., Allgöwer, M. Klinische Erfahrungen mit der Messung des zentralen Venendruckes. *Schweiz. Med. Wochschr.*, **97**, 1414–20 (1967)
27. Eastridge, C. E., Hughes, F. A., Jr. Central venous pressure monitoring. A useful aid in the management of shock. *Am. J. Surg.*, **113**, 648–52 (1967)
28. Feurstein, V. Grundlagen und Ergebnisse der Venendruckmessung zur Prüfung des zirkulierenden Blutvolumens. *Anaesthesiologie und Wiederbelebung* (Springer, Berlin, 1965)
29. Hughes, R. E., Magovern, G. J. The relationship between right atrial pressure and blood volume. *Arch. Surg.*, **79**, 238–43 (1959)

30. MacLean, L. D., Duff, J. H. The use of central venous pressure as a guide to volume replacement in shock. *Diseases Chest,* **48,** 199–205 (1965)

31. MacLean, L. D., Duff, J. H., Scott, H. M., Peretz, D. I. Treatment of shock in man based on hemodynamic diagnosis. *Surg. Gynecol. Obstet.,* **120,** 1–16 (1965)

32. Wilson, J. N., Grow, J. B., Demong, C. V., Prevadel, A. E., Owens, J. C. Central venous pressures in optimal blood volume maintenance. *Arch. Surg.,* **85,** 563–78 (1962)

33. Landis, E. M., Pappenheimer, J. R. Exchange of substances through the capillary walls. *Circulation,* **II,** 961–1034 (See Ref. 4)

34. Mayerson, H. S. The physiologic importance of lymph. *Circulation,* **II,** 1035–73 (See Ref. 4)

35. Renkin, E. M. Transcapillary exchange in relation to capillary circulation. In *Proc. Symp. Biol. Interfaces Flows and Exchanges. J. Gen. Physiol.,* **52,** Part 2, 96S–108S (1968)

36. Schultze, H. E., Heremans, J. F. *Molecular biology of human proteins. With special reference to plasma proteins,* **1** (Elsevier, Amsterdam, 1966)

37. Wiedeman, M. P. Patterns of the arteriovenous pathways. *Circulation,* **II,** 891–934 (1963) (See Ref. 4)

38. Wiederhielm, C. A. Dynamics of transcapillary fluid exchange. In *Proc. Symp. Biol. Interfaces Flows and Exchanges. J. Gen. Physiol.,* **52,** Part 2, 29S–63S (1968)

39. Wiederhielm, C. A. Analysis of small vessel function. In *Physical Bases of Circulatory Transport. Regulation and Exchange,* 313–26 (Reeve, E. B., Guyton, A. C., Eds., Saunders, Philadelphia, 1967)

40. Zweifach, B. W., Intaglietta, M. Fluid exchange across the blood capillary interface. *Fed. Proc.,* **25,** 1784–88 (1966)

41. Rusznyak, I., Földi, M., Szabo, G. *Lymphatics and lymph circulation* (Pergamon, New York, 1967)

42. Mellander, S., Johansson, B. Control of resistance, exchange and capacitance functions in the peripheral circulation. *Pharmacol. Rev.,* **20,** 117–96 (1968)

43. Shires, T., Williams, J., Brown, F. Simultaneous measurement of

plasma volume, extracellular fluid volume and red blood cell mass in man, utilizing I^{131}, $S^{35}O_4$ and Cr^{51}. *J. Lab. Clin. Med.,* **55,** 776–83 (1960)

44. Reinhardt, H. W., Behrenbeck, D. W. Untersuchungen an wachen Hunden über die Einstellung der Natriumbilanz. I. Die Bedeutung des Extracellulärraumes für die Einstellung der Natrium-Tagesbilanz. *Pflügers Arch.,* **295,** 266–79 (1967)

45. Behrenbeck, D. W., Reinhardt, H. W. Untersuchungen an wachen Hunden über die Einstellung der Natriumbilanz. II. Postprandiale Elektrolyt- und Wasserbilanz bei unterschiedlicher Kochsalzzufuhr. *Pflügers Arch.,* **295,** 280–92 (1967)

46. Kramer, K., Boylan, J. W., Keck, W. Regulation of total body sodium in the mammalian organism. *Nephron,* **6,** 379–87 (1969)

46a. Skillman, J. J., Awwad, H. K., Moore, F. D. Plasma protein kinetics of the early transcapillary refill after hemorrhage in man. *Surg. Gynecol. Obstet.,* **125,** 983–96 (1967)

46b. Greenway, C. V., Lawson, A. E., Mellander, S The effects of stimulation of the hepatic nerves, infusions of noradrenaline and occlusion of the carotid arteries on liver blood flow in the anaesthetized cat. *J. Physiol.,* **192,** 21–41 (1967)

47. Ingraham, R. C., Wiggers, H. C. Alkalizing agents and fluid priming in hemorrhagic shock. *Am. J. Physiol.,* **144,** 505–12 (1945)

48. Guyton, A. C. A concept of negative interstitial pressure based on pressures in implanted perforated capsules. *Circ. Res.,* **12,** 399–414 (1963)

49. Guyton, A. C. Interstitial fluid pressure, II. Pressure-volume curves of interstitial space. *Circ. Res.,* **16,** 452–60 (1965)

50. Guyton, A. C., Scheel, K., Murphree, D. Interstitial fluid pressure, III. Its effect on resistance to tissue fluid mobility. *Circ. Res.,* **19,** 412–19 (1966)

50a. Gersh, I., Catchpole, H. R. The nature of ground substance of connective tissue. *Perspect. Biol. Med.,* **3,** 282–319 (1960)

51. Hopkinson, B. R., Border, J. R., Heyden, W. C., Schenk, W. G., Jr. Interstitial fluid pressure

changes during hemorrhage and blood replacement with and without hypotension. *Surgery, 64,* 68–74 (1968)

52. Anas, P., Neely, W. A., Hardy, J. D. Interstitial fluid pressure changes in endotoxin shock. *Surgery, 63,* 938–41 (1968)

53. Stromberg, D. D., Wiederhielm, C. A. Effect of colloid concentration gradients on negative pressures in implanted capsules (In press)

54. Scholander, P. F., Hargens, A. R., Miller, S. L. Negative pressure in the interstitial fluid of animals. *Science,* **161,** 321–28 (1968)

55. Gauer, O. H., Henry, J. P., Sieker, O. H. Changes in central venous pressure after moderate hemorrhage and transfusion in man. *Circ. Res.,* **4,** 79–84 (1956)

56. Shires, T., Coln, D., Carrico, J., Lightfoot, S. Fluid therapy in hemorrhagic shock. *Arch. Surg.,* **88,** 688–93 (1964)

57. Robinson, J. D. Regulating ion pumps to control cell volume. *J. Theor. Biol.,* **19,** 90–96 (1968)

58. Tosteson, D. C., Hoffman, J. F. Regulation of cell volume by active cation transport in high and low potassium sheep red cells. *J. Gen. Physiol.,* **44,** 169–94 (1960)

59. Kjellmer, I., An indirect method for estimating tissue pressure with special reference to tissue pressure in muscle during exercise. *Acta Physiol. Scand.,* **62,** 31–40 (1964)

60. Wells, H. S., Youmans, J. B., Miller, D. G., Jr. Tissue pressure (intracutaneous, subcutaneous and intramuscular) as related to venous pressure, capillary filtration, and other factors. *J. Clin. Invest.,* **17,** 489–99 (1938)

61. Horstmann, E. Beobachtungen zur Motorik der Lymphgefässe. *Pflügers Arch.,* **269,** 511–19 (1959)

62. Borst, J. G. G. The maintenance of an adequate cardiac output by the regulation of the urinary excretion of water and sodium chloride; an essential factor in the genesis of oedema. *Acta Med. Scand.,* **130,** *Suppl. 207,* 1–71 (1948)

63. Pitts, R. F. *Physiology of the kidney and body fluids* (Yearbook Med. Publ., Chicago, 1968)

64. Kaufmann, W., Müller, A. A. Expansion des Plasmavolumens nach rascher Verminderung der zir-

kulierenden Blutmenge. *Z. Kreislaufforsch,* **47,** 719–31 (1958)

65. Öberg, B. Effects of cardiovascular reflexes on net capillary fluid transfer. *Acta Physiol. Scand.,* **62,** *Suppl.* 229, 1–98 (1964)

66. Mellander, S., Öberg, B. Transcapillary fluid absorption and other vascular reactions in the human forearm during reduction of the circulating blood volume. *Acta Physiol. Scand.,* **71,** 37–46 (1967)

67. Johnston, B. D. Nerve endings in the human endocardium. *Am. J. Anat.,* **122,** 621–30 (1968)

68. Nonidez, J. F. Studies on the innervation of the heart. *Am. J. Anat.,* **65,** 361–413 (1939)

69. Hakumäki, M. O. K., Bergström, R. M., Huopaniemi, T. H., Sarajas, H. S. S. Vagal impulses from the atrial stretch receptors in relation to intra-atrial pressure. *Scand. J. Clin. Lab. Invest., Suppl. 101,* **21,** 64 (1968) *Abstr.*

70. Williams, T. H. Mitral and tricuspid valve innervation. *Brit. Heart J.,* **26,** 105–15 (1964)

71. Semenov, S. P. Experimental and morphological study of cardiac afferents. *Arkh. Anat.,* **45,** 72–83 (1963)

72. Ellison, J. P., Williams, T. H. Sympathetic nerve pathways to the human heart, and their variations. *Am. J. Anat.,* **124,** 149–62 (1969)

73. Ledsome, J. R., Linden, R. J. A reflex increase in heart rate from distension of the pulmonary-vein-atrial junctions. *J. Physiol.,* **170,** 456–73 (1964)

74. Ledsome, J. R., Linden, R. J. The effect of distending a pouch of the left atrium on the heart rate. *J. Physiol.,* **193,** 121–29 (1967)

75. Ledsome, J. R., Linden, R. J. The role of left atrial receptors in the diuretic response to left atrial distension. *J. Physiol.,* **198,** 487–503 (1968)

76. Edis, A. J., Shepherd, J. T. Circulatory reflexes from stretch of pulmonary vein-atrial junctions. *Physiologist,* **12,** 213 (1969)

77. Carswell, F., Hainsworth, R., Ledsome, J. R. The response of the perfused hind limb to stimulation of left atrial receptors. *J. Physiol.,* **198,** 97–98 (1968) *Abstr.*

78. Goetz, K. L., Hermreck, A. S., Trank, J. W. Contribution of atrial receptors to diuresis following

plasma expansion in conscious dogs. *Fed. Proc.,* **28,** 584 (1969)

79. Dieudonné, J. M. Tissue-cavitary difference in pressure of dog myocardium under stress. *Am. J. Physiol.,* **213,** 107–11 (1967)

80. Kolatat, T., Ascanio, G., Tallarida, R. J., Oppenheimer, M. J. Action potentials in the sensory vagus at the time of coronary infarction. *Am. J. Physiol.,* **213,** 71–78 (1967)

81. Brown, A. M. Mechanoreceptors in or near the coronary arteries. *J. Physiol.,* **177,** 203–14 (1965)

82. Thomas, S. Reflex increase in urine flow by veratridine. *Quart. J. Exptl. Physiol.,* **52,** 313–18 (1967)

83. Paintal, A. S. Mechanism of stimulation of type J pulmonary receptors. *J. Physiol.,* **203,** 511–32 (1969)

84. Henry, J. P., Meehan, J. P., Greenberg, T., Richmond, W. H. The response of atrial stretch receptors to acute changes in central venous pressure during experimental heart failure. *Fed. Proc.,* **28,** 270 (1969)

85. Eliahou, H. E., Clarke, S. D., Bull, G. M. Atrial pulsation during acute distension and its possible significance in the regulation of blood volume. *Clin. Sci.,* **19,** 377–90 (1960)

86. Payne, R. M., Stone, H. L., Engelken, E. J. Atrial function during volume loading. *Fed. Proc.,* **28,** 517 (1969)

87. Wright, F. S., Davis, J. O., Johnston, C. I., Howards, S. S. Renal sodium excretion after volume expansion with saline and blood. *Proc. Soc. Exptl. Biol. Med.,* **128,** 1044–51 (1968)

88. Earley, L. E., Daugharty, T. M. Sodium metabolism. *New England J. Med.,* **281,** 72–86 (1969)

89. Nizet, A. Influence of serum albumin and dextran on sodium and water excretion by the isolated dog kidney. *Pflügers Arch.,* **301,** 7–15 (1968)

90. Kumada, M., Schmidt, R. M., Tan, K. S., Sagawa, K. Cardiovascular responses to hemorrhage under pulsatile and nonpulsatile forcings of the carotid sinus. *Physiologist,* **12,** 277 (1969)

91. Share, L. Extracellular fluid volume and vasopressin secretion. In *Frontiers in Neuroendocrinology* (Ganong, W. F., Martini, L., Eds., Oxford Univ. Press, 1969)

92. Godley, J. A., Myers, J. W., Rosenbaum, D. A. Cardiovascular and renal function during continuous negative pressure breathing in dogs. *J. Appl. Physiol.,* **22,** 568–72 (1967)

93. Shu'ayb, W. A., Moran, W. H., Jr., Zimmermann, B. Studies of the mechanism of antidiuretic hormone secretion and the post-commissurotomy dilutional syndrome. *Ann. Surg.,* **162,** 690–701 (1965)

94. Johnson, J. A., Moore, W. W., Segar, W. E. Small changes in left atrial pressure and plasma antidiuretic hormone titers in dogs. *Am. J. Physiol.,* **217,** 210–14 (1969)

95. Lydtin, H., Hamilton, W. H. Effect of acute changes in left atrial pressure on urine flow in unanesthetized dogs. *Am. J. Physiol.,* **207,** 530 (1964)

96. Kilburn, K. Fluid volume control and induced arrhythmias. *Clin. Res.,* **12,** 186 (1964)

97. Gilmore, J. P. Contribution of baroreceptors to the control of renal function. *Circ. Res.,* **14,** 301–17 (1964)

98. Michaelis, L. L., Gilmore, J. P. Renal effects of electrical stimulation of the carotid sinus nerve. *Surgery,* **65,** 797–801 (1969)

99. Gilmore, J. P., Weisfeldt, M. L. Contribution of intravascular receptors to the renal responses following intravascular volume expansion. *Circ. Res.,* **17,** 144–54 (1965)

100. Perlmutt, J. H. Contribution of carotid and vagal reflex mechanisms. *Fed. Proc.,* **27,** 1149–55 (1968)

101. Pearce, J. W., Lichardus, B. Effects of vagotomy and renal denervation on renal response to blood volume expansion. *Can. J. Physiol. Pharmacol.,* **45,** 689–703 (1967)

102. Gilmore, J. P. Contribution of cardiac nerves to the control of body salt and water. *Fed. Proc.,* **27,** 1156–59 (1968)

103. Cooper, T., Gilbert, J. W., Jr., Bloodwell, R. D., Crout, J. R. Chronic extrinsic cardiac denervation by regional neural ablation. *Circ. Res.,* **9,** 275–81 (1961)

104. Gilmore, J. P., Daggett, W. M. Response of the chronic cardiac denervated dog to acute volume expansion. *Am. J. Physiol.,* **210,** 509–12 (1966)

105. Knox, F. G., Davis, B. B., Berliner, R. W. Effect of chronic cardiac

denervation on renal response to saline infusion. *Am. J. Physiol.,* **213,** 174–78 (1967)

106. Willman, V. L., Merjavy, J. P., Pennell, R., Hanlon, C. R. Response of the autotransplanted heart to blood volume expansion. *Ann. Surg.,* **166,** 513–17 (1967)

107. Lower, R. R. Cardiac transplantation without complete cardiac denervation. *Am. Heart J.,* **72,** 841–42 (1966)

108. Lower, R. R., Shumway, N. E. Studies on orthotopic homotransplantation of the canine heart. *Surg. Forum,* **11,** 18–23 (1960)

109. Michaelis, L. L., Gilmore, J. P. The effect of acute spinal cord section upon the renal response to intravascular volume expansion. *Nephron,* **6,** 62–69 (1969)

110. Pearce, J. W., Sonnenberg, H. Effects of spinal section and renal denervation on the renal response to blood volume expansion. *Can. J. Physiol. Pharmacol.,* **43,** 211–24 (1965)

110a. Pearce, J. W., Sonnenberg, H., Lichardus, B., Veress, A. T. Interaction of extrarenal and intrarenal factors in 'volume natriuresis' (To be published *Proc. Intern. Nephrol. Congr., Karger*)

111. Smith, O. A., Jr., Nathan, M. A., Clarke, N. P. Central nervous system pathways mediating blood pressure. In *Hypertension,* **XVI,** 9–22 (Am. Heart Assoc., New York, 1968)

112. Chai, C. Y., Wang, S. C. Integration of sympathetic cardiovascular mechanisms in medulla oblongata of the cat. *Am. J. Physiol.,* **215,** 1310–15 (1968)

113. Ueda, H., Yasuda, H., Takabatake, Y., Iizuka, M., Iizuka, T., Ihori, M., Yamamoto, M., Sakamoto, Y. Increased renin release evoked by mesencephalic stimulation in the dog. *Japan. Heart J.,* **8,** 498–506 (1967)

114. Bargainer, J. D., Woods, J. W. Renal responses to changes in blood volume in the absence of hypothalamic input from atrial receptors. *Johns Hopkins Med. J.,* **119,** 371–77 (1966)

115. Bisset, G. W., Hilton, S. M., Poisner, A. M. Hypothalamic pathways for independent release of vasopressin and oxytocin. *Proc. Roy. Soc. Biol.,* **166,** 422–42 (1966)

116. Clark, B. J., Rocha e Silva, M., Jr. An afferent pathway for the selective release of vasopressin in response to carotid occlusion and haemorrhage in the cat. *J. Physiol.,* **191,** 529–42 (1967)

117. Tindal, J. S., Knaggs, G. S., Turvey, A. The afferent path of the milk-ejection reflex in the brain of the guinea pig. *J. Endocrinol.,* **38,** 337–49 (1967)

118. Woods, W. H., Holland, R. C., Powell, E. W. Connections of cerebral structures functioning in neurohypophysial hormone release. *Brain Res.,* **12,** 26–46 (1969)

119. Hayward, J. N., Baker, M. A. Diuretic and thermoregulatory responses to preoptic cooling in the monkey. *Am. J. Physiol.,* **214,** 843–50 (1968)

120. Segar, W. E., Moore, W. W. The regulation of antidiuretic hormone release in man. I. Effects of change in position and ambient temperature on blood ADH levels. *J. Clin. Invest.,* **47,** 2143–51 (1968)

121. Stricker, E. M. Osmoregulation and volume regulation in rats: inhibition of hypovolemic thirst by water. *Am. J. Physiol.,* **217,** 98–105 (1969)

122. Houpt, K. A., Epstein, A. N. The renin-angiotensin mediation of hypotensive drinking. *Physiologist,* **12,** 257 (1969) *Abstr.*

123. Daniels, A. E., Ogden, E. Vernikos-Danellis, J., Effects of centrally administered angiotensin II in the unanesthetized rat. *Physiologist,* **12,** 205 (1969) *Abstr.*

124. Dorn, J. B., Levine, N., Kaley, G., Rothballer, A. B. Natriuresis induced by injection of hypertonic saline into the third cerebral ventricle of dogs. *Proc. Soc. Exptl. Biol. Med.,* **131,** 240–42 (1969)

125. Mouw, D. R., Vander, A. J. Evidence for brain sodium receptors controlling renal sodium excretion and plasma renin activity. *Physiologist,* **12,** 310 (1969) *Abstr.*

126. Andersson, B., Olsson, K., Warner, R. G. Dissimilarities between the central control of thirst and the release of antidiuretic hormone (ADH). *Acta Physiol. Scand..* **71,** 57–64 (1967)

127. Fichman, M. P., Bethune, J. E. The role of andrenocorticoids in the inappropriate antidiuretic hormone

syndrome. *Ann. Internal Med.*, **63**, 806–20 (1968)
128. Wise, B. L. Inappropriate secretion of ADH caused by obstruction of ventriculo-atrial shunts. *J. Neurosurg.*, **28**, 429–33 (1968)
129. Carter, N. W., Rector, F. C., Jr., Seldin, D. W. Hyponatremia in cerebral disease resulting from the inappropriate secretion of antidiuretic hormone. *New Engl. J. Med.*, **264**, 67–72 (1961)
130. Share, L. Vasopressin, its bioassay and the physiological control of its release. *Am. J. Med.*, **42**, 701–12 (1967)
131. Henry, J. P., Gupta, P. D., Meehan, J. P., Sinclair, R., Share, L. The role of afferents from the low-pressure system in the release of antidiuretic hormone during non-hypotensive hemorrhage. *Can. J. Physiol. Pharmacol.*, **46**, 287–95 (1968)
132. Share, L. Role of peripheral receptors in the increased release of vasopressin in response to hemorrhage. *Endocrinology*, **81**, 1140–46 (1967)
133. Tata, P. S., Buzalkov, R. Vasopressin studies in the rat. III. Inability of ethanol anesthesia to prevent ADH secretion due to pain and hemorrhage. *Pflügers Arch.*, **290**, 294–97 (1966)
134. Johnson, J. A., Moore, W. W., Segar, W. E. Small changes in left atrial pressure and plasma antidiuretic hormone titers in dogs. *Am. J. Physiol.*, **217**, 210–14 (1969)
134a. Saito, T., Yoshida, S., Nakao, K. Release of antidiuretic hormone from neurohypophysis in response to hemorrhage and infusion of hypertonic saline in dogs. *Endocrinology*, **85**, 72–78 (1969)
135. Gauer, O. H. Osmocontrol versus volume control. *Fed. Proc.*, **27**, 1132–36 (1968)
136. Arndt, J. O. Diuresis induced by water infusion into the carotid loop and its inhibition by small hemorrhage. *Pflügers Arch.*, **282**, 313–22 (1965)
137. Haberich, F. J. Osmoreception in the portal circulation. *Fed. Proc.*, **27**, 1137–41 (1968)
138. Haberich, F. J., Aziz, O., Nowacki, P. E. Über einen osmoreceptorisch tätigen Mechanismus in der Leber. *Pflügers Arch.*, **285**, 73–89 (1965)
139. Nowacki, P. E., Aziz, O., Haberich, F. J. Über die Rehydrierung von wachen Durstratten durch enterale

oder parenterale Wasserinfusion. *Pflügers Arch.*, **289**, R89 (1966) *Abstr.*
140. Haberich, F. J., Dennhard, R., Ohm, W. The removal of the hepatic branches of the vagal nerve in the unanesthetized rat and its influence on the hepatogenic diuretic mechanism. *Pflügers Arch.*, **307**, R80 (1969) *Abstr.*
141. Haberich, F. J., Gottwald, P. Chr., Köhler, D., Drechsler, H. Das Verhalten der Perspiratio insensibilis und der Urinsekretion des Menschen bei der enteralen und parenteralen Infusion von Wasser und verschieden konzentrierten Kochsalzlösungen unter klimakonstanten Bedingungen. *Pflügers Arch.*, **297**, R74 (1967) *Abstr.*
142. Lydtin, H. Untersuchungen über Mechanismen der Osmo- und Volumenregulation. II. Untersuchungen über den Einfluss intravenös, intraportal und oral zugeführter hypotoner Kochsalzlösungen auf die Diurese des Hundes. *Z. Ges. Exptl. Med.*, **149**, 193–210 (1969)
143. Lydtin, H. Untersuchungen über Mechanismen der Osmo- und Volumenregulation. III. Untersuchungen am Menschen über die Wirkung von oral und intravenös zugeführten Kochsalzlösungen auf die Harnausscheidung. *Z. Ges. Exptl. Med.*, **149**, 211–25 (1969)
144. Schneider, E. G., Davis, J. O., Robb, C. A., Baumber, J. S., Johnson, J. A., Wright, F. S. Lack of evidence for an hepatic osmoreceptor mechanism in conscious dogs. *Physiologist*, **12**, 350 (1969) *Abstr.*
145. Hakumäki, M. O. K. Effect of the left atrial pressure on vagal afferent discharge from the left atrium, and on the sympathetic postganglionic discharge to the heart. *Acta Physiol. Scand.*, **74**, 255–56 (1968)
146. Webb-Peploe, M. M. The isovolumetric spleen: index of reflex changes in splanchnic vascular capacity. *Am. J. Physiol.*, **216**, 407–13 (1969)
147. Henry, J. P., Cabaud, H. E., Hinderleider, C. D., Meehan, J. P. Splenic contraction in response to non-hypotensive hemorrhage. *Physiologist*, **10**, 200 (1967)
148. Hinderleider, C. D., Cabaud, H. E., Henry, J. P., Meehan, J. P. Failure of contraction of the spleen during non-hypotensive hemorrhage in

cardiac denervated dogs. *Fed. Proc.*, **27**, 329 (1968) *Abstr.*

149. Gill, J. R., Jr., Bartter, F. C. Adrenergic nervous system in sodium metabolism. II. Effects of guanethidine on the renal response to sodium deprivation in normal man. *New Engl. J. Med.*, **275**, 1466–71 (1966)

150. Gill, J. R., Jr., Carr, A. A., Fleischmann, L. E., Casper, A. G. T., Bartter, F. C. Effects of pentolinium on sodium excretion in dogs with constriction of the vena cava. *Am. J. Physiol.*, **212**, 191–96 (1967)

151. Dieter, E. Der Einfluß der Kreislauffüllung auf die Aktivität der Nierennerven beim Frosch. *Pflügers Arch.*, **270**, 215–26 (1960)

152. Gill, J. R., Jr., Casper, A. G. T. Role of the sympathetic nervous system in the renal response to hemorrhage. *J. Clin. Invest.*, **48**, 915–22 (1969)

153. Berne, R. M., Hoffman, W. K., Jr., Kagan, A., Levy, M. N. Response of the normal and denervated kidney to L-epinephrine and L-norepinephrine. *Am. J. Physiol.*, **171**, 564–71 (1952)

154. Vander, A. J. Effect of catecholamines and the renal nerves on renin secretion in anesthetized dogs. *Am. J. Physiol.*, **209**, 659–62 (1965)

155. Trueta, J., Barclay, A. E., Daniel, P. M., Franklin, K. J., Prichard, M. M. L. *Studies of the renal circulation* (Thomas, Springfield, Ill., 1947)

156. Tuttle, E. P., Jr., Sadler, J. H. Local renal tissue fluid turnover rates by thermal washout technique. *Free Commun. Intern. Congr. Nephrol.*, **3**, 287 (1966)

157. Horster, M., Thurau, K. Micropuncture studies on the filtration rate of single superficial and juxtamedullary glomeruli in the rat kidney. *Pflügers Arch.*, **301**, 162–81 (1968)

158. Carriere, S., Thorburn, G. D., O'Morchoe, C. C. C., Barger, A. C. Intrarenal distribution of blood flow in dogs during hemorrhagic hypotension. *Circ. Res.*, **19**, 167–79 (1966)

159. Pomeranz, B. H., Birtch, A. G., Barger, A. C. Neural control of intrarenal blood flow. *Am. J. Physiol.*, **215**, 1067–81 (1968)

160. Hollenberg, N. K., Epstein, M., Rosen, S. M., Basch, R. I., Oken, D. E., Merrill, J. P. Acute oliguric renal failure in man. Evidence for preferential renal cortical ischemia. *Medicine*, **47**, 455–70 (1968)

161. Arndt, J. O., Reineck, H., Gauer, O. H. Ausscheidungsfunktion und Hämodynamik der Nieren bei Dehnung des linken Vorhofes am narkotisierten Hund. *Pflügers Arch.*, **277**, 1–15 (1963)

162. Lydtin, H. Untersuchungen über Mechanismen der Osmo- und Volumenregulation. I. Über den Einfluss akuter Änderungen des Drucks im linken Vorhof auf die Diurese. Untersuchungen am wachen und narkotisierten Hund. *Z. Ges. Exptl. Med.*, **149**, 91–131 (1966)

163. Fisher, R. D., Grunfeld, J. P., Barger, A. C. Antidiuretic hormone and renal circulation. *Physiologist*, **12**, 226 (1969) *Abstr.*

164. Ledsome, J. R., Linden, R. J., O'Connor, W. J. The mechanism by which distension of the left atrium produces diuresis in anaesthetized dogs. *J. Physiol.*, **159**, 87–100 (1961)

165. Baïsset, A., Montastruc., P. Blocage par la vasopressine de la diurèse provoquée chez le chien par distension atriale où par respiration en dépression. *C. R. Soc. Biol.*, **162**, 995–99 (1968)

166. Wågermark, J., Ungerstedt, U., Ljungqvist, A. Sympathetic innervation of the juxtaglomerular cells of the kidney. *Circ. Res.*, **22**, 149–53 (1968)

167. Vander, A. J., Luciano, J. R. Effects of mercurial diuresis and acute sodium depletion on renin release in dog. *Am. J. Physiol.*, **212**, 651–56 (1967)

168. Vander, A. J., Luciano, J. R. Neural and humoral control of renin release in salt depletion. *Circ. Res.*, **21**, Suppl. 2, 69–75 (1967)

169. Korz, R., Fischer, F., Behn, C. Renin-angiotensin System bei simulierter Hypervolämie durch Immersion. *Klin. Wochschr.* (In press)

170. Bunag, R. D., Page, I. H., McCubbin, J. W. Neural stimulation of release of renin. *Circ. Res.*, **19**, 851–58 (1966)

171. Hodge, R. L., Lowe, R. D., Vane, J. R. The effects of alteration of blood-volume on the concentration of circulating angiotensin in anaes-

thetized dogs. *J. Physiol.*, **185,** 613–26 (1966)

172. Hodge, R. L., Lowe, R. D., Ng, K. K. F., Vane, J. R. Role of the vagus nerve in the control of the concentration of angiotensin II in the circulation. *Nature,* **221,** 177–79 (1969)

173. Fabre, L. F., Jr., Farmer, R. W., Davis, H. W., McBee, G., Farrell, G. Biphasic stimulation of aldosterone secretion during hemorrhage in dogs. *Circ. Res.,* **24,** 893–900 (1969)

174. Mills, I. H., De Wardener, H. E., Hayter, C. J., Clapham, W. F. Studies on the afferent mechanism of the sodium chloride diuresis which follows intravenous saline in the dog. *Clin. Sci.,* **21,** 259–64 (1961)

175. De Wardener, H. E., Mills, I. H., Clapham, W. F., Hayter, C. J. Studies on the efferent mechanism of the sodium diuresis which follows the administration of intravenous saline in the dog. *Clin. Sci.,* **21,** 249–58 (1961)

176. Davis, J. O., Holman, J. E., Carpenter, C. C. J., Urquhart, J., Higgins, J. T., Jr. An extraadrenal factor essential for chronic renal sodium retention in presence of increased sodium-retaining hormone. *Circ. Res.,* **14,** 17–31 (1964)

177. Davis, J. O., Johnston, C. I., Howards, S. S., Wright, F. S. Humoral factors in the regulation of renal sodium excretion. *Fed. Proc.,* **26,** 60–69 (1967)

178. Cirksena, W. J., Dirks, J. H., Berliner, R. W. Effect of thoracic cava obstruction on response of proximal tubule sodium reabsorption to saline infusion. *J. Clin. Invest.,* **45,** 179–86 (1966)

179. Knox, F. G., Howards, S. S., Wright, F. S., Davis, B. B., Berliner, R. W. Effect of dilution and expansion of blood volume on proximal sodium reabsorption. *Am. J. Physiol.,* **215,** 1041–48 (1968)

180. Levinsky, N. G. Nonaldosterone influences on renal sodium transport. *Ann. N.Y. Acad. Sci.,* **139,** 295–303 (1966)

181. Rector, F. C., Jr., Martinez-Maldonado, M., Kurtzman, N. A., Sellman, J. C., Oerther, F., Seldin, D. W. Demonstration of a hormonal inhibitor of proximal tubular reabsorption during expansion of extracellular volume with iso-

tonic saline. *J. Clin. Invest.,* **47,** 761–73 (1968)

182. Wright, F. S., Brenner, B. M., Bennett, C. M., Keimowitz, R. I., Berliner, R. W., Schrier, R. W., Verroust, P. J., De Wardener, H. E., Holzgreve, H. Failure to demonstrate a hormonal inhibitor of proximal sodium reabsorption. *J. Clin. Invest.,* **48,** 1107–13 (1969)

183. Pearce, J. W., Sonnenberg, H., Lichardus, B., Veress, A. T. Interaction of extrarenal and intrarenal factors in 'volume natriuresis' (To be published Proc. Intern. Nephrol. Congr., Karger, 1970)

184. Cort, J. H. The source and chemical nature of the natriuretic activity of plasma evoked by saluretic "volume reflexes." *Can. J. Physiol. Pharmacol.,* **46,** 325–33 (1968)

185. Cort, J. H., Douša, T., Pliška, V., Lichardus, B., Šáfářová, J., Vranešić, M., Rudinger, J. Saliuretic activity of blood during carotid occlusion in the cat. *Am. J. Physiol.,* **215,** 921–27 (1968)

186. Sedlakava, E., Lichardus, B., Cort, J. H. Plasma saliuretic activity: Its nature and relation to oxytocin analogs. *Science,* **164,** 580–82 (1969)

187. Linkenbach, H. J., Eckert, P., Gauer, O. H. Nachweis eines diuretischen Faktors im menschlichen Serum während der durch Expansion des intrathorakalen Blutvolumens ausgelösten Diurese. *Pflügers Arch.,* **293,** 107–14 (1967)

188. Jahn, H., Stephan, F., Stahl, J. Activité diuretique dans le sang et les urines après saignée chez le chien. *Arch. Sci. Physiol.,* **14,** 421–33 (1960)

189. Krück, F. Influence of humoral factors on renal tubular sodium handling. *Nephron,* **6,** 205–16 (1969)

190. Kessler, E., Hughes, R. C., Orlando, C., Shamlou, G. Comparative effects of saline and isoncotic albumin in saline on sodium excretion. *Proc. Soc. Exptl. Biol. Med.,* **125,** 543–48 (1967)

191. Vereerstraeten, P., Toussaint, C. Effects of plasmapheresis on renal hemodynamics and sodium excretion in dogs. *Pflügers Arch.,* **306,** 92–102 (1969)

192. Lewy, J. E., Windhager, E. E. Peritubular control of proximal tubular fluid reabsorption in the rat kid-

ney. *Am. J. Physiol.*, **214**, 943–54 (1968)

193. Graveline, D. E., Balke, B. The physiologic effects of hypodynamics induced by water immersion. *USAF School of Aviation Medicine, Brooks AFB Texas, Res. Rept.* 60–88, **11**, Sept. (1960)

194. Graveline, D. E., Jackson, M. M. Diuresis associated with prolonged water immersion. *J. Appl. Physiol.*, **17**, 519–24 (1962)

195. Bazett, H. C. Studies on the effects of baths on man. I. Relationship between the effects produced and the temperature of the bath. *Am. J. Physiol.*, **70**, 412–29 (1924)

196. Bazett, H. C., Thurlow, S., Crowell, C., Stewart, W. Studies on the effects of baths on man. II. The diuresis caused by warm baths, together with some observations on urinary tides. *Am. J. Physiol.*, **70**, 430–52 (1924)

197. McCally, M. Immersion techniques and the evaluation of deconditioning countermeasures. In *Symp. Hypogravic Hypodynamic Environments* (Murray, R. H., Ed, NASA Tech. Rept., to be published)

198. Piemme, T. E. Body fluid volume and renal relationships to gravity. In *Hypodynamics and Hypogravics*, 133–61 (McCally, M., Ed., Academic, New York, London, 1968)

199. Wunder, C. C., Duling, B., Bengele, H. Gravity as a biological determinant. Chap. 1, 1–69 (See Ref. 198)

200. Boehm, G., Ekert, F. Über die röntgenologisch fassbaren Einwirkungen von gewöhnlichen und therapeutischen Bädern auf die zentralen Kreislauforgane beim Herzgessunden. *Deut. Arch. Klin. Med.*, **182**, 598–610 (1938)

201. Hood, W. B., Jr., Murray, R. H., Urschel, C. W., Bowers, J. A., Goldman, J. K. Circulatory effects of water immersion upon human subjects. *Aerospace Med.*, **39**, 579–84 (1968)

202. Hunt, N. C. Positive pressure breathing during water immersion. *Aerospace Med.*, **38**, 731–35 (1967)

203. Smith, H. W. Salt and water volume receptors. *Am. J. Med.*, **23**, 623–52 (1957)

204. Behn, C., Gauer, O. H., Kirsch, K., Eckert, P. Effects of sustained intrathoracic vascular distention on body fluid distribution and renal excretion in man. *Pflügers Arch.*, **313**, 123–35 (1969)

205. Kaiser, D., Eckert, P., Gauer, O. H., Linkenbach, H. J. Die Diurese bei Immersion in ein thermoindifferentes Vollbad. *Pflügers Arch.*, **306**, 247–61 (1969)

206. Eckert, P., Kirsch, K., Behn, C., Gauer, O. H. Wasser- und Salzhaushalt bei langdauernder Immersion in Wasserbad. *Pflügers Arch.*, **297**, R70 (1967)

207. Graybiel, A., Clark, B. Symptoms resulting from prolonged immersion in water : The problem of zero G asthenia. *Aerospace Med.*, **32**, 181–96 (1961)

208. Kaiser, D., Linkenbach, H. J., Gauer, O. H. Änderung des Plasmavolumens des Menschen bei Immersion in ein thermoindifferentes Wasserbad. *Pflügers Arch.*, **308**, 166–73 (1969)

209. McCally, M. Plasma volume response to water immersion. Implications for space flight. *Aerospace Med.*, **35**, 130–32 (1964)

210. McCally, M., Pohl, S. A., Samson, P. A. Relative effectiveness of selected space flight deconditioning countermeasures. *Aerospace Med.*, **39**, 722–34 (1968)

211. White, P. D., Nyberg, J. W., Finney, L. M., White, W. J. A comparative study of the physiological effects of immersion and bed rest. *NASA Douglas Rept. DAC-59226* (1966)

212. Eckert, P. *Untersuchungen zur Rolle des antidiuretischen Hormons bei der volumenbedingten Diurese* (Inaugural dissertation, Berlin, 1965)

213. Kaiser, D., Gauer, O. H. Einwirkung von Adiuretin auf die Homöostase des menschlichen Kreislaufs im Bade. (Simulierte Schwerelosigkeit) *Pflügers Arch.*, **283**, R69–70 (1965) *Abstr.*

214. Hunt, N. C. Immersion diuresis. *Aerospace Med.*, **38**, 176–80 (1967)

215. Goodall, McC., McCally, M., Graveline, D. E. Urinary adrenaline and noradrenaline response to simulated weightless state. *Am. J. Physiol.*, **206**, 431–36 (1964)

216. Korz, R., Pontzen, W., Behn, C. Renaler Phenolsulfonphthaleintransport bei Vergrösserung des zentralen Blutvolumes durch Immersion. *Klin. Wochschr.* **47**, 1220–25 (1969)

217. Echt, M. *Untersuchung über das Verhalten des Druck-Umfangsquotienten und der Durchblutung*

am *Unterarm sowie der Herzfrequenz bei simulierter Schwerelosigkeit (Immersion im Wasserbad)* (Inaugural dissertation, Berlin) (In preparation)

218. Kaiser, D., Gauer, O. H. Untersuchungen über den Venentonus am Unterarm bei simulierter Schwerelosigkeit. *Pflügers Arch.*, **289**, R76 (1966) *Abstr.*

219. Framing, H. D. Veränderungen der maximalen Sauerstoffaufnahme, des Leistungspulsindex und der Maximalkraft von Trainierten und Untrainierten nach langfristiger Immersion in Wasser. *Pflügers Arch.*, **307**, R91 (1969) *Abstr.*

220. Rogge, J. D., Moore, W. W., Segar, W. E., Fasola, A. F. Effect of +Gz and +Gx accleration on peripheral venous ADH levels in humans, *J. Appl. Physiol*, **23**, 870–74 (1967)

221. Watson, J. F., Rapp, R. M. Effect of forward acceleration on renal function. *J. Appl. Physiol.*, **17**, 413–16 (1962)

222. Bengele, H. H., Jr. Water intake and urine output of rats during chronic centrifugation. *Am. J. Physiol.*, **216**, 659–65 (1969)

223. Bengele, H. H., Jr. *The influence of chronic centrifugation on renal function in the rat* (Thesis, Dept. Physiol., Univ. Iowa, 1969)

224. Murray, R. H., Thompson, L. J., Bowers, J. A., Albright, C. D. Hemodynamic effects of graded hypovolemia and vasodepressor syncope induced by lower body negative pressure. *Am. Heart J.*, **76**, 799–811 (1968)

225. Lamb, L. E., Stevens, P. M. Influence of lower body negative pressure on the level of hydration during bed rest. *Aerospace Med.*, **36**, 1145–51 (1965)

226. Miller, P. B., Johnson, R. L., Lamb, L. E. Effects of moderate physical exercise during four weeks of bed rest on circulatory functions in man. *Aerospace Med.*, **36**, 1077–82 (1965)

227. Gauer, O. H., Eckert, P., Kaiser, D., Linkenbach, H. J. Fluid metabolism and circulation during and after simulated weightlessness. In: Basic environmental problems of man in space, Edited by H. Bjurstedt, *Proc. 2nd Intern. Symp. Man in Space, Paris, 1965*, 212–21 (Springer-Verlag, Vienna, 1967)

228. Gauer, O. H., Haber, H. Man under gravity-free conditions. *German Aviation Medicine, World War II*, **1**, 641–44 (Dept. Air Force, Supt. Doc. U. S. Govt. Printing Office, Washington, D.C., 1950)

229. Adey, W. R., Cockett, A. K., Mack, P. B., Meehan, J. P., Pace, N. Biosatellite III: Preliminary Findings. *Science*, **166**, 492–93 (1969)

230. Dietlein, L. F. Spaceflight deconditioning effects: Overview and summary of cardiovascular consequences. In *Symp. Hypogravic Hypodynamic Environments* (Murray, R. H., Ed., NASA Tech. Rept., to be published)

231. Webb, P., Weight loss in men in space. *Science,* **155**, 558–60 (1667)

232. Lutwak, L., Whedon, G. D., LaChance, P. A., Reid, J. M., Lipscomb, H. S. Mineral, electrolyte and nitrogen balance studies of the Gemini-VII fourteen-day orbital space flight. *J. Clin. Endocrinol.*, **29**, 1140–56 (1969)

233. Gurowski, N. N., Communication at the third international symposium on basic environmental problems of man in space (Intern. Astronaut. Found., Intern. Acad. Astronaut., Geneva, 1968)

234. Berry, C. A., Coons, D. O., Catterson, A. D., Kelly, G. F. Man's response to long-duration flight in the Gemini Spacecraft. *Gemini Mid-program Conf., NASA, Houston*, 235–61 (1966)

235. Berry, C A. Preliminary clinical report of the medical aspects of Apollo VII and VIII. *Aerospace Med.*, **40**, 245 (1969)

236. Barger, A. C., Maldowney, F. P., Liebowitz, M. R. The role of the kidney in pathogenesis of congestive heart failure. *Circulation*, **20**, 273 (1959)

237. Wood, P. Polyuria in paroxysmal tachycardia and paroxysmal atrial flutter and fibrillation *Brit. Heart J.*, **25**, 273–82 (1963)

238. Mersch, F. D., Arndt, J. O. Der Dehnungszustand der Herzvorhöfe unter dem Einfluss künstlicher Herzfrequenzänderungen bei narkotisierten Katzen. *Pflügers Arch.*, **311**, 55–72 (1969)

239. Haynal, I., Matsch, J. Spastic urine. In *Paroxysmal Tachycardia*, Chap. 13, 111–30 (Akad. Kiado, Budapest, 1968)

240. Ghose, R. R., Joekes, A. M., Kyriacou, E. H. Renal response to paroxysmal tachycardia. *Brit. Heart*

J., 27, 684–87 (1965)
241. Moran, W. H., Jr., Zimmermann, B. Mechanisms of antidiuretic hormone (ADH) control of importance to the surgical patient. Surgery, 62, 639–44 (1967)
242. Windhager, E. E. Kidney, water, and electrolytes. Ann. Rev. Physiol., 31, 117–72 (1969)
243. Sagawa, K. Overall circulatory regulation. Ann. Rev. Physiol., 31, 295–330 (1969)
244. Mason, D. T., Bartter, F. C. Autonomic regulation of blood volume. Anesthesiology, 29, 681–92 (1968)
245. Houdas, Y. L'autorégulation du volume plasmatique. J. Physiol. (Paris), 61, 43–74 (1969)
246. Riecker, G. Niere und Volumenregulation des Kreislaufs. Verhandl. Deut. Ges. Kreislaufforsch., 33, 30–47 (1967)
247. Vander, A. J. Control of renin release. Physiol. Rev., 47, 359–82 (1967)
248. Frazier, H. S. Renal regulation of sodium balance. New Engl. J. Med., 279, 868–75 (1968)

SOME RELATED ARTICLES APPEARING
IN OTHER *ANNUAL REVIEWS*

From the *Annual Review of Biochemistry,* Volume 39 (1970)
Burgus, Roger, and Guillemin, Roger. Hypothalamic Releasing Factors
Kaback, H. Ronald. Transport
Roberts, Eugene, and Matthysse, Steven. Neurochemistry: At the Cross-
roads of Neurobiology

From the *Annual Review of Medicine,* Volume 21 (1970)
De Clercq, Erik, and Merigan, Thomas C. Current Concepts of Interferon
and Interferon Induction
Dupré, John. Regulation of the Secretions of the Pancreas
Gill, John R., Jr. Edema
Keele, C. A. Chemical Causes of Pain and Itch
Kleeman, Charles R. Hypo-Osmolar Syndromes Secondary to Impaired
Water Excretion
Mills, Ivor H. Renal Regulation of Sodium Excretion
Porte, Daniel, Jr., and Bagdade, John H. Human Insulin Secretion: An
Integrated Approach

From the *Annual Review of Pharmacology,* Volume 10 (1970)
Burgen, A. S. V. Receptor Mechanisms
Mendez, Rafael, and Kabela, Emilio. Cardiac Pharmacology
Weiner, Norman. Regulation of Norepinephrine Biosynthesis

From the *Annual Review of Psychology,* Volume 21 (1970)
Baker, Howard D., and Baker, Barbara N. Visual Sensitivity
Clark, Brant. The Vestibular System
Elkind, David, and Sameroff, Arnold. Developmental Psychology
Rosner, Burton S. Brain Functions

AUTHOR INDEX

597

SUBJECT INDEX

CUMULATIVE INDEXES

VOLUMES 28 -32

INDEX OF CONTRIBUTING AUTHORS

INDEX OF CHAPTER TITLES

VOLUMES 28-32